Non-Alcoholic Fatty Liver Disease Research 2016

Non-Alcoholic Fatty Liver Disease Research 2016

Special Issue Editors

Amedeo Lonardo
Giovanni Targher

MDPI • Basel • Beijing • Wuhan • Barcelona • Belgrade

MDPI

Special Issue Editors

Amedeo Lonardo
Azienda USL Modena
Italy

Giovanni Targher
University of Verona
Italy

Editorial Office
MDPI
St. Alban-Anlage 66
Basel, Switzerland

This is a reprint of articles from the Special Issue published online in the open access journal *International Journal of Molecular Sciences* (ISSN 1422-0067) from 2015 to 2017 (available at: http://www.mdpi.com/journal/ijms/special_issues/nafld2016)

For citation purposes, cite each article independently as indicated on the article page online and as indicated below:

LastName, A.A.; LastName, B.B.; LastName, C.C. Article Title. *Journal Name* **Year**, *Article Number*, Page Range.

ISBN 978-3-03897-600-4 (Pbk)
ISBN 978-3-03897-601-1 (PDF)

Contents

About the Special Issue Editors

Amedeo Lonardo is vice-Director of the Unit of Internal Medicine of "Ospedale Civile Sant'Agostino Estense", Baggiovara Modena, affiliated with the Azienda Ospedaliero-Universitaria of Modena. His research interests include NAFLD as a cause and a consequence of metabolic syndrome; fatty liver disorders owing to varying etiopathogenesis (NAFLD, HCV infection, hypobetalipoproteinemia); NAFLD and insulin resistance; NAFLD-cirrhosis and NAFLD-HCC. On these specific topics, Dr. Lonardo has published 170 scientific articles.

Giovanni Targher is an Associate Professor and Senior Consultant in the Section of Endocrinology, Diabetes and Metabolism, Department of Medicine, University of Verona, and at Azienda Ospedaliera Universitaria Integrata, Verona, Italy. His main research interests are NAFLD and its relationships with cardiovascular disease, chronic kidney disease, type 2 diabetes mellitus and other extra-hepatic complications. He has published over 350 original articles, reviews or editorials (mostly on the topic of NAFLD).

Preface to "Non-Alcoholic Fatty Liver Disease Research 2016"

This book covers a selection of recent research topics and current review articles in the field of nonalcoholic fatty liver disease (NAFLD) that have been published in a monographic Special Issue of the IJMS journal entitled "Non-Alcoholic Fatty Liver Disease Research 2016".

We felt honored, and happily accepted to serve as Guest Editors for this monographic Special Issue of the IJMS journal. The facts have shown that we did the right thing! It was indeed a demanding job, which saw us committed for more than one year. However, this book is truly gratifying for us and for all those prestigious Authors whose thirty-five contributions are published here. We are proud of the participation of so many, highly qualified research groups and thus would like to thank each and every one for the time and commitment they dedicated to this outstanding editorial initiative. Similarly, we are also indebted to all Reviewers: if not for their expert opinions, the monographic Special Issue and this book would never have come to light.

We believe that the research topics and articles included in this book reinforce the view that the global health burden of NAFLD is not only restricted to progressive liver disease (nonalcoholic steatohepatitis, cirrhosis, liver failure, liver transplantation and hepatocellular carcinoma), but also embraces major extra-hepatic complications. In particular, the leading causes of death among patients with NAFLD are cardiovascular disease, followed by non-liver malignancy and liver diseases. Indeed, NAFLD is a multisystem disease, which plays an important role in the development of cardiovascular disease, type 2 diabetes mellitus, chronic kidney disease and other cardiometabolic disorders by disrupting the regulation of multiple metabolic and inflammatory pathways. Moreover, NAFLD is also linked to other invalidating chronic diseases such as hepatitis C virus, HIV infections, extra-hepatic cancers (mainly colo-rectal neoplasms), and chronic plaque psoriasis.

Collectively, we believe that the articles included in this book provide an updated, state-of-the-art view on the aforementioned topics and testimony that NAFLD research has reached a considerable scientific standard across the world and that most patients with NAFLD will benefit from it in the foreseeable future. Based on the published data, more careful surveillance of patients with NAFLD and aggressive management in a subset of them is highly recommended. However, further research is urgently needed to better understand the genetic modifiers, the natural history, the molecular pathogenesis of NAFLD and the biological mechanisms by which NAFLD may promote the development of major hepatic and extra-hepatic complications. This promises also to disclose novel and effective treatment strategies for this increasingly prevalent disease, which will ever increasingly impact on the burden of global health in the near future.

Amedeo Lonardo, Giovanni Targher
Special Issue Editors

International Journal of
Molecular Sciences

MDPI

Editorial

NAFLD: Is There Anything New under the Sun?

Amedeo Lonardo [1],* and Giovanni Targher [2],*

[1] Division of Internal Medicine, Department of Biomedical, Metabolic and Neural Sciences,
     Azienda Ospedaliero-Universitaria, Ospedale Civile di Baggiovara, 41125 Modena, Italy
[2] Section of Endocrinology, Diabetes and Metabolism, Department of Medicine, University and Azienda
     Ospedaliera Universitaria Integrata of Verona, 37126 Verona, Italy
*   Correspondence: a.lonardo@libero.it (A.L.); giovanni.targher@univr.it (G.T.);
     Tel.: +39-059-3961807 (A.L.); +39-045-8123748 (G.T.)

Received: 15 August 2017; Accepted: 10 September 2017; Published: 12 September 2017

1. Introduction

Nonalcoholic fatty liver disease (NAFLD) is an "umbrella" definition that encompasses a spectrum of histological liver changes ranging from simple steatosis to nonalcoholic steatohepatitis (NASH) with/without fibrosis, "cryptogenic" cirrhosis, and hepatocellular carcinoma (HCC), occurring in a dysmetabolic *milieu*, though in the absence of excessive alcohol consumption and other competing etiologies of chronic liver disease [1].

NAFLD has become a leading cause of end-stage liver disease necessitating liver transplantation and a major cause of HCC in many regions of the world [2]. However, owing to its systemic nature, NAFLD is also strongly associated with the metabolic syndrome [3,4] and excess cardiovascular risk [5]. Over the last 20 years, the amount of scientific information on NAFLD has surged [6], owing to the fact that NAFLD, being closely linked to the so-called *"diabesity"* epidemic [1], has become a major public health problem imposing a substantial clinical and economic burden on many societies worldwide [7,8].

On this background, we felt honored, and happily accepted, to serve as Guest Editors for a monographic special issue of the *IJMS* journal entitled *"Non-Alcoholic Fatty Liver Disease Research 2016"*. Facts have shown that we did the right thing! It was indeed a demanding job, which saw us committed for more than 1 year. Finally, however, this monographic special issue is a true gratification for us and for all those prestigious authors whose thirty-five contributions are published here. We are proud of the participation of so many highly qualified research groups and thus would like to thank each and every one for the time and commitment they dedicated to this outstanding editorial initiative. Similarly, we are also indebted to all reviewers: if not for their expert opinions, this special issue would never have come to light.

2. Epidemiology

Although NAFLD has reached pandemic proportions, understanding that there are certain physiological and metabolic factors that can modulate the development and progression of this liver disease may assist physicians in conducting a guided NAFLD screening among high-risk groups of individuals [9,10].

Confirming this paradigm, Losekann et al. examined the prevalence of NASH and risk factors for hepatic fibrosis in 250 patients with morbid obesity submitted to bariatric surgery at a referral center in Southern Brazil [11]. The authors found that hepatic steatosis and NASH were present in nearly 90% and 70% of cases, respectively. Hepatic fibrosis, which affected nearly 45% of these patients, was significantly associated with older age and increased serum alanine aminotransferase and triglyceride levels, thus identifying a subset of morbidly obese patients with more severe liver disease. Finally, the diagnosis of cirrhosis was established in as many as 2% of cases [11]. Collectively, these data further support the notion that physicians should maintain a high index of suspicion that certain high-risk patient groups, such as those with morbid obesity, are more likely to develop fibrosing NASH.

3. Diagnosis

By definition, NAFLD still remains a histological diagnosis that requires not only the demonstration of a steatogenic liver disease but also the exclusion of alternative etiologies of chronic liver disease, except for cardiometabolic ones [1,10]. However, given that liver biopsy is an invasive procedure, is costly, and is not completely free of potential risks and acute complications, it cannot be proposed to each individual patient in clinical practice. Moreover, various histological scoring systems are now available. On these grounds, research has addressed multiple non-invasive biomarkers as well as "pros" and "cons" of various histological scoring systems.

Lombardi et al. assessed whether, among the routinely available serum biomarkers, elevated levels of serum uric acid and ferritin may play an additional role as predictors of NAFLD severity [12]. However, based on their revision of the literature, the authors concluded that the power of these two serum biomarkers appears to be too low if considered alone, suggesting that they should best be included in a wider perspective together with other biochemical and metabolic biomarkers in order to predict liver damage noninvasively [12].

Bringing this topic further, Baratta et al. evaluated the role, if any, of the lysosomal acid lipase (LAL) deficiency in diagnosing advanced NAFLD [13]. LAL is a key enzyme responsible for hydrolyzing the cholesteryl esters and triglycerides. In children, Wolman disease is the early onset phenotype of LAL deficiency which rapidly leads to death. Conversely, cholesterol ester storage disease (CESD) is a late onset phenotype that occurs with hepatic steatosis, hepatomegaly, elevated serum aminotransferase levels, and high low-density lipoprotein (LDL)-cholesterol, high triglycerides and low high-density lipoprotein (HDL)-cholesterol levels. Natural history and clinical manifestations of the LAL deficiency in adults are not well defined, and the diagnosis of this disease is often incidental. Based on their review of the literature, Baratta et al. suggested a significant association between reduced LAL activity levels and the pathogenesis and progression of NAFLD [13]. They also pointed out the clinical circumstances under which reduced LAL activity levels should be suspected.

Consistent with these findings, Shteyer et al., by studying LAL activity levels in patients with microvesicular, idiopathic cirrhosis or NAFLD found that a LAL activity level of 0.5 was the most sensitive for detecting both histologic and non-invasive markers for liver disease severity in these patients [14]. However, additional research is required to better elucidate whether LAL deficiency is a cause or a consequence of advanced hepatic fibrosis, and whether LAL deficiency may be useful for the diagnosis of fibrosing NAFLD.

Despite remarkable advances in non-invasive algorithms developed from tests based on biochemical variables, imaging techniques, or liver stiffness evaluation, the diagnostic phenotype of NAFLD and NASH continues to rely on liver tissue evaluation. NAFLD and NASH are two complex entities, not only for clinical and basic scientists, but also for liver pathologists. Even though much progress has been made, scoring methods gauge injury, but do not replace diagnostic assessment and thus pathologists still need to be trained to identify diagnostic patterns of disease first, and then to apply appropriate scoring systems. Dr. Brunt is among the most experienced liver pathologists worldwide, given that her name is linked to the original proposal for grading and staging NAFLD, which is largely utilized in clinical practice [15] as well as to the Clinical Research Network (CRN) scoring system, which is more appropriate in the research setting [16]. It was, therefore, a pleasure to read her comprehensive review addressing the "pros" and "cons" of the four existent histological scoring systems of NAFLD (i.e., the Brunt proposal for grading and staging; the Clinical Research Network-NASH scoring system; the Fatty Liver Inhibition of Progression (FLIP) algorithm, and the Pediatric NAFLD histologic score), which have specific fields of applications [17]. We fully agree with Dr. Brunt's conclusions that, as we learn to better use these different histological scoring systems, there remain the expectations for more "pros" and fewer "cons" [17].

4. Genetics, Epigenetics, Pathophysiology, and Molecular Pathogenesis

Genetics plays an ever increasingly appreciated pathogenic role in NAFLD development and progression, and an improved understanding of the molecular pathophysiology of NAFLD promises to disclose novel molecular pathways to be manipulated through innovative intervention schemes [1,10]. This is the reason why a substantial proportion of the contributions included in this monographic special issue are devoted to this specific topic.

Telomeres (i.e., repeat DNA sequences located at the terminal portion of chromosomes) shorten during mitosis, thus protecting the tips of chromosomes. Chronic degenerative conditions associated with high cell replication rate are associated with progressive telomere attrition which promotes DNA destabilization and cell aging in mammals, but also disturbed nutrient sensing, which could lead to the development of metabolic disorders such as NAFLD, cryptogenic cirrhosis, and type 2 diabetes mellitus [18–20]. In an article by Donati et al., after extensively reviewing the literature the authors concluded that modulation of telomerase or sheltering can be exploited to prevent NAFLD progression, and to define specific treatments for different stages of liver disease [20].

In an article by Ban et al., the authors addressed extracellular vesicles (EVs) as a promising tool for the non-invasive diagnosis of NAFLD [21]. The EVs are submicron membrane-bound structures that play a key role in the cell-to-cell cross talks and are either secreted from stressed and activated cells or formed during apoptosis. Based on the data published in the literature, the authors concluded that it can be reasonably assumed that once EVs become a routinely measured parameter for the assessment of NAFLD, their utility might be further projected to the treatment of the liver disease in its early stages and, potentially, the reversal of NASH [21].

Nuño-Lámbarri et al. reviewed experimental pathology and human NAFLD [22]. These authors further highlighted the importance of both oxidative/nitrative protein stress and mitochondrial dysfunction, which play a major role in stimulating NAFLD damage, as well as the importance of novel non-invasive biomarkers, such as retinol-binding protein-4, lumican, transgelin-2, and hemoglobin, which also play a role in NAFLD pathogenesis [22].

Similar to the oxidative stress, lipidomic analysis also has double significance as a pathogenic and diagnostic. For example, Gambino et al. reported that the elevated levels of serum free fatty acids observed in patients with NAFLD were mainly due to the levels of palmitic and oleic acids (which are the most abundant serum free fatty acids) as well as of those of serum linoleic acid and an imbalance in the n-3/n-6 fatty acids ratio [23].

The gut-liver axis plays a major role in NASH pathogenesis [1]. Consistent with this view, Houghton et al. identified gut microbiota as an emerging key element of personalized medicine and nutrition, and extensively reviewed how lifestyle interventions (diet and physical exercise) may affect gut microbiota, thus influencing the prognosis of NAFLD [24]. Similarly, Machado and Cortez-Pinto also addressed those lines of evidence linking NAFLD with intestinal dysbiosis [25]. They discussed that intestinal dysbiosis may promote the development of obesity through modulation of the energy harvested from the diet, as well as through direct modulation of adipose tissue and hepatic metabolism. Moreover, intestinal bacterial products and perturbed metabolism of choline and bile acids may be hepatotoxic. Dysbiosis can weaken the intestinal barrier, thus allowing bacterial products to invade the bloodstream and inducing systemic chronic inflammation and liver injury [25]. This impressive amount of emerging data on gut microbiota fuels expectations, however, it conflicts with the inadequacy of available studies which are small, heterogeneous, short-term, and do not properly address hepatic histology/risk for progressive liver disease. Hence, the lack of solid evidence still precludes us implementing probiotics in the management of NAFLD or NASH. Extensive preclinical studies comparing different approaches in different animal models of NASH would be important, and fecal microbiota transplantation also deserves further evaluation.

In an article by Aragonès et al., the authors analyzed the hepatic expression of patatin-like phospholipase domain containing 3 (PNPLA3) and other lipid metabolism-related genes in 55 morbidly obese patients (undergoing bariatric surgery) with normal liver histology ($n = 18$), simple steatosis (*n* = 20), and NASH (*n* = 17). These authors found that, compared to patients with normal liver histology, liver PNPLA3 expression was significantly increased in patients with NAFLD. Notably, the hepatic expression of PNPLA3 was even greater in those with NASH. In addition, the expression of the transcription factors liver X receptor (LXR)-α, peroxisome proliferator-activated receptor (PPAR)-α, and sterol regulatory element binding transcription factor (SREBP)-2 was also significantly associated with liver PNPLA3 expression. These findings are compatible with the notion that PNPLA3 is closely related to hepatic fat accumulation, and plays a role in the development and progression of NAFLD [26].

Petäjä and Yki-Järvinen reviewed the pertinent literature aimed at defining how much liver fat content is normal depending on the methods available and at evaluating the cardiometabolic effects of liver fat content as a function of different types of NAFLD (i.e., metabolic-related vs. genetic-related NAFLD) [27]. Based on liver histology, normal liver fat content is defined as macroscopic steatosis in less than 5% of hepatocytes. Based on proton magnetic resonance spectroscopy, normal liver fat content has been defined as ≤5.6%, which corresponds to histologic liver fat of nearly 15%. Whether or not these "normal values" of liver fat content are of clinical relevance with respect to the future development of hepatic fibrosis remains uncertain. NAFLD is a heterogeneous disease. While metabolic-related NAFLD is closely associated with metabolic syndrome features and an increased risk of incident type 2 diabetes and cardiovascular disease, NAFLD caused by either the PNPLA3 or the trans-membrane 6 superfamily member 2 (TM6SF2) genetic variants is usually not accompanied by increased insulin resistance [27]. In other words, it appears that "*not all NAFLD forms were created equal*" in terms of associated cardiometabolic risk [28]. Specifically, addressing the pathogenesis of cardiovascular disease associated with NAFLD, Pisano et al. reported that elevated ferritin levels and mild increased iron stores (i.e., a common finding in patients with NAFLD) may contribute to the development of vascular damage. Moreover, iron depletion may protect from accelerated atherogenesis in both experimental models and human studies [29].

In an article by Machado and Diehl, the authors reported on the Hedgehog (Hh) signaling pathway, which is a known orchestrator of integrated regenerative response by the different cellular players involved in wound-healing. The Hh pathway, which is usually quiescent in the normal liver, will become activated during liver injury. Both experimental and clinical data have consistently confirmed that activation of the Hh pathway mirrors the severity of NASH. Consistently, direct inhibition of the Hh pathway via pharmacological route may prevent liver disease progression in rodent NASH models and, in humans, the Hh pathway activity decreases as NASH improves, thus supporting a promising role of the Hh pathway as a therapeutic target in NASH [30].

Caligiuri et al. reported on the complex and multifactorial nature of NASH pathogenesis, which involves genetic and epigenetic factors; dietary factors; mitochondrial dysfunction and apoptosis; necroptosis; endoplasmic reticulum stress; hypoxia; inflammation; Hh pathway; nuclear receptors; pattern recognition receptors and inflammasomes; adipokines; and gut microbiome [31]. The authors concluded that continuing research is key in providing new targets and biomarkers for the management of NAFLD [31].

In an article by France et al., the authors examined the relationship between liver fat content and indices of lipolysis, and determined whether the degree of lipolysis may reflect insulin resistance or metabolic liver disease [32]. The authors found that glycerol was inversely related to liver fat content, suggesting down-regulation of fatty acid trafficking consistent with the classical paradigm proposed for NAFLD pathogenesis. Levels of ceruloplasmin were also inversely related to liver fat content, which remains an unexplained finding [32].

5. Clinical Features and Comorbidities

When addressing clinical features and comorbidities, it must be re-emphasized that NAFLD is a systemic disease [33–35] (Figure 1), which is strongly associated with an increased risk of incident fatal and nonfatal cardiovascular events [5,36], and chronic kidney disease [36,37].

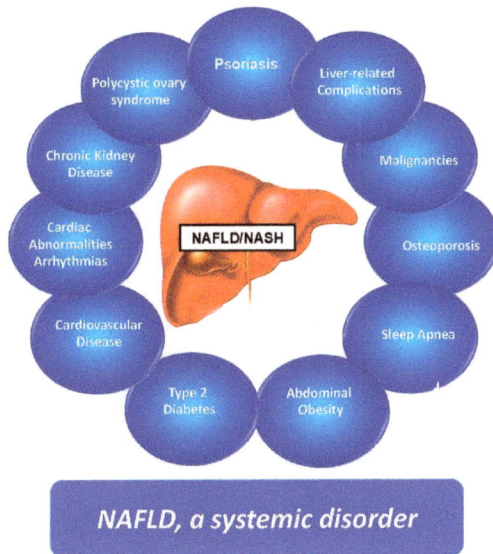

Figure 1. Nonalcoholic fatty liver disease (NAFLD) as a systemic disorder. This figure depicts the ever enlarging protean clinical spectrum of NAFLD. The variety and heterogeneity of the organ systems involved in patients with NAFLD witnesses the systemic nature of this common liver disease. (Modified from [36]).

The concurrence of chronic plaque psoriasis was almost anecdotally reported in three NAFLD cases observed in 2001 [38], and has now turned into a solid line of research. On this background, it can be better appreciated, as reported by Mantovani et al., that there is now substantial evidence supporting a strong association between the presence and severity of NAFLD and chronic plaque psoriasis, which argues for more careful evaluation and surveillance of NAFLD among patients with psoriasis [39].

The initial paradigm of NAFLD being the "hepatic manifestation of the metabolic syndrome" has undergone a significant evolution and now the relationship between NAFLD and the metabolic syndrome is deemed to be mutual and bidirectional [3,4,36,40]. Wainwright and Byrne highlighted that NAFLD predisposes to the development of metabolic syndrome features, which can, in their turn, increase the risk of development and progression of NAFLD [41]. The authors went further in discussing recent insights from studies of PNPLA3 and trans-membrane 6 superfamily member 2 (TM6SF2) genotypes, which may further contribute to understanding how and why metabolic syndrome features and liver disease are linked in NAFLD [41].

In their comparative NAFLD-hepatitis C virus review of the literature, Ballestri et al. depicted the liver as the "fourth musketeer" (Figure 2) involved in the pathogenesis of hepatic insulin resistance and type 2 diabetes mellitus [42].

Further attesting to the strong relationship between NAFLD and metabolic syndrome features, Perticone et al., by studying endothelium-dependent vasodilation in nearly 300 never-treated hypertensive patients, suggested that NAFLD is an early marker of endothelial dysfunction in these patients [43].

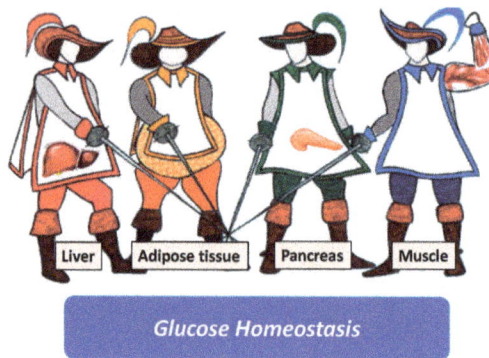

Figure 2. Liver as the fourth "musketeer". This figure identifies adipose tissue, skeletal muscles, and pancreas as the three key organ systems controlling glucose homeostasis in humans. Together with these three organ systems, the liver also plays a key role in glucose disposal in health. Consistently, a large number of studies based on both the NAFLD and the hepatitis C virus (HCV)-related liver disease spectrum have highlighted the pathogenic role of the liver in the development of type 2 diabetes mellitus. (Modified from ref. [42]).

Clearly, if NAFLD is closely linked with both circulatory endothelial dysfunction and metabolic syndrome features, one might anticipate that NAFLD may also predispose to the development of chronic kidney disease (CKD). In their review of published and ongoing studies, Marcuccilli and Chonchol addressed this interesting topic and concluded that there is now substantial evidence linking NAFLD to CKD development [44]. The mechanisms underlying these two diseases are complexly inter-woven; thus, additional experimental and clinical research is required, including data on both liver and kidney histology. Of interest, lifestyle changes aimed at weight loss and increased physical activity may prevent and benefit both diseases. Finally, physicians' awareness may lead to screening of CKD among patients with NAFLD and thus to earlier detection and treatment and to improved outcomes in patients with NAFLD and spared organ transplantations [44].

In an article by Villela-Nogueira et al., the authors reviewed the published data on the association between NAFLD and increased aortic stiffness, i.e., a marker of increased cardiovascular risk [45]. Although the underlying biological mechanisms linking NAFLD and increased arterial stiffness remain largely unknown, they possibly involve shared pathways of chronic inflammation and imbalance in adipokine profile [45].

Sanna et al. critically appraised key studies on NAFLD-associated extra-hepatic cancers and speculated on how NAFLD may influence carcinogenesis at these sites [46]. Beyond the increased risk of incident HCC, probably mediated by NASH, substantial epidemiological evidence is now accumulating for a role of NAFLD as a possible risk factor for certain extra-hepatic cancers, particularly in the gastrointestinal tract [46]. Based on the wealth of published data, health care providers taking care of patients with NAFLD should be vigilant for any signs and symptoms suggestive of cancer, particularly colorectal cancers, and promptly refer these patients for further assessment and management whenever indicated.

6. Clinical Course and Natural History

The clinical course of NAFLD is characterized by the development of cardiovascular disease and other metabolic comorbidities and by the possible progression of liver disease itself [1,47,48].

Calzadilla Bertot and Adams further highlighted that, although only a small proportion of individuals with NAFLD will develop cirrhosis, the large proportion of the population affected by NAFLD has led to predictions that NAFLD will become a leading cause of end-stage liver disease, liver transplantation, and HCC over the next decade [49]. HCC may arise in non-cirrhotic livers in the setting of NAFLD and is closely associated with the presence of metabolic syndrome and male sex. Along with metabolic syndrome features, other genetic and environmental factors also play a role in the progression of NAFLD [49].

On this background, Gitto and Villa addressed a specific and often overlooked aspect. These authors reported that following liver transplant both recurrent and de novo NAFLD can be found, which usually follows an indolent course with very few cases of liver fibrosis progression [50]. Clinicians should therefore use the diagnosis of NAFLD in the post-liver transplant phase as a marker of increased cardiovascular and CKD risks [50].

7. Pediatric Nonalcoholic Fatty Liver Disease

Compared to the disease as seen in adults, pediatric NAFLD has both similarities and differences [51]. Temple et al. reported that NAFLD affects up to 20% of the general pediatric age-group population, and it is projected to become the major cause of liver pathology, liver failure, and liver transplantation in childhood and adolescence in Western countries over the next decade [52]. However, pediatric NAFLD remains an under-studied, under-recognized, and thus potentially under-managed condition [52].

In their original study Pacifico et al. investigated whether overweight or obese children with NAFLD suffered from impaired renal function, as determined by both estimated glomerular filtration rate and urinary albumin excretion [53]. Data have indeed confirmed that children with NAFLD were at risk for early renal dysfunction. Recognition of this risk in these young patients may help in halting the progression of subclinical kidney disease [53].

8. NAFLD and Hepatitis C Virus

Historically, comparative studies of NAFLD vs. hepatitis C virus (HCV)-related liver disease have been key in promoting an improved understanding of the pathogenesis and natural history of both liver diseases [54–57].

According to Adinolfi et al., data have shown that hepatic steatosis was a feature of chronic HCV infection and a potentially finalistic condition favoring the persistence and replication of HCV [58]. Hepatic steatosis might thus be a useful marker for identifying those HCV patients at higher risk of liver disease progression, development of extra-hepatic diseases, and, possibly, reduced response rate to novel antivirals [58]. Bringing this consolidated comparative analysis further, Shigefuku et al. aimed at elucidating the difference in liver disease progression (measuring various fibrosis markers, liver function, and hepatic tissue blood flow) in 139 patients with NAFLD and 152 patients with chronic HCV [59]. The authors concluded that, compared to those with HCV-related liver disease, patients with NAFLD exhibited significant changes in hepatic blood flow during the earliest stage of hepatic fibrosis, suggesting that patients with NAFLD need to be followed carefully [59].

9. Management

It is now universally agreed that lifestyle changes (diet and physical activity) should be offered to all patients with NAFLD and that treatment of all coexisting cardiometabolic risk factors will often require multiple pharmacological interventions [1,10,60]. Regarding the management of NAFLD, this monographic special issue includes two articles of clinical relevance and two experimental studies.

As regards the role of diet in humans, based on their review of published articles, Stachowska et al. pinpointed that the action of nutrients may be affected by some gene polymorphisms [61]. Therefore, individualization of diet for patients with NAFLD and particularly the nutrient-induced insulin output ratio in people sensitive to fat appears to be a useful tool for determining specific nutritional strategies for patients with NAFLD [61]. Hernandez-Rodas et al., in their turn, extensively reviewed the results of interventions in lifestyle, diet, and behavioral therapies and research results in human, animal, and cell models [62].

Finally, this single-topic special issue also includes two experimental studies. In the first one, Walenbergh et al. reported that subcutaneous injection of 2-hydroxypropyl-β-cyclodextrin could be a useful tool to improve intracellular cholesterol levels in the context of the metabolic syndrome in a mouse model featuring hyperlipidemic low-density lipoprotein (LDL)-receptor knockout animals, possibly through modulation of phytosterols and oxysterols [63]. In the second study, Ideta et al. established a novel NAFLD model mouse, using monosodium glutamate and a high-fat diet, and investigated the effect of teneligliptin (i.e., an oral dipeptidyl-peptidase-4 inhibitor) on the risk of NAFLD progression [64]. They reported that this drug significantly attenuated hepatic lipogenesis by activating $5'$ adenosine monophosphate (AMP)-activated protein kinase (AMPK) and down-regulating the expression of multiple genes involved in lipogenesis [64]. However, the clinical relevance of both experimental studies [63,64] remains to be further evaluated.

10. Conclusions

We believe that the *"Non-Alcoholic Fatty Liver Disease Research 2016"* monographic special issue of the *IJMS* journal further reinforces the notion that the global health burden of NAFLD is not only confined to progressive liver disease, but also embraces major extra-hepatic complications. In particular, the leading causes of mortality among patients with NAFLD are cardiovascular disease, followed by non-liver malignancy and liver disease. Indeed, NAFLD is a multisystem disease, which by disrupting the regulation of multiple metabolic and inflammatory pathways, plays an important role in the development of cardiovascular disease, type 2 diabetes mellitus, and other metabolic disorders.

Collectively, the published papers provide testimony that NAFLD research has now reached an elevated scientific standard and that most patients with NAFLD will benefit from it. For example, based on the published data, close surveillance of most patients with NAFLD and aggressive management in a subset of them is now highly recommendable. However, further research is needed to better understand the genetic modifiers, natural history, molecular pathogenesis of NAFLD, and biological mechanisms by which NAFLD may contribute to the increased cardiometabolic risk. This promises also to disclose novel and effective treatment strategies for this increasingly prevalent disease, which will ever increasingly impact on the burden of global health in the near future.

Acknowledgments: We are indebted to Jacqueline Mole for her editing of English.

Author Contributions: Both authors researched the data for the article, provided substantial contributions to discussions of its content, wrote the article and undertook review and/or editing of the manuscript before submission.

Conflicts of Interest: The authors declare no conflict of interest.

Abbreviations

AMPK	AMP-Activated Protein Kinase
CRN	Clinical Research Network
EVs	Extracellular Vesicles
FLIP	Fatty Liver Inhibition of Progression
HCC	Hepatocellular Carcinoma
Hh	Hedgehog
LAL	Lysosomal Acid Lipase
NAFLD	Nonalcoholic Fatty Liver Disease
NASH	Nonalcoholic Steatohepatitis
PNPLA3	Patatin-Like Phospholipase Domain Containing 3
TM6SF2	Trans-Membrane 6 Superfamily Member 2

References

1. Italian Association for the Study of the Liver (AISF). AISF position paper on nonalcoholic fatty liver disease (NAFLD): Updates and future directions. *Dig. Liver Dis.* **2017**, *49*, 471–483.
2. Younossi, Z.M.; Koenig, A.B.; Abdelatif, D.; Fazel, Y.; Henry, L.; Wymer, M. Global epidemiology of nonalcoholic fatty liver disease-Meta-analytic assessment of prevalence, incidence, and outcomes. *Hepatology* **2016**, *64*, 73–84. [CrossRef] [PubMed]
3. Ballestri, S.; Zona, S.; Targher, G.; Romagnoli, D.; Baldelli, E.; Nascimbeni, F.; Roverato, A.; Guaraldi, G.; Lonardo, A. Nonalcoholic fatty liver disease is associated with an almost twofold increased risk of incident type 2 diabetes and metabolic syndrome. Evidence from a systematic review and meta-analysis. *J. Gastroenterol. Hepatol.* **2016**, *31*, 936–944. [CrossRef] [PubMed]
4. Ballestri, S.; Nascimbeni, F.; Romagnoli, D.; Lonardo, A. The independent predictors of non-alcoholic steatohepatitis and its individual histological features. Insulin resistance, serum uric acid, metabolic syndrome, alanine aminotransferase and serum total cholesterol are a clue to pathogenesis and candidate targets for treatment. *Hepatol. Res.* **2016**, *46*, 1074–1087. [PubMed]
5. Targher, G.; Byrne, C.D.; Lonardo, A.; Zoppini, G.; Barbui, C. Non-alcoholic fatty liver disease and risk of incident cardiovascular disease: A meta-analysis. *J. Hepatol.* **2016**, *65*, 589–600. [CrossRef] [PubMed]
6. Lonardo, A.; Loria, P.; Argo, C.; Caldwell, S. Perspectives on cellular dysfunction in nonalcoholic steatohepatitis: A case of "multiorganelle failure"? Proceedings of a virtual workshop on nonalcoholic steatohepatitis. *Expert Rev. Gastroenterol. Hepatol.* **2011**, *5*, 135–139. [CrossRef] [PubMed]
7. Farrell, G.C.; Wong, V.W.; Chitturi, S. NAFLD in Asia—As common and important as in the West. *Nat. Rev. Gastroenterol. Hepatol.* **2013**, *10*, 307–318. [CrossRef] [PubMed]
8. Younossi, Z.M.; Blissett, D.; Blissett, R.; Henry, L.; Stepanova, M.; Younossi, Y.; Racila, A.; Hunt, S.; Beckerman, R. The economic and clinical burden of nonalcoholic fatty liver disease in the United States and Europe. *Hepatology* **2016**, *64*, 1577–1586. [CrossRef] [PubMed]
9. Lonardo, A.; Bellentani, S.; Argo, C.K.; Ballestri, S.; Byrne, C.D.; Caldwell, S.H.; Cortez-Pinto, H.; Grieco, A.; Machado, M.V.; Miele, L.; et al. Epidemiological modifiers of non-alcoholic fatty liver disease: Focus on high-risk groups. *Dig. Liver Dis.* **2015**, *47*, 997–1006. [CrossRef] [PubMed]
10. European Association for the Study of the Liver (EASL); European Association for the Study of Diabetes (EASD); European Association for the Study of Obesity (EASO). EASL-EASD-EASO Clinical Practice Guidelines for the management of non-alcoholic fatty liver disease. *J. Hepatol.* **2016**, *64*, 1388–1402.
11. Losekann, A.; Weston, A.; de Mattos, A.; Tovo, C.; de Carli, L.; Espindola, M.; Pioner, S.; Coral, G. Non-alcoholic steatohepatitis (NASH): Risk factors in morbidly obese patients. *Int. J. Mol. Sci.* **2015**, *16*, 25552–25559. [CrossRef] [PubMed]
12. Lombardi, R.; Pisano, G.; Fargion, S. Role of serum uric acid and ferritin in the development and progression of NAFLD. *Int. J. Mol. Sci.* **2016**, *17*, 548. [CrossRef] [PubMed]
13. Baratta, F.; Pastori, D.; Polimeni, L.; Tozzi, G.; Violi, F.; Angelico, F.; del Ben, M. Does Lysosomial acid lipase reduction play a role in adult non-alcoholic fatty liver disease? *Int. J. Mol. Sci.* **2015**, *16*, 28014–28021. [CrossRef] [PubMed]
14. Shteyer, E.; Villenchik, R.; Mahamid, M.; Nator, N.; Safadi, R. Low serum lysosomal acid lipase activity correlates with advanced liver disease. *Int. J. Mol. Sci.* **2016**, *17*, 312. [CrossRef] [PubMed]
15. Brunt, E.M.; Janney, C.G.; Di Bisceglie, A.M.; Neuschwander-Tetri, B.A.; Bacon, B.R. Nonalcoholic steatohepatitis: A proposal for grading and staging the histological lesions. *Am. J. Gastroenterol.* **1999**, *94*, 2467–2474. [CrossRef] [PubMed]
16. Kleiner, D.E.; Brunt, E.M.; van Natta, M.; Behling, C.; Contos, M.J.; Cummings, O.W.; Ferrell, L.D.; Liu, Y.C.; Torbenson, M.S.; Unalp-Arida, A.; et al. Nonalcoholic steatohepatitis clinical research network. Design and validation of a histological scoring system for nonalcoholic fatty liver disease. *Hepatology* **2005**, *41*, 1313–1321. [CrossRef] [PubMed]
17. Brunt, E. Nonalcoholic fatty liver disease: Pros and cons of histologic systems of evaluation. *Int. J. Mol. Sci.* **2016**, *17*, 97. [CrossRef] [PubMed]
18. Kirchner, H.; Shaheen, F.; Kalscheuer, H.; Schmid, S.M.; Oster, H.; Lehnert, H. The telomeric complex and metabolic disease. *Genes* **2017**, *8*, 176. [CrossRef] [PubMed]

19. Laish, I.; Mannasse-Green, B.; Hadary, R.; Konikoff, F.M.; Amiel, A.; Kitay-Cohen, Y. Aneuploidy and asynchronous replication in non-alcoholic fatty liver disease and cryptogenic cirrhosis. *Gene* **2016**, *593*, 162–166. [CrossRef] [PubMed]

20. Donati, B.; Valenti, L. Telomeres NAFLD and chronic liver disease. *Int. J. Mol. Sci.* **2016**, *17*, 383. [CrossRef] [PubMed]

21. Ban, L.; Shackel, N.; McLennan, S. Extracellular vesicles: A new frontier in biomarker discovery for non-alcoholic fatty liver disease. *Int. J. Mol. Sci.* **2016**, *17*, 376. [CrossRef] [PubMed]

22. Nuño-Lámbarri, N.; Barbero-Becerra, V.; Uribe, M.; Chávez-Tapia, N. Mitochondrial molecular pathophysiology of nonalcoholic fatty liver disease: A proteomics approach. *Int. J. Mol. Sci.* **2016**, *17*, 281. [CrossRef] [PubMed]

23. Gambino, R.; Bugianesi, E.; Rosso, C.; Mezzabotta, L.; Pinach, S.; Alemanno, N.; Saba, F.; Cassader, M. Different serum free fatty acid profiles in NAFLD subjects and healthy controls after oral fat load. *Int. J. Mol. Sci.* **2016**, *17*, 479. [CrossRef] [PubMed]

24. Houghton, D.; Stewart, C.; Day, C.; Trenell, M. Gut microbiota and lifestyle interventions in NAFLD. *Int. J. Mol. Sci.* **2016**, *17*, 447. [CrossRef] [PubMed]

25. Machado, M.; Cortez-Pinto, H. Diet microbiota obesity and NAFLD: A dangerous quartet. *Int. J. Mol. Sci.* **2016**, *17*, 481. [CrossRef] [PubMed]

26. Aragonès, G.; Auguet, T.; Armengol, S.; Berlanga, A.; Guiu-Jurado, E.; Aguilar, C.; Martínez, S.; Sabench, F.; Porras, J.; Ruiz, M.; et al. PNPLA3 expression is related to liver steatosis in morbidly obese women with non-alcoholic fatty liver disease. *Int. J. Mol. Sci.* **2016**, *17*, 630. [CrossRef] [PubMed]

27. Petäjä, E.; Yki-Järvinen, H. Definitions of normal liver fat and the association of insulin sensitivity with acquired and genetic NAFLD—A systematic review. *Int. J. Mol. Sci.* **2016**, *17*, 633. [CrossRef] [PubMed]

28. Lonardo, A.; Ballestri, S.; Targher, G. "Not all forms of NAFLD were created equal". Do metabolic syndrome-related NAFLD and PNPLA3-related NAFLD exert a variable impact on the risk of early carotid atherosclerosis? *Atherosclerosis* **2017**, *257*, 253–255. [CrossRef] [PubMed]

29. Pisano, G.; Lombardi, R.; Fracanzani, A. Vascular damage in patients with nonalcoholic fatty liver disease: Possible role of iron and ferritin. *Int. J. Mol. Sci.* **2016**, *17*, 675. [CrossRef] [PubMed]

30. Verdelho Machado, M.; Diehl, A. Role of hedgehog signaling pathway in NASH. *Int. J. Mol. Sci.* **2016**, *17*, 857. [CrossRef] [PubMed]

31. Caligiuri, A.; Gentilini, A.; Marra, F. Molecular pathogenesis of NASH. *Int. J. Mol. Sci.* **2016**, *17*, 1575. [CrossRef] [PubMed]

32. France, M.; Kwok, S.; Soran, H.; Williams, S.; Ho, J.; Adam, S.; Canoy, D.; Liu, Y.; Durrington, P. Liver fat measured by MR spectroscopy: Estimate of imprecision and relationship with serum glycerol, caeruloplasmin and non-esterified fatty acids. *Int. J. Mol. Sci.* **2016**, *17*, 1089. [CrossRef] [PubMed]

33. Lonardo, A.; Bellini, M.; Tondelli, E.; Frazzoni, M.; Grisendi, A.; Pulvirenti, M.; Della Casa, G. Nonalcoholic steatohepatitis and the "bright liver syndrome": Should a recently expanded clinical entity be further expanded? *Am. J. Gastroenterol.* **1995**, *90*, 2072–2074. [PubMed]

34. Byrne, C.D.; Targher, G. NAFLD: A multisystem disease. *J. Hepatol.* **2015**, *62* (Suppl. 1), S47–S64. [CrossRef] [PubMed]

35. Petta, S.; Valenti, L.; Bugianesi, E.; Targher, G.; Bellentani, S.; Bonino, F.; Special Interest Group on Personalised Hepatology of the Italian Association for the Study of the Liver (AISF). A "systems medicine" approach to the study of non-alcoholic fatty liver disease. *Dig. Liver Dis.* **2016**, *48*, 333–342. [CrossRef] [PubMed]

36. Adams, L.A.; Anstee, Q.M.; Tilg, H.; Targher, G. Non-alcoholic fatty liver disease and its relationship with cardiovascular disease and other extrahepatic diseases. *Gut* **2017**, *66*, 1138–1153. [CrossRef] [PubMed]

37. Targher, G.; Byrne, C.D. Non-alcoholic fatty liver disease: An emerging driving force in chronic kidney disease. *Nat. Rev. Nephrol.* **2017**, *13*, 297–310. [CrossRef] [PubMed]

38. Lonardo, A.; Loria, P.; Carulli, N. Concurrent non-alcoholic steatohepatitis and psoriasis. Report of three cases from the POLI. ST. ENA study. *Dig. Liver Dis.* **2001**, *33*, 86–87. [CrossRef]

39. Mantovani, A.; Gisondi, P.; Lonardo, A.; Targher, G. Relationship between non-alcoholic fatty liver disease and psoriasis: A novel hepato-dermal axis? *Int. J. Mol. Sci.* **2016**, *17*, 217. [CrossRef] [PubMed]

40. Lonardo, A.; Ballestri, S.; Marchesini, G.; Angulo, P.; Loria, P. Nonalcoholic fatty liver disease: A precursor of the metabolic syndrome. *Dig. Liver Dis.* **2015**, *47*, 181–190. [CrossRef] [PubMed]

41. Wainwright, P.; Byrne, C. Bidirectional relationships and disconnects between NAFLD and features of the metabolic syndrome. *Int. J. Mol. Sci.* **2016**, *17*, 367. [CrossRef] [PubMed]
42. Ballestri, S.; Nascimbeni, F.; Romagnoli, D.; Baldelli, E.; Targher, G.; Lonardo, A. Type 2 Diabetes in non-alcoholic fatty liver disease and hepatitis C virus infection—Liver: The "Musketeer" in the spotlight. *Int. J. Mol. Sci.* **2016**, *17*, 355. [CrossRef] [PubMed]
43. Perticone, M.; Cimellaro, A.; Maio, R.; Caroleo, B.; Sciacqua, A.; Sesti, G.; Perticone, F. Additive effect of non-alcoholic fatty liver disease on metabolic syndrome-related endothelial dysfunction in hypertensive patients. *Int. J. Mol. Sci.* **2016**, *17*, 456. [CrossRef] [PubMed]
44. Marcuccilli, M.; Chonchol, M. NAFLD and chronic kidney disease. *Int. J. Mol. Sci.* **2016**, *17*, 562. [CrossRef] [PubMed]
45. Villela-Nogueira, C.; Leite, N.; Cardoso, C.; Salles, G. NAFLD and increased aortic stiffness: Parallel or common physiopathological mechanisms? *Int. J. Mol. Sci.* **2016**, *17*, 460. [CrossRef] [PubMed]
46. Sanna, C.; Rosso, C.; Marietti, M.; Bugianesi, E. Non-alcoholic fatty liver disease and extra-hepatic cancers. *Int. J. Mol. Sci.* **2016**, *17*, 717. [CrossRef] [PubMed]
47. Ballestri, S.; Nascimbeni, F.; Romagnoli, D.; Baldelli, E.; Lonardo, A. The role of nuclear receptors in the pathophysiology, natural course, and drug treatment of NAFLD in humans. *Adv. Ther.* **2016**, *33*, 291–319. [CrossRef] [PubMed]
48. Lonardo, A.; Sookoian, S.; Chonchol, M.; Loria, P.; Targher, G. Cardiovascular and systemic risk in nonalcoholic fatty liver disease—Atherosclerosis as a major player in the natural course of NAFLD. *Curr. Pharm. Des.* **2013**, *19*, 5177–5192. [CrossRef] [PubMed]
49. Calzadilla Bertot, L.; Adams, L. The natural course of non-alcoholic fatty liver disease. *Int. J. Mol. Sci.* **2016**, *17*, 774. [CrossRef] [PubMed]
50. Gitto, S.; Villa, E. Non-alcoholic fatty liver disease and metabolic syndrome after liver transplant. *Int. J. Mol. Sci.* **2016**, *17*, 490. [CrossRef] [PubMed]
51. Crespo, M.; Lappe, S.; Feldstein, A.E.; Alkhouri, N. Similarities and differences between pediatric and adult nonalcoholic fatty liver disease. *Metabolism* **2016**, *65*, 1161–1171. [CrossRef] [PubMed]
52. Temple, J.; Cordero, P.; Li, J.; Nguyen, V.; Oben, J. A Guide to non-alcoholic fatty liver disease in childhood and adolescence. *Int. J. Mol. Sci.* **2016**, *17*, 947. [CrossRef] [PubMed]
53. Pacifico, L.; Bonci, E.; Andreoli, G.; di Martino, M.; Gallozzi, A.; De Luca, E.; Chiesa, C. The impact of nonalcoholic fatty liver disease on renal function in children with overweight/obesity. *Int. J. Mol. Sci.* **2016**, *17*, 1218. [CrossRef] [PubMed]
54. Lonardo, A.; Adinolfi, L.E.; Loria, P.; Carulli, N.; Ruggiero, G.; Day, C.P. Steatosis and hepatitis C virus: Mechanisms and significance for hepatic and extrahepatic disease. *Gastroenterology* **2004**, *126*, 586–597. [CrossRef] [PubMed]
55. Targher, G.; Bertolini, L.; Padovani, R.; Rodella, S.; Arcaro, G.; Day, C. Differences and similarities in early atherosclerosis between patients with non-alcoholic steatohepatitis and chronic hepatitis B and C. *J. Hepatol.* **2007**, *46*, 1126–1132. [CrossRef] [PubMed]
56. Lonardo, A.; Adinolfi, L.E.; Restivo, L.; Ballestri, S.; Romagnoli, D.; Baldelli, E.; Nascimbeni, F.; Loria, P. Pathogenesis and significance of hepatitis C virus steatosis: An update on survival strategy of a successful pathogen. *World J. Gastroenterol.* **2014**, *20*, 7089–7103. [CrossRef] [PubMed]
57. Rinaldi, L.; Nascimbeni, F.; Giordano, M.; Masetti, C.; Guerrera, B.; Amelia, A.; Fascione, M.C.; Ballestri, S.; Romagnoli, D.; Zampino, R.; et al. Clinical features and natural history of cryptogenic cirrhosis compared to hepatitis C virus-related cirrhosis. *World J. Gastroenterol.* **2017**, *23*, 1458–1468. [CrossRef] [PubMed]
58. Adinolfi, L.; Rinaldi, L.; Guerrera, B.; Restivo, L.; Marrone, A.; Giordano, M.; Zampino, R. NAFLD and NASH in HCV infection: Prevalence and significance in hepatic and extrahepatic manifestations. *Int. J. Mol. Sci.* **2016**, *17*, 803. [CrossRef] [PubMed]
59. Shigefuku, R.; Takahashi, H.; Nakano, H.; Watanabe, T.; Matsunaga, K.; Matsumoto, N.; Kato, M.; Morita, R.; Michikawa, Y.; Tamura, T.; et al. Correlations of hepatic hemodynamics liver function and fibrosis markers in nonalcoholic fatty liver disease: Comparison with chronic hepatitis related to hepatitis C virus. *Int. J. Mol. Sci.* **2016**, *17*, 1545. [CrossRef] [PubMed]
60. Lonardo, A.; Ballestri, S.; Targher, G.; Loria, P. Diagnosis and management of cardiovascular risk in nonalcoholic fatty liver disease. *Expert Rev. Gastroenterol. Hepatol.* **2015**, *9*, 629–650. [CrossRef] [PubMed]

61. Stachowska, E.; Ryterska, K.; Maciejewska, D.; Banaszczak, M.; Milkiewicz, P.; Milkiewicz, M.; Gutowska, I.; Ossowski, P.; Kaczorowska, M.; Jamioł-Milc, D.; et al. Nutritional strategies for the individualized treatment of non-alcoholic fatty liver disease (NAFLD) based on the nutrient-induced insulin output ratio (NIOR). *Int. J. Mol. Sci.* **2016**, *17*, 1192. [CrossRef] [PubMed]
62. Hernandez-Rodas, M.; Valenzuela, R.; Videla, L. Relevant aspects of nutritional and dietary interventions in non-alcoholic fatty liver disease. *Int. J. Mol. Sci.* **2015**, *16*, 25168–25198. [CrossRef] [PubMed]
63. Walenbergh, S.; Houben, T.; Hendrikx, T.; Jeurissen, M.; van Gorp, P.; Vaes, N.; Damink, S.; Verheyen, F.; Koek, G.; Lütjohann, D.; et al. Weekly treatment of 2-hydroxypropyl-β-cyclodextrin improves intracellular cholesterol levels in LDL receptor knockout mice. *Int. J. Mol. Sci.* **2015**, *1*, 21056–21069. [CrossRef] [PubMed]
64. Ideta, T.; Shirakami, Y.; Miyazaki, T.; Kochi, T.; Sakai, H.; Moriwaki, H.; Shimizu, M. The DIPEPTIDYL peptidase-4 Inhibitor teneligliptin attenuates hepatic lipogenesis via AMPK activation in non-alcoholic fatty liver disease model mice. *Int. J. Mol. Sci.* **2015**, *16*, 29207–29218. [CrossRef] [PubMed]

International Journal of
Molecular Sciences

MDPI

Article

Non-Alcoholic Steatohepatitis (NASH): Risk Factors in Morbidly Obese Patients

Alexandre Losekann [1], Antonio C. Weston [2], Angelo A. de Mattos [1], Cristiane V. Tovo [1], Luis A. de Carli [2], Marilia B. Espindola [2], Sergio R. Pioner [2] and Gabriela P. Coral [1,*]

[1]   Post-Graduation Program, Hepatology at Universidade Federal de Ciências da Saúde de Porto Alegre (UFCSPA), Porto Alegre 90.050-170, Brasil; alosekann@gmail.com (A.L.); angeloamattos@gmail.com (A.A.M.); cris.tovo@terra.com.br (C.V.T.)
[2]   Centro de Tratamento da Obesidade (CTO), Hospital Santa Casa de Misericórdia de Porto Alegre, Porto Alegre 92.010-300, Brasil; drweston@terra.com.br (A.C.W.); luizdecarli@plugin.com.br (L.A.C.); mariliae@brturbo.com.br (M.B.E.); srpioner@terra.com.br (S.R.P.)
*   Author to whom correspondence should be addressed; g.coral@terra.com.br; Tel.: +55-51-3214-8158; Fax: +55-51-3214-8238.

Academic Editors: Amedeo Lonardo and Giovanni Targher
Received: 15 August 2015; Accepted: 14 October 2015; Published: 23 October 2015

Abstract: The aim was to investigate the prevalence of non-alcoholic steatohepatitis (NASH) and risk factors for hepatic fibrosis in morbidly obese patients submitted to bariatric surgery. This retrospective study recruited all patients submitted to bariatric surgery from January 2007 to December 2012 at a reference attendance center of Southern Brazil. Clinical and biochemical data were studied as a function of the histological findings of liver biopsies done during the surgery. Steatosis was present in 226 (90.4%) and NASH in 176 (70.4%) cases. The diagnosis of cirrhosis was established in four cases (1.6%) and fibrosis in 108 (43.2%). Risk factors associated with NASH at multivariate analysis were alanine aminotransferase (ALT) >1.5 times the upper limit of normal (ULN); glucose $\geq$ 126 mg/dL and triglycerides $\geq$ 150 mg/dL. All patients with ALT $\geq$1.5 times the ULN had NASH. When the presence of fibrosis was analyzed, ALT > 1.5 times the ULN and triglycerides $\geq$ 150 mg/dL were risk factors, furthermore, there was an increase of 1% in the prevalence of fibrosis for each year of age increase. Not only steatosis, but NASH is a frequent finding in MO patients. In the present study, ALT $\geq$ 1.5 times the ULN identifies all patients with NASH, this finding needs to be further validated in other studies. Moreover, the presence of fibrosis was associated with ALT, triglycerides and age, identifying a subset of patients with more severe disease.

Keywords: NAFLD; NASH; morbidly obese; liver fibrosis

---

1. Introduction

Nonalcoholic fatty liver disease (NAFLD) embraces a wide range of manifestations that includes simple steatosis (SS), non-alcoholic steatohepatitis (NASH), cirrhosis and hepatocellular carcinoma [1,2]. The real prevalence of NASH is not known, as the disease is usually asymptomatic and that the definitive diagnosis is possible only by the histopathological assessment [3,4]. In a study conducted in a tertiary public hospital in south Brazil, the prevalence of NASH was 3.18% in obese patients without diabetes mellitus (DM) [5].

Morbidly obese (MO) patients, defined as body mass index (BMI) $\geq$35 and experiencing obesity-related health conditions or $\geq$40 kg/m^2, are a subgroup with higher risk of NAFLD. In these patients, the prevalence of NAFLD is estimated from 84% to 96% and of NASH from 25% to 55%. In those with NASH, there is bridging fibrosis or cirrhosis at a rate of 12% and 2% respectively [4,6].

This study aimed to estimate the prevalence of NASH and the risk factors for fibrosis in MO patients submitted to bariatric surgery (BS).

2. Results

A total of 250 patients were evaluated; 200 (80%) were women, with an average age of 36.8 ± 10.2 years. The average BMI was 43.6 ± 5.2 kg/m^2. Type 2 diabetes was identified in 12.8% and arterial hypertension in 41.3%.

Simple steatosis was present in 226 (90.4%) patients and were classified as mild in 76 (30.4%); moderate in 71 (28.4%) and severe in 79 (31.6%). NASH was diagnosed in 176 (70.4%) cases, being mild degree in 120 (48.4%) cases; moderate in 50 (20%) cases, and severe in 6 (2.4%) cases. Fibrosis was reported in 108 (43.2%) biopsies, 95 (38%) of them were mild; 2 (0.8%) moderate; and 7 severe (2.8%). Cirrhosis was diagnosed in 4 (1.6%) cases.

The risk factors related to NASH in bivariate analysis (Table 1) were: Mean value of AST, mean value of ALT, ALT ≥ 1.5 times the ULN, mean value of TG, TG ≥ 150 mg/dL and mean value of glucose. All patients with ALT ≥1.5 times the ULN had NASH. After the adjustment by the multivariate model, the following variables remain associated with NASH (Table 2): ALT > 1.5 times the ULN; glucose ≥ 126 mg/dL and TG ≥ 150 mg/dL.

Some risk factors associated to fibrosis by bivariate analysis (Table 3) were the same as those associated with NASH: Mean value of AST, mean value of ALT, ALT > 1.5 times the ULN, mean value of TG, TG ≥ 150 mg/dL and mean value of glucose. In addition, glucose ≥ 126 mg/dL and age were also associated with fibrosis. The mean age of patients with fibrosis was 40.0 ± 11.4 and without fibrosis, 34.8 ± 9.3 (p = 0.001). After the adjustment by the multivariate model (Table 2), the following variables remain associated with fibrosis: ALT > 1.5 times the ULN, TG ≥ 150 mg/dL and age: For a year of age increase, there is an increase of 1% in the prevalence of fibrosis (PR = 1.01; 95% CI = 1.00–1.02; p = 0.006).

Table 1. Bivariate analysis according to the presence of non-alcoholic steatohepatitis (NASH).

Variable *	Total Sample	With NASH	Without NASH	p
Age (years)	37.2 ± 10.6 (n = 183)	37.6 ± 11.0 (n = 141)	35.5 ± 9.0 (n = 42)	0.208
Female	153 (80.1) (n = 191)	113 (79) (n = 143)	40 (83.3) (n = 48)	0.661
BMI (kg/m^2)	43.7 ± 5.2 (n = 191)	43.5 ± 5.0 (n = 143)	44.1 ± 5.7 (n = 48)	0.535
Ferritin (μ/L)	119 (67–208) (n = 169)	123 (75–239) (n = 128)	97 (58.5–173) (n = 41)	0.120
Iron (μ/L)	76.4 ± 25.2 (n = 163)	75.8 ± 24.1 (n = 125)	78.4 ± 29.1 (n = 38)	0.587
** AST (U/L)	24 (19–31) (n = 183)	25 (20–34) (n = 139)	21.5 (16.3–26.8) (n = 44)	0.007
** ALT (U/L)	29 (21–47.8) (n = 183)	32 (23–51) (n = 139)	25 (17–29.5) (n = 44)	<0.001
ALT > 1.5 × U/L	28 (15.2) (n = 183)	28 (20.1) (n = 139)	0 (0.0) (n = 44)	0.002
Glucose (mg/dL)	103.7 ± 34.3 (n = 188)	106.7 ± 37.7 (n = 142)	94.5 ± 17.9 (n = 46)	0.036
Glucose ≥ 126 mg/dL	24 (12.8) (n = 188)	22 (15.5) (n = 142)	2 (4.3) (n = 46)	0.086
Platelets (10^3/mm^3)	278.5 ± 68.6 (n = 172)	283.3 ± 64.8 (n = 131)	269 ± 68.8 (n = 41)	0.233
Total cholesterol (mg/dL)	193 ± 42 (n = 186)	196.6 ± 42.8 (n = 138)	182.9 ± 38.3 (n = 48)	0.052
LDL-C (mg/dL)	116 ± 41 (n = 186)	117.4 ± 41.1 (n = 138)	112 ± 41.1 (n = 48)	0.438
HDL-C (mg/dL)	48.9 ± 13.7 (n = 186)	48.4 ± 13.5 (n = 138)	50.2 ± 14.3 (n = 48)	0.427
TG (mg/dL)	122 (91–193) (n = 186)	134 (96–198) (n = 138)	105 (72–135) (n = 48)	0.004
TG ≥ 150 mg/dL	68 (36.3) (n = 186)	58 (42.0) (n = 138)	9 (18.8) (n = 48)	0.007

* Variables described by mean ± standard deviation, median (percentiles 25–75) or n (%); ** Normal values for ALT: 14–42 U/L and for AST: 10–42 U/L; n = number of cases; NASH = nonalcoholic steatohepatitis; BMI = body mass index; AST = aspartate aminotransferase; ALT = alanine aminotransferase; LDL-C = low density lipoprotein; HDL-C = high density lipoprotein.

Table 2. Multivariate analysis according to the presence of NASH and fibrosis.

Variables	NASH		Fb	
	PR (95% CI)	p	PR (95% CI)	p
ALT > 1.5 ULN	1.31 (1.22–1.41)	<0.001	1.22 (1.00–1.48)	0.048
Glucose ≥ 126 mg/dL	1.16 (1.02–1.32)	0.022	1.22 (0.99–1.50)	0.058
TGs ≥ 150 mg/dL	1.15 (1.01–1.30)	0.035	1.24 (1.07–1.45)	0.005
Age	*	*	1.01 (1.00–1.02)	0.006

* did not present a *p* value <0.20 in the bivariate analysis.

Table 3. Bivariate analysis according to the presence of fibrosis.

Variable *	With Fb	Without Fb	p
Age (years)	40.0 ± 11.4 (*n* = 83)	34.8 ± 9.3 (*n* = 100)	0.001
Female	67 (79.8) (*n* = 84)	86 (80.4) (*n* = 107)	1.000
BMI (kg/m²)	43.4 ± 5.4 (*n* = 84)	43.9 ± 5.0 (*n* = 107)	0.479
Ferritin (μ/L)	127 (81–293) (*n* = 73)	109 (56–97) (*n* = 96)	0.080
Iron (μ/L)	75.8 ± 22.5 (*n* = 73)	76.9 ± 27.4 (*n* = 90)	0.790
** AST (U/L)	25 (19–43) (*n* = 83)	24 (18–28) (*n* = 100)	0.040
** ALT (U/L)	30 (24–54) (*n* = 83)	26 (19–39) (*n* = 100)	0.008
** ALT > 1.5 × U/L	19 (22.9) (*n* = 83)	9 (8.9) (*n* = 100)	0.015
Glycemia (mg/dL)	110.9 ± 40 (*n* = 83)	98.0 ± 27.9 (*n* = 105)	0.014
Glycemia ≥ 126 mg/dL	17 (20.5) (*n* = 83)	7 (6.7) (*n* = 105)	0.009
Platelets (10³/mm³)	273.6 ± 59.3 (*n* = 77)	285 ± 70.6 (*n* = 95)	0.261
Total cholesterol (mg/dL)	198.9 ± 42.3 (*n* = 80)	188.7 ± 41.4 (*n* = 106)	0.102
LDL-C (mg/dL)	116.3 ± 38.4 (*n* = 80)	115.8 ± 43.1 (*n* = 106)	0.934
HDL-C (mg/dL)	49.2 ± 14.2 (*n* = 80)	48.6 ± 13.3 (*n* = 106)	0.776
TG (mg/dL)	148.5 (100–199) (*n* = 80)	112.5 (83.8–158) (*n* = 106)	0.005
TG ≥ 150 mg/dL	40 (50) (*n* = 80)	27 (25.5) (*n* = 106)	0.001

* Variables described by mean ± standard deviation, median (percentiles 25–75) or n (%); ** Normal values for ALT: 14–42 U/L and for AST: 10–42 U/L; *n* = number of cases; Fb = fibrosis; BMI = body mass index; AST = aspartate aminotransferase; ALT = alanine aminotransferase; LDL-C = low density lipoprotein; HDL-C = high density lipoprotein; TG = triglycerides.

3. Discussion

More recently, BS has become an accepted therapeutic option for MO patients and has been associated with histological improvement of NAFLD [7–10]. When liver biopsies performed before and after the weight loss caused by the surgery were compared, it was shown that this treatment determines an improvement or stabilization of SS, NASH and fibrosis [9,10]. However, in cirrhosis, the likelihood of regression is reduced and there is an increase in morbidity and mortality after BS [8–12].

In the present study, NAFLD was present in 90.4% of the MO patients submitted to BS. This result is consistent with the literature that reports a prevalence varying between 84% and 96% of NAFLD [4,13]. In the same way, the degree of steatosis was uniformly distributed in 30.4%, 28.4% and 31.6%, as mild, moderate and severe degree respectively, and NASH was found in approximately 70%, with a moderate correlation with the degree of steatosis. Other authors found a prevalence of NASH between 55% and 60%, but in these cases, the histopathological diagnostic criteria were not homogeneous, which makes the actual prevalence of NASH difficult to be established [3,11].

Bedossa *et al.* [14] proposed recently a score and algorithm for the histopathological definition of NASH in patients with MO. Patients should be classified as having NASH only if they have unequivocal hepatocyte ballooning. According to these criteria, a prevalence of NASH in 34% in patients with MO was found, which is lower than the observed in other studies [3,11], including ours. A possible explanation for this finding is that Bedossa *et al.* used more specific criteria for the diagnosis of NASH. In the present study, fibrosis was present in 48.3% of patients; out of these, 38% were mild and only 4.4% were considered severe. Although cirrhosis is not a contraindication for BS, there is a risk of hepatic decompensation with rapid weight loss [15].

New noninvasive clinical and biochemical markers of fibrosis in NASH have been evaluated [3]. Age, obesity, hypertension, DM, the levels of bilirubin and the ALT/AST ratio greater than 1 has been associated with the presence of NASH or fibrosis [3,13,16–18]. Contrary to other studies [19,20], the present results did not show a positive correlation of BMI with the degree of steatosis, NASH and fibrosis. BMI does not always properly reflect the degree of visceral adiposity, significantly more involved in the physiopathology of NAFLD. It is possible that there is a closer correlation between the liver damage and the measure of abdominal circumference; however, this data was not evaluated in the present study.

The results of the present study demonstrated that all patients whose ALT values were greater than 1.5 times the ULN (15% of the sample) presented NASH, and ALT was also strongly associated with fibrosis. This data can represent a cutoff and has not yet been reported in the literature for this subgroup of patients.

This study showed an association among serum levels of TG and glucose with NASH. These findings were already described in former studies concerning the risk factors of NASH [13,18,21]. In addition to high levels of TG, we found that the presence of fibrosis was also correlated with age; this association has been described before [20,22]. Furthermore, an increase in age raises the prevalence of fibrosis linearly.

Although several non-invasive markers for prediction of advanced fibrosis are available (aspartate aminotransferase-to-platelet ratio index - APRI; NAFLD fibrosis score; body mass index, ASL/ALT ratio and diabetes mellitus - BARD; FIB-4) [16,23–25], the present study suggests that patients with MO and more advanced age, high levels of ALT and TG should best be submitted to a full diagnostic evaluation such as liver biopsy to better assessment of hepatic damage.

In conclusion, this study showed a high prevalence of NASH in patients with MO and identifies a subset of patients with a higher risk of more advanced disease.

4. Experimental Section

This is a retrospective cohort study, where MO patients were submitted to BS from 2007 to 2012 at the Obesity Treatment Center of a tertiary reference center (Santa Casa de Porto Alegre, SCPA) in southern Brazil. Age, gender, the presence of comorbidities (diabetes, arterial hypertension) and body mass index (BMI) were evaluated. The dosage of ferritin, aspartate (AST) and alanine (ALT) aminotransferases, fasting glucose, platelets, total cholesterol, triglycerides (TG), high (HDL-C) and low (LDL-C) density lipoproteins was done up to 90 days before procedure. These variables were compared with the histological results of liver biopsies obtained in the trans-operative period.

Patients aged less than 18 years, those who presented serological markers for viral hepatitis, as well as patients with other causes of chronic liver disease and history of alcohol intake >20 g/day were excluded.

Liver biopsies were routinely stained with Hematoxylin-Eosin, Perls and Masson's trichrome and evaluated by the same liver pathologist who was blinded to the clinical data.

Simple steatosis (SS) was considered to be present over 5% of the sample and scored as suggested by Brunt: Mild steatosis was defined when present in 5% to 33%; moderate steatosis when present in 33% to 66%, and severe steatosis when greater than 66% [26]. To diagnose NASH, steatosis associated with hepatocyte ballooning and/or inflammatory infiltrate were the main findings, and was classified using NAFLD Activity Score (NAS) as mild (A1), moderate (A2) and severe (A3), according to classification described by the Pathology Committee of the NASH Clinical Research Network. The degree of fibrosis (Fb) was classified as stage A1, when sinusoidal/discrete cellular Fb was present; degree 1B, when sinusoidal/dense and diffuse Fb was identified; and 1c for portal Fb. Stage 2 was considered when there was pericellular/perisinusoidal associated with periportal Fb, and stage 3 in the presence of the anterior changes associated to bridging Fb. Finally, stage 4 corresponds to cirrhosis [27]. In the statistical analysis, the degree of Fb was classified as mild (stages 1A, 1B, 1C); moderate (stage 2); severe (stage 3) or cirrhosis (stage 4).

Int. J. Mol. Sci. **2015**, *16*, 25552–25559

The data were analyzed using the SPSS (Statistical Package for the Social Sciences) Inc., Chicago, IL, USA, version 18.0. The sample size supports a minimum difference between groups of 20%, power of 85% and a significance level of 5%. To control confounding factors and analyze the variables independently associated with NASH and fibrosis, the Poisson regression analysis was applied. To evaluate the association, the prevalence ratio (PR) was used, with the 95% confidence interval (CI) to estimate the risk in the population. To control the multicollinearity, two regression models were made, one of them inserting the glycemia and the other the TG. The criteria for entering the variable in the multivariate model was that it should have a value of $p < 0.20$ in the bivariate analysis. To evaluate the association between the categorical variables, the Pearson chi-square test was applied, and for the continuous or ordinal variables, the Spearman (r_s) correlation test was used. p values of <0.05 were considered significant. This study was approved by the Institutional review board of SCPA. For this type of study formal consent was not required.

Author Contributions: Alexandre Losekann and Gabriela P. Coral conceptualized and designed this manuscript; Alexandre Losekann, Antonio C. Weston, Luiz A. de Carli, Marilia B. Espindola and Sergio R. Pioner collected and analyzed the data; Alexandre Losekann, Angelo A. de Mattos, Cristiane V. Tovo and Gabriela P. Coral reviewed the literature and wrote the paper; all authors approved the final version of the manuscript.

Conflicts of Interest: The authors declare no conflict of interest.

Abbreviations

ALT: alanine aminotransferase; AST: aspartate aminotransferase; APRI: aspartate aminotransferase-to-platelet ratio index; BARD: body mass index, ASL/ALT ratio and diabetes mellitus; BMI: body mass index; BS: bariatric surgery; CI: confidence interval; DM: diabetes mellitus; Fb: fibrosis; HDL-C: high density lipoproteins; LDL-C: low density lipoproteins; MO: morbidly obese; NAFLD: Nonalcoholic fatty liver disease; NAS: NAFLD Activity Score; NASH: non-alcoholic steatohepatitis; PR: prevalence ratio; r_s:Spearman correlation test; SCPA: Santa Casa de Porto Alegre; SPSS: Statistical Package for the Social Sciences; SS: simple steatosis; TG: triglycerides; ULN: upper limit of normal.

References

1. Brunt, E.M. Nonalcoholic steatohepatitis. *Semin. Liver Dis.* **2004**, *24*, 3–20.
2. White, D.L.; Kanwal, F.; El-Serag, H.B. Associations between nonalcoholic fatty liver disease and risk for hepatocellular cancer based on systematic review. *Clin. Gastroenterol. Hepatol.* **2012**, *10*, 1342–1359.
3. Musso, G.; Gambino, R.; Cassader, M.; Pagano, G. Meta-analysis: natural history of non-alcoholic fatty liver disease (NAFLD) and diagnostic accuracy of non-invasive tests for liver disease severity. *Ann. Med.* **2011**, *43*, 617–649. [CrossRef] [PubMed]
4. Clark, J.M. The epidemiology of nonalcoholic fatty liver disease in adults. *J. Clin. Gastroenterol.* **2006**, *40*, 5–10.
5. Zamin, I., Jr.; de Mattos, A.A.; Zettler, C.G. Nonalcoholic steatohepatitis in nondiabetic obese patients. *Can. J. Gastroenterol.* **2002**, *16*, 303–307. [PubMed]
6. Ratziu, V.; Giral, P.; Charlotte, F.; Bruckert, E.; Thibault, V. Liver fibrosis in overweight patients. *Gastroenterology* **2000**, *118*, 1117–1123. [CrossRef]
7. Chalasani, N.; Younossi, Z.; Lavine, J.E.; Diehl, A.M.; Brunt, E.M.; Cusi, K.; Charlton, M.; Sanyal, A.J. The diagnosis and management of non-alcoholic fatty liver disease: Practice Guideline by the American Association for the Study of Liver Diseases, American College of Gastroenterology, and the American Gastroenterological Association. *Hepatology* **2012**, *55*, 2005–2023. [CrossRef] [PubMed]
8. De Andrade, A.R.; Cotrim, H.P.; Alves, E.; Soares, D.; Rocha, R. Nonalcoholic fatty liver disease in severely obese individuals: The influence of bariatric surgery. *Ann. Hepatol.* **2008**, *7*, 364–368. [PubMed]
9. Mathurin, P.; Hollebecque, A.; Arnalsteen, L.; Buob, D.; Leteurtre, E.; Caiazzo, R.; Pigeyre, M.; Verkindt, H.; Dharancy, S.; Louvet, A.; *et al.* Prospective study of the long-term effects of bariatric surgery on liver injury in patients without advanced disease. *Gastroenterology* **2009**, *137*, 532–540. [CrossRef] [PubMed]
10. Moretto, M.; Kupski, C.; da Silva, V.D.; Padoin, A.V.; Mottin, C.C. Effect of bariatric surgery on liver fibrosis. *Obes. Surg.* **2012**, *22*, 1044–1049. [PubMed]

11. Mummadi, R.R.; Kasturi, K.S.; Chennareddygari, S.; Sood, G.K. Effect of bariatric surgery on nonalcoholic fatty liver disease: systematic review and meta-analysis. *Clin. Gastroenterol. Hepatol.* **2008**, *6*, 1396–1402. [CrossRef] [PubMed]

12. Mosko, J.D.; Nguyen, G.C. Increased perioperative mortality following bariatric surgery among patients with cirrhosis. *Clin. Gastroenterol. Hepatol.* **2011**, *9*, 897–901. [CrossRef] [PubMed]

13. Ong, J.P.; Elariny, H.; Collantes, R.; Younoszai, A.; Chandhoke, V.; Reines, H.D.; Goodman, Z.; Younossi, Z.M. Predictors of nonalcoholic steatohepatitis and advanced fibrosis in morbidly obese patients. *Obes. Surg.* **2005**, *15*, 310–315. [CrossRef] [PubMed]

14. Bedossa, P.; Poitou, C.; Veyrie, N.; Bouillot, J.L.; Basdevant, A.; Paradis, V.; Tordjman, J.; Clement, K. Histopathological algorithm and scoring system for evaluation of liver lesions in morbidly obese patients. *Hepatology* **2012**, *56*, 1751–1759. [CrossRef] [PubMed]

15. D'Albuquerque, L.A.C.; Gonzalez, A.M.; Whale, R.C.; de Oliveira Souza, E.; Mancero, J.M.; de Oliveira e Silva, A. Liver transplantation for subacute hepatocellular failure due to massive steatohepatitis after bariatric surgery. *Liver Transpl.* **2008**, *14*, 881–885. [CrossRef] [PubMed]

16. Angulo, P. Long-term mortality in nonalcoholic fatty liver disease: Is liver histology of any prognostic significance? *Hepatology* **2010**, *51*, 373–375. [CrossRef] [PubMed]

17. Chisholm, J.; Seki, Y.; Toouli, J.; Stahl, J.; Collins, J.; Kow, L. Serologic predictors of nonalcoholic steatohepatitis in a population undergoing bariatric surgery. *Surg. Obes. Relat. Dis.* **2012**, *8*, 416–422. [CrossRef] [PubMed]

18. Praveenraj, P.; Gomes, R.M.; Kumar, S.; Karthikeyan, P.; Shankar, A.; Parthasarathi, R.; Senthilnathan, P.; Rajapandian, S.; Palanivelu, C. Prevalence and predictors of non-alcoholic fatty liver disease in morbidly obese south indian patients undergoing bariatric surgery. *Obes. Surg.* **2015**, *25*, 2078–2087. [PubMed]

19. Pagano, G.; Pacini, G.; Musso, G.; Gambino, R.; Mecca, F.; Depetris, N.; Cassader, M.; David, E.; Cavallo-Perin, P.; Rizzetto, M. Nonalcoholic steatohepatitis, insulin resistance, and metabolic syndrome: further evidence for an etiologic association. *Hepatology* **2002**, *35*, 367–372. [CrossRef] [PubMed]

20. Rocha, R.; Cotrim, H.P.; Carvalho, F.M.; Siqueira, A.C.; Braga, H.; Freitas, L.A. Body mass index and waist circumference in non-alcoholic fatty liver disease. *J. Hum. Nutr. Diet.* **2005**, *18*, 365–370. [CrossRef] [PubMed]

21. Chitturi, S.; Abeygunasekera, S.; Farrell, G.C.; Holmes-Walker, J.; Hui, J.M.; Fung, C. NASH and insulin resistance: Insulin hypersecretion and specific association with the insulin resistance syndrome. *Hepatology* **2002**, *35*, 373–379. [CrossRef] [PubMed]

22. Guidorizzi de Siqueira, A.C.; Cotrim, H.P.; Rocha, R.; Carvalho, F.M.; de Freitas, L.A.; Barreto, D.; Gouveia, L.; Landeiro, L. Non-alcoholic fatty liver disease and insulin resistance: Importance of risk factors and histological spectrum. *Eur. J. Gastroenterol. Hepatol.* **2005**, *17*, 837–841. [CrossRef] [PubMed]

23. Kruger, F.C.; Daniels, C.R.; Kidd, M.; Swart, G.; Brundyn, K.; van Rensburg, C.; Kotze, M. APRI: A simple bedside marker for advanced fibrosis that can avoid liver biopsy in patients with NAFLD/NASH. *South Afr. Med. J.* **2011**, *101*, 477–480.

24. Harrison, S.A.; Oliver, D.; Arnold, H.L.; Gogia, S.; Neuschwander-Tetri, B.A. Development and validation of a simple NAFLD clinical scoring system for identifying patients without advanced disease. *Gut* **2008**, *57*, 1441–1447. [CrossRef] [PubMed]

25. Shah, A.G.; Lydecker, A.; Murray, K.; Tetri, B.N.; Contos, M.J.; Sanyal, A.J.; Nash Clinical Research Network. Use of the FIB4 index for non-invasive evaluation of fibrosis in nonalcoholic fatty liver disease. *Clin. Gastroenterol. Hepatol.* **2009**, *7*, 1104–1112. [CrossRef] [PubMed]

26. Brunt, E.M.; Janney, C.G.; Di Bisceglie, A.M.; Neuschwander-Tetri, B.A.; Bacon, B.R. Nonalcoholic steatohepatitis: A proposal for grading and staging the histological lesions. *Am. J. Gastroenterol.* **1999**, *94*, 2467–2474. [CrossRef] [PubMed]

27. Kleiner, D.E.; Brunt, E.M.; van Natta, M.; Behling, C.; Contos, M.J.; Cummings, O.W.; Ferrell, L.D.; Liu, Y.C.; Torbenson, M.S.; Unalp-Arida, A.; *et al.* Design and validation of a histological scoring system for nonalcoholic fatty liver disease. *Hepatology* **2005**, *41*, 1313–1321. [CrossRef] [PubMed]

International Journal of
Molecular Sciences

MDPI

Review

Role of Serum Uric Acid and Ferritin in the Development and Progression of NAFLD

Rosa Lombardi, Giuseppina Pisano and Silvia Fargion *

Department of Pathophysiology and Transplantation, IRCCS "Ca' Granda" IRCCS Foundation,
Poiliclinico Hospital, University of Milan, Centro delle Malattie Metaboliche del Fegato, Milan 20122, Italy;
rosalombardi@hotmail.it (R.L.); pinaz81@hotmail.com (G.P.)
* Correspondence: silvia.fargion@unimi.it; Tel.: +39-02-5503-3301

Academic Editors: Amedeo Lonardo and Giovanni Targher
Received: 3 March 2016; Accepted: 5 April 2016; Published: 12 April 2016

Abstract: Nonalcoholic fatty liver disease (NAFLD), tightly linked to the metabolic syndrome (MS), has emerged as a leading cause of chronic liver disease worldwide. Since it is potentially progressive towards non-alcoholic steatohepatitis (NASH) and hepatic fibrosis, up to cirrhosis and its associated complications, the need for predictive factors of NAFLD and of its advanced forms is mandatory. Despite the current "gold standard" for the assessment of liver damage in NAFLD being liver biopsy, in recent years, several non-invasive tools have been designed as alternatives to histology, of which fibroscan seems the most promising. Among the different serum markers considered, serum uric acid (SUA) and ferritin have emerged as possible predictors of severity of liver damage in NAFLD. In fact, as widely described in this review, they share common pathogenetic pathways and are both associated with hepatic steatosis and MS, thus suggesting a likely synergistic action. Nevertheless, the power of these serum markers seems to be too low if considered alone, suggesting that they should be included in a wider perspective together with other metabolic and biochemical parameters in order to predict liver damage.

Keywords: SUA; liver damage; fibrosis; NASH; serum markers; oxidative stress; insulin resistance; metabolic syndrome

1. Introduction

Nonalcoholic fatty liver disease (NAFLD), tightly linked to metabolic syndrome (MS), has emerged as a leading cause of chronic liver disease worldwide with a rapidly growing prevalence in the general population, ranging between 20% and 30%, and paralleling the epidemics of obesity and type 2 diabetes mellitus (T2DM) all over the world [1,2]. NAFLD encompasses a clinical-pathologic spectrum of liver diseases ranging from simple steatosis to nonalcoholic steatohepatitis (NASH), the more aggressive form of NAFLD, which can progress to cirrhosis and its associated complications [3,4].

Unfortunately, the only validated method to diagnose NASH, the potentially evolving form of NAFLD, is liver biopsy. Nonetheless, this procedure is limited by intra and inter-observer variability, sampling errors and invasiveness, thus letting impossible its feasibility in such a large number of patients with NAFLD. Several scores have been designed in the attempt to diagnose NASH and fibrosis stage without histological data, but the debate on their real utility is still ongoing [5]. Fibroscan is emerging as a reliable tool to identify fibrosis in a non-invasive way, but still the large "grey area" of its results does not allow one to discriminate the entity of fibrosis in a large portion of patients with NAFLD [6].

During the last few years, among the several parameters evaluated as possible predictors of NAFLD, serum uric acid (SUA) and ferritin have emerged. In fact, increasing evidence has shown that SUA levels as well as high ferritin are associated with the metabolic insulin resistance syndrome, higher body fat content and more severe liver damage.

2. Uric Acid

Serum uric acid (SUA) is a product of purine metabolism in humans and originates from hypoxanthine after a double enzyme catalysis by xanthine oxidase (XO) in the liver. Its production is regulated by the endogenous (nucleoproteins originating from cellular metabolism) and exogenous (dietary) precursor proteins delivered to the liver, whereas its excretion is controlled by the kidneys through renal plasma flow, glomerular filtration and proximal tubular exchange. Therefore, an impairment in this balance, caused by either an over generation of uric acid, like in MS and diets rich in fructose and purines or by a reduction in its excretion, as in acute renal failure or consequent to some drugs (ciclosporin, ethambutol, pyrazinamide, and cytotoxic chemotherapy), can lead to high SUA levels [7,8].

3. Serum Uric Acid and Metabolic Syndrome Clinical Manifestations

SUA is the most common and well-studied risk factor for developing gout. In addition, beyond contributing to the pathogenesis of gout, arthritis, and chronic nephropathy, hyperuricemia is associated with the so-called "cardio-metabolic diseases" including cardiovascular disease and all the metabolic diseases associated with MS [9]. Several studies reported a significantly higher prevalence of MS (up to 60%) and its components such as hypertension, hyperinsulinemia, hypertriglyceridemia and diabetes in the hyperuricemic population, suggesting that hyperuricemia might be an indicator for early diagnosis of MS and of its different clinical manifestations [10–12]. Moreover, a meta-analysis of prospective cohort studies provided strong evidence that a high level of SUA is a risk factor for developing T2DM in middle-aged and older people, independently of other established metabolic risk features [13].

4. Serum Uric Acid and Nonalcoholic Fatty Liver Disease (NAFLD)

Lonardo *et al.* [14] firstly described an association between NAFLD and serum uric acid levels in a small case-control study of Italian patients with ultrasound-diagnosed NAFLD.

The relationship between SUA and NAFLD was then confirmed in cross-sectional and prospective studies in which SUA resulted to be an independent risk factor for NAFLD [15,16]. More recently in two different meta-analyses of prospective studies including very large numbers of participants, it was shown a significant higher risk of NAFLD in subjects with higher SUA compared to those with lower levels. A linear dose-response effect between SUA and NAFLD was reported with each 1 mg increase of SUA leading to 21% rise in NAFLD risk [17,18]. Moreover, in patients with established coronary artery disease, hyperuricemia was reported to be a potent predictor of mortality in overweight or obese patients in whom liver steatosis was highly prevalent [19].

The mutual relationship between NAFLD and SUA was shown in another study aimed at exploring the causal relationship and underlying mechanisms linking NAFLD and hyperuricemia. By analyzing prospectively a cohort of 5541 patients, NAFLD resulted strongly associated with the risk of developing hyperuricemia over a period of seven years. In a second part of the same study, xantine oxidase was demonstrated to be the mediator of this relationship through the activation of the ucleotide-binding oligomerization domain-like (NOD-like) receptor family pyrin domain containing 3 (NLRP3) inflammasome [20] in both in HepG2 cells and mice, as explained in the next pharagraph. However, a major limitation of these study designs is their inability to show the biological mechanisms underpinning the association between SUA and NAFLD. Furthermore, experimental animal models supporting this association do not always mirror human biology.

Interestingly, Sirota *et al.* [21] examined the association between SUA levels and NAFLD in a large population-based study from the United States including 10,732 non-diabetic adults who participated in the National Health and Nutrition Examination Survey 1988–1994. The Authors found that the odds ratio for NAFLD was significantly higher in patients with the highest SUA values (3rd and 4th quartiles) compared to subjects in the lowest quartiles. In addition, after adjusting for the known risk factors, uric acid (4th quartile) remained significantly associated with NAFLD. Thus, they concluded that elevated SUA level is independently associated with ultrasound-diagnosed NAFLD and with increasing severity of NAFLD as evaluated by ultrasonography. These data were in line with previous results by Petta *et al.* [22] obtained in a group of patients with histologically proven NAFLD. They had demonstrated that hyperuricemia was associated with histological features of liver disease, representing an independent risk factor for higher grade of steatosis, lobular inflammation and higher NAFLD Activity Score (NAS), the histological score routinely used for the diagnosis and grading of NASH. Thus, these data confirm and extend the results obtained in Asiatic subjects also to Caucasian patients, consolidating the relationship between NAFLD and SUA.

Finally, Afzali *et al.* [23], on the basis of the observation that elevated SUA levels strongly reflect and may even cause oxidative stress, insulin resistance (IR), and MS, and that experimental, and in *in vitro* models indicate that uric acid is able to induce inflammatory responses, all known risk factors involved in the pathogenesis and in the progression of liver disease of different etiology, addressed the question whether the baseline SUA level was associated with the incidence of hospitalization or death due to cirrhosis. These authors analyzed 5518 participants from the first National Health and Nutrition Examination Survey during a mean follow-up of 12.9 years (range 5.4–21 years) and demonstrated that subjects with the higher uric acid values had a higher risk of cirrhosis related hospitalization or death even after adjustment for important causes and risk factors of chronic liver disease. In addition, patients with higher SUA levels had a greater probability of elevated serum ALT and GGT. They suggested that the negative effect of SUA was mediated by the induction by uric acid of endothelial dysfunction, IR, oxidative stress and systemic inflammation, which are known risk factors for the development and progression of liver disease of different etiology. However, despite this fascinating hypothesis, a major limitation of these results obtained in clinical studies is that the direct demonstration in patients with NAFLD of the mechanisms underpinning the negative effect of SUA is still missing.

5. Relationship between Uric Acid and NAFLD/Metabolic Syndrome: Possible Mechanisms

Accumulating clinical evidence suggests that hyperuricemia is strongly associated with MS/NAFLD, and abnormal glucose metabolism and IR, as well as oxidative stress and NLRP3 inflammasome involvement, have been pointed out as possible linking conditions [11,24]. The possible interactions of the different mechanisms involved are schematically depicted in Figure 1.

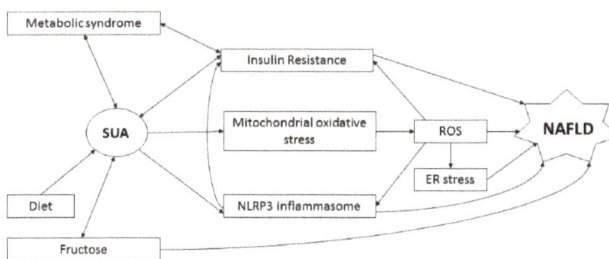

Figure 1. Pathogenetic pathways of the association between serum uric acid and NAFLD. Abbreviations: SUA, serum uric acid; ROS, reactive oxygen species; ER, endoplasmic reticulum; NAFLD, non-alcoholic fatty liver disease.

Furthermore, a very recent study by a Chinese group, has focused on the progression of NAFLD in hyperuricemic subjects, showing a key role of perturbations of phospholipases, purine nucleotide degradation and Liver X receptor/retinoid X receptor. In particular, they demonstrated an increase in oxidative stress and IR driven by an upregulation of phospatidic acid and cholesterol ester metabolism and a downregulation of the acid uric precursor, namely inosin [25].

5.1. Interaction between Uric Acid and Insulin

Insulin acts on the proximal renal tubule fostering acid uric reabsorption and increasing renal cellular metabolism, thus leading to hyperuricemia. Indeed, elevated SUA levels may prompt the development of IR by reducing endothelial nitric oxide (NO) bioavailability and supply to cells [26].

In addition, in an experimental model, mice fed with hyperuricemia-inducing diet (HUA) presented significantly lower insulin sensitivity and impaired glucose metabolism compared to those with a standard diet, as well as higher levels of both serum and intrahepatic triglycerides. In particular, hyperuricemia inhibited a protein kinase B (AKT) response to insulin by decreasing its phosphorylation and conversely increasing the phosphorylation of the insulin receptor substrate-1 (IRS1) in liver, muscle and fat tissue, thus fostering the onset of IR. This effect seems to be secondary to uric acid induced radical oxygen species (ROS) and activation of the NLRP3 inflammasome [27,28]. These data were confirmed also in HepG2 cell cultures exposed to different concentrations of uric acid. Not surprisingly, administration of probenecid, a uric acid transport inhibitor into cells, or the antioxidant *N*-acetylcisteine, diminished intracellular triglycerides accumulation and improved insulin-signaling.

5.2. Uric Acid and Lipid Metabolism

Beyond hyperinsulinemia, uric acid is responsible of mitochondrial oxidative stress [29], sterol regulatory element-binding protein 1 (SREBP-1) activation induced by endoplasmic reticulum (ER) stress [30] and NLRP3 inflammasome involvement [31], all causative factors of lipid metabolism impairment.

Moreover, evidence suggests that uric acid could originate from fructose metabolism, which is well known for inducing hepatic steatosis being directly metabolized to triglycerides in the liver [32], and be responsible for mitochondrial oxidative stress. In turn, SUA amplifies the lipogenic effect of fructose by upregulating its metabolic enzymatic reactions [33]. In cultured HepG2 cellular lines exposed to fructose, increased intracellular levels of uric acid and triglycerides were registered. Interestingly, allopurinol effectively prevented the formation of uric acid after exposure to fructose [29].

5.3. Mitochondrial and Endoplasmic Reticulum (ER) Oxidative Stress

Oxidative stress plays a key-role in steatosis induced by uric acid. In the study by Lanaspa *et al.* [29], cellular exposure to high SUA levels determined mitochondrial oxidative stress with generation of ROS by nicotinamide adenine dinucleotide phosphate (NADPH) oxidase. As a result, the activity of aconitase, an enzyme involved in the acid citric circle, was markedly reduced leading to accumulation of citrate, a substrate for hepatic *de novo* lipogenesis and subsequent intracellular fat generation.

Furthermore, ROS production promotes ER stress, which is determinant of fat accumulation in steatosis. In fact, alterations in its homeostasis have been demonstrated in human HepG2 cells and mice models of fatty liver [34,35]. ER is a site of protein folding and production of lipids and sterols. If a perturbation in this compartment occurs, misfolded and unfolded proteins accumulate and activate the unfolded protein response (UPR) signaling pathways, which regulate hepatic lipid metabolism and promote fat accumulation in the liver because of the expression of genes encoding for lipogenic enzymes driven by the transcriptional factor SREBP-1c. Uric acid has been shown to induce the expression of unfolded response protein (URP)-inducible and to increase the cleavage of SREBP-1c into the mature form and its nuclear translocation, thus enhancing the *de novo* lipogenesis. This data has been shown in both HepG2 cells and primary mice hepatocytes [30].

Despite these data, acute elevations seem to provide antioxidant protection, and uric acid contributes >50% of the antioxidant capacity of our organism. In fact, it has a direct effect on the inhibition of free radicals, protecting the cell membrane and DNA. The antioxidant activity of SUA also occurs in the brain, being a protector for several disease such as multiple sclerosis and neurodegenerative disease, as well as cardiac and renal toxicity [36]. Thus, an eventually beneficial action could be speculated also on the liver.

In addition, there is still no consensus if uric acid is a protective or a risk factor; however, it seems that the quantity and the duration of the concentration of the uric acid in the blood is essential for this answer, possibly being the acute increase in its protective levels whereas chronic elevated levels are dangerous.

5.4. The Ucleotide-Binding Oligomerization Domain-Like (NOD-Like) Receptor Family Pyrin Domain Containing 3 (NLRP3) Inflammasome

Another factor which has been reported to be strongly involved in the pathogenesis of uric acid toxicity is NLRP3 inflammasome, an intracellular multiprotein complex that is assembled and activated by pathogen-associated and damage-associated molecular patterns with subsequent production of pro-inflammatory and pro-fibrotic cytokines (IL-1β and IL-18). It plays a central role in obesity and IR and has been involved in dyslipidemia and lipid accumulation in hepatocytes [28,31]. The NLRP3 inflammasome is activated by uric acid, both directly and indirectly through ROS production [37] and recent evidence has demonstrated that it contributes to hepatic steatosis and insulin resistance in a murine model [28]. This suggestion was confirmed in cultured HepG2 and L02 cellular lines, where the NLRP3 inflammasome knock-down cells decreased the uric acid-induced hepatic free fatty acids (FFAs) accumulation [31].

In conclusion, SUA is able to regulate lipid production and to foster the onset of metabolic disorders and NAFLD through multifaceted pathways. Thereby, evidence is accumulating on the benefit of lowering SUA levels in NAFLD by using drugs commonly employed in the treatment of hyperuricemia, like allopurinol or probenecid.

6. Ferritin

Hyperferritinemia is a frequent finding in the general population, is detected in 30%–40% of the patients with MS/NAFLD, and has been suggested as a marker of severity of the disease.

The difficulty in the interpretation of increased ferritin is related to the multiple causes that can lead to its increase, initially identified as marker of iron overload, following the increase of transferrin saturation, and also in the presence of severe hepatic necrosis. Furthermore, other more frequent causes need to be considered, namely the presence of inflammation, since ferritin behaves as a protein of acute phase and it can also be induced in the setting of systemic inflammation, like in rheumatologi, infectious or neoplastic diseases, and alcohol abuse, where ferritin levels rapidly decrease with alcohol abstinence. However, enlarging the most common cause of hyperferritinemia identified in the last years is the presence of the MS, to which NAFLD is frequently associated.

7. Ferritin and Metabolic Syndrome Clinical Manifestations

Hyperferritinemia is detected in about one-third of patients with NAFLD and the MS and its levels seem to be directly correlated with the severity of IR [38,39].

The first reports on the relationship between ferritin, IR/T2DM and the MS study in Europe were published in the 1990s. In 1998, Ford *et al.* [40] reported the results of a case-control study in Europe, demonstrating that subjects with hyperferritinemia had a 2.4-fold higher risk of developing T2DM. In addition, Salonen [41] showed in a prospective study that increased ferritin levels precede the development of diabetes and Kim obtained the same results in a very large cohort of Korean subjects [42]. In addition, cross-sectional studies found that elevated ferritin levels were associated with central obesity [43], hypertension [44], and dyslipidemia [45], all manifestations of the MS. Moreover, Iwasaki highlighted an association between serum ferritin, visceral fat and subcutaneous adiposity and suggested that serum ferritin concentration may be a useful indicator of systemic fat content and degree of IR [46]. In addition, Alam *et al.* [47] demonstrated that obesity led to hyperferritinemia irrespective of actual body iron story, advocating a state of subclinical inflammation responsible for high levels of ferritin.

Others demonstrated in population-based studies that moderate to markedly increased ferritin concentrations represent a biological biomarker predictive of early death in a dose-dependent manner [48]. Thus, even if in this study, information on the presence of liver steatosis was lacking, it is very likely that ferritin may be a predictor of early death also in the setting of NAFLD.

8. Ferritin and NAFLD

The tight link between ferritin and insulin dysregulation was shown by Fernandez-Real [49], who proposed ferritin as a marker of IR. Zelber-Sagi *et al.* [50]demonstrated that among different metabolic features, insulin was the strongest predictor of increased serum ferritin levels and that the association between serum ferritin and MS was mediated by NAFLD.

A French group coined the term of *"dysmetabolic iron overload syndrome"* (DIOS), to indicate subjects with increased ferritin levels, with normal or only mildly increased transferrin saturation, in the presence of liver steatosis, IR and two or more components of the MS, along with moderate hepatic iron accumulation with the typical pattern of mixed parenchymal and mesenchymal iron deposition [51]. However, it was also observed that several patients with NAFLD, IR and manifestations of MS may have increased ferritin even in the absence of increased iron stores.

In addition, Kim *et al.* [42] reported that serum ferritin levels predict incident non-alcoholic fatty liver disease in healthy Korean men.

9. Relationship between Ferritin and NAFLD/Metabolic Syndrome: Possible Mechanisms

Numerous data demonstrate that hepatic iron accumulation could elicit the onset of metabolic imbalance and liver damage and figure out the DIOS or more recently called "insulin-resistance associated with iron overload syndrome".

The liver has a central role in iron metabolism as it is the principle source of hepcidin, the regulatory peptide hormone of iron homeostasis. In fact, in response to several stimuli, like excessive iron deposits, inflammatory signals (IL-6) or ER-stress, hepcidin is overexpressed and determines a reduction in iron intestinal absorption and an increase in iron retention from macrophage and hepatocytes [52,53]. In addition, hepatocyte necrosis, with subsequent erythrophagocytosis by macrophages, and the systemic inflammatory state induced by obesity and NAFLD itself, may predispose individuals to increased hepcidin levels.

Many mechanisms linking iron and liver damage have been described. Firstly, iron, once accumulated in the liver, causes oxidative stress through the Fenton and Haber–Weiss chemistry with production of ROS and damage to membranes, proteins and DNA. Secondly, ferritin itself, which is the expression of iron storage in the liver, behaves as a real pro-inflammatory cytokine directly activating the hepatic stellate cells via Nuclear Factor κB (NFκB) cascade and inducing fibrogenesis [54]. Nevertheless, the role of hepatic iron and progression of liver disease is still to be fully elucidated.

In addition, very recent data suggest a possible role of splenic iron accumulation in promoting liver damage. However, these results need further confirmations [55].

9.1. Pathogenesis of DIOS (Dysmetabolic Iron Overload Syndrome)

Several explanations for the correlation between high ferritin levels and NAFLD have been proposed, namely IR, erythrophagocytosis by hepatic macrophages and dysregulation of proteins and pathways involved in iron homeostasis. Among the latter, hepcidin seems to have a key role in iron accumulation in NAFLD [56,57], as increased levels of this peptide have been detected in these patients [58,59], as well in the paediatric NAFLD population [60]. Furthermore, an influence of genetic factors has been considered, in particular the heterozygosis state of β-thalassemia and mutations in the HFE gene responsible for hereditary hemochromatosis (HH) [38,61,62] (Figure 2).

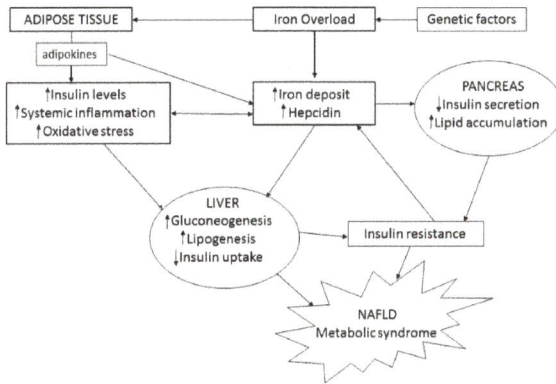

Figure 2. Pathogenetic pathways of the association between ferritin and NAFLD. Up arrow in the boxes: increase; down arrow in the boxes: decrease.

9.2. Hyperferritinemia and Insulin-Resistance

The relationship between hyperferritinemia and IR seems to be mutual. In fact, early *in vitro* studies have suggested that insulin might determine a rapid and marked stimulation of iron uptake by fat cells, by a redistribution of transferrin receptors from an intracellular membrane compartment to the cell surface [49]. On the other hand, systemic iron overload may prompt the onset of diabetes mellitus (DM) consequent to an impairment in pancreatic β-cells function due to intra-parenchymal iron deposition. In fact, because of oxidative stress, β-cells are less sensitive to glucose stimulation and die by to apoptosis with consequent reduction in insulin production [63].

The effect of iron overload on glucose metabolism has been investigated in animal models. In a study by Choi *et al.* [64], mice fed with a standard diet enriched in iron, presented higher levels of ferritin, hepcidin and inflammatory cytokines, as well as a higher degree of IR and metabolic dysregulations, mainly driven by an overexpression of genes involved in either gluconeogenesis or lipogenesis. These features were exasperated in mice fed with high fat diet (HFD) enriched with iron, suggesting a synergistic effect of fat and iron. The authors have speculated that insulin stimulates ferritin synthesis via inflammatory pathways and enhances hepcidin expression. On the other hand, iron interferes with insulin inhibition of glucose production by the liver and decreases the hepatic extraction and metabolism of insulin, leading to peripheral hyperinsulinemia. These data were confirmed by Dongiovanni *et al.* [65], who showed that an iron-enriched diet in mice led to the development of IR, probably due to the secretion of adipokines by the visceral adipose tissue consequent to iron accumulation.

Recent data by Vecchi *et al.* [66] further explored the relationship between glucose and iron metabolism and showed a new regulatory pathway in iron homeostasis driven by gluconeogenic stimuli and with the major actors being hepcidin and PPARGC1A, a transcriptional coactivator of genes involved in gluconeogenesis. Therefore, in conditions like NAFLD, obesity and T2DM, persistently activated gluceoneogenesis may result in overstimulation of hepcidin and iron accumulation.

The interplay between iron and insulin has been also confirmed by experimental data that showed how iron depletion could elicit an over expression and higher affinity of insulin receptors, as well as an increase in the expression of molecules involved in the intracellular signal cascade activated by insulin receptors and of genes involved in glucose uptake [57].

9.3. Hyperferritinemia and Adipose Tissue

The adipose tissue behaves as an endocrine organ, which under a condition of chronic inflammation, as in NAFLD, releases adipokines in the bloodstream, thus altering glucose and iron homeostasis and may determine a condition of subclinical inflammation itself [47,67]. Many adipokines play a central role in this scenario, namely adiponectin, leptin and resistin [57]. Adiponectin, which is an anti-steatotic and anti-inflammatory adipokine, is reduced in dysmetabolic conditions like NAFLD, IR and T2DM, and seems to predict the severity of liver inflammation and fibrosis. In fact, it has the capability of inducing the transcription of key genes in iron metabolism, like the hemeoxygenase-1 (HO-1), determining lower iron levels in hepatocytes, thus preventing apoptosis. Conversely, leptin, an adipokine involved in the control of food intake and energy consumption, seems to upregulate hepcidin synthesis, thus contributing to DIOS pathogenesis.

Finally, resistin is able to either impair glucose tolerance or reduce glucose uptake from muscular tissue or induce an inhibitor of insulin signaling namely SOCS3 (Suppressor of cytokine signaling 3), thus eliciting a condition of IR.

In line with this are the results by Beckry *et al.* [68] who have shown the ectopic expression of hepcidin in white adipose tissue of obese individuals and that of leptin, usually increased in obese subjects, was able to enhance hepcidin mRNA *in vitro*. In addition, Green *et al.* [69] have demonstrated how isolated primary rat adipocytes exposed to iron become insulin-resistant decreasing insulin mediated glucose transport and fostering lipolisis. On the other hand, a "portal vein theory" has been proposed and comprises the concept that visceral adipose tissue and/or the gut release into the portal vein increasing amounts of FFAs and pro-inflammatory factors, which, in turn, reach the liver and contribute to the onset of hepatic IR and steatosis. However, further studies are needed for a better comprehension of this casual link [70].

10. Hyperferritinemia and Severity of Liver Damage in NAFLD

Iron and ferritin have been hypothesized to foster the progression of organ damage, including hepatic and cardiovascular diseases.

In 2001, our group showed that hyperferritinemia with normal transferrin saturation was a hallmark of a glucose/lipid metabolism disorder and, when associated with multiple metabolic abnormalities and iron overload, identified patients at risk for NASH. Interestingly, we observed that patients in whom ferritin remained elevated despite lifestyle modifications (diet, weight loss, physical activity) differed from those whose ferritin normalized, presenting the former a more severe liver disease. We hypothesized that the increase of ferritin possibly reflected a synergistic induction of its synthesis because of increased iron stores, hepatic steatosis and subclinical inflammation. In contrast, when the increase in serum ferritin was a consequence only of altered lipid metabolism, it was reversible with diet and unrelated to iron stores [71].

Since then, several other studies analyzed the relationship between ferritin, iron overload and severity of liver damage in patients with NAFLD. Bugianesi *et al.* [38] demonstrated that increased ferritin levels are markers of severe histologic damage, but not of iron overload and that iron burden and HFE mutations do not contribute significantly to hepatic fibrosis in the majority of patients with NAFLD. Manousou *et al.* [72] evaluated in 111 NAFLD patients the relationship between serum ferritin and features of MS with respect to histological inflammation and/or fibrosis. Interestingly, ferritin resulted a good predictor of advanced liver disease, with respect to both NASH and fibrosis. In addition, Kowdley *et al.* [73] demonstrated that elevated serum ferritin is an independent predictor of histologic severity and advanced fibrosis among patients with NAFLD. He found in a cohort of 628 biopsy-proven NAFLD with hyperferritinemia that ferritin, besides being significantly associated with markers of liver damage (elevated serum ALT, AST and decreased platelets) and of iron overload (iron, transferrin-iron saturation and iron stain grade), was associated with more severe histologic features of NAFLD, including steatosis, hepatocellular ballooning, increased NAFLD Activity Score (NAS) and diagnosis of NASH. In addition, ferritin was also independently associated with advanced hepatic fibrosis and with higher NAS, the latter even among patients without hepatic iron deposition. The authors concluded that serum ferritin was useful to identify NAFLD patients at risk for NASH and advanced fibrosis.

These data were confirmed in a cohort of 108 Korean biopsy proven NAFLD patients in whom a positive correlation between ferritin level, metabolic alterations, liver fibrosis and NASH was found. Nevertheless, the association between ferritin and histology resulted weaker compared to another serum marker resulting from hepatocytes apoptosis, namely fragmented cytokeratin-18 (CK-18) [74].

Conversely, Angulo *et al.* [75] retrospectively analyzed in 1404 NAFLD patients the accuracy of serum ferritin in determining the presence and severity of liver fibrosis, and whether combining non-invasive fibrosis scoring systems with serum ferritin analysis could increase the accuracy of those tests. Although serum levels of ferritin correlated with more-severe liver fibrosis; however, either the performance of ferritin resulted unsatisfactorily for any grade of fibrosis or the accuracy of the non-invasive scores did not change with inclusion of serum ferritin. On the basis of adjusted multiple logistic regression analysis, they concluded that serum ferritin levels alone had a low level of diagnostic accuracy for the presence or severity of liver fibrosis in patients with NAFLD.

Similar results were reported by Yoneda *et al.* [76], who analyzed 1201 biopsy-proven NAFLD patients previously enrolled into the Japan Study Group of NAFLD and belonging to a large Japanese cohort database of NAFLD patients. By comparing serum ferritin levels and hepatic histology, the authors showed that ferritin increased with increasing histological grade of steatosis, lobular inflammation and ballooning and that at multivariate analyses it was independently associated with steatosis grade and fibrotic stage. However, ferritin showed a suboptimal performance as predictive test of any degree of liver fibrosis, possibly because several other factors including sex and metabolic features could have interfered. The conclusion of the study was that serum ferritin had a low diagnostic accuracy for detecting fibrosis in NAFLD patients when considered alone.

Nevertheless, ferritin has also been included in serum panels in order to detect liver damage non-invasively. One of these is the NAFIC score, which relies on ferritin, insulin and type IV collagen serum levels and which has been tested in a cohort of 147 biopsy-proven NAFLD and validated in another cohort of 355 patients from nine hepatologic centers in Japan. A cut-off of two has been identified to diagnose the presence of NASH in NAFLD patients, with a sensitivity and a specificity of 63% and 83%, respectively. Later, a new modified NAFIC score was created including higher insulin values that presented a better diagnostic performance (sensitivity 74%, specificity 75% and Area under Receiving Operating Characteristic—AUROC 0.801) [77].

Another score which includes ferritin as a variable is the FibroMeter NAFLD score. It consists of a panel of serum markers and has been shown to have a high diagnostic accuracy for staging liver fibrosis. In particular, in a study of 235 NAFLD patients, it showed an AUROC of 0.94 for significant fibrosis ($\geqslant$F2), 0.93 for severe fibrosis (F3), and 0.9 for cirrhosis [5,78].

In conclusion, increasing data aimed at pointing ferritin as possible predictive factor of liver damage are accumulating. Despite conflicting and still not conclusive results, it could be speculated that ferritin might be used as a surrogate marker, especially if combined with other metabolic and biochemical variables, to identify a more severe liver disease, even if with an intermediate sensitivity and specificity.

11. Does Hyperferritinemia Reflect Iron Overload?

In an attempt to clarify whether the increase in ferritin observed in patients with NAFLD reflects iron overload, studies were performed to define a possible association between ferritin and both liver siderosis and mutations in genes involved in iron metabolism. Interestingly, HFE mutations responsible for hereditary hemochromatosis resulted non significantly associated either to liver siderosis or hyperferritinemia and also liver damage did not result as being influenced by the presence of these mutations [62]. *Vice versa*, liver damage defined either by more severe fibrosis or presence of NASH, resulted as significantly associated with the presence of liver siderosis and β thalassemia traits [79]. However, the large majority of studies concluded that the increased ferritin values observed in patients with NAFLD reflect increased iron stores and acquired and genetic factors predisposing individuals to lipid and iron metabolism alterations in the presence of subclinical inflammation.

12. Iron Depletion in Patients with Hyperferritinemia, Metabolic Alterations and NAFLD

Iron is known for causing oxidative stress through the Fenton and Haber–Weiss chemistry with production of ROS and damage to membranes, proteins and DNA, thus being capable of inducing liver damage and fibrosis. Ferritin is the primary iron-storage protein and serum ferritin concentration has historically been used to predict severe fibrosis in chronic liver diseases.

Several studies showed that iron depletion therapy was followed by a reduction in plasma glucose and by an improvement of insulin sensitivity. Facchini *et al.* in 2002 [80] demonstrated in a small series of NAFLD patients, with and without increased ferritin levels, that iron removal in carbohydrate intolerant patients with clinical evidence of nonalcoholic fatty liver disease was able to improve insulin sensitivity in the short term (without changes in body weight). Fernandez-Real showed in a randomized trial that blood letting in high-ferritin T2DM improved insulin sensitivity and secretion [81]. In addition, Valenti *et al.* [82] demonstrated that iron depletion by venesection, in patients with moderate iron overload associated with NAFLD, determined a decrease of both IR and transaminases, as well as of ferritin levels.

Despite these encouraging data, confirmed also in following studies, the role of iron depletion in the improvement in liver histology and the natural history of liver disease is still under definition because of the lack of studies including a large number of patients.

13. Conclusions

NAFLD is recognized as the leading cause of chronic liver disease worldwide, and, in a percentage of cases, it is potentially progressive towards advanced fibrosis and severe complications. As a consequence, the need for predictive factors of NAFLD and especially of its progressive forms is mandatory. In recent years, SUA and ferritin have emerged as possible predictors of hepatic steatosis and liver damage. Interestingly, some studies have reported high SUA levels in patients with hyperferritinemia and *vice versa*, thus suggesting a mutual relationship and a synergistic action [83–85].

In fact, as extensively depicted in this review, SUA and ferritin share common pathogenic mechanisms, in particular oxidative stress and IR, and are associated with metabolic features, among the latter obesity and T2DM are the most important. Therefore, it could be speculated that both SUA and ferritin are the main actors in the multifaceted and complicated scenario of NAFLD and its dysmetabolic features.

However, given that the majority of studies are based on observational data, well-designed prospective studies including a large series of patients of different ethnicities are warranted before a definite role of SUA and ferritin in the pathogenesis of NAFLD can be established. In addition, it could be of interest to evaluate whether treating hyperuricemia and hyperferritinemia may lead to NAFLD improvement, and, in turn, whether regression of NAFLD is accompanied by a normalization of SUA and ferritin levels.

Author Contributions: Rosa Lombardi wrote the first version of the manuscript, Giuseppina Pisano made the extensive revision of literature and Silvia Fargion revised the final version of the manuscript.

Conflicts of Interest: The authors declare no conflict of interest.

References

1. Williams, C.D.; Stengel, J.; Asike, M.I.; Torres, D.M.; Shaw, J.; Contreras, M.; Landt, C.L.; Harrison, S.A. Prevalence of nonalcoholic fatty liver disease and nonalcoholic steatohepatitis among a largely middle-aged population utilizing ultrasound and liver biopsy: A prospective study. *Gastroenterology* **2011**, *140*, 124–131. [CrossRef] [PubMed]
2. Lonardo, A.; Ballestri, S.; Marchesini, G.; Angulo, P.; Loria, P. Nonalcoholic fatty liver disease: A precursor of the metabolic syndrome. *Dig. Liver Dis.* **2015**, *47*, 181–190. [CrossRef] [PubMed]
3. Anstee, Q.M.; Targher, G.; Day, C.P. Progression of NAFLD to diabetes mellitus, cardiovascular disease or cirrhosis. *Nat. Rev. Gastroenterol. Hepatol.* **2013**, *10*, 330–344. [CrossRef] [PubMed]

4. Serfaty, L.; Lemoine, M. Definition and natural history of metabolic steatosis: Clinical aspects of NAFLD, NASH and cirrhosis. *Diabetes Metab.* **2008**, *34*, 634–637. [CrossRef]
5. Buzzetti, E.; Lombardi, R.; de Luca, L.; Tsochatzis, E.A. Noninvasive assessment of fibrosis in patients with nonalcoholic fatty liver disease. *Int. J. Endocrinol.* **2015**, *2015*, 343828. [CrossRef] [PubMed]
6. Tsochatzis, E.A.; Gurusamy, K.S.; Ntaoula, S.; Cholongitas, E.; Davidson, B.R.; Burroughs, A.K. Elastography for the diagnosis of severity of fibrosis in chronic liver disease: A meta-analysis of diagnostic accuracy. *J. Hepatol.* **2011**, *54*, 650–659. [CrossRef] [PubMed]
7. Mount, D.B.; Kwon, C.Y.; Zandi-Nejad, K. Renal urate transport. *Rheum. Dis. Clin. N. Am.* **2006**, *32*, 313–331. [CrossRef] [PubMed]
8. Richette, P.; Bardin, T. Gout. *Lancet* **2010**, *375*, 318–328. [CrossRef]
9. Zhang, M.L.; Gao, Y.X.; Wang, X.; Chang, H.; Huang, G.W. Serum uric acid and appropriate cutoff value for prediction of metabolic syndrome among Chinese adults. *J. Clin. Biochem. Nutr.* **2013**, *52*, 38–42. [CrossRef] [PubMed]
10. Choi, H.K.; Ford, E.S. Prevalence of the metabolic syndrome in individuals with hyperuricemia. *Am. J. Med.* **2007**, *120*, 442–447. [CrossRef] [PubMed]
11. Kodama, S.; Saito, K.; Yachi, Y.; Asumi, M.; Sugawara, A.; Totsuka, K.; Saito, A.; Sone, H. Association between serum uric acid and development of type 2 diabetes. *Diabetes Care* **2009**, *32*, 1737–1742. [CrossRef] [PubMed]
12. Lin, S.D.; Tsai, D.H.; Hsu, S.R. Association between serum uric acid level and components of the metabolic syndrome. *J. Chin. Med. Assoc.* **2006**, *69*, 512–516. [CrossRef]
13. Lv, Q.; Meng, X.F.; He, F.F.; Chen, S.; Su, H.; Xiong, J.; Gao, P.; Tian, X.J.; Liu, J.S.; Zhu, Z.H.; *et al.* High serum uric acid and increased risk of type 2 diabetes: A systemic review and meta-analysis of prospective cohort studies. *PLoS ONE* **2013**, *8*, e56864.
14. Lonardo, A.; Loria, P.; Leonardi, F.; Borsatti, A.; Neri, P.; Pulvirenti, M.; Verrone, A.M.; Bagni, A.; Bertolotti, M.; Ganazzi, D.; *et al.* Fasting insulin and uric acid levels but not indices of iron metabolism are independent predictors of non-alcoholic fatty liver disease. A case-control study. *Dig. Liver Dis.* **2002**, *34*, 204–211. [CrossRef]
15. Li, Y.; Xu, C.; Yu, C.; Xu, L.; Miao, M. Association of serum uric acid level with non-alcoholic fatty liver disease: A cross-sectional study. *J. Hepatol.* **2009**, *50*, 1029–1034. [PubMed]
16. Ryu, S.; Chang, Y.; Kim, S.G.; Cho, J.; Guallar, E. Serum uric acid levels predict incident nonalcoholic fatty liver disease in healthy Korean men. *Metabolism* **2011**, *60*, 860–866. [CrossRef] [PubMed]
17. Liu, Z.; Que, S.; Zhou, L.; Zheng, S. Dose-response relationship of serum uric acid with metabolic syndrome and non-alcoholic fatty liver disease incidence: A meta-analysis of prospective studies. *Sci. Rep.* **2015**, *5*, 14325. [CrossRef] [PubMed]
18. Yuan, H.; Yu, C.; Li, X.; Sun, L.; Zhu, X.; Zhao, C.; Zhang, Z.; Yang, Z. Serum uric acid levels and risk of metabolic syndrome: A dose-response meta-analysis of prospective studies. *J. Clin. Endocrinol. Metab.* **2015**, *100*, 4198–4207. [CrossRef] [PubMed]
19. Chen, J.H.; Chuang, S.Y.; Chen, H.J.; Yeh, W.T.; Pan, W.H. Serum uric acid level as an independent risk factor for all-cause, cardiovascular, and ischemic stroke mortality: A Chinese cohort study. *Arthritis Rheum.* **2009**, *61*, 225–232. [CrossRef] [PubMed]
20. Xu, C.; Wan, X.; Xu, L.; Weng, H.; Yan, M.; Miao, M.; Sun, Y.; Xu, G.; Dooley, S.; Li, Y.; *et al.* Xanthine oxidase in non-alcoholic fatty liver disease and hyperuricemia: One stone hits two birds. *J. Hepatol.* **2015**, *62*, 1412–1419. [CrossRef] [PubMed]
21. Sirota, J.C.; McFann, K.; Targher, G.; Johnson, R.J.; Chonchol, M.; Jalal, D.I. Elevated serum uric acid levels are associated with non-alcoholic fatty liver disease independently of metabolic syndrome features in the United States: Liver ultrasound data from the National Health and Nutrition Examination Survey. *Metabolism* **2013**, *62*, 392–399. [CrossRef] [PubMed]
22. Petta, S.; Camma, C.; Cabibi, D.; Di Marco, V.; Craxi, A. Hyperuricemia is associated with histological liver damage in patients with non-alcoholic fatty liver disease. *Aliment. Pharmacol. Ther.* **2011**, *34*, 757–766. [PubMed]
23. Afzali, A.; Weiss, N.S.; Boyko, E.J.; Ioannou, G.N. Association between serum uric acid level and chronic liver disease in the United States. *Hepatology* **2010**, *52*, 578–589. [CrossRef] [PubMed]
24. Abreu, E.; Fonseca, M.J.; Santos, A.C. Association between hyperuricemia and insulin resistance. *Acta Med. Port.* **2011**, *24*, 565–574. [PubMed]

25. Tan, Y.; Liu, X.; Zhou, K.; He, X.; Lu, C.; He, B.; Niu, X.; Xiao, C.; Xu, G.; Bian, Z.; *et al.* The potential biomarkers to identify the development of steatosis in hyperuricemia. *PLoS ONE* **2016**, *11*, e0149043. [CrossRef] [PubMed]

26. Li, C.; Hsieh, M.C.; Chang, S.J. Metabolic syndrome, diabetes, and hyperuricemia. *Curr. Opin. Rheumatol.* **2013**, *25*, 210–216. [CrossRef] [PubMed]

27. Zhu, Y.; Hu, Y.; Huang, T.; Zhang, Y.; Li, Z.; Luo, C.; Luo, Y.; Yuan, H.; Hisatome, I.; Yamamoto, T.; *et al.* High uric acid directly inhibits insulin signalling and induces insulin resistance. *Biochem. Biophys. Res. Commun.* **2014**, *447*, 707–714. [CrossRef] [PubMed]

28. Vandanmagsar, B.; Youm, Y.H.; Ravussin, A.; Galgani, J.E.; Stadler, K.; Mynatt, R.L.; Ravussin, E.; Stephens, J.M.; Dixit, V.D. The NLRP3 inflammasome instigates obesity-induced inflammation and insulin resistance. *Nat. Med.* **2011**, *17*, 179–188. [CrossRef] [PubMed]

29. Lanaspa, M.A.; Sanchez-Lozada, L.G.; Choi, Y.J.; Cicerchi, C.; Kanbay, M.; Roncal-Jimenez, C.A.; Ishimoto, T.; Li, N.; Marek, G.; Duranay, M.; *et al.* Uric acid induces hepatic steatosis by generation of mitochondrial oxidative stress: potential role in fructose-dependent and -independent fatty liver. *J. Biol. Chem.* **2012**, *287*, 40732–40744. [CrossRef] [PubMed]

30. Choi, Y.J.; Shin, H.S.; Choi, H.S.; Park, J.W.; Jo, I.; Oh, E.S.; Lee, K.Y.; Lee, B.H.; Johnson, R.J.; Kang, D.H. Uric acid induces fat accumulation via generation of endoplasmic reticulum stress and SREBP-1c activation in hepatocytes. *Lab. Investig.* **2014**, *94*, 1114–1125. [CrossRef] [PubMed]

31. Wan, X.; Xu, C.; Lin, Y.; Lu, C.; Li, D.; Sang, J.; He, H.; Liu, X.; Li, Y.; Yu, C. Uric acid regulates hepatic steatosis and insulin resistance through the NLRP3 inflammasome-dependent mechanism. *J. Hepatol.* **2015**. [CrossRef]

32. Ackerman, Z.; Oron-Herman, M.; Grozovski, M.; Rosenthal, T.; Pappo, O.; Link, G.; Sela, B.A. Fructose-induced fatty liver disease: hepatic effects of blood pressure and plasma triglyceride reduction. *Hypertension* **2005**, *45*, 1012–1018. [CrossRef] [PubMed]

33. Lanaspa, M.A.; Sanchez-Lozada, L.G.; Cicerchi, C.; Li, N.; Roncal-Jimenez, C.A.; Ishimoto, T.; Le, M.; Garcia, G.E.; Thomas, J.B.; Rivard, C.J.; *et al.* Uric acid stimulates fructokinase and accelerates fructose metabolism in the development of fatty liver. *PLoS ONE* **2012**, *7*, e47948. [CrossRef] [PubMed]

34. Pagliassotti, M.J. Endoplasmic reticulum stress in nonalcoholic fatty liver disease. *Annu. Rev. Nutr.* **2012**, *32*, 17–33. [CrossRef] [PubMed]

35. Zhang, C.; Chen, X.; Zhu, R.M.; Zhang, Y.; Yu, T.; Wang, H.; Zhao, H.; Zhao, M.; Ji, Y.L.; Chen, Y.H.; *et al.* Endoplasmic reticulum stress is involved in hepatic SREBP-1c activation and lipid accumulation in fructose-fed mice. *Toxicol. Lett.* **2012**, *212*, 229–240. [CrossRef] [PubMed]

36. De Oliveira, E.P.; Burini, R.C. High plasma uric acid concentration: causes and consequences. *Diabetol. Metab. Syndr.* **2012**, *4*, 12. [CrossRef] [PubMed]

37. Martinon, F.; Petrilli, V.; Mayor, A.; Tardivel, A.; Tschopp, J. Gout-associated uric acid crystals activate the NALP3 inflammasome. *Nature* **2006**, *440*, 237–241. [CrossRef] [PubMed]

38. Bugianesi, E.; Manzini, P.; D'Antico, S.; Vanni, E.; Longo, F.; Leone, N.; Massarenti, P.; Piga, A.; Marchesini, G.; Rizzetto, M. Relative contribution of iron burden, HFE mutations, and insulin resistance to fibrosis in nonalcoholic fatty liver. *Hepatology* **2004**, *39*, 179–187. [CrossRef] [PubMed]

39. Fernandez-Real, J.M.; Ricart-Engel, W.; Arroyo, E.; Balanca, R.; Casamitjana-Abella, R.; Cabrero, D.; Fernandez-Castaner, M.; Soler, J. Serum ferritin as a component of the insulin resistance syndrome. *Diabetes Care* **1998**, *21*, 62–68. [CrossRef] [PubMed]

40. Ford, E.S.; Cogswell, M.E. Diabetes and serum ferritin concentration among U.S. adults. *Diabetes Care* **1999**, *22*, 1978–1983. [CrossRef] [PubMed]

41. Salonen, J.T.; Tuomainen, T.P.; Nyyssonen, K.; Lakka, H.M.; Punnonen, K. Relation between iron stores and non-insulin dependent diabetes in men: Case-control study. *BMJ* **1998**, *317*, 727. [CrossRef] [PubMed]

42. Kim, C.W.; Chang, Y.; Sung, E.; Shin, H.; Ryu, S. Serum ferritin levels predict incident non-alcoholic fatty liver disease in healthy Korean men. *Metabolism* **2012**, *61*, 1182–1188. [CrossRef] [PubMed]

43. Gillum, R.F. Association of serum ferritin and indices of body fat distribution and obesity in Mexican American men—The third national health and nutrition examination survey. *Int. J. Obes. Relat. Metab. Disord.* **2001**, *25*, 639–645. [CrossRef] [PubMed]

44. Piperno, A.; Trombini, P.; Gelosa, M.; Mauri, V.; Pecci, V.; Vergani, A.; Salvioni, A.; Mariani, R.; Mancia, G. Increased serum ferritin is common in men with essential hypertension. *J. Hypertens.* **2002**, *20*, 1513–1518. [CrossRef] [PubMed]

45. Williams, M.J.; Poulton, R.; Williams, S. Relationship of serum ferritin with cardiovascular risk factors and inflammation in young men and women. *Atherosclerosis* **2002**, *165*, 179–184. [CrossRef]

46. Iwasaki, T.; Nakajima, A.; Yoneda, M.; Yamada, Y.; Mukasa, K.; Fujita, K.; Fujisawa, N.; Wada, K.; Terauchi, Y. Serum ferritin is associated with visceral fat area and subcutaneous fat area. *Diabetes Care* **2005**, *28*, 2486–2491. [CrossRef] [PubMed]

47. Alam, F.; Memon, A.S.; Fatima, S.S. Increased Body Mass Index may lead to Hyperferritinemia Irrespective of Body Iron Stores. *Pak. J. Med. Sci.* **2015**, *31*, 1521–1526. [PubMed]

48. Ellervik, C.; Marott, J.L.; Tybjaerg-Hansen, A.; Schnohr, P.; Nordestgaard, B.G. Total and cause-specific mortality by moderately and markedly increased ferritin concentrations: General population study and metaanalysis. *Clin. Chem.* **2014**, *60*, 1419–1428. [CrossRef] [PubMed]

49. Fernandez-Real, J.M.; Lopez-Bermejo, A.; Ricart, W. Cross-talk between iron metabolism and diabetes. *Diabetes* **2002**, *51*, 2348–2354. [CrossRef] [PubMed]

50. Zelber-Sagi, S.; Nitzan-Kaluski, D.; Halpern, Z.; Oren, R. NAFLD and hyperinsulinemia are major deter4.minants of serum ferritin levels. *J. Hepatol.* **2007**, *46*, 700–707. [CrossRef] [PubMed]

51. Moirand, R.; Mortaji, A.M.; Loreal, O.; Paillard, F.; Brissot, P.; Deugnier, Y. A new syndrome of liver iron overload with normal transferrin saturation. *Lancet* **1997**, *349*, 95–97. [CrossRef]

52. Corradini, E.; Meynard, D.; Wu, Q.; Chen, S.; Ventura, P.; Pietrangelo, A.; Babitt, J.L. Serum and liver iron differently regulate the bone morphogenetic protein 6 (BMP6)-SMAD signaling pathway in mice. *Hepatology* **2011**, *54*, 273–284. [CrossRef] [PubMed]

53. Vecchi, C.; Montosi, G.; Zhang, K.; Lamberti, I.; Duncan, S.A.; Kaufman, R.J.; Pietrangelo, A. ER stress controls iron metabolism through induction of hepcidin. *Science* **2009**, *325*, 877–880. [CrossRef] [PubMed]

54. Fargion, S.; Valenti, L.; Fracanzani, A.L. Beyond hereditary hemochromatosis: New insights into the relationship between iron overload and chronic liver diseases. *Dig. Liver Dis.* **2011**, *43*, 89–95. [CrossRef] [PubMed]

55. Murotomi, K.; Arai, S.; Uchida, S.; Endo, S.; Mitsuzumi, H.; Tabei, Y.; Yoshida, Y.; Nakajima, Y. Involvement of splenic iron accumulation in the development of nonalcoholic steatohepatitis in Tsumura Suzuki Obese Diabetes mice. *Sci. Rep.* **2016**, *6*, 22476. [CrossRef] [PubMed]

56. Corradini, E.; Pietrangelo, A. Iron and steatohepatitis. *J. Gastroenterol. Hepatol.* **2012**, *27*, 42–46. [CrossRef] [PubMed]

57. Dongiovanni, P.; Fracanzani, A.L.; Fargion, S.; Valenti, L. Iron in fatty liver and in the metabolic syndrome: a promising therapeutic target. *J. Hepatol.* **2011**, *55*, 920–932. [CrossRef] [PubMed]

58. Boga, S.; Alkim, H.; Alkim, C.; Koksal, A.R.; Bayram, M.; Yilmaz Ozguven, M.B.; Tekin Neijmann, S. The relationship of serum hemojuvelin and hepcidin levels with iron overload in nonalcoholic fatty liver disease. *J. Gastrointest. Liver Dis.* **2015**, *24*, 293–300.

59. Senates, E.; Yilmaz, Y.; Colak, Y.; Ozturk, O.; Altunoz, M.E.; Kurt, R.; Ozkara, S.; Aksaray, S.; Tuncer, I.; Ovunc, A.O. Serum levels of hepcidin in patients with biopsy-proven nonalcoholic fatty liver disease. *Metab. Syndr. Relat. Disord.* **2011**, *9*, 287–290. [CrossRef] [PubMed]

60. Demircioglu, F.; Gorunmez, G.; Dagistan, E.; Goksugur, S.B.; Bekdas, M.; Tosun, M.; Kizildag, B.; Kismet, E. Serum hepcidin levels and iron metabolism in obese children with and without fatty liver: Case-control study. *Eur. J. Pediatr.* **2014**, *173*, 947–951. [CrossRef] [PubMed]

61. Neri, S.; Pulvirenti, D.; Signorelli, S.; Ignaccolo, L.; Tsami, A.; Mauceri, B.; Misseri, M.; Interlandi, D.; Cutuli, N.; Castellino, P. The HFE gene heterozygosis H63D: A cofactor for liver damage in patients with steatohepatitis? Epidemiological and clinical considerations. *Intern. Med. J.* **2008**, *38*, 254–258. [CrossRef] [PubMed]

62. Valenti, L.; Dongiovanni, P.; Fracanzani, A.L.; Fargion, S. HFE mutations in nonalcoholic fatty liver disease. *Hepatology* **2008**, *47*, 1794–1795. [CrossRef] [PubMed]

63. McClain, D.A.; Abraham, D.; Rogers, J.; Brady, R.; Gault, P.; Ajioka, R.; Kushner, J.P. High prevalence of abnormal glucose homeostasis secondary to decreased insulin secretion in individuals with hereditary haemochromatosis. *Diabetologia* **2006**, *49*, 1661–1669. [CrossRef] [PubMed]

64. Choi, J.S.; Koh, I.U.; Lee, H.J.; Kim, W.H.; Song, J. Effects of excess dietary iron and fat on glucose and lipid metabolism. *J. Nutr. Biochem.* **2013**, *24*, 1634–1644. [CrossRef] [PubMed]

65. Dongiovanni, P.; Ruscica, M.; Rametta, R.; Recalcati, S.; Steffani, L.; Gatti, S.; Girelli, D.; Cairo, G.; Magni, P.; Fargion, S.; *et al.* Dietary iron overload induces visceral adipose tissue insulin resistance. *Am. J. Pathol.* **2013**, *182*, 2254–2263. [CrossRef] [PubMed]

66. Vecchi, C.; Montosi, G.; Garuti, C.; Corradini, E.; Sabelli, M.; Canali, S.; Pietrangelo, A. Gluconeogenic signals regulate iron homeostasis via hepcidin in mice. *Gastroenterology* **2014**, *146*, 1060–1069. [CrossRef] [PubMed]

67. Marra, F.; Bertolani, C. Adipokines in liver diseases. *Hepatology* **2009**, *50*, 957–969. [CrossRef] [PubMed]

68. Bekri, S.; Gual, P.; Anty, R.; Luciani, N.; Dahman, M.; Ramesh, B.; Iannelli, A.; Staccini-Myx, A.; Casanova, D.; Ben Amor, I.; *et al.* Increased adipose tissue expression of hepcidin in severe obesity is independent from diabetes and NASH. *Gastroenterology* **2006**, *131*, 788–796. [CrossRef] [PubMed]

69. Green, A.; Basile, R.; Rumberger, J.M. Transferrin and iron induce insulin resistance of glucose transport in adipocytes. *Metabolism* **2006**, *55*, 1042–1045. [CrossRef] [PubMed]

70. Item, F.; Konrad, D. Visceral fat and metabolic inflammation: the portal theory revisited. *Obes. Rev.* **2012**, *13*, 30–39. [CrossRef] [PubMed]

71. Fargion, S.; Mattioli, M.; Fracanzani, A.L.; Sampietro, M.; Tavazzi, D.; Fociani, P.; Taioli, E.; Valenti, L.; Fiorelli, G. Hyperferritinemia, iron overload, and multiple metabolic alterations identify patients at risk for nonalcoholic steatohepatitis. *Am. J. Gastroenterol.* **2001**, *96*, 2448–2455. [CrossRef] [PubMed]

72. Manousou, P.; Kalambokis, G.; Grillo, F.; Watkins, J.; Xirouchakis, E.; Pleguezuelo, M.; Leandro, G.; Arvaniti, V.; Germani, G.; Patch, D.; *et al.* Serum ferritin is a discriminant marker for both fibrosis and inflammation in histologically proven non-alcoholic fatty liver disease patients. *Liver Int.* **2011**, *31*, 730–739. [CrossRef] [PubMed]

73. Kowdley, K.V.; Belt, P.; Wilson, L.A.; Yeh, M.M.; Neuschwander-Tetri, B.A.; Chalasani, N.; Sanyal, A.J.; Nelson, J.E.; Network, N.C.R. Serum ferritin is an independent predictor of histologic severity and advanced fibrosis in patients with nonalcoholic fatty liver disease. *Hepatology* **2012**, *55*, 77–85. [CrossRef] [PubMed]

74. Kim, Y.S.; Jung, E.S.; Hur, W.; Bae, S.H.; Choi, J.Y.; Song, M.J.; Kim, C.W.; Jo, S.H.; Lee, C.D.; Lee, Y.S.; *et al.* Noninvasive predictors of nonalcoholic steatohepatitis in Korean patients with histologically proven nonalcoholic fatty liver disease. *Clin. Mol. Hepatol.* **2013**, *19*, 120–130. [CrossRef] [PubMed]

75. Angulo, P.; George, J.; Day, C.P.; Vanni, E.; Russell, L.; de la Cruz, A.C.; Liaquat, H.; Mezzabotta, L.; Lee, E.; Bugianesi, E. Serum ferritin levels lack diagnostic accuracy for liver fibrosis in patients with nonalcoholic fatty liver disease. *Clin. Gastroenterol. Hepatol.* **2014**, *12*, 1163–1169. [CrossRef] [PubMed]

76. Yoneda, M.; Thomas, E.; Sumida, Y.; Imajo, K.; Eguchi, Y.; Hyogo, H.; Fujii, H.; Ono, M.; Kawaguchi, T.; Schiff, E.R. Clinical usage of serum ferritin to assess liver fibrosis in patients with non-alcoholic fatty liver disease: Proceed with caution. *Hepatol. Res.* **2014**, *44*, E499–E502. [CrossRef] [PubMed]

77. Nakamura, A.; Yoneda, M.; Sumida, Y.; Eguchi, Y.; Fujii, H.; Hyogo, H.; Ono, M.; Suzuki, Y.; Kawaguchi, T.; Aoki, N.; *et al.* Modification of a simple clinical scoring system as a diagnostic screening tool for non-alcoholic steatohepatitis in Japanese patients with non-alcoholic fatty liver disease. *J. Diabetes Investig.* **2013**, *4*, 651–658. [CrossRef] [PubMed]

78. Cales, P.; Boursier, J.; Oberti, F.; Hubert, I.; Gallois, Y.; Rousselet, M.C.; Dib, N.; Moal, V.; Macchi, L.; Chevailler, A.; *et al.* FibroMeters: A family of blood tests for liver fibrosis. *Gastroenterol. Clin. Biol.* **2008**, *32*, 40–51. [CrossRef]

79. Valenti, L.; Canavesi, E.; Galmozzi, E.; Dongiovanni, P.; Rametta, R.; Maggioni, P.; Maggioni, M.; Fracanzani, A.L.; Fargion, S. β-Globin mutations are associated with parenchymal siderosis and fibrosis in patients with non-alcoholic fatty liver disease. *J. Hepatol.* **2010**, *53*, 927–933. [CrossRef] [PubMed]

80. Facchini, F.S.; Hua, N.W.; Stoohs, R.A. Effect of iron depletion in carbohydrate-intolerant patients with clinical evidence of nonalcoholic fatty liver disease. *Gastroenterology* **2002**, *122*, 931–939. [CrossRef] [PubMed]

81. Fernandez-Real, J.M.; Penarroja, G.; Castro, A.; Garcia-Bragado, F.; Hernandez-Aguado, I.; Ricart, W. Blood letting in high-ferritin type 2 diabetes: effects on insulin sensitivity and β-cell function. *Diabetes* **2002**, *51*, 1000–1004. [CrossRef] [PubMed]

82. Valenti, L.; Fracanzani, A.L.; Dongiovanni, P.; Bugianesi, E.; Marchesini, G.; Manzini, P.; Vanni, E.; Fargion, S. Iron depletion by phlebotomy improves insulin resistance in patients with nonalcoholic fatty liver disease and hyperferritinemia: evidence from a case-control study. *Am. J. Gastroenterol.* **2007**, *102*, 1251–1258. [CrossRef] [PubMed]

83. Chen, S.C.; Huang, Y.F.; Wang, J.D. Hyperferritinemia and hyperuricemia may be associated with liver function abnormality in obese adolescents. *PLoS ONE* **2012**, *7*, e48645. [CrossRef] [PubMed]
84. Ghio, A.J.; Ford, E.S.; Kennedy, T.P.; Hoidal, J.R. The association between serum ferritin and uric acid in humans. *Free Radic. Res.* **2005**, *39*, 337–342. [CrossRef] [PubMed]
85. Mainous, A.G., 3rd; Knoll, M.E.; Everett, C.J.; Matheson, E.M.; Hulihan, M.M.; Grant, A.M. Uric acid as a potential cue to screen for iron overload. *J. Am. Board Fam. Med.* **2011**, *24*, 415–421. [CrossRef] [PubMed]

International Journal of
Molecular Sciences

MDPI

Review

Does Lysosomial Acid Lipase Reduction Play a Role in Adult Non-Alcoholic Fatty Liver Disease?

Francesco Baratta [1,†], Daniele Pastori [1,†], Licia Polimeni [1], Giulia Tozzi [2], Francesco Violi [3], Francesco Angelico [4,*,‡] and Maria Del Ben [3,‡]

[1] Department of Internal Medicine and Medical Specialities and Department of Anatomical, Histological, Forensic Medicine and Orthopedics Sciences-Sapienza University, Rome 00185, Italy; francesco.baratta@uniroma1.it (F.B.); daniele.pastori@uniroma1.it (D.P.); licia.polimeni@uniroma1.it (L.P.)

[2] Unit for Neuromuscular and Neurodegenerative Diseases, Children's Hospital and Research Institute "Bambino Gesù", Rome 00165, Italy; giulia.tozzi@opbg.net

[3] Department of Internal Medicine and Medical Specialities, Sapienza University, Rome 00185, Italy; francesco.violi@uniroma1.it (F.V.); maria.delben@uniroma1.it (M.D.B.)

[4] Department of Public Health and Infectious Diseases, Sapienza University, Policlinico Umberto I, I Clinica Medica, Viale del Policlinico 155, Rome 00161, Italy

* Correspondence: francesco.angelico@uniroma1.it; Tel./Fax: +39-064-997-2249

† These authors contributed equally to this work.

‡ Joint senior authors.

Academic Editor: Amedeo Lonardo

Received: 13 October 2015; Accepted: 17 November 2015; Published: 25 November 2015

Abstract: Lysosomal Acid Lipase (LAL) is a key enzyme involved in lipid metabolism, responsible for hydrolysing the cholesteryl esters and triglycerides. Wolman Disease represents the early onset phenotype of LAL deficiency rapidly leading to death. Cholesterol Ester Storage Disease is a late onset phenotype that occurs with fatty liver, elevated aminotransferase levels, hepatomegaly and dyslipidaemia, the latter characterized by elevated LDL-C and low HDL-C. The natural history and the clinical manifestations of the LAL deficiency in adults are not well defined, and the diagnosis is often incidental. LAL deficiency has been suggested as an under-recognized cause of dyslipidaemia and fatty liver. Therefore, LAL activity may be reduced also in non-obese patients presenting non-alcoholic fatty liver disease (NAFLD), unexplained persistently elevated liver transaminases or with elevation in LDL cholesterol. In these patients, it could be indicated to test LAL activity. So far, very few studies have been performed to assess LAL activity in representative samples of normal subjects or patients with NAFLD. Moreover, no large study has been carried out in adult subjects with NAFLD or cryptogenic cirrhosis.

Keywords: lysosomial acid lipase; non-alcoholic fatty liver disease; Wolman Disease; cholesterol ester storage disease; hypercholesterolemia

1. Introduction

Non-alcoholic fatty liver disease (NAFLD) is a spectrum of disorders characterized by excessive hepatic fat accumulation that occurs in individuals in the absence of significant alcohol consumption or chronic viral infection. NAFLD is the most common hepatic disease involving a growing number of people worldwide. In the general population, the prevalence of NAFLD is about 20%–30%, and reaches 70%–90% in obese or diabetic patients [1]. The early stage of NAFLD is represented by simple steatosis, where the main histologic finding is the presence of fatty liver; in some cases simple steatosis my evolve in non-alcoholic steatohepatitis (NASH), where steatosis is associated with hepatocellular injury and inflammation with or without fibrosis.

Traditionally, NAFLD has been interpreted as a benign condition; however, more recent evidence suggests that NAFLD may progress to advanced liver disease such as cirrhosis, hepatocellular carcinoma, and end stage hepatic failure [2].

NAFLD is the result of many different pathogenic mechanisms which cause lipid accumulation into hepatocytes [3], increased oxidative stress, pro-inflammatory changes [4], and eventually fibrosis in a subset of individuals.

The mechanisms underlying the evolution of simple steatosis to NASH and/or liver cirrhosis are not yet clarified, and the progression of NAFLD is not predictable.

Nowadays, NAFLD is a major cause of cryptogenic cirrhosis, whose prevalence has increased over the last years especially in patients with a history of obesity and type 2 diabetes. NAFLD is the third most common indication for liver transplantation in the United States and is projected to eventually overtake the hepatitis C virus and alcoholic liver disease and to become the main cause of liver transplants [5].

2. Non-Alcoholic Fatty Liver Disease and Cardiovascular Disease

Prospective studies suggested that, in patients with NAFLD, cardiovascular disease (CVD) is the first cause of death [6]. Thus, atherosclerosis is the primary cause of morbidity for these subjects, and many of them will be suffering from CVD before the development of liver-related complications [7].

The association between NAFLD and CV risk has been largely investigated [8], but a definite explanation has not been provided. Among the proposed mechanisms, it has been suggested that NAFLD, especially in its more advanced forms, might act itself as a stimulus for the release of pro-atherogenic factors contributing actively to the onset of CVD [9].

The association of steatosis with different pro-atherogenic conditions is another plausible reason accounting for an increased CV risk [10]. Thus, patients with NAFLD disclosed systemic signs of atherosclerosis, such as increased carotid intima-media thickness and endothelial dysfunction [11].

Common metabolic disorders, such as dyslipidaemia, type 2 diabetes [12] and central obesity, have been associated with both simple liver steatosis and progressive NASH.

Besides, it has been also suggested that fatty liver can be considered an hepatic consequence of the insulin resistance related to the metabolic syndrome (MetS) [13,14], which is a highly pro-atherogenic condition that involves approximately 20% of the non-diabetic population in the western countries meeting the ATPIII diagnostic criteria [15].

Insulin resistance is a paramount pathophysiological moment in the MetS, and according to the "two hit" hypothesis, is also considered to play a central role in the first stage of fatty liver infiltration [16]. However, whether MetS with insulin resistance promotes fatty liver or whether NAFLD itself induces chronic hyperinsulinemia by impaired insulin degradation, is still under debate. The current opinion is that there is a strong bidirectional association between NAFLD and MetS [9].

However, not all NAFLD cases could be explained by insulin resistance; in fact, not all subjects with MetS will develop NAFLD and not all subjects with NAFLD have MetS or will develop it.

PNPLA3 and Non-Metabolic NAFLD

Patatin-like phospholipase domain-containing protein 3 (PNPLA3) is a gene encoding a lipase enzyme expressed in adipocytes. The mutation of PNPLA3, such as the PNPLA3 MM genotype, showed to be strongly associated with the presence of NAFLD and NASH [17]. Patients with PNPLA3 MM genotype do not show classical metabolic features commonly described in NAFLD patients with wild type genotype. In fact, normal peripheral and hepatic insulin sensitivity has been described in NAFLD patients with PNLPA3 mutation [18,19].

In addition, NAFLD patients with PNPLA3 mutation showed a lower CV risk compared to "metabolic" NAFLD patients, questioning as to whether NAFLD represents an independent CV risk factor.

3. Clinical Presentations of Genetic LAL Deficiency

Lysosomal Acid Lipase (LAL) deficiency is a rare autosomal recessive genetic disease characterized by the accumulation of cholesteryl esters (CE) and triglycerides in many tissues, caused by mutations of the gene encoding LAL, namely *LIPA* gene [20]. The most common *LIPA* gene mutation is the E8SJM variant, and its frequency is 0.0025 in the general population; this translates into a carrier frequency of about one in 200 in Western countries [21].

LAL deficiency is a heterogeneous disease and two main different phenotypes may be present; the Wolman Disease represents the early onset of LAL deficiency and manifests itself during the first six months of life, and it is rapidly fatal for the patient. Babies with LAL deficiency show growth retardation associated with malabsorption, hepatosplenomegaly, severe liver dysfunction, rapidly progressive anaemia and multi-organ failure. Adrenal calcification is the pathognomonic sign of Wolman Disease. The survival beyond one year of age is very rare.

Cholesterol Ester Storage Disease (CESD) is a late onset phenotype that occurs with fatty liver, elevated aminotransferase levels, hepatomegaly and dyslipidaemia characterized by elevated low-density lipoprotein cholesterol (LDL-C) and low high-density lipoprotein cholesterol (HDL-C) with or without triglyceride elevation. CESD may manifest in infancy, childhood or adulthood, and it remains often unrecognized since symptoms can overlap with other conditions. Patients have a more variable age of clinical presentation, ranging from five years to 44 years or over, and milder clinical courses [22].

The natural history and the clinical manifestations of the disease in children and adults are less well defined and the diagnosis is often incidental. Lipid abnormalities are common, and patients may present early signs of systemic atherosclerosis. Moreover, hepatomegaly and microvescicular steatosis with liver cell damage and splenomegaly are common features of the disease [23].

Clinical phenotype and the severity of LAL deficiency depend on the magnitude of the residual enzymatic activity. Therefore, finding steatosis and NASH in non-obese patients with lipid abnormalities may help in differentiating LAL deficiency from other metabolic causes of NAFLD such as MetS, type 2 diabetes, hypertriglyceridemia and central obesity [24].

4. Liver Histology in LAL Deficiency

The relationship between LAL deficiency and histological liver alterations was investigated only in subjects with CESD or Wolman Disease.

Based on available data, all patients with *LIPA* gene disorders have liver steatosis. Often, the differential diagnosis with other causes of fatty liver can be difficult and a definitive diagnosis can be done only by histological analysis of liver biopsy specimens.

In paraffin fixed specimen, the main feature is represented by a pervasive and homogeneous microvescicolar steatosis, although this aspect is not specific for CESD [23]. Conversely, in unfixed frozen samples, the finding of cholesterol ester crystals, using polarized light, is a distinctive feature of CESD [25].

Recently, Hůlková H. *et al.* [25] provided a new immunohistochemistry method to better identify CESD, in both paraffin-fixed and frozen biopsy specimen. The presence of luminal cathepsin D and membrane lysosomal markers namely lysosomal-associated membrane protein 1 and 2, and lysosomal integral membrane protein 2 around the lipid vacuoles, confirms the intra-lysosomal lipid accumulation. Moreover, the presence of macrophage with intracellular ceroid accumulation is another common histological finding in patients with CESD. The presence of this specific feature, namely ceroid induction, localized in lysosomes from macrophage, but not in those from hepatocytes, supports the diagnosis of CESD.

5. The Role of LAL in Lipid Metabolism

LAL is a key enzyme involved in intracellular lipid metabolism and trafficking; it is responsible for the intra-lysosomal hydrolysis of LDL CE and triglycerides into free cholesterol and free fatty acids [26]. Therefore, the reduction of LAL activity determines intra-lysosomal lipid accumulation and a consecutive reduction of free cholesterol in cytosol [27]. This can promote an increase of the activity of the sterol regulatory element-binding proteins (SREBPs), leading to increased lipogenesis, cholesterol biosynthesis and VLDL production. At the same time, there is also a reduction of the expression of liver X receptors (LXRs) leading to reduced efflux of cholesterol and HDL production. Therefore, abnormalities in serum lipids are induced.

The main evidence of lipid serum alterations, in LAL activity deficiency, derives from studies performed in patients with homozygous genetic disorders for *LIPA* gene.

The most common lipoprotein alterations in patients with homozygous LAL deficiency are type IIa (high LDL-C with normal triglycerides) and type IIb dyslipidaemias (high LDL-C and triglycerides), combined with low HDL-C. In these patients, dyslipidaemia has been associated with accelerated atherosclerosis. Therefore, in the presence of a type IIa dyslipidaemia, the differential diagnosis with heterozygous familial hypercholesterolemia (HeFH) is very important but not always easy to perform. The presence of family history for premature CVD and/or for hypercholesterolemia may contribute to make FH diagnosis. By contrast, in the absence of diagnostic criteria for HeFH, diagnosis of LAL deficiency should be suspected.

Further studies were carried out in heterozygous patients for *LIPA* gene mutation. A recent review on patients with different LIPA mutations [23], reported an increase of total and LDL-C, and most patients had a severe LDL-C elevation (>200 mg/dL). In 65 patients, HDL cholesterol was determined, and, in 57 of those, it was found to be reduced. Premature atherosclerosis was also documented in some patients. Based on the above study, it appears that the occurrence of lipid alterations and of accelerated atherosclerosis is similar in patients with LAL deficiency due to homozygous and heterozygous mutation of *LIPA* gene. LAL deficiency should more often be considered in dyslipidemic patients with combined hyperlipidemia and low HDL-C.

Only one study explored lipid data in patients with non-genetic LAL activity reduction. Authors reported a moderate elevation of total and LDL-C in NAFLD patients with lower LAL activity. No differences were reported in HDL-C and triglycerides.

All the above data suggest a negative correlation between LAL activity and total and LDL-C elevation.

6. The Role of LAL in Atherosclerosis

It has been recently hypothesized that changes in LAL activity could contribute to the atherosclerotic process. The formation and accumulation of foam cells within wall arteries is a key pathophysiological moment in the formation of atherosclerotic plaque [28].

Foam cells derived from oxidation of lipid products, mostly in the form of CE, that cannot be metabolized upon LDL receptor pathway and are recognized and removed by scavenger receptors expressed on macrophages and smooth muscular cells, leading to accumulation of cholesterol in these cells [27]. Thus, CE are physiologically hydrolysed in the lysosomes by LAL to generate free cholesterol, which, after being re-esterified in the endoplasmic reticulum, can form cytosolic lipid droplets. The accumulation of free cholesterol in lysosomes during the atherosclerotic process could inhibit LAL activity, causing accumulation of CE in cells. LAL is also present within the extracellular space of atherosclerotic intima [29].

Physiopathology findings have been confirmed by interventional studies on mice with recombinant human LAL, in which a reversal of atherosclerotic lesions have been observed [27].

7. Who Should Be Tested for LAL Activity?

LAL activity reduction should always be suspected in non-obese patients presenting with NAFLD and/or cryptogenic cirrhosis, unexplained persistently elevated liver transaminases or with elevation in LDL-C and decreased HDL-C (Table 1). An accurate anamnesis is necessary to exclude potential causes contributing to fatty liver, such as viral causes, alcohol abuse or the presence of familial hypercholesterolemia [24].

In these patients, it could be indicated to test LAL activity, using the dried blood spot (DBS) test. The DBS is a simple test used to determine LAL activity by comparing total lipase activity to lipase activity in the presence of a highly specific inhibitor (Lalistat 2) of LAL. It allows the differentiation of healthy subjects from affected individuals. All patients with LAL reduction ($\leqslant$0.40 nmol/spot/h) detected by DBS should perform genetic tests to detect LAL gene mutations [30].

Table 1. Clinical suspicion of lysosomal acid lipase (LAL) reduction.

Who Should Be Tested for LAL Activity?
Patients with unexplained:
•Liver Dysfunction ($\geqslant$1 of the following)
Persistent elevation of ALT
Presence of hepatomegaly
Hepatic steatosis
AND/OR
•Dislipidemia ($\geqslant$1 of the following)
High LDL-C ($\geqslant$160 mg/dL–4.1 mmol/L)
Low HDL-C ($\leqslant$40 mg/dL–1.0 mmol/L in males; $\leqslant$50 mg/dL–1.3 mmol/L in females)

8. Current Research Status on LAL Activity and NAFLD

Very few studies have been performed so far to assess LAL activity in representative samples of normal adult subjects or patients with NAFLD. Moreover, no large study has been carried out in adult subjects with NAFLD, and prevalence of *LIPA* gene mutation in this setting is unknown. Only one study investigated the clinical phenotype of patients with heterozygous mutations for *LIPA* genes. However, this study was focused only on lipid panel results and did not show data about hepatic condition or about other biochemical values [21].

In vitro, it has been demonstrated that several factors may modulate LAL activity [31]. In particular, enhanced LAL activity was associated with eicosanoids, gonadotropins and glucagon, and reduced activity was correlated with Lp(a), LDL remnants and oxidized LDL concentrations.

We recently reported, for the first time, reduced blood LAL activity in adult patients with NAFLD [32]. LAL activity was significantly reduced in 240 patients with NAFLD, as compared to 100 adult subjects [0.78 (0.61–1.01) *vs.* 1.15 (0.94–1.72) nmol/spot/h, $p < 0.001$]. NAFLD patients with LAL activity below median had higher values of serum total cholesterol ($p < 0.05$) and LDL-C ($p < 0.05$), and increased serum liver enzymes (ALT, $p < 0.001$; AST, $p < 0.01$; GGT, $p < 0.01$). We also observed a progressive decrease of LAL activity from patients with simple steatosis [0.84 (0.62–1.08) nmol/spot/h, $p < 0.001$ *vs.* HS] to those with biopsy-proven NASH [0.67 (0.51–0.77) nmol/spot/h, $p < 0.001$ *vs.* HS; $p < 0.001$, among groups].

However, at present, there are no data on certain epigenetic modulation of LAL activity *in vivo* models. Thus, studies are needed to better clarify mechanisms of epigenetic modulation of LAL activity and their potential role as therapeutic targets. For example, we do not know if an intervention on modifiable cardio-metabolic risk factors typically associated with NAFLD, such as metabolic syndrome, overweight, increased oxidative stress, may have a role in modulating LAL activity.

In addition, it is not known if the improvement in LAL activity may translate into a reduction of fatty liver content in adult NAFLD patients.

9. Future Directions

Altogether these data indicated that modifications in LAL activity are associated with dyslipidaemia and liver dysfunction [21]. In fact, both serum lipoprotein alterations and NAFLD are common and share many possible pathophysiological mechanisms. Moreover, it is not surprising that LAL activity reduction could be also an unrecognized contributing factor in the development and progression of NAFLD to cryptogenic cirrhosis.

Therefore, the identification of clinical and metabolic risk factors, especially those modifiable, which are able to modulate LAL activity, may have important clinical implications for the management of patients with NAFLD. Moreover, future research should also address epigenetic modulation of LAL activity and also take into consideration the effect of drug treatments. This would be particularly important to better understand the contribution of LAL in the complex scenario of NAFLD.

Recently, Burton BK *et al.* reported an impressive reduction of hepatic fat content as assessed by means of magnetic resonance imaging in patients with severe LAL deficiency treated for 20 weeks with enzyme replacement therapy with Sebelipase alfa [33]. These findings were paralleled by improvement in serum liver enzymes and lipid levels. The study was carried out in subjects with confirmed enzyme activity-based diagnosis performed by dried blood spots using the inhibitor Lalistat 2. Almost 50% of patients had bridging fibrosis at liver biopsy and 31% had cirrhosis.

These findings, together with those showing low LAL activity in patients with NAFLD and NASH [32], suggest a strong association between impaired LAL activity and fatty liver pathogenesis and progression. Thus, LAL activity seems to be linked to NAFLD through several mechanisms including lipid metabolism alterations, intra-hepatic fat accumulation and pro-atherosclerotic functions (Figure 1).

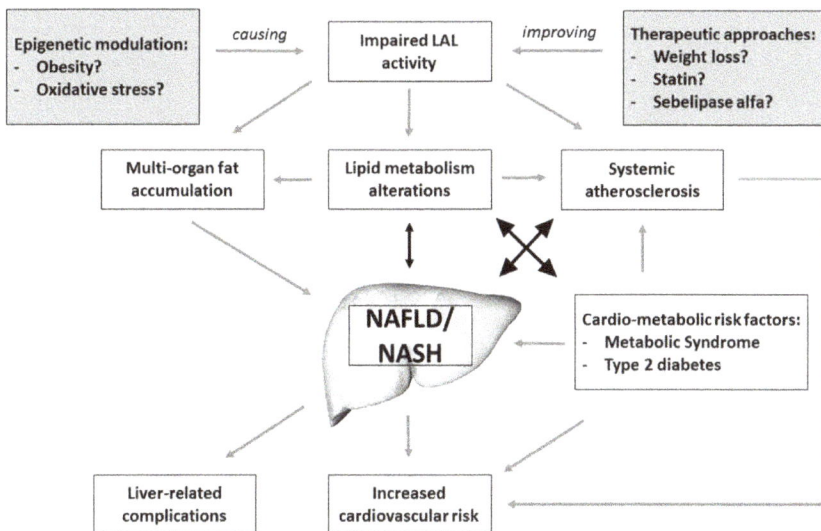

Figure 1. Putative mechanisms linking impaired LAL activity and NAFLD/NASH.

Finally, we speculate that LAL activity reduction may become a possible new target for the treatment of NAFLD. In fact, enzyme-replacement therapy may soon be available. This treatment will be indicated for patients with more severe, genetic LAL deficiency, where treatment will be lifesaving. However, in a recent clinical trial lead on CESD patients, treatment with sebelipase was associated with a significant reduction in fatty liver content in almost all treated patients [33]. Based on this evidence, we may speculate that, in the future, enzyme-replacement therapy could be also indicated for less severe LAL deficiency, especially in patients with more advanced forms of NAFLD, such as those with NASH or cryptogenic cirrhosis. Therefore, we believe that it is important to test NAFLD patients for LAL activity to identify a subgroup of patients at higher risk for liver disease progression.

Author Contributions: Francesco Baratta, Licia Polimeni, Giulia Tozzi and Daniele Pastori drafted the article or revised it critically. Maria Del Ben, Francesco Violi and Francesco Angelico gave final approval of the version to be published.

Conflicts of Interest: The authors declare no conflict of interest.

References

1. Vernon, G.; Baranova, A.; Younossi, Z.M. Systematic review: The epidemiology and natural history of non-alcoholic fatty liver disease and non-alcoholic steatohepatitis in adults. *Aliment. Pharmacol. Ther.* **2011**, *34*, 274–285. [CrossRef] [PubMed]

2. Kawano, Y.; Cohen, D.E. Mechanisms of hepatic triglyceride accumulation in non-alcoholic fatty liver disease. *J. Gastroenterol.* **2013**, *48*, 434–441. [CrossRef] [PubMed]

3. Takaki, A.; Kawai, D.; Yamamoto, K. Multiple hits, including oxidative stress, as pathogenesis and treatment target in non-alcoholic steatohepatitis (NASH). *Int. J. Mol. Sci.* **2013**, *14*, 20704–20728. [CrossRef] [PubMed]

4. Pastori, D.; Baratta, F.; Carnevale, R.; Cangemi, R.; del Ben, M.; Bucci, T.; Polimeni, L.; Labbadia, G.; Nocella, C.; Scardella, L.; *et al.* Similar reduction of cholesterol-adjusted vitamin e serum levels in simple steatosis and non-alcoholic steatohepatitis. *Clin. Transl. Gastroenterol.* **2015**, *6*, e113. [CrossRef] [PubMed]

5. Kemmer, N.; Neff, G.W.; Franco, E.; Osman-Mohammed, H.; Leone, J.; Parkinson, E.; Cece, E.; Alsina, A. Nonalcoholic fatty liver disease epidemic and its implications for liver transplantation. *Transplantation* **2013**, *96*, 860–862. [CrossRef] [PubMed]

6. Soderberg, C.; Stal, P.; Askling, J.; Glaumann, H.; Lindberg, G.; Marmur, J.; Hultcrantz, R. Decreased survival of subjects with elevated liver function tests during a 28-year follow-up. *Hepatology* **2010**, *51*, 595–602. [CrossRef] [PubMed]

7. Ballestri, S.; Lonardo, A.; Bonapace, S.; Byrne, C.D.; Loria, P.; Targher, G. Risk of cardiovascular, cardiac and arrhythmic complications in patients with non-alcoholic fatty liver disease. *World J. Gastroenterol.* **2014**, *20*, 1724–1745. [CrossRef] [PubMed]

8. Bhatia, L.S.; Curzen, N.P.; Calder, P.C.; Byrne, C.D. Non-alcoholic fatty liver disease: A new and important cardiovascular risk factor? *Eur. Heart J.* **2012**, *33*, 1190–1200. [CrossRef] [PubMed]

9. Del Ben, M.; Baratta, F.; Polimeni, L.; Angelico, F. Non-alcoholic fatty liver disease and cardiovascular disease: Epidemiological, clinical and pathophysiological evidences. *Internal Emerg. Med.* **2012**, *7*, S291–S296. [CrossRef] [PubMed]

10. Sookoian, S.; Castano, G.O.; Burgueno, A.L.; Rosselli, M.S.; Gianotti, T.F.; Mallardi, P.; Martino, J.S.; Pirola, C.J. Circulating levels and hepatic expression of molecular mediators of atherosclerosis in nonalcoholic fatty liver disease. *Atherosclerosis* **2010**, *209*, 585–591. [CrossRef] [PubMed]

11. Pastori, D.; Loffredo, L.; Perri, L.; Baratta, F.; Scardella, L.; Polimeni, L.; Pani, A.; Brancorsini, M.; Albanese, F.; Catasca, E.; *et al.* Relation of nonalcoholic fatty liver disease and framingham risk score to flow-mediated dilation in patients with cardiometabolic risk factors. *Am. J. Cardiol.* **2015**, *115*, 1402–1406. [CrossRef] [PubMed]

12. Targher, G.; Bertolini, L.; Padovani, R.; Rodella, S.; Tessari, R.; Zenari, L.; Day, C.; Arcaro, G. Prevalence of nonalcoholic fatty liver disease and its association with cardiovascular disease among type 2 diabetic patients. *Diabetes Care* **2007**, *30*, 1212–1218. [CrossRef] [PubMed]

13. Targher, G.; Marra, F.; Marchesini, G. Increased risk of cardiovascular disease in non-alcoholic fatty liver disease: Causal effect or epiphenomenon? *Diabetologia* **2008**, *51*, 1947–1953. [CrossRef] [PubMed]

14. Marchesini, G.; Bugianesi, E.; Forlani, G.; Cerrelli, F.; Lenzi, M.; Manini, R.; Natale, S.; Vanni, E.; Villanova, N.; Melchionda, N.; *et al.* Nonalcoholic fatty liver, steatohepatitis, and the metabolic syndrome. *Hepatology* **2003**, *37*, 917–923. [CrossRef] [PubMed]

15. Del Ben, M.; Polimeni, L.; Baratta, F.; Pastori, D.; Loffredo, L.; Angelico, F. Modern approach to the clinical management of non-alcoholic fatty liver disease. *World J. Gastroenterol.* **2014**, *20*, 8341–8350. [PubMed]

16. Day, C.P.; James, O.F. Steatohepatitis: A tale of two "hits"? *Gastroenterology* **1998**, *114*, 842–845. [CrossRef]

17. Wood, K.L.; Miller, M.H.; Dillon, J.F. Systematic review of genetic association studies involving histologically confirmed non-alcoholic fatty liver disease. *BMJ Open Gastroenterol.* **2015**, *2*, e000019. [CrossRef] [PubMed]

18. Del Ben, M.; Polimeni, L.; Brancorsini, M.; di Costanzo, A.; D'Erasmo, L.; Baratta, F.; Loffredo, L.; Pastori, D.; Pignatelli, P.; Violi, F.; *et al.* Non-alcoholic fatty liver disease, metabolic syndrome and patatin-like phospholipase domain-containing protein3 gene variants. *Eur. J. Intern. Med.* **2014**, *25*, 566–570. [CrossRef] [PubMed]

19. Della Corte, C.; Fintini, D.; Giordano, U.; Cappa, M.; Brufani, C.; Majo, F.; Mennini, C.; Nobili, V. Fatty liver and insulin resistance in children with hypobetalipoproteinemia: The importance of aetiology. *Clin. Endocrinol.* **2013**, *79*, 49–54. [CrossRef] [PubMed]

20. Thelwall, P.E.; Smith, F.E.; Leavitt, M.C.; Canty, D.; Hu, W.; Hollingsworth, K.G.; Thoma, C.; Trenell, M.I.; Taylor, R.; Rutkowski, J.V.; *et al.* Hepatic cholesteryl ester accumulation in lysosomal acid lipase deficiency: Non-invasive identification and treatment monitoring by magnetic resonance. *J. Hepatol.* **2013**, *59*, 543–549. [CrossRef] [PubMed]

21. Muntoni, S.; Wiebusch, H.; Jansen-Rust, M.; Rust, S.; Schulte, H.; Berger, K.; Pisciotta, L.; Bertolini, S.; Funke, H.; Seedorf, U.; *et al.* Heterozygosity for lysosomal acid lipase E8SJM mutation and serum lipid concentrations. *Nutr. Metab. Cardiovasc. Dis.* **2013**, *23*, 732–736. [CrossRef] [PubMed]

22. Pisciotta, L.; Fresa, R.; Bellocchio, A.; Pino, E.; Guido, V.; Cantafora, A.; di Rocco, M.; Calandra, S.; Bertolini, S. Cholesteryl ester storage disease (CESD) due to novel mutations in the LIPA gene. *Mol. Genet. Metab.* **2009**, *97*, 143–148. [CrossRef] [PubMed]

23. Bernstein, D.L.; Hulkova, H.; Bialer, M.G.; Desnick, R.J. Cholesteryl ester storage disease: Review of the findings in 135 reported patients with an underdiagnosed disease. *J. Hepatol.* **2013**, *58*, 1230–1243. [CrossRef] [PubMed]

24. Reiner, Z.; Guardamagna, O.; Nair, D.; Soran, H.; Hovingh, K.; Bertolini, S.; Jones, S.; Coric, M.; Calandra, S.; Hamilton, J.; *et al.* Lysosomal acid lipase deficiency—An under-recognized cause of dyslipidaemia and liver dysfunction. *Atherosclerosis* **2014**, *235*, 21–30. [CrossRef] [PubMed]

25. Hulkova, H.; Elleder, M. Distinctive histopathological features that support a diagnosis of cholesterol ester storage disease in liver biopsy specimens. *Histopathology* **2012**, *60*, 1107–1113. [CrossRef] [PubMed]

26. Fasano, T.; Pisciotta, L.; Bocchi, L.; Guardamagna, O.; Assandro, P.; Rabacchi, C.; Zanoni, P.; Filocamo, M.; Bertolini, S.; Calandra, S. Lysosomal lipase deficiency: Molecular characterization of eleven patients with wolman or cholesteryl ester storage disease. *Mol. Genet. Metab.* **2012**, *105*, 450–456. [CrossRef] [PubMed]

27. Dubland, J.A.; Francis, G.A. Lysosomal acid lipase: At the crossroads of normal and atherogenic cholesterol metabolism. *Front. Cell Dev. Biol.* **2015**, *3*, 3. [CrossRef] [PubMed]

28. Stocker, R.; Keaney, J.F., Jr. Role of oxidative modifications in atherosclerosis. *Physiol. Rev.* **2004**, *84*, 1381–1478. [CrossRef] [PubMed]

29. Hakala, J.K.; Oksjoki, R.; Laine, P.; Du, H.; Grabowski, G.A.; Kovanen, P.T.; Pentikainen, M.O. Lysosomal enzymes are released from cultured human macrophages, hydrolyze LDL *in vitro*, and are present extracellularly in human atherosclerotic lesions. *Arterioscler. Thromb. Vasc. Biol.* **2003**, *23*, 1430–1436. [CrossRef] [PubMed]

30. Hamilton, J.; Jones, I.; Srivastava, R.; Galloway, P. A new method for the measurement of lysosomal acid lipase in dried blood spots using the inhibitor lalistat 2. *Clin. Chim. Acta* **2012**, *413*, 1207–1210. [CrossRef] [PubMed]

31. Zschenker, O.; Illies, T.; Ameis, D. Overexpression of lysosomal acid lipase and other proteins in atherosclerosis. *J. Biochem.* **2006**, *140*, 23–38. [CrossRef] [PubMed]

32. Baratta, F.; Pastori, D.; del Ben, M.; Polimeni, L.; Labbadia, G.; di Santo, S.; Piemonte, F.; Tozzi, G.; Violi, F.; Angelico, F. Reduced lysosomal acid lipase activity in adult patients with non-alcoholic fatty liver disease. *EBioMedicine* **2015**, *2*, 750–754. [CrossRef] [PubMed]

33. Burton, B.K.; Balwani, M.; Feillet, F.; Baric, I.; Burrow, T.A.; Camarena Grande, C.; Coker, M.; Deegan, P.; Consuelo-Sanchez, A.; di Rocco, M.; *et al.* A phase 3 trial of sebelipase alfa in lysosomal acid lipase deficiency. *N. Engl. J. Med.* **2015**, *373*, 1010–1020. [CrossRef] [PubMed]

International Journal of
Molecular Sciences

MDPI

Article

Low Serum Lysosomal Acid Lipase Activity Correlates with Advanced Liver Disease

Eyal Shteyer [1,2,*,†], Rivka Villenchik [1,†], Mahmud Mahamid [3,4], Nidaa Nator [1] and Rifaat Safadi [1,4]

[1] The Liver Unit, Gastroenterology Institute, Hadassah Medical Center, Hadassah Medical School,
    The Hebrew University, Jerusalem 9112001, Israel; eshteyer@hotmail.com (R.V.);
    nidaa@hadassah.org.il (N.N.); safadi@hadassah.org.il (R.S.)
[2] Pediatric Gastroenterology Institute, Shaare Zedek Medical Center, Hadassah Medical School,
    The Hebrew University, Jerusalem 9103102, Israel
[3] Liver Unit, Gastroenterology Institute, Shaare Zedek Medical Center, Hadassah Medical School,
    The Hebrew University, Jerusalem 9112001, Israel; mmahamid@szmc.org.il
[4] Liver Unit, Holy Family Hospital; Safed Medical School, Bar Ilan University, Nazareth 1641110, Israel
* Correspondence: eyals@szmc.org.il; Tel.: +972-508-946-462; Fax: +972-2-655-5756
† These authors contributed equally to this work.

Academic Editors: Amedeo Lonardo and Giovanni Targher
Received: 12 December 2015; Accepted: 18 February 2016; Published: 27 February 2016

Abstract: Fatty liver has become the most common liver disorder and is recognized as a major health burden in the Western world. The causes for disease progression are not fully elucidated but lysosomal impairment is suggested. Here we evaluate a possible role for lysosomal acid lipase (LAL) activity in liver disease. To study LAL levels in patients with microvesicular, idiopathic cirrhosis and nonalcoholic fatty liver disease (NAFLD). Medical records of patients with microvesicular steatosis, cryptogenic cirrhosis and NAFLD, diagnosed on the basis of liver biopsies, were included in the study. Measured serum LAL activity was correlated to clinical, laboratory, imaging and pathological data. No patient exhibited LAL activity compatible with genetic LAL deficiency. However, serum LAL activity inversely predicted liver disease severity. A LAL level of 0.5 was the most sensitive for detecting both histologic and noninvasive markers for disease severity, including lower white blood cell count and calcium, and elevated γ-glutamyltransferase, creatinine, glucose, glycated hemoglobin, uric acid and coagulation function. Serum LAL activity <0.5 indicates severe liver injury in patients with fatty liver and cirrhosis. Further studies should define the direct role of LAL in liver disease severity and consider the possibility of replacement therapy.

Keywords: lysosomal acid lipase; cholesteryl ester storage disease; non-alcoholic liver disease; non-alcoholic steatohepatitis; cirrhosis

1. Introduction

Fatty liver has become the most common liver disorder [1] and is recognized as a major health burden in the Western world. The spectrum of histological abnormalities includes simple steatosis (steatosis without other liver injuries) and nonalcoholic steatohepatitis in its more extreme forms [2]. Over 30% of adults in developed countries suffer from hepatic fat accumulation [3]. Among these patients, 60% are diabetic, obese or morbidly obese [3–5].

The earliest stage of nonalcoholic fatty liver disease (NAFLD) consists of hepatic steatosis or lipid deposition in the cytoplasm of hepatocytes [6,7]. Hepatic steatosis may progress to the more aggressive necro-inflammatory form of NAFLD, nonalcoholic steatohepatitis (NASH) [2]. NASH patients, as compared to those with steatosis, have a much greater risk for developing liver cirrhosis, a significant risk factor for development of hepatocellular carcinoma [7–9]. It is still unclear what leads to the progression from simple steatosis to advanced liver disease. In some cases hepatic steatosis is merely a marker for other diseases, such as microvesicular steatosis in metabolic diseases [10] and in viral hepatitis [11].

An emerging cause for fatty liver and hepatic dysfunction is lysosomal acid lipase deficiency (LAL-d). Pronounced LAL-d is a rare autosomal recessive storage disorder, leading to lysosomal accumulation of lipids, predominately cholesteryl esters and triglycerides in various tissues and cell types. In LAL-deficient hepatocytes increased levels of cholesterol lead to substantial increases in very low-density lipoprotein (VLDL)-cholesterol production and secretion, the normal way of exporting cholesterol from the liver. This in turn leads to enhanced low-density lipoprotein (LDL)-cholesterol secretion and thus may be an important enhancer of hypercholesterolemia in LAL-d [12]. LAL-d is classified as either Wolman disease (WD) or cholesteryl ester storage disease (CESD), both characterized by very low LAL activity [13–15]. CESD usually has a later onset than WD, and primarily affects the liver, with a wide spectrum of involvement ranging from early onset disease with severe cirrhosis to later onset of slowly progressive hepatic disease with survival into adulthood. Subsequently, complications of fatty liver disease with mixed hyperlipidemia lead to accelerated atherosclerosis, which dominates the clinical picture. Moreover, CESD patients exhibit many abnormalities that overlap with those in more common liver disorders such as nonalcoholic fatty liver disease (NAFLD), making the diagnosis of CESD much more challenging. Therefore, the importance of LAL-d in dyslipidemia and liver dysfunction was recently suggested for the NAFLD spectrum [9]. Furthermore, low LAL activity has been reported only in patients with NAFLD, underscoring the potential role of LAL in NAFLD [16].

The aim of the current study was to further evaluate LAL activity in patients with liver diseases that may be attributed to LAL-d: fatty liver with microvesicular steatosis, cryptogenic cirrhosis and NAFLD.

2. Results

2.1. Basic Characterization of the Study Population

Seventy-four patients diagnosed with cirrhosis according to the International Classification of Diseases 9 (ICD9) classification, and having an available liver biopsy were identified. Sixty-three were excluded due to clear etiology for their liver disease, thus not meeting the diagnostic criteria for cryptogenic cirrhosis. Two of the remaining patients underwent liver transplantation and five others declined to participate in the study. From the 15 patients with histology of microvesicular steatosis, two were excluded due to other overt etiology and four patients refused to participate in the trial. Nine NAFLD-patients with macrovesicular steatosis were also included. Altogether, the 22 patients in the study were analyzed as one group and as two groups, designated as higher-risk for LAL-d (13 patients, nine with microvesicular steatosis and four with cryptogenic cirrhosis) and lower-risk for LAL-d (nine patients with metabolic syndrome and NAFLD).

The mean age of all 22 patients participating in the study was 32.4 ± 23.3 (range 3.0–71.8) years, with similar distribution of males and females (Table 1). The ethnic origin of most participants was Arab and the rest were defined as Ashkenazi or Sephardi Jews. The age of the high-risk group was significantly lower ($p = 0.001$), while the rate of consanguinity and family history of fatty liver or cirrhosis were higher in this group ($p > 0.05$). As expected, systemic blood pressure, body mass index (BMI), and waist circumference were significantly higher in the low-risk group ($p = 0.023$–0.028, $p = 0.006$ and $p = 0.006$, respectively).

Table 1. Baseline characteristics of participants.

Parmeters	Discriptors	High Risk *n* = 13	Low Risk *n* = 9	Total *n* = 22	*p*
Age, years	Mean ± SD	17.2 ± 12.3	54.3 ± 17.1	32.4 ± 23.3	0.0001
	Median	14.2	59.2	24.9	-
	Range	3.0–39.9	21.7–71.8	3.0–71.8	-
Gender, Male, %	-	61.5	44.4	54.5	0.666
Origin, %	Ashkenazi Jew	15.4	22.2	18.2	1.000
	Sephardi Jew	7.7	11.1	9.1	-
	Arab	76.9	66.7	72.7	-
Consanguinity, %	-	58.3	22.2	42.9	0.184
Familial Fatty liver, %	-	58.3	12.5	40	0.070
Familial Cirrhosis, %	-	33.3	0	21.1	0.245
Smoking, %	-	15.4	33.3	22.7	0.609
SBP, mmHg	Mean ± SD	116.9 ± 10.3	128.2 ± 10.3	121.8 ± 11.6	0.028
	Median	117.0	131.0	125.0	-
DBP, mmHg	Mean ± SD	66.1 ± 14.8	77.9 ± 6.1	71.1 ± 13.1	0.023
	Median	69.5	79.0	74.0	-
BMI, kg/m^2	Mean ± SD	22.1 ± 6.8	33.4 ± 8.5	28.0 ± 89.5	0.006
	Median	19.95	30.1	26.2	-
Waist C., m	Mean ± SD	0.79 ± 0.11	1.07 ± 0.16	0.98 ± 0.2	0.006
	Median	0.80	1.01	0.95	-

SBP = Systolic blood pressure; DBP = Diastolic blood pressure; BMI = Body mass index; Waist C. = Waist circumference; SD = Standard deviation; m = meters; *n* = number of patients. *p* Value calculated by: Fisher's Exact Test, Exact Significance (2-sided); Mann-Whitney Test, Exact Significance (2*(1-tailed Sig.)).

Differences between groups were found for several laboratory tests. Alkaline phosphatase serum levels were significantly higher in the high-risk group (198.5 ± 76 *vs.* 94 ± 33. *p* < 0.001); this may be attributed to the younger age of the patients in this group. In contrast, the low-risk group had significantly higher levels of urea (8.3 ± 2 *vs.* 11.9 ± 2.9 *p* < 0.006), uric acid (234.8 ± 50 *vs.* 347 ± 66, *p* < 0.006) and hematocrit (36.3 ± 5 *vs.* 41 ± 4, *p* < 0.03). A significant difference was also noted in white blood cell count (WBC), glycated hemoglobin (HbA1c) and thyroid-stimulating hormone (TSH). Abdominal imaging and liver histologic assessments showed higher fibrosis scorings in the high-risk group (*p* = 0.01). However, imaging signs of portal hypertension and NAS biopsy scores were similar (Table 2).

Table 2. Imaging and histologic characterization of participants.

Total (*n* = 22)	High Risk Study Group (*n* = 13)	Low Risk Control Group (*n* = 9)	Total (*n* = 22)	*p* Value
Fatty liver, Imaging test, *n*	4 (31%)	9 (100%)	13 (59%)	0.002
Hepatomegaly, Imaging test, *n*	6 (46%)	2 (22%)	8 (36%)	0.380
Splenomegaly, Imaging test, *n*	6 (46%)	3 (33%)	9 (41%)	0.674
Hepatic Fibrosis, Imaging test, *n*	3 (23%)	1 (11%)	4 (18%)	0.616
Portal Hypertension, Imaging test, *n*	3 (23%)	1 (11%)	4 (18%)	0.616
Macrovesicular steatosis, Liver pathology, *n*	7 (54%)	2 (22%)	9 (41%)	0.620
Microvesicular steatosis, Liver pathology, *n*	7 (54%)	0	7 (32%)	0.044
Liver fibrosis score, mean ± SD	2.4 ± 1.1	1 ± 1.3	1.9 ± 1.3	0.01
NAS scoring, Liver pathology	2.8 ± 2	2.2 ± 2.2	2.6 ± 2	1.000

Imaging test = Ultrasound (US), Computed tomography (CT) or Magnetic resonance imaging (MRI); *p* value calculated by Fisher's Exact Test, Exact Significance (2-sided).

2.2. Lysosomal Acid Lipase (LAL) Activity

Mean LAL activity was 0.74 (median 0.8, ±0.28) nmol/punch/h, and was similar in both risk groups. Subsequently, the entire cohort was analyzed according to two LAL cutoffs: 0.5 and

0.6 nmol/punch/h. Characterization of the cohort according to the cutoffs revealed similar composition with respect to age, gender, origin, weight, MBI, waist circumference, smoking rate, consanguinity, family history (of fatty liver or cirrhosis) and blood pressure (Table 3).

Table 3. Baseline characteristics of participants according to LAL cutoffs.

Parmeters	Discriptors	LAL 0.5 Cutoff			LAL 0.6 Cutoff		
		<0.5 (n = 6)	≥0.5 (n = 16)	p	<0.6 (n = 7)	≥0.6 (n = 15)	p
Age, years	Mean ± SD	46.3 ± 18.4	27.2 ± 23.3	0.08	40.7 ± 22.4	28.5 ± 23.5	0.26
	Median	52.5	18.6		47.4	21.7	
Males, n		2	10	0.34	3	9	0.65
Jew, n	Ashkenazi	2	2		2	2	
Jew, n	Sephardi	0	2	0.57	0	2	0.60
Arab, n	Palestinian	4	12		5	11	
Consanguinity , n		2	7	1.00	3	6	1.00
Familial Fatty liver, n		2	6	1.00	2	6	1.00
Familial Cirrhosis, n		0	4	1.00	0	4	0.53
Smoking, n		1	4	1.00	1	4	1.00
SBP, mmHg	Mean ± SD	122.17 ± 9.95	121.60 ± 12.52	0.97	121.14 ± 9.48	122.07 ± 12.85	0.69
	Median	122.50	126.00		120.00	126.00	
DBP, mmHg	Mean ± SD	79.17 ± 8.59	67.93 ± 13.39	0.09	75.86 ± 11.75	68.79 ± 13.47	0.29
	Median	77.50	70.00		74.00	71.50	
BMI, kg/m²	Mean ± SD	33.89 ± 12.77	25.66 ± 7.07	0.19	33.89 ± 12.77	25.66 ± 7.07	0.19
	Median	36.33	24.96		36.33	24.96	
Waist C., m	Mean ± SD	1.16 ± 0.21	0.90 ± 0.13	0.08	1.16 ± 0.21	0.90 ± 0.13	0.08
	Median	1.19	0.94		1.19	0.94	

SBP = Systolic blood pressure; DBP = Diastolic blood pressure; BMI = Body mass index; SD = Standard deviation; m = meters; *n* = number of patients; Waist C. = Waist Circumference. *p* Value calculated by: Fisher's Exact Test, Exact Significance (2-sided); Mann-Whitney Test, Exact Significance (2*(1-tailed Sig.)).

Table 4 shows selected parameters that differed significantly when analyzed according to LAL cutoffs. Significant differences were found for WBC, platelets (PLT), International Normalized Ratio (INR), γ-glutamyltransferase (γGT), total protein, albumin, calcium, uric acid, creatinine, glucose and HbA1c. Other parameters that were analyzed but were not significantly different included hematological (hemoglobin, hematocrit (HCT)), biochemical (sodium, alanine aminotransferase (ALT), aspartate aminotransferase (AST), alkaline phosphatase (ALP), total bilirubin, direct bilirubin, phosphorous, urea, triglycerides, low-density lipoproteins (LDL), high-density lipoproteins (HDL) and total cholesterol), metabolic and inflammatory markers (TSH, vitamin D 25, ammonia, ferritin, C-reactive protein (CRP)), as well as α-fetoprotein (αFP). A threshold of LAL <0.5 was found to characterize six patients. All had marked macrosteatosis and hepatomegaly. LAL <0.5 identified eight severity markers of liver disease, including low calcium levels, a low WBC, high creatinine levels, high uric acid, high glucose and HbA1c, and high γGT and prolonged INR. The seven patients with a LAL threshold <0.6 were the six mentioned above (for the LAL <0.5 threshold) and a child from the high-risk group with severe microvesicular steatosis and liver fibrosis complicated by portal hypertension. LAL <0.6 identified seven additional markers, including lower serum calcium, total protein and platelets, and increased glucose, HbA1c, uric acid and INR.

Table 4. Laboratory results of participants, according to LAL cutoffs.

| Parmeters | LAL Cutoff 0.5 | | | | | | | LAL Cutoff 0.6 | | | | | | |
| | LAL < 0.5 n = 6 | | | LAL ≥ 0.5 n = 16 | | | p | LAL < 0.6 n = 7 | | | LAL ≥ 0.6 n = 15 | | | p |
	Mean	Median	SD	Mean	Median	SD		Mean	Median	SD	Mean	Median	SD	
WBC	6.64	7.01	1.36	9.33	8.76	3.31	**0.029**	6.95	7.11	1.49	9.37	8.59	3.43	0.079
PLT(x1000)	193	207	96	292	273	110	0.095	194	200	87	298	284	111	**0.046**
INR	1.25	1.17	0.28	1.06	1.02	0.11	**0.046**	1.23	1.09	0.26	1.05	1.02	0.12	**0.022**
γGT	147.02	135.50	104.84	61.70	35.00	59.41	**0.036**	129.44	108.00	106.41	64.84	37.50	60.91	0.100
Total protein	66.80	67.00	10.83	75.86	76.00	6.14	0.070	66.67	67.00	9.69	76.62	76.00	5.66	**0.012**
Albumin	38.17	43.00	10.94	43.80	44.00	5.68	0.178	37.86	43.00	10.02	44.36	44.50	5.46	0.056
Calcium	2.34	2.38	0.19	2.53	2.46	0.12	**0.012**	2.34	2.38	0.19	2.53	2.46	0.12	**0.012**
Uric acid	382.25	380.26	64.44	269.43	280.00	64.18	**0.020**	382.25	380.26	64.44	269.43	280.00	64.18	**0.012**
Creatinine	64.14	62.03	20.71	44.78	45.00	17.75	**0.049**	60.12	60.00	21.69	45.37	45.76	18.22	**0.020**
Glucose	6.60	6.46	0.80	5.18	5.01	0.91	**0.005**	6.70	6.72	0.78	5.04	4.90	0.74	0.142
HbA1c	6.12	6.10	0.55	5.51	5.50	0.18	**0.048**	6.12	6.10	0.55	5.51	5.50	0.18	**<0.001**

p = p value, calculated by Mann-Whitney Test, Exact Significance [2*(1-tailed Sig)]. Significant values are in bold.

Abdominal imaging and liver histologi c characterization were also analyzed according to the LAL cutoffs (Table 5). There were no significant differences between LAL-groups. However, in the ⩾0.5 group the NAS score was significantly higher and the fibrosis score was marginally higher compared to the <0.5 group (p = 0.06) (Table 5). In conclusion, the LAL 0.5 threshold was the most sensitive for detecting both histologic and noninvasive markers for disease severity.

Table 5. Imaging and histologic characterization of participants according to LAL cutoffs.

LAL Cutoff	LAL 0.5			LAL 0.6		
	<0.5 (n = 6)	⩾0.5 (n = 16)	p	<0.6 (n = 7)	⩾0.6 (n = 15)	p
Fatty liver, Image, n	4	9	1.0	4	9	1.0
Hepatomegaly, Image, n	2	6	1.0	3	5	1.0
Splenomegaly, Image, n	4	5	0.18	5	4	0.07
Cirrhosis Liver, Image, n	1	3	1.0	1	3	1.0
PTH, Image, n	2	2	0.29	3	1	0.08
NAS score	2.1	3.7	0.03	3.3	2	0.1
Fibrosis score	1.75	3	0.06	1.8	2.75	0.1

p = p-value, calculated by Fisher's Exact Test, Exact Significance (2-sided); NAS: Nonalcoholic steatohepatitis score, PTH = Portal Hypertension.

3. Discussion

Fatty liver disease is emerging as the leading liver disease with no current effective treatment. Although in most cases a metabolic syndrome is the cause of hepatic steatosis, other causes of fatty liver should also be considered. One of those diagnoses is lysosomal acid lipase deficiency (LAL-d), which is hopefully soon to be treatable with encouraging results from enzyme replacement therapy (Sebelipase Alfa, Kanuma®, New Haven, CT, USA). This was indeed our initial motivation for the current study. We aimed to assess LAL activity in patients with liver disease in order to provide suitable therapy. Thus, we measured levels of LAL in patients with cryptogenic cirrhosis, microvesicular steatosis and nonalcoholic fatty liver disease (NAFLD) related to a metabolic syndrome. Although no LAL-d was found, and no patient was eligible for enzyme replacement therapy, we did find that low LAL activity was associated with liver disease severity.

Our initial aim in the study was to compare patients with higher likelihood of genetically-low LAL activity (cryptogenic cirrhosis and microvesicular steatosis) to patients with NAFLD who we thought would be less likely to have low LAL activity. However, Baratta *et al.* [16] reported recently that patients with NAFLD have low LAL activity. As we could not find any statistical difference in LAL levels when we compared the two groups, we concluded that our study supports the study by Baratta *et al.* [16]. Subsequently, we analyzed our data according to two LAL levels. The analysis revealed significant differences that could be attributed to liver disease severity. A LAL threshold of 0.5 identified six patients with significantly higher histologic scorings and eight noninvasive markers (including low calcium levels and white blood cell count, and high creatinine, uric acid, glucose and HbA1c, and γGT levels and prolonged INR). A LAL threshold of 0.6 detected seven patients with seven markers (including low PLT count, calcium levels and total protein; prolonged INR; and high uric acid, glucose and HbA1c), but could not differentiate on the basis of histologic severity.

The blood work that was found to be different in patients with low LAL activity levels signifies indirect measures for liver disease severity. Low platelets and white blood counts serve as indirect markers for cirrhosis because of portal hypertension and hypersplenism. An elevated creatinine level, which is a marker of advanced liver disease and a strong predictor of survival in cirrhosis and [17] hepatorenal syndrome patients [18–20], was also observed in the lower-risk LAL group. With respect to insulin resistance, higher glucose and HbA1c levels were also observed for patients in the low LAL group and may signify more advanced fatty liver disease [21]. Interestingly, higher γGT levels were observed in the lower risk LAL group. This observation corresponds with the other disease severity markers, as γGT is regarded to be an independent predictive marker of morbidity and mortality in cardiovascular-related disorders, including coronary arterial disease, and congestive heart failure [17,22–25]. Higher uric acid levels may be a result of hypovolemia but also of advanced liver injury, accompanied by malnutrition and protein breakup, or a secondary renal injury [21]. Furthermore, when assessing the NAS score we found higher scores for NASH and fibrosis at low LAL levels. Taken together, all measures that were found to be different in the low LAL group signify hepatic and overall disease severity.

The association between low LAL activity and severity of liver injury merits further discussion. It may be considered that low LAL activity in patients with severe liver disease is merely a consequence of an overall decrease in viable hepatocytes that leads to lower protein production. On the other hand, various studies in animal models suggest that lower LAL activity may be part of the pathogenesis of fatty liver disease. The mechanism of lipid accumulation in hepatocytes is not completely elucidated but the role of lipases, including LAL is significant [26]. Autophagy is the key process in hepatic lipid metabolism and steatosis [27], and is the common pathway for the other liver diseases included in our study. Thus, other enzymes may be affected in our cohort. Nevertheless, the importance of measuring LAL activity lies in the potential for treatment with enzyme replacement therapy. Furthermore, the lysosomal-associated NK cells are crucial to prevent fibrosis progression in liver diseases [28,29] and LAL decrease uncovers an additional possible mechanism.

The major limitation of the study is the number of patients and the age range. Despite these limitations we still observed significant differences between the groups of patients with lower and higher LAL activity. It is hard to draw clear conclusions from these observation but they may set a basis for further studies to elucidate the role of LAL in each group of patients within a larger cohort.

4. Materials and Methods

4.1. Study Design

This study was conducted in the Liver Unit, Hadassah Medical Center, Jerusalem, Israel. The local ethics committee of Hadassah Medical Center approved the study (application 920120061, 24/05/2012) and written informed consent was obtained from all the participants or legal guardians in cases of minors. Patients aged 1–75 years who underwent liver biopsy during the years 2006–2012 were screened for the diagnosis of cryptogenic cirrhosis (according to ICD9 registration), microvesicular steatosis (according to liver pathology reports) and NAFLD with macrovesicular steatosis.

Exclusion criteria included daily alcohol intake >10 g/day, exposure to any other hepatotoxic agents, or evidence of other liver disease. Therefore, patients were excluded with the presence of serum hepatitis B surface antigen (HBsAg), hepatitis C viral (HCV) antibodies, HCV RNA, positive autoimmune serology, evidence for hemochromatosis, Wilson's disease (low ceruloplasmin serum levels and high liver tissue copper content) or α-1-antitrypsin disease (low α-1-antitrypsin levels with suggestive biopsy). Abdominal ultrasound was performed to exclude masses, obstruction of bile or blood vessels, but also provided features of liver steatosis and cirrhosis.

4.2. Study Groups

The cohort of patients was analyzed both as a whole group and as two groups: one consisting of patients with cryptogenic cirrhosis or microvesicular steatosis, and a second consisting of patients with NAFLD and macrovesicular steatosis.

4.3. Clinical Characterizations

Body mass index (BMI), blood pressure, waist circumference, concomitant diseases and medications were recorded at the time of LAL evaluation. Any results of abdominal imaging (Abdominal Ultrasound, Computerized Tomography and Magnetic Resonance) were documented, focusing on fatty liver appearance, hepatomegaly and splenomegaly and hepatic fibrosis (irregular hepatic appearance).

4.4. NAFLD Activity Score (NAS)

This score represented the sum of scores for steatosis, lobular inflammation, and ballooning, ranging from 0 to 8 according to Kleiner *et al.* [30]. Subjects with a NAS activity score of 0–2 were considered as having NAFLD. Biopsies with an activity score of 3 or more were considered as NASH. Fibrosis was ranked as follows: 0-none, 1-perisinusoidal or periportal, 2-perisinusoidal and periportal, 3-bridging fibrosis, 4-cirrhosis.

4.5. LAL Activity in Dried Blood Spots (DBS)

The test was performed as described previously by Hamilton *et al.* [31]. DBS values of 0.37–2.30 nmol/punch/h were interpreted as normal, 0.15–0.40 nmol/punch/h as carriers and <0.03 nmol/punch/h as CESD patients.

4.6. Statistical Analysis

All clinical, laboratory, imaging and pathological parameters were compared between the two groups using the *t*-test and the nonparametric Mann-Whitney *U* test. Categorical parameters were compared using Fisher's exact test. All statistical tests were bilateral and a *p*-value of 5% or less was considered statistically significant.

5. Conclusions

In the current study we found that LAL activity correlates with hepatic steatosis and dysfunction. Our findings suggest a possible role for LAL in the pathogenesis of liver dysfunction and future studies may assist in finding subseta of patients who will benefit from enzyme replacement therapy. As our cohort is small, further larger groups should be studied in order to substantiate our findings.

Acknowledgments: This study was supported by grants from the Israel Scientific Foundation (ISF), the Chief Scientist of the Israeli Ministry of Health, and the Israel-American Bi-national Scientific Foundation (BSF) awards.

Author Contributions: Eyal Shteyer and Rifaat Safadi conceived and designed the experiments; Rivka Villenchik, Mahmud Mahamid and Nidaa Nator recruited the patients; Eyal Shteyer, Rivka Villenchik and Rifaat Safadi analyzed the data; Eyal Shteyer, Rivka Villenchik and Rifaat Safadi wrote the paper.

Conflicts of Interest: The authors declare no conflict of interest.

References

1. Bellentani, S.; Marino, M. Epidemiology and natural history of non-alcoholic fatty liver disease (NAFLD). *Ann. Hepatol.* **2009**, *8*, S4–S8. [PubMed]
2. Sun, B.; Karin, M. Obesity, inflammation, and liver cancer. *J. Hepatol.* **2012**, *56*, 704–713. [CrossRef] [PubMed]
3. Machado, M.V.; Cortez-Pinto, H. Non-alcoholic fatty liver disease: What the clinician needs to know. *World J. Gastroenterol.* **2014**, *20*, 12956–12980. [CrossRef] [PubMed]
4. Gupte, P.; Amarapurkar, D.; Agal, S.; Baijal, R.; Kulshrestha, P.; Pramanik, S.; Patel, N.; Madan, A.; Amarapurkar, A. Non-alcoholic steatohepatitis in type 2 diabetes mellitus. *J. Gastroenterol. Hepatol.* **2004**, *19*, 854–858. [CrossRef] [PubMed]
5. Del Gaudio, A.; Boschi, L.; del Gaudio, G.A.; Mastrangelo, L.; Munari, D. Liver damage in obese patients. *Obes. Surg.* **2002**, *12*, 802–804. [CrossRef] [PubMed]
6. Baffy, G.; Brunt, E.M.; Caldwell, S.H. Hepatocellular carcinoma in non-alcoholic fatty liver disease: An emerging menace. *J. Hepatol.* **2012**, *56*, 1384–1391. [CrossRef] [PubMed]
7. Cohen, J.C.; Horton, J.D.; Hobbs, H.H. Human fatty liver disease: Old questions and new insights. *Science* **2011**, *332*, 1519–1523. [CrossRef] [PubMed]
8. Michelotti, G.A.; Machado, M.V.; Diehl, A.M. NAFLD, NASH and liver cancer. *Nat. Rev. Gastroenterol. Hepatol.* **2013**, *10*, 656–665. [CrossRef] [PubMed]

9. Reiner, Z.; Guardamagna, O.; Nair, D.; Soran, H.; Hovingh, K.; Bertolini, S.; Jones, S.; Ćorić, M.; Calandra, S.; Hamilton, J.; *et al.* Lysosomal acid lipase deficiency—An under-recognized cause of dyslipidaemia and liver dysfunction. *Atherosclerosis* **2014**, *235*, 21–30. [CrossRef] [PubMed]

10. Bernstein, D.L.; Hulkova, H.; Bialer, M.G.; Desnick, R.J. Cholesteryl ester storage disease: Review of the findings in 135 reported patients with an underdiagnosed disease. *J. Hepatol.* **2013**, *58*, 1230–1243. [CrossRef] [PubMed]

11. Haga, Y.; Kanda, T.; Sasaki, R.; Nakamura, M.; Nakamoto, S.; Yokosuka, O. Nonalcoholic fatty liver disease and hepatic cirrhosis: Comparison with viral hepatitis-associated steatosis. *World J. Gastroenterol.* **2015**, *21*, 12989–12995. [CrossRef] [PubMed]

12. Ginsberg, H.N.; Le, N.A.; Short, M.P.; Ramakrishnan, R.; Desnick, R.J. Suppression of apolipoprotein B production during treatment of cholesteryl ester storage disease with lovastatin. Implications for regulation of apolipoprotein B synthesis. *J. Clin. Investig.* **1987**, *80*, 1692–1697. [CrossRef] [PubMed]

13. Aslanidis, C.; Ries, S.; Fehringer, P.; Buchler, C.; Klima, H.; Schmitz, G. Genetic and biochemical evidence that CESD and Wolman disease are distinguished by residual lysosomal acid lipase activity. *Genomics* **1996**, *33*, 85–93. [CrossRef] [PubMed]

14. Saito, S.; Ohno, K.; Suzuki, T.; Sakuraba, H. Structural bases of Wolman disease and cholesteryl ester storage disease. *Mol. Genet. Metab.* **2012**, *105*, 244–248. [CrossRef] [PubMed]

15. Pagani, F.; Pariyarath, R.; Garcia, R.; Stuani, C.; Burlina, AB.; Ruotolo, G.; Rabusin, M.; Baralle, F.E. New lysosomal acid lipase gene mutants explain the phenotype of Wolman disease and cholesteryl ester storage disease. *J. Lipid Res.* **1998**, *39*, 1382–1388. [PubMed]

16. Baratta, F.; Pastori, D.; del Ben, M.; Polimeni, L.; Labbadia, G.; di Santo, S.; Piemonte, F.; Tozzi, G.; Violi, F.; Angelico, F. Reduced lysosomal acid lipase activity in adult patients with non-alcoholic fatty liver disease. *EBioMedicine* **2015**, *2*, 750–754. [CrossRef] [PubMed]

17. Jiang, S.; Jiang, D.; Tao, Y. Role of γ-glutamyltransferase in cardiovascular diseases. *Exp. Clin. Cardiol.* **2013**, *18*, 53–56. [PubMed]

18. Li, G.; Shi, W.; Hug, H.; Chen, Y.; Liu, L.; Yin, D. Nonalcoholic fatty liver disease associated with impairment of kidney function in nondiabetes population. *Biochem. Med.* **2012**, *22*, 92–99. [CrossRef]

19. Lau, T.; Ahmad, J. Clinical applications of the model for end-stage liver disease (MELD) in hepatic medicine. *Hepat. Med.* **2013**, *5*, 1–10. [PubMed]

20. Hartleb, M.; Gutkowski, K. Kidneys in chronic liver diseases. *World J. Gastroenterol.* **2012**, *18*, 3035–3049. [CrossRef] [PubMed]

21. Miyake, T.; Kumagi, T.; Furukawa, S.; Tokumoto, Y.; Hirooka, M.; Abe, M.; Hiasa, Y.; Matsuura, B.; Onji, M. Non-alcoholic fatty liver disease: Factors associated with its presence and onset. *J. Gastroenterol. Hepatol.* **2013**, *28*, 71–78. [CrossRef] [PubMed]

22. Lee, D.S.; Evans, J.C.; Robins, S.J.; Wilson, P.W.; Albano, I.; Fox, C.S.; Wang, T.J.; Benjamin, E.J.; D′Agostino, R.B.; Vasan, R.S. γ Glutamyl transferase and metabolic syndrome, cardiovascular disease, and mortality risk: The framingham heart study. *Arterioscler Thromb. Vasc. Biol.* **2007**, *27*, 127–133. [CrossRef] [PubMed]

23. Onat, A.; Can, G.; Ornek, E.; Cicek, G.; Ayhan, E.; Dogan, Y. Serum γ-glutamyltransferase: Independent predictor of risk of diabetes, hypertension, metabolic syndrome, and coronary disease. *Obesity* **2012**, *20*, 842–848. [CrossRef] [PubMed]

24. Liu, C.F.; Zhou, W.N.; Fang, N.Y. γ-Glutamyltransferase levels and risk of metabolic syndrome: A meta-analysis of prospective cohort studies. *Int. J. Clin. Pract.* **2012**, *66*, 692–698. [CrossRef] [PubMed]

25. Nakchbandi, I.A. Osteoporosis and fractures in liver disease: Relevance, pathogenesis and therapeutic implications. *World J. Gastroenterol.* **2014**, *20*, 9427–9438. [PubMed]

26. Czaja, M.J. Autophagy in health and disease. 2. Regulation of lipid metabolism and storage by autophagy: Pathophysiological implications. *Am. J. Physiol. Cell Physiol.* **2010**, *298*, C973–C978. [CrossRef] [PubMed]

27. Singh, R.; Kaushik, S.; Wang, Y.; Xiang, Y.; Novak, I.; Komatsu, M.; Keiji, T.; Cuervo, A.M.; Czaja, M.J. Autophagy regulates lipid metabolism. *Nature* **2009**, *458*, 1131–1135. [CrossRef] [PubMed]

28. Melhem, A.; Muhanna, N.; Bishara, A.; Alvarez, C.E.; Ilan, Y.; Bishara, T.; Horani, A.; Nassar, M.; Friedman, S.L.; Safadi, R. Anti-fibrotic activity of NK cells in experimental liver injury through killing of activated HSC. *J. Hepatol.* **2006**, *45*, 60–71. [CrossRef] [PubMed]

29. Gur, C.; Doron, S.; Kfir-Erenfeld, S.; Horwitz, E.; Abu-Tair, L.; Safadi, R.; Mandelboim, O. NKp46-mediated killing of human and mouse hepatic stellate cells attenuates liver fibrosis. *Gut* **2012**, *61*, 885–893. [CrossRef] [PubMed]

30. Kleiner, D.E.; Brunt, E.M.; van Natta, M.; Polimeni, L.; Labbadia, G.; di Santo, S.; Piemonte, F.; Tozzi, G.; Violi, F.; Angelico, F. Design and validation of a histological scoring system for nonalcoholic fatty liver disease. *Hepatology* **2005**, *41*, 1313–1321. [CrossRef] [PubMed]

31. Hamilton, J.; Jones, I.; Srivastava, R.; Galloway, P. A new method for the measurement of lysosomal acid lipase in dried blood spots using the inhibitor Lalistat 2. *Clin. Chim. Acta* **2012**, *413*, 1207–1210. [CrossRef] [PubMed]

International Journal of
Molecular Sciences

MDPI

Review

Nonalcoholic Fatty Liver Disease: Pros and Cons of Histologic Systems of Evaluation

Elizabeth M. Brunt

Department of Pathology and Immunology, Washington University School of Medicine, Campus Box 8118, St. Louis, MO 63110, USA; ebrunt@wustl.edu; Tel.: +314-747-0143

Academic Editors: Amedeo Lonardo and Giovanni Targher
Received: 15 December 2015; Accepted: 7 January 2016; Published: 13 January 2016

Abstract: The diagnostic phenotype of nonalcoholic fatty liver disease (NAFLD)—in particular, the most significant form in terms of prognosis, nonalcoholic steatohepatitis (NASH)—continues to rely on liver tissue evaluation, in spite of remarkable advances in non-invasive algorithms developed from serum-based tests and imaging-based or sonographically-based tests for fibrosis or liver stiffness. The most common tissue evaluation remains percutaneous liver biopsy; considerations given to the needle size and the location of the biopsy have the potential to yield the most representative tissue for evaluation. The pathologist's efforts are directed to not only global diagnosis, but also assessment of severity of injury. Just as in other forms of chronic liver disease, these assessments can be divided into necroinflammatory activity, and fibrosis with parenchymal remodeling, in order to separately analyze potentially reversible (grade) and non-reversible (stage) lesions. These concepts formed the bases for current methods of evaluating the lesions that collectively comprise the phenotypic spectra of NAFLD. Four extant methods have specific applications; there are pros and cons to each, and this forms the basis of the review.

Keywords: nonalcoholic fatty liver disease; nonalcoholic steatohepatitis; pathology

1. Introduction

The value of liver biopsy evaluation for diagnosis in clinical care and effectiveness of intervention in clinical research in the field of nonalcoholic fatty liver disease (NAFLD) has remained unquestioned as knowledge in the field has continued to grow over the course of the last three and a half decades since the publication attributed as one of the early descriptions in humans [1]. Currently several clinical algorithms based on serum-based tests can be used to predict the likelihood of NAFLD, nonalcoholic steatohepatitis (NASH) or presence or severity of fibrosis, reviewed [2]. As well, sonographically-based tests of liver "stiffness" and imaging-based tests for presence of hepatic fat are variably validated and becoming more available [3]. The unquestioned value of all non-invasive testing is for patient follow-up; in sophisticated hands, these tests also play a role in determination of need for liver biopsy, as the latter, an invasive test with known low but potential risk of morbidity cannot be utilized as a screening test [4]. The best noninvasive tests have been developed and validated against the "gold-standard" of liver biopsy in order to produce equivalent information regarding the state of the liver parenchyma.

Liver biopsy cannot be considered a "perfect" test, however, but the short-comings of this can largely be overcome once understood. For instance, the consideration of sampling "error" [5] was detailed in a study in 2005 that demonstrated differences in grade and stage by the blinded pathologist even when biopsies were obtained from the identical location. However, as in most chronic liver diseases, this "error" is likely a reflection of the disease heterogeneity of NAFLD, and must be accounted for by providing sufficient numbers of subjects in clinical trials. Another less well-known short-coming of liver biopsy, particularly when done by radiologists, or in the setting of bariatric surgery, is the use of appropriately sized (*i.e.*, large-bore) needles, [6], and potential differences between the right and left lobes of the liver. For instance, the subcapsular portal tracts in the left lobe are larger and closer to the capsule than in the right lobe; if not aware of this, a pathologist can misinterpret the seemingly enlarged portal structures from a left lobe biopsy for fibrotic portal structures, particularly if a small bore needle has been used to obtain the biopsy. Determining histologic inflammation in the liver parenchyma will not lead to valid results from a biopsy obtained in a surgical procedure, as anesthesia alone will lead to parenchymal and perivenular collections of polymorphonuclear leukocytes, collectively known as "surgical hepatitis". Discerning which foci were present prior to anesthesia, and which are due to surgical hepatitis is not possible. Further, if a study protocol includes biopsy, agreement of exact location should be made in advance with all investigators so that pre and post intervention biopsies are truly comparable. Finally, the interpreting pathologist's expertise and familiarity with the spectra of lesions in the disease process are factors to be considered in NAFLD, as in any other form of liver disease [7,8].

Once the decision for liver biopsy has been made, whether for clinical (*i.e.*, diagnostic or prognostic) purposes, or for clinical trial protocol, the next steps involve the histopathologic interpretation for diagnosis, and for semi-quantitative lesion evaluations, if requested, for protocol or study purposes. Methods for these are the subjects of the remainder of this review.

2. Diagnosing Fatty Liver Disease in Liver Biopsy

Before any form of assessment of severity of injury or fibrosis can be applied, the pathologist must be certain that the biopsy actually is diagnostic of the clinically presumptive disease; this basic exercise applies to all forms of liver disease. NAFLD is an umbrella term applied to a range of histopathologic phenotypes in adults, adolescents and children. It is important that the pathologist report is limited to the findings noted, and count on the clinical team to put these together with all information regarding possible etiologies that may present in a similar manner, including, for instance, Wilson disease, other inborn errors of metabolism, and alcoholic liver disease. Discussed in detail in recent reviews [9], they will be briefly summarized herein. In adults, prior to advanced fibrosis and parenchymal remodeling (nodularity), the parenchyma shows varying degrees of steatosis within the zone 3 hepatocytes (those around the terminal hepatic venule). The large and small droplet steatosis is termed macrovesicular due to the fact it is either a single large droplet or several droplets readily separable to the microscopic eye. Often, the two are co-existent in the same hepatocyte. Thus, the term, "large and small droplet macrovesicular steatosis" is applied. When only steatosis is present in the biopsy, the diagnostic term, NAFL, is given. For this, >5% of hepatocytes within the biopsy must be occupied by this type of visible fat droplets. In a minority of cases, non-zonal clusters of hepatocytes also have true microvesicular steatosis; an association was noted with greater severity of disease in these cases in a large series from the NASH Clinical Research Network (CRN) [10]. The terminal "D" of NAFLD is removed by convention, as steatosis is considered non-progressive, although exceptions have been noted in subjects, most of whom subsequently gain weight or the metabolic status changed [11,12].

The second component of NAFLD is inflammatory cells; these may be seen within the acini (aka lobules), or in portal tracts, or both. The inflammatory components of this disease are quite complex, but with the routine hematoxylin and eosin stain to the pathologist's view microscopically, can be divided into mononuclear cells (lymphocytes, monocytes), eosinophils, polymorphonuclear cells (pmn's), and Kupffer cells. Even occasional plasma cells can be noted. Kupffer cells are pigmented, enlarged and either singly or in clusters surrounding an apoptotic hepatocyte (microgranuloma) or a fat droplet (lipogranuloma). Lipogranulomas often have an associated eosinophilic leukocyte, and when adjacent to a terminal hepatic venule or within a portal tract, may also have collagen. Epithelioid or caseating granulomatous inflammation are not features of NAFLD, and deserve further attention. Pmn's surrounding individual hepatocytes, referred to as "satellitosis", are indicative of alcoholic hepatitis; clusters of pmn's signify possible sepsis or may occur if the biopsy is obtained during a surgical procedure when the patient is under anesthesia. Thus, caution is warranted when pmn clusters are easily noted; attempting to "count" inflammatory foci in such a specimen is not advisable.

Portal inflammation consists of similar cell types as described above (except the macrophages are not Kupffer cells) in varying degrees, including lipogranulomas. Other types of granulomatous inflammation should be further evaluated. Bile duct injury may be seen, but should be further evaluated. Marked portal inflammation and lymphoid aggregates, diffuse interface activity, and plasma-cell rich infiltrates are all lesions that deserve further investigation. Numerous polymorphonuclear leukocytes, when present, are typically present as cholangitis, cholangiolitis/pericholangitis and indicate an extra-hepatic biliary process such as obstruction or pancreatitis, or alcoholic liver disease. Canalicular bile plugs in zone 3 correlate with these findings and warrant further investigation. Cholangiolar bile is indicative of sepsis. The combination of macrovesicular steatosis and inflammation has been termed steatosis with inflammation; this is not, however, diagnostic of steatohepatitis.

2.1. Nonalcoholic Steatohepatitis (NASH)

For the diagnosis of NASH, the most recognized form of injury in NAFLD with potential to progress to fibrosis and cirrhosis and its complications, there is a requirement not only for the steatosis and inflammation as described above, but also for a particular form of hepatocyte injury known as ballooning. While some authorities have stated that steatosis with inflammation and perisinusoidal fibrosis are adequate for a diagnosis of steatohepatitis, it is not clear that this group of findings represents a lesion with actual potential of progression, or represents a step in regression of steatohepatitis (*i.e.*, loss of ballooning). The NASH CRN Pathology Committee categorizes this within a set of lesions as "Borderline, Zone 3", and specifies that hepatocellular ballooning must be present for a diagnosis of steatohepatitis. NASH can be diagnosed in the absence of fibrosis. The initial collagen deposition in adult NASH is in the perisinusoidal spaces in zone 3; with progression, fibrosis is additionally noted in periportal spaces, often associated with a ductular reaction. More advanced fibrosis is indicated by bridging between vascular structures: central veins to central veins (via perisinusoidal spaces); central–portal; portal–portal; with nodularity of the intervening parenchyma. Cirrhosis is the final outcome of advanced fibrosis and remodeling. Residual perisinusoidal fibrosis may or may not remain.

An intriguing and important concept in NASH is that with advanced disease, *i.e.*, fibrosis and architectural remodeling with bridging fibrosis and nodularity, and ultimately the vascular remodeling of cirrhosis, the lesions of activity described above may or may not continue to be present. Investigators have used this information to justify a correlation with the assignment of the diagnosis of "cryptogenic cirrhosis" to cases in which no identifying lesions of active liver disease can be found. In a strict sense, however, without a prior biopsy diagnosis of NASH, this may not be correct in all cases. Many cases of cryptogenic cirrhosis, in fact, may be burned-out cirrhosis from other causes such as prior alcohol abuse, autoimmune hepatitis, heterozygous α-1-antitrypsin liver disease, or even more rare processes (e.g., keratin mutations). However, there are bona fide cases of burned-out NASH in which there remain histologic "hints": e.g., foci of perisinusoidal fibrosis, occasional ballooned hepatocytes, rare Mallory–Denk bodies in a non-alcohol user. If there is a prior biopsy with NASH, the "burned-out" cirrhosis is no longer "cryptogenic", but is cirrhosis secondary to prior NASH.

2.2. Pediatric Nonalcoholic Fatty Liver Disease (NAFLD)

Pediatric NAFLD is known to be unique in its pre-cirrhotic histopathologic features. This has been accepted since the seminal descriptions of Schwimmer *et al.* in 2005 [13], and validated subsequently by others. Interestingly, as of yet, there is no accepted diagnosis of "steatohepatitis" in children, although clearly the end results, cirrhosis and hepatocellular carcinoma, do occur. The initial findings in children are of large droplet macrovesicular steatosis either in a periportal or panacinar distribution and when inflammation is present, it is more common in the portal collagen than in the lobules. Ballooned hepatocytes are few if any. Portal expansion by fibrosis occurs initially, and perisinusoidal fibrosis may or may never be seen. The categorization of Borderline, Zone 1 has been utilized by the NASH CRN for the above-described lesions.

3. Grading and Staging the Lesions of NAFLD

Four current methods of semi-quantitatively evaluating histologic lesions of NAFLD are summarized in Table 1; they include a proposal referred to as the "Brunt" system [14], the NASH CRN Pathology Committee system for NAFLD Activity Score (NAS) and fibrosis score [15], the "Fatty Liver Inhibition of Progression (FLIP)" algorithm [16,17] and a pediatric score based on weighted values for the features of NAFLD, the Pediatric NAFLD Histologic Score [18]. The first was restricted to adults and to NASH; the middle two can apply to the full range of NAFLD; the NASH CRN system alone applies to adults and children.

3.1. Brunt Proposal for Grading and Staging

The proposal for grading and staging the lesions of NASH was made when the disease itself was still being questioned as an entity other than surreptitious alcoholism; it was clear that further work would not progress until a systematic method of analyzing the pathology was in place. Thus, this proposal was just that: a first proposed method to separately analyze grade and stage, similarly to what was being done with other forms of chronic hepatitis, but with adjustments for the lesions of fatty liver disease [14]. There was systematic review of 52 adult biopsies from 51 clinically diagnosed subjects with NASH with semi-quantitative assessment and notation of location of steatosis, and ballooning; semi-quantitative assessment for lobular and portal inflammation and Periodic Acid Schiff after diastase digestion (PASd) Kupffer cells, Mallory–Denk bodies, acidophil bodies, iron, and glycogenated nuclei, lipogranulomas and locations of fibrosis, zone 3 perisinusoidal, portal/periportal, and bridging. "Gestalt" diagnosis of severity of each case (mild, moderate, severe) then followed. The "global grade" was based on review of the semi-quantitative lesions and impression-based grades, and focused in particular on steatosis, hepatocellular ballooning, zone 3 accentuation of injury. It was noted that the initial, and often persistent form of fibrosis is perisinusoidal; this differs from the distinctly portal-based fibrosis of chronic hepatitis and biliary fibrosis. The so-called "Brunt" method continued the paradigm of maintaining separation of grade (lesions of activity) and stage (lesions of fibrosis and parenchymal remodeling), as had been established by the systems for evaluation in chronic hepatitis [19]. The method of grading and staging was written to be applied after the diagnosis of NASH had been rendered, and was considered a "global" assessment such that grades 1–3, mild, moderate and severe, were evaluations of combinations of steatosis, lobular and portal inflammation and ballooning. Hepatocyte ballooning was noted as the major determinant of severity and steatosis amount was the least determinant; inflammation increased with each grade. Fibrosis was scored according to the observed location and extent of collagen deposition as described above. Grade and stage were noted to be disparate, as in chronic hepatitis although none of the low stage biopsies showed severe steatohepatitis. Higher grade did correlate with higher mean aspartate aminotransferase (AST), but not with alanine aminotransferase (ALT). This system was created for NASH, and thus did not take into account the full spectrum of NAFLD, nor did the system address lesions of pediatric NAFLD. Although the system has been widely utilized and applied, it was never formally validated. It is, however, a useful benchmark for diagnosing NASH as it highlighted the increasing severity of ballooning with increased severity of grade. This proposal also documented the characteristic fibrosis of adult NASH.

Table 1. Histologic methods of semi-quantitative evaluation of nonalcoholic fatty liver disease (NAFLD).

System/Characteristics	Brunt System [14]	NASH CRN [15]	* SAF/** FLIP Algorithm [16,17]	Pediatric NAFLD Histologic Score [18]
			Adults	Children
Patient Population	Adults only	Adults + Children	All NAFLD	Peds NAFLD
Applicable to	NASH	All NAFLD		
Grade	Mild, Moderate, Severe; S + LI, PI + B; Unweighted but steatosis does not affect score; LI + PI, ballooning increase incrementally with score	NAFLD Activity Score (NAS): S + LI + B = 0–8; Unweighted scores for each lesion	Steatosis is not a component of activity Activity: LI + B; * SAF: Steatosis + Activity + Fibrosis = $S_x A_x F_x$; ** FLIP: Fatty Liver Inhibition of Progression algorithm for diagnosis	Weighted sums of S + LI + PI + B, see text
Details of Scoring	Steatosis 0: 0; 1: 0%–33%; 2: 34%–66%; 3: >66%	Steatosis 0: <5%; 1: 5%–33%; 2: 34%–66%; 3: >67%	Steatosis 0: <5%; 1: 5%–33%; 2: 34%–66%; 3: >67%	Same as NASH CRN plus Portal Inflammation 0-2
	LI 0:0; 1: 1–2/20x; 2: 2–4/20X; 3: >4/20X	LI 0:0; 1: <2/20x; 2: 2–4/20X; 3: >4/20X	LI 0: 0; 1: <2/20x; 2: 2/20x; –	
	PI: 0: none; 1: mild; 2: moderate; 3: severe	Ballooning: 0: None; 1: Few; 2: Many	Ballooning: 0-2; 0: 0; 1: clusters, reticulated cytoplasm; 2: enlarged hepatocytes; –	
	Ballooning	Prominent	–	
	Acinar location	–	–	
	Mild	–	–	
	Marked	–	–	
	Fibrosis Stage 0: none; 1: zone 3 perisinusoidal; 2: 1 + periportal; 3: bridging; 4: cirrhosis	Fibrosis Stage 0: none; 1a: zone 3 perisinusoidal, delicate; 1b: zone 3 perisinusoidal, dense; 1c: portal only; 2: 1a or 1b + periportal; 3: bridging; 4: cirrhosis	Fibrosis Stage F0: 0; F1: zone 3 perisinusoidal (all), or portal only; F2: zone 3 + periportal; F3: bridging; F4: cirrhosis	Fibrosis Stage: As with NASH CRN

Table 1. *Cont.*

System/Characteristics	Brunt System [14]	NASH CRN [15]	* SAF/** FLIP Algorithm [16,17]	Pediatric NAFLD Histologic Score [18]
Fibrosis Stages	0–4	0–4; # 1a, 1b, 1c	0–4; # 1a, 1b, 1c	0–4
Scoring Method Used for diagnosis	Minimal criteria for dx	Correlates but does not replace; used in clinical trials for feature comparisons	Yes, for diagnosis	Yes, for diagnosis
Clinical Associations	Grade: AST	ALT, AST	AST, ALT	WC, MetSynd, TG, Fibrosis in biopsy

S = steatosis amount; LI = lobular inflammation; PI = portal inflammation; B = ballooning; # 1a, 1b, 1c: see text. ALT = alanine aminotransferase; AST = aspartate aminotransferase; WC = Waist circumference; MetSynd = Metabolic Syndrome; TG = triglyceride levels.

3.2. NASH Clinical Research Network (CRN) Scoring System

The National Institute of Digestive Diseases and Kidney (NIDDK) of the National Institutes of Health (NIH) established the NASH Clinical Research Network (CRN) in order to undertake multicenter observational and interventional trials. The Pathology Committee was tasked with developing and validating a method for semi-quantitatively evaluating changes in histologic features in these studies. The result was a feature-based system referred to commonly as the NAFLD Activity Score (NAS) [15]. This is a score for lesions of activity based on carefully analyzed results of 32 twice-reviewed biopsies of adults and 18 once reviewed biopsies of children by a group of 9 liver pathologists. The review consisted of 14 lesions of NAFLD (the same as above in similar fashion, plus presence of foci of microvesicular steatosis, megamitochondria, and microgranulomas) and three diagnostic categories: NASH, not NASH and borderline. The lesions that ultimately comprised the NAS were determined by multiple logistic regression to correspond with the separately derived diagnoses of NASH: macrovesicular steatosis, lobular inflammation and ballooning. The final NAS was based on unweighted scores of each, and ranged from 0 to 8. As noted in Table 1, although the lesion scores are unweighted, the fact that steatosis and lobular inflammation range from 0 to 3 whereas ballooning range from 0 to 2, gives steatosis more weight in the NAS. The separately derived diagnoses of NASH mostly correlated with scores $\geqslant 5$; NAS < 3 had been diagnosed as not NASH. Fibrosis stage was a modification of the Brunt system in order to account for pediatric portal-only fibrosis (stage 1c); zone 3 delicate (1a) or dense (1b) fibrosis were created for the purpose of clinical trials. The manuscript that presented the NAS described other observations of importance that remain relevant today: the diagnosis does not rest solely on the presence of particular lesions; the score was not created to replace a pathologist's diagnosis or as a severity scale or to measure rapidity of progression, but rather as a method of analysis in assessing overall histologic change. A subsequent study of 976 centrally reviewed adult biopsies from the NASH CRN highlighted the significance of separating the pattern-based pathologists' activity of diagnosis from the feature-based score [20]. Although there was significant overlap between the diagnosis and the NAS, some details are worth re-iterating. While 75% of definite steatohepatitis cases had NAS $\geqslant 5$, 28% of borderline diagnoses and 7% of "not NASH" also had NAS $\geqslant 5$. Thus, for clinical trial entry, or for clinical management, if the NAS were the basis of decision making, the latter and last cases would be "mis-categorized". Further, and of most importance, in a regression model, while both the diagnosis of steatohepatitis and the NAS were statistically strongly associated with liver enzymes (ALT and AST) in both the one variable (either NAS or NASH diagnosis) and two variable (both NAS and NASH diagnosis) models, and features of Metabolic Syndrome, diabetes, and measures of insulin resistance, the homeostatic model assessment of insulin resistance and the quantitative insulin sensitivity check index (HOMA-IR and QUICKI) were associated with both in the one variable model, these latter features only remained statistically associated with the diagnosis of steatohepatitis in the two variable model. Thus, the implication is strong that not only are the particular histologic features of steatohepatitis important, but the overall pattern of those features (*i.e.*, the determination of diagnosis) is important in correlation with liver injury, as well as underlying factors of the disease process.

3.3. Fatty Liver Inhibition of Progression (FLIP) Algorithm

A third approach to adult NAFLD scoring has been proposed and validated by Bedossa *et al.* [17]; the score was developed in 679 liver biopsies from morbidly obese patients undergoing bariatric surgery with at least one metabolic complication (*i.e.*, diabetes, hypertension, dyslipidemia or obstructive sleep apnea), and validated in 60 liver biopsies of subjects with metabolic syndrome, but not morbid obesity. The algorithm, subsequently tested for observer variability by two groups of pathologists, a European study group, the Fatty Liver Inhibition of Progression (FLIP) pathology group, and a pathology group of general pathologists with varying amounts of liver pathology training [16]. The score is based on two now recognized concepts; even though large droplet macrovesicular steatosis is an obviously recognized, and required, feature of non-cirrhotic NAFLD, it is likely not a driver in progression of disease, thus, the feature should not carry much weight, if any at all, in a histologic score. However, ballooning and lobular inflammation have been noted in several studies to be significant features in progressive disease, thus, these should be more weighted as determinants of progression. Thus, the "activity score" is derived from the combination of the semi-quantitative values of the two [17]. The details for semi-quantitative scores differ slightly from prior methods: lobular inflammation ranges from 0 to 2 (instead of 0–3), ballooning 0–2 (with descriptions of ballooning as detailed in Table 1). As the final score is meant to represent a diagnosis, steatosis (S_x) must be >0, activity (ballooning plus lobular inflammation (A_x) must be $\geqslant 2$, in which ballooning is at least 1. Fibrosis is based on the NASH CRN scale, and reported as "F". One of the primary advantages of this score is the manner of reporting: by giving a subscore for each component of the SAF (Steatosis + Activity + Fibrosis), the amount of steatosis and fibrosis are communicated and one may make comparisons for the features with other biopsies from the same patient. Activity, the most important of the scores is an additive score, so, similar to the NAS, one cannot determine how much is ballooning and how much is lobular inflammation, thus, as with the NAS, improvement in either would not be visible by the SAF alone. Increased values of the SAF correlated well with increased values of serum AST and ALT. Correlations with known metabolic features of NAFLD/NASH, such as markers of insulin resistance, were not reported for the different activity scores that discriminate NAFLD and NASH.

The second study done by the FLIP pathologists and a group of community pathologists [16] was done to test the validity of the SAF algorithm in non-bariatric subjects as well as to test the usefulness of such an algorithm for practical use. Both groups of pathologists' diagnoses improved when the SAF was utilized and both groups had high kappa values when utilizing the SAF. One of the discussed concepts was the challenge for pathologists to make the distinction(s) of NASH and non-NASH in liver biopsy material, whereas use of an algorithm such as the SAF could mitigate against the necessity of such. An example given was a case of steatosis with only fibrosis, but no other features. Additionally, the graphic of the SAF score showed that it could be possible to have $S > 0$ $A_{1(B1+L0)}$ (*i.e.*, steatosis > 0, activity score of 1 because of ballooning score of 1 but no lobular inflammation) with a final diagnosis of "steatosis". Both of these examples are troublesome and highlight the oversimplification of the SAF on its own. The former could potentially fit into a "borderline" category of either zone 1 or zone 3 depending on where the fibrosis is located and the latter could fit into borderline zone 3, also depending if the ballooning and steatosis were in zone 3. Alternatively, both could fit into examples of resolution of prior NASH, and one would want to compare them with prior biopsies. Although both of the studies that proposed and discussed the values of the SAF reiterated that it was not meant to replace a written pathology report, neither mentioned the authors' concepts of fundamentals of NASH diagnosis other than the presence of the lesions in the SAF. Zonal localization and accentuation of lesions in adults and children were not assessed, nor can they be, by the algorithm proposed.

3.4. Pediatric NAFLD Histologic Score

The final scoring system proposed is specifically for the pediatric group by Alkhouri *et al.* [18]. The score proposed was developed from 203 biopsies of children with NASH or "notNASH" according to the pathologist's diagnosis, and given NAS and fibrosis scores according to the NIDDK NASH CRN system with the exception of adding a portal inflammation score of 0–2 for none, mild or moderate portal inflammation. After logistic regression, each feature was weighted and a final Pediatric NAFLD Histologic Score (PNHS) was developed that can be calculated by entering their values into the website [21]. Both the training and validation sets had high area under receiver operating curve (AUROC) values. Interestingly, 65.9% of NASH biopsies had ballooning, as did 4.4% of notNASH biopsies, but 34.1% of NASH biopsies also were diagnosed as such without ballooning. The NAS was greater in NASH biopsies than in notNASH biopsies (mean values 4.5 ± 1.4 *vs.* 2.2 ± 0.59, $p < 0.001$), as expected, as was fibrosis >0 ($p < 0.001$). The score was developed in order to better reflect pediatric "NASH" than the term "borderline" steatohepatitis for both clinical care and clinical trials. Whether it has been in use long enough to accomplish this goal or not cannot be clearly stated at this time. The need to utilize a website for determination of a score and therefore a diagnostic category is interesting and the goal worthwhile, but the concept is somewhat worrisome to diagnostic pathologists as the suggestion that a calculated algorithm can actually replace the interpretative experience that is involved in deriving a final diagnosis is not something one accepts with certainty. The "art" of interpretation continues to play a role in all fields of medicine, regardless of the rigor with which it is applied.

4. Conclusions

It is apparent that NAFLD and NASH are complex entities, not only for clinicians, basic scientists, but also for diagnostic pathologists. Even though much progress has been made, it is worthwhile to remember that scoring methods are measures of injury, but not replacements of diagnostic assessment, and thus, pathologists need to first be trained to recognize patterns of disease, and then to apply appropriate scoring systems. There are pros and cons to any scoring system for all disease processes, as discussed above for NAFLD and NASH. As continued work is done, however, the expectations for more "pros" and fewers "cons" remain.

Acknowledgments: The author would like to thank Amedeo Lonardo and Giovanni Targher for the honor of the invitation to write this review.

Author Contributions: The author has written the text alone.

Conflicts of Interest: The author declares no conflict of interest.

References

1. Ludwig, J.; Viggiano, T.R.; McGill, D.B.; Oh, B.J. Nonalcoholic steatohepatitis: Mayo Clinic experiences with a hitherto unnamed disease. *Mayo Clin. Proc.* **1980**, *55*, 434–438. [PubMed]

2. Brunt, E.M.; Neuschwander-Tetri, B.A.; Burt, A.D. Fatty Liver Disease: Alcoholic and Nonalcoholic. In *MacSween's Pathology of the Liver*, 6th ed.; Burt, A.D., Portmann, B., Ferrell, L., Eds.; Churchill Livingstone/Elsevier: Edinburgh, UK, 2012; pp. 293–359.

3. Brunt, E.M.; Wong, V.W.-S.; Nobili, V.; Day, C.P.; Sookoian, S.; Maher, J.J.; Sirlin, C.; Neuschwander-Tetri, B.A.; Rinella, M.E. Nonalcoholic fatty liver disease. *Nat. Rev. Prim.* **2015**. in press. [CrossRef]

4. Torres, D.M.; Williams, C.D.; Harrison, S.A. Features, diagnosis, and treatment of nonalcoholic fatty liver disease. *Clin. Gastroenterol. Hepatol.* **2012**, *10*, 837–858. [CrossRef] [PubMed]

5. Ratziu, V.; Charlotte, F.; Heurtier, A.; Gombert, S.; Giral, P.; Bruckert, E.; Grimaldi, A.; Capron, F.; Poynard, T. Sampling variability of liver biopsy in nonalcoholic fatty liver disease. *Gastroenterology* **2005**, *128*, 1898–1906. [CrossRef] [PubMed]

6. Larson, S.P.; Bowers, S.P.; Palekar, N.A.; Ward, J.A.; Pulcini, J.P.; Harrison, S.A. Histopathologic variability between the right and left lobes of the liver in morbidly obese patients undergoing Roux-en-Y bypass. *Clin. Gastroenterol. Hepatol.* **2007**, *5*, 1329–1332. [CrossRef] [PubMed]

7. Vuppalanchi, R.; Unalp, A.; van Natta, M.L.; Cummings, O.W.; Sandrasegaran, K.E.; Hameed, T.; Tonascia, J.; Chalasani, N. Effects of liver biopsy sample length and number of readings on histologic yield for nonalcoholic fatty liver disease. *Clin. Gastroenterol. Hepatol.* **2009**, *7*, 481–486. [CrossRef] [PubMed]

8. Bedossa, P.; Bioulacsage, P.; Callard, P.; Chevallier, M.; Degott, C.; Deugnier, Y.; Fabre, M.; Reynes, M.; Voigt, J.J.; Zafrani, E.S.; *et al.* Intraobserver and interobserver variations in liver biopsy interpretation in patients with chronic hepatitis c. *Hepatology* **1994**, *20*, 15–20.

9. Kleiner, D.E.; Brunt, E.M. Nonalcoholic fatty liver disease: Pathologic patterns and biopsy evaluation in clinical research. *Semin. Liver Dis.* **2012**, *32*, 3–13. [CrossRef] [PubMed]

10. Tandra, S.; Yeh, M.M.; Brunt, E.M.; Vuppalanchi, R.; Cummings, O.W.; Unalp-Arida, A.; Wilson, L.A.; Chalasani, N. Presence and significance of microvesicular steatosis in nonalcoholic fatty liver disease. *J. Hepatol.* **2011**, *55*, 654–659. [CrossRef] [PubMed]

11. Pais, R.; Charlotte, F.; Fedchuk, L.; Bedossa, P.; Lebray, P.; Poynard, T.; Ratziu, V. A systematic review of follow-up biopsies reveals disease progression in patients with non-alcoholic fatty liver. *J. Hepatol.* **2013**, *59*, 550–556. [CrossRef] [PubMed]

12. McPherson, S.; Hardy, T.; Henderson, E.; Burt, A.D.; Day, C.P.; Anstee, Q.M. Evidence of NAFLD progression from steatosis to fibrosing-steatohepatitis using paired biopsies: Implications for prognosis and clinical management. *J. Hepatol.* **2015**, *62*, 1148–1155. [CrossRef] [PubMed]

13. Schwimmer, J.B.; Behling, C.; Newbury, R.; Deutsch, R.; Nievergelt, C.; Schork, N.J.; Lavine, J.E. Histopathology of pediatric nonalcoholic fatty liver disease. *Hepatology* **2005**, *42*, 641–649. [CrossRef] [PubMed]

14. Brunt, E.M.; Janney, C.G.; di Bisceglie, A.M.; Neuschwander-Tetri, B.A.; Bacon, B.R. Nonalcoholic steatohepatitis: A proposal for grading and staging the histological lesions. *Am. J. Gastroenterol.* **1999**, *94*, 2467–2474. [CrossRef] [PubMed]

15. Kleiner, D.E.; Brunt, E.M.; van Natta, M.; Behling, C.; Contos, M.J.; Cummings, O.W.; Ferrell, L.D.; Liu, Y.C.; Torbenson, M.S.; Unalp-Arida, A.; *et al.* Design and validation of a histological scoring system for nonalcoholic fatty liver disease. *Hepatology* **2005**, *41*, 1313–1321. [CrossRef] [PubMed]

16. Bedossa, P. Utility and appropriateness of the fatty liver inhibition of progression (FLIP) algorithm and steatosis, activity, and fibrosis (SAF) score in the evaluation of biopsies of nonalcoholic fatty liver disease. *Hepatology* **2014**, *60*, 565–575. [CrossRef] [PubMed]

17. Bedossa, P.; Poitou, C.; Veyrie, N.; Bouillot, J.-L.; Basdevant, A.; Paradis, V.; Tordjman, J.; Clement, K. Histopathological algorithm and scoring system for evaluation of liver lesions in morbidly obese patients. *Hepatology* **2012**, *56*, 1751–1759. [CrossRef] [PubMed]

18. Alkhouri, N.; de Vito, R.; Alisi, A.; Yerian, L.; Lopez, R.; Feldstein, A.E.; Nobili, V. Development and validation of a new histological score for pediatric non-alcoholic fatty liver disease. *J. Hepatol.* **2012**, *57*, 1312–1318. [CrossRef] [PubMed]

19. Brunt, E.M. Grading and staging the histopathological lesions of chronic hepatitis: The Knodell histology activity index and beyond. *Hepatology* **2000**, *31*, 241–246. [CrossRef] [PubMed]

20. Brunt, E.M.; Kleiner, D.E.; Wilson, L.; Belt, P.; Neuschwander-Tetri, B.A. NASH Clinical Research Network (CRN). The NAS and the histopathologic diagnosis of NASH: Distinct clinicopathologic meanings. *Hepatology* **2011**, *53*, 810–820. [CrossRef] [PubMed]

21. Pediatric NAFLD Histologic Score. Available online: http://rcc.simpal.com/RCEval.cgi?RCID=RPCxtv#RESULT (accessed on 15 November 2015).

International Journal of
Molecular Sciences

MDPI

Review

Telomeres, NAFLD and Chronic Liver Disease

Benedetta Donati and Luca Valenti *

Department of Pathophysiology and Transplantation, Università degli Studi di Milano,
Fondazione IRCCS Ca' Granda Ospedale Policlinico Milano, 20122 Milano, Italy; benedetta.donati@unimi.it
* Correspondence: luca.valenti@unimi.it; Tel.: +39-025-032-0278

Academic Editors: Amedeo Lonardo and Giovanni Targher
Received: 25 February 2016; Accepted: 10 March 2016; Published: 15 March 2016

Abstract: Telomeres consist of repeat DNA sequences located at the terminal portion of chromosomes that shorten during mitosis, protecting the tips of chromosomes. During chronic degenerative conditions associated with high cell replication rate, progressive telomere attrition is accentuated, favoring senescence and genomic instability. Several lines of evidence suggest that this process is involved in liver disease progression: (a) telomere shortening and alterations in the expression of proteins protecting the telomere are associated with cirrhosis and hepatocellular carcinoma; (b) advanced liver damage is a feature of a spectrum of genetic diseases impairing telomere function, and inactivating germline mutations in the telomerase complex (including *human Telomerase Reverse Transcriptase (hTERT)* and *human Telomerase RNA Component (hTERC)*) are enriched in cirrhotic patients independently of the etiology; and (c) experimental models suggest that telomerase protects from liver fibrosis progression. Conversely, reactivation of telomerase occurs during hepatocarcinogenesis, allowing the immortalization of the neoplastic clone. The role of telomere attrition may be particularly relevant in the progression of nonalcoholic fatty liver, an emerging cause of advanced liver disease. Modulation of telomerase or shelterins may be exploited to prevent liver disease progression, and to define specific treatments for different stages of liver disease.

Keywords: telomere; telomerase; liver disease progression; nonalcoholic fatty liver disease; cirrhosis; hepatocellular carcinoma

1. Introduction

In humans, telomeres consist of thousands copies of six base repeats (TTAGGG) located at the extremities of the chromosomes that protect chromosomes tips from end-to-end fusion, rearrangement and translocation. Telomere length is progressively shortened at each mitosis, due to the inability of the DNA polymerase complex to replicate the very 5' end of the lagging strand (attrition). For this reason, telomere shortening may function as a "mitotic clock" to sense somatic cells aging. When telomeres become critically short, a DNA-damage program is activated, leading to apoptosis or cell senescence. On the contrary, immortal cells (cancer, stem and germ cells) constitutionally express telomerase, a ribonuclear enzymatic complex associated with telomeres that is responsible for stabilizing telomere length by synthesizing new DNA sequences and adding them to the end of the chromosomes during DNA replication [1]. Telomerase comprises two essential components: Telomerase reverse transcriptase (hTERT) and its RNA template, the telomerase RNA component (hTERC). Dyskerin complex binds to hTERC, in order to protect it and to stabilize the telomerase complex. It includes four nucleolar proteins: Dyskerin (DKC1) and Nucleolar protein family A member 1, 2 and 3 (NOLA1-NOLA2-NOLA3) [2–4]. Besides telomerase, the Shelterin complex, which binds specifically to telomeres, plays a fundamental role in the protection of chromosome ends facilitating telomerase-based telomere elongation [5]. It is composed of six core proteins: the telomeric repeat binding factors 1 and 2 (TRF1-TRF2) that bind telomeric double strand DNA, the protection of telomeres

1 (POT1), which binds the 3' telomeric region of single strand DNA avoiding the degradation by nuclease, and the TRF-1 interacting protein 2 (TIN2), the POT1-TIN2 organizing protein (TPP1) and the repressor/activator protein 1 (RAP1), that interact with the other proteins bound to telomere stabilizing the complex (Figure 1; [6,7]). Mutations of proteins involved in maintenance and repair of telomeres are responsible for telomeropathies [8,9]: a spectrum of progressive genetic diseases exemplified in the most severe cases by dyskeratosis congenita (DKC), whose common autosomal recessive form is caused by mutations in *DKC1*. They are degenerative and age-dependent diseases, characterized by premature senescence of the stem cell compartment, determining increased risk of organ failure and cancer, with possible involvement of the hematopoietic compartment, lungs, mucous membranes, skin, and also the liver. Consistently, loss-of-function mutations in *hTERT* and *hTERC* may cause a spectrum of familial liver diseases [10]. Telomere length is a strong hereditable tract and telomere shortening is accentuated in chronic degenerative condition associated with high cell replication rate. Thus, involvement of telomeres and telomerase mutations seems to be important in predisposition to liver disease progression towards hepatocellular carcinoma (HCC). Indeed, the incidence of HCC increases with age, and, in particular, in nonalcoholic fatty liver disease (NAFLD), where there is a strong aggregation of familial cases [11].

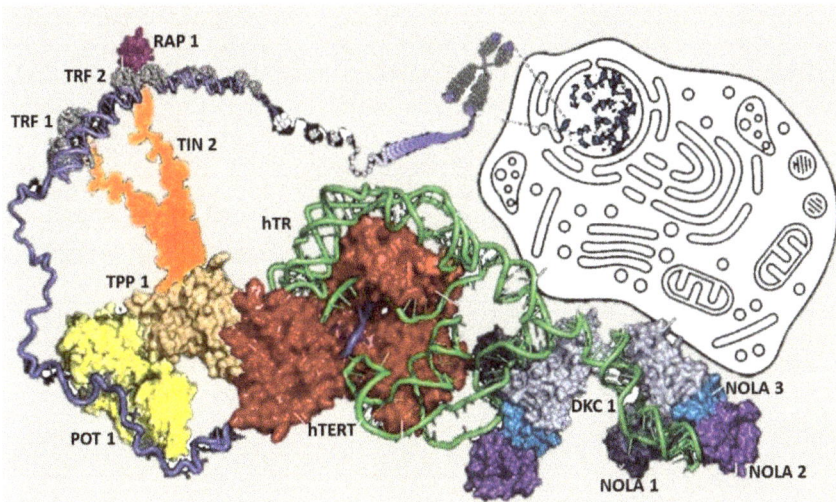

Figure 1. Model representing the telomeres associated proteins. Telomerase (including hTERT (**red**) and hTERC (**green**)) represents the principal catalytic subunit. The Shelterin complex is anchored by binding of the proteins TRF1 and TRF2 to double-stranded telomeric repeats. TRF1 and TRF2 are bridged to the single-stranded telomeric-repeat G-strand DNA-binding protein POT1 through TIN2 and TPP1. Additionally, shelterin RAP1 binds directly to TRF2. Dyskerin complex involving NOLA proteins, interacts and stabilizes the non-overlapping regions of hTERC.

2. Telomerase and Telomere Diseases

2.1. Telomere Shortening Related to Cellular Senescence Characterizes Human Cirrhosis

The role of ageing in liver fibrosis progression has been largely demonstrated, and older age and duration of liver disease remain the major and more validated risk factors for liver disease progression, together with male gender and alcohol abuse [12,13]. Cellular ageing is generally referred to as replicative senescence, a condition strictly linked to telomerase and telomere biology. Indeed, telomere shortening limited the replicative capacity of cells and the number of cells participating in tissue regeneration. Thus, the regenerative potential of an organ depends on the size of the population of cells with sufficient telomere reserves required for cell proliferation. Consistently, in chronic disease associated with tissue regeneration, such as cirrhosis, an elevated regenerative pressure is generated on the proliferating subpopulation of cells, which undergoes several rounds of cell division that, in turn, accelerate the rate of telomere shortening [14]. When telomeres become critically short, a DNA damage program is activated, leading to cell senescence or apoptosis (due to the Hayflick limit), further reducing the number of cell with regenerative capacity.

Several lines of evidence correlate shortened telomeres with liver fibrosis. Kitada *et al.* [15] first described a progressive reduction of telomere length during liver disease progression. Urabe *et al.* [16] confirmed these data and described telomerase re-activation in poorly differentiated HCC, consistently with an increase of telomere length compared to those well differentiated. In the normal liver, progressive telomere shortening has been correlated with age. Consistently, reduction of telomere length in cirrhotic tissue was more marked in patients who developed cirrhosis at younger age [17]. Additionally, reduction of telomere length is considered a hallmark of cirrhotic tissue independently of the etiology of liver disease (e.g., viral hepatitis, autoimmune hepatitis, alcohol abuse ...) [18]. Thus, excessive telomere shortening, caused either by telomerase gene mutations or acquired factors, may impair the hepatocyte regenerative ability in response to chronic injury, facilitating fibrosis progression [19,20]. A causal role of telomere shortening in fibrosis progression has been experimentally demonstrated in telomerase deficient mice. After three generations, these mice developed shortened telomeres and displayed diminished capacity for liver regeneration, and with accelerated development of cirrhosis after liver injury. On the contrary, overexpression of TERT activity improved liver function and protected mice from development of hepatic steatosis and fibrosis [21].

Consistently, shortened telomere length in cirrhotic patients was correlated with the expression of known markers of cellular senescence, such as β-galactosidase, p16, p21 and p53 not only in hepatocytes but also in non-parenchymal cells, such as biliary cells [22,23]. The p53 protein represents the key regulator point for various signaling pathways of senescence: p53 phosphorylation and consequent activation inhibits cell division primarily inducing p21 expression, which, in turn, activates pRb through inhibition of a cyclin-dependent kinase (Cdk) complex. The activated pRb inhibits the transcription of E2F target genes that are required for cell cycle progression. pRB can alternatively be activated by p16, another Cdk inhibitor, that typically accumulates in senescent cells [23].

Cellular senescence may have a dual role in liver disease: in a first phase, it seems to contribute to liver impairment by reducing the hepatocytes and progenitor cell population, while, in a second phase, the subsequent senescence of HSC (epatic stellate cells) due to long-standing activation of fibrogenesis may protect from further fibrosis progression [24–26]. In particular, progression of human fibrosis is often characterized by a state of chronic inflammation that results in a condition of cell death and tissue regeneration, involving also a massive expansion of hepatic progenitor cells in order to restore the lost hepatocytes. Ductular reaction typical of this condition has been shown to produce chemotactic stimuli for induction of inflammatory cells and activation of pro-fibrotic hepatic stellate cells (HSC). Moreover, due to the epithelial to mesenchymal transition, progenitors and biliary epithelial cells may provide a portion of myofibroblasts, contributing to fibrosis progression [27]. When the wound is filled, the activated HSC undergo apoptosis or cellular senescence and consequently are eliminated by immune cells. In this way, HSC induce the recruitment of other immune cells at the site of tissue injury that, in turn, help in arresting liver fibrosis progression. However, it has recently been shown that later, senescent HSC may favor HCC development by secreting pro-carcinogenic mediators (the senescence associated secretory program: SASP) [28].

2.2. Telomerase Mutations Are Hallmarks of Liver Fibrosis

Genetic studies have proven that mutations in telomerase represent the underlying cause of accelerated telomere shortening and organ failure in some rare human diseases, including some forms of DKC [29], which may be characterized by liver injury and development of complications of portal hypertension. Moreover, evidence suggests that telomere attrition is also involved in liver disease progression in humans. Indeed, a spectrum of familial liver disease with autosomal dominant transmission and incomplete penetrance has been associated with inheritance of *hTERT* and *hTERC* mutations [10,30]. In these pedigrees, liver disease was characterized by development of steatosis, with possible progression to cirrhosis and HCC. Furthermore, a significant enrichment of missense mutations in the *hTERT* and *hTERC* genes was observed in 7% of patients and one patient, respectively, of a US cohort including 134 patients with cirrhosis of different etiologies (NAFLD, but also alcohol abuse and Hepatitis C virus infection), as compared to healthy controls. These mutations impaired hTERT enzymatic activity, as they were associated with reduced telomere length in the peripheral blood of patients and reduced telomerase activity *in vitro* [19]. These data were substantially confirmed in a larger series of 521 German patients with cirrhosis, of whom 3% carried functional *hTERT* mutations again independently from the etiology of the liver disease [31]. These observations indicate that, in at least a proportion of patients who developed cirrhosis, fibrosis progression may be favored by genetic risk variants facilitating telomere shortening and cell senescence in the presence of triggering factors.

2.3. Telomere Shortening Induces Genomic Instability in Hepatocellular Carcinoma (HCC)

Thus, telomere shortening is a hallmark of cirrhosis, the main risk factor for the development of liver cancer [32]. The state of chronic inflammation characteristic of injured liver, results *per se* in oxidative DNA damage leading to genomic and epigenomic alterations, pushing cells toward a malignant phenotype. Deregulation of key oncogenes and tumor-suppressor genes, such as *TP53*, *β-catenin*, *ErbB receptor family members* and *p16(INK4a)* have been observed both in early and advance HCC. Impaired function of p53 most likely induces alterations in DNA damage response machinery, resulting in loss of DNA repairing and avoiding cellular apoptosis, thus contributing to an increased mutation rate. Moreover, aberrant DNA methylation patterns have been reported in the earliest stages of hepatocarcinogenesis, and to a greater extent in tumor progression. Finally, karyotypic analysis of HCCs revealed that recurrent regions of copy number change and allelic imbalances are present in 90% of cases, thus highlighting the possibility for new cancer gene targets reside in these loci [33,34]. In this context, telomere shortening may favor carcinogenesis by directly facilitating genomic instability. Telomere shortening plays a pivotal role in inducing genomic alteration first favoring chromosomes segregation defect. Indeed, shortened telomeres have been associated with the typical karyotipic alterations in HCC (chromosome 8 alterations), especially in the presence of *TP53* mutations [33,35].

Moreover, loss of *hTERT* has been shown to affect the overall configuration of chromatin and to diminish the capacity for DNA repair of double strand breaks (DSB) [36]. Therefore, current data suggest a model whereby telomere shortening drives chromosomal instability during early stages of hepatic carcinogenesis, while telomerase re-activation is involved in malignant progression, as it restores chromosomal stability necessary for cellular immortalization.

2.4. Elongation of Telomeres and Telomerase Complex Reactivation during Advance Hepatocarcinogenesis

While the majority of tumors display shortened telomeres compared to non-neoplastic tissues, nevertheless telomere lengthening has been observed in various tumors at advanced stage, including colorectal, and head and neck cancers [37]. In HCC tissues, long telomeres and increased telomerase activity were also shown to be a significant reflection of poor prognostic factors, associated with clinicopathological features of aggressive behavior [38]. Indeed, HCC tumor progression is associated with the reactivation of telomerase, which is necessary for the immortalization of the neoplastic clone [39,40]. Accordingly, *hTERT* was found upregulated in dysplastic liver nodules and to be more than 10-fold induced in overt HCC tissue compared to the surrounding non-neoplastic tissue [41] independently from the etiology of liver disease [42].

On the contrary, a specific gene signature of the Shelterin complex has been identified for each cause of liver disease. Indeed, Shelterin overexpressed in HCC developed upon HCV infection or in the presence of alcohol abuse, and displayed a diminished expression in HCC developed upon

HBV infection [5]. In particular, longer telomeres have been observed in HCCs expressing markers of stemness, such as CK19, EpCAM and CD133, generally considered more aggressive than the conventional, negative for these markers [43,44]. It is known that there is heterogeneity in the expression patterns of stemness-related markers within the same tumors. Interestingly, the analysis of telomere length among different cells according to EpCAM expression status has shown that longer telomeres were present in HCC tumor cells that expressed EpCAM, compared to tumor cells that were EpCAM-negative [45]. Additionally, stemness–related markers were correlated with the expression of the Shelterin proteins. Increased TPP1, TRF2, RAP1, and POT1 expression were observed in HCC tissues expressing "stemness"-related markers compared to conventional HCCs, and their expression was correlated with poorer prognosis and reduced disease-free survival [45]. On the other hand, shortened telomeres and low POT1 expression have been observed in HCCs expressing HepPar1, a marker of hepatocytes differentiation. Additionally, Kim *et al.* [46] demonstrated that TPP1 expression was correlated with hTERT expression, supporting previous findings indicating TPP1 as a positive regulator of telomere maintenance that may represent a good target for cancer therapy as it plays a dominant role in the recruitment of hTERT to telomeres.

Elongation of telomere may also be due to higher expression of DKC1 in HCC compared to noncancerous liver tissue where the level of the protein was absent or very low. DKC1 expression has been validated as an independent risk factor for adverse overall mortality, and it was correlated with advanced HCC clinical stage (grade III–IV) and recurrence independently of hTERT expression [47]. Considering that *DKC1* is the direct and conserved transcriptional target of c-myc responsible for proliferative activity of cancer cells [48], this suggests that the role of DKC1 on cancer progression may be independent of its involvement in telomerase complex function.

Additionally, elongation of telomeres in 7% of HCC cases is associated with alternative lengthening of telomeres (ALT), the telomerase-independent telomere maintenance mechanism, which is thought to be dependent on homologous recombination. The ALT-positive cells are characterized by telomere length heterogeneity, as well as increased chromosomal instability [49].

2.5. Mechanisms of Reactivation of Telomerase in HCC Tissue

Several mechanisms have been shown to lead to telomerase activation during hepatic carcinogenesis. *hTERT* promoter mutations have been described as the most frequent somatic genetic alteration in HCC, with an overall frequency of 60% in Western countries, in particular in patients with chronic HCV infection [50,51]. Interestingly, these somatic mutations occur not only in cancer tissue but in 6%–19% of the cases have been observed also in the early cirrhotic tissue, while usually somatic mutations in oncogene or oncosuppressor genes occur in a more advanced stage of tumorigenesis [51,52]. These promoter mutations represent the most important mechanism of reactivation of telomerase during hepatocarcinogenesis. Indeed, they create new binding sites for specific transcription factors, which consequently induce hTERT overexpression [53,54]. No promoter mutations have been individuated in studies involving cholangiocarcinoma [52] and hepatoblastoma [55], while a minority of patients affected by hepatocholangiocarcinoma presented these kinds of mutations. This evidence suggests that telomerase involvement is dependent on the origin of the cancer cells [56]. In HCC, due to HBV infection, the reactivation of telomerase is generally due to the insertion of the HBV virus in *hTERT* gene, more frequently in the promoter [57,58]. Integration of HBV was detected in 22% of the HBV positive samples, whereas *hTERT* focal amplification, another mechanism likely inducing increased telomerase activity, in 6.7% of the cases. In the same study, *hTERT* promoter mutations were mutually exclusive with HBV genome integration in the *hTERT* locus and were almost mutually exclusive with *hTERT* focal amplifications [59].

2.6. Telomerase Promotes Hepatic Carcinogenesis by Multiple Pathways

Besides telomere protection and maintenance, several *in vitro* and *in vivo* studies in which *hTERT* has been exogenously expressed revealed novel telomerase functions in tumorigenesis independently of *hTERC* [60]. First, hTERT can act as a transcription factor in the Wnt-β-catenin signaling pathway, regulating the expression of Wnt target genes, which play a role in tumorigenesis. Indeed, hTERT interacts with BRG1, a chromatin remodeler binding to β-catenin and involved in the Wnt signaling [61], and promotes the expression of several β-catenin target genes in a BRG1-dependent way. Consistently, *hTERT* was found to interact with the same promoter elements recognized by BRG1 and β-catenin [62]. Actually, the relationship between hTERT and the Wnt-β-catenin pathway is bidirectional: indeed, *β-catenin* deficient human cell lines showed shorter telomere and reduced telomerase activity, and *hTERT* appears as a direct target of β-catenin through the binding to TCF4 transcription factor [63]. Furthermore, hTERT and BRG1 interact with nucleostemin, a GTP-binding protein overexpressed in stem cells and cancers [64], which is essential to drive transcriptional programs relevant for the maintenance of the cancer stem cells phenotype [65]. In this case, hTERT contributes to tumorigenesis increasing the proportion of stem cells within a tumor.

Further functions of hTERT in tumorigenesis are related to its localization in mitochondria. Here, telomerase plays a role as an RNA-dependent RNA polymerase (RdRP) paired to a mitochondrial non-coding RNA, the mitochondrial RNA processing endoribonuclease (RMRP) [66]. hTERT represents the only RdRP identified in mammals and hTERT-RMRP complex leads to the production of double-stranded RMRP RNA molecules, subsequently processed into 22-nucleotide siRNAs by RNA-induced silencing complex (RISC) [66]. Since RMRP has several cellular functions, including mRNA cleavage of cell cycle genes [67], hTERT may influence cellular proliferation, both increasing cell division and reducing apoptosis, independently of activation of Wnt signaling.

Finally, hTERT can increase cancer cell fitness, improving mitochondrial activity and resistance to apoptosis. Indeed, mt-TERT, through its reverse transcriptase domain, can provide mt-DNA replication and repair using mt-tRNAs as the template [68]. Additionally, Sahin *et al.* [60,69] noticed that *Tert* and *Terc* late generation knockout mice showed a p53-mediated repression of peroxisome proliferator-activated receptor gγ coactivator-1 α and β (Pgc-1α and Pgc-1β), the master regulators of mitochondrial physiology and metabolism, resulting in altered mitochondrial biogenesis and function and increased reactive oxygen species.

2.7. Telomeres and Nonalcoholic Fatty Liver Disease (NAFLD)

Following the epidemic of obesity and type 2 diabetes, NAFLD is becoming the most frequent liver disease in Western countries. Established risk factors for disease progression in NAFLD include older age and presence of features of the metabolic syndrome, such as obesity, insulin resistance, and hypertension. However, progression of liver disease to cirrhosis and HCC is generally limited to the subgroup of patients who developed non-alcoholic steatohepatitis (NASH), a condition characterized by active inflammation and fibrosis [70]. Genetic factors have also been shown to influence disease progression in NAFLD. Besides the most validated factors influencing lipid metabolism, such as the I148M variant of *PNPLA3*, the influence of variants involved in fibrogenesis has recently been described.

Genetic data indicate that NAFLD is commonly observed in patients with telomeropathies, suggesting that steatosis may either be a consequence of hepatocellular senescence, as also observed in animal models, or a trigger for liver disease progression [10,21]. Fibrosis stage and liver disease progression are also strictly linked to cell senescence. Consistently, hepatocyte expression of p21, playing a pivotal role in the induction and maintenance of cellular senescence, was associated with fibrosis stage in NAFLD and increase liver related morbidity and mortality [71]. Additionally, the rs762623 variant in the promoter region of *Cyclin-dependent Kinase 1A* (*CDKN1A*) gene, encoding for p21 protein, was associated with the development but not the progression of fibrosis in NAFLD independently from well-recognized *PNPLA3* I148M status [72]. This polymorphism has been associated with reduced p21 expression by abolishing an E2F transcription factor binding site. Thereby these data suggest that *CDKN1A* rs762623 G > A polymorphism favors HSC proliferation by limiting p21 induction, due to DNA damage and telomere shortening, but it may not predispose to severe fibrosis because it antagonizes cellular senescence [73]. Interestingly, *CDKN1A* variants have previously been described in association with rapid progression of idiopathic pulmonary fibrosis, another degenerative condition characterized by cellular senescence and impairment of telomeres [74].

Telomere attrition may also be involved in mediating cancer susceptibility in NAFLD. We reported the occurrence of HCC in NAFLD in a family where a novel missense *hTERT* mutation was segregated with idiopathic familial pulmonary fibrosis and NAFLD. This rare Glu668Asp variant located in the motif 3c of the reverse transcriptase domain of the protein likely led to reduced telomeres length by directly interfering with hTERT enzymatic activity [75]. This finding suggested us to investigate the presence of *hTERT* germline coding mutations in a cohort of patients who developed HCC without recognized risk factors (cryptogenic) or were affected only by NAFLD, which, in the absence of other predisposing conditions, is *per se* a relatively weak risk factor for progressive liver disease. We observed a highly significant enrichment of germline coding mutations in NAFLD HCC. In fact, 10% of NASH HCC were carriers of mutations, while no mutations were identified in 30 NASH cirrhosis and in healthy controls. The rare mutations modifying the sequence of the protein identified (three missense and one frameshift) were located in the N-terminal domain of interaction with hTERC or in the catalytic domain, likely impairing the activity of the telomerase complex. However, the relatively small number of patients analyzed did not allow for correlation of the presence of *hTERT* mutations with HCC prognosis. Additionally, in the same study, we found that telomeres are progressively shortened in peripheral blood leukocytes of NAFLD HCC patients compared to cirrhosis and controls [76]. These data point out a possible causal role for telomere attrition and telomerase mutations in influencing susceptibility towards HCC in NAFLD patients. As telomere shortening was not always correlated with the presence of *hTERT* mutations, this suggests that mutations in other genes contributing to the maintenance of telomeres or epigenetic mechanisms may result in a similar phenotype (genetic heterogeneity) and contribute to the phenotypic expression of heterozygous *hTERT* mutations.

3. Conclusions

Telomeres and telomerase play an important role in the onset and progression of liver disease independently of the underlying etiology. However, the role of telomere attrition and cell senescence is most likely magnified in NAFLD, where genetic risk factors and ageing have a large impact on the predisposition to advanced liver damage in combination with acquired risk factors. The role of telomeres in the pathogenesis of liver disease may be explained by the following hypothesis. Triggering factors, such as obesity and insulin resistance in the case of NAFLD, induce a condition of chronic hepatic damage and regeneration characterized by progressive hepatocytes telomere shortening and senescence. When hepatocytes reach senescence, liver regeneration decreases, but chronic damage remains. Concomitantly, other cell types, such as HSCs, become activated and form fibrotic tissue in area of hepatocyte loss. In this context, germline *hTERT* loss-of-function mutations accelerate telomere shortening, favoring fibrosis development and thus creating a favorable microenvironment for cancer onset. Moreover, telomere attrition and germline *hTERT* loss-of-function mutations may exert a direct pro-carcinogenic effect by promoting genomic instability, both inducing telomere shortening and impairing telomerase activity in DNA repair and chromatin organization [36]. Within this context, the presence of heterozygous mutations does not prevent the reactivation of the telomerase wild type allele at later stages of carcinogenesis, which is necessary for the indefinite replication of the neoplastic clone (Figure 2).

Several studies suggest the use of telomerase inhibitors for HCC treatment. These molecules will hopefully be able to arrest early tumor growth by blocking telomerase, having an almost immediate effect since they likely act on a phenotype of still short telomeres [77]. Moreover, they could arrest inflammatory and HSC telomerase activity, and, consequently, telomere elongation, which has been described as a feature of cirrhotic tissue surrounding tumors [18], thus having a beneficial effect both on the cirrhotic and the cancer tissue. Additionally, inhibition of telomerase may enhance chemosensitivity of cancer cells to chemotherapeutic agents [78]. *Vice versa*, treatment based on molecules that activate telomerase may be useful at the first stage of liver disease and in patients carrying telomerase complex mutations, in order to permit tissue regeneration by avoiding hepatocyte telomere shortening and senescence. This could be exploited by transplantation of liver cells engineered for *hTERT* gene expression, by directly delivering hTERT to the organ, or by small molecules enhancing telomerase activity. However, to date, it is not known how to manage both the carcinogenic potential of *hTERT*-immortalized hepatocytes, and the hepatotoxicity linked to gene delivery [77].

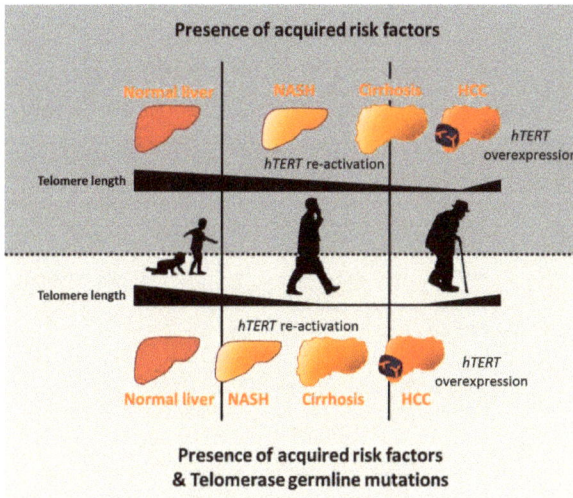

Figure 2. Hypothesis for telomeres' role in pathogenesis of nonalcoholic fatty liver disease (NAFLD) progression toward cirrhosis and hepatocellular carcinoma (HCC). The model shows that, in the presence of triggering acquired risk factors such as obesity and insulin resistance, the liver undergoes cycle of damage and regeneration that requires telomerase re-activation. However, degenerative chronic conditions lead to telomere shortening and fibrosis progression towards cirrhosis, the main risk factor for HCC. In carriers of telomerase germline loss-of-function mutations, this process is accelerated due to telomerase inability to elongate telomeres, thus impairing tissue regeneration. Moreover, telomerase mutations may have a direct pro-carcinogenic effect by inducing genomic instability. Finally, telomere re-elongation in cancer tissue was triggered by different mechanisms, among which, overexpression of *hTERT* is necessary for the immortalization of the neoplastic clone.

Interestingly, both the inhibition and the activation of telomerase may be useful in different stages of liver disease, and, at the same time, may have important side effects due also to the impairment of the physiological expression of this gene in other organs and tissues. Thus, how to act in order to modulate telomerase activity remains controversial. Further studies are necessary in order to better understand the impact of telomeres and telomerase on the different levels of liver disease progression, and consequently how to act to prevent telomerase related damage.

Conflicts of Interest: The authors declare no conflict of interest.

Abbreviations

The following abbreviations are used in this manuscript:

NAFLD	Non-alcoholic fatty liver disease
HCC	Hepatocellular carcinoma
hTERT	Human telomerase Reverse Transcriptase
hTERC	Human telomerase RNA Component
DKC1	Dyskerin
NOLA1-NOLA2- NOLA3	Nucleolar protein family A member 1, 2 and 3
TRF1-TRF2	Telomeric repeat- binding factors 1 and 2
POT1	Protection of telomeres 1
TIN2	TRF-1 interacting protein 2
TPP1	POT1-TIN2 organizing protein
RAP1	repressor/activator protein 1
pRb	Retinoblastoma 1
Cdk	Cyclin-dependent kinase
E2F	Transcription factor E2F
ErbB	Epidermal Growth Factor Receptor family members
INK4a	Cyclin-dependent kinase inhibitor 2A
K19	Keratin 19
EpCAM	Epithelial Cell Adhesion Molecule
ALT	Alternative Lengthening of Telomeres
BRG1	SWI/SNF related, matrix associated, actin dependent regulator of chromatin, subfamily a, member 4
TCF4	Transcription factor 4
RdRP	RNA-dependent RNA polymerase
RMRP	RNA component of mitochondrial RNA processing endoribonuclease
siRNA	Silencing RNA
RISC	RNA-induced silencing complex
Pgc-1α/β	Peroxisome proliferator-activated receptor γ coactivator-1 α/β
NASH	Non-alcoholic steatohepatitis
CDKN1A	Cyclin-dependent kinase inhibitor 1A

References

1. Blackburn, E.H. Structure and function of telomeres. *Nature* **1991**, *350*, 569–573. [CrossRef] [PubMed]
2. Egan, E.D.; Collins, K. Specificity and stoichiometry of subunit interactions in the human telomerase holoenzyme assembled *in vivo*. *Mol. Cell. Biol.* **2010**, *30*, 2775–2786. [CrossRef] [PubMed]
3. Reichow, S.L.; Hamma, T.; Ferre-D'Amare, A.R.; Varani, G. The structure and function of small nucleolar ribonucleoproteins. *Nucleic Acids Res.* **2007**, *35*, 1452–1464. [CrossRef] [PubMed]
4. Wang, C.; Meier, U.T. Architecture and assembly of mammalian H/ACA small nucleolar and telomerase ribonucleoproteins. *EMBO J.* **2004**, *23*, 1857–1867. [CrossRef] [PubMed]
5. El Idrissi, M.; Hervieu, V.; Merle, P.; Mortreux, F.; Wattel, E. Cause-specific telomere factors deregulation in hepatocellular carcinoma. *J. Exp. Clin. Cancer Res.* **2013**, *32*, 64. [CrossRef] [PubMed]
6. De Lange, T. Shelterin: The protein complex that shapes and safeguards human telomeres. *Genes Dev.* **2005**, *19*, 2100–2110. [CrossRef] [PubMed]
7. Xin, H.; Liu, D.; Wan, M.; Safari, A.; Kim, H.; Sun, W.; O'Connor, M.S.; Songyang, Z. TPP1 is a homologue of ciliate TEBP-β and interacts with POT1 to recruit telomerase. *Nature* **2007**, *445*, 559–562. [CrossRef] [PubMed]
8. Dokal, I. Dyskeratosis congenita. A disease of premature ageing. *Lancet* **2001**, *358*, S27. [CrossRef]
9. Calado, R.T.; Young, N.S. Telomere diseases. *N. Eng. J. Med.* **2009**, *361*, 2353–2365. [CrossRef] [PubMed]
10. Calado, R.T.; Regal, J.A.; Kleiner, D.E.; Schrump, D.S.; Peterson, N.R.; Pons, V.; Chanock, S.J.; Lansdorp, P.M.; Young, N.S. A spectrum of severe familial liver disorders associate with telomerase mutations. *PLoS ONE* **2009**, *4*, e7926. [CrossRef] [PubMed]

11. Dongiovanni, P.; Romeo, S.; Valenti, L. Hepatocellular carcinoma in nonalcoholic fatty liver: Role of environmental and genetic factors. *World J. Gastroenterol.* **2014**, *20*, 12945–12955. [CrossRef] [PubMed]

12. Pinzani, M. Pathophysiology of liver fibrosis. *Dig. Dis.* **2015**, *33*, 492–497. [CrossRef] [PubMed]

13. Poynard, T.; Mathurin, P.; Lai, C.L.; Guyader, D.; Poupon, R.; Tainturier, M.H.; Myers, R.P.; Muntenau, M.; Ratziu, V.; Manns, M.; *et al.* A comparison of fibrosis progression in chronic liver diseases. *J. Hepatol.* **2003**, *38*, 257–265.

14. Satyanarayana, A.; Wiemann, S.U.; Buer, J.; Lauber, J.; Dittmar, K.E.; Wustefeld, T.; Blasco, M.A.; Manns, M.P.; Rudolph, K.L. Telomere shortening impairs organ regeneration by inhibiting cell cycle re-entry of a subpopulation of cells. *EMBO J.* **2003**, *22*, 4003–4013. [CrossRef] [PubMed]

15. Kitada, T.; Seki, S.; Kawakita, N.; Kuroki, T.; Monna, T. Telomere shortening in chronic liver diseases. *Biochem. Biophys. Res. Commun.* **1995**, *211*, 33–39. [CrossRef] [PubMed]

16. Urabe, Y.; Nouso, K.; Higashi, T.; Nakatsukasa, H.; Hino, N.; Ashida, K.; Kinugasa, N.; Yoshida, K.; Uematsu, S.; Tsuji, T. Telomere length in human liver diseases. *Liver* **1996**, *16*, 293–297. [CrossRef] [PubMed]

17. Aikata, H.; Takaishi, H.; Kawakami, Y.; Takahashi, S.; Kitamoto, M.; Nakanishi, T.; Nakamura, Y.; Shimamoto, F.; Kajiyama, G.; Ide, T. Telomere reduction in human liver tissues with age and chronic inflammation. *Exp. Cell Res.* **2000**, *256*, 578–582. [CrossRef] [PubMed]

18. Wiemann, S.U.; Satyanarayana, A.; Tsahuridu, M.; Tillmann, H.L.; Zender, L.; Klempnauer, J.; Flemming, P.; Franco, S.; Blasco, M.A.; Manns, M.P.; *et al.* Hepatocyte telomere shortening and senescence are general markers of human liver cirrhosis. *FASEB J.* **2002**, *16*, 935–942. [CrossRef] [PubMed]

19. Calado, R.T.; Brudno, J.; Mehta, P.; Kovacs, J.J.; Wu, C.; Zago, M.A.; Chanock, S.J.; Boyer, T.D.; Young, N.S. Constitutional telomerase mutations are genetic risk factors for cirrhosis. *Hepatology* **2011**, *53*, 1600–1607. [CrossRef] [PubMed]

20. Chaiteerakij, R.; Roberts, L.R. Telomerase mutation: A genetic risk factor for cirrhosis. *Hepatology* **2011**, *53*, 1430–1432. [CrossRef] [PubMed]

21. Rudolph, K.L.; Chang, S.; Millard, M.; Schreiber-Agus, N.; Depinho, R.A. Inhibition of experimental liver cirrhosis in mice by telomerase gene delivery. *Science* **2000**, *287*, 1253–1258. [CrossRef] [PubMed]

22. Sasaki, M.; Ikeda, H.; Yamaguchi, J.; Nakada, S.; Nakanuma, Y. Telomere shortening in the damaged small bile ducts in primary biliary cirrhosis reflects ongoing cellular senescence. *Hepatology* **2008**, *48*, 186–195. [CrossRef] [PubMed]

23. Gutierrez-Reyes, G.; del Carmen Garcia de Leon, M.; Varela-Fascinetto, G.; Valencia, P.; Perez Tamayo, R.; Rosado, C.G.; Labonne, B.F.; Rochilin, N.M.; Garcia, R.M.; Valadez, J.A.; *et al.* Cellular senescence in livers from children with end stage liver disease. *PLoS ONE* **2010**, *5*, e10231. [CrossRef]

24. Krizhanovsky, V.; Yon, M.; Dickins, R.A.; Hearn, S.; Simon, J.; Miething, C.; Yee, H.; Zender, L.; Lowe, S.W. Senescence of activated stellate cells limits liver fibrosis. *Cell* **2008**, *134*, 657–667. [CrossRef] [PubMed]

25. Schnabl, B.; Purbeck, C.A.; Choi, Y.H.; Hagedorn, C.H.; Brenner, D. Replicative senescence of activated human hepatic stellate cells is accompanied by a pronounced inflammatory but less fibrogenic phenotype. *Hepatology* **2003**, *37*, 653–664. [CrossRef] [PubMed]

26. Ramakrishna, G.; Rastogi, A.; Trehanpati, N.; Sen, B.; Khosla, R.; Sarin, S.K. From cirrhosis to hepatocellular carcinoma: New molecular insights on inflammation and cellular senescence. *Liver Cancer* **2013**, *2*, 367–383. [CrossRef] [PubMed]

27. Richardson, M.M.; Jonsson, J.R.; Powell, E.E.; Brunt, E.M.; Neuschwander-Tetri, B.A.; Bhathal, P.S.; Dixon, J.B.; Weltman, M.D.; Tilg, H.; Moschen, A.R.; *et al.* Progressive fibrosis in nonalcoholic steatohepatitis: Association with altered regeneration and a ductular reaction. *Gastroenterology* **2007**, *133*, 80–90. [CrossRef] [PubMed]

28. Yoshimoto, S.; Loo, T.M.; Atarashi, K.; Kanda, H.; Sato, S.; Oyadomari, S.; Iwakura, Y.; Oshima, K.; Morita, H.; Hattori, M.; *et al.* Obesity-induced gut microbial metabolite promotes liver cancer through senescence secretome. *Nature* **2013**, *499*, 97–101. [CrossRef] [PubMed]

29. Vulliamy, T.; Marrone, A.; Goldman, F.; Dearlove, A.; Bessler, M.; Mason, P.J.; Dokal, I. The RNA component of telomerase is mutated in autosomal dominant dyskeratosis congenita. *Nature* **2001**, *413*, 432–435. [CrossRef] [PubMed]

30. Armanios, M.Y.; Chen, J.J.-L.; Cogan, J.D.; Alder, J.K.; Ingersoll, R.G.; Markin, C.; Lawson, W.E.; Xie, M.; Vulto, I.; Phillips, J.A.; *et al.* Telomerase Mutations in Families with Idiopathic Pulmonary Fibrosis. *N. Eng. J. Med.* **2007**, *356*, 1317–1326. [CrossRef] [PubMed]

31. Hartmann, D.; Srivastava, U.; Thaler, M.; Kleinhans, K.N.; N'Kontchou, G.; Scheffold, A.; Bauer, K.; Kratzer, R.F.; Kloos, N.; Katz, S.F.; *et al.* Telomerase gene mutations are associated with cirrhosis formation. *Hepatology* **2011**, *53*, 1608–1617. [CrossRef] [PubMed]

32. El-Serag, H.B.; Rudolph, K.L. Hepatocellular carcinoma: Epidemiology and molecular carcinogenesis. *Gastroenterology* **2007**, *132*, 2557–2576. [CrossRef] [PubMed]

33. Plentz, R.R.; Schlegelberger, B.; Flemming, P.; Gebel, M.; Kreipe, H.; Manns, M.P.; Rudolph, K.L.; Wilkens, L. Telomere shortening correlates with increasing aneuploidy of chromosome 8 in human hepatocellular carcinoma. *Hepatology* **2005**, *42*, 522–526. [CrossRef] [PubMed]

34. Farazi, P.A.; DePinho, R.A. Hepatocellular carcinoma pathogenesis: From genes to environment. *Nat. Rev. Cancer* **2006**, *6*, 674–687. [CrossRef] [PubMed]

35. Farazi, P.A.; Glickman, J.; Jiang, S.; Yu, A.; Rudolph, K.L.; DePinho, R.A. Differential impact of telomere dysfunction on initiation and progression of hepatocellular carcinoma. *Cancer Res.* **2003**, *63*, 5021–5027. [PubMed]

36. Masutomi, K.; Possemato, R.; Wong, J.M.; Currier, J.L.; Tothova, Z.; Manola, J.B.; Ganesan, S.; Lansdorp, P.M.; Collins, K.; Hahn, W.C. The telomerase reverse transcriptase regulates chromatin state and DNA damage responses. *Proc. Nat. Acad. Sci. USA* **2005**, *102*, 8222–8227. [CrossRef] [PubMed]

37. Plentz, R.R.; Wiemann, S.U.; Flemming, P.; Meier, P.N.; Kubicka, S.; Kreipe, H.; Manns, M.P.; Rudolph, K.L. Telomere shortening of epithelial cells characterises the adenoma-carcinoma transition of human colorectal cancer. *Gut* **2003**, *52*, 1304–1307.

38. Oh, B.K.; Kim, H.; Park, Y.N.; Yoo, J.E.; Choi, J.; Kim, K.S.; Lee, J.J.; Park, C. High telomerase activity and long telomeres in advanced hepatocellular carcinomas with poor prognosis. *Lab. Invest.* **2008**, *88*, 144–152.

39. Oh, B.K.; Jo Chae, K.; Park, C.; Kim, K.; Lee, W.J.; Han, K.H.; Park, Y.N. Telomere shortening and telomerase reactivation in dysplastic nodules of human hepatocarcinogenesis. *J. Hepatol.* **2003**, *39*, 786–792. [CrossRef]

40. Ju, Z.; Rudolph, K.L. Telomeres and telomerase in cancer stem cells. *Eur. J. Cancer* **2006**, *42*, 1197–1203. [CrossRef] [PubMed]

41. Llovet, J.M.; Chen, Y.; Wurmbach, E.; Roayaie, S.; Fiel, M.I.; Schwartz, M.; Thung, S.N.; Khitrov, G.; Zhang, W.; Villanueva, A.; *et al.* A molecular signature to discriminate dysplastic nodules from early hepatocellular carcinoma in HCV cirrhosis. *Gastroenterology* **2006**, *131*, 1758–1767. [CrossRef] [PubMed]

42. Saini, N.; Srinivasan, R.; Chawla, Y.; Sharma, S.; Chakraborti, A.; Rajwanshi, A. Telomerase activity, telomere length and human telomerase reverse transcriptase expression in hepatocellular carcinoma is independent of hepatitis virus status. *Liver Int.* **2009**, *29*, 1162–1170. [CrossRef] [PubMed]

43. Yamashita, T.; Forgues, M.; Wang, W.; Kim, J.W.; Ye, Q.; Jia, H.; Budhu, A.; Zanetti, K.A.; Chen, Y.; Qin, L.X.; *et al.* EpCAM and alpha-fetoprotein expression defines novel prognostic subtypes of hepatocellular carcinoma. *Cancer Res.* **2008**, *68*, 1451–1461. [CrossRef] [PubMed]

44. Kim, H.; Choi, G.H.; Na, D.C.; Ahn, E.Y.; Kim, G.I.; Lee, J.E.; Cho, J.Y.; Yoo, J.E.; Choi, J.S.; Park, Y.N. Human hepatocellular carcinomas with "Stemness"-related marker expression: Keratin 19 expression and a poor prognosis. *Hepatology* **2011**, *54*, 1707–1717. [CrossRef] [PubMed]

45. Kim, H.; Yoo, J.E.; Cho, J.Y.; Oh, B.K.; Yoon, Y.S.; Han, H.S.; Lee, H.S.; Jang, J.J.; Jeong, S.H.; Kim, J.W.; *et al.* Telomere length, TERT and shelterin complex proteins in hepatocellular carcinomas expressing "stemness"-related markers. *J. Hepatol.* **2013**, *59*, 746–752. [CrossRef] [PubMed]

46. Tejera, A.M.; Stagno d'Alcontres, M.; Thanasoula, M.; Marion, R.M.; Martinez, P.; Liao, C.; Flores, J.M.; Tarsounas, M.; Blasco, M.A. TPP1 is required for TERT recruitment, telomere elongation during nuclear reprogramming, and normal skin development in mice. *Dev. Cell* **2010**, *18*, 775–789. [CrossRef] [PubMed]

47. Liu, B.; Zhang, J.; Huang, C.; Liu, H. Dyskerin overexpression in human hepatocellular carcinoma is associated with advanced clinical stage and poor patient prognosis. *PLoS ONE* **2012**, *7*, e43147. [CrossRef] [PubMed]

48. Alawi, F.; Lee, M.N. DKC1 is a direct and conserved transcriptional target of c-MYC. *Biochem. Biophys. Res. Commun.* **2007**, *362*, 893–898. [CrossRef] [PubMed]

49. Heaphy, C.M.; Subhawong, A.P.; Hong, S.M.; Goggins, M.G.; Montgomery, E.A.; Gabrielson, E.; Netto, G.J.; Epstein, J.I.; Lotan, T.L.; Westra, W.H.; *et al.* Prevalence of the alternative lengthening of telomeres telomere maintenance mechanism in human cancer subtypes. *Am. J. Pathol.* **2011**, *179*, 1608–1615. [PubMed]

50. Cevik, D.; Yildiz, G.; Ozturk, M. Common telomerase reverse transcriptase promoter mutations in hepatocellular carcinomas from different geographical locations. *World J. Gastroenterol.* **2015**, *21*, 311–317. [CrossRef] [PubMed]

51. Nault, J.C.; Mallet, M.; Pilati, C.; Calderaro, J.; Bioulac-Sage, P.; Laurent, C.; Laurent, A.; Cherqui, D.; Balabaud, C.; Zucman-Rossi, J. High frequency of telomerase reverse-transcriptase promoter somatic mutations in hepatocellular carcinoma and preneoplastic lesions. *Nat. Commun.* **2013**, *4*, 2218. [CrossRef] [PubMed]

52. Quaas, A.; Oldopp, T.; Tharun, L.; Klingenfeld, C.; Krech, T.; Sauter, G.; Grob, T.J. Frequency of TERT promoter mutations in primary tumors of the liver. *Virchows Arch.* **2014**, *465*, 673–677. [CrossRef] [PubMed]

53. Horn, S.; Figl, A.; Rachakonda, P.S.; Fischer, C.; Sucker, A.; Gast, A.; Kadel, S.; Moll, I.; Nagore, E.; Hemminki, K.; *et al.* TERT promoter mutations in familial and sporadic melanoma. *Science* **2013**, *339*, 959–961. [CrossRef] [PubMed]

54. Huang, F.W.; Hodis, E.; Xu, M.J.; Kryukov, G.V.; Chin, L.; Garraway, L.A. Highly recurrent TERT promoter mutations in human melanoma. *Science* **2013**, *339*, 957–959. [CrossRef] [PubMed]

55. Eichenmuller, M.; Trippel, F.; Kreuder, M.; Beck, A.; Schwarzmayr, T.; Haberle, B.; Cairo, S.; Leuschner, I.; von Schweinitz, D.; Strom, T.M.; *et al.* The genomic landscape of hepatoblastoma and their progenies with HCC-like features. *J. Hepatol.* **2014**, *61*, 1312–1320. [CrossRef] [PubMed]

56. Nault, J.C.; Zucman-Rossi, J. TERT promoter mutations in primary liver tumors. *Clin. Res. Hepatol. Gastroenterol.* **2016**, *40*, 9–14. [CrossRef] [PubMed]

57. Paterlini-Brechot, P.; Saigo, K.; Murakami, Y.; Chami, M.; Gozuacik, D.; Mugnier, C.; Lagorce, D.; Brechot, C. Hepatitis B virus-related insertional mutagenesis occurs frequently in human liver cancers and recurrently targets human telomerase gene. *Oncogene* **2003**, *22*, 3911–3916. [CrossRef] [PubMed]

58. Sung, W.K.; Zheng, H.; Li, S.; Chen, R.; Liu, X.; Li, Y.; Lee, N.P.; Lee, W.H.; Ariyaratne, P.N.; Tennakoon, C.; *et al.* Genome-wide survey of recurrent HBV integration in hepatocellular carcinoma. *Nat. Genet.* **2012**, *44*, 765–769. [CrossRef] [PubMed]

59. Totoki, Y.; Tatsuno, K.; Covington, K.R.; Ueda, H.; Creighton, C.J.; Kato, M.; Tsuji, S.; Donehower, L.A.; Slagle, B.L.; Nakamura, H.; *et al.* Trans-ancestry mutational landscape of hepatocellular carcinoma genomes. *Nat. Gene.* **2014**, *46*, 1267–1273. [CrossRef] [PubMed]

60. Chiodi, I.; Mondello, C. Telomere-independent functions of telomerase in nuclei, cytoplasm, and mitochondria. *Front. Oncol.* **2012**, *2*, 133. [CrossRef] [PubMed]

61. Barker, N.; Hurlstone, A.; Musisi, H.; Miles, A.; Bienz, M.; Clevers, H. The chromatin remodelling factor BRG-1 interacts with β-catenin to promote target gene activation. *EMBO J.* **2001**, *20*, 4935–4943. [CrossRef] [PubMed]

62. Park, J.I.; Venteicher, A.S.; Hong, J.Y.; Choi, J.; Jun, S.; Shkreli, M.; Chang, W.; Meng, Z.; Cheung, P.; Ji, H.; *et al.* Telomerase modulates Wnt signalling by association with target gene chromatin. *Nature* **2009**, *460*, 66–72. [CrossRef] [PubMed]

63. Zhang, Y.; Toh, L.; Lau, P.; Wang, X. Human telomerase reverse transcriptase (hTERT) is a novel target of the Wnt/β-catenin pathway in human cancer. *J. Biol. Chem.* **2012**, *287*, 32494–32511. [CrossRef] [PubMed]

64. Tsai, R.Y.; McKay, R.D. A nucleolar mechanism controlling cell proliferation in stem cells and cancer cells. *Genes Dev.* **2002**, *16*, 2991–3003. [PubMed]

65. Okamoto, N.; Yasukawa, M.; Nguyen, C.; Kasim, V.; Maida, Y.; Possemato, R.; Shibata, T.; Ligon, K.L.; Fukami, K.; Hahn, W.C.; *et al.* Maintenance of tumor initiating cells of defined genetic composition by nucleostemin. *Proc. Nat. Acad. Sci. USA* **2011**, *108*, 20388–20393.

66. Maida, Y.; Yasukawa, M.; Furuuchi, M.; Lassmann, T.; Possemato, R.; Okamoto, N.; Kasim, V.; Hayashizaki, Y.; Hahn, W.C.; Masutomi, K. An RNA-dependent RNA polymerase formed by TERT and the RMRP RNA. *Nature* **2009**, *461*, 230–235. [CrossRef] [PubMed]

67. Esakova, O.; Krasilnikov, A.S. Of proteins and RNA: The RNase P/MRP family. *Rna* **2010**, *16*, 1725–1747. [CrossRef] [PubMed]

68. Sharma, N.K.; Reyes, A.; Green, P.; Caron, M.J.; Bonini, M.G.; Gordon, D.M.; Holt, I.J.; Santos, J.H. Human telomerase acts as a hTR-independent reverse transcriptase in mitochondria. *Nucleic Acids Res.* **2012**, *40*, 712–725. [CrossRef] [PubMed]

69. Sahin, E.; DePinho, R.A. Axis of ageing: Telomeres, p53 and mitochondria. *Nat. Rev. Mol. Cell Biol.* **2012**, *13*, 397–404. [CrossRef] [PubMed]

70. Dongiovanni, P.; Valenti, L. Genetics of nonalcoholic fatty liver disease. *Metabolism* **2015**. (in press). [CrossRef] [PubMed]

71. Aravinthan, A.; Scarpini, C.; Tachtatzis, P.; Verma, S.; Penrhyn-Lowe, S.; Harvey, R.; Davies, S.E.; Allison, M.; Coleman, N.; Alexander, G. Hepatocyte senescence predicts progression in non-alcohol-related fatty liver disease. *J. Hepatol.* **2013**, *58*, 549–556. [CrossRef] [PubMed]

72. Aravinthan, A.; Mells, G.; Allison, M.; Leathart, J.; Kotronen, A.; Yki-Jarvinen, H.; Daly, A.K.; Day, C.P.; Anstee, Q.M.; Alexander, G. Gene polymorphisms of cellular senescence marker p21 and disease progression in non-alcohol-related fatty liver disease. *Cell Cycle* **2014**, *13*, 1489–1494.

73. Valenti, L.; Dongiovanni, P. CDKN1A: A double-edged sword in fatty liver? *Cell Cycle* **2014**, *13*, 1371–1372. [CrossRef] [PubMed]

74. Korthagen, N.M.; van Moorsel, C.H.; Barlo, N.P.; Kazemier, K.M.; Ruven, H.J.; Grutters, J.C. Association between variations in cell cycle genes and idiopathic pulmonary fibrosis. *PLoS ONE* **2012**, *7*, e30442. [CrossRef] [PubMed]

75. Valenti, L.; Dongiovanni, P.; Maggioni, M.; Motta, B.M.; Rametta, R.; Milano, M.; Fargion, S.; Reggiani, P.; Fracanzani, A.L. Liver transplantation for hepatocellular carcinoma in a patient with a novel telomerase mutation and steatosis. *J. Hepatol.* **2013**, *58*, 399–401. [CrossRef] [PubMed]

76. Donati, B.; Vanni, E.; Dongiovanni, P.; Iavarone, M.; Rametta, R.; Rosso, C.; Carnelutti, A.; Petta, S.; Fracanzani, A.L.; Reeves, H.L.; *et al.* O071: Telomerase reverse transcriptase mutations are associated with hepatocellular carcinoma in nash. *J. Hepatol.* **2015**, *62*, S226. [CrossRef]

77. Lechel, A.; Manns, M.P.; Rudolph, K.L. Telomeres and telomerase: New targets for the treatment of liver cirrhosis and hepatocellular carcinoma. *J. Hepatol.* **2004**, *41*, 491–497. [CrossRef] [PubMed]

78. Lee, K.H.; Rudolph, K.L.; Ju, Y.J.; Greenberg, R.A.; Cannizzaro, L.; Chin, L.; Weiler, S.R.; DePinho, R.A. Telomere dysfunction alters the chemotherapeutic profile of transformed cells. *Proc. Nat. Acad. Sci. USA* **2001**, *98*, 3381–3386. [CrossRef] [PubMed]

International Journal of
Molecular Sciences

MDPI

Review

Extracellular Vesicles: A New Frontier in Biomarker Discovery for Non-Alcoholic Fatty Liver Disease

Linda A. Ban [1], Nicholas A. Shackel [2] and Susan V. McLennan [1,*]

[1]   Greg Brown Diabetes and Endocrine Laboratory, Charles Perkins Centre, University of Sydney, NSW 2006, Australia; linda.ban@sydney.edu.au

[2]   Liver Cell Biology Laboratory, Centenary Institute of Cancer Medicine and Cell Biology, Camperdown, NSW 2006, Australia; n.shackel@centenary.usyd.edu.au

*   Correspondence: sue.mclennan@sydney.edu.au; Tel.: +61-2-8627-1892

Academic Editors: Amedeo Lonardo and Giovanni Targher
Received: 24 February 2016; Accepted: 2 March 2016; Published: 14 March 2016

Abstract: In recent years, the global burden of obesity and diabetes has seen a parallel rise in other metabolic complications, such as non-alcoholic fatty liver disease (NAFLD). This condition, once thought to be a benign accumulation of hepatic fat, is now recognized as a serious and prevalent disorder that is conducive to inflammation and fibrosis. Despite the rising incidence of NAFLD, there is currently no reliable method for its diagnosis or staging besides the highly invasive tissue biopsy. This limitation has resulted in the study of novel circulating markers as potential candidates, one of the most popular being extracellular vesicles (EVs). These submicron membrane-bound structures are secreted from stressed and activated cells, or are formed during apoptosis, and are known to be involved in intercellular communication. The cargo of EVs depends upon the parent cell and has been shown to be changed in disease, as is their abundance in the circulation. The role of EVs in immunity and epigenetic regulation is widely attested, and studies showing a correlation with disease severity have made these structures a favorable target for diagnostic as well as therapeutic purposes. This review will highlight the research that is available on EVs in the context of NAFLD, the current limitations, and projections for their future utility in a clinical setting.

Keywords: biomarkers; diagnosis; exosomes; extracellular vesicles; microvesicles; NAFLD; non-alcoholic steatohepatitis (NASH); steatosis; steatohepatitis

---

1. Introduction

Obesity is rapidly evolving into a global pandemic, and poses a significant healthcare and socioeconomic burden. Its increased prevalence in both developed and developing nations has seen a rise in other serious metabolic complications, such as cardiovascular disease, type 2 diabetes mellitus and non-alcoholic fatty liver disease (NAFLD). Although diabetes is a common risk factor for NAFLD progression and *vice versa* [1–4], lean or non-diabetic patients also develop NAFLD [5–7], and so biochemical rather than anthropometric parameters would likely be of greater utility in diagnosis or prognosis of the disease.

To address this issue, the World Gastroenterology Organisation (WGO) recently published a set of comprehensive guidelines on the assessment and management of NAFLD [8], with emphasis on the distinction between simple steatosis and non-alcoholic steatohepatitis (NASH). The latter represents the advanced manifestation of the NAFLD spectrum whereby inflammation and fibrosis are also present, and is a condition which is much easier to identify than simple steatosis. However, limitations with current diagnostic methods, such as unreliable imaging techniques and serum markers, have meant that tissue biopsy remains the gold standard for NASH diagnosis [9–14]. Irrespective of this, biopsy is a highly invasive procedure and subject to variability through sampling error [15–17].

Moreover, it cannot predict disease progression, and, for this reason, there is increasing emphasis on the identification of stable non-invasive markers specific for liver disease progression.

At this stage, effective early detection is poor as patients usually do not report symptoms until they have progressed to NASH or cirrhosis. Serum biochemistry that reveals elevated liver transaminases in the absence of excessive alcohol consumption or other liver disease is the most typical indicator of NAFLD, while anthropometric data such as a high body mass index (considered obese if above 35 kg/m^2) may warrant further screening for visceral fat accumulation in the liver [8]. It must nonetheless be stressed that despite the increased likelihood, not all obese individuals will develop NAFLD/NASH, and so probing for markers of steatosis in global metabolic disorders should therefore address what is known about the mechanisms of disease within the target organ. Ideal marker candidates should reflect not only the presence of NAFLD, but also the severity of disease, which is vital for early diagnosis as well grading progression [13].

This review aims to introduce the concept of using circulating cell-derived vesicles as novel markers of NAFLD, with an emphasis on their role in diagnosis and the assessment of disease pathology. Drawing on recent evidence from the literature, the paradigm of "marker *versus* mediator" will be discussed, as well as insight into their potential as therapeutic targets.

2. Novel Biomarkers in Liver Disease

In the latter half of the last century, shedding of vesicles from the cell membrane was identified as an inconsequential by-product of cell degradation [18,19]. However, clinical studies supported by research findings have recently pointed to the regulated secretion of these extracellular vesicles and their role in intercellular communication. Moreover, the abundance as well as the phenotype of circulating vesicles is reported to change in many disease states, including liver diseases [20–23] and metabolic disorders such as diabetes and obesity [24–27]. As such, much interest has been invested in characterising these structures for their potential utility in diagnostics, especially for conditions where this is otherwise notoriously difficult, such as NAFLD.

2.1. Extracellular Vesicles: What Are They?

Extracellular vesicles (EVs) are collectively represented by three subclasses of membrane-bound structures that are distinguished based on their size, typical markers, and biogenesis [28–30] (see Figure 1). Exosomes are the smallest vesicles, usually below 100 nm in diameter, and are formed within multivesicular bodies (MVB) that release their contents into the interstitium upon fusion with the cell membrane. These exocytosed EVs are characterised by their expression of membrane tetraspanins, most notably CD63, as well as the endosomal sorting complex required for transport (ESCRT)-associated protein Alix, both of which reflect the MVB origin of exosomes [29,31,32].

In contrast, microvesicles (MVs) are shed directly from the cell membrane by a "budding" process and typically range in size from around 100 to 1000 nm, although these values are somewhat arbitrary and subclass overlap may exist [29]. MVs are identified by the expression of phosphatidylserine (PS) on their surface, which is indicative of their release from activated or apoptotic cells. In these cells PS is externalized, whereas in quiescent cells the membrane PS has a cytosolic orientation [33,34]. Most studies utilise the fact that Annexin V—a soluble protein used in the detection of apoptotic cells—binds with high affinity to PS and is therefore a useful marker of the MV subclass. Meanwhile, some groups have argued that a majority of circulating MVs are in fact PS-negative, whilst others have proposed that measurement of lactadherin may be a more sensitive alternative to Annexin V [35–37]. Despite ongoing controversies in their characterisation, both EV populations have ultimately been shown to impart functional properties of their parent cells through the transfer of proteins, mRNAs, and particularly microRNAs (or miRNAs) that are subsequently involved in epigenetic regulation [38,39].

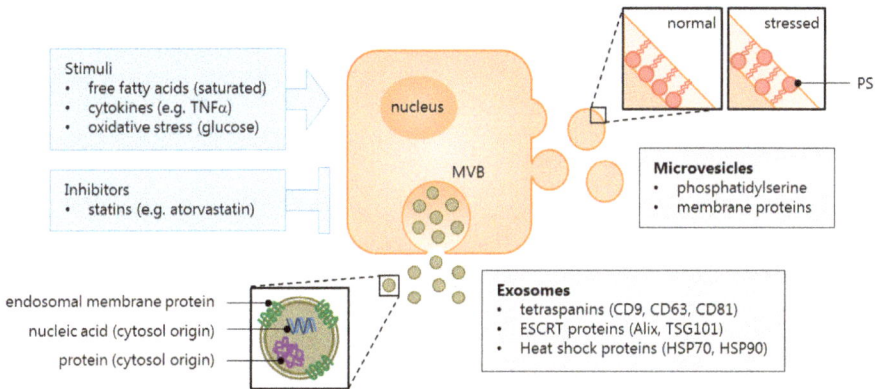

Figure 1. Extracellular vesicle characterisation. Cells respond to a variety of stimuli that cause inflammation and metabolic stress, which result in their activation, impaired functioning, or apoptosis. This mechanism drives the release of extracellular vesicles (EVs), which signal to paracrine or distal effectors the condition of the cell microenvironment. Effector cells may, in turn, respond by selectively imparting regulatory molecules—small nucleic acids (mRNA and miRNA), lipids, and proteins—contained within EVs, that are taken up by the recipient cell. The EV subclasses are identified by membrane markers that denote the site of their biogenesis. Exosomes typically express endosomal membrane proteins, such as tetraspanins, while microvesicles are understood to contain phosphatidylserine. These lipoproteins are normally oriented towards the cytosol to maintain the cell membrane asymmetry, but during conditions that stimulate EV release, the molecules become everted. Abbreviations: ESCRT = endosomal sorting complex required for transport; MVB = multivesicular body; PS = phosphatidylserine.

Finally, apoptotic bodies represent the largest EV subclass in terms of their size, ranging from one to four microns. Since this is comparable with platelets, studies that use size exclusion techniques to isolate circulating EVs, such as ultracentrifugation or filtration, will usually lose this population of vesicles with larger contaminants [40]. Furthermore, as apoptotic bodies are formed during the compartmentalization of apoptotic cells, they are generally assumed to be inert particles destined for phagocytosis, although their horizontal gene-transfer capacity has been documented [41,42].

2.2. Role of Extracellular Vesicles in Liver Disease

Almost all cell types ubiquitously release low levels of extracellular vesicles. In normal physiology, most circulating EVs are derived from platelets and endothelial cells, and have been shown to be important in common haemostatic events such as coagulation [43]. While vesicles of the same origin have been implicated in disease complications of a pro-coagulative nature [44,45], there is still a paucity of knowledge regarding the dynamics of EV secretion by different cell types and in particular how the secreted EVs interact to advance the pathogenesis of a given disease. Controlled *in vitro* experiments have provided the most direct lines of evidence for EV regulation, including how the stimulus for release may affect their phenotype [46]. There is a wealth of research using liver injury models to explore EV-mediated fibrosis [47–49], transcriptomic signalling [50–54], and targeted immunotherapy [55–57] in artificial cell culture systems. However, *in vivo* studies present an added degree of complexity due to the difficulty of identifying liver specific EVs within the circulating pool. For this reason, most studies have opted to focus on circulating vesicle characterisation and their temporal changes in relation to liver disease development [58–63], while others have pointed to roles in extrahepatic cancer metastasis to the liver [64–66], although functional relationships have yet to be explored.

Some groups have approached the study of EVs from a more organ-targeted perspective, assessing their role as paracrine mediators. Most of these studies evaluate the effect of EVs in fibrogenesis, for example, the shuttling of pro-fibrogenic connective tissue growth factor (CTGF) between hepatic stellate cells on the one hand [47], or the CTGF inhibiting miRNA-214 between stellate cells and hepatocytes or adjacent stellate cells on the other hand [48]. Immune-mediated modulation has also been suggested; one study had demonstrated a role for T cell-derived EVs in the induction of stellate cell fibrolytic activity, as defined by an increase in the gene expression of matrix metalloproteinases (MMPs) [49]. The findings concluded that this response from the stellate cells was likely mediated by the homodimeric interaction of CD147 at the EV-cell interface. A pro-inflammatory glycoprotein, CD147 had previously been implicated in liver disease pathogenesis by our group [67,68] as well as having a well document role in tumour metastasis, which more recently had been attributed to EV-mediated translocation [69–71]. Secreted vesicles have also been linked to paracrine signalling in the tumour microenvironment, whereby miRNAs shuttled from hepatoma cells were able to modulate protein expression in adjacent hepatocytes and to increase their proliferative potential [50,51]. Silencing of these miRNAs, in turn, had abrogated the pro-tumorigenic effects, while another study had suggested a role for liver stem cell-derived EVs in miRNA-mediated tumour suppression [52].

2.3. Markers or Mediators of Liver Disease?

Taken together, this body of evidence highlights the growing expanse of EV research pertaining to liver disease, and on the contrary, a relative paucity of data regarding the involvement of EVs in NAFLD progression to NASH. Additionally, it introduces the "marker *versus* mediator" paradigm when addressing the functionality of EVs. This plays an important role in EV analysis; for instance, in the context of NAFLD, global changes in the circulating pool (marker) may not reflect the local interactions within specific tissues, such as the liver, that drive pathogenesis at these sites (mediator). However, a circulating profile that is unique to a given disease etiology would still substantiate the use of EVs as non-invasive diagnostic markers, a concept that is discussed further in the section below.

3. Studies in Non-Alcoholic Fatty Liver Disease

Liver research involving EVs as disease mediators faces a number of inherent challenges. The most important of these is finding a link between the circulating EV populations and a specific contribution from the liver. From a biomarker perspective, it could be argued that a quantitative or phenotypic change in circulating EVs with disease may validate their diagnostic utility, especially if these changes are intensified with NAFLD progression (see Table 1). Unfortunately, given the complex biological determinants of EV secretion, rather than a linear relationship we are more likely to see dynamic responses from different tissues during the course of pathogenesis (see Figure 2). For a start, NAFLD is not an isolated condition and, generally speaking, occurs as a complication of other metabolic disorders where global insulin resistance is also present. Therefore, multiple tissues may be affected by the resulting oxidative stress and fatty acid flux, which in turn promotes the activation of immune cells and their migration to these sites. Consequently, the extrahepatic release of EVs may in fact mask the pathogenesis of NAFLD. For this reason, and the lack of a specifically hepatic molecular marker, ideal studies should examine the circulating EVs against their liver-derived counterparts, where possible.

Table 1. Extracellular vesicle markers in non-alcoholic fatty liver disease (NAFLD) studies.

Vesicle Source		Marker(s)	Key Study Findings	Citation
Circulating	Lymphoid cells	CD4 CD8 Va24/Vb11	Enriched in NAFLD, positively correlated with serum ALT and liver biopsy	[72]
	Myeloid cells	CD14 CD15	Variable; CD14+ (monocyte origin) enriched in NAFLD, positively correlated with serum ALT; CD15+ (neutrophil origin) opposite trend	[72]
	Erythrocytes	TER119	Comprise the majority of circulating EVs during Western diet	[73]
	Platelets	CD41 CD62P	Conflicting data for abundance in NAFLD; reduced with statin intervention	[72,74]
	Liver	ASGPR1 CES1 miR-122 miR-192	Enriched in NAFLD; miR-122 and miR-192 correlated with decreased liver expression	[75–77]
	Endothelial	CD144	Enriched in NAFLD; reduced with statin intervention	[74]
Tissue derived	Adipose	adiponectin IL-6 MCP-1 MIF	Enriched in adipose origin; with the exception of adiponectin, enriched in visceral *versus* subcutaneous adipose	[78]
	Hepatocytes	Vanin-1	Enriched in steatotic hepatocytes (HepG2 cells treated with palmitate)	[76]

Abbreviations: ALT = alanine transaminase; ASGPR1 = asialoglycoprotein receptor 1; CES1 = (liver) carboxylesterase 1; IL-6 = interleukin 6; iNKT = invariant natural killer T [cell]; MCP-1 = monocyte chemotactic protein 1; MIF = (macrophage) migration inhibitory factor; NAFLD = non-alcoholic fatty liver disease; Va24/Vb11 = T cell receptor covariants a24/b11.

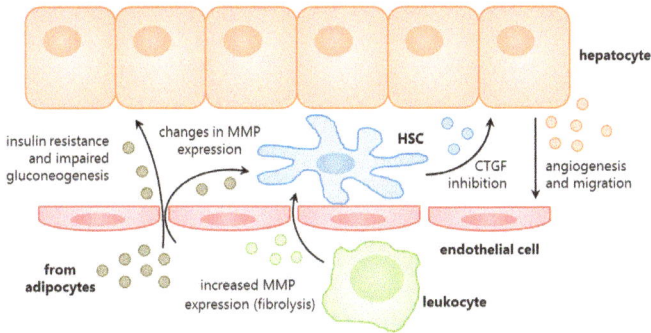

Figure 2. Extracellular vesicle roles in non-alcoholic fatty liver disease (NAFLD). EVs are involved in intercellular communication within the liver tissue, between hepatic cells as well as other tissues involved in mediating NAFLD pathogenesis, such as adipose and circulating (liver-homing) leukocytes. Collectively, these EVs are involved in a dynamic response that may exacerbate tissue injury, as well as promoting repair and matrix remodelling. Abbreviations: CTGF = connective tissue growth factor; HSC = hepatic stellate cell; MMP = matrix metalloproteinase.

3.1. Animal Studies

The fact that such issues remain to be addressed can be explained by the relative infancy of this field of research. To date, there are fewer than a dozen studies to have documented a role for EV signalling in a model of NAFLD, the earliest reported as late as 2009 in mice [79]. To better define a role for EVs in the development of hepatic steatosis, researchers have sought to replicate the clinical observations in rodent models of NAFLD, simulated by administering a choline-deficient diet (CDD) or high-fat diet (HFD) *ad libitum* for several weeks, the latter of which more accurately reflects the development of human metabolic syndrome. It should also be noted, that while CDD animals have comparable liver triglycerides to HFD animals, and a much more rapid progression to hepatic fibrosis, other typical changes such as increased body weight and fat depots, insulin resistance, and elevated fasting glucose and fatty acids are not observed [80]. This is due to the fact that, while HFD feeding increases lipid production, choline deficiency results in mitochondrial dysfunction and hence prevents the normal breakdown of lipids [81]. In saying that, contrary to what would be expected, EV studies in rodent models of NAFLD showed similar trends for both diets (see Table 2).

Table 2. Important findings for extracellular vesicles in the context of NAFLD.

	Key Study Findings	Disease Model	Vesicle Source	Methods	Citation
Rodent	NAFLD-inducing diet increases circulating EV abundance	HFD CDD	plasma	FC	[74–76]
	Circulating EV abundance correlates with NAFLD progression	CDD	plasma	FC	[75,76]
	NAFLD-inducing diet increases circulating liver-derived EVs	HFD CDD	plasma serum	RT-qPCR	[75–77]
	NAFLD-inducing diet changes circulating EV contents	CDD	plasma	LCMS WB	[75,76]
	NAFLD-inducing diet changes circulating EV interactions with cells	HFD	plasma	FC	[79]
Human	Circulating EV abundance correlates with NAFLD progression	NASH	plasma	FC	[72]
	Circulating EV contents can distinguish NAFLD from other liver diseases	NASH	plasma serum	FC microarray	[72,82]

Abbreviations: CDD = choline deficient diet, EV = extracellular vesicle, FC = flow cytometry, HFD = high-fat diet, LCMS = liquid chromatography with mass spectrometry, NAFLD = non-alcoholic fatty liver disease, NASH = non-alcoholic steatohepatitis, RT-qPCR = real-time quantitative polymerase chain reaction, WB = western blot.

In the original study, Deng and colleagues described a phenomenon in their chronic HFD model whereby circulating EVs that were adoptively transferred to healthy animals were engulfed by myeloid cells that subsequently accumulated in the liver [79]. This phenotype was not observed when EVs were transferred from animals on a normal chow diet, which may suggest a selective, EV-driven mechanism for hepatic inflammation as a concomitant to steatosis. While these findings are yet to be reproduced, other groups have instead begun to more comprehensively examine the profile of circulating EVs to better understand their temporal regulation, contents, and possible intervention strategies. Indeed it was shown that vesicles tend to increase on a background of NAFLD, and do so in a time-dependent manner, according to data obtained from flow cytometry experiments [74–76].

To evaluate how the liver contributes to this population, EVs were assessed for their expression of miRNA-122, a molecule that is enriched in mammalian livers and is shown to be involved in early NAFLD progression [83–85]. Consistent with previous findings, rodent studies confirmed an increase in circulating EV-associated miRNA-122 accompanied by a decrease in the liver expression of this molecule [75–77]. Furthermore, one study demonstrated that when miRNA-122 was trafficked in EVs, it was not associated with its protein binding partner Argonaute 2, a phenomenon that is otherwise typically observed in non-disease conditions [75]. While other miRNAs and proteins were not correlated against disease severity, Povero and colleagues had employed mass spectrometry to identify an EV-specific proteome in NAFLD that was distinct from healthy controls [75]. These findings complement a previous study done by the group, in which they confirm a role for EV-bound Vanin-1 in hepatocyte vesicle uptake by an endothelial cell line, with subsequent angiogenic behaviour that is only observed when EVs are derived from hepatocytes subjected to lipotoxic stress [76].

Taken together, these studies establish a solid foundation for understanding the role of EVs in NAFLD, however, some notable limitations exist. Firstly, changes in EV phenotype were not correlated against histological severity of liver disease, which would otherwise give some insight into their prognostic value. Furthermore, perhaps an emphasis on distinguishing NAFLD from other underlying liver pathologies would give EVs a stronger diagnostic utility, as had been addressed in the clinical studies below.

3.2. Human Studies

The pioneering study to involve human subjects was published three years later by Kornek and colleagues, who for the first time had suggested a correlation between the circulating abundance of leukocyte-derived EVs and disease severity, as determined by liver transaminase levels, biopsy grade, and NAFLD activity score (NAS) [72]. These findings still provide the most compelling evidence in clinical samples for the prognostic value of EVs in NASH development, and have been extensively cited. The authors have additionally noted a distinction between the circulating NAFLD EV profile and that seen in hepatitis C patients. This is further supported by another study where transcriptomic analysis revealed that serum exosome-derived miRNAs are capable of differentiating multiple aetiologies of liver disease, as well as disease from normal liver controls [82]. Similar to the first study, it was shown that the expression level of some miRNAs was regulated either positively or negatively with histological features of disease, such as inflammation and fibrosis. However, these results were limited to the cohort with chronic hepatitis and no such data was available for NAFLD progression to NASH.

More recent studies have described the modulation of hepatocyte and stellate cell activity by EVs isolated from visceral (peritoneal) adipose tissue. While the subjects did not necessarily present with NAFLD, the *ex vivo* experimental designs instead aimed to establish a role for EVs in potentially mediating this disease. As such, Kranendonk and colleagues showed that adipocyte EVs from non-obese patients were capable of interfering with insulin signalling and gluconeogenesis when directly exposed to a hepatocyte cell line [78]. Furthermore, the concentration of EVs correlated positively with expression of liver transaminases, which supports the evidence for their role in hepatocyte dysfunction. In another study, albeit on a smaller scale, adipose tissue isolated from obese patients released EVs in culture that subsequently altered the gene expression of an MMP inhibitor, TIMP-1, in both hepatocytes and stellate cells [86]. Collectively, these findings suggest a novel mechanism of NAFLD pathogenesis by EVs through adipocyte-mediated hepatic cell stress and tissue remodelling.

4. Understanding the Role of Secreted Vesicles

With the urgency to develop a non-invasive biomarker for the diagnosis and staging of NAFLD, research into the biology of extracellular vesicles has provided an opportunity to explore a novel mechanism of disease pathogenesis that can also be harnessed as a clinical tool. However, there is still a long way to go before EV-related assays will have translational utility. Besides the obvious question of disease and tissue specificity, current techniques used in the isolation and characterisation of EVs remain laborious, and suffer from a lack of standardization, as well as high variability. It will undoubtedly take a few years before the processing of EVs from blood and other bodily fluids as "liquid biopsies" becomes economically viable, reproducible and validated. Until then we are unlikely to see their use in routine clinical practice.

While much can be learned from the studies described in this review, the concept of analysing EVs in the context of NAFLD is still very much a small niche in the literature. One reason could be the limitations mentioned above, or a focus on more accessible biochemistries such as liver transaminases and soluble miRNA-122. But then why look at circulating EVs? Perhaps the answer lies in their active role in disease; they may not only confirm the presence of NAFLD, but also give an insight into which tissues are interacting and how this is driving pathogenesis. It has been shown that adipose tissue EVs taken from obese individuals are capable of signalling to hepatic cells to remodel their extracellular milieu, while these cells in turn may communicate via EVs with the sinusoid to promote angiogenesis [76,86]. Circulating vesicles have also been implicated in the innate immune response that accompanies steatosis, pointing to a role in the progression from early NAFLD to NASH [72,79]. From a physiological perspective, it makes sense to encapsulate certain molecules that are otherwise prone to enzymatic degradation, especially in a complex or unpredictable disease environment. However, if preservation of these molecules within EVs leads to a heightened stimulation of inflammatory cells, as previously suggested, this mechanism may in turn be responsible for the exacerbation of tissue injury.

Whether EVs can be considered as friend or foe in metabolic diseases is still a grey area, and likely depends on the tissue of origin. Their use as a biomarker is further complicated by the possibility of temporal fluctuation or waning, as is seen with liver enzymes in models of NAFLD [87,88], which limits their predictive value. Furthermore, high-powered micrographs of liver sections have shown that hepatic EVs are predominantly located in the perisinusoidal region [75,76], which may indicate their entrapment in the liver, contrary to previous findings described in this review and also within the same studies. This idea is supported by the fact that the sinusoidal endothelium undergoes defenestration with progressive fibrosis, as well as aging [89], which may restrict the normal flux of vesicles and macromolecules within the liver. Alternatively, the accumulation of fibrous tissue in the perisinusoid may also limit the passage of EVs, or provide selective permeability to smaller vesicles. However, whether this is a protective mechanism or passive consequence of disease is yet to be elucidated.

What Does the Future Hold?

The multifaceted nature of EVs suggests that these structures may have potential value beyond their use as circulating biomarkers in NAFLD. For instance, cancer studies have explored the transfer of oncogenes and an oncogenic phenotype through EV uptake in cell culture models [41,90,91], which may provide a target for therapeutic intervention. Indeed, it was shown that incubating hepatoma cells with various anti-cancer drugs promoted the secretion of immunogenic EVs that were capable of enhancing natural killer (NK) cell responses [55,56]. Conversely, exposing macrophages to such drugs may induce the release of EV-derived miRNAs, which suppress cancer growth by epigenetic regulation [57]. This concept has been extended to NAFLD models, where it was found that administering cholesterol-lowering drugs to high-fat fed rodents can attenuate the release of EVs, however the exact implication of this was not discussed, except for a potential reduction in liver cell death [73,74].

Another approach is to use the vesicles themselves as a mode or target of therapy, not simply a marker of injury. This idea has been investigated since the late 1980s, whereby synthetic EVs were used as a vehicle for drug delivery in both *in vitro* and *in vivo* models of liver injury [92,93]. It is also possible that in the future, endogenous EVs may be harvested for similar purposes, providing an efficient technique for tissue-specific delivery of molecules. The advantage of this autologous transfer system is that the vesicles are less likely to be rejected by the patient, however still sufficiently immunogenic to elicit a response [79].

5. Conclusions

With the rapid advancement of technology, it can be expected that once EVs become a routine parameter for assessment of disease status—of especial value in conditions that are difficult to diagnose, such as NAFLD—their utility may be further projected to the treatment of disease in its early stages,

Int. J. Mol. Sci. **2016**, *17*, 376

and potentially the reversal of chronic disorders like NASH. While there is still a long way to go, for the time being it is important to focus on controlling the underlying metabolic disorders through traditional intervention methods and lifestyle changes, which would also slow the progression of its comorbidities. However, detection of NAFLD and its staging continues to be a problem with invasive techniques such as biopsy being the gold standard. For this reason, EV analysis has promise as a non-invasive diagnostic tool.

Acknowledgments: Linda A. Ban is supported by a grant from the Greg Brown Diabetes and Endocrine Trust Fund.

Author Contributions: Linda A. Ban and Susan V. McLennan conceived the study; Linda A. Ban and Nicholas A. Shackel designed the figures; Susan V. McLennan and Nicholas A. Shackel reviewed/edited the manuscript; Linda A. Ban researched the data and wrote the manuscript.

Conflicts of Interest: The authors declare no conflict of interest.

Abbreviations

The following abbreviations are used in this manuscript:

ALT	alanine transaminase
ASGPR1	asialoglycoprotein receptor 1
CDD	choline-deficient diet
CES1	carboxylesterase 1
CTGF	connective tissue growth factor
ESCRT	endosomal sorting complex required for transport
EV	extracellular vesicle
FC	flow cytometry
HFD	high-fat diet
HSC	hepatic stellate cell
IL-6	interleukin 6
iNKT cell	invariant natural killer T cell
LC-MS/MS	liquid chromatography with tandem mass spectrometry
MCP-1	monocyte chemotactic protein 1
MIF	[macrophage] migration inhibitory factor
miRNA	microRNA
MMP	matrix metalloproteinase
MV	microvesicle
MVB	multivesicular body
NAFLD	non-alcoholic fatty liver disease
NAS	NAFLD activity score
NASH	non-alcoholic steatohepatitis
NK cell	natural killer cell
PS	phosphatidylserine
RT-qPCR	real-time quantitative polymerase chain reaction
TEM	transmission electron microscopy
TIMP-1	tissue inhibitor of metalloproteinase 1
WB	western blot
WGO	World Gastroenterology Organisation

References

1. Hui, E.; Xu, A.; Bo Yang, H.; Lam, K.S. Obesity as the common soil of non-alcoholic fatty liver disease and diabetes: Role of adipokines. *J. Diabetes Investig.* **2013**, *4*, 413–425. [CrossRef] [PubMed]
2. Bugianesi, E.; Vanni, E.; Marchesini, G. NASH and the risk of cirrhosis and hepatocellular carcinoma in type 2 diabetes. *Curr. Diabetes Rep.* **2007**, *7*, 175–180. [CrossRef]

3. Williams, K.H.; Shackel, N.A.; Gorrell, M.D.; McLennan, S.V.; Twigg, S.M. Diabetes and nonalcoholic fatty liver disease: A pathogenic duo. *Endocr. Rev.* **2013**, *34*, 84–129. [CrossRef] [PubMed]

4. Adams, L.A.; Harmsen, S.; St Sauver, J.L.; Charatcharoenwitthaya, P.; Enders, F.B.; Therneau, T.; Angulo, P. Nonalcoholic fatty liver disease increases risk of death among patients with diabetes: A community-based cohort study. *Am. J. Gastroenterol.* **2010**, *105*, 1567–1573. [CrossRef] [PubMed]

5. Feng, R.N.; Du, S.S.; Wang, C.; Li, Y.C.; Liu, L.Y.; Guo, F.C.; Sun, C.H. Lean-non-alcoholic fatty liver disease increases risk for metabolic disorders in a normal weight chinese population. *World J. Gastroenterol.* **2014**, *20*, 17932–17940. [PubMed]

6. Kumar, R.; Rastogi, A.; Sharma, M.K.; Bhatia, V.; Garg, H.; Bihari, C.; Sarin, S.K. Clinicopathological characteristics and metabolic profiles of non-alcoholic fatty liver disease in indian patients with normal body mass index: Do they differ from obese or overweight non-alcoholic fatty liver disease? *Indian J. Endocrinol. Metab.* **2013**, *17*, 665–671. [CrossRef] [PubMed]

7. Younossi, Z.M.; Stepanova, M.; Negro, F.; Hallaji, S.; Younossi, Y.; Lam, B.; Srishord, M. Nonalcoholic fatty liver disease in lean individuals in the united states. *Medicine* **2012**, *91*, 319–327. [CrossRef] [PubMed]

8. LaBrecque, D.R.; Abbas, Z.; Anania, F.; Ferenci, P.; Khan, A.G.; Goh, K.L.; Hamid, S.S.; Isakov, V.; Lizarzabal, M.; Penaranda, M.M.; *et al.* World gastroenterology organisation global guidelines: Nonalcoholic fatty liver disease and nonalcoholic steatohepatitis. *J. Clin. Gastroenterol.* **2014**, *48*, 467–473. [CrossRef] [PubMed]

9. Deffieux, T.; Gennisson, J.L.; Bousquet, L.; Corouge, M.; Cosconea, S.; Amroun, D.; Tripon, S.; Terris, B.; Mallet, V.; Sogni, P.; *et al.* Investigating liver stiffness and viscosity for fibrosis, steatosis and activity staging using shear wave elastography. *J. Hepatol.* **2015**, *62*, 317–324. [CrossRef] [PubMed]

10. Khov, N.; Sharma, A.; Riley, T.R. Bedside ultrasound in the diagnosis of nonalcoholic fatty liver disease. *World J. Gastroenterol.* **2014**, *20*, 6821–6825. [CrossRef] [PubMed]

11. Myers, R.P.; Pomier-Layrargues, G.; Kirsch, R.; Pollett, A.; Beaton, M.; Levstik, M.; Duarte-Rojo, A.; Wong, D.; Crotty, P.; Elkashab, M. Discordance in fibrosis staging between liver biopsy and transient elastography using the FibroScan XL probe. *J. Hepatol.* **2012**, *56*, 564–570. [CrossRef] [PubMed]

12. Myers, R.P.; Pomier-Layrargues, G.; Kirsch, R.; Pollett, A.; Duarte-Rojo, A.; Wong, D.; Beaton, M.; Levstik, M.; Crotty, P.; Elkashab, M. Feasibility and diagnostic performance of the FibroScan XL probe for liver stiffness measurement in overweight and obese patients. *Hepatology* **2012**, *55*, 199–208. [CrossRef] [PubMed]

13. Pais, R.; Charlotte, F.; Fedchuk, L.; Bedossa, P.; Lebray, P.; Poynard, T.; Ratziu, V.; Group, L.S. A systematic review of follow-up biopsies reveals disease progression in patients with non-alcoholic fatty liver. *J. Hepatol.* **2013**, *59*, 550–556. [CrossRef] [PubMed]

14. Zelber-Sagi, S.; Yeshua, H.; Shlomai, A.; Blendis, L.; Leshno, M.; Levit, S.; Halpern, Z.; Oren, R. Sampling variability of transient elastography according to probe location. *Eur. J. Gastroenterol. Hepatol.* **2011**, *23*, 507–514. [CrossRef] [PubMed]

15. Athyros, V.G.; Katsiki, N.; Karagiannis, A.; Mikhailidis, D.P. Statins and nonalcoholic fatty liver disease: A bright future? *Expert Opin. Investig. Drugs* **2013**, *22*, 1089–1093. [CrossRef] [PubMed]

16. Angulo, P. Long-term mortality in nonalcoholic fatty liver disease: Is liver histology of any prognostic significance? *Hepatology* **2010**, *51*, 373–375. [CrossRef] [PubMed]

17. Arun, J.; Jhala, N.; Lazenby, A.J.; Clements, R.; Abrams, G.A. Influence of liver biopsy heterogeneity and diagnosis of nonalcoholic steatohepatitis in subjects undergoing gastric bypass. *Obes. Surg.* **2007**, *17*, 155–161. [CrossRef] [PubMed]

18. Wolf, P. The nature and significance of platelet products in human plasma. *Br. J. Haematol.* **1967**, *13*, 269–288. [CrossRef] [PubMed]

19. Dalton, A.J. Microvesicles and vesicles of multivesicular bodies *versus* "virus-like" particles. *J. Natl. Cancer Inst.* **1975**, *54*, 1137–1148.

20. Bala, S.; Petrasek, J.; Mundkur, S.; Catalano, D.; Levin, I.; Ward, J.; Alao, H.; Kodys, K.; Szabo, G. Circulating microRNAs in exosomes indicate hepatocyte injury and inflammation in alcoholic, drug-induced, and inflammatory liver diseases. *Hepatology* **2012**, *56*, 1946–1957. [CrossRef] [PubMed]

21. Kornek, M.; Schuppan, D. Microparticles: Modulators and biomarkers of liver disease. *J. Hepatol.* **2012**, *57*, 1144–1146. [CrossRef] [PubMed]

22. Lemoinne, S.; Thabut, D.; Housset, C.; Moreau, R.; Valla, D.; Boulanger, C.M.; Rautou, P.E. The emerging roles of microvesicles in liver diseases. *Nat. Rev. Gastroenterol. Hepatol.* **2014**, *11*, 350–361. [CrossRef] [PubMed]

23. Royo, F.; Falcon-Perez, J.M. Liver extracellular vesicles in health and disease. *J. Extracell. Vesicles* **2012**, *1*. [CrossRef] [PubMed]

24. Ferrante, S.C.; Nadler, E.P.; Pillai, D.K.; Hubal, M.J.; Wang, Z.; Wang, J.M.; Gordish-Dressman, H.; Koeck, E.; Sevilla, S.; Wiles, A.A.; *et al.* Adipocyte-derived exosomal miRNAs: A novel mechanism for obesity-related disease. *Pediatr. Res.* **2015**, *77*, 447–454. [CrossRef] [PubMed]

25. Goichot, B.; Grunebaum, L.; Desprez, D.; Vinzio, S.; Meyer, L.; Schlienger, J.L.; Lessard, M.; Simon, C. Circulating procoagulant microparticles in obesity. *Diabetes Metab.* **2006**, *32*, 82–85. [CrossRef]

26. Nomura, S.; Inami, N.; Shouzu, A.; Urase, F.; Maeda, Y. Correlation and association between plasma platelet-, monocyte- and endothelial cell-derived microparticles in hypertensive patients with type 2 diabetes mellitus. *Platelets* **2009**, *20*, 406–414. [CrossRef] [PubMed]

27. Wang, Y.; Chen, L.M.; Liu, M.L. Microvesicles and diabetic complications—Novel mediators, potential biomarkers and therapeutic targets. *Acta Pharmacol. Sin.* **2014**, *35*, 433–443. [CrossRef] [PubMed]

28. Akers, J.C.; Gonda, D.; Kim, R.; Carter, B.S.; Chen, C.C. Biogenesis of extracellular vesicles (EV): Exosomes, microvesicles, retrovirus-like vesicles, and apoptotic bodies. *J. Neuro-Oncol.* **2013**, *113*, 1–11. [CrossRef] [PubMed]

29. Cocucci, E.; Meldolesi, J. Ectosomes and exosomes: Shedding the confusion between extracellular vesicles. *Trends Cell Biol.* **2015**, *25*, 364–372. [CrossRef] [PubMed]

30. Kreimer, S.; Belov, A.M.; Ghiran, I.; Murthy, S.K.; Frank, D.A.; Ivanov, A.R. Mass-spectrometry-based molecular characterization of extracellular vesicles: Lipidomics and proteomics. *J. Proteome Res.* **2015**, *14*, 2367–2384. [CrossRef] [PubMed]

31. Hurley, J.H.; Odorizzi, G. Get on the exosome bus with ALIX. *Nat. Cell Biol.* **2012**, *14*, 654–655. [CrossRef] [PubMed]

32. Pols, M.S.; Klumperman, J. Trafficking and function of the tetraspanin CD63. *Exp. Cell Res.* **2009**, *315*, 1584–1592. [CrossRef] [PubMed]

33. Schutters, K.; Reutelingsperger, C. Phosphatidylserine targeting for diagnosis and treatment of human diseases. *Apoptosis Int. J. Program. Cell Death* **2010**, *15*, 1072–1082. [CrossRef] [PubMed]

34. Spronk, H.M.; ten Cate, H.; van der Meijden, P.E. Differential roles of tissue factor and phosphatidylserine in activation of coagulation. *Thromb. Res.* **2014**, *133*, S54–S56. [CrossRef] [PubMed]

35. Albanyan, A.M.; Murphy, M.F.; Rasmussen, J.T.; Heegaard, C.W.; Harrison, P. Measurement of phosphatidylserine exposure during storage of platelet concentrates using the novel probe lactadherin: A comparison study with annexin V. *Transfusion* **2009**, *49*, 99–107. [CrossRef] [PubMed]

36. Connor, D.E.; Exner, T.; Ma, D.D.; Joseph, J.E. The majority of circulating platelet-derived microparticles fail to bind annexin V, lack phospholipid-dependent procoagulant activity and demonstrate greater expression of glycoprotein Ib. *Thromb. Haemost.* **2010**, *103*, 1044–1052. [CrossRef] [PubMed]

37. Dasgupta, S.K.; Guchhait, P.; Thiagarajan, P. Lactadherin binding and phosphatidylserine expression on cell surface-comparison with annexin A5. *Transl. Res. J. Lab. Clin. Med.* **2006**, *148*, 19–25. [CrossRef] [PubMed]

38. Quesenberry, P.J.; Goldberg, L.R.; Aliotta, J.M.; Dooner, M.S.; Pereira, M.G.; Wen, S.; Camussi, G. Cellular phenotype and extracellular vesicles: Basic and clinical considerations. *Stem Cells Dev.* **2014**, *23*, 1429–1436. [CrossRef] [PubMed]

39. Xiong, W.; Sun, L.P.; Chen, X.M.; Li, H.Y.; Huang, S.A.; Jie, S.H. Comparison of microRNA expression profiles in HCC-derived microvesicles and the parental cells and evaluation of their roles in HCC. *J. Huazhong Univ. Sci. Technol. Med. Sci.* **2013**, *33*, 346–352. [CrossRef] [PubMed]

40. Witwer, K.W.; Buzas, E.I.; Bemis, L.T.; Bora, A.; Lasser, C.; Lotvall, J.; Nolte-'t Hoen, E.N.; Piper, M.G.; Sivaraman, S.; Skog, J.; *et al.* Standardization of sample collection, isolation and analysis methods in extracellular vesicle research. *J. Extracell. Vesicles* **2013**, *2*. [CrossRef] [PubMed]

41. Bergsmedh, A.; Szeles, A.; Henriksson, M.; Bratt, A.; Folkman, M.J.; Spetz, A.L.; Holmgren, L. Horizontal transfer of oncogenes by uptake of apoptotic bodies. *Proc. Natl. Acad. Sci. USA* **2001**, *98*, 6407–6411. [CrossRef] [PubMed]

42. Elmore, S. Apoptosis: A review of programmed cell death. *Toxicol. Pathol.* **2007**, *35*, 495–516. [CrossRef] [PubMed]

43. Lynch, S.F.; Ludlam, C.A. Plasma microparticles and vascular disorders. *Br. J. Haematol.* **2007**, *137*, 36–48. [CrossRef] [PubMed]

44. Ogasawara, F.; Fusegawa, H.; Haruki, Y.; Shiraishi, K.; Watanabe, N.; Matsuzaki, S. Platelet activation in patients with alcoholic liver disease. *Tokai J. Exp. Clin. Med.* **2005**, *30*, 41–48. [PubMed]

45. Stravitz, R.T.; Bowling, R.; Bradford, R.L.; Key, N.S.; Glover, S.; Thacker, L.R.; Gabriel, D.A. Role of procoagulant microparticles in mediating complications and outcome of acute liver injury/acute liver failure. *Hepatology* **2013**, *58*, 304–313. [CrossRef] [PubMed]

46. Bernimoulin, M.; Waters, E.K.; Foy, M.; Steele, B.M.; Sullivan, M.; Falet, H.; Walsh, M.T.; Barteneva, N.; Geng, J.G.; Hartwig, J.H.; *et al.* Differential stimulation of monocytic cells results in distinct populations of microparticles. *J. Thromb. Haemost.* **2009**, *7*, 1019–1028. [CrossRef] [PubMed]

47. Charrier, A.; Chen, R.; Chen, L.; Kemper, S.; Hattori, T.; Takigawa, M.; Brigstock, D.R. Exosomes mediate intercellular transfer of pro-fibrogenic connective tissue growth factor (CCN2) between hepatic stellate cells, the principal fibrotic cells in the liver. *Surgery* **2014**, *156*, 548–555. [CrossRef] [PubMed]

48. Chen, L.; Charrier, A.; Zhou, Y.; Chen, R.; Yu, B.; Agarwal, K.; Tsukamoto, H.; Lee, L.J.; Paulaitis, M.E.; Brigstock, D.R. Epigenetic regulation of connective tissue growth factor by microRNA-214 delivery in exosomes from mouse or human hepatic stellate cells. *Hepatology* **2014**, *59*, 1118–1129. [CrossRef] [PubMed]

49. Kornek, M.; Popov, Y.; Libermann, T.A.; Afdhal, N.H.; Schuppan, D. Human t cell microparticles circulate in blood of hepatitis patients and induce fibrolytic activation of hepatic stellate cells. *Hepatology* **2011**, *53*, 230–242. [CrossRef] [PubMed]

50. Kogure, T.; Lin, W.L.; Yan, I.K.; Braconi, C.; Patel, T. Intercellular nanovesicle-mediated microRNA transfer: A mechanism of environmental modulation of hepatocellular cancer cell growth. *Hepatology* **2011**, *54*, 1237–1248. [CrossRef] [PubMed]

51. Kogure, T.; Yan, I.K.; Lin, W.L.; Patel, T. Extracellular vesicle-mediated transfer of a novel long noncoding RNA TUC339: A mechanism of intercellular signaling in human hepatocellular cancer. *Genes Cancer* **2013**, *4*, 261–272. [CrossRef] [PubMed]

52. Fonsato, V.; Collino, F.; Herrera, M.B.; Cavallari, C.; Deregibus, M.C.; Cisterna, B.; Bruno, S.; Romagnoli, R.; Salizzoni, M.; Tetta, C.; *et al.* Human liver stem cell-derived microvesicles inhibit hepatoma growth in scid mice by delivering antitumor microRNAs. *Stem Cells* **2012**, *30*, 1985–1998. [CrossRef] [PubMed]

53. Momen-Heravi, F.; Bala, S.; Kodys, K.; Szabo, G. Exosomes derived from alcohol-treated hepatocytes horizontally transfer liver specific miRNA-122 and sensitize monocytes to LPS. *Sci. Rep.* **2015**, *5*, 9991. [CrossRef] [PubMed]

54. Takahashi, K.; Yan, I.K.; Kogure, T.; Haga, H.; Patel, T. Extracellular vesicle-mediated transfer of long non-coding RNA ror modulates chemosensitivity in human hepatocellular cancer. *FEBS Open Bio* **2014**, *4*, 458–467. [CrossRef] [PubMed]

55. Lv, L.H.; Wan, Y.L.; Lin, Y.; Zhang, W.; Yang, M.; Li, G.L.; Lin, H.M.; Shang, C.Z.; Chen, Y.J.; Min, J. Anticancer drugs cause release of exosomes with heat shock proteins from human hepatocellular carcinoma cells that elicit effective natural killer cell antitumor responses *in vitro*. *J. Biol. Chem.* **2012**, *287*, 15874–15885. [CrossRef] [PubMed]

56. Xiao, W.; Dong, W.; Zhang, C.; Saren, G.; Geng, P.; Zhao, H.; Li, Q.; Zhu, J.; Li, G.; Zhang, S.; *et al.* Effects of the epigenetic drug MS-275 on the release and function of exosome-related immune molecules in hepatocellular carcinoma cells. *Eur. J. Med. Res.* **2013**, *18*, 61. [CrossRef] [PubMed]

57. Zhang, J.; Shan, W.F.; Jin, T.T.; Wu, G.Q.; Xiong, X.X.; Jin, H.Y.; Zhu, S.M. Propofol exerts anti-hepatocellular carcinoma by microvesicle-mediated transfer of miR-142–3p from macrophage to cancer cells. *J. Transl. Med.* **2014**, *12*, 279. [CrossRef] [PubMed]

58. Li, Y.; Zhang, L.; Liu, F.; Xiang, G.; Jiang, D.; Pu, X. Identification of endogenous controls for analyzing serum exosomal miRNA in patients with hepatitis B or hepatocellular carcinoma. *Dis. Markers* **2015**, *2015*, 893594. [CrossRef] [PubMed]

59. Sugimachi, K.; Matsumura, T.; Hirata, H.; Uchi, R.; Ueda, M.; Ueo, H.; Shinden, Y.; Iguchi, T.; Eguchi, H.; Shirabe, K.; *et al.* Identification of a bona fide microRNA biomarker in serum exosomes that predicts hepatocellular carcinoma recurrence after liver transplantation. *Br. J. Cancer* **2015**, *112*, 532–538. [CrossRef] [PubMed]

60. Sun, L.; Hu, J.; Xiong, W.; Chen, X.; Li, H.; Jie, S. MicroRNA expression profiles of circulating microvesicles in hepatocellular carcinoma. *Acta Gastro-Enterol. Belg.* **2013**, *76*, 386–392.

61. Wang, H.; Hou, L.; Li, A.; Duan, Y.; Gao, H.; Song, X. Expression of serum exosomal microRNA-21 in human hepatocellular carcinoma. *BioMed Res. Int.* **2014**, *2014*, 864894. [CrossRef] [PubMed]

62. Brodsky, S.V.; Facciuto, M.E.; Heydt, D.; Chen, J.; Islam, H.K.; Kajstura, M.; Ramaswamy, G.; Aguero-Rosenfeld, M. Dynamics of circulating microparticles in liver transplant patients. *J. Gastrointest. Liver Dis.* **2008**, *17*, 261–268.

63. Freeman, C.M.; Quillin, R.C., 3rd; Wilson, G.C.; Nojima, H.; Johnson, B.L., 3rd; Sutton, J.M.; Schuster, R.M.; Blanchard, J.; Edwards, M.J.; Caldwell, C.C.; *et al.* Characterization of microparticles after hepatic ischemia-reperfusion injury. *PLoS ONE* **2014**, *9*, e97945. [CrossRef] [PubMed]

64. Costa-Silva, B.; Aiello, N.M.; Ocean, A.J.; Singh, S.; Zhang, H.; Thakur, B.K.; Becker, A.; Hoshino, A.; Mark, M.T.; Molina, H.; *et al.* Pancreatic cancer exosomes initiate pre-metastatic niche formation in the liver. *Nat. Cell Biol.* **2015**, *17*, 816–826. [CrossRef] [PubMed]

65. Eldh, M.; Olofsson Bagge, R.; Lasser, C.; Svanvik, J.; Sjostrand, M.; Mattsson, J.; Lindner, P.; Choi, D.S.; Gho, Y.S.; Lotvall, J. MicroRNA in exosomes isolated directly from the liver circulation in patients with metastatic uveal melanoma. *BMC Cancer* **2014**, *14*, 962. [CrossRef] [PubMed]

66. Wang, X.; Ding, X.; Nan, L.; Wang, Y.; Wang, J.; Yan, Z.; Zhang, W.; Sun, J.; Zhu, W.; Ni, B.; *et al.* Investigation of the roles of exosomes in colorectal cancer liver metastasis. *Oncol. Rep.* **2015**, *33*, 2445–2453. [CrossRef] [PubMed]

67. Calabro, S.R.; Maczurek, A.E.; Morgan, A.J.; Tu, T.; Wen, V.W.; Yee, C.; Mridha, A.; Lee, M.; d'Avigdor, W.; Locarnini, S.A.; *et al.* Hepatocyte produced matrix metalloproteinases are regulated by CD147 in liver fibrogenesis. *PLoS ONE* **2014**, *9*, e90571. [CrossRef] [PubMed]

68. Lee, A.; Rode, A.; Nicoll, A.; Maczurek, A.E.; Lim, L.; Lim, S.; Angus, P.; Kronborg, I.; Arachchi, N.; Gorelik, A.; *et al.* Circulating CD147 predicts mortality in advanced hepatocellular carcinoma. *J. Gastroenterol. Hepatol.* **2016**, *31*, 459–466. [CrossRef] [PubMed]

69. Sidhu, S.S.; Mengistab, A.T.; Tauscher, A.N.; LaVail, J.; Basbaum, C. The microvesicle as a vehicle for emmprin in tumor-stromal interactions. *Oncogene* **2004**, *23*, 956–963. [CrossRef] [PubMed]

70. Millimaggi, D.; Mari, M.; D'Ascenzo, S.; Carosa, E.; Jannini, E.A.; Zucker, S.; Carta, G.; Pavan, A.; Dolo, V. Tumor vesicle-associated CD147 modulates the angiogenic capability of endothelial cells. *Neoplasia* **2007**, *9*, 349–357. [CrossRef] [PubMed]

71. Zhang, W.; Zhao, P.; Xu, X.L.; Cai, L.; Song, Z.S.; Cao, D.Y.; Tao, K.S.; Zhou, W.P.; Chen, Z.N.; Dou, K.F. Annexin A2 promotes the migration and invasion of human hepatocellular carcinoma cells *in vitro* by regulating the shedding of CD147-harboring microvesicles from tumor cells. *PLoS ONE* **2013**, *8*, e67268. [CrossRef] [PubMed]

72. Kornek, M.; Lynch, M.; Mehta, S.H.; Lai, M.; Exley, M.; Afdhal, N.H.; Schuppan, D. Circulating microparticles as disease-specific biomarkers of severity of inflammation in patients with hepatitis c or nonalcoholic steatohepatitis. *Gastroenterology* **2012**, *143*, 448–458. [CrossRef] [PubMed]

73. Baron, M.; Leroyer, A.S.; Majd, Z.; Lalloyer, F.; Vallez, E.; Bantubungi, K.; Chinetti-Gbaguidi, G.; Delerive, P.; Boulanger, C.M.; Staels, B.; *et al.* PPARα activation differently affects microparticle content in atherosclerotic lesions and liver of a mouse model of atherosclerosis and NASH. *Atherosclerosis* **2011**, *218*, 69–76. [CrossRef] [PubMed]

74. Ajamieh, H.; Farrell, G.C.; McCuskey, R.S.; Yu, J.; Chu, E.; Wong, H.J.; Lam, W.; Teoh, N.C. Acute atorvastatin is hepatoprotective against ischaemia-reperfusion injury in mice by modulating enos and microparticle formation. *Liver Int.* **2015**, *35*, 2174–2186. [CrossRef] [PubMed]

75. Povero, D.; Eguchi, A.; Li, H.; Johnson, C.D.; Papouchado, B.G.; Wree, A.; Messer, K.; Feldstein, A.E. Circulating extracellular vesicles with specific proteome and liver microRNAs are potential biomarkers for liver injury in experimental fatty liver disease. *PLoS ONE* **2014**, *9*, e113651. [CrossRef] [PubMed]

76. Povero, D.; Eguchi, A.; Niesman, I.R.; Andronikou, N.; de Mollerat du Jeu, X.; Mulya, A.; Berk, M.; Lazic, M.; Thapaliya, S.; Parola, M.; *et al.* Lipid-induced toxicity stimulates hepatocytes to release angiogenic microparticles that require vanin-1 for uptake by endothelial cells. *Sci. Signal.* **2013**, *6*, ra88. [CrossRef] [PubMed]

77. Csak, T.; Bala, S.; Lippai, D.; Satishchandran, A.; Catalano, D.; Kodys, K.; Szabo, G. MicroRNA-122 regulates hypoxia-inducible factor-1 and vimentin in hepatocytes and correlates with fibrosis in diet-induced steatohepatitis. *Liver Int.* **2015**, *35*, 532–541. [CrossRef] [PubMed]

78. Kranendonk, M.E.; Visseren, F.L.; van Herwaarden, J.A.; Nolte-'t Hoen, E.N.; de Jager, W.; Wauben, M.H.; Kalkhoven, E. Effect of extracellular vesicles of human adipose tissue on insulin signaling in liver and muscle cells. *Obesity* **2014**, *22*, 2216–2223. [CrossRef] [PubMed]

79. Deng, Z.B.; Liu, Y.; Liu, C.; Xiang, X.; Wang, J.; Cheng, Z.; Shah, S.V.; Zhang, S.; Zhang, L.; Zhuang, X.; *et al.* Immature myeloid cells induced by a high-fat diet contribute to liver inflammation. *Hepatology* **2009**, *50*, 1412–1420. [CrossRef] [PubMed]

80. Raubenheimer, P.J.; Nyirenda, M.J.; Walker, B.R. A choline-deficient diet exacerbates fatty liver but attenuates insulin resistance and glucose intolerance in mice fed a high-fat diet. *Diabetes* **2006**, *55*, 2015–2020. [CrossRef] [PubMed]

81. Anstee, Q.M.; Goldin, R.D. Mouse models in non-alcoholic fatty liver disease and steatohepatitis research. *Int. J. Exp. Pathol.* **2006**, *87*, 1–16. [CrossRef] [PubMed]

82. Murakami, Y.; Toyoda, H.; Tanahashi, T.; Tanaka, J.; Kumada, T.; Yoshioka, Y.; Kosaka, N.; Ochiya, T.; Taguchi, Y.H. Comprehensive miRNA expression analysis in peripheral blood can diagnose liver disease. *PLoS ONE* **2012**, *7*, e48366.

83. Lagos-Quintana, M.; Rauhut, R.; Yalcin, A.; Meyer, J.; Lendeckel, W.; Tuschl, T. Identification of tissue-specific microRNAs from mouse. *Curr. Biol. CB* **2002**, *12*, 735–739. [PubMed]

84. Barad, O.; Meiri, E.; Avniel, A.; Aharonov, R.; Barzilai, A.; Bentwich, I.; Einav, U.; Gilad, S.; Hurban, P.; Karov, Y.; *et al.* MicroRNA expression detected by oligonucleotide microarrays: System establishment and expression profiling in human tissues. *Gen. Res.* **2004**, *14*, 2486–2494. [CrossRef] [PubMed]

85. Yamada, H.; Ohashi, K.; Suzuki, K.; Munetsuna, E.; Ando, Y.; Yamazaki, M.; Ishikawa, H.; Ichino, N.; Teradaira, R.; Hashimoto, S. Longitudinal study of circulating miR-122 in a rat model of non-alcoholic fatty liver disease. *Clin. Chim. Acta Int. J. Clin. Chem.* **2015**, *446*, 267–271. [CrossRef] [PubMed]

86. Koeck, E.S.; Iordanskaia, T.; Sevilla, S.; Ferrante, S.C.; Hubal, M.J.; Freishtat, R.J.; Nadler, E.P. Adipocyte exosomes induce transforming growth factor β pathway dysregulation in hepatocytes: A novel paradigm for obesity-related liver disease. *J. Surg. Res.* **2014**, *192*, 268–275. [CrossRef] [PubMed]

87. Itagaki, H.; Shimizu, K.; Morikawa, S.; Ogawa, K.; Ezaki, T. Morphological and functional characterization of non-alcoholic fatty liver disease induced by a methionine-choline-deficient diet in c57bl/6 mice. *Int. J. Clin. Exp. Pathol.* **2013**, *6*, 2683–2696. [PubMed]

88. Verma, S.; Jensen, D.; Hart, J.; Mohanty, S.R. Predictive value of alt levels for non-alcoholic steatohepatitis (NASH) and advanced fibrosis in non-alcoholic fatty liver disease (NAFLD). *Liver Int.* **2013**, *33*, 1398–1405. [CrossRef] [PubMed]

89. Fraser, R.; Cogger, V.C.; Dobbs, B.; Jamieson, H.; Warren, A.; Hilmer, S.N.; le Couteur, D.G. The liver sieve and atherosclerosis. *Pathology* **2012**, *44*, 181–186. [CrossRef] [PubMed]

90. Redzic, J.S.; Kendrick, A.A.; Bahmed, K.; Dahl, K.D.; Pearson, C.G.; Robinson, W.A.; Robinson, S.E.; Graner, M.W.; Eisenmesser, E.Z. Extracellular vesicles secreted from cancer cell lines stimulate secretion of MMP-9, IL-6, TGF-β1 and emmprin. *PLoS ONE* **2013**, *8*, e71225. [CrossRef] [PubMed]

91. He, M.; Qin, H.; Poon, T.C.; Sze, S.C.; Ding, X.; Co, N.N.; Ngai, S.M.; Chan, T.F.; Wong, N. Hepatocellular carcinoma-derived exosomes promote motility of immortalized hepatocyte through transfer of oncogenic proteins and RNAs. *Carcinogenesis* **2015**, *36*, 1008–1018. [CrossRef] [PubMed]

92. Farazuddin, M.; Dua, B.; Zia, Q.; Khan, A.A.; Joshi, B.; Owais, M. Chemotherapeutic potential of curcumin-bearing microcells against hepatocellular carcinoma in model animals. *Int. J. Nanomed.* **2014**, *9*, 1139–1152.

93. Laakso, T.; Edman, P.; Brunk, U. Biodegradable microspheres VII: Alterations in mouse liver morphology after intravenous administration of polyacryl starch microparticles with different biodegradability. *J. Pharm. Sci.* **1988**, *77*, 138–144. [CrossRef] [PubMed]

International Journal of
Molecular Sciences

MDPI

Review

Mitochondrial Molecular Pathophysiology of Nonalcoholic Fatty Liver Disease: A Proteomics Approach

Natalia Nuño-Lámbarri [1,†], **Varenka J. Barbero-Becerra** [1,†], **Misael Uribe** [2] and
Norberto C. Chávez-Tapia [1,2,*]

1   Traslational Research Unit, Médica Sur Clinic & Foundation, Mexico City 14050, Mexico;
    nnunol@medicasur.org.mx (N.N.-L.); vbarberob@medicasur.org.mx (V.J.B.-B.)
2   Obesity and Digestive Diseases Unit, Médica Sur Clinic & Foundation, Mexico City 14050, Mexico;
    muribe@medicasur.org.mx
*   Correspondence: nchavezt@medicasur.org.mx; Tel.: +525-55-424-7200 (ext. 6850)
†   These authors contributed equally to this work.

Academic Editor: Amedeo Lonardo
Received: 23 December 2015; Accepted: 19 February 2016; Published: 15 March 2016

Abstract: Nonalcoholic fatty liver disease (NAFLD) is a chronic liver condition that can progress to nonalcoholic steatohepatitis, cirrhosis and cancer. It is considered an emerging health problem due to malnourishment or a high-fat diet (HFD) intake, which is observed worldwide. It is well known that the hepatocytes' apoptosis phenomenon is one of the most important features of NAFLD. Thus, this review focuses on revealing, through a proteomics approach, the complex network of protein interactions that promote fibrosis, liver cell stress, and apoptosis. According to different types of *in vitro* and murine models, it has been found that oxidative/nitrative protein stress leads to mitochondrial dysfunction, which plays a major role in stimulating NAFLD damage. Human studies have revealed the importance of novel biomarkers, such as retinol-binding protein 4, lumican, transgelin 2 and hemoglobin, which have a significant role in the disease. The post-genome era has brought proteomics technology, which allows the determination of molecular pathogenesis in NAFLD. This has led to the search for biomarkers which improve early diagnosis and optimal treatment and which may effectively prevent fatal consequences such as cirrhosis or cancer.

Keywords: proteomics; NAFLD; mitochondrial dysfunction

1. Introduction

Non-alcoholic fatty liver disease (NAFLD) is a clinicopathological condition that is commonly associated with dyslipidemia, insulin resistance, cardiovascular disease, obesity metabolic syndrome and type 2 diabetes mellitus (T2DM) [1]. Moreover, the liver is targeted by signals from other tissues, including adipose tissue, the gut and its microbiota [2], comprising a wide spectrum of liver damage, ranging from simple steatosis to steatohepatitis [3], which is a major health problem affecting an estimated 25% of the adult population worldwide. Although NAFLD is highly prevalent on all continents, the highest prevalence rates were reported in South America (31%) and the Middle East (32%) while the lowest prevalence was reported in Africa (14%). Also, the prevalence between the United States and Europe is similar, and an interesting finding was the relatively high prevalence found in the Asian population (27%) [4].

NAFLD can progress to nonalcoholic steatohepatitis (NASH) in 12%–40% of cases. NASH can be distinguished by the presence of hepatocyte ballooning, apoptosis, inflammatory infiltrates, and collagen deposition. Over a period of 10–15 years, 15% of patients with NASH will exhibit progression to liver cirrhosis. Annually, 4% of hepatic decompensation is generated by cirrhosis that has not been caused by viral hepatitis, while the overall risk of generating cancer in 10 years is 10% [5].

Currently, proteomics are an essential approach that have improved the study of the complex pathogenesis of NAFLD, becoming more outstanding since they have been applied in the health sciences and industry [6] and being useful in the determination of pathophysiology and identifying new markers for disease diagnosis [7].

Proteomics provide essential information of the biologically active entity named protein, which includes its post-translational modifications and interactions with other proteins [8]. Proteomic techniques are primarily based on electrophoresis and mass spectrometry [9]. In recent years, genomics, proteomics, and bioinformatic techniques have been developed synergistically and have experienced a surprising development, which has brought about major advances in medicine.

1.1. Identification of Specific Proteins through in Vitro Studies

In vitro models are necessary for elucidating the mechanisms of liver damage in NAFLD, as they are for understanding the complex network of cellular interactions, apoptosis and oxidative stress, the mechanisms that lead to mitochondrial damage which promotes fibrosis.

Hepatic oxidative stress and injury are mechanisms associated with polyploidy, which is one of the most dramatic changes that can occur in the genome [10]. A hepatocyte NAFLD model has shown that oxidative stress triggers the activation of a G2/M DNA damage checkpoint, preventing the activation of the cyclin B1/CDK1 complex, which causes an inefficient progression through the S/G2 phases, suggesting that polyploidy in mononuclear cell populations is an early event in NAFLD development [11].

During liver injury, perpetuation of the insult induces progressive deterioration of hepatic damage with the production of extracellular matrix (ECM) remodeling components, which contribute to uncontrolled ECM turnover [12], leading to an excessive accumulation of extracellular proteins, proteoglycans, and carbohydrates that ends in a pathological state that is called fibrosis [13]. Components of the fibrotic liver ECM had been previously cataloged by sodium dodecyl sulfate polyacrylamide gel electrophoresis (SDS–PAGE) separation and mass spectrometry (GeLC-MS)–based proteomics approaches [14]. An *in vitro* liver fibrosis model using mass spectrometry analysis in cell-derived ECM identified 61 structural or secreted ECM proteins (48 proteins for a hepatic stellate cell line, LX-2, and 31 proteins for human foreskin fibroblasts) [14]. Several proteins identified in this study have been linked with fibrotic processes that occur in the liver and other organs; fibrillin, which was previously implicated in the activation of transforming growth factor β (TGF-β) storage, was among those proteins [15]. Furthermore, two new fibrotic constituent proteins identified in this study, CYR61 and Wnt-5a, were also validated in the fibrotic liver [14]. GELC-MS–based proteomics coupled to an ECM-enrichment strategy in an *in vitro* model of liver fibrosis may be a valuable tool for determining the mechanisms underlying fibrosis and for the identification of novel therapeutic targets or biomarkers.

Fibrosis is not the only mechanism of liver damage; apoptosis has also been studied since it is one of the most important features of NAFLD [16]. The participation of certain proteins, such as cytochrome b5, annexin A5 and A6, and protein disulfide isomerase fragments, has been confirmed in murine and human cell apoptosis models [17]. On the other hand, it has been reported that cholesterol induces Bax and caspase-3 [18], which may be important proteins for apoptosis; however, cholesterol did not increase the expression of p53 and Bcl-2 in steatotic cells, suggesting an important role for cell death mechanisms in hepatocytes [19].

Furthermore, proteomic techniques could be useful in other scenarios such as liver regeneration; an analysis was performed through label-free quantitative mass spectrometry in which human embryonic stem cells were differentiated into hepatocyte-like cells to investigate the effects of the cell secretome, which demonstrated that hepatocyte-like cells derived from stem cells contribute to the recovery from injured liver tissue in mice by delivering trophic factors that support liver regeneration [20].

The application of this strategy to different *in vitro* disease models may therefore significantly improve identifying specific proteins, and provide the first step toward elucidating the mechanisms which underlie fibrosis and novel therapeutic targets or biomarkers.

1.2. In Vivo NAFLD Studies

Obesity is related to several diseases, such as NAFLD and NASH, being linked to mitochondrial dysfunction and deficiency of nitric oxide (NO). Chronic consumption of a high-fat diet (HFD) in a murine model induces NASH, and it is accompanied by profound changes in mitochondrial bioenergetics. Conversely, HFD decreased the activity of cytochrome c oxidase and increased sensitivity to the NO-dependent inhibition of mitochondrial respiration [21]. According to HFD intake, a densitometry analysis revealed that 22 proteins were significantly altered, whereas 67 proteins remained unchanged. The last events are a bit far from proposing a mechanism; however, this response could be considered as a regulatory mechanism according to the microenvironment where it develops (Figure 1) [21].

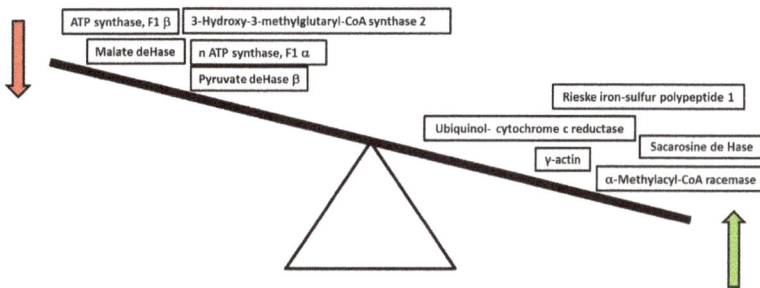

Figure 1. Mitochondrial proteins altered by high-fat diet.

Chronic exposure of mice to a HFD induces hepatic steatosis, modifying the liver mitochondrial proteome, including changes in proteins related to oxidative phosphorylation, protein folding, and lipid and sulfur amino acid metabolism [21]. Mitochondrial dysfunction may be generated by high concentrations of reactive oxygen species (ROS) which inhibit the respiratory chain and integrity of mitochondrial DNA and also contribute to organelle toxicity, the suppression of fatty acid oxidation and the rise in lipid peroxidation [22].

Liver steatosis may be due to an excess of fatty acids (FA), glucose, lipotoxicity, or insulin resistance (IR), and it induces *de novo* lipid synthesis by the activation of nuclear receptors such as sterol regulatory element-binding protein 1 (SREBP-1), carbohydrate-responsive element-binding protein (ChREBP-1), and peroxisome proliferator-activated receptor γ (PPARγ) [23]. Moreover, PPARγ activation increased cellular free FA uptake, exceeding the adaptive pathways of hepatic lipid export and catabolism, suggesting an adipogenic transformation of hepatocytes [24]. The presence of steatosis is tightly associated with chronic hepatic inflammation, an effect mediated in part by activation of the Ikκ-b/NF-κB signaling pathway.

A murine model of steatosis induced with a HFD increases NF-κB activity, which is associated with the elevated hepatic expression of pro-inflammatory cytokines such as TNF-α and IL-1 which are activated by ROS created by lipid peroxidation, responsible not only for promoting insulin resistance and Kupffer cell activation, but also for mediating cholesterol and triglyceride metabolism [25,26].

TNF-α act upon leukocyte infiltration in the liver, contributing to intracellular oxidative stress and mitochondrial dysfunction; in fact, TNF receptor adaptor proteins initiate the phosphorylation of mitogen-activated protein kinases (MAPK 1), which in turn activate c-Jun N-terminal kinases

(JNK) [27]. Prolonged activation of the downstream signaling molecule JNK was found to promote inflammation and apoptosis [28], amplifying hepatocyte damage [29].

Studies in JNK2 knockout mice indicated that this protein might be important for caspase 8 activation and apoptosis mitochondrial pathways in response to TNF-α [30]. Treatment with anti-TNF-α antibodies improved mitochondrial respiration and inflammation, and alleviated hepatic steatosis in mouse models of NASH [31]. Also, it has been seen that Gegenqinlian decoction (GGQLD), a Chinese herbal medicine, can decrease serum elevated TNF-α levels, being an optimal approach for managing lipid metabolic, inflammatory, and histological abnormalities via the PPARγ/TNF-α pathway in NAFLD [26].

Mitochondria adjust to lipid accumulation in hepatocytes raising the levels of β-oxidation; nevertheless, increased substrate transfer to the mitochondrial electron transport chain leads to a rise in ROS production and finally insulin resistance, playing an important role in hepatic lipid metabolism [32]. In a murine model study, with the use of gel electrophoresis (DIGE) and MALDI-TOF techniques, 95 proteins were identified to exhibit significant changes during the development of NAFLD, whereas protein down-regulation was observed for enoyl coenzyme A hydratase (ECHS1), which catalyzes the second step of the mitochondrial β-oxidation of fatty acids, probably because of HFD-related hepatic steatosis [33]. These findings suggest an important role for ECHS1 in lipid accumulation in *in vivo* NAFLD models [34].

Furthermore, the HFD-mediated decrease in ATP synthase subunits (F1α and β) may also compromise mitochondrial energy conservation; these findings, together with a decrease in the content of malate and pyruvate dehydrogenase, which are key mitochondrial metabolism enzymes, provide strong evidence supporting the occurrence of bioenergetics dysfunction in response to chronic exposure to a HFD, which can be linked to NAFLD liver proteome changes [35]. Moreover, some proteins associated with acetyl-CoA intake and oxidative stress are molecular markers of hepatic steatosis in ob/ob mice that have been identified by liver mitochondrial 2D-DIGE proteomics [36]. Also, a comparative study of liver mitochondrial proteomics, using Ingenuity Pathway Analysis software (IPA; Ingenuity Systems, Mountain View, Redwood City, CA, USA), found that among the 1100 protein analyzed, aldehyde dehydrogenase 2 (ALDH2), and 3-hydroxy-3-methylglutaryl-CoA synthase 2 (HMGCS2) were altered [37]. In summary, analysis of sub-mitochondrial and cellular proteomes indicates that metabolic adaptations occurring in hypertriglyceridemic mice hepatocytes induce an enhanced acetyl-CoA, glycerol-3-phosphate, ATP and Nicotinamide adenine dinucleotide phosphate (NADPH) availability for *de novo* triglyceride (TG) biosynthesis. They also strongly suggest that the cytosol of HuApoC-III mouse hepatocytes is the subject of an important oxidative stress, probably as a result of free fatty acid (FFA) over-accumulation, iron overload and enhanced activity of some ROS-producing catabolic enzymes [38].

Also, the increase of intracellular triacylglycerols may be promoted by the inhibition of lipoprotein assembly and secretion [23]. Recently it has been found that fetuin A is an adaptor protein for saturated fatty acid–induced activation of Toll-like receptor 4 signaling, promoting lipid-induced insulin resistance; also, fetuin B secretion from the liver is increased by steatosis and diminishes glucose lowering through insulin-independent mechanisms [39].

It is important to study alcoholic fatty liver disease (AFLD) since it shares some hepatocyte injury mechanisms with NAFLD. AFLD appears in 90% of people who consume ⩾60 mg per day of alcohol; however, both have the deterioration of mitochondrial functions because of protein nitration in common [40]. Under normal conditions, these function capacity alterations can be managed by properly using the antioxidant host defense system and by the removal of nitrated proteins, which can serve as a defense mechanism against nitroxidative stress–related harmful consequences [35].

Peroxynitrite and protein nitration were suggested to be the main causes of acute and chronic AFLD injury models [41]. Also, several mouse models have been used to evaluate the effect of protein nitration on nitroxidative stress [42]. For instance, the role of protein nitration has been studied in mouse strains with ablated genes that are involved in the regulation of superoxide and NO levels [43] in which the identification of peptides that originate from nitrated proteins can be performed using matrix-assisted laser desorption/ionization time-of-flight mass spectrometry (MALDI-TOF MS) [44,45].

Moreover, knockout inducible nitric oxide synthase (iNOS) mice with a Lieber–De Carli ethanol liquid diet exhibit a markedly decreased level of nitrated proteins, which confers resistance to AFLD and, together with protein nitration, inhibits complex I (NADH ubiquinone oxidoreductase) and complex V (ATP synthase) activities in models of acute and chronic alcohol exposure [46,47].

The authors suggest that these damaging effects are probably caused by protein nitration, as the administration of iNOS inhibitors and peroxynitrite scavengers, such as uric acid, ameliorated the ethanol-induced nitration and the inhibition of activity and mitochondrial depletion of ATP synthase. In addition, the deletion of superoxide dismutase 2 (SOD2) would scavenge superoxide and block peroxynitrite formation, yielding the extension of mitochondrial DNA depletion, whereas SOD2 over-expression yielded opposite outcomes [47].

On the other hand, cytosolic SOD1 also exhibits a protective role against ethanol-mediated hepatic damage [48]. In SOD1-deficient mice, the levels of protective hepatic ATP content and SOD2 expression were decreased, whereas oxidative damage and nitro-Tyr formation were elevated in response to ethanol feeding, thus leading to greater hepatic injury [41]. Up to this point, evidence suggests that hepatic mitochondria from ethanol-fed murine models are more sensitive to NO and reactive nitrogen species. It seems that after ethanol exposure, mitochondrial liver dysfunction might develop a cytosolic antioxidant defense, which could be an important feature of chronic hepatotoxicity damaging the proteome and genome [49].

In regards to the inflammatory response, it is important to mention that ethanol hepatotoxicity was significantly prevented through a mechanism that involves a decrease in tumor necrosis factor α (TNF-α) formation, in hepatocytes isolated from alcohol-fed rats, through the SDS–PAGE technique [50]. It was not surprising that TNF-α knockout mice exhibited a significantly less severe ethanol-mediated hepatotoxicity, markedly accompanied by lower levels of protein Tyr nitration [51].

The Fernandez-Checa group have shown that mitochondrial free cholesterol loading in steatohepatitis sensitizes to TNF and Fas through mitochondrial glutathione (GSH) depletion [31]. Protein Tyr nitration and its functional consequences might explain the role of protein nitration in promoting many forms of liver disease, including AFLD and NAFLD [52]. The levels of protein nitration are correlated with the increased levels of hepatic transaminases, steatosis, and necrosis [43]. It is also very important to study the NO bioavailability throughout the course of NAFLD. In an HFD mouse model, it was shown that NO contents were initially increased, causing mitochondrial damage accompanied by alterations in mitochondrial proteins, such as thiolase, complex I (NADH ubiquinone oxidoreductase), aldehyde dehydrogenase 2 (ALDH2), and complex V (ATP synthase); in contrast, NO levels decreased at later stages of NAFLD [43]. NO might be an encouraging inflammatory regulatory marker according to the NAFLD damage stage.

1.3. Human Studies

Based on the hypothesis that liver injury in NAFLD and NASH is caused by protein effectors, as described for the *in vitro* and *in vivo* models, human studies are critical because they may help establish biomarkers that can be used for an earlier diagnosis and more effective treatments.

Dr. Feldstein's group reported that extracellular vesicle (EV) proteomes carry a selective antigenic composition that might be used to diagnose NAFLD non-invasively. They analyzed cell death, inflammation, and antioxidant and pathological angiogenesis in steatotic mice, finding that some functional activities of oxidoreductase, hydrolase, endopeptidase inhibitors, signal transducers and lipid binding proteins were abundantly expressed in EVs [53]. Another study in patients with simple steatosis showed that a group of cytochrome P450 family proteins, such as CYP2E1, CYP4A11, and CYP2C9, are upregulated, being associated with lipid droplets (LDs). On the other hand, mitochondrial proteins were found to be downregulated, suggesting that these enzymes are involved in NAFLD development and mitochondrial dysfunction. Increased adipose differentiation-related protein

(ADRP) and fatty acid synthase (FAS) mRNA and protein expression were found to be upregulated in the LD fractions of patients with steatosis. It has been recently recognized that in fatty liver disease, the LD-associated protein 17β-HSD13 expression was upregulated [54].

There are several molecules that have been associated with liver damage progression. For instance, two important proteomic studies in adult patients using liver tissue and serum respectively, with and without NAFLD, revealed an increased expression of lumican (a keratan sulphate proteoglycan involved in collagen cross-linking and epithelial–mesenchymal transition) [55]. The expression of lumican was similarly abundant in obese patients with normal liver histology and in obese patients with simple steatosis; however, it was over-expressed in mild progressive NASH patients [56]. Thus, lumican is expressed differentially across the progressive stages of NAFLD, and not just in patients with moderate to advanced fibrosis, raising the possibility of over-expressed hepatic lumican as an early marker of a profibrotic state in patients with NAFLD [57]. Also, fatty acid-binding protein 1 (FABP-1) is another protein involved in multiple biological functions, such as intracellular fatty acid transport, cholesterol and phospholipid metabolism, which plays an important facilitative role in hepatic fatty acid oxidation [58,59]. FABP-1 is relatively over-expressed in patients with simple steatosis compared with those with obesity; however, throughout the NAFLD stages, it was observed that FABP-1 was significantly under-expressed in patients with mild and progressive NASH [60].

A novel analysis of hepatic peptides performed on an electrospray ionization mass spectrometry (ESI-MS) biosystem (an analytical technique that can provide both qualitative (structure) and quantitative (molecular mass or concentration) information on analyte molecules after their conversion to ions) [61] was conducted on several phenotypes of fatty liver disease, where 1362 hepatic proteins were assessed. Several proteins were consistently abundant among study groups, whereas albumin, hemoglobinβ, hemoglobinα, dihydropyrimidinase, enolase, the metal-transport protein ATX1, and HSP gp96 were likely differentially abundant because of the biological effects of increased hepatic lipid content or inflammation [56]. Furthermore, it has been observed that serum and hepatic TNF-α levels are elevated in patients with NAFLD, correlating with the animal models which had already been studied. Conversely, inhibition of TNF-α signaling improves insulin resistance (IR) and histological parameters of NAFLD [26].

In another study which involved NAFLD patients who underwent bariatric surgery, quantified protein peak intensity levels were selected from SELDI-TOF mass spectrometry [62]; the results revealed that fibrinogen γ was elevated, playing a role in blood clotting and serving as a depot for active fibroblast growth factor receptor 2 (FGF2) in the blood, and it may be connected to liver fibrosis [63]. However, the role of fibrinogen γ in NAFLD remains speculative and needs to be well defined. Moreover, this study involves patients with varying stages of NAFLD. Several protein biomarkers were identified and classified from priority 1 to 4, according to quality identification (ID); priority 1 proteins have the greatest likelihood of correct ID (multiple unique sequences identified), such as transgelin 2, retinol-binding protein 4, lumican, and paraoxonase 1, among others [62].

Importantly, it seems that each protein may have biological significance in the microenvironment in which it is expressed. For instance, the fibrinogen β chain, retinol-binding protein 4 (RBP4), serum amyloid P component, lumican, transgelin 2, and CD5 antigen-like exhibit differential levels of expression among patient groups and present a global success rate of 76%, whereas complement component C7, the insulin-like growth factor acid labile subunit, and transgelin 2 present a global success rate of 90% wherein they are characterized by simple steatosis and NASH and are able to accurately differentiate between control subjects and patients with all forms of NAFLD [62]. RBP4 is an important protein synthesized by the liver and adipose tissue, carrying vitamin A in the blood; it has been involved in the development of IR and has been related to increased NAFLD severity [64].

NAFLD development has been associated with elevated serum hemoglobin levels, being independent of body mass index, type 2 diabetes, and other metabolic diseases [29,65]. One of the potential explanations for the observed associations between increased hemoglobin and NAFLD may be related to oxidative stress, catalyzed by iron excess accumulation and probably causing thrombosis, leading to hepatocyte injury [66,67]. The relationship between serum hemoglobin and NAFLD may be partially modulated by haptoglobin levels, which act as an antioxidant binding to free hemoglobin and inhibiting the hemoglobin-induced oxidative damage [65]. Furthermore, excessive erythrocytosis increased hemoglobin in NAFLD subjects without a diagnosis of metabolic syndrome (MS), and this should be considered in the selection of cases for histological assessment of disease severity and progression [68]. On the other hand, Lixin Zhu *et al.* showed that in NASH, hemoglobin is highly expressed and synthesized in hepatocytes, being released into the circulatory system and providing a possible explanation for serum free hemoglobin [69]. Therefore, hemoglobin measurements should be considered part of the clinical evaluation markers for severity of liver damage in patients with NAFLD [67,70].

Finding clinical biomarkers that have arisen from proteomic technologies, which reveal biological reactions and could distinguish NAFLD from NASH, is of great importance (Table 1). However, accurate human studies which involved protein analysis related to mitochondrial dysfunction are lacking. Oxidative-nitrated stress proteins play a major role in stimulating damage in various hepatic diseases, including AFLD and NAFLD mediated by ethanol. As these proteins are essential for normal mitochondrial function, protein nitration might lead to irreversible modification of the respiratory-chain proteins [29].

2. Conclusions

In vitro studies are the basis for elucidating the pathogenic network that is involved in NAFLD, which is interesting because of the recognition of some proteins involved in liver fibrosis. Conversely, *in vivo* studies have focused on the bioenergetics dysfunction caused by chronic exposure to HFD, which can be linked to changes in protein interactions in the liver proteome between NAFLD and NASH (Figure 2) [14]. Human studies have revealed the importance of novel proteins that were identified as having a high rate of confidence in the presence of NAFLD and NASH and seem to emerge as good marker candidates (Table 1). Deeper and more accurate human studies will be required to identify the network of complex proteomes that underlies the pathogenesis related to mitochondrial dysfunction, where its functional consequences might explain the pathophysiological mechanism which follows many forms of liver diseases.

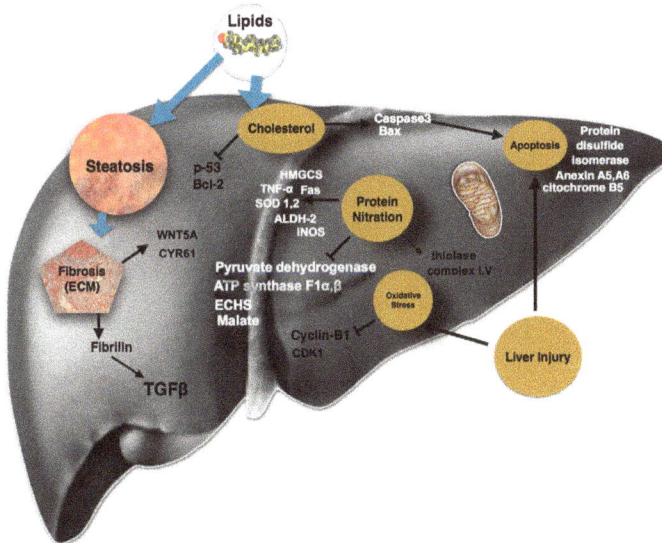

Figure 2. Activation and inhibition of different proteins in NAFLD.

Table 1. Proteins involved in NAFLD and potential markers for NAFLD.

Research Context	Protein	Implications and Findings	Study	Year
Cell Cycle	Cyclin B1 CDK1	Polyploidy in mononuclear cell populations is an early event in NAFLD development.	Gentric, Maillet *et al.* [11]	2015
Fibrosis	Fibrillin	Mechanisms underlying fibrotic processes. Early marker of a profibrotic state in patients with NAFLD.	Lorena, Darby *et al.* [15]	2004
	TGF-β CYR61		Rashid, Humphries *et al.* [14]	2012
	Wnt-5a		Fitzpatrick and Dhawan [57]	2014
	Lumican Fibrinogeny FGF2		Younossi, Baranova *et al.* [63]	2005
Apoptosis	Cytochrome b5	Important role for cell death mechanisms in hepatocytes.	Jayaraman, Roberts *et al.* [17]	2005
	Annexin A5		Yamaguchi, Chen *et al.* [18]	2004
	Annexin A6 Bax		Zhu, Xie *et al.* [19]	2014
	Caspase 3 Caspase 8		Sabapathy, Hochedlinger *et al.* [30]	2004
Lipid synthesis	SREBP-1 ChREBP-1	Adaptive pathways of hepatic lipid export and catabolism.	Anderson and Borlak [23]	2008
	PPARγ Acetyl-CoA Glycerol-3-phosphate	Hepatocytes are subjected to an important oxidative stress.	Al Sharif, Alov *et al.* [24]	2014
	Fetuin A Fetuin B	Promote lipid-induced insulin resistance.	Ehx, Gerin *et al.* [38]	2014
Inflammation	NF-κB	Promote insulin resistance, Kupffer cells activation, cholesterol and triglyceride metabolism, intracellular oxidative stress.	Cai, Yuan *et al.* [25]	2005
	TNF-α IL-1		Wang, Liu *et al.* [26]	2015
	MAPK1 JNK		Lim, Dillon *et al.* [29]	2014
β-Oxidation	ECHS1	Lipid accumulation in NAFLD.	Zhang, Yang *et al.* [33]	2010
			Lewis, Hagstrom *et al.* [34]	2002
Oxidative stress	ALDH2 HMGCS2	Acetyl-CoA consumption and oxidative stress as molecular markers of hepatic steatosis. Catalyze the accumulation of iron in excess.	Douette, Navet *et al.* [36]	2005
	Hemoglobin Haptoglobin		Peinado, Diaz-Ruiz *et al.* [37]	2014
Antioxidants	SOD2	Protective role in mitochondrial DNA depletion, and hepatic ATP content.	Mansouri, Tarhuni *et al.* [47]	2010
	SOD1		Kessova, *et al.* [48]	2003
Lipid droplets	CYP2E1 CYP4A11 CYP2C9	Enzymes involved in mitochondrial dysfunction and the development of NAFLD.	Su, Wang *et al.* [54]	2014
Lipid metabolism	FABP-1	Intracellular fatty acid transport, cholesterol and phospholipid metabolism, and plays an important facilitative role in hepatic fatty acid oxidation.	Binas and Erol Higuchi [58]	2007
			Kato *et al.* [59]	2011

Cyclin-dependent kinase 1 (CDK1), Transforming growth factor beta (TGFβ), Cysteine-rich angiogenic inducer 61 (CYR61), Wingless-Type MMTV Integration Site Family, Member 5A (Wnt-5a), Fibroblast Growth Factor 2 (FGF2), BCL2-Associated X Protein (Bax), Sterol regulatory element-binding protein 1 (SREBP-1), Carbohydrate-responsive element-binding protein 1 (ChREBP-1), Peroxisome proliferator-activated receptor gamma (PPARγ), Nuclear factor κB (NF-κB), Tumor necrosis factor α (TNF-α), Interleukin 1 (IL-1), Mitogen-activated protein kinase 1 (MAPK1), c-Jun N-terminal kinase (JNK), Enoyl-CoA hydratase short chain 1 (ECHS1), Aldehyde dehydrogenase 2 (ALDH2), 3-hydroxy-3-methylglutaryl-CoA synthase 2 (HMGCS2), Superoxide dismutase 1 (SOD1), Superoxide dismutase 2 (SOD2), Cytochrome P450 family 2 subfamily E member 1 (CYP2E1), Cytochrome P450 family 4 subfamily A member 11 (CYP4A11), Cytochrome P450 family 2 subfamily C member 9 (CYP2C9) and Fatty acid binding protein 1 (FABP-1).

Acknowledgments: This study was supported by the Médica Sur Clinic and Foundation. It is it appreciated the assistance received by Victor Medina Lopez in the correction and improvement of this article.

Author Contributions: Natalia Nuño-Lámbarri and Varenka J. Barbero-Becerra wrote the article; Misael Uribe and Norberto C. Chávez-Tapia revised and corrected the final version of the manuscript.

Conflicts of Interest: The authors declare no conflict of interest.

References

1. Ballestri, S.; Zona, S.; Targher, G.; Romagnoli, D.; Baldelli, E.; Nascimbeni, F.; Roverato, A.; Guaraldi, G.; Lonardo, A. Nonalcoholic fatty liver disease is associated with an almost two-fold increased risk of incident type 2 diabetes and metabolic syndrome. Evidence from a systematic review and meta-analysis. *J. Gastroenterol. Hepatol.* **2015**. [CrossRef]
2. Petta, S.; Valenti, L.; Bugianesi, E.; Targher, G.; Bellentani, S.; Bonino, F.; Special Interest Group on Personalised Hepatology of the Italian Association for the Study of the Liver (AISF). A "systems medicine" approach to the study of non-alcoholic fatty liver disease. *Dig. Liver Dis.* **2016**, *48*, 333–342. [PubMed]
3. Lomonaco, R.; Sunny, N.E.; Bril, F.; Cusi, K. Nonalcoholic fatty liver disease: Current issues and novel treatment approaches. *Drugs* **2013**, *73*, 1–14. [CrossRef] [PubMed]
4. Younossi, Z.M.; Koenig, A.B.; Abdelatif, D.; Fazel, Y.; Henry, L.; Wymer, M. Global epidemiology of non-alcoholic fatty liver disease-meta-analytic assessment of prevalence, incidence and outcomes. *Hepatology* **2015**. [CrossRef] [PubMed]
5. Fuchs, M. Non-alcoholic Fatty liver disease: The bile Acid-activated farnesoid x receptor as an emerging treatment target. *J. Lipids* **2012**, *2012*, 934396. [CrossRef] [PubMed]
6. Enriquez, J. Genomics and the world's economy. *Science* **1998**, *281*, 925–926. [CrossRef] [PubMed]
7. Blackstock, W.P.; Weir, M.P. Proteomics: Quantitative and physical mapping of cellular proteins. *Trends Biotechnol.* **1999**, *17*, 121–127. [CrossRef]
8. Gerold, G.; Bruening, J.; Pietschmann, T. Decoding protein networks during virus entry by quantitative proteomics. *Virus Res.* **2015**. [CrossRef] [PubMed]
9. Larbi, N.B.; Jefferies, C. 2D-DIGE: Comparative proteomics of cellular signalling pathways. *Methods Mol. Biol.* **2009**, *517*, 105–132. [PubMed]
10. Celton-Morizur, S.; Desdouets, C. Polyploidization of liver cells. *Adv. Exp. Med. Biol.* **2010**, *676*, 123–135. [PubMed]
11. Gentric, G.; Maillet, V.; Paradis, V.; Couton, D.; L'Hermitte, A.; Panasyuk, G.; Fromenty, B.; Celton-Morizur, S.; Desdouets, C. Oxidative stress promotes pathologic polyploidization in nonalcoholic fatty liver disease. *J. Clin. Investig.* **2015**, *125*, 981–992. [CrossRef] [PubMed]
12. Mormone, E.; George, J.; Nieto, N. Molecular pathogenesis of hepatic fibrosis and current therapeutic approaches. *Chem. Biol. Interact.* **2011**, *193*, 225–231. [CrossRef] [PubMed]
13. Riedman, S.L. Mechanisms of hepatic fibrogenesis. *Gastroenterology* **2008**, *134*, 1655–1669. [CrossRef] [PubMed]
14. Rashid, S.T.; Humphries, J.D.; Byron, A.; Dhar, A.; Askari, J.A.; Selley, J.N.; Knight, D.; Goldin, R.D.; Thursz, M.; Humphries, M.J. Proteomic analysis of extracellular matrix from the hepatic stellate cell line LX-2 identifies CYR61 and Wnt-5a as novel constituents of fibrotic liver. *J. Proteome Res.* **2012**, *11*, 4052–4064. [CrossRef] [PubMed]
15. Lorena, D.; Darby, I.A.; Reinhardt, D.P.; Sapin, V.; Rosenbaum, J.; Desmoulière, A. Fibrillin-1 expression in normal and fibrotic rat liver and in cultured hepatic fibroblastic cells: Modulation by mechanical stress and role in cell adhesion. *Lab. Investig.* **2004**, *84*, 203–212. [CrossRef] [PubMed]
16. Williams, K.H.; Vieira De Ribeiro, A.J.; Prakoso, E.; Veillard, A.S.; Shackel, N.A.; Brooks, B.; Bu, Y.; Cavanagh, E.; Raleigh, J.; McLennan, S.V.; *et al.* Circulating dipeptidyl peptidase-4 activity correlates with measures of hepatocyte apoptosis and fibrosis in non-alcoholic fatty liver disease in type 2 diabetes mellitus and obesity: A dual cohort cross-sectional study. *J. Diabetes* **2015**, *7*, 809–819. [CrossRef] [PubMed]
17. Jayaraman, A.; Roberts, K.A.; Yoon, J.; Yarmush, D.M.; Duan, X.; Lee, K.; Yarmush, M.L. Identification of neutrophil gelatinase-associated lipocalin (NGAL) as a discriminatory marker of the hepatocyte-secreted protein response to IL-1β: A proteomic analysis. *Biotechnol. Bioeng.* **2005**, *91*, 502–515. [CrossRef] [PubMed]
18. Yamaguchi, H.; Chen, J.; Bhalla, K.; Wang, H.-G. Regulation of Bax activation and apoptotic response to microtubule-damaging agents by p53 transcription-dependent and -independent pathways. *J. Biol. Chem.* **2004**, *279*, 39431–39437. [CrossRef] [PubMed]
19. Zhu, C.; Xie, P.; Zhao, F.; Zhang, L.; An, W.; Zhan, Y. Mechanism of the promotion of steatotic HepG2 cell apoptosis by cholesterol. *Int. J. Clin. Exp. Pathol.* **2014**, *7*, 6807–6813.

20. Woo, D.H.; Kim, S.K.; Lim, H.J.; Heo, J.; Park, H.S.; Kang, G.Y.; Kim, S.E.; You, H.J.; Hoeppner, D.J.; Kim, Y.; *et al.* Direct and indirect contribution of human embryonic stem cell-derived hepatocyte-like cells to liver repair in mice. *Gastroenterology* **2012**, *142*, 602–611. [CrossRef] [PubMed]

21. Eccleston, H.B.; Andringa, K.A.; Betancourt, A.M.; Betancourt, A.L.; Mantena, S.K.; Swain, T.M.; Tinsley, H.N.; Nolte, R.N.; Nagy, T.R.; Nagy, G.A.; *et al.* Chronic exposure to a high-fat diet induces hepatic steatosis, impairs nitric oxide bioavailability, and modifies the mitochondrial proteome in mice. *Antioxid. Redox Signal.* **2011**, *15*, 447–459.

22. Garcia-Ruiz, C.; Fernandez-Checa, J.C. Mitochondrial glutathione: Hepatocellular survival-death switch. *J. Gastroenterol. Hepatol.* **2006**, *21*, S3–S6. [CrossRef] [PubMed]

23. Anderson, N.; Borlak, J. Molecular mechanisms and therapeutic targets in steatosis and steatohepatitis. *Pharmacol. Rev.* **2008**, *60*, 311–357. [CrossRef] [PubMed]

24. Al Sharif, M.; Alov, P.; Vitcheva, V.; Pajeva, I.; Tsakovska, I. Modes-of-action related to repeated dose toxicity: Tissue-specific biological roles of PPARγ ligand-dependent dysregulation in nonalcoholic fatty liver disease. *PPAR Res.* **2014**, *2014*, 432647. [CrossRef] [PubMed]

25. Cai, D.; Yuan, M.; Frantz, D.F.; Melendez, P.A.; Hansen, L.; Lee, J.; Shoelson, S.E. Local and systemic insulin resistance resulting from hepatic activation of IKK-β and NF-κB. *Nat. Med.* **2005**, *11*, 183–190. [CrossRef] [PubMed]

26. Wang, Y.L.; Liu, L.J.; Zhao, W.J.; Li, J.X. Intervening TNF-α via PPARγ with gegenqinlian decoction in experimental nonalcoholic fatty liver disease. *Evid. Based Complement. Altern. Med.* **2015**, *2015*, 715638. [CrossRef] [PubMed]

27. Schwabe, R.F.; Brenner, D.A. Mechanisms of Liver Injury. I. TNF-α-induced liver injury: Role of IKK, JNK, and ROS pathways. *Am. J. Physiol. Gastrointest. Liver Physiol.* **2006**, *290*, G583–G589. [CrossRef] [PubMed]

28. Chen, Y.R.; Wang, X.; Templeton, D.; Davis, R.J.; Tan, T.H. The role of c-Jun N-terminal kinase (JNK) in apoptosis induced by ultraviolet C and γ radiation. Duration of JNK activation may determine cell death and proliferation. *J. Biol. Chem.* **1996**, *271*, 31929–31936. [CrossRef] [PubMed]

29. Lim, J.W.; Dillon, J.; Miller, M. Proteomic and genomic studies of non-alcoholic fatty liver disease—Clues in the pathogenesis. *World J. Gastroenterol.* **2014**, *20*, 8325–8340. [CrossRef] [PubMed]

30. Sabapathy, K.; Hochedlinger, K.; Nam, S.Y.; Bauer, A.; Karin, M.; Wagner, E.F. Distinct roles for JNK1 and JNK2 in regulating JNK activity and c-Jun-dependent cell proliferation. *Mol. Cell* **2004**, *15*, 713–725. [CrossRef] [PubMed]

31. Mari, M.; Caballero, F.; Colell, A.; Morales, A.; Caballeria, J.; Fernandez, A.; Enrich, C.; Fernandez-Checa, J.C.; García-Ruiz, C. Mitochondrial free cholesterol loading sensitizes to TNF- and Fas-mediated steatohepatitis. *Cell Metab.* **2006**, *4*, 185–198. [CrossRef] [PubMed]

32. Gusdon, A.M.; Song, K.X.; Qu, S. Nonalcoholic fatty liver disease: Pathogenesis and therapeutics from a mitochondria-centric perspective. *Oxid. Med. Cell. Longev.* **2014**, *2014*, 637027. [CrossRef] [PubMed]

33. Zhang, X.; Yang, J.; Guo, Y.; Ye, H.; Yu, C.; Xu, C.; Xu, L.; Wu, S.; Sun, W.; Wei, H.; *et al.* Functional proteomic analysis of nonalcoholic fatty liver disease in rat models: Enoyl-coenzyme a hydratase down-regulation exacerbates hepatic steatosis. *Hepatology* **2010**, *51*, 1190–1199. [CrossRef] [PubMed]

34. Lewis, D.L.; Hagstrom, J.E.; Loomis, A.G.; Wolff, J.A.; Herweijer, H. Efficient delivery of siRNA for inhibition of gene expression in postnatal mice. *Nat. Genet.* **2002**, *32*, 107–108. [CrossRef] [PubMed]

35. Pessayre, D.; Mansouri, A.; Fromenty, B. Nonalcoholic steatosis and steatohepatitis. V. Mitochondrial dysfunction in steatohepatitis. *Am. J. Physiol. Gastrointest. Liver Physiol.* **2002**, *282*, G193–G199. [CrossRef] [PubMed]

36. Douette, P.; Navet, R.; Gerkens, P.; de Pauw, E.; Leprince, P.; Sluse-Goffart, C.; Sluse, F.E. Steatosis-induced proteomic changes in liver mitochondria evidenced by two-dimensional differential in-gel electrophoresis. *J. Proteome Res.* **2005**, *4*, 2024–2031. [CrossRef] [PubMed]

37. Peinado, J.R.; Diaz-Ruiz, A.; Frühbeck, G.; Malagon, M.M. Mitochondria in metabolic disease: Getting clues from proteomic studies. *Proteomics* **2014**, *14*, 452–466. [CrossRef] [PubMed]

38. Ehx, G.; Gérin, S.; Mathy, G.; Franck, F.; Oliveira, H.C.; Vercesi, A.E.; Sluse, F.E. Liver proteomic response to hypertriglyceridemia in human-apolipoprotein C-III transgenic mice at cellular and mitochondrial compartment levels. *Lipids Health Dis.* **2014**, *13*, 116. [CrossRef] [PubMed]

39. Meex, R.C.; Hoy, A.J.; Morris, A.; Brown, R.D.; Lo, J.C.Y.; Burke, M.; Goode, R.J.A.; Kingwell, B.A.; Kraakman, M.J.; Febbraio, M.A.; *et al.* Fetuin B is a secreted hepatocyte factor linking steatosis to impaired glucose metabolism. *Cell Metab.* **2015**, *22*, 1078–1089. [CrossRef] [PubMed]

40. Ray, S.; Khanra, D.; Sonthalia, N.; Kundu, S.; Biswas, K.; Talukdar, A.; Saha, M.; Bera, H. Clinico-biochemical correlation to histological findings in alcoholic liver disease: A single centre study from eastern India. *J. Clin. Diagn. Res.* **2014**, *8*, MC01–MC05. [CrossRef] [PubMed]

41. Larosche, I.; Lettéron, P.; Berson, A.; Fromenty, B.; Huang, T.T.; Moreau, R.; Pessayre, D.; Mansouri, A. Hepatic mitochondrial DNA depletion after an alcohol binge in mice: Probable role of peroxynitrite and modulation by manganese superoxide dismutase. *J. Pharmacol. Exp. Ther.* **2010**, *332*, 886–897. [CrossRef] [PubMed]

42. McKim, S.E.; Gäbele, E.; Isayama, F.; Lambert, J.C.; Tucker, L.M.; Wheeler, M.D.; Connor, H.D.; Mason, R.P.; Doll, M.A.; Hein, D.W.; *et al.* Inducible nitric oxide synthase is required in alcohol-induced liver injury: Studies with knockout mice. *Gastroenterology* **2003**, *125*, 1834–1844. [CrossRef] [PubMed]

43. Abdelmegeed, M.A.; Song, B.J. Functional roles of protein nitration in acute and chronic liver diseases. *Oxid. Med. Cell. Longev.* **2014**, *2014*, 149627. [CrossRef] [PubMed]

44. Sanyal, A.J.; Campbell-Sargent, C.; Mirshahi, F.; Rizzo, W.B.; Contos, M.J.; Sterling, R.K.; Luketic, V.A.; Shiffman, M.L.; Clore, J.N. Nonalcoholic steatohepatitis: Association of insulin resistance and mitochondrial abnormalities. *Gastroenterology* **2001**, *120*, 1183–1192. [CrossRef] [PubMed]

45. Rodriguez-Suarez, E.; Mato, J.M.; Elortza, F. Proteomics analysis of human nonalcoholic fatty liver. *Methods Mol. Biol.* **2012**, *909*, 241–258. [PubMed]

46. Venkatraman, A.; Shiva, S.; Wigley, A.; Ulasova, E.; Chhieng, D.; Bailey, S.M.; Darley-Usmar, V.M. The role of iNOS in alcohol-dependent hepatotoxicity and mitochondrial dysfunction in mice. *Hepatology* **2004**, *40*, 565–573. [CrossRef] [PubMed]

47. Mansouri, A.; Tarhuni, A.; Larosche, I.; Reyl-Desmars, F.; Demeilliers, C.; Degoul, F.; Nahon, P.; Sutton, A.; Moreau, R.; Fromenty, B.; *et al.* MnSOD overexpression prevents liver mitochondrial DNA depletion after an alcohol binge but worsens this effect after prolonged alcohol consumption in mice. *Dig. Dis.* **2010**, *28*, 756–775. [CrossRef] [PubMed]

48. Kessova, I.G.; Ho, Y.S.; Thung, S.; Cederbaum, A.I. Alcohol-induced liver injury in mice lacking Cu, Zn-superoxide dismutase. *Hepatology* **2003**, *38*, 1136–1145. [CrossRef] [PubMed]

49. Venkatraman, A.; Landar, A.; Davis, A.J.; Chamlee, L.; Sanderson, T.; Kim, H.; Page, G.; Pompilius, M.; Ballinger, S.; Darley-Usmar, V.; *et al.* Modification of the mitochondrial proteome in response to the stress of ethanol-dependent hepatotoxicity. *J. Biol. Chem.* **2004**, *279*, 22092–22101. [CrossRef] [PubMed]

50. Zelickson, B.R.; Benavides, G.A.; Johnson, M.S.; Chacko, B.K.; Venkatraman, A.; Landar, A.; Betancourt, A.M.; Bailey, S.M.; Darley-Usmar, V.M. Nitric oxide and hypoxia exacerbate alcohol-induced mitochondrial dysfunction in hepatocytes. *Biochim. Biophys. Acta* **2011**, *1807*, 1573–1582. [CrossRef] [PubMed]

51. Smathers, R.L.; Galligan, J.J.; Stewart, B.J.; Petersen, D.R. Overview of lipid peroxidation products and hepatic protein modification in alcoholic liver disease. *Chem. Biol. Interact.* **2011**, *192*, 107–112. [CrossRef] [PubMed]

52. Charbonneau, A.; Marette, A. Inducible nitric oxide synthase induction underlies lipid-induced hepatic insulin resistance in mice: Potential role of tyrosine nitration of insulin signaling proteins. *Diabetes* **2010**, *59*, 861–871. [CrossRef] [PubMed]

53. Povero, D.; Eguchi, A.; Li, H.; Johnson, C.D.; Papouchado, B.G.; Wree, A.; Messer, K.; Feldstein, A.E. Circulating extracellular vesicles with specific proteome and liver microRNAs are potential biomarkers for liver injury in experimental fatty liver disease. *PLoS ONE* **2014**, *9*, e113651. [CrossRef] [PubMed]

54. Su, W.; Wang, Y.; Jia, X.; Wu, W.; Li, L.; Tian, X.; Li, S.; Wang, C.; Xu, H.; Cao, J.; *et al.* Comparative proteomic study reveals 17β-HSD13 as a pathogenic protein in nonalcoholic fatty liver disease. *Proc. Natl. Acad. Sci. USA* **2014**, *111*, 11437–11442. [CrossRef] [PubMed]

55. Krishnan, A.; Li, X.; Kao, W.Y.; Viker, K.; Butters, K.; Masuoka, H.; Knudsen, B.; Gores, G.; Charlton, M. Lumican, an extracellular matrix proteoglycan, is a novel requisite for hepatic fibrosis. *Lab. Investig.* **2012**, *92*, 1712–1725. [CrossRef] [PubMed]

56. Charlton, M.; Viker, K.; Krishnan, A.; Sanderson, S.; Veldt, B.; Kaalsbeek, A.J.; Kendrick, M.; Thompson, G.; Que, F.; Swain, J.; *et al.* Differential expression of lumican and fatty acid binding protein-1: New insights into the histologic spectrum of nonalcoholic fatty liver disease. *Hepatology* **2009**, *49*, 1375–1384. [CrossRef] [PubMed]

57. Fitzpatrick, E.; Dhawan, A. Noninvasive biomarkers in non-alcoholic fatty liver disease: Current status and a glimpse of the future. *World J. Gastroenterol.* **2014**, *20*, 10851–10863. [CrossRef] [PubMed]

58. Binas, B.; Erol, E. FABPs as determinants of myocellular and hepatic fuel metabolism. *Mol. Cell. Biochem.* **2007**, *299*, 75–84. [CrossRef] [PubMed]

59. Higuchi, N.; Kato, M.; Tanaka, M.; Miyazaki, M.; Takao, S.; Kohjima, M.; Kotoh, K.; Enjoji, M.; Nakamuta, M.; Takayanagi, R. Effects of insulin resistance and hepatic lipid accumulation on hepatic mRNA expression levels of apoB, MTP and L-FABP in non-alcoholic fatty liver disease. *Exp. Ther. Med.* **2011**, *2*, 1077–1081. [PubMed]

60. Veerkamp, J.H.; van Moerkerk, H.T. Fatty acid-binding protein and its relation to fatty acid oxidation. *Mol. Cell. Biochem.* **1993**, *123*, 101–106. [CrossRef] [PubMed]

61. Ho, C.S.; Lam, C.W.; Chan, M.H.; Cheung, R.C.; Law, L.K.; Lit, L.C.; Ng, K.F.; Suen, M.W.; Tai, H.L. Electrospray ionisation mass spectrometry: Principles and clinical applications. *Clin. Biochem. Rev.* **2003**, *24*, 3–12. [PubMed]

62. Bell, L.N.; Theodorakis, J.L.; Vuppalanchi, R.; Saxena, R.; Bemis, K.G.; Wang, M.; Chalasani, N. Serum proteomics and biomarker discovery across the spectrum of nonalcoholic fatty liver disease. *Hepatology* **2010**, *51*, 111–120. [CrossRef] [PubMed]

63. Younossi, Z.M.; Baranova, A.; Ziegler, K.; del Giacco, L.; Schlauch, K.; Born, T.L.; Elariny, H.; Gorreta, F.; VanMeter, A.; Younoszai, A. A genomic and proteomic study of the spectrum of nonalcoholic fatty liver disease. *Hepatology* **2005**, *42*, 665–674. [CrossRef] [PubMed]

64. Janke, J.; Engeli, S.; Boschmann, M.; Adams, F.; Böhnke, J.; Luft, F.C.; Sharma, A.M.; Jordan, J. Retinol-binding protein 4 in human obesity. *Diabetes* **2006**, *55*, 2805–2810. [CrossRef] [PubMed]

65. Yu, C.; Xu, C.; Xu, L.; Yu, J.; Miao, M.; Li, Y. Serum proteomic analysis revealed diagnostic value of hemoglobin for nonalcoholic fatty liver disease. *J. Hepatol.* **2012**, *56*, 241–247. [CrossRef] [PubMed]

66. Jiang, Y.; Zeng, J.; Chen, B. Hemoglobin combined with triglyceride and ferritin in predicting non-alcoholic fatty liver. *J. Gastroenterol. Hepatol.* **2014**, *29*, 1508–1514. [CrossRef] [PubMed]

67. Akyuz, U.; Yesil, A.; Yilmaz, Y. Characterization of lean patients with nonalcoholic fatty liver disease: Potential role of high hemoglobin levels. *Scand. J. Gastroenterol.* **2015**, *50*, 341–346. [CrossRef] [PubMed]

68. Yilmaz, Y.; Senates, E.; Ayyildiz, T.; Colak, Y.; Tuncer, I.; Ovunc, A.O.; Dolar, E.; Kalayci, C. Characterization of nonalcoholic fatty liver disease unrelated to the metabolic syndrome. *Eur. J. Clin. Investig.* **2012**, *42*, 411–418. [CrossRef] [PubMed]

69. Liu, W.; Baker, S.S.; Baker, R.D.; Nowak, N.J.; Zhu, L. Upregulation of hemoglobin expression by oxidative stress in hepatocytes and its implication in nonalcoholic steatohepatitis. *PLoS ONE* **2011**, *6*, e24363. [CrossRef] [PubMed]

70. Trak-Smayra, V.; Dargere, D.; Noun, R.; Albuquerque, M.; Yaghi, C.; Gannagé-Yared, M.H.; Bedossa, P.; Paradis, V. Serum proteomic profiling of obese patients: Correlation with liver pathology and evolution after bariatric surgery. *Gut* **2009**, *58*, 825–832. [CrossRef] [PubMed]

International Journal of
Molecular Sciences

MDPI

Article

Different Serum Free Fatty Acid Profiles in NAFLD Subjects and Healthy Controls after Oral Fat Load

Roberto Gambino *, Elisabetta Bugianesi, Chiara Rosso, Lavinia Mezzabotta, Silvia Pinach, Natalina Alemanno, Francesca Saba and Maurizio Cassader

Department of Medical Sciences, University of Turin, C.so Dogliotti 14, 10126 Torino, Italy;
elisabetta.bugianesi@unito.it (E.B.); crosso3@cittadellasalute.to.it (C.R.); lavinia.mezzabotta@unito.it (L.M.);
silvia.pinach@unito.it (S.P.); natalina.alemanno@unito.it (N.A.); francescasaba85@yahoo.it (F.S.);
maurizio.cassader@unito.it (M.C.)
* Correspondence: roberto.gambino@unito.it; Tel./Fax: +39-011-633-5493

Academic Editors: Amedeo Lonardo and Giovanni Targher
Received: 24 February 2016; Accepted: 23 March 2016; Published: 31 March 2016

Abstract: Background: Free fatty acid (FFA) metabolism can impact on metabolic conditions, such as obesity and nonalcoholic fatty liver disease (NAFLD). This work studied the increase in total FFA shown in NAFLD subjects to possibly characterize which fatty acids significantly accounted for the whole increase. Methods: 21 patients with NAFLD were selected according to specified criteria. The control group consisted of nine healthy subjects. All subjects underwent an oral standard fat load. Triglycerides; cholesterol; FFA; glucose and insulin were measured every 2 h with the determination of fatty acid composition of FFA. Results: higher serum FFA levels in NAFLD subjects are mainly due to levels of oleic, palmitic and linoleic acids at different times. Significant increases were shown for docosahexaenoic acid, linolenic acid, eicosatrienoic acid, and arachidonic acid, although this was just on one occasion. In the postprandial phase, homeostatic model assessment HOMA index positively correlated with the $\omega 3/\omega 6$ ratio in NAFLD patients. Conclusions: the higher serum levels of FFA in NAFLD subjects are mainly due to levels of oleic and palmitic acids which are the most abundant circulating free fatty acids. This is almost exactly corresponded with significant increases in linoleic acid. An imbalance in the n-3/n-6 fatty acids ratio could modulate postprandial responses with more pronounced effects in insulin-resistant subjects, such as NAFLD patients.

Keywords: nonalcoholic fatty liver disease; free fatty acids; insulin resistance

---

1. Introduction

Free fatty acid (FFA) metabolism can widely impact on metabolic health. Several metabolic conditions, such as obesity, insulin resistance, type 2 diabetes, and non-alcoholic steatohepatitis, are associated with increased total concentrations of serum free fatty acids [1,2]. Nonalcoholic fatty liver disease (NAFLD) encompasses a spectrum of conditions characterized histologically by hepatic steatosis in individuals without significant alcohol consumption and negative viral, congenital and autoimmune liver disease markers. Hepatic lipid accumulation results from an imbalance between lipid availability and lipid disposal [3,4]. In this context, the composition of serum FFA has been poorly studied so far, especially in the postprandial state [5]. High levels of saturated fatty acids (SFA) were reported to increase coronary risk [6,7].

The liver is the main organ regulating fatty acid metabolism. Several sources supply the liver with a continuous flux of fatty acids [8]. In particular, in the fasting state free fatty acids coming from the lipolysis in adipose tissue fuel the liver. In the fed state, there are two major forms of dietary fatty acids which are available to the liver. In esterified forms, fatty acids are carried to the liver by triacylglycerol–rich chylomicron remnant particles and, as FFA, they stem from the so called spillover mechanism: in the spillover mechanism, FFA are released from chylomicron triacylglycerol by the activity of lipoprotein lipase (LPL, n. EC 3.1.1.34) in peripheral tissues, mainly adipose tissue [9]. Moreover, hepatic "*de novo*" lipogenesis (DNL) from non-lipid precursor increases the content of fatty acid in the liver.

After SFA exposure, *in vitro* experiments had shown that different cell types were induced to synthetize proinflammatory cytokines; they were more prone to apoptosis and had impaired insulin signaling [10,11]. By contrast, the exposure of monounsaturated fatty acids does not seem to trigger apoptosis [12]. Different signaling mechanisms were suggested in order to explain how SFA triggers apoptosis in hepatic cells. Endoplasmic reticulum (ER) stress, mitochondrial dysfunction, Jun N-terminal kinase (JNK) signaling and lipotoxicity are the main molecular mechanisms through which fatty acids exert their deleterious effects on the human metabolism. Wistar rats fed with a diet high in saturated fats showed liver damage and hepatic ER stress [13]. ER stress was due to a decreased fluidity of the lipid bilayer for abnormal incorporation of saturated phospholipids [14]. Excess of unesterified SFA is assembled into saturated phospholipid species leading to stiffening of cellular membranes [15]. Dysregulation of mitochondrial metabolism is due to an imbalance between the glycolytic fluxes and tricarboxylic acid (TCA) cycle since palmitate inhibits glycolytic flux and up regulates TCA cycle and anaplerotic fluxes [16]. The altered mitochondrial metabolism generates an elevated level of reacting oxygen species (ROS) stimulating apoptosis. An accelerated mitochondrial metabolism was observed in NAFLD patients [17]. Additionally, under either ER stress or oxidative stress, molecular signaling arises from JNK activation. Palmitate-induced JNK phosphorylation can be reversed in hepatic cells with administration of antioxidants [18]. SFA shows also a high degree of lipotoxicity. For instance, ceramide synthesis was associated with apoptosis in a hemopoietic precursor cell line [19] and with insulin resistance [20]. In this context, circulating FFAs, which should provide the substrate for triacylglycerol formation, may turn out to be cytotoxic in certain circumstances, such as under insulin resistance. NAFLD is characterized by elevated serum concentration of FFAs, hepatocyte apoptosis, progressive inflammation and fibrosis. In this work, we investigated the composition of circulating FFA in normal and NAFLD subjects during fasting and after a standard oral lipid load. Cultured hepatocytes incubated with FFA of various lengths demonstrated an inverse correlation between FA chain lengths and NAFLD induction [21].

The aim of our work was to study in depth the well-known significant increase in total free fatty acids shown in NAFLD subjects, and to possibly characterize which fatty acids significantly accounted for the whole increase, with specific regard to their classification (saturated, *n*-3, *n*-6 polyunsaturated fatty acids).

2. Results

Main basal features of the patients and control subjects are reported in Table 1. After oral fat load in NAFLD patients, triglycerides reached their maximum peak after around 4 h and they circulated at higher levels than in control subjects. The differences were significant at all times (Figure 1a). The trend of FFA over a 4 h period after the oral fat load is different between NAFLD patients and control subjects (Figure 1b). NAFLD patients showed higher FFA levels than control subjects from baseline through the end of the oral fat load with significant differences at times 60, 150, 180 and 210 min.

Table 1. Subjects baseline physical characteristics and fasting blood measurements.

Parameters	Control Group (*n* = 9)	NAFLD Group (*n* = 21)	*p*
Age (year)	27 ± 2	40 ± 9	0.001
BMI (kg/m^2)	21 ± 2	28 ± 4	0.002
Systolic blood pressure (mmHg)	119 ± 4	125 ± 8	0.049
Waist (cm)	73 ± 6	94 ± 8	0.000001
Diastolic blood pressure (mmHg)	80 ± 0	82 ± 9	0.615
Glucose (mg/dL)	91 ± 5	98 ± 11	0.097
Triglycerides (mg/dL)	59 ± 19	100 ± 49	0.021

Table 1. *Cont.*

Parameters	Control Group (*n* = 9)	NAFLD Group (*n* = 21)	*p*
Cholesterol (mg/dL)	168 ± 27	182 ± 34	0.306
HDL-Chol (mg/dL)	54 ± 13	42 ± 8	0.007
HDL$_2$-Chol (mg/dL)	20 ± 8	12 ± 4	0.003
HDL$_3$-Chol (mg/dL)	34.22 ± 5	30 ± 5	0.072
LDL-Chol (mg/dL)	107 ± 27	125 ± 29	0.139
FFA (mmol/L)	0.73 ± 0.41	1.07 ± 0.59	0.131
sdLDL (mg/dL)	21 ± 11	31 ± 18	0.127
c-Peptide (pM/mL)	0.54 ± 0.13	0.92 ± 0.35	0.004
Insulin (μU/mL)	6.28 ± 1.99	12.7 ± 7.68	0.021
AST (U/L)	20 ± 4	33 ± 10	0.002
ALT (U/L)	16 ± 4	64 ± 30	0.001
GGT (U/L)	14 ± 12	80 ± 74	0.021
ALP (U/L)	51 ± 21	75 ± 23	0.016
HOMA-IR	1.42 ± 0.49	3.16 ± 2.13	0.024
QUICKI index	0.367 ± 0.02	0.333 ± 0.03	0.008

Abbreviations: HDL-Chol, High density lipoprotein-Cholesterol; HDL$_2$-Chol, High density lipoprotein 2-Cholesterol; HDL$_3$-Chol, High density lipoprotein 3-Cholesterol; LDL-Chol, Low density lipoprotein-Cholesterol; FFA, free fatty acids; sdLDL, small dense low-density lipoproteins; AST, aspartate aminotransferase; ALT, alanine aminotransferase; GGT, gamma-glutamyltransferase; ALP, alkaline phosphatase; HOMA-IR, homeostatic model assessment-insulin resistance; QUICKI index, quantitative insulin sensitivity check index.

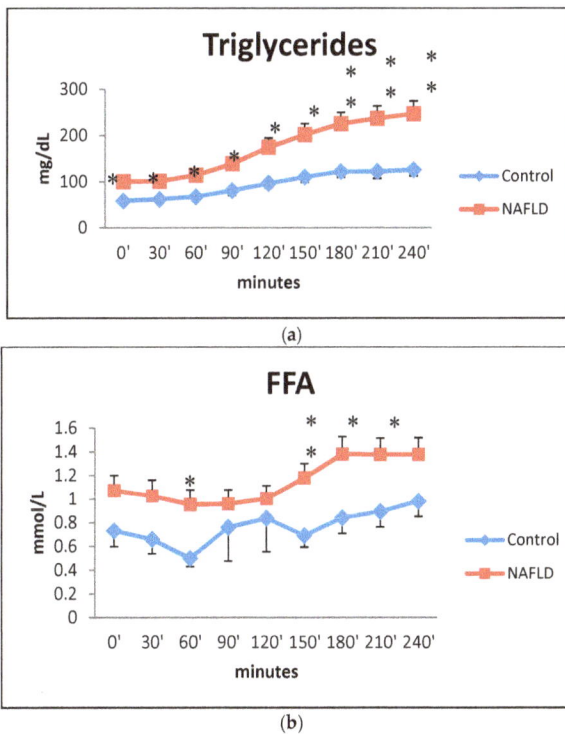

(a)

(b)

Figure 1. Time courses for total plasma triglycerides (box **a**) and free fatty acids (box **b**) concentrations during the oral fat meal in control (filled diamonds) and nonalcoholic fatty liver disease (NAFLD) (filled squares) subjects. Values are expressed as mean ±SEM. * $p < 0.05$, ** $p < 0.01$.

The trend of glycemia is dotted in Figure 2a and it shows a slight decrease from baseline to 90 min both in NAFLD and control group and then a constant course up to 240 min with a statistically significant difference at 210 min. Insulin curve showed in NAFLD patients a major peak at 30 min and higher levels than in control subjects. At all times, except at 180 min, there were statistically significant differences (Figure 2b).

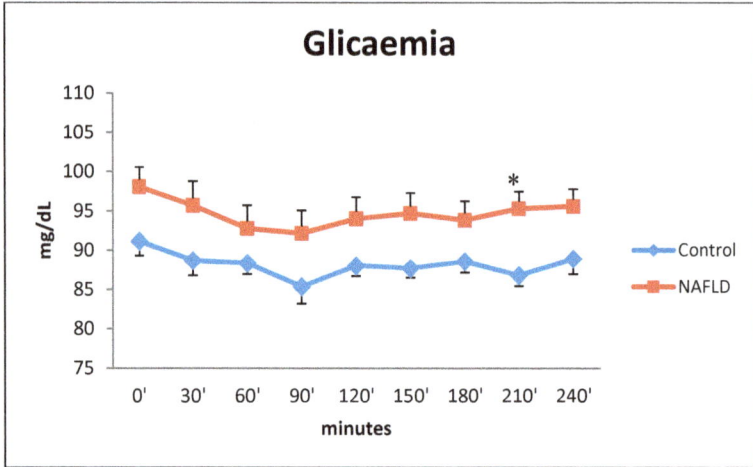

(a)

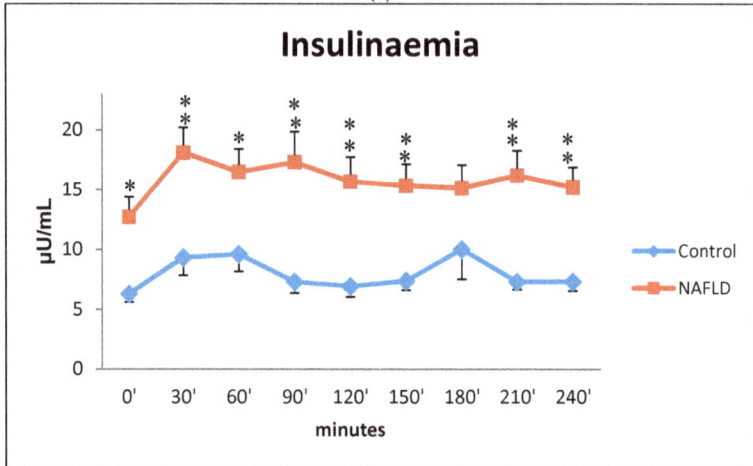

(b)

Figure 2. Time courses for glucose (box **a**) and insulin (box **b**) concentrations during the oral fat meal in control (filled diamonds) and NAFLD (filled squares) subjects. Values are expressed as mean ± SEM. * $p < 0.05$, ** $p < 0.01$.

Fatty acid values are given as percentage contents (mmol/100 mmol total fatty acids) since the between-individual variations in the molar concentration of total serum FFA is very high [22]. Figure 3 shows the trends of saturated fatty acids lauric (12:0) (a), myristic (14:0) (b) and stearic (18:0) (STA) (c) which did not present significant statistical differences between the two groups.

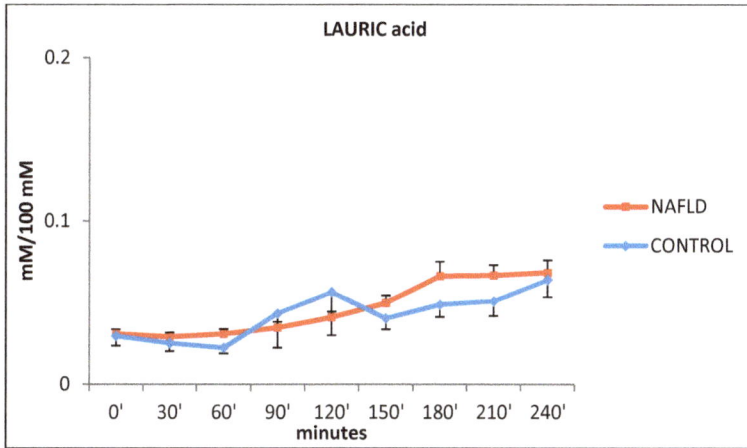

(a)

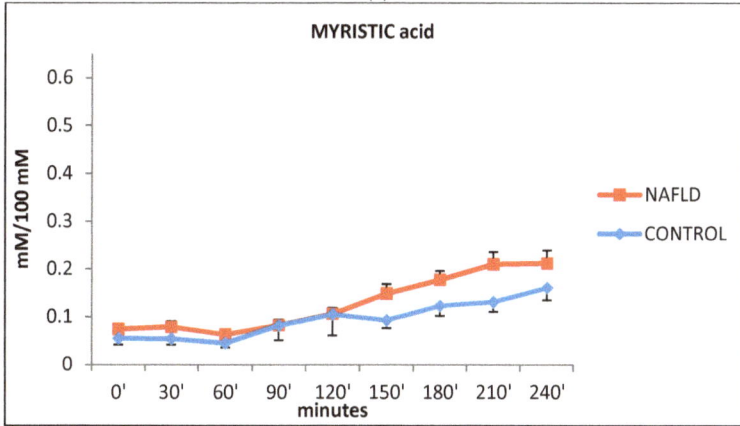

(b)

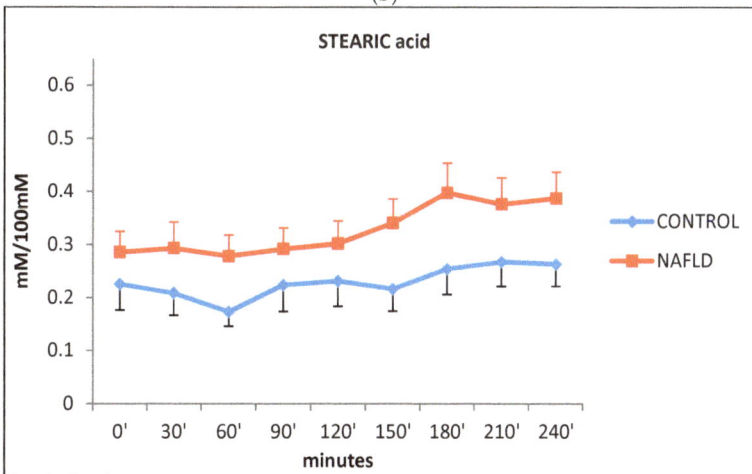

(c)

Figure 3. Change in plasma levels of saturated lauric (box **a**), myristic (box **b**) and stearic (box **c**) acid during the oral fat meal in control (filled diamonds) and NAFLD (filled squares) subjects. Values are expressed as mean ± SEM.

105

Figure 4 shows the trends of oleic acid (18:1*n*-9) (OLA) eluted with palmitic acid (16:0) (PAL), a saturated fatty acid. Oleic and palmitic acids amounts reached their peak at 180 min in NAFLD patients and were statistically higher in NAFLD patients than in control subjects at times 60, 150, and 210 min.

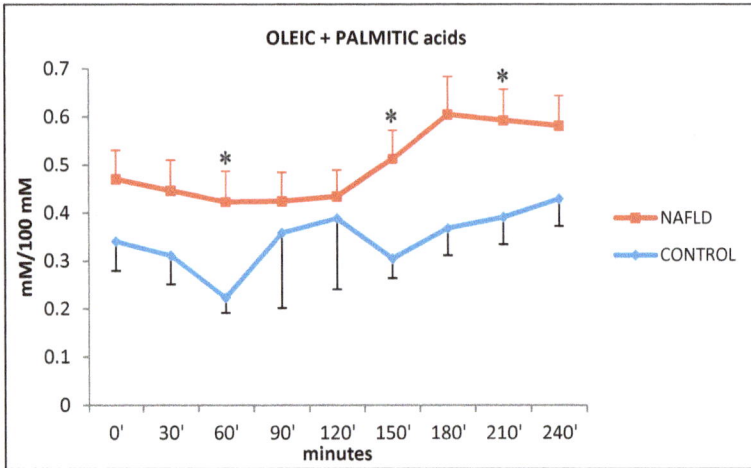

Figure 4. Change in plasma levels of oleic + palmitic acid during the oral fat meal in control (filled diamonds) and NAFLD (filled squares) subjects. Values are expressed as mean $\pm$ SEM. * $p < 0.05$.

The monounsaturated palmitoleic acid (16:1*n*-7) fell from baseline to 90 min in NAFLD subjects and from baseline to 150 min in control subjects. Then, in both group palmitoleic acids rose progressively up until the end of the test. No significant differences were observed between NAFLD and control subjects (Figure 5a).

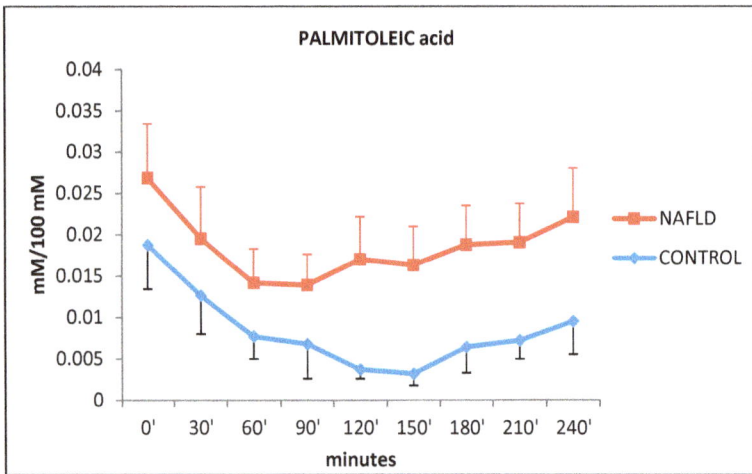

(a)

Figure 5. *Cont.*

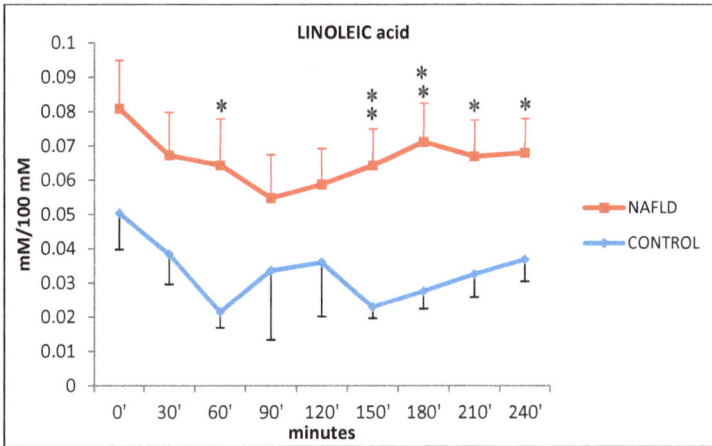

(b)

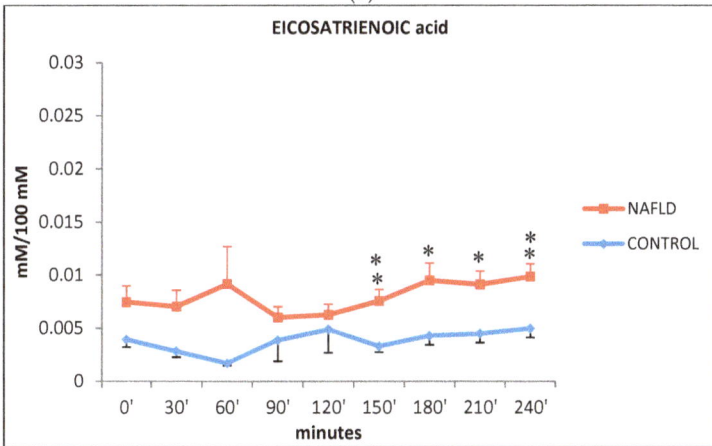

(c)

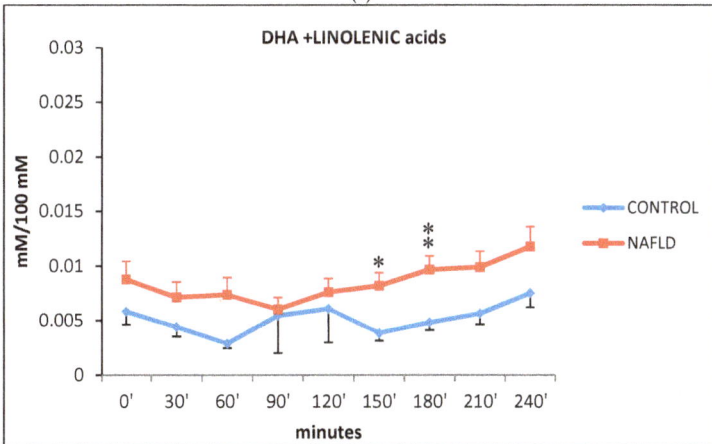

(d)

Figure 5. *Cont.*

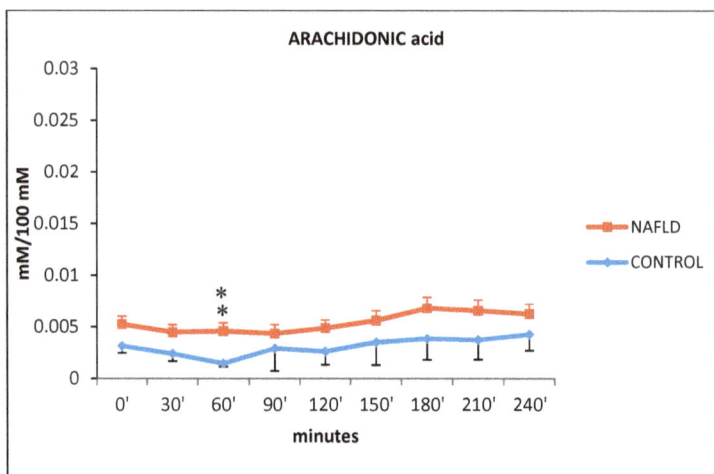

(e)

Figure 5. Change in plasma levels of palmitoleic (box **a**), linoleic (box **b**) eicosatrienoic (box c), DHA + linolenic (**d**) and arachidonic (**e**) acids during the oral fat meal in control (filled diamonds) and NAFLD (filled squares) subjects. Values are expressed as mean $\pm$ SEM. * $p < 0.05$, ** $p < 0.01$.

Linoleic acid (18:2*n*-6) (LNA) throughout the fat load showed significant differences at times 60, 150, 180, 210, and 240 min between NAFLD and control subjects (Figure 5b).

Eicosatrienoic acid (20:3*n*-9) in NAFLD patients had higher levels than in control subjects with significant differences from 150 min to the end of the fat oral test (Figure 5c).

Docosahexaenoic (22:6*n*-3) (DHA) and linolenic acids (18:3*n*-3) (ALA), two polyunsaturated fatty acids, are significantly increased in NAFLD patients at 150 and 180 min, compared to control subjects (Figure 5d).

Arachidonic acid (20:4*n*-6) (ARA) showed an almost flat trend in both NAFLD and control group with a significant difference at 60 min (Figure 5e).

The n-3/n-6 ratio measured at every time is not statistically different between control and NAFLD groups. HOMA-IR was higher in NAFLD subjects compared to the control subjects (3.16 ± 2.13 *vs.* 1.42 ± 0.49, $p = 0.024$). HOMA index positively correlated with the n-3/n-6 ratio at time 210 and 240 min in NAFLD patients ($r = 0.55$, $p = 0.0122$ and $r = 0.47$, $p = 0.035$, respectively) (Figure 6a,b).

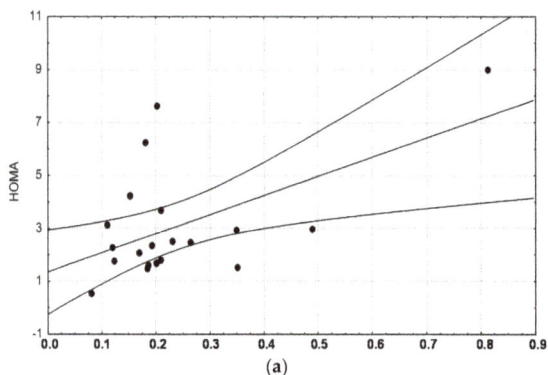

(a)

Figure 6. *Cont.*

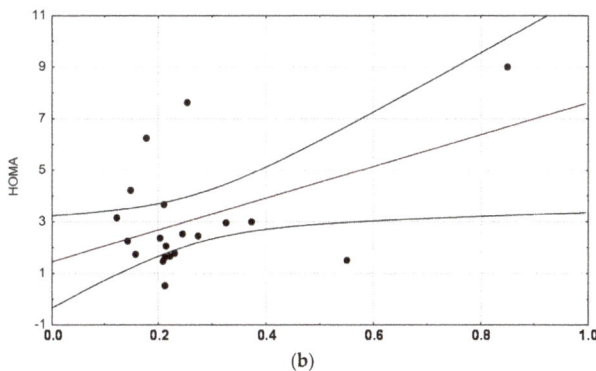

(b)

Figure 6. Correlation between homeostatic model assessment HOMA index and n-3/n-6 ratio at time 210 min in NAFLD patients (box 6a); correlation between HOMA index and n-3/n-6 ratio at time 240 min in NAFLD patients (box 6b); Figure 6a: PUFA n-3/n-6 at 210 min *vs.* HOMA in NAFLD; *r* = 0.54883, PUFA n-3/n-6 at 210 min; Figure 6b: PUFA n-3/n-6 at 240 min *vs.* HOMA in NAFLD; *r* = 0.47351, PUFA n-3/n-6 at 240 min.

3. Discussion

Free fatty acids derived from the diet can directly enter the circulation through spillover into the plasma FFA pool [23]. Other potential sources of fats causing fatty liver include adipose tissue from where non-esterified fatty acids flow to the liver, *de novo* lipogenesis and through the uptake of intestinally derived chylomicron remnants [24]. After a fatty meal, the FFA profile mirrors that of the meal [25]. We performed an abbreviated 4-hour postprandial fat load which was a valid surrogate for longer oral fat loads [26].

In the postprandial phase, the high insulinaemia and triglyceridemia observed in NAFLD patients confirms the insulin resistance state in these subjects [27]. Insulin does not suppress hormone-sensitive lipase in adipose tissue as in healthy subjects; therefore, in the postprandial phase, adipocyte-derived FFA mix with fatty acids coming from the diet and they can reach the liver.

The peak of triglycerides starts at around 4 h after the fatty meal in NAFLD subjects whilst in control subjects the peak is reached earlier. That means a delayed clearance of triglyceride-rich lipoproteins in NAFLD patients [28].

FFA levels are high in NAFLD patients compared to normal subjects with a trend similar to that of oleic and palmitic acid levels (Figures 1b and 4). This study shows that the higher serum levels of free fatty acids in NAFLD subjects are mainly due to levels of oleic (n9) and palmitic acids (reported as unique value in the data presented) which are the most abundant circulating free fatty acids (60, 150, and 210 min after the oral fat load) (Figures 1b and 4). Almost at the same time, linoleic acid (n6) levels increase significantly (60, 150, 180, 210, 240 min) (Figure 5b). Significant increases were also shown for docosahexaenoic acid (n3), linolenic acid (n-3) (Figure 5d), eicosatrienoic acid (n-9) (Figure 5c), and arachidonic acid (n6) (Figure 5e), although just on one occasion.

High levels of oleic and palmitic acids have molecular implications: oleic acid is the preferred substrate for the synthesis of triglycerides, and cholesteryl esters [29]. Palmitic acid is the substrate for isoforms 1 and 6 of fatty acid elongase (Elov-1 and Elov-6) which are converted into stearic acid [30]. Stearic acid is rapidly converted to oleic acid by the enzyme stearoyl-CoA 9-desaturase (SCD, No. EC 1.14.19.1) in mammalian cells [31]. A single double bond between carbon 9 and 10 is introduced in the chain of palmitic and stearic acids to be converted to palmitoleate and oleate, respectively [24]. The cellular ratio of oleic and stearic acids can affect membrane fluidity and signal transduction leading to an altered composition of membrane phospholipids, triglycerides and cholesterol esters [32]. Subjects exhibiting a hypertriglyceridemic response to a low-fat, high-carbohydrate diet show an increase in the oleic to stearic acids ratio [33].

Eicosatrienoic acid is significantly increased towards the end of the test in NAFLD subjects (Figure 5c). This increase is unlikely to be due to the meal composition since eicosatrienoic acid is of a negligible amount in dairy cream. Rather, eicosatrienoic acid might be derived from oleic acid metabolism [34].

Linolenic and DHA acids are two PUFA n-3 that coelute in our HPLC method. They significantly increase in NAFLD subjects at time 150 and 180 min. Humans have the ability to metabolize linolenic acids to their longer chain DHA even if this conversion is less than 1% in adults [35]. Further studies are needed to verify its physiological functions. The competition between n-3 and n6 fatty acids for the same enzymes and transport systems might explain why linoleic acid showed a flat trend throughout the test, even though they were found at higher concentrations in NAFLD patients than in control subjects.

The n-3/n-6 ratio measured every 30 min is not statistically different even if the ratio is slightly higher in control subjects than in NAFLD patients. When the n-3/n-6 ratio was correlated with HOMA-IR, it was found that HOMA index positively correlated with the n-3/n-6 ratio at times 210 and 240 min only in NAFLD patients (Figure 6a,b). Therefore, subjects who have a basal insulin resistance have higher n-3/n-6 ratio towards the end of the test as if higher n-3 fatty acids could worsen the clearance of triglycerides in NAFLD subjects. On the contrary, in healthy subjects with optimal insulin sensitivity, n-3 fatty acids could have beneficial influence on the lipid clearance. Our data seem to be in contrast with previous studies suggesting that increasing consumption of n-3 PUFA could improve lipid metabolism both in the fasting and postprandial states [36] even if modifying the n-3/n-6 polyunsaturated fatty acid ratio of a high-saturated fat challenge did not acutely change postprandial triglyceride response in men with metabolic syndrome [37]. It is likely for n-3 PUFA to need more than 8 h to exert beneficial effects in subjects with an impaired lipid metabolism [35]. Amount and type of dietary fatty acids can influence postprandial response [38]. Therefore, an imbalance in the n-3/n-6 fatty acids ratio could modulate postprandial response with more pronounced effects in insulin resistant subjects, such as NAFLD patients.

This preliminary study has some limitations due to the reduced number of control subjects available for the study which prevents us from matching by age, sex, BMI and also by physical activity on daily bases. The patients enrolled should be matched for a *de novo* clinical investigation to expand these preliminary results.

4. Experimental Section

4.1. Subjects

Twenty-one patients (ethics committee of University Hospital San Giovanni Battista of Torino, 00096648, 30 December 2009) with NAFLD (mean age $\pm$ SD, 40 $\pm$ 9 years, BMI 27.5 $\pm$ 3.9 kg/m^2) attending our Liver Unit were selected according to the following criteria: persistently (at least 12 months) elevated aspartate aminotransferases (AST) and alanine aminotransferases (ALT) in the absence of significant alcohol consumption (defined as <20 in men and <10 g/day in women); ultrasonographic presence of bright liver without any other liver or biliary tract disease. At ultrasounds, the diagnosis of NAFLD was based on four parameters: diffuse hyperechoic echotexture ("bright liver"), increased liver echotexture compared with the kidneys, vascular blurring and deep attenuation. Control subjects had a normal ultrasound liver scan.

Conditions known to be associated with fatty liver were ruled out by the following exclusion criteria: a Body Mass Index (BMI) $\geqslant$35 kg/m^2; positive serum markers of viral, autoimmune or celiac disease; abnormal copper metabolism or thyroid function indices; a diagnosis of diabetes mellitus based on plasma glucose $\geqslant$126 mg/dL in fasting conditions or $\geqslant$200 mg/dL at +2 h on a standard oral glucose tolerance test, serum total cholesterol $\geqslant$220 mg/dL, serum triglycerides

$\geqslant 160$ mg/dL. The patients did not take drugs known to be steatogenic or to affect glucose metabolism and were not exposed to occupational hepatotoxins. The control group consisted of 9 healthy subjects (mean age $\pm$ SD, 27 $\pm$ 2 years, BMI 21.2 $\pm$ 1.6 kg/m^2) with normal liver enzymes and abdomen ultrasound scan (see Table 1).

4.2. Oral Fat Load

NAFLD patients and controls underwent a standard oral fat load to investigate the metabolism of triglyceride-rich lipoproteins and FFAs. The standard fat load consisted of a mixture of dairy cream (38% fat) and egg yolk for a total energy content of 745.22 Kcal. The fat meal was composed of 79.96 g fats, whose 54.32 g was of saturated fatty acids, 21.80 g of monounsaturated fatty acids, 2.82 g of polyunsaturated fatty acids, and 0.45 g of cholesterol. The Table 2 shows the amounts of the most represented fatty acids in the fat meal given to every participant.

Table 2. Fatty acid composition of lipid mixture prepared for the oral fat load.

Fatty Acids	200 g Dairy Cream (38% fat)	NO. 1 Egg Yolk	Total Fat Load
C12:0 (g)	3.02		
C14:0 (g)	9.18	0.013	
C16:0 (g)	21.40	1.020	
C18:0 (g)	7.54	0.630	
Total SFA (g)	52.75	1.67	54.32
C18:1 (g)	18.00	1.30	
Total MUFA (g)	20.48	1.33	21.81
C18:2 (g)	1.52	0.650	
C18:3 (g)	0.20	0.019	
C20:4 (g)		0.120	
Total PUFA (g)	2.07	0.74	2.82
Total fat (g)	75.30	4.66	79.96
Cholesterol (mg)	228.00	213.92	441.92
Proteins (g)	1.60	2.53	4.12
Carbohydrates (g)	2.28		2.28
Kcal	693.20	52.02	745.22

The fat load was consumed during a period of 5 min; subjects kept fasting and strenuous activity was forbidden during the test, since exercise can reduce postprandial lipemia. A catheter (Venflon Viggo AB, Helsingborg, Sweden) inserted in the antecubital vein and kept patent during the test was used to draw blood samples at baseline and every 30 min for 4 h for biochemical determinations. Blood samples were collected in tubes containing EDTA as anticoagulant and plasma was immediately frozen. All subjects provided their informed consent for the study, which was conducted in conformance with the Helsinki Declaration.

4.3. Biochemical Analyses

Serum glucose was measured by the glucose oxidase method (Sentinel, Milan, Italy) with an intra-assay variation coefficient of 1.07% and an inter-assay variation coefficient of 2.33%.

Triglycerides (Tg) and cholesterol (Chol) were assayed by enzymatic colorimetric assays (Sentinel, Milan, Italy) with an intra-assay variation coefficient of 2.99% and an inter-assay variation coefficient of 3.46% for triglycerides and with an intra-assay variation coefficient of 2.2% and an inter-assay variation coefficient of 3.38% for cholesterol.

HDL-Chol was determined by enzymatic colorimetric assay after precipitation of LDL and VLDL fractions using heparin-MnCl$_2$ solution and centrifugation at 4 °C [39], and it had an intra-assay variation coefficient of 2.5% and an inter-assay variation coefficient of 4.1%.

HDL$_2$- and HDL$_3$-Chol levels were determined according to Gidez *et al.* [40]: HDL$_2$ and HDL$_3$ lipoproteins were separated after precipitation of Apo B-containing lipoproteins with heparin-MnCl$_2$, and HDL$_2$ particles were further precipitated with dextran sulphate. HDL$_3$-Chol was determined in the supernatant. HDL$_2$-Chol was obtained by subtracting HDL$_3$-Chol from total HDL-Chol.

LDL-Chol was measured with a standardized homogeneous enzymatic colorimetric method in order to avoid triglycerides effects on LDL-Chol determination (Sentinel, Milan, Italy).

QUICKI was calculated from fasting glucose and insulin values as previously reported [41].

HOMA was calculated using units of millimoles per liter for glucose and microunits per milliliter for insulin [42].

The determination of fatty acid composition of free fatty acids was performed by high performance liquid chromatography (HPLC) coupled with a fluorescence detector [43]. This procedure enables the analyses of the content and profile of free fatty acids in total lipids extract. For free fatty acids' analyses, we prepared an acidified sample mixture containing a small volume of serum and 10% acetic acid. The mixture was applied onto C$_{18}$ minicolumn and the column was washed with 10% acetic acid. The fatty acids were eluted with ethyl ether. The ether phase was evaporated and dried under vacuum at room temperature; the residue was dissolved into the derivatization solution containing the labeling fluorescent compound. A very small volume was injected in a HPLC reverse phase column and the free fatty acids profile was obtained within 45 min. Concentrations of each free fatty acid were obtained from a calibration curve made of 10 fatty acids run at 5 levels.

4.4. Statistical Analysis

Data were expressed as means ± SD. Between-group comparisons (NAFLD *vs.* control groups) were performed by using independent "*t*-test". To assess correlations between data, the Pearson correlation coefficient was calculated. Differences were considered statistically significant at $p < 0.05$.

5. Conclusions

The postprandial lipid metabolism in NAFLD subjects is very complex and partially understood. Although the excessive flow of FFA from adipose tissue, especially from abdominal obesity (Table 1), to the liver is considered to be the most important trigger of the NAFLD, little is known about the type of free fatty acids reaching the liver. In literature, there are few data dealing with levels of different circulating free fatty acids, but these data were usually measured only at baseline and come from small groups of subjects [5]; however, they confirmed a significant increase of oleic, palmitoleic and palmitic acids at baseline.

Taking into account the results coming out of this study, it would seem advisable for NAFLD subjects to not only follow a saturated fatty acid-free diet, but also be careful not to consume large amounts of n-3/n-6 PUFA. Obviously, these preliminary data should be further confirmed with larger clinical trials which could help to develop tailored nutritional interventions aimed to improving lipid metabolism in NAFLD subjects with the use of dynamic tests.

Acknowledgments: Funded by FP7/2007-2013 under grant agreement No. HEALTH-F2-2009-241762 for the project FLIP and by PRIN 2009ARYX4T.

Author Contributions: Roberto Gambino conceived of the study, performed HPLC analyses and participated in its design and coordination and helped to draft the manuscript; Elisabetta Bugianesi was involved in the planning of the study and commented on the draft manuscript; Chiara Rosso was involved in the planning of the study and selection of subjects; Lavinia Mezzabotta was involved in the planning of the study and selection of subjects; Silvia Pinach carried out biochemical analyses and commented on the draft manuscript; Natalina Alemanno carried out biochemical analyses; Francesca Saba performed HPLC analyses; Maurizio Cassader was involved in the planning of the study and commented on the draft manuscript; All authors read and approved the final manuscript.

Conflicts of Interest: The authors declare no conflict of interest.

References

1. Kooner, J.S.; Baliga, R.R.; Wilding, J.; Crook, D.; Packard, C.J.; Banks, L.M.; Peart, S.; Aitman, T.J.; Scott, J. Abdominal obesity, impaired nonesterified fatty acid suppression, and insulin-mediated glucose disposal are early metabolic abnormalities in families with premature myocardial infarction. *Arterioscler. Thromb. Vasc. Biol.* **1998**, *18*, 1021–1026. [CrossRef] [PubMed]

2. Zoratti, R.; Godsland, I.F.; Chaturvedi, N.; Crook, D.; Crook, D.; Stevenson, J.C.; McKeigue, P.M. Relation of plasma lipids to insulin resistance, nonesterified fatty acid levels, and body fat in men from three ethnic groups: Relevance to variation in risk of diabetes and coronary disease. *Metabolism* **2000**, *49*, 245–252. [CrossRef]

3. Musso, G.; Gambino, R.; Cassader, M. Recent insights into hepatic lipid metabolism in non-alcoholic fatty liver disease (NAFLD). *Prog. Lipid Res.* **2009**, *48*, 1–26. [CrossRef] [PubMed]

4. Musso, G.; Gambino, R.; de Michieli, F.; Biroli, G.; Fagà, E.; Pagano, G.; Cassader, M. Association of liver disease with postprandial large intestinal triglyceride-rich lipoprotein accumulation and pro/antioxidant imbalance in normolipidemic non-alcoholic steatohepatitis. *Ann. Med.* **2008**, *40*, 383–394. [CrossRef] [PubMed]

5. De Almeida, I.T.; Cortez-Pinto, H.; Fidalgo, G.; Rodrigues, D.; Camilo, M.E. Plasma total and free fatty acids composition in human non-alcoholic steatohepatitis. *Clin. Nutr.* **2002**, *21*, 219–223. [CrossRef] [PubMed]

6. Seidelin, K.N.; Myrup, B.; Fischer-Hansen, B. *n*-3 fatty acids in adipose tissue and coronary artery disease are inversely related. *Am. J. Clin. Nutr.* **1992**, *55*, 1117–1119. [PubMed]

7. Musso, G.; Gambino, R.; Pacini, G.; de Michieli, F.; Cassader, M. Prolonged saturated fat-induced, glucose-dependent insulinotropic polypeptide elevation is associated with adipokine imbalance and liver injury in nonalcoholic steatohepatitis: Dysregulated enteroadipocyte axis as a novel feature of fatty liver. *Am. J. Clin. Nutr.* **2009**, *89*, 558–567. [CrossRef] [PubMed]

8. Marinou, K.; Adiels, M.; Hodson, L.; Frayn, K.N.; Karpe, F.; Fielding, B.A. Young women partition fatty acids towards ketone body production rather than VLDL-TAG synthesis, compared with young men. *Br. J. Nutr.* **2011**, *105*, 857–865. [CrossRef] [PubMed]

9. Nelson, R.H.; Basu, R.; Johnson, C.M.; Rizza, R.A.; Miles, J.M. Splanchnic spillover of extracellular lipase-generated fatty acids in overweight and obese humans. *Diabetes* **2007**, *56*, 2878–2884. [CrossRef] [PubMed]

10. Hardy, S.; El-Assaad, W.; Przybytkowski, E.; Joly, E.; Prentki, M.; Langelier, Y. Saturated fatty acid induced-apoptosis in MDA-MB-231 breast cancer cells—A role for cardiolipin. *J. Biol. Chem.* **2003**, *278*, 31861–31870. [CrossRef] [PubMed]

11. Musso, G.; Gambino, R.; Durazzo, M.; Biroli, G.; Carello, M.; Faga, E.; Pacini, G.; de Michieli, F.; Rabbione, L.; Premoli, A.; *et al.* Adipokines in NASH: Postprandial lipid metabolism as a link between adiponectin and liver disease. *Hepatology* **2005**, *42*, 1175–1183. [CrossRef] [PubMed]

12. Okere, I.; Chandler, M.; McElfresh, T.; Rennison, J.H.; Sharov, V.; Sabbah, H.N.; Tserng, K.T.; Hoit, B.D.; Ernsberger, P.; Young, M.E.; *et al.* Differential effects of saturated and unsaturated fatty acid diets on cardiomyocyte apoptosis, adipose distribution, and serum leptin. *Am. J. Physiol. Heart Circ. Physiol.* **2006**, *291*, H38–H44. [CrossRef] [PubMed]

13. Wang, D.; Wei, Y.R.; Pagliassotti, M.J. Saturated fatty acids promote endoplasmic reticulum stress and liver injury in rats with hepatic steatosis. *Endocrinology* **2006**, *147*, 943–951. [CrossRef] [PubMed]

14. Spector, A.A.; Yorek, M.A. Membrane lipid-composition and cellular function. *J. Lipid Res.* **1985**, *26*, 1015–1035. [PubMed]

15. Borradaile, N.M.; Han, X.; Harp, J.D.; Gale, S.E.; Ory, D.S.; Schaffer, J.E. Disruption of endoplasmic reticulum structure and integrity in lipotoxic cell death. *J. Lipid Res.* **2006**, *47*, 2726–2737. [CrossRef] [PubMed]

16. Satapati, S.; Sunny, N.E.; Kucejova, B.; Fu, X.; He, T.T.; Méndez-Lucas, A.; Shelton, J.M.; Perales, J.C.; Browning, J.D.; Burgess, S.C. Elevated TCA cycle function in the pathology of diet-induced hepatic insulin resistance and fatty liver. *J. Lipid Res.* **2012**, *53*, 1080–1092. [CrossRef] [PubMed]

17. Sunny, N.E.; Parks, E.J.; Browning, J.D.; Burgess, S.C. Excessive hepatic mitochondrial TCA cycle and gluconeogenesis in humans with nonalcoholic fatty liver disease. *Cell Metab.* **2011**, *14*, 804–810. [CrossRef] [PubMed]

18. Nakamura, S.; Takamura, T.; Matsuzawa-Nagata, N.; Takayama, H.; Misu, H.; Noda, H.; Nabemoto, S.; Kurita, S.; Ota, T.; Ando, H.; *et al.* Palmitate induces insulin resistance in H4IIEC3 hepatocytes through reactive oxygen species produced by mitochondria. *J. Biol. Chem.* **2009**, *284*, 14809–14818. [CrossRef] [PubMed]

19. Paumen, M.B.; Ishida, Y.; Muramatsu, M.; Yamamoto, M.; Honjo, T. Inhibition of carnitine palmitoyltransferase I augments sphingolipid synthesis and palmitate-induced apoptosis. *J. Biol. Chem.* **1997**, *272*, 3324–3329. [CrossRef] [PubMed]

20. Summers, S.A. Ceramides in insulin resistance and lipotoxicity. *Prog. Lipid Res.* **2006**, *45*, 42–72. [CrossRef] [PubMed]

21. Maeda, K.; Cao, H.; Kono, K.; Gorgun, C.Z.; Furuhashi, M.; Uysal, K.T.; Cao, Q.; Atsumi, G.; Malone, H.; Krishnan, B.; *et al.* Adipocyte/macrophage fatty acid binding proteins control integrated metabolic responses in obesity and diabetes. *Cell Metab.* **2005**, *1*, 107–119. [CrossRef] [PubMed]

22. Yli-Jama, P.; Meyer, H.E.; Ringstad, J.; Pedersen, J.I. Serum free fatty acid pattern and risk of myocardial infarction: A case-control study. *J. Intern. Med.* **2002**, *251*, 19–28. [CrossRef] [PubMed]

23. Miles, J.M.; Park, Y.S.; Walewicz, D.; Russell-Lopez, C.; Windsor, S.; Isley, W.L.; Coppack, S.W.; Harris, W.S. Systemic and forearm triglyceride metabolism: Fate of lipoprotein lipase-generated glycerol and free fatty acids. *Diabetes* **2004**, *53*, 521–527. [CrossRef] [PubMed]

24. Havel, R.J.; Hamilton, R.L. Hepatic catabolism of remnant lipoproteins: Where the action is. *Arterioscler. Thromb. Vasc. Biol.* **2004**, *24*, 213–215. [PubMed]

25. Griffiths, A.J.; Humphreys, S.M.; Clark, M.L.; Fielding, B.A.; Frayn, K.N. Immediate metabolic availability of dietary fat in combination with carbohydrate. *Am. J. Clin. Nutr.* **1994**, *59*, 53–59. [PubMed]

26. Weiss, E.P.; Fields, D.A.; Mittendorfer, B.; Dorien Haverkort, A.M.; Klein, S. Reproducibility of postprandial lipemia test and validity of an abbreviated 4-h test. *Metabolism* **2008**, *57*, 1479–1485. [CrossRef] [PubMed]

27. Musso, G.; Gambino, R.; De Michieli, F.; Cassader, M.; Rizzetto, M.; Durazzo, M.; Fagà, E.; Silli, B.; Pagano, G. Dietary habits and their relation to insulin resistance in nonalcoholic steatohepatitis. *Hepatology* **2003**, *37*, 909–916. [CrossRef] [PubMed]

28. Cassader, M.; Gambino, R.; Musso, G.; Depetris, N.; Mecca, F.; Cavallo-Perin, P.; Pacini, G.; Rizzetto, M.; Pagano, G. Postprandial triglyceride-rich lipoprotein metabolism and insulin sensitivity in nonalcoholic steatohepatitis patients. *Lipids* **2001**, *36*, 1117–1124. [CrossRef] [PubMed]

29. Ntambi, J.M.; Miyazaki, M. Regulation of stearoyl-CoA desaturases and role in metabolism. *Prog. Lipid Res.* **2004**, *43*, 91–104. [CrossRef]

30. Inagaki, K.; Aki, T.; Fukuda, Y.; Kawamoto, S.; Shigeta, S.; Ono, K.; Suzuki, O. Identification and expression of a rat fatty acid elongase involved in the biosynthesis of C18 fatty acids. *Biosci. Biotechnol. Biochem.* **2002**, *66*, 613–621. [CrossRef] [PubMed]

31. Sampath, H.; Ntambi, J.M. The fate and intermediary metabolism of stearic acid. *Lipids* **2005**, *40*, 1187–1191. [CrossRef] [PubMed]

32. Sun, Y.; Hao, M.M.; Luo, Y.; Liang, C.P.; Silver, D.L.; Cheng, C.; Maxfield, F.R.; Tall, A.R. Stearoyl-CoA desaturase inhibits ATP-binding cassette transporter A1-mediated cholesterol efflux and modulates membrane domain structure. *J. Biol. Chem.* **2003**, *278*, 5813–5820. [CrossRef] [PubMed]

33. Attie, A.D.; Krauss, R.M.; Gray-Keller, M.P.; Brownlie, A.; Miyazaki, M.; Kastelein, J.J.; Lusis, A.J.; Stalenhoef, A.F.; Stoehr, J.P.; Hayden, M.R.; *et al.* Relationship between stearoyl-CoA desaturase activity and plasma triglycerides in human and mouse hypertriglyceridemia. *J. Lipid Res.* **2002**, *43*, 1899–1907. [CrossRef] [PubMed]

34. Le, H.D.; Meisel, J.A.; de Meijer, V.E.; Gura, K.M.; Puder, M. The essentiality of arachidonic acid and docosahexaenoic acid. *Prostaglandins Leukot. Essent. Fatty Acids* **2009**, *81*, 165–170. [CrossRef] [PubMed]

35. Brenna, J.T.; Salem, N., Jr.; Sinclair, A.J.; Cunnane, S.C. α-Linolenic acid supplementation and conversion to *n*-3 long-chain polyunsaturated fatty acids in humans. *Prostaglandins Leukot. Essent. Fatty Acids* **2009**, *80*, 85–91. [CrossRef] [PubMed]

36. Roche, H.M.; Gibney, M.J. Effect of long-chain *n*-3 polyunsaturated fatty acids on fasting and postprandial triacylglycerol metabolism. *Am. J. Clin. Nutr.* **2000**, *71*, 232s–237s. [PubMed]

37. Tulk, H.; Robinson, L. Modifying the *n*-6/*n*-3 polyunsaturated fatty acid ratio of a high-saturated fat challenge does not acutely attenuate postprandial changes in inflammatory markers in men with metabolic syndrome. *Metabolism* **2009**, *58*, 1709–1716. [CrossRef] [PubMed]

38. Song, Z.; Yang, L.; Shu, G.; Lu, H.; Sun, G. Effects of the *n*-6/*n*-3 polyunsaturated fatty acids ratio on postprandial metabolism in hypertriacylglycerolemia patients. *Lipids Health Dis.* **2013**, *12*, 181–188. [CrossRef] [PubMed]

39. Warnick, G.R.; Albers, J.J. A comprehensive evolution of the heparin manganese precipitation procedure for estimating high density lipoprotein cholesterol. *J. Lipid Res.* **1978**, *29*, 65–76.

40. Gidez, L.I.; Miller, G.J.; Burnstein, M.; Slagle, S.; Eder, H.A. Separation and quantitation of subclasses of human plasma HDL by a single precipitation procedure. *J. Lipid Res.* **1982**, *23*, 1206–1216. [PubMed]

41. Katz, A.; Nambi, S.S.; Mather, K.; Baron, A.D.; Follmann, D.A.; Sullivan, G.; Quon, M.J. Quantitative insulin sensitivity check index: A simple, accurate method for assessing insulin sensitivity in humans. *J. Clin. Endocrinol. Metab.* **2000**, *85*, 2402–2410. [CrossRef] [PubMed]

42. Matthews, D.R.; Hosker, J.P.; Rudenski, A.S.; Naylor, B.A.; Treacher, D.F.; Turner, R.C. Homeostasis model assessment: Insulin resistance and β-cell function from fasting plasma glucose and insulin concentrations in man. *Diabetologia* **1985**, *28*, 412–419. [CrossRef] [PubMed]

43. Matsuzawa, T.; Mishima, K.; Nishii, M.; Ito, M. Serum fatty acids analysis by high performance liquid chromatography, after enzymatic hydrolysis and isolation by Sep-Pak C18 minicolumn. *Biochem. Int.* **1987**, *15*, 693–702. [PubMed]

International Journal of
Molecular Sciences

MDPI

Review

Gut Microbiota and Lifestyle Interventions in NAFLD

David Houghton [1,*], Christopher J. Stewart [2], Christopher P. Day [1,3] and Michael Trenell [1,*]

[1] Institute of Cellular Medicine, Newcastle University, Newcastle upon Tyne NE4 6BE, UK;
    chris.day@newcastle.ac.uk
[2] Alkek Center for Metagenomics and Microbiome Research, Department of Molecular Virology and
    Microbiology, Baylor College of Medicine, Houston, TX 77030, USA; Christopher.Stewart@bcm.edu
[3] Liver Unit, Newcastle upon Tyne Hospitals NHS Trust, Freeman Hospital,
    Newcastle upon Tyne NE7 7DN, UK
*   Correspondence: david.houghton@ncl.ac.uk (D.H.); michael.trenell@newcastle.ac.uk (M.T.);
    Tel.: +44-191-208-6935 (M.T.); Fax: +44-191-208-8264 (D.H.); +44-191-208-5685 (M.T.)

Academic Editors: Giovanni Targher and Amedeo Lonardo
Received: 29 February 2016; Accepted: 15 March 2016; Published: 25 March 2016

Abstract: The human digestive system harbors a diverse and complex community of microorganisms that work in a symbiotic fashion with the host, contributing to metabolism, immune response and intestinal architecture. However, disruption of a stable and diverse community, termed "dysbiosis", has been shown to have a profound impact upon health and disease. Emerging data demonstrate dysbiosis of the gut microbiota to be linked with non-alcoholic fatty liver disease (NAFLD). Although the exact mechanism(s) remain unknown, inflammation, damage to the intestinal membrane, and translocation of bacteria have all been suggested. Lifestyle intervention is undoubtedly effective at improving NAFLD, however, not all patients respond to these in the same manner. Furthermore, studies investigating the effects of lifestyle interventions on the gut microbiota in NAFLD patients are lacking. A deeper understanding of how different aspects of lifestyle (diet/nutrition/exercise) affect the host–microbiome interaction may allow for a more tailored approach to lifestyle intervention. With gut microbiota representing a key element of personalized medicine and nutrition, we review the effects of lifestyle interventions (diet and physical activity/exercise) on gut microbiota and how this impacts upon NAFLD prognosis.

Keywords: NAFLD; gut microbiota; lifestyle; diet and exercise

1. Non-Alcoholic Fatty Liver Disease (NAFLD)

Non-alcoholic fatty liver disease (NAFLD) represents a spectrum of liver disease including simple steatosis, non-alcoholic steatohepatitis (NASH), fibrosis and cirrhosis, in the absence of excessive alcohol consumption [1]. NAFLD is the leading aetiology of liver disease [2], although factors leading to the development of NAFLD and progression to more advanced liver disease are poorly understood [3]. NAFLD is strongly associated with metabolic syndrome and its features including insulin resistance, obesity, hyperlipidemia, low high density lipoproteins (HDL), and hypertension and is considered the hepatic manifestation of the metabolic syndrome [4].

The incidence of NAFLD is closely associated with dietary intake and lack of physical activity, which typically manifests in obesity [5]. NAFLD is further accompanied by excess risk of type 2 diabetes mellitus (T2DM) and cardiovascular disease (CVD) [6]. The multifactorial aetiology of NAFLD is determined by both the patient's genetics and the environmental factors to which they are exposed, which may account for the substantial inter-patient variability common to the disease [7]. Although genetic polymorphisms have been attributed to account for a small portion of the patient inter-variability, there are additional contributing factors that have also been identified, spanning epigenetics, hormones, nutrition and physical inactivity [5,7]. Despite advances in NAFLD pathology, the reasons for the large inter-patient variability in progression remains incompletely understood. Consequently, a potential new diagnostic and therapeutic target receiving considerable attention is the collection of microorganisms that reside the gastrointestinal (GI) system. Despite humans being >99% identical genetically, the collection of bacteria, fungi, archea, virus, and phage are hugely diverse and highly individual from one person to the next. Termed the gut microbiota, bacteria in the gut alone accounts for around 70% of the total bacteria in the body and include 500–1000 different bacterial species [8–11].

Bacterial evolutionary linages are represented by phylogenetic trees, demonstrating the relatedness of bacteria to one another, classified from life, domain, kingdom, phylum, class, order, family, genus and finally species. The majority of research into gut microbiota has focused on phylum (Firmicutes, Bacteroidetes, *etc.*), genus (*Bacteroides*, *Lactobacillus*, *etc.*), and species (*Roseburia* spp. and *Eubacterium* spp.).

2. Gut Microbiota

Historical evidence spanning eight decades has demonstrated a link between the bacteria in the GI system and the liver, present from early fetal life and throughout life [8,12]. The gut microbiota in a healthy individual has been shown to be stable, absent of clinical manipulation (e.g., antibiotics), provided that a healthy diet and physical activity, combined with a healthy lifestyle (e.g., limited alcohol, not smoking, *etc.*) are maintained [13–18]. A healthy balance of bacteria in the GI system ensures that the gut microbiota works in a symbiotic nature with the host and its functions include maintaining a supply of essential nutrients, metabolism, immune response and intestinal architecture [19]. However, a change in the diversity leading to a reduced abundance of beneficial bacteria, with increased prevalence of potentially pathogenic bacteria can occur, which has been termed "dysbiosis" [17]. Dysbiosis of the gut microbiota has been associated with many disease states from early infancy [20], through childhood [21] and into adulthood [18]. Thus, manipulation of the gut microbiome to ensure a non-dysbiotic state offers attractive therapeutic for a range of conditions and overall health status.

Synonymous to NAFLD, inter-patient variability of the gut microbiota is well recognized, with each individual harboring a unique collection of microorganisms from the thousands that can potentially colonize, primarily from the phyla Firmicutes, Bacteroides and Actinobacteria [15,22]. Until recently, the majority of research published focused on these phyla, specifically the Firmicutes and Bacteroides, which are dominant in the gut microbiota from year three of life. However, recent advances in the throughput and affordability of deoxyribonucleic acid (DNA) sequencing technologies and associated bioinformatics [23] has facilitated an increased understanding of the pathophysiology of a number of diseases and adverse health conditions including obesity, metabolic syndrome, diabetes and cardiovascular disease [18,24–26], all of which are closely associated with NAFLD [4].

3. Gut Microbiota and NAFLD

NAFLD is a complex disease and with advances in the pathology of the disease new pharmacotherapy treatments are being developed [27,28]. However, lifestyle interventions accompanied by weight loss of between 5% and 10% remain the cornerstone of treatment [27,29]. The effectiveness of lifestyle changes are unprecedented with improvements in metabolic control and liver histology, and when accompanied by greater than 10% weight loss NASH resolution, fibrosis regression and reductions NAFLD activity score [30,31]. However, the difficulty in implementing and maintaining these lifestyle interventions in clinical practice in NAFLD is well documented, with randomized long-term studies lacking [32,33].

Due to the intimate relationship between liver and GI tract, it is unsurprising that gut microbiota dysbiosis has been linked with hepatic fat accumulation, and all stages of NAFLD in both animals and humans [7,34–41]. Although the exact mechanism linking the gut microbiota with NAFLD development and progression remains unknown, potential explanations include bacterial overgrowth, gut leakiness, increased endotoxemia absorption, and inflammation [3,36,42–45]. The increased knowledge of the gut microbiota in recent years has enhanced the understanding of the metabolic and immunological potential and microbial–host interactions, primarily in gut, but also in the liver and other organs. The role and identity of microbial produced metabolites and their direct function locally in the gut and also at other body sites remains unknown. However, increasing evidence suggests the gut microbiota as a genuine target for therapeutic interventions in the management of NAFLD (Figure 1) [8,19].

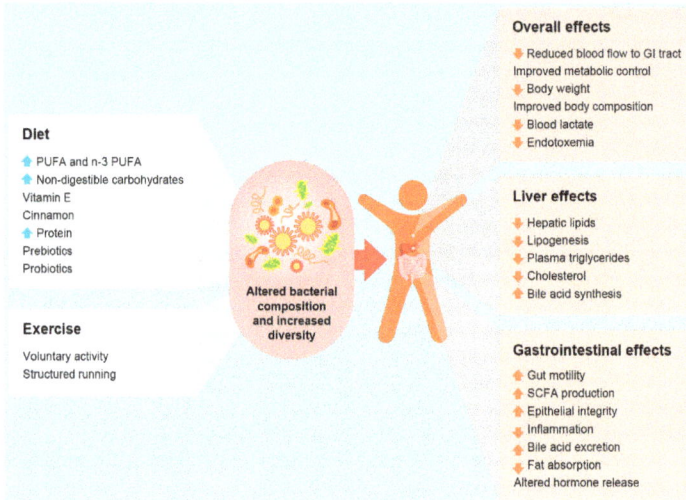

Diet
⬆ PUFA and n-3 PUFA
⬆ Non-digestible carbohydrates
Vitamin E
Cinnamon
⬆ Protein
Prebiotics
Probiotics

Exercise
Voluntary activity
Structured running

Altered bacterial composition and increased diversity

Overall effects
⬇ Reduced blood flow to GI tract
Improved metabolic control
⬇ Body weight
Improved body composition
⬇ Blood lactate
⬇ Endotoxemia

Liver effects
⬇ Hepatic lipids
⬇ Lipogenesis
⬇ Plasma triglycerides
⬇ Cholesterol
⬆ Bile acid synthesis

Gastrointestinal effects
⬆ Gut motility
⬆ SCFA production
⬆ Epithelial integrity
⬇ Inflammation
⬆ Bile acid excretion
⬇ Fat absorption
Altered hormone release

Figure 1. Impact of lifestyle interventions on gut microbiota and non-alcoholic fatty liver disease (NAFLD) and its risk factors (⬆ and ⬇ arrows denote increase or decrease in variables, respectively).

This review provides an overview of gut microbiota and its relationship with NAFLD by reviewing published data on how diet, nutrition and exercise modulate the gut microbiota and the liver. The purpose of this review is to assess the impact that lifestyle interventions (excluding pharmaceutical and surgical) have on gut microbiota and how this may interact with NAFLD development and progression.

4. Lifestyle Interventions in NAFLD

As the incidence of NAFLD increases [1], the individual and societal burden of its management weigh heavily on health care systems throughout the world, and the need for treatments to combat this is crucial [46]. Although the understanding of NAFLD has increased considerably in the last 20 years, the exact cause of why some people develop more severe forms of NAFLD is not fully understood. The development of NAFLD results from two key factors: (1) greater calories consumed compared to those expended; and (2) genetic susceptibility. Although genetic susceptibility cannot be altered (excluding epigenetic changes), calories consumed and expended can be modified, and has led to a large body of research undertaken investigating the impact of various lifestyle modification interventions [27,29]. Lifestyle interventions that lead to a reduction in weight and/or an increase in physical activity/exercise have consistently been shown to reduce hepatic lipids, improve glucose control and insulin sensitivity [29], and more recently improve liver histology [30,31]. The control of calories consumed *vs.* those expended may incorporate a number of interventions including exercise/physical activity independent of weight loss [47–49], diet modification [50–52] or diet and exercise/physical activity [30,31,53,54]. However, why some patients respond to interventions, and others do not is unknown. Modulation of the gut microbiota through the various lifestyle modifications discussed here may provide an insight into the inter-patient variability observed in NAFLD, and improve the number of people who may respond to specific lifestyle interventions to treat NAFLD.

5. Diet and Gut Microbiota

Exposure to environmental factors plays a significant role in the pathophysiology of NAFLD [6], particular dietary intake [55]. A regular healthy balanced diet has been shown to maintain a stable and healthy gut microbiota and reduce the risk of numerous diseases [56,57]. Recent evidence has emphasized the importance of calorie excess, in contrast to macronutrient content, as a major contributor to weight gain [58]. This is particularly important given the highly calorific content of the Western diet (high in fat and carbohydrates), which is associated with an altered gut microbiota and increased risk of developing obesity and NAFLD [35,46,59]. Although there are some conflicting findings, a strong association has been reported between obesity and changes in the gut microbiota, which may be responsible for enhanced energy harvest, weight gain and metabolic syndrome [60–62]. The link between the diet and the composition and function of the gut microbiota is unsurprising given that dietary components provide nutrients for bacteria, which then produce metabolites involved in energy balance, metabolism, immune response and the pathophysiology of NAFLD [63–65]. Indeed, bacteria in the gut are responsible for the digestion and production of many essential vitamins and minerals. The link between diet, gut microbiota, and health has been elegantly shown in animal models. Animals that were switched from low fat/fiber rich plant diets, to high fat/high sugar diets had significant increases in Bacilli and Erysipelotrichi from the Firmicutes phylum, which were associated with a significant decrease in the abundance of members of the Bacteroidetes phylum [66]. Furthermore, the role of the gut microbiome alone in causing obesity, independent of diet, was first demonstrated by Ley *et al.* [67] who showed mice transplanted an "obese microbiota" would have significantly greater weight gain than mice transplanted with a "lean microbiota". The substantial impact of the diet has also been shown in humans, where a rural African diet (high in fiber and vegetables) had a higher relative abundance of Bacteroidetes and a lower relative abundance of Firmicutes compared with the urban European diet (high in fat and sugar, low in fiber and vegetables). Even more interesting was that the samples from Africa had two bacterial species (*Prevottela* and *Xylanibacter*) that were not detectable in the European samples. Further evidence has been reported when comparing a control diet *vs.* diets high in non-digestible carbohydrates, where the authors reported that the non-digestible carbohydrates produce significant changes in the composition of the gut microbiota within a number of days [62].

Although there are contrasting results in the specific bacterial taxa that are modulated through the diet, the key message is that the diet is able to have a direct and long-term impact on the gut microbiota composition and function, which has a profound implication for health. Any modulation of the diet, such as an increase in non-digestible carbohydrates and/or weight loss has the potential to alter the gut microbiota and potentially disease phenotype, such as NAFLD. This approach of modulating the gut microbiota by modifying the dietary components (fats, proteins and carbohydrates), probiotics (living microorganisms that provide health effects on the host), and prebiotics (ingredients that are selectively fermented and modulate the changes in both the composition and activity of the gut microbiota) has been established for some time, although the links between specific bacteria with disease and mechanisms are often lacking [68]. This paper will now report the impact that macronutrients (fats, proteins and carbohydrates), probiotics and prebiotics manipulation has on the gut microbiota and the NAFLD phenotype.

6. Fat

Although the exact pathophysiology of NAFLD is unknown, the accumulation of lipids in the liver is a key pre-requisite for development and progression [69]. The cause of lipid accumulation in the liver is complex, but has been linked with an influx of fatty acids from fat depots, *de-novo* lipogenesis, and excess dietary fat intake, leading to steatosis. Increased fat intake is a common finding in NAFLD patients [70,71], thus regulation of fat intake has been highlighted as potential target for therapeutic intervention to reduce hepatic lipids [72]. Contrasting results have been reported in human studies that have used a high fat diet to increase hepatic lipid content [73,74], whereas others have reported no effect of a high fat diet on hepatic lipids [75,76]. The lack of consistency is likely to be due to the duration of the studies (10 days–3 weeks) and the various forms of fat used (saturated, polyunsaturated (PUFA) and mono-unsaturated (MUFA)). Furthermore, in a regular Western style diet the high fat content is normally supplemented by high carbohydrates and therefore it may be the combination of fat and carbohydrates that stimulate the development and progression of NAFLD [77]. The Western diet associated with NAFLD has also been associated with gut microbiota dysbiosis, which represents a potential source for the inter-patient variability observed in NAFLD, and progression from simple steatosis to NASH [36,78].

Although the exact mechanisms of how high fat diets lead to the development of NAFLD through gut microbiota modulation are unknown, research has predominantly focused on gut barrier function [77], leaky gut, endotoxemia, gut derived toxins and inflammation [45,79]. Despite the links between high fat diets, NAFLD, and the gut microbiota, there is a need to identify specific microbial changes that may be causative, which would highlight potential targets for diagnosis and treatment. The majority of studies investigating the impact that a high fat diet can have on the gut microbiota have been based around changes in the Firmicutes:Bacteroidetes ratio. This was firstly shown by Turnbaugh, *et al.* [80] in germ free mice that were fed a high fat diet and failed to develop obesity. Once inoculated with the microbiota from a mouse fed a high fat diet, the mice had increased weight, hepatic lipogenesis, fat deposition and insulin resistance, which was associated with an increase in Firmicutes and a subsequent decrease in Bacteroidetes [80]. This has subsequently been supported by decreases in *Eubacterium rectale*, *Blautia coccoides*, *Bifidobacteria* sp. and *Bacteroides* sp. [81–84]. Although these studies have identified that the gut microbiota is modulated with a high fat diet, the changes reported are limiting in their specificity (phylum changes rather than species), and the exact mechanism(s) linking these changes with NAFLD require further investigation.

There have been a number of mechanisms that have been identified to play a role in gut microbiota dysbiois associated with a high fat diet and the development of NAFLD including gut barrier dysfunction and translocation of microbes from the gut. Increased endotoxemia and inflammation in human [85–87] and animal studies [81,88–90] further suggests insulin resistance to be a key to the development of NAFLD and NASH [90,91]. High fat diets have also been shown to modulate the levels of Gammaproteobacteria and Erysipelotrichi, which have been shown to lead to choline deficiency, liver fat accumulation and NASH [65,92–94]. In addition, the ability of high fat diets to alter the gut microbiota and subsequently bile acids metabolism and synthesis by alleviating farnesoid X receptor (FXR) [95–97]. Although not exhaustive, the mechanisms discussed here have all been shown to have a direct impact upon the liver, therefore modulation of the gut microbiota in the presence of a high fat diet may offer the potential to reduce the risk and development of NAFLD.

The obvious treatment may be to put NAFLD patients on a low fat diet which have been shown to be effective in weight loss, reduce liver fat, improve metabolic control and modulate the gut microbiota [10,30,98]. However, managing and maintaining such diets can be difficult [32,33]. A number of alternative options for patients who may struggle with converting to a low fat diet include changing the form of fat consumed and increasing non-digestible carbohydrates. MUFA, PUFA and *n*-3 PUFA have been incorporated into dietary studies and shown to restore aspects of the high fat gut microbiota dysbiosis, including changes in Clostridia, Enterobacteriales, *Bifidobacterium* and *Lactobacillus casei* (Table 1) [99,100]. Although these studies do not report how these changes link with NAFLD, potential explanations may include reduced gut leakiness and inflammation, although these were not confirmed. In human studies, increases in MUFA, PUFA and *n*-3 PUFA have been shown to reduce hepatic lipid content and improve metabolic control in NAFLD patients [73,100], potentially due to increase fatty acid oxidation, redistribution of fatty acids and down regulation of gene expression of sterol regulatory element binding protein 1 (SREBP1-c) and factor for apoptosis (FAS). It is important to emphasize that the changes reported here did not influence weight, therefore suggesting the changes in the gut microbiota and hepatic lipids are diet driven rather than weight loss.

The use of non-digestible carbohydrates has been researched for a number of years and shown to be an effective treatment for increasing satiety, reducing blood glucose, insulin resistance, fat digestion and inducing weight loss [101]. Furthermore, non-digestible carbohydrates are effective in modulating gut microbiota and maintaining a healthy GI system [64]. However, the impact upon the gut microbiota in the presence of a high fat diet and mediators of NAFLD are lacking. Arabinoxylan and chitin-glucan have been shown to be effective at modulating the gut microbiota by increasing Bifidobacteria and restoring the abundance of *Bacteroides-Prevotella* spp., *Roseburia* spp., and *Clostridium* cluster fourteen a (XIVa) that were reduced following a high fat diet (Table 1). These changes in the gut microbiota were also supported by reductions in body fat, hepatic lipids, serum and hepatic cholesterol and insulin resistance, independent of calories consumed [102,103]. There is also evidence that, in the presence of high fat diets, chitosan and arabinoxylan are able to increase fat, bile acids and cholesterol in the feces. These studies suggest that non-digestible carbohydrates are able to modulate the gut microbiota, even in the presence of a high fat diet, potentially by binding to fat/cholesterol or inhibiting pancreatic lipase [101,104,105].

Table 1. Significant bacterial changes following dietary manipulation in the presence of high fat intake. XIV; fourteen, ↑ and ↓ denote increase or decrease in variable, respectively.

Intervention/Treatment	Model Used	Non-Microbiome Changes	Bacterial Changes	Reference
Polyunsaturated fatty acids	Cells	Inhibit growth of mucus	↑ *Lactobacillus casei*	[99]
Oleic acid and *n*-3 fatty acids (EPA and DHA)	Mice	↓ Body Weight	↑ *Clostridial* cluster XIV ↑ Enterobacteriales ↑ Firmicutes ↓ *Bifidobacterium*	[100]
Arabinoxylans	Mice	Improved gut barrier function ↓ Circulating inflammatory markers ↓ Adipocyte size ↓ Body weight gain ↓ Serum cholesterol ↓ Hepatic cholesterol ↓ Insulin resistance	↑ *Prevotella* spp. ↑ *Roseburia* spp. ↑ *Bifidobacterium*	[102]
Chitin-Glucan	Mice	↓ Body weight gain ↓ Fat Mass ↓ Fasting Glucose ↓ Hepatic Lipids ↓ Cholesterol	↑ *Clostridial* cluster XIV	[103]

Although a low fat diet may be preferable for patients with NAFLD, such a considerable change from an established lifestyle will be difficult for patients with NAFLD to incorporate. It is also important to recognize that, in general, a reduction in fat intake is typically accompanied by an increase in carbohydrate content. The data here suggest that changing the type of fat ingested and incorporating a larger proportion of non-digestible carbohydrates into the diet may be effective modulating the gut microbiota, reducing hepatic lipids and ameliorating risk factors associated with NAFLD. However, further work is required to assess the impact of diet on the gut microbiota specifically and further human intervention studies in patients with NAFLD are required to assess this.

7. Carbohydrates

Carbohydrates provide a crucial energy source for the host and gut microbiota [25]. Carbohydrate fermentation, specifically non-digestible carbohydrates, is a core activity of the human gut microbiota, driving the energy and carbon economy of the colon [106]. The move towards the Western style diet, which is high in processed carbohydrates and low in non-digestible carbohydrates, has been attributed to the rise and prevalence of obesity and NAFLD in these demographics [8,65,107]. This was recently confirmed in a meta-analysis where fructose was linked with poor liver health, although this was confounded by excessive energy intake, which is likely to be due to high fructose intake [108].

Excessive intake of calories in NAFLD is associated with sugar intake, with fructose being identified as having a crucial role to play (potentially due to altered hormone release). With regard to NAFLD, excess fructose, which is primarily metabolized in the liver, is linked to elevated steatosis [109–111]. Fructose has also been suggested to be a key driver in alteration of gut microbiota, potentially causing dysbiosis, as well as increased intestinal permeability and endotoxins in portal blood [112,113]. Notably, such factors have been previously reported in NAFLD [114]. Increased endotoxins and inflammatory cytokines have been identified to be part of the multiple hits hypothesis that exposes the liver to inflammation and injury [91]. Furthermore, endotoxemia is also linked with activation of Kupffer cells through toll like receptor dependent mechanisms, weight gain, poor metabolic control and increased plasma triglycerides, hepatic lipogenic enzymes and hepatic steatosis [111,113,115–118].

Replacing non-digestible carbohydrates with simple carbohydrates, such as fructose, will alter the substrate made available to the gut microbiota and ultimately affect the metabolic outputs and the microbial composition [67,106,119]. Numerous studies have reported that reducing non-digestible carbohydrates in the diet significantly reduces the levels of *Roseburia* spp. and *Eubacterium rectale* subgroup of cluster XIVa from the Firmicutes phylum and bifidobacteria from the Actinobacteria phylum [98,120]. More recently, the same group have also shown that increasing the levels of non-digestible carbohydrates can increase levels of *Ruminococcus bromii* (phylum:Firmicutes), however, these changes were dependent on the individuals initial microbiota profile [62]. These changes reflect the impact that non-digestible carbohydrates have on gut microbiota and subsequent health implications, although studies linking carbohydrates intake, such as non-digestible carbohydrates and fructose, with specific bacterial changes in NAFLD are lacking.

There are few studies investigating the effects of high carbohydrate intake similar to the Western diet on the gut microbiota composition. Ferrere, *et al.* [121] reported increased relative abundance of the class Erysipelotrichi (phylum:Firmicutes) following high fructose diet. Turnbaugh, Backhed, Fulton and Gordon [84] also reported that a high carbohydrate diet was able to increase the relative abundance of bacteria from the class Mollicutes (phylum:Firmicutes) and enrich genes that encode fructose metabolism, but reduce genes required for starch and sucrose metabolism. The authors suggested that the increase in Mollicutes might reduce microbial diversity, including a reduction in the relative abundance of the genus *Bacteroides* (phylum:Bacteroidetes), which is associated with poor health [61]. However, in humans Boursier, Mueller, Barret, Machado, Fizanne, Araujo-Perez, Guy, Seed, Rawls, David, Hunault, Oberti, Cales and Diehl [7] reported increased levels of *Bacteroides* in NASH patients compared to controls, which suggests that the data which we extrapolate from animal models require validation in human populations. Further studies should ascertain the effect of high fructose diets on specific bacteria to potentially identify targets for treatment.

The cornerstone of NAFLD treatment is weight loss, through diet and/or physical activity/exercise, which is effective in improving both liver histology [30] and modulating the gut microbiota [10,31]. In recent years a reduction in calories in the form of carbohydrates has been prevalent in many fad diets. Although initially effective for weight loss, such diets also have a substantial impact upon the gut microbiota and short chain fatty acids (SCFA) [98]. SCFA contribute around 10% of our daily energy requirements and provide a hospitable environment for cross feeding between microbial communities [108]. Specifically, a reduction in butyrate and butyrate producing bacteria has been shown in such diets, which may have detrimental effects on the GI structure and immune response [98,106,120]. An alternative would be to increase the amount of non-digestible carbohydrates consumed, which has been shown to be effective in maintaining a healthy gut microbiota [67] and ameliorating obesity and insulin resistance, which appear to be necessary for the development of NAFLD [122,123]. Furthermore, SCFA, including butyrate have been shown to contribute towards maintaining epithelial integrity, gut motility, hormone secretion, reducing appetite and inflammation [106], all of which are associated with NAFLD [122,123]. Increased intake of non-digestible carbohydrates has also been shown to improve glucose uptake, adipokine profile, and alter colonic fermentation, although the latter was only confirmed with breath tests [124]. Oligofructose specifically has also been shown to induce weight loss, reduce calories consumed and improved glucose uptake [125]. The authors also reported reductions in grehlin and increased peptide YY response, which have both been associated with changes in the gut microbiota following dietary intervention [126,127].

Further treatments to combat the detrimental effects of a high carbohydrate diet may involve increased protein intake, Vitamin E, and cinnamon [128–131]. All of which have been shown to be effective in reducing weight gain, body fat, adipocyte size, insulin resistance and hepatic steatosis. Although these all show promise, there are currently no data on whether these may be able to modulate the gut microbiota in NAFLD patients and should be explored further. Increased intake of carbohydrates, specifically fructose, is undoubtedly linked with NAFLD, due to either metabolism in the liver or through increasing calories consumed. Replacement of these simple carbohydrates with non-digestible carbohydrates provides potential to have a direct impact upon gut microbiota dysbiosis and have a positive effect on mediators of NAFLD.

8. Protein

Like carbohydrate, an increase in protein in the diet at the expense of carbohydrates and fat had been utilized in a number of fad diets to facilitate weight loss [132]. However, the effect that protein may have on the gut microbiota in humans, and specifically NAFLD are lacking. Furthermore, the small number of studies investigating the effects of high protein diets have predominantly focused on the products produced during fermentation [64]. This is surprising given the amount of protein that reaches the colon in a healthy diet (12–18 g), which would be expected to rise in a high protein diet [133], and provide nutrients for bacterial proliferation. Although an essential macronutrient, excess protein has been linked with potentially damaging effects on the gut microbiota and intestinal structure through toxic substances produced [64,133–135]. The small number of studies that have reported the impact that high protein diets have on the gut microbiota have reported high levels of *Clostridium* spp. and *Bacteroides* spp., with concurrent reductions in *Bifidobacterium* spp., *Roseburia* spp., and *Eubacterium* spp. [136,137]. The reductions in *Bifidobacterium* spp., *Roseburia* spp., and *Eubacterium* spp. bacterial species are associated with butyrate production, endotoxemia, mucus barrier function, and insulin sensitivity [81,136]. This suggests that the decreases in these bacteria may be detrimental to health and increase the risk of NAFLD [35–37,40,138,139].

Various animal models have been used to investigate the impact of protein on the gut microbiome with the main findings summarized in Table 2. In cats the authors utilized a high protein/low carbohydrate and a moderate protein and carbohydrate diet for eight weeks [140]. Ordination analysis of this data demonstrated that increases in the abundance of genre *Clostridium*, *Faecalibacterium*, *Ruminococcus*, *Blautia* and *Eubacterium* were clustered with plasma triglycerides. Contrastingly, piglets fed a high protein diet showed little microbial change, except reductions in *Faecalibacterium prausnitzii*, but were shown to have a higher increase in colonic permeability and higher cytokine secretion [141]. Whether this small change in bacteria can be directly attributed to the bacterial changes remains to be seen. However, the differing animal models and protein sources may account for the difference reported here. Further animal data from chickens and rats fed diets high in protein showed reductions in hepatic lipids and adipose tissue [142–144]. More recently, high protein diets have been shown to be effective for reducing hepatic lipids, blood lipids, body fat, CVD risk and improve insulin sensitivity and anti-oxidative potential [132,145–149]. Potential explanations for these results have been linked with increased satiety, increased energy expenditure, reduced hepatic lipid oxidation, cell death, hormone release in the GI system and bile acid metabolism [126,127,150], all of which are associated with the pathophysiology of NAFLD [123].

Table 2. Significant bacterial changes following high protein intake (↑ and ↓ denote increase or decrease in variable, respectively).

Intervention/Treatment	Model Used	Non-Microbiome Changes	Bacterial Changes	Reference
High Protein/Moderate Carbohydrates High Protein/Low Carbohydrates	Obese Men	↑ Branch chain amino acids ↑ Phenylacetic acid ↑ N-nitroso compounds ↓ Butyrate ↓ Phenolic acids	↓ *Roseburia* ↓ *Eubacterium*	[137]
High Protein/Low Carbohydrates	Kittens		↑ *Clostridium* ↑ *Faecalibacterium* ↑ *Ruminococcus* ↑ *Blautia* ↑ *Eubacterium*	[140]
High Protein	Piglets	↑ Branch chain amino acids ↑ Colonic Permeability ↑ Cytokine Secretion	↓ *Faecalibacterium prausnitzii*	[141]

Although there has been no direct link between the gut microbiota, NAFLD, and a high protein diet, there is evidence that an excess of 36 g/day of protein was identified as a risk factor for increasing the risk of NAFLD [111]. Furthermore, in T2DM an increase in protein intake resulted in reduced insulin sensitivity, increased gluconeogenesis and increase glucagon [151,152].

Overall, there are contrasting evidence on whether diets high in protein may be an effective treatment for gut microbiota modulation and NAFLD management. Discrepancies are likely due to differing study designs, including the source of protein (animal *vs.* plant protein), varying manipulations of the diets (protein to carbohydrate and fat ratios) populations sampled (Healthy, NAFLD, T2DM, obese, *etc.*) and study duration. The optimal benefits of diets high in protein to modulate the gut microbiota and aid with NAFLD management strategies should be explored further.

9. Prebiotics and Probiotics

Given the connection between the gut microbiota, diet, and health [65,84], coupled to issues with sustained dietary modification, an alternative approach utilizes pre- and probiotics to indirectly or directly confer beneficial colonizers of the GI, respectively [153]. Although there are various definitions, prebiotics is most commonly referred to as ingredients that are selectively fermented and modulate the changes in both the composition and activity of the gut microbiota [68,154]. Probiotics are different in that they are living (viable) microorganisms which have the ability to provide health effects on the host when provided in adequate amounts, similar to the bacteria that are already present [155].

10. Prebiotics

Fructans are the most extensively studied prebiotics and have been linked with modulation of the gut microbiota (summarized in Table 3), resulting in positive health benefits. In animal models, the administration of prebiotics increased 18 potentially beneficial species, notably *Bifidobacterium* spp. (Phylum: Actinobacteria) and Bacteroidetes [156–158]. Changes in gut microbiota are also associated with appetite regulation, improved glucose tolerance, increased satiety, reduced ghrelin, plasma triglycerides, oxidative stress and inflammation and calories consumed [82,158–160].

Further animal data have demonstrated that prebiotics are able to reduce hepatic lipids, cholesterol, plasma triglycerides and increase the SCFA propionate [161–163]. Daubioul, Rousseau, Demeure, Gallez, Taper, Declerck and Delzenne [161] suggested that the improved lipid profile and hepatic lipids were due to changes in the gut microbiota, which ultimately altered metabolites of fermentation. Alterations in the acetate:propionate ratio has been shown to reduce lipogenesis and account for the reductions in hepatic lipids. Although the authors suggest that the changes in SCFA are due to modulation of the gut microbiota, the authors failed to measure specific bacteria, focusing rather on the metabolites. It is intriguing that increased SCFA production, specifically butyrate and propionate, protect against diet-induced obesity in mice [164]. However, such studies underscore the need to understand the complex interplay between microbial–host interaction in gut and to which extent the bacterial community is causing the phenotypes observed.

In human cohorts, where systematic study is challenging, studies elucidating the exact effects and mechanisms of prebiotics on the gut microbiota and resulting microbial–host interaction are lacking. Studies in healthy and T2DM patients have provided similar results, reporting increased satiety and reduced ghrelin, body weight, glucose, and inflammation [125,157,165,166]. There is a need for studies investigating the effects of prebiotics in NAFLD. In a small pilot study in biopsy confirmed NASH patients, Daubioul, *et al.* [167] reported that prebiotics had a positive impact on liver aminotransferases and insulin, but no effects on plasma triglycerides. A recent study reported that prebiotics were effective at significantly reducing inflammatory cytokines, liver aminotransferases, insulin sensitivity and steatosis in NASH patients [168]. Notably, the study compares lifestyle alone with lifestyle and prebiotics, thus it is difficult to ascertain how much affect the prebiotics with no other lifestyle interventions alone would have. As with existing animal data, such studies lack analysis of the gut microbiota and thus relating potential mechanisms to changes in the gut microbiota is not possible.

A recent meta-analysis analyzing 26 randomized controlled trials concluded that prebiotics were effective in increasing satiety and improving insulin sensitivity [169]. While specific effects of prebiotics on the gut microbiota remain poorly understood, the majority of studies have reported increases in Bifidobacteria [170–173]. Dewulf, *et al.* [174] also reported an increase in Bifidobacteria, as well as increased levels of *Faecalibacterium prausnitzii* and reductions in *Bacteroides intestinalis*, *Bacteroides vulgatus* and *Propionibacterium*, which they associated with endotoxemia, although they failed to report any changes in plasma endotoxemia. Although these studies demonstrate promise that prebiotics may be used as a potential treatment for NAFLD, further work is required to investigate additional overall changes in the gut microbiome. Rapid advances in NGS and other 'omic technologies offer promise for more systematic understanding of entire treatment mechanisms. In addition, there are currently no studies that have reported the effects of prebiotics on hepatic lipids or liver histology, and evidence linking specific bacteria with the pathophysiology of NAFLD is lacking.

Table 3. Significant bacterial changes following prebiotic consumption (↑ and ↓ denote increase or decrease in variable, respectively).

Intervention/Treatment	Model Used	Non-Microbiome Changes	Bacterial Changes	Reference
Prebiotic Diet	Mice	Improved Glucose Tolerance Improved Leptin Sensitivity ↑ GLP-1 ↑ L-cell GLP-1 ↓ Fat Mass ↓ Oxidative Stress ↓ Inflammation	↓ Firmicutes ↑ Bacteroidetes Changed 102 taxa	[162]
Prebiotics—Xylo-oligosaccharide and inulin	Human	↑ Butyrate ↑ Propionate ↓ Acetate ↓ P-creso ↓ Lipopolysaccharides	↑ *Bifidobacterium*	[164]
Prebiotics—β2-1 Fructans	Human		↑ *Bifidobacterium*	[172]
Prebiotic—Galactooligosaccharides (GOSs)	Human	↑ Phagocytosis ↑ Natural killer cells ↓ Inflammation	↑ *Bifidobacterium*	[173]
Prebiotic—Galactooligosaccharides (GOSs)	Human	↓ Inflammation ↓ IgA ↓ Calcoprotectin ↓ Cholesterol ↓ Insulin	↑ *Bifidobacterium*	[174]

Table 3. *Cont.*

Intervention/Treatment	Model Used	Non-Microbiome Changes	Bacterial Changes	Reference
Prebiotics—Inulin type fructans	Human	↓ Fat Mass ↓ Plasma Lactate ↓ Phosphatidylcholine	↑ *Bifidobacterium* ↑ *Faecalibacterium prausnitzi* ↓ *Bacteroides intestinalis* ↓ *Bacteroides vulgatus* ↓ *Propionibacterium*	[175]

11. Probiotics

Probiotics have been suggested as a potential treatment for patients with NAFLD, due to their apparent ability to modulate the gut microbiota (Table 4) and impact upon metabolic control, inflammation, lipid profile and intestinal permeability [155,175], and have been systematically reviewed in detail elsewhere [176]. However, the exact mechanisms of how probiotics are able to do this are not fully understood. Although not exhaustive, proposed mechanisms include direct microbe-to-microbe interaction and competition with pathogenic bacteria potentially leading to eradication and a healthy balance of gut microbiota [62,177]. Furthermore, probiotics have been shown to be effective at improving epithelial barrier integrity [178] and stimulating the host immune response [179,180].

One of the first studies to investigate the use of probiotics was conducted over 10 years ago in mice. The authors demonstrated that a course of a common brand of probiotics called VSL#3, which included *Streptococcus thermophiles*, *Lactobacillus* (species: *acidophilus, delbrueckii, casei* and *plantarum*) and *Bifidobacterium* (species: *breve, longum and infantis*) over four weeks was as effective as an anti-TNF antibody at improving liver histology, reducing hepatic lipids, and reducing serum alanine aminotransferase [181]. Importantly, the authors also reported a reduction in pro-inflammatory cytokines and hepatic insulin resistance resulting from modulation of the gut microbiota, although they failed to assess this. This early study into probiotics demonstrates potential for ameliorating multiple hits that are associated with the pathophysiology and development of NAFLD [69,91]. Subsequent to this pioneering study, further animal work has reported that probiotics are effective at reducing cholesterol, low density lipoproteins (LDL), very low density lipoproteins (VLDL), triglycerides [182,183], fat depots [184], hepatic lipid content [185–187], steatotic and peroxidase factors and liver aminotransferase [188,189]. There is also evidence demonstrating improvements in hepatic insulin resistance and metabolic control [81,186,190,191]

There is also a body of evidence that has reported reduced inflammation and endotoxemia following probiotic administration period. An exaggerated and damaging inflammatory response occurs in a range of conditions and current evidence associates dysbiosis of the gut microbiota with inflammation, although it is unclear if this is cause or effect. This is especially prevalent in the case of the mucosa and tight protein junctions, where pathogenic bacteria cause damage and increase gut permeability leading to chronic inflammation and endotoxemia [155,192]. Direct modulation of the gut microbiota with viable organisms in probiotics has been shown to reduce hepatic inflammation [188], circulating inflammatory markers [181,191,193], endotoxemia in portal blood [194] and provide essential nutrients for maintaining intestinal epithelium integrity [178,195].

Although these data do imply that probiotics may play a role in the therapeutic management of NAFLD, human data are lacking. In obese children who were non-compliant to lifestyle interventions, probiotics significantly reduced alanine aminotransferase (ALT) and anti-peptidoglycan-polysaccharide antibodies, but did not reduce liver fat [196]. In three well-designed randomized controlled studies, the authors observed that probiotics high in *Lactobacillus gasseri* reduced abdominal adiposity and serum lipids [197–199]. However, the duration of these studies was relatively short and the effects on liver steatosis and specific bacterial changes were not reported.

Similar results have been shown in patients with liver disease, where probiotics have been shown to be effective at restoring neutrophil phagocytic capacity in cirrhosis and reducing IL-10, IL-6 and TNF-α secretion and toll like receptor expression [200,201]. More specifically, in NAFLD, the administration of probiotics resulted in a significant reduction liver aminotransferase [202,203], although no changes in hepatic lipids, liver histology or gut microbiota were reported.

The majority of the studies discussed suggest that gut microbiota modulation following consumption of probiotics was responsible for the beneficial effects observed. Early animal data from Cani, Neyrinck, Fava, Knauf, Burcelin, Tuohy, Gibson and Delzenne [81] demonstrated that supplementing mice on a high fat diet with *Bifidobacterium* restored the levels of *Bifidobacterium* comparable to controls on a normal chow fed diet. More recently Bifidobacteria added to animal feed has been shown to increase the abundance of *Bifidobacterium* and *Clostridiaceae* and reduce the abundance of *Enterobacteria* and Eubacteriaceae [184,187,191,193,204]. The changes in bacterial diversity discussed here were also supported by reductions in inflammatory cytokines, endotoxemia, hepatic lipids and gut permeability.

Table 4. Significant bacterial changes following probiotic consumption (↑ and ↓ denote increase or decrease in variable, respectively).

Intervention/Treatment	Model Used	Non-Microbiome Changes	Bacterial Changes	Reference
Probiotic—oligofructose and Bifidobacterium species	Mice	↓ Endotoxemia Improved glucose tolerance	↑ *Bifidobacterium*	[81]
Probiotic—Bifidobacterium longum	Rat	↓ Endotoxemia ↓ Inflammation ↓ Intestinal myeloperoxidase ↓ Body Weight ↓ Fat Depots ↓ Systolic Blood Pressure Improve insulin sensitivity	↑ *Bifidobacterium*	[185]
Probiotic—Bifidobacterium longum or Lactobacillus acidophilus	Rat	↓ Hepatic Lipids	↑ *Bifidobacterium longum* ↑ *Lactobacillus acidophilus*	[188]
Probiotic—Bifidobacterium pseudocatenulatum	Mice	↓ Cholesterol ↓ Triglycerides ↓ Glucose levels ↓ Insulin resistance ↓ Leptin ↓ Inflammation ↓ Hepatic Lipids	↑ *Bifidobacterium* ↓ *Enterobacteria*	[192]
Probiotic—Bifidobacterium pseudocatenulatum	Mice	↓ Inflammation ↓ Endotoxemia ↓ B cells ↓ Macrophages ↓ Cholesterol ↓ Body Weight Gain ↓ Triglycerides ↓ Insulin resistance	↓ *Firmicutes* ↓ *Proteobacteria*	[194]
Probiotic—Bifidobacterium breve	Mice	↑ Propionate	↑ *Clostridiaceae* ↓ *Eubacteriaceae*	[205]

Although existing data suggest probiotics represent a safe and effective treatment option for NAFLD, there are instances where probiotics were ineffective, such as in Crohn's disease [205] and Helicobacter infections [206]. Such results may simply represent inefficiency of the probiotics selected for these studies and it is plausible different probiotic combinations may yield different results. It should be noted that probiotics are regarded as safe, with little data showing any adverse effects of supplementation. As each disease is uniquely complex, so too must the probiotic selected for treatment, with better characterization of the disease mechanism informing the specific probiotics to use [62]. Important considerations also include the route of administration, dosage, how often to take the treatment, and for how long. As we better understand the most effective means of administering probiotics as well as which specific combinations of bacteria to use, the efficacy of treatment should become apparent. In the era of personalized medicine it is feasible that each NAFLD patient can have their gut microbiota profile determined, allowing probiotics to be tailored to the individual.

12. Exercise

Exercise is well recognized for its health benefits and its ability to attenuate the risk of CVD, obesity, mental disorders, diabetes and intestinal diseases [207,208]. More specifically exercise has been shown to be effective at modulating hepatic steatosis and its mediators, improve body composition, liver and adipose tissue insulin sensitivity independent of weight loss [29,47–49,209]. Furthermore exercise (both endurance and high intensity) training has been shown to attenuate inflammation and improve insulin secretion by upregulating glucagon-like peptide-1 secretion in the GI tract and pancreas [209–211]. Despite the strong associations among exercise, liver health, metabolic control and inflammation, evidence linking exercise, the gut microbiota and NAFLD in humans is lacking. Understanding the interplay between the triad and resulting mechanisms in NAFLD will be fundamental to translating therapeutics into clinical practice.

In a recent study, Clarke, *et al.* [212] investigated the effects of effects of exercise in rugby players compared sedentary overweight and obese controls. The authors observed that the highly active rugby players had a significantly more diverse gut microbiota and lower levels of inflammatory and metabolic markers compared to the controls. Specifically, the authors identified increased relative abundance of Firmicutes, Proteobacteria and reduced relative abundance of Bacteroidetes. These observations are based on extremities of a population with vastly different diet and calorie consumption, thus linking findings directly to the gut microbiota is challenging [18,213]. The authors acknowledge these confounding variables, stating future studies must be well designed in an attempt to isolate the effects that exercise may have on the gut microbiota.

Although animal models do not offer a direct comparison with humans, the control over interventions allows an excellent model to develop disease states and may make it easier to tease out the impact that exercise alone may have on the gut microbiota. To date, there are no animal studies looking specifically at exercise and the gut microbiota in an animal model of NAFLD. There are, however, a number of other animal studies that have investigated the effects of exercise on the gut microbiota in type 2 diabetes [214], obesity, CVD [215], high fat intake [216,217] and low activity levels [218], which are all risk factors for the development and progression of NAFLD [5,6], summarized in Table 5.

Table 5. Significant bacterial changes following exercise (↑ and ↓ denote increase or decrease in variable, respectively).

Intervention/Treatment	Model Used	Non-Microbiome Changes	Bacterial Changes	Reference
Controlled treadmill running	Mice		↑ *Lactobacillus* spp. ↑ *Clostridium leptum* (C-IV) ↓ *Clostridium* cluster (C-XI) ↓ *Bifidobacterium* spp	[215]
Controlled treadmill running	Rat	↓ Blood Lactate	↑ *Allocaculum* ↑ *Pseudomonas* ↑ *Lactobacillus* ↓ *Streptococcus* ↓ *Aggregatibacter* ↓ *Sutturella*	[216]
Voluntary wheel running	Mice	↓ Body Weight ↓ Body Fat ↓ Blood glucose ↑ Heart:Body Weight	↑ Bacteroidetes ↓ Firmicutes ↓ Actinobacteria	[217]

Table 5. *Cont.*

Intervention/Treatment	Model Used	Non-Microbiome Changes	Bacterial Changes	Reference
Controlled wheel running	Mice		↓ *Streptococcus* ↓ Bacteroidetes ↑ Firmicutes	[218]
Voluntary wheel running	Rat	↓ Body Fat ↑ Lean Body Mass ↓ Non-esterified fatty acids ↓ Cholesterol	↓ Firmicutes ↑ Cyanobacteria ↑ Proteobacteia	[219]
Voluntary wheel running	Rat	↑ Cecal size and weight ↑ Butyrate production ↓ Body Weight	↑ SM7/11 ↑ T2-87	[220]
Voluntary and forced treadmill running	Mice	↓ Body Weight	↑ *Dorea* ↑ *Anaerotruncus* ↑ *Nautilia* ↑ *Coprococcus* ↑ *Oscillospira* ↓ *Turicibacter* ↓ *Moryella* ↓ *Prevotella*	[221]
Voluntary wheel running	Mice	↓ Body Weight	↑ Enterococcsceae ↑ Staphylococcsceae ↓ Erysipelotrichaceae	[222]
Voluntary wheel running	Rat	↑ Body Weight ↑ Serum Leptin ↓ Serum Ghrelin	↑ *B. Coccoides-E Rectale* ↑ *Lactobacillus* ↓ *Clostridium* ↓ *Enteroccocus* ↓ *Prevotella* ↓ *Bacteroides*	[223]
Voluntary wheel running	Rat	↑ Body Weight ↑ Lean Body Mass	↓ *Rikenellaceae* g_AF12 ↓ *Rikenellaceae* g ↓ *Desulfovibrio* spp ↑ *Blautia* spp ↑ *Turicibacter* ↑ *Anaerostipes* spp ↑ *Methanosphaera*	[224]
Single Peak Exercise Test	Human	↑ Bacteria in blood	↑ Actinobacteria ↑ Firmicutes	[225]

The first animal study to investigate the effects of exercise on the gut microbiota was performed nearly a decade ago using rats who voluntarily exercised for five weeks [219]. Rats that exercised had a distinctly different bacterial cluster from the sedentary rats, with a significant increase in bacterial producing bacterium (SM7/11 and T2-87). The exercised mice also consumed fewer calories, had reduced body weight and an in increase in butyrate. Both voluntary and forced exercise has since been shown to elicit significant clustering and increased richness of the gut microbiota, with distinctive changes in the abundance of genus *Lactobacillus, Bifidobacterium, Dorea, Turicibacter, Anaerotruncus* and species *Enterococcus faecium* when compared with sedentary animals [220–222].

The role of genetic and epigenetic predisposition is unclear, but the gut microbiota evolves with the host from birth [8,12]. Therefore, early manipulation of the microbiota may have beneficial effects later in life. Genetically altered rats with low activity levels from birth had a greater shift in bacterial diversity when compare to the highly active rats [218]. Furthermore, this extenuated increase in bacterial diversity in the low activity rats was supported by a greater improvement in body composition and serum lipid profile, when compared with the highly active mice. The beneficial effects of exercise early in life suggests that even in those with a genetic predisposition to be sedentary may be able to modulate their gut microbiota and risk factors for NAFLD. Further evidence was presented when exercising juvenile and adults rats [223]. Juvenile rats had greater shifts in bacterial composition when compared with the exercising adult rats, which were closely related to body composition of the rats. These studies together suggest that early stimulus and the activity predisposition (low *vs.* high) may be involved in characterizing gut microbiota phenotypes.

Further exercise studies have investigated the effects of exercise on the gut microbiota in hypertension, obesity and diabetes, which are all closely associated with NAFLD [6]. Petriz, Castro,

Almeida, Gomes, Fernandes, Kruger, Pereira and Franco [215] exercised obese and hypertensive rats five times per week for four weeks and observed altered composition and diversity of the gut microbiota, with specific increases in *Allobaculum* in hypertensive rats, and *Pseudomonas* and *Lactobacillus* in the obese rats. In a similar exercise intervention, Lambert, Myslicki, Bomhof, Belke, Shearer and Reimer [214] exercised diabetic and control mice and compared them with matched sedentary controls. The authors observed a significant increase in the abundance of several Firmicutes species and reductions in the abundance of *Bacteroides* spp., which had previously been reported in humans [212]. The only human study to look at the acute effects of exercise on gut microbiota was performed in patients with myalgic encephalomyelitis/chronic fatigue syndrome compared to healthy controls [224]. The authors reported that following a single maximal exercise bout the gut microbiota of patients was significantly altered in comparison with controls. Furthermore the patients had a significantly larger level of bacteria recovered in the blood when compared with the healthy controls. Although the authors only conducted a single bout of exercise, they suggest that the altered gut microbiota led to an increase in bacterial translocation and may contribute to worsening myalgic encephalomyelitis/chronic fatigue syndrome. The increased bacteria in the blood may be due to an increase in inflammatory cytokines (IL-6, IL-8, IL-1β, and TNF-α), which have been shown to be required to initiate villus injury and reduce intestinal barrier function [210]. However, the authors failed to report on inflammation, and it must be pointed out that the exercise performed was maximal, which would not be routinely performed. Despite this there is a large body of evidence demonstrating that exercise is able to reduce inflammation [211], hepatic lipids [29], and improves metabolic control [47,209,225,226]. However, further work would need to compare different modalities of exercise and intensities to assess their impact on the gut microbiota, liver fat, metabolic control, inflammation and patients health.

Inter-study variability has been reported by Petriz, Castro, Almeida, Gomes, Fernandes, Kruger, Pereira and Franco [215], who reported increased relative abundance of *Allobaculum*, *Pseudomonas* and *Lactobacillus*. However, Liu, Park, Holscher, Padilla, Scroggins, Welly, Britton, Koch, Vieira-Potter and Swanson [218] reported increased relative abundance of Christensenellaceae, Helicobacteraceae and Desulfovibrionaceae, and Choi, Eum, Rampersaud, Daunert, Abreu and Toborek [221] reported increased relative abundance of the family Enterococcaceae and decreased relative abundance of Erysipelotrichaceae.

Possible reasons for discrepancy reported between studies may include; varying disease type and status amongst studies, exercise intervention duration and/or intensity, diet incorporated (ranging from high fat diet to regular animal chow) and body composition changes. Of particular note, the varying methods and technologies used to extract and sequence the 16S rRNA gene creates potential sources of bias between studies.

Exercise does appear to be able to modulate the gut microbiota and reduce the risk of NAFLD, however, the mechanism(s) remain unknown. Potential mechanisms include: (1) increased butyrate production, which is linked with colonic epithelial cell proliferation and modulation of mucosal immunity and exclusion of pathogens [215,219,227]; (2) increased primary bile acid secretion and cholesterol turnover [228]; (3) growth of beneficial bacteria [221]; and (4) increased core body temperature and reduced blood flow to the GI system reducing gut transit time and substrate delivery to the microbiota [218,229,230]. Although the exact mechanism remains elusive and methodological bias hinders direct cross-study comparisons, existing data indicate that exercise may be able to modulate the composition, diversity and relative abundance of the gut microbiota in NAFLD patients. Further investigation of the impact of exercise on gut microbiota is required and may address why some patients respond to exercise and some do not.

13. Conclusions

The gut microbiota has been studied for decades, however, recent developments in 16S rRNA gene sequencing, coupled to advances in computational processing of data has enhanced our understanding of the microbial–host interactions [23]. The gut microbiota has been associated with a range of diseases, from obesity, metabolic syndrome, diabetes, and cardiovascular disease [18,24–26] to NAFLD [7,34,36–41]. However, existing studies are largely focused on profiling the bacterial community and fail to provide functional information between the gut microbiota and the host. Ultimately, it still remains unknown whether the gut microbiome is *causing* the disease, or simply an *effect* of disease pathophysiology.

This review reveals that diet, pre/probiotics, and exercise play a significant role in the function and diversity of the gut microflora. To date, studies have predominantly focused on pre-clinical models, which have limitations in the transferability of their data to humans. Although much is known, significant questions about how lifestyle therapies may influence the gut microbiota as a therapeutic target for NAFLD care. However, the links between the gut microbiota and NAFLD should continue to be explored to:

(1)   better understand inter-patient variability;
(2)   develop potential biomarkers for NAFLD development and progression;
(3)   understand the mechanism(s) linking the gut microbiota and NAFLD;
(4)   develop an understanding of how aspects of lifestyle interventions interact with the gut microbiota and how this may impact upon health; and
(5)   tailor prebiotics and probiotics to influence health for each individual.

Furthermore, although these lifestyle interventions clearly impact upon NAFLD, understanding of how they interact with the gut microbiota and NAFLD is lacking and requires longitudinal studies with large sample sizes. For example, the diet has been shown to modulate the gut microbiota in days [62], but these changes are generally reversed in a similar time frame. Therefore, we need to understand the best mechanisms for modulating the long-term establishment of a healthy gut microbiota and the resulting health implications this may have.

As technologies are increasingly developed and the associated costs are reduced, there is huge potential to systematically determine the importance of both the presence of certain bacteria and their ultimate function is a given community. For understanding such complex processes and interaction at the microbe and host levels, there is a need to integrate multiple techniques in a systems biology approach. A focus on large-scale collaborative studies that explore many relevant biological samples to comprehensively determine disease mechanisms and therapeutic efficiency is necessary. This represents an important time for life sciences and the prospect of advances in diseases such as NAFLD is promising.

Author Contributions: David Houghton, Christopher J. Stewart, Christopher P. Day and Michael Trenell participated in the study concept and design. David Houghton and Christopher J. Stewart conducted the literature search and acquisition of the literature presented. David Houghton, Christopher J. Stewart, Christopher P. Day and Michael Trenell drafted the manuscript, read and approved the final manuscript.

Conflicts of Interest: The authors declare no conflict of interest.

References

1.   Anstee, Q.M.; McPherson, S.; Day, C.P. How big a problem is non-alcoholic fatty liver disease? *BMJ* **2011**, *343*, d3897. [CrossRef] [PubMed]
2.   Harrison, S.A.; Day, C.P. Benefits of lifestyle modification in NAFLD. *Gut* **2007**, *56*, 1760–1769. [CrossRef] [PubMed]
3.   Henao-Mejia, J.; Elinav, E.; Jin, C.; Hao, L.; Mehal, W.Z.; Strowig, T.; Thaiss, C.A.; Kau, A.L.; Eisenbarth, S.C.; Jurczak, M.J.; *et al.* Inflammasome-mediated dysbiosis regulates progression of NAFLD and obesity. *Nature* **2012**, *482*, 179–185. [CrossRef] [PubMed]
4.   De Alwis, N.M.; Day, C.P. Non-alcoholic fatty liver disease: The mist gradually clears. *J. Hepatol.* **2008**, *48*, S104–S112. [CrossRef] [PubMed]

5. Ratziu, V.; Sheikh, M.Y.; Sanyal, A.J.; Lim, J.K.; Conjeevaram, H.; Chalasani, N.; Abdelmalek, M.; Bakken, A.; Renou, C.; Palmer, M.; *et al.* A phase 2, randomized, double-blind, placebo-controlled study of GS-9450 in subjects with nonalcoholic steatohepatitis. *Hepatology* **2012**, *55*, 419–428. [CrossRef] [PubMed]

6. Anstee, Q.M.; Targher, G.; Day, C.P. Progression of NAFLD to diabetes mellitus, cardiovascular disease or cirrhosis. *Nat. Rev. Gastroenterol. Hepatol.* **2013**, *10*, 330–344. [CrossRef] [PubMed]

7. Boursier, J.; Mueller, O.; Barret, M.; Machado, M.; Fizanne, L.; Araujo-Perez, F.; Guy, C.D.; Seed, P.C.; Rawls, J.F.; David, L.A.; *et al.* The Severity of NAFLD Is Associated with Gut Dysbiosis and Shift in the Metabolic Function of the Gut Microbiota. Available online: http://www.mdlinx.com/gastroenterology/medical-news-article/2015/11/30/nafld-metabolic-function/6431385/ (accessed on 24 March 2016).

8. Abu-Shanab, A.; Quigley, E.M. The role of the gut microbiota in nonalcoholic fatty liver disease. *Nat. Rev. Gastroenterol. Hepatol.* **2010**, *7*, 691–701. [CrossRef] [PubMed]

9. Ley, R.E.; Peterson, D.A.; Gordon, J.I. Ecological and evolutionary forces shaping microbial diversity in the human intestine. *Cell* **2006**, *124*, 837–848. [CrossRef] [PubMed]

10. Ley, R.E.; Turnbaugh, P.J.; Klein, S.; Gordon, J.I. Microbial ecology: Human gut microbes associated with obesity. *Nature* **2006**, *444*, 1022–1023. [CrossRef] [PubMed]

11. Whitman, W.B.; Coleman, D.C.; Wiebe, W.J. Prokaryotes: The unseen majority. *Proc. Natl. Acad. Sci. USA* **1998**, *95*, 6578–6583. [CrossRef] [PubMed]

12. Hoefert, B. Bacteria findings in duodenal juice of healthy and sick. *Zschr. Klin. Med.* **1921**, *92*, 221–235.

13. Caballero, F.; Fernandez, A.; Matias, N.; Martinez, L.; Fucho, R.; Elena, M.; Caballeria, J.; Morales, A.; Fernandez-Checa, J.C.; Garcia-Ruiz, C. Specific contribution of methionine and choline in nutritional nonalcoholic steatohepatitis: Impact on mitochondrial S-adenosyl-L-methionine and glutathione. *J. Biol. Chem.* **2010**, *285*, 18528–18536. [CrossRef] [PubMed]

14. Claesson, M.J.; Cusack, S.; O'Sullivan, O.; Greene-Diniz, R.; de Weerd, H.; Flannery, E.; Marchesi, J.R.; Falush, D.; Dinan, T.; Fitzgerald, G.; *et al.* Composition, variability, and temporal stability of the intestinal microbiota of the elderly. *Proc. Natl. Acad. Sci. USA* **2011**, *108*, 4586–4591. [CrossRef] [PubMed]

15. Clemente, J.C.; Ursell, L.K.; Parfrey, L.W.; Knight, R. The impact of the gut microbiota on human health: An integrative view. *Cell* **2012**, *148*, 1258–1270. [CrossRef] [PubMed]

16. Faith, J.J.; Guruge, J.L.; Charbonneau, M.; Subramanian, S.; Seedorf, H.; Goodman, A.L.; Clemente, J.C.; Knight, R.; Heath, A.C.; Leibel, R.L.; *et al.* The long-term stability of the human gut microbiota. *Science* **2013**, *341*, 1237439. [CrossRef] [PubMed]

17. Holzapfel, W.H.; Haberer, P.; Snel, J.; Schillinger, U.; Huis in't Veld, J.H. Overview of gut flora and probiotics. *Int. J. Food Microbiol.* **1998**, *41*, 85–101. [CrossRef]

18. Sommer, F.; Backhed, F. The gut microbiota—Masters of host development and physiology. *Nat. Rev. Microbiol.* **2013**, *11*, 227–238. [CrossRef] [PubMed]

19. Hooper, L.V.; Gordon, J.I. Commensal host-bacterial relationships in the gut. *Science* **2001**, *292*, 1115–1118. [CrossRef] [PubMed]

20. Stewart, C.J.; Marrs, E.C.; Nelson, A.; Lanyon, C.; Perry, J.D.; Embleton, N.D.; Cummings, S.P.; Berrington, J.E. Development of the preterm gut microbiome in twins at risk of necrotising enterocolitis and sepsis. *PLoS ONE* **2013**, *8*, e73465. [CrossRef] [PubMed]

21. Stewart, J.A.; Chadwick, V.S.; Murray, A. Investigations into the influence of host genetics on the predominant eubacteria in the faecal microflora of children. *J. Med. Microbiol.* **2005**, *54*, 1239–1242. [CrossRef] [PubMed]

22. Qin, J.; Li, R.; Raes, J.; Arumugam, M.; Burgdorf, K.S.; Manichanh, C.; Nielsen, T.; Pons, N.; Levenez, F.; Yamada, T.; *et al.* A human gut microbial gene catalogue established by metagenomic sequencing. *Nature* **2010**, *464*, 59–65. [CrossRef] [PubMed]

23. Round, J.L.; Mazmanian, S.K. The gut microbiota shapes intestinal immune responses during health and disease. *Nat. Rev. Immunol.* **2009**, *9*, 313–323. [CrossRef] [PubMed]

24. DuPont, A.W.; DuPont, H.L. The intestinal microbiota and chronic disorders of the gut. *Nat. Rev. Gastroenterol. Hepatol.* **2011**, *8*, 523–531. [CrossRef] [PubMed]

25. Russell, W.R.; Duncan, S.H.; Flint, H.J. The gut microbial metabolome: Modulation of cancer risk in obese individuals. *Proc. Nutr. Soc.* **2013**, *72*, 178–188. [CrossRef] [PubMed]

26. Vrieze, A.; van Nood, E.; Holleman, F.; Salojarvi, J.; Kootte, R.S.; Bartelsman, J.F.; Dallinga-Thie, G.M.; Ackermans, M.T.; Serlie, M.J.; Oozeer, R.; *et al.* Transfer of intestinal microbiota from lean donors increases insulin sensitivity in individuals with metabolic syndrome. *Gastroenterology* **2012**, *143*, 913–916. [CrossRef] [PubMed]

27. Hardy, T.; Anstee, Q.M.; Day, C.P. Nonalcoholic fatty liver disease: New treatments. *Curr. Opin. Gastroenterol.* **2015**, *31*, 175–183. [CrossRef] [PubMed]

28. Taylor, R. Pathogenesis of type 2 diabetes: Tracing the reverse route from cure to cause. *Diabetologia* **2008**, *51*, 1781–1789. [CrossRef] [PubMed]

29. Thoma, C.; Day, C.P.; Trenell, M.I. Lifestyle interventions for the treatment of non-alcoholic fatty liver disease in adults: A systematic review. *J. Hepatol.* **2012**, *56*, 255–266. [CrossRef] [PubMed]

30. Vilar-Gomez, E.; Martinez-Perez, Y.; Calzadilla-Bertot, L.; Torres-Gonzalez, A.; Gra-Oramas, B.; Gonzalez-Fabian, L.; Friedman, S.L.; Diago, M.; Romero-Gomez, M. Weight loss via lifestyle modification significantly reduces features of nonalcoholic steatohepatitis. *Gastroenterology* **2015**, *149*, 367–378. [CrossRef] [PubMed]

31. Promrat, K.; Kleiner, D.E.; Niemeier, H.M.; Jackvony, E.; Kearns, M.; Wands, J.R.; Fava, J.L.; Wing, R.R. Randomized controlled trial testing the effects of weight loss on nonalcoholic steatohepatitis. *Hepatology* **2010**, *51*, 121–129. [CrossRef] [PubMed]

32. Dudekula, A.; Rachakonda, V.; Shaik, B.; Behari, J. Weight loss in nonalcoholic fatty liver disease patients in an ambulatory care setting is largely unsuccessful but correlates with frequency of clinic visits. *PLoS ONE* **2014**, *9*, e111808. [CrossRef] [PubMed]

33. Yamada, T.; Hara, K.; Svensson, A.K.; Shojima, N.; Hosoe, J.; Iwasaki, M.; Yamauchi, T.; Kadowaki, T. Successfully achieving target weight loss influences subsequent maintenance of lower weight and dropout from treatment. *Obesity* **2015**, *23*, 183–191. [CrossRef] [PubMed]

34. Bacchi, E.; Moghetti, P. Exercise for hepatic fat accumulation in type 2 diabetic subjects. *Int. J. Endocrinol.* **2013**, *2013*, 309191. [CrossRef] [PubMed]

35. Boursier, J.; Diehl, A.M. Implication of gut microbiota in nonalcoholic fatty liver disease. *PLoS Pathog.* **2015**, *11*, e1004559. [CrossRef] [PubMed]

36. Cani, P.D. When specific gut microbes reveal a possible link between hepatic steatosis and adipose tissue. *J. Hepatol.* **2014**, *61*, 5–6. [CrossRef] [PubMed]

37. Farhadi, A.; Gundlapalli, S.; Shaikh, M.; Frantzides, C.; Harrell, L.; Kwasny, M.M.; Keshavarzian, A. Susceptibility to gut leakiness: A possible mechanism for endotoxaemia in non-alcoholic steatohepatitis. *Liver Int.* **2008**, *28*, 1026–1033. [CrossRef] [PubMed]

38. Le Roy, T.; Llopis, M.; Lepage, P.; Bruneau, A.; Rabot, S.; Bevilacqua, C.; Martin, P.; Philippe, C.; Walker, F.; Bado, A.; *et al.* Intestinal microbiota determines development of non-alcoholic fatty liver disease in mice. *Gut* **2013**, *62*, 1787–1794. [CrossRef] [PubMed]

39. Mouzaki, M.; Comelli, E.M.; Arendt, B.M.; Bonengel, J.; Fung, S.K.; Fischer, S.E.; McGilvray, I.D.; Allard, J.P. Intestinal microbiota in patients with nonalcoholic fatty liver disease. *Hepatology* **2013**, *58*, 120–127. [CrossRef] [PubMed]

40. Wigg, A.J.; Roberts-Thomson, I.C.; Dymock, R.B.; McCarthy, P.J.; Grose, R.H.; Cummins, A.G. The role of small intestinal bacterial overgrowth, intestinal permeability, endotoxaemia, and tumour necrosis factor α in the pathogenesis of non-alcoholic steatohepatitis. *Gut* **2001**, *48*, 206–211. [CrossRef] [PubMed]

41. Zhu, L.; Baker, S.S.; Gill, C.; Liu, W.; Alkhouri, R.; Baker, R.D.; Gill, S.R. Characterization of gut microbiomes in nonalcoholic steatohepatitis (NASH) patients: A connection between endogenous alcohol and NASH. *Hepatology* **2013**, *57*, 601–609. [CrossRef] [PubMed]

42. Cani, P.D.; Osto, M.; Geurts, L.; Everard, A. Involvement of gut microbiota in the development of low-grade inflammation and type 2 diabetes associated with obesity. *Gut Microbes* **2012**, *3*, 279–288. [CrossRef] [PubMed]

43. Kirsch, R.; Clarkson, V.; Verdonk, R.C.; Marais, A.D.; Shephard, E.G.; Ryffel, B.; de la, M.H.P. Rodent nutritional model of steatohepatitis: Effects of endotoxin (lipopolysaccharide) and tumor necrosis factor α deficiency. *J. Gastroenterol. Hepatol.* **2006**, *21*, 174–182. [CrossRef] [PubMed]

44. Nolan, J.P. Intestinal endotoxins as mediators of hepatic injury—An idea whose time has come again. *Hepatology* **1989**, *10*, 887–891. [CrossRef] [PubMed]

45. Nolan, J.P.; Leibowitz, A.I. Endotoxins in liver disease. *Gastroenterology* **1978**, *75*, 765–766. [PubMed]

46. Trenell, M.I. Sedentary behaviour, physical activity, and NAFLD: Curse of the chair. *J. Hepatol.* **2015**, *63*, 1064–1065. [CrossRef] [PubMed]

47. Hallsworth, K.; Fattakhova, G.; Hollingsworth, K.G.; Thoma, C.; Moore, S.; Taylor, R.; Day, C.P.; Trenell, M.I. Resistance exercise reduces liver fat and its mediators in non-alcoholic fatty liver disease independent of weight loss. *Gut* **2011**, *60*, 1278–1283. [CrossRef] [PubMed]

48. Hickman, I.J.; Byrne, N.M.; Croci, I.; Chachay, V.S.; Clouston, A.D.; Hills, A.P.; Bugianesi, B.; Whitehead, J.P.; Gastaldelli, A.; O'Moore-Sullivan, T.M.; *et al.* Randomised study of the metabolic and histological effects of exercise in non alcoholic steatohepatitis. *J. Diabetes Metab.* **2013**, *4*. [CrossRef]

49. Johnson, N.A.; Sachinwalla, T.; Walton, D.W.; Smith, K.; Armstrong, A.; Thompson, M.W.; George, J. Aerobic exercise training reduces hepatic and visceral lipids in obese individuals without weight loss. *Hepatology* **2009**, *50*, 1105–1112. [CrossRef] [PubMed]

50. Kirk, E.; Reeds, D.N.; Finck, B.N.; Mayurranjan, S.M.; Patterson, B.W.; Klein, S. Dietary fat and carbohydrates differentially alter insulin sensitivity during caloric restriction. *Gastroenterology* **2009**, *136*, 1552–1560. [CrossRef] [PubMed]

51. Viljanen, A.P.; Iozzo, P.; Borra, R.; Kankaanpaa, M.; Karmi, A.; Lautamaki, R.; Jarvisalo, M.; Parkkola, R.; Ronnemaa, T.; Guiducci, L.; *et al.* Effect of weight loss on liver free fatty acid uptake and hepatic insulin resistance. *J. Clin. Endocrinol. Metab.* **2009**, *94*, 50–55. [CrossRef] [PubMed]

52. Wong, V.W.; Chan, R.S.; Wong, G.L.; Cheung, B.H.; Chu, W.C.; Yeung, D.K.; Chim, A.M.; Lai, J.W.; Li, L.S.; Sea, M.M.; *et al.* Community-based lifestyle modification programme for non-alcoholic fatty liver disease: A randomized controlled trial. *J. Hepatol.* **2013**, *59*, 536–542. [CrossRef] [PubMed]

53. Lazo, M.; Solga, S.F.; Horska, A.; Bonekamp, S.; Diehl, A.M.; Brancati, F.L.; Wagenknecht, L.E.; Pi-Sunyer, F.X.; Kahn, S.E.; Clark, J.M. Effect of a 12-month intensive lifestyle intervention on hepatic steatosis in adults with type 2 diabetes. *Diabetes Care* **2010**, *33*, 2156–2163. [CrossRef] [PubMed]

54. Oza, N.; Eguchi, Y.; Mizuta, T.; Ishibashi, E.; Kitajima, Y.; Horie, H.; Ushirogawa, M.; Tsuzura, T.; Nakashita, S.; Takahashi, H.; *et al.* A pilot trial of body weight reduction for nonalcoholic fatty liver disease with a home-based lifestyle modification intervention delivered in collaboration with interdisciplinary medical staff. *J. Gastroenterol.* **2009**, *44*, 1203–1208. [CrossRef] [PubMed]

55. Lim, J.S.; Mietus-Snyder, M.; Valente, A.; Schwarz, J.M.; Lustig, R.H. The role of fructose in the pathogenesis of NAFLD and the metabolic syndrome. *Nat. Rev. Gastroenterol. Hepatol.* **2010**, *7*, 251–264. [CrossRef] [PubMed]

56. Costello, E.K.; Lauber, C.L.; Hamady, M.; Fierer, N.; Gordon, J.I.; Knight, R. Bacterial community variation in human body habitats across space and time. *Science* **2009**, *326*, 1694–1697. [CrossRef] [PubMed]

57. Zoetendal, E.G.; Akkermans, A.D.; De Vos, W.M. Temperature gradient gel electrophoresis analysis of 16s rrna from human fecal samples reveals stable and host-specific communities of active bacteria. *Appl. Environ. Microbiol.* **1998**, *64*, 3854–3859. [PubMed]

58. Sacks, F.M.; Bray, G.A.; Carey, V.J.; Smith, S.R.; Ryan, D.H.; Anton, S.D.; McManus, K.; Champagne, C.M.; Bishop, L.M.; Laranjo, N.; *et al.* Comparison of weight-loss diets with different compositions of fat, protein, and carbohydrates. *N. Engl. J. Med.* **2009**, *360*, 859–873. [CrossRef] [PubMed]

59. Weinsier, R.L.; Hunter, G.R.; Heini, A.F.; Goran, M.I.; Sell, S.M. The etiology of obesity: Relative contribution of metabolic factors, diet, and physical activity. *Am. J. Med.* **1998**, *105*, 145–150. [CrossRef]

60. Karlsson, F.; Tremaroli, V.; Nielsen, J.; Backhed, F. Assessing the human gut microbiota in metabolic diseases. *Diabetes* **2013**, *62*, 3341–3349. [CrossRef] [PubMed]

61. Ley, R.E.; Backhed, F.; Turnbaugh, P.; Lozupone, C.A.; Knight, R.D.; Gordon, J.I. Obesity alters gut microbial ecology. *Proc. Natl. Acad. Sci. USA* **2005**, *102*, 11070–11075. [CrossRef] [PubMed]

62. Walker, A.W.; Ince, J.; Duncan, S.H.; Webster, L.M.; Holtrop, G.; Ze, X.; Brown, D.; Stares, M.D.; Scott, P.; Bergerat, A.; *et al.* Dominant and diet-responsive groups of bacteria within the human colonic microbiota. *ISME J.* **2011**, *5*, 220–230. [CrossRef] [PubMed]

63. Saghizadeh, M.; Ong, J.M.; Garvey, W.T.; Henry, R.R.; Kern, P.A. The expression of TNF α by human muscle. Relationship to insulin resistance. *J. Clin. Investig.* **1996**, *97*, 1111–1116. [CrossRef] [PubMed]

64. Scott, K.P.; Gratz, S.W.; Sheridan, P.O.; Flint, H.J.; Duncan, S.H. The influence of diet on the gut microbiota. *Pharmacol. Res.* **2013**, *69*, 52–60. [CrossRef] [PubMed]

65. Spencer, M.D.; Hamp, T.J.; Reid, R.W.; Fischer, L.M.; Zeisel, S.H.; Fodor, A.A. Association between composition of the human gastrointestinal microbiome and development of fatty liver with choline deficiency. *Gastroenterology* **2011**, *140*, 976–986. [CrossRef] [PubMed]

66. Turnbaugh, P.J.; Ridaura, V.K.; Faith, J.J.; Rey, F.E.; Knight, R.; Gordon, J.I. The effect of diet on the human gut microbiome: A metagenomic analysis in humanized gnotobiotic mice. *Sci. Transl. Med.* **2009**, *1*, 6ra14. [CrossRef] [PubMed]

67. De Filippo, C.; Cavalieri, D.; di Paola, M.; Ramazzotti, M.; Poullet, J.B.; Massart, S.; Collini, S.; Pieraccini, G.; Lionetti, P. Impact of diet in shaping gut microbiota revealed by a comparative study in children from europe and rural africa. *Proc. Natl. Acad. Sci. USA* **2010**, *107*, 14691–14696. [CrossRef] [PubMed]

68. Gibson, G.R.; Roberfroid, M.B. Dietary modulation of the human colonic microbiota: Introducing the concept of prebiotics. *J. Nutr.* **1995**, *125*, 1401–1412. [PubMed]

69. Day, C.P.; James, O.F. Steatohepatitis: A tale of two "hits"? *Gastroenterology* **1998**, *114*, 842–845. [CrossRef]

70. Musso, G.; Gambino, R.; De Michieli, F.; Cassader, M.; Rizzetto, M.; Durazzo, M.; Faga, E.; Silli, B.; Pagano, G. Dietary habits and their relations to insulin resistance and postprandial lipemia in nonalcoholic steatohepatitis. *Hepatology* **2003**, *37*, 909–916. [CrossRef] [PubMed]

71. Toshimitsu, K.; Matsuura, B.; Ohkubo, I.; Niiya, T.; Furukawa, S.; Hiasa, Y.; Kawamura, M.; Ebihara, K.; Onji, M. Dietary habits and nutrient intake in non-alcoholic steatohepatitis. *Nutrition* **2007**, *23*, 46–52. [CrossRef] [PubMed]

72. Donnelly, K.L.; Smith, C.I.; Schwarzenberg, S.J.; Jessurun, J.; Boldt, M.D.; Parks, E.J. Sources of fatty acids stored in liver and secreted via lipoproteins in patients with nonalcoholic fatty liver disease. *J. Clin. Investig.* **2005**, *115*, 1343–1351. [CrossRef] [PubMed]

73. Westerbacka, J.; Lammi, K.; Hakkinen, A.M.; Rissanen, A.; Salminen, I.; Aro, A.; Yki-Jarvinen, H. Dietary fat content modifies liver fat in overweight nondiabetic subjects. *J. Clin. Endocrinol. Metab.* **2005**, *90*, 2804–2809. [CrossRef] [PubMed]

74. Van Herpen, N.A.; Schrauwen-Hinderling, V.B.; Schaart, G.; Mensink, R.P.; Schrauwen, P. Three weeks on a high-fat diet increases intrahepatic lipid accumulation and decreases metabolic flexibility in healthy overweight men. *J. Clin. Endocrinol. Metab.* **2011**, *96*, E691–E695. [CrossRef] [PubMed]

75. Marina, A.; von Frankenberg, A.D.; Suvag, S.; Callahan, H.S.; Kratz, M.; Richards, T.L.; Utzschneider, K.M. Effects of dietary fat and saturated fat content on liver fat and markers of oxidative stress in overweight/obese men and women under weight-stable conditions. *Nutrients* **2014**, *6*, 4678–4690. [CrossRef] [PubMed]

76. Utzschneider, K.M.; Bayer-Carter, J.L.; Arbuckle, M.D.; Tidwell, J.M.; Richards, T.L.; Craft, S. Beneficial effect of a weight-stable, low-fat/low-saturated fat/low-glycaemic index diet to reduce liver fat in older subjects. *Br. J. Nutr.* **2013**, *109*, 1096–1104. [CrossRef] [PubMed]

77. Delarue, J.; Lalles, J.P. Nonalcoholic fatty liver disease: Roles of the gut and the liver and metabolic modulation by some dietary factors and especially long-chain *n*-3 PUFA. *Mol. Nutr. Food Res.* **2016**, *60*, 147–159. [CrossRef] [PubMed]

78. Tilg, H.; Moschen, A.R. Insulin resistance, inflammation, and non-alcoholic fatty liver disease. *Trends Endocrinol. Metab.* **2008**, *19*, 371–379. [CrossRef] [PubMed]

79. Cani, P.D.; Amar, J.; Iglesias, M.A.; Poggi, M.; Knauf, C.; Bastelica, D.; Neyrinck, A.M.; Fava, F.; Tuohy, K.M.; Chabo, C.; *et al.* Metabolic endotoxemia initiates obesity and insulin resistance. *Diabetes* **2007**, *56*, 1761–1772. [CrossRef] [PubMed]

80. Turnbaugh, P.J.; Ley, R.E.; Mahowald, M.A.; Magrini, V.; Mardis, E.R.; Gordon, J.I. An obesity-associated gut microbiome with increased capacity for energy harvest. *Nature* **2006**, *444*, 1027–1031. [CrossRef] [PubMed]

81. Cani, P.D.; Neyrinck, A.M.; Fava, F.; Knauf, C.; Burcelin, R.G.; Tuohy, K.M.; Gibson, G.R.; Delzenne, N.M. Selective increases of bifidobacteria in gut microflora improve high-fat-diet-induced diabetes in mice through a mechanism associated with endotoxaemia. *Diabetologia* **2007**, *50*, 2374–2383. [CrossRef] [PubMed]

82. Hildebrandt, M.A.; Hoffmann, C.; Sherrill-Mix, S.A.; Keilbaugh, S.A.; Hamady, M.; Chen, Y.Y.; Knight, R.; Ahima, R.S.; Bushman, F.; Wu, G.D. High-fat diet determines the composition of the murine gut microbiome independently of obesity. *Gastroenterology* **2009**, *137*, 1716–1724. [CrossRef] [PubMed]

83. Murphy, E.F.; Cotter, P.D.; Healy, S.; Marques, T.M.; O'Sullivan, O.; Fouhy, F.; Clarke, S.F.; O'Toole, P.W.; Quigley, E.M.; Stanton, C.; *et al.* Composition and energy harvesting capacity of the gut microbiota: Relationship to diet, obesity and time in mouse models. *Gut* **2010**, *59*, 1635–1642. [CrossRef] [PubMed]

84. Turnbaugh, P.J.; Backhed, F.; Fulton, L.; Gordon, J.I. Diet-induced obesity is linked to marked but reversible alterations in the mouse distal gut microbiome. *Cell Host Microbe* **2008**, *3*, 213–223. [CrossRef] [PubMed]

85. Ghanim, H.; Abuaysheh, S.; Sia, C.L.; Korzeniewski, K.; Chaudhuri, A.; Fernandez-Real, J.M.; Dandona, P. Increase in plasma endotoxin concentrations and the expression of toll-like receptors and suppressor of cytokine signaling-3 in mononuclear cells after a high-fat, high-carbohydrate meal: Implications for insulin resistance. *Diabetes Care* **2009**, *32*, 2281–2287. [CrossRef] [PubMed]

86. Pendyala, S.; Walker, J.M.; Holt, P.R. A high-fat diet is associated with endotoxemia that originates from the gut. *Gastroenterology* **2012**, *142*, 1100–1101. [CrossRef] [PubMed]

87. Pussinen, P.J.; Havulinna, A.S.; Lehto, M.; Sundvall, J.; Salomaa, V. Endotoxemia is associated with an increased risk of incident diabetes. *Diabetes Care* **2011**, *34*, 392–397. [CrossRef] [PubMed]

88. Amar, J.; Chabo, C.; Waget, A.; Klopp, P.; Vachoux, C.; Bermudez-Humaran, L.G.; Smirnova, N.; Berge, M.; Sulpice, T.; Lahtinen, S.; *et al.* Intestinal mucosal adherence and translocation of commensal bacteria at the early onset of type 2 diabetes: Molecular mechanisms and probiotic treatment. *EMBO Mol. Med.* **2011**, *3*, 559–572. [CrossRef] [PubMed]

89. Caesar, R.; Tremaroli, V.; Kovatcheva-Datchary, P.; Cani, P.D.; Backhed, F. Crosstalk between gut microbiota and dietary lipids aggravates wat inflammation through TLR signaling. *Cell Metab.* **2015**, *22*, 658–668. [CrossRef] [PubMed]

90. Su, L.; Wang, J.H.; Cong, X.; Wang, L.H.; Liu, F.; Xie, X.W.; Zhang, H.H.; Fei, R.; Liu, Y.L. Intestinal immune barrier integrity in rats with nonalcoholic hepatic steatosis and steatohepatitis. *Chin. Med. J.* **2012**, *125*, 306–311. [PubMed]

91. Tilg, H.; Moschen, A.R. Evolution of inflammation in nonalcoholic fatty liver disease: The multiple parallel hits hypothesis. *Hepatology* **2010**, *52*, 1836–1846. [CrossRef] [PubMed]

92. Corbin, K.D.; Zeisel, S.H. Choline metabolism provides novel insights into nonalcoholic fatty liver disease and its progression. *Curr. Opin. Gastroenterol.* **2012**, *28*, 159–165. [CrossRef] [PubMed]

93. Jiang, X.C.; Li, Z.; Liu, R.; Yang, X.P.; Pan, M.; Lagrost, L.; Fisher, E.A.; Williams, K.J. Phospholipid transfer protein deficiency impairs apolipoprotein-b secretion from hepatocytes by stimulating a proteolytic pathway through a relative deficiency of vitamin e and an increase in intracellular oxidants. *J. Biol. Chem.* **2005**, *280*, 18336–18340. [CrossRef] [PubMed]

94. Dumas, M.E.; Barton, R.H.; Toye, A.; Cloarec, O.; Blancher, C.; Rothwell, A.; Fearnside, J.; Tatoud, R.; Blanc, V.; Lindon, J.C.; *et al.* Metabolic profiling reveals a contribution of gut microbiota to fatty liver phenotype in insulin-resistant mice. *Proc. Natl. Acad. Sci. USA* **2006**, *103*, 12511–12516. [CrossRef] [PubMed]

95. Fukiya, S.; Arata, M.; Kawashima, H.; Yoshida, D.; Kaneko, M.; Minamida, K.; Watanabe, J.; Ogura, Y.; Uchida, K.; Itoh, K.; *et al.* Conversion of cholic acid and chenodeoxycholic acid into their 7-oxo derivatives by bacteroides intestinalis AM-1 isolated from human feces. *FEMS Microbiol. Lett.* **2009**, *293*, 263–270. [CrossRef] [PubMed]

96. Islam, K.B.; Fukiya, S.; Hagio, M.; Fujii, N.; Ishizuka, S.; Ooka, T.; Ogura, Y.; Hayashi, T.; Yokota, A. Bile acid is a host factor that regulates the composition of the cecal microbiota in rats. *Gastroenterology* **2011**, *141*, 1773–1781. [CrossRef] [PubMed]

97. Sayin, S.I.; Wahlstrom, A.; Felin, J.; Jantti, S.; Marschall, H.U.; Bamberg, K.; Angelin, B.; Hyotylainen, T.; Oresic, M.; Backhed, F. Gut microbiota regulates bile acid metabolism by reducing the levels of tauro-β-muricholic acid, a naturally occurring fxr antagonist. *Cell Metab.* **2013**, *17*, 225–235. [CrossRef] [PubMed]

98. Duncan, S.H.; Lobley, G.E.; Holtrop, G.; Ince, J.; Johnstone, A.M.; Louis, P.; Flint, H.J. Human colonic microbiota associated with diet, obesity and weight loss. *Int. J. Obes.* **2008**, *32*, 1720–1724. [CrossRef] [PubMed]

99. Kankaanpaa, P.E.; Salminen, S.J.; Isolauri, E.; Lee, Y.K. The influence of polyunsaturated fatty acids on probiotic growth and adhesion. *FEMS Microbiol. Lett.* **2001**, *194*, 149–153. [CrossRef] [PubMed]

100. Mujico, J.R.; Baccan, G.C.; Gheorghe, A.; Diaz, L.E.; Marcos, A. Changes in gut microbiota due to supplemented fatty acids in diet-induced obese mice. *Br. J. Nutr.* **2013**, *110*, 711–720. [CrossRef] [PubMed]

101. Bozzetto, L.; Prinster, A.; Annuzzi, G.; Costagliola, L.; Mangione, A.; Vitelli, A.; Mazzarella, R.; Longobardo, M.; Mancini, M.; Vigorito, C.; *et al.* Liver fat is reduced by an isoenergetic MUFA diet in a controlled randomized study in type 2 diabetic patients. *Diabetes Care* **2012**, *35*, 1429–1435. [CrossRef] [PubMed]

102. Houghton, D.; Wilcox, M.D.; Chater, P.I.; Brownlee, I.A.; Seal, C.J.; Pearson, J.P. Biological activity of alginate and its effect on pancreatic lipase inhibition as a potential treatment for obesity. *Food Hydrocoll.* **2015**, *49*, 18–24. [CrossRef] [PubMed]

103. Neyrinck, A.M.; Possemiers, S.; Druart, C.; van de Wiele, T.; De Backer, F.; Cani, P.D.; Larondelle, Y.; Delzenne, N.M. Prebiotic effects of wheat arabinoxylan related to the increase in *Bifidobacteria*, *Roseburia* and *Bacteroides*/*Prevotella* in diet-induced obese mice. *PLoS ONE* **2011**, *6*, e20944. [CrossRef] [PubMed]

104. Neyrinck, A.M.; Possemiers, S.; Verstraete, W.; De Backer, F.; Cani, P.D.; Delzenne, N.M. Dietary modulation of *Clostridial* cluster xiva gut bacteria (*Roseburia* spp.) by chitin-glucan fiber improves host metabolic alterations induced by high-fat diet in mice. *J. Nutr. Biochem.* **2012**, *23*, 51–59. [CrossRef] [PubMed]

105. Lopez, H.W.; Levrat, M.A.; Guy, C.; Messager, A.; Demigne, C.; Remesy, C. Effects of soluble corn bran arabinoxylans on cecal digestion, lipid metabolism, and mineral balance (Ca, Mg) in rats. *J. Nutr. Biochem.* **1999**, *10*, 500–509. [CrossRef]

106. Wydro, P.; Krajewska, B.; Hac-Wydro, K. Chitosan as a lipid binder: A langmuir monolayer study of chitosan-lipid interactions. *Biomacromolecules* **2007**, *8*, 2611–2617. [CrossRef] [PubMed]

107. Flint, H.J.; Scott, K.P.; Louis, P.; Duncan, S.H. The role of the gut microbiota in nutrition and health. *Nat. Rev. Gastroenterol. Hepatol.* **2012**, *9*, 577–589. [CrossRef] [PubMed]

108. David, L.A.; Maurice, C.F.; Carmody, R.N.; Gootenberg, D.B.; Button, J.E.; Wolfe, B.E.; Ling, A.V.; Devlin, A.S.; Varma, Y.; Fischbach, M.A.; *et al.* Diet rapidly and reproducibly alters the human gut microbiome. *Nature* **2014**, *505*, 559–563. [CrossRef] [PubMed]

109. Chung, M.; Ma, J.T.; Patel, K.; Berger, S.; Lau, J.; Lichtenstein, A.H. Fructose, high-fructose corn syrup, sucrose, and nonalcoholic fatty liver disease or indexes of liver health: A systematic review and meta-analysis. *Am. J. Clin. Nutr.* **2014**, *100*, 833–849. [CrossRef] [PubMed]

110. Collison, K.S.; Saleh, S.M.; Bakheet, R.H.; Al-Rabiah, R.K.; Inglis, A.L.; Makhoul, N.J.; Maqbool, Z.M.; Zaidi, M.Z.; Al-Johi, M.A.; Al-Mohanna, F.A. Diabetes of the liver: The link between nonalcoholic fatty liver disease and HFCS-55. *Obesity* **2009**, *17*, 2003–2013. [CrossRef] [PubMed]

111. Saad, M.F.; Khan, A.; Sharma, A.; Michael, R.; Riad-Gabriel, M.G.; Boyadjian, R.; Jinagouda, S.D.; Steil, G.M.; Kamdar, V. Physiological insulinemia acutely modulates plasma leptin. *Diabetes* **1998**, *47*, 544–549. [CrossRef] [PubMed]

112. Zelber-Sagi, S.; Nitzan-Kaluski, D.; Goldsmith, R.; Webb, M.; Blendis, L.; Halpern, Z.; Oren, R. Long term nutritional intake and the risk for non-alcoholic fatty liver disease (NAFLD): A population based study. *J. Hepatol.* **2007**, *47*, 711–717. [CrossRef] [PubMed]

113. Bergheim, I.; Weber, S.; Vos, M.; Kramer, S.; Volynets, V.; Kaserouni, S.; McClain, C.J.; Bischoff, S.C. Antibiotics protect against fructose-induced hepatic lipid accumulation in mice: Role of endotoxin. *J. Hepatol.* **2008**, *48*, 983–992. [CrossRef] [PubMed]

114. Spruss, A.; Kanuri, G.; Wagnerberger, S.; Haub, S.; Bischoff, S.C.; Bergheim, I. Toll-like receptor 4 is involved in the development of fructose-induced hepatic steatosis in mice. *Hepatology* **2009**, *50*, 1094–1104. [CrossRef] [PubMed]

115. Thuy, S.; Ladurner, R.; Volynets, V.; Wagner, S.; Strahl, S.; Konigsrainer, A.; Maier, K.P.; Bischoff, S.C.; Bergheim, I. Nonalcoholic fatty liver disease in humans is associated with increased plasma endotoxin and plasminogen activator inhibitor 1 concentrations and with fructose intake. *J. Nutr.* **2008**, *138*, 1452–1455. [PubMed]

116. Bizeau, M.E.; Pagliassotti, M.J. Hepatic adaptations to sucrose and fructose. *Metabolism* **2005**, *54*, 1189–1201. [CrossRef] [PubMed]

117. Pagliassotti, M.J.; Prach, P.A.; Koppenhafer, T.A.; Pan, D.A. Changes in insulin action, triglycerides, and lipid composition during sucrose feeding in rats. *Am. J. Physiol.* **1996**, *271*, R1319–R1326. [PubMed]

118. Poulsom, R. Morphological changes of organs after sucrose or fructose feeding. *Prog. Biochem. Pharmacol.* **1986**, *21*, 104–134. [PubMed]

119. Spruss, A.; Kanuri, G.; Stahl, C.; Bischoff, S.C.; Bergheim, I. Metformin protects against the development of fructose-induced steatosis in mice: Role of the intestinal barrier function. *Lab. Investig.* **2012**, *92*, 1020–1032. [CrossRef] [PubMed]

120. Walker, A.W.; Duncan, S.H.; McWilliam Leitch, E.C.; Child, M.W.; Flint, H.J. Ph and peptide supply can radically alter bacterial populations and short-chain fatty acid ratios within microbial communities from the human colon. *Appl. Environ. Microbiol.* **2005**, *71*, 3692–3700. [CrossRef] [PubMed]

121. Duncan, S.H.; Belenguer, A.; Holtrop, G.; Johnstone, A.M.; Flint, H.J.; Lobley, G.E. Reduced dietary intake of carbohydrates by obese subjects results in decreased concentrations of butyrate and butyrate-producing bacteria in feces. *Appl. Environ. Microbiol.* **2007**, *73*, 1073–1078. [CrossRef] [PubMed]

122. Ferrere, G.; Leroux, A.; Wrzosek, L.; Puchois, V.; Gaudin, F.; Ciocan, D.; Renoud, M.L.; Naveau, S.; Perlemuter, G.; Cassard, A.M. Activation of kupffer cells is associated with a specific dysbiosis induced by fructose or high fat diet in mice. *PLoS ONE* **2016**, *11*, e0146177. [CrossRef] [PubMed]

123. Pagano, G.; Pacini, G.; Musso, G.; Gambino, R.; Mecca, F.; Depetris, N.; Cassader, M.; David, E.; Cavallo-Perin, P.; Rizzetto, M. Nonalcoholic steatohepatitis, insulin resistance, and metabolic syndrome: Further evidence for an etiologic association. *Hepatology* **2002**, *35*, 367–372. [CrossRef] [PubMed]

124. Vrieze, A.; Holleman, F.; Zoetendal, E.G.; de Vos, W.M.; Hoekstra, J.B.; Nieuwdorp, M. The environment within: How gut microbiota may influence metabolism and body composition. *Diabetologia* **2010**, *53*, 606–613. [CrossRef] [PubMed]

125. Nilsson, A.C.; Ostman, E.M.; Holst, J.J.; Bjorck, I.M. Including indigestible carbohydrates in the evening meal of healthy subjects improves glucose tolerance, lowers inflammatory markers, and increases satiety after a subsequent standardized breakfast. *J. Nutr.* **2008**, *138*, 732–739. [PubMed]

126. Parnell, J.A.; Reimer, R.A. Weight loss during oligofructose supplementation is associated with decreased ghrelin and increased peptide YY in overweight and obese adults. *Am. J. Clin. Nutr.* **2009**, *89*, 1751–1759. [CrossRef] [PubMed]

127. Hashidume, T.; Sasaki, T.; Inoue, J.; Sato, R. Consumption of soy protein isolate reduces hepatic srebp-1c and lipogenic gene expression in wild-type mice, but not in FXR-deficient mice. *Biosci. Biotechnol. Biochem.* **2011**, *75*, 1702–1707. [CrossRef] [PubMed]

128. Jakubowicz, D.; Froy, O. Biochemical and metabolic mechanisms by which dietary whey protein may combat obesity and type 2 diabetes. *J. Nutr. Biochem.* **2013**, *24*, 1–5. [CrossRef] [PubMed]

129. Faure, P.; Rossini, E.; Lafond, J.L.; Richard, M.J.; Favier, A.; Halimi, S. Vitamin e improves the free radical defense system potential and insulin sensitivity of rats fed high fructose diets. *J. Nutr.* **1997**, *127*, 103–107. [PubMed]

130. Noguchi, Y.; Nishikata, N.; Shikata, N.; Kimura, Y.; Aleman, J.O.; Young, J.D.; Koyama, N.; Kelleher, J.K.; Takahashi, M.; Stephanopoulos, G. Ketogenic essential amino acids modulate lipid synthetic pathways and prevent hepatic steatosis in mice. *PLoS ONE* **2010**, *5*, e12057. [CrossRef] [PubMed]

131. Pichon, L.; Huneau, J.F.; Fromentin, G.; Tome, D. A high-protein, high-fat, carbohydrate-free diet reduces energy intake, hepatic lipogenesis, and adiposity in rats. *J. Nutr.* **2006**, *136*, 1256–1260. [PubMed]

132. Qin, B.; Nagasaki, M.; Ren, M.; Bajotto, G.; Oshida, Y.; Sato, Y. Cinnamon extract prevents the insulin resistance induced by a high-fructose diet. *Horm. Metab. Res.* **2004**, *36*, 119–125. [PubMed]

133. Halton, T.L.; Hu, F.B. The effects of high protein diets on thermogenesis, satiety and weight loss: A critical review. *J. Am. Coll. Nutr.* **2004**, *23*, 373–385. [CrossRef] [PubMed]

134. Cummings, J.H. Carbohydrate and protein digestion: The substrate available for fermentation. In *The Large Intestine in Nutrition and Disease*; Danone Institute: Brussels, Belgium, 1997; pp. 15–42.

135. Smith, E.A.; Macfarlane, G.T. Enumeration of human colonic bacteria producing phenolic and indolic compounds: Effects of pH, carbohydrate availability and retention time on dissimilatory aromatic amino acid metabolism. *J. Appl. Bacteriol.* **1996**, *81*, 288–302. [CrossRef] [PubMed]

136. Smith, E.A.; Macfarlane, G.T. Studies on amine production in the human colon: Enumeration of amine forming bacteria and physiological effects of carbohydrate and pH. *Anaerobe* **1996**, *2*, 285–297.

137. Russell, W.R.; Gratz, S.W.; Duncan, S.H.; Holtrop, G.; Ince, J.; Scobbie, L.; Duncan, G.; Johnstone, A.M.; Lobley, G.E.; Wallace, R.J.; *et al.* High-protein, reduced-carbohydrate weight-loss diets promote metabolite profiles likely to be detrimental to colonic health. *Am. J. Clin. Nutr.* **2011**, *93*, 1062–1072. [PubMed]

138. Shen, Q.; Chen, Y.A.; Tuohy, K.M. A comparative *in vitro* investigation into the effects of cooked meats on the human faecal microbiota. *Anaerobe* **2010**, *16*, 572–577. [PubMed]

139. Aron-Wisnewsky, J.; Gaborit, B.; Dutour, A.; Clement, K. Gut microbiota and non-alcoholic fatty liver disease: New insights. *Clin. Microbiol. Infect.* **2013**, *19*, 338–348. [PubMed]

140. Schnabl, B.; Brenner, D.A. Interactions between the intestinal microbiome and liver diseases. *Gastroenterology* **2014**, *146*, 1513–1524. [PubMed]

141. Hooda, S.; Vester Boler, B.M.; Kerr, K.R.; Dowd, S.E.; Swanson, K.S. The gut microbiome of kittens is affected by dietary protein: Carbohydrate ratio and associated with blood metabolite and hormone concentrations. *Br. J. Nutr.* **2013**, *109*, 1637–1646. [PubMed]

142. Boudry, G.; Jamin, A.; Chatelais, L.; Gras-Le Guen, C.; Michel, C.; Le Huerou-Luron, I. Dietary protein excess during neonatal life alters colonic microbiota and mucosal response to inflammatory mediators later in life in female pigs. *J. Nutr.* **2013**, *143*, 1225–1232. [CrossRef] [PubMed]

143. Cohen, A.M.; Teitelbaum, A. Effect of different levels of protein in sucrose and starch diets on lipid synthesis in the rat. *Isr. J. Med. Sci.* **1966**, *2*, 727–732. [PubMed]

144. Masoro, E.J.; Chaikoff, I.L.; Chernick, S.S.; Felts, J.M. Previous nutritional state and glucose conversion to fatty acids in liver slices. *J. Biol. Chem.* **1950**, *185*, 845–856. [PubMed]

145. Yeh, Y.Y.; Leveille, G.A. Effect of dietary protein on hepatic lipogenesis in the growing chick. *J. Nutr.* **1969**, *98*, 356–366. [PubMed]

146. Bortolotti, M.; Maiolo, E.; Corazza, M.; van Dijke, E.; Schneiter, P.; Boss, A.; Carrel, G.; Giusti, V.; Le, K.A.; Quo Chong, D.G.; *et al.* Effects of a whey protein supplementation on intrahepatocellular lipids in obese female patients. *Clin. Nutr.* **2011**, *30*, 494–498. [CrossRef] [PubMed]

147. Farnsworth, E.; Luscombe, N.D.; Noakes, M.; Wittert, G.; Argyiou, E.; Clifton, P.M. Effect of a high-protein, energy-restricted diet on body composition, glycemic control, and lipid concentrations in overweight and obese hyperinsulinemic men and women. *Am. J. Clin. Nutr.* **2003**, *78*, 31–39. [PubMed]

148. Jenkins, D.J.; Kendall, C.W.; Vidgen, E.; Augustin, L.S.; van Erk, M.; Geelen, A.; Parker, T.; Faulkner, D.; Vuksan, V.; Josse, R.G.; *et al.* High-protein diets in hyperlipidemia: Effect of wheat gluten on serum lipids, uric acid, and renal function. *Am. J. Clin. Nutr.* **2001**, *74*, 57–63. [PubMed]

149. Samaha, F.F.; Iqbal, N.; Seshadri, P.; Chicano, K.L.; Daily, D.A.; McGrory, J.; Williams, T.; Williams, M.; Gracely, E.J.; Stern, L. A low-carbohydrate as compared with a low-fat diet in severe obesity. *N. Engl. J. Med.* **2003**, *348*, 2074–2081. [CrossRef] [PubMed]

150. Yang, H.Y.; Tzeng, Y.H.; Chai, C.Y.; Hsieh, A.T.; Chen, J.R.; Chang, L.S.; Yang, S.S. Soy protein retards the progression of non-alcoholic steatohepatitis via improvement of insulin resistance and steatosis. *Nutrition* **2011**, *27*, 943–948. [CrossRef] [PubMed]

151. Gentile, C.L.; Nivala, A.M.; Gonzales, J.C.; Pfaffenbach, K.T.; Wang, D.; Wei, Y.; Jiang, H.; Orlicky, D.J.; Petersen, D.R.; Pagliassotti, M.J.; *et al.* Experimental evidence for therapeutic potential of taurine in the treatment of nonalcoholic fatty liver disease. *Am. J. Physiol. Regul. Integr. Comp. Physiol.* **2011**, *301*, R1710–R1722. [CrossRef] [PubMed]

152. Linn, T.; Geyer, R.; Prassek, S.; Laube, H. Effect of dietary protein intake on insulin secretion and glucose metabolism in insulin-dependent diabetes mellitus. *J. Clin. Endocrinol. Metab.* **1996**, *81*, 3938–3943. [PubMed]

153. Linn, T.; Santosa, B.; Gronemeyer, D.; Aygen, S.; Scholz, N.; Busch, M.; Bretzel, R.G. Effect of long-term dietary protein intake on glucose metabolism in humans. *Diabetologia* **2000**, *43*, 1257–1265. [CrossRef] [PubMed]

154. Delzenne, N.M.; Neyrinck, A.M.; Backhed, F.; Cani, P.D. Targeting gut microbiota in obesity: Effects of prebiotics and probiotics. *Nat. Rev. Endocrinol.* **2011**, *7*, 639–646. [CrossRef] [PubMed]

155. Slavin, J. Fiber and prebiotics: Mechanisms and health benefits. *Nutrients* **2013**, *5*, 1417–1435. [CrossRef] [PubMed]

156. Moschen, A.R.; Kaser, S.; Tilg, H. Non-alcoholic steatohepatitis: A microbiota-driven disease. *Trends Endocrinol. Metab.* **2013**, *24*, 537–545. [CrossRef] [PubMed]

157. Cani, P.D.; Joly, E.; Horsmans, Y.; Delzenne, N.M. Oligofructose promotes satiety in healthy human: A pilot study. *Eur. J. Clin. Nutr.* **2006**, *60*, 567–572. [CrossRef] [PubMed]

158. Cani, P.D.; Knauf, C.; Iglesias, M.A.; Drucker, D.J.; Delzenne, N.M.; Burcelin, R. Improvement of glucose tolerance and hepatic insulin sensitivity by oligofructose requires a functional glucagon-like peptide 1 receptor. *Diabetes* **2006**, *55*, 1484–1490. [CrossRef] [PubMed]

159. Everard, A.; Lazarevic, V.; Derrien, M.; Girard, M.; Muccioli, G.G.; Neyrinck, A.M.; Possemiers, S.; van Holle, A.; Francois, P.; de Vos, W.M.; *et al.* Responses of gut microbiota and glucose and lipid metabolism to prebiotics in genetic obese and diet-induced leptin-resistant mice. *Diabetes* **2011**, *60*, 2775–2786. [CrossRef] [PubMed]

160. Cani, P.D.; Dewever, C.; Delzenne, N.M. Inulin-type fructans modulate gastrointestinal peptides involved in appetite regulation (glucagon-like peptide-1 and ghrelin) in rats. *Br. J. Nutr.* **2004**, *92*, 521–526. [CrossRef] [PubMed]

161. Sugatani, J.; Wada, T.; Osabe, M.; Yamakawa, K.; Yoshinari, K.; Miwa, M. Dietary inulin alleviates hepatic steatosis and xenobiotics-induced liver injury in rats fed a high-fat and high-sucrose diet: Association with the suppression of hepatic cytochrome p450 and hepatocyte nuclear factor 4α expression. *Drug Metab. Dispos.* **2006**, *34*, 1677–1687. [CrossRef] [PubMed]

162. Daubioul, C.; Rousseau, N.; Demeure, R.; Gallez, B.; Taper, H.; Declerck, B.; Delzenne, N. Dietary fructans, but not cellulose, decrease triglyceride accumulation in the liver of obese zucker FA/FA rats. *J. Nutr.* **2002**, *132*, 967–973. [PubMed]

163. Fiordaliso, M.; Kok, N.; Desager, J.P.; Goethals, F.; Deboyser, D.; Roberfroid, M.; Delzenne, N. Dietary oligofructose lowers triglycerides, phospholipids and cholesterol in serum and very low density lipoproteins of rats. *Lipids* **1995**, *30*, 163–167. [CrossRef] [PubMed]

164. Parnell, J.A.; Reimer, R.A. Effect of prebiotic fibre supplementation on hepatic gene expression and serum lipids: A dose-response study in JCR:LA-cp rats. *Br. J. Nutr.* **2010**, *103*, 1577–1584. [CrossRef] [PubMed]

165. Lin, H.V.; Frassetto, A.; Kowalik, E.J., Jr.; Nawrocki, A.R.; Lu, M.M.; Kosinski, J.R.; Hubert, J.A.; Szeto, D.; Yao, X.; Forrest, G.; *et al.* Butyrate and propionate protect against diet-induced obesity and regulate gut hormones via free fatty acid receptor 3-independent mechanisms. *PLoS ONE* **2012**, *7*, e35240. [CrossRef] [PubMed]

166. Archer, B.J.; Johnson, S.K.; Devereux, H.M.; Baxter, A.L. Effect of fat replacement by inulin or lupin-kernel fibre on sausage patty acceptability, post-meal perceptions of satiety and food intake in men. *Br. J. Nutr.* **2004**, *91*, 591–599. [CrossRef] [PubMed]

167. Dehghan, P.; Pourghassem Gargari, B.; Asghari Jafar-abadi, M. Oligofructose-enriched inulin improves some inflammatory markers and metabolic endotoxemia in women with type 2 diabetes mellitus: A randomized controlled clinical trial. *Nutrition* **2014**, *30*, 418–423. [CrossRef] [PubMed]

168. Daubioul, C.; Horsmans, Y.; Lambert, P.; Danse, E.; Delzenne, N.M. Effects of oligofructose on glucose and lipid metabolism in patients with nonalcoholic steatohepatitis: Results of a pilot study. *Eur. J. Clin. Nutr.* **2005**, *59*, 723–726. [CrossRef] [PubMed]

169. Malaguarnera, M.; Vacante, M.; Antic, T.; Giordano, M.; Chisari, G.; Acquaviva, R.; Mastrojeni, S.; Malaguarnera, G.; Mistretta, A.; Li Volti, G.; *et al. Bifidobacterium longum* with fructo-oligosaccharides in patients with non alcoholic steatohepatitis. *Dig. Dis. Sci.* **2012**, *57*, 545–553. [CrossRef] [PubMed]

170. Kellow, N.J.; Coughlan, M.T.; Reid, C.M. Metabolic benefits of dietary prebiotics in human subjects: A systematic review of randomised controlled trials. *Br. J. Nutr.* **2014**, *111*, 1147–1161. [CrossRef] [PubMed]

171. Lecerf, J.M.; Depeint, F.; Clerc, E.; Dugenet, Y.; Niamba, C.N.; Rhazi, L.; Cayzeele, A.; Abdelnour, G.; Jaruga, A.; Younes, H.; *et al.* Xylo-oligosaccharide (XOS) in combination with inulin modulates both the intestinal environment and immune status in healthy subjects, while XOS alone only shows prebiotic properties. *Br. J. Nutr.* **2012**, *108*, 1847–1858. [CrossRef] [PubMed]

172. Lomax, A.R.; Cheung, L.V.; Tuohy, K.M.; Noakes, P.S.; Miles, E.A.; Calder, P.C. B2-1 fructans have a bifidogenic effect in healthy middle-aged human subjects but do not alter immune responses examined in the absence of an *in vivo* immune challenge: Results from a randomised controlled trial. *Br. J. Nutr.* **2012**, *108*, 1818–1828. [CrossRef] [PubMed]

173. Vulevic, J.; Drakoularakou, A.; Yaqoob, P.; Tzortzis, G.; Gibson, G.R. Modulation of the fecal microflora profile and immune function by a novel trans-galactooligosaccharide mixture (B-GOS) in healthy elderly volunteers. *Am. J. Clin. Nutr.* **2008**, *88*, 1438–1446. [PubMed]

174. Vulevic, J.; Juric, A.; Tzortzis, G.; Gibson, G.R. A mixture of trans-galactooligosaccharides reduces markers of metabolic syndrome and modulates the fecal microbiota and immune function of overweight adults. *J. Nutr.* **2013**, *143*, 324–331. [CrossRef] [PubMed]

175. Dewulf, E.M.; Cani, P.D.; Claus, S.P.; Fuentes, S.; Puylaert, P.G.; Neyrinck, A.M.; Bindels, L.B.; de Vos, W.M.; Gibson, G.R.; Thissen, J.P.; *et al.* Insight into the prebiotic concept: Lessons from an exploratory, double blind intervention study with inulin-type fructans in obese women. *Gut* **2013**, *62*, 1112–1121. [CrossRef] [PubMed]

176. Lirussi, F.; Mastropasqua, E.; Orando, S.; Orlando, R. Probiotics for non-alcoholic fatty liver disease and/or steatohepatitis. *Cochrane Database Syst. Rev.* **2007**, *1*, CD005165. [PubMed]

177. Tarantino, G.; Finelli, C. Systematic review on intervention with prebiotics/probiotics in patients with obesity-related nonalcoholic fatty liver disease. *Future Microbiol.* **2015**, *10*, 889–902. [CrossRef] [PubMed]

178. Solga, S.F.; Diehl, A.M. Non-alcoholic fatty liver disease: Lumen-liver interactions and possible role for probiotics. *J. Hepatol.* **2003**, *38*, 681–687. [CrossRef]

179. Wang, Y.; Liu, Y.; Sidhu, A.; Ma, Z.; McClain, C.; Feng, W. *Lactobacillus rhamnosus* GG culture supernatant ameliorates acute alcohol-induced intestinal permeability and liver injury. *Am. J. Physiol. Gastrointest. Liver Physiol.* **2012**, *303*, G32–G41. [CrossRef] [PubMed]

180. Spruss, A.; Bergheim, I. Dietary fructose and intestinal barrier: Potential risk factor in the pathogenesis of nonalcoholic fatty liver disease. *J. Nutr. Biochem.* **2009**, *20*, 657–662. [CrossRef] [PubMed]

181. Reid, G.; Younes, J.A.; Van der Mei, H.C.; Gloor, G.B.; Knight, R.; Busscher, H.J. Microbiota restoration: Natural and supplemented recovery of human microbial communities. *Nat. Rev. Microbiol.* **2011**, *9*, 27–38. [CrossRef] [PubMed]

182. Li, Z.; Yang, S.; Lin, H.; Huang, J.; Watkins, P.A.; Moser, A.B.; Desimone, C.; Song, X.Y.; Diehl, A.M. Probiotics and antibodies to TNF inhibit inflammatory activity and improve nonalcoholic fatty liver disease. *Hepatology* **2003**, *37*, 343–350. [CrossRef] [PubMed]

183. Paik, H.D.; Park, J.S.; Park, E. Effects of bacillus polyfermenticus scd on lipid and antioxidant metabolisms in rats fed a high-fat and high-cholesterol diet. *Biol. Pharm. Bull.* **2005**, *28*, 1270–1274. [CrossRef] [PubMed]

184. Yadav, H.; Jain, S.; Sinha, P.R. Oral administration of dahi containing probiotic *Lactobacillus acidophilus* and *Lactobacillus casei* delayed the progression of streptozotocin-induced diabetes in rats. *J. Dairy Res.* **2008**, *75*, 189–195. [CrossRef] [PubMed]

185. Chen, J.J.; Wang, R.; Li, X.F.; Wang, R.L. *Bifidobacterium longum* supplementation improved high-fat-fed-induced metabolic syndrome and promoted intestinal reg i gene expression. *Exp. Biol. Med.* **2011**, *236*, 823–831. [CrossRef] [PubMed]

186. Lee, H.Y.; Park, J.H.; Seok, S.H.; Baek, M.W.; Kim, D.J.; Lee, K.E.; Paek, K.S.; Lee, Y. Human originated bacteria, *Lactobacillus rhamnosus* PL60, produce conjugated linoleic acid and show anti-obesity effects in diet-induced obese mice. *Biochim. Biophys. Acta* **2006**, *1761*, 736–744. [CrossRef] [PubMed]

187. Ma, X.; Hua, J.; Li, Z. Probiotics improve high fat diet-induced hepatic steatosis and insulin resistance by increasing hepatic nkt cells. *J. Hepatol.* **2008**, *49*, 821–830. [CrossRef] [PubMed]

188. Xu, R.Y.; Wan, Y.P.; Fang, Q.Y.; Lu, W.; Cai, W. Supplementation with probiotics modifies gut flora and attenuates liver fat accumulation in rat nonalcoholic fatty liver disease model. *J. Clin. Biochem. Nutr.* **2012**, *50*, 72–77. [CrossRef] [PubMed]

189. Esposito, E.; Iacono, A.; Bianco, G.; Autore, G.; Cuzzocrea, S.; Vajro, P.; Canani, R.B.; Calignano, A.; Raso, G.M.; Meli, R. Probiotics reduce the inflammatory response induced by a high-fat diet in the liver of young rats. *J. Nutr.* **2009**, *139*, 905–911. [CrossRef] [PubMed]

190. Velayudham, A.; Dolganiuc, A.; Ellis, M.; Petrasek, J.; Kodys, K.; Mandrekar, P.; Szabo, G. VSL#3 probiotic treatment attenuates fibrosis without changes in steatohepatitis in a diet-induced nonalcoholic steatohepatitis model in mice. *Hepatology* **2009**, *49*, 989–997. [PubMed]

191. Al-Salami, H.; Butt, G.; Fawcett, J.P.; Tucker, I.G.; Golocorbin-Kon, S.; Mikov, M. Probiotic treatment reduces blood glucose levels and increases systemic absorption of gliclazide in diabetic rats. *Eur. J. Drug Metab. Pharmacokinet.* **2008**, *33*, 101–106. [CrossRef] [PubMed]

192. Cano, P.G.; Santacruz, A.; Trejo, F.M.; Sanz, Y. Bifidobacterium cect 7765 improves metabolic and immunological alterations associated with obesity in high-fat diet-fed mice. *Obesity* **2013**, *21*, 2310–2321. [CrossRef] [PubMed]

193. Eslamparast, T.; Eghtesad, S.; Hekmatdoost, A.; Poustchi, H. Probiotics and nonalcoholic fatty liver disease. *Middle East J. Dig. Dis.* **2013**, *5*, 129–136. [PubMed]

194. Moya-Perez, A.; Neef, A.; Sanz, Y. Bifidobacterium pseudocatenulatum cect 7765 reduces obesity-associated inflammation by restoring the lymphocyte-macrophage balance and gut microbiota structure in high-fat diet-fed mice. *PLoS ONE* **2015**, *10*, e0126976.

195. Fan, J.G.; Xu, Z.J.; Wang, G.L. Effect of lactulose on establishment of a rat non-alcoholic steatohepatitis model. *World J. Gastroenterol.* **2005**, *11*, 5053–5056. [CrossRef] [PubMed]

196. Kanauchi, O.; Fujiyama, Y.; Mitsuyama, K.; Araki, Y.; Ishii, T.; Nakamura, T.; Hitomi, Y.; Agata, K.; Saiki, T.; Andoh, A.; *et al.* Increased growth of bifidobacterium and eubacterium by germinated barley foodstuff,

accompanied by enhanced butyrate production in healthy volunteers. *Int. J. Mol. Med.* **1999**, *3*, 175–179. [CrossRef] [PubMed]

197. Vajro, P.; Mandato, C.; Licenziati, M.R.; Franzese, A.; Vitale, D.F.; Lenta, S.; Caropreso, M.; Vallone, G.; Meli, R. Effects of *Lactobacillus rhamnosus* strain GG in pediatric obesity-related liver disease. *J. Pediatr. Gastroenterol. Nutr.* **2011**, *52*, 740–743. [CrossRef] [PubMed]

198. Kadooka, Y.; Sato, M.; Imaizumi, K.; Ogawa, A.; Ikuyama, K.; Akai, Y.; Okano, M.; Kagoshima, M.; Tsuchida, T. Regulation of abdominal adiposity by probiotics (*Lactobacillus gasseri* SBT2055) in adults with obese tendencies in a randomized controlled trial. *Eur. J. Clin. Nutr.* **2010**, *64*, 636–643. [CrossRef] [PubMed]

199. Kadooka, Y.; Sato, M.; Ogawa, A.; Miyoshi, M.; Uenishi, H.; Ogawa, H.; Ikuyama, K.; Kagoshima, M.; Tsuchida, T. Effect of *Lactobacillus gasseri* SBT2055 in fermented milk on abdominal adiposity in adults in a randomised controlled trial. *Br. J. Nutr.* **2013**, *110*, 1696–1703. [CrossRef] [PubMed]

200. Osawa, K.; Miyoshi, T.; Yamauchi, K.; Koyama, Y.; Nakamura, K.; Sato, S.; Kanazawa, S.; Ito, H. Nonalcoholic hepatic steatosis is a strong predictor of high-risk coronary-artery plaques as determined by multidetector ct. *PLoS ONE* **2015**, *10*, e0131138. [CrossRef] [PubMed]

201. Loguercio, C.; Federico, A.; Tuccillo, C.; Terracciano, F.; D'Auria, M.V.; De Simone, C.; del Vecchio Blanco, C. Beneficial effects of a probiotic vsl#3 on parameters of liver dysfunction in chronic liver diseases. *J. Clin. Gastroenterol.* **2005**, *39*, 540–543. [PubMed]

202. Stadlbauer, V.; Mookerjee, R.P.; Hodges, S.; Wright, G.A.; Davies, N.A.; Jalan, R. Effect of probiotic treatment on deranged neutrophil function and cytokine responses in patients with compensated alcoholic cirrhosis. *J. Hepatol.* **2008**, *48*, 945–951. [CrossRef] [PubMed]

203. Aller, R.; De Luis, D.A.; Izaola, O.; Conde, R.; Gonzalez Sagrado, M.; Primo, D.; de La Fuente, B.; Gonzalez, J. Effect of a probiotic on liver aminotransferases in nonalcoholic fatty liver disease patients: A double blind randomized clinical trial. *Eur. Rev. Med. Pharmacol. Sci.* **2011**, *15*, 1090–1095. [PubMed]

204. Loguercio, C.; De Simone, T.; Federico, A.; Terracciano, F.; Tuccillo, C.; Di Chicco, M.; Carteni, M. Gut-liver axis: A new point of attack to treat chronic liver damage? *Am. J. Gastroenterol.* **2002**, *97*, 2144–2146. [CrossRef] [PubMed]

205. Wall, R.; Marques, T.M.; O'Sullivan, O.; Ross, R.P.; Shanahan, F.; Quigley, E.; Dinan, T.G.; Kiely, B.; Fitzgerald, G.F.; Cotter, P.D.; *et al.* Contrasting effects of *Bifidobacterium breve* NCIMB 702258 and *Bifidobacterium breve* DPC 6330 on the composition of murine brain fatty acids and gut microbiota. *Am. J. Clin. Nutr.* **2012**, *95*, 1278–1287. [CrossRef] [PubMed]

206. Shen, J.; Ran, H.Z.; Yin, M.H.; Zhou, T.X.; Xiao, D.S. Meta-analysis: The effect and adverse events of *lactobacilli* versus placebo in maintenance therapy for crohn disease. *Intern. Med. J.* **2009**, *39*, 103–109. [CrossRef] [PubMed]

207. Lionetti, E.; Indrio, F.; Pavone, L.; Borrelli, G.; Cavallo, L.; Francavilla, R. Role of probiotics in pediatric patients with *Helicobacter pylori* infection: A comprehensive review of the literature. *Helicobacter* **2010**, *15*, 79–87. [CrossRef] [PubMed]

208. Friedenreich, C.; Norat, T.; Steindorf, K.; Boutron-Ruault, M.C.; Pischon, T.; Mazuir, M.; Clavel-Chapelon, F.; Linseisen, J.; Boeing, H.; Bergman, M.; *et al.* Physical activity and risk of colon and rectal cancers: The european prospective investigation into cancer and nutrition. *Cancer Epidemiol. Biomark. Prev.* **2006**, *15*, 2398–2407. [CrossRef] [PubMed]

209. Warburton, D.E.; Nicol, C.W.; Bredin, S.S. Health benefits of physical activity: The evidence. *CMAJ* **2006**, *174*, 801–809. [CrossRef] [PubMed]

210. Marcinko, K.; Sikkema, S.R.; Samaan, M.C.; Kemp, B.E.; Fullerton, M.D.; Steinberg, G.R. High intensity interval training improves liver and adipose tissue insulin sensitivity. *Mol. Metab.* **2015**, *4*, 903–915. [CrossRef] [PubMed]

211. Ellingsgaard, H.; Hauselmann, I.; Schuler, B.; Habib, A.M.; Baggio, L.L.; Meier, D.T.; Eppler, E.; Bouzakri, K.; Wueest, S.; Muller, Y.D.; *et al.* Interleukin-6 enhances insulin secretion by increasing glucagon-like peptide-1 secretion from l cells and α cells. *Nat. Med.* **2011**, *17*, 1481–1489. [CrossRef] [PubMed]

212. Petersen, A.M.; Pedersen, B.K. The anti-inflammatory effect of exercise. *J. Appl. Physiol.* **2005**, *98*, 1154–1162. [CrossRef] [PubMed]

213. Clarke, S.F.; Murphy, E.F.; O'Sullivan, O.; Lucey, A.J.; Humphreys, M.; Hogan, A.; Hayes, P.; O'Reilly, M.; Jeffery, I.B.; Wood-Martin, R.; *et al.* Exercise and associated dietary extremes impact on gut microbial diversity. *Gut* **2014**, *63*, 1913–1920. [CrossRef] [PubMed]

214. Maslowski, K.M.; Mackay, C.R. Diet, gut microbiota and immune responses. *Nat. Immunol.* **2011**, *12*, 5–9. [CrossRef] [PubMed]

215. Lambert, J.E.; Myslicki, J.P.; Bomhof, M.R.; Belke, D.D.; Shearer, J.; Reimer, R.A. Exercise training modifies gut microbiota in normal and diabetic mice. *Appl. Physiol. Nutr. Metab.* **2015**, *40*, 749–752. [CrossRef] [PubMed]

216. Petriz, B.A.; Castro, A.P.; Almeida, J.A.; Gomes, C.P.; Fernandes, G.R.; Kruger, R.H.; Pereira, R.W.; Franco, O.L. Exercise induction of gut microbiota modifications in obese, non-obese and hypertensive rats. *BMC Genom.* **2014**, *15*, 511. [CrossRef] [PubMed]

217. Evans, C.C.; LePard, K.J.; Kwak, J.W.; Stancukas, M.C.; Laskowski, S.; Dougherty, J.; Moulton, L.; Glawe, A.; Wang, Y.; Leone, V.; *et al.* Exercise prevents weight gain and alters the gut microbiota in a mouse model of high fat diet-induced obesity. *PLoS ONE* **2014**, *9*, e92193. [CrossRef] [PubMed]

218. Kang, S.S.; Jeraldo, P.R.; Kurti, A.; Miller, M.E.; Cook, M.D.; Whitlock, K.; Goldenfeld, N.; Woods, J.A.; White, B.A.; Chia, N.; *et al.* Diet and exercise orthogonally alter the gut microbiome and reveal independent associations with anxiety and cognition. *Mol. Neurodegener.* **2014**, *9*, 36. [CrossRef] [PubMed]

219. Liu, T.W.; Park, Y.M.; Holscher, H.D.; Padilla, J.; Scroggins, R.J.; Welly, R.; Britton, S.L.; Koch, L.G.; Vieira-Potter, V.J.; Swanson, K.S. Physical activity differentially affects the cecal microbiota of ovariectomized female rats selectively bred for high and low aerobic capacity. *PLoS ONE* **2015**, *10*, e0136150. [CrossRef] [PubMed]

220. Matsumoto, M.; Inoue, R.; Tsukahara, T.; Ushida, K.; Chiji, H.; Matsubara, N.; Hara, H. Voluntary running exercise alters microbiota composition and increases n-butyrate concentration in the rat cecum. *Biosci. Biotechnol. Biochem.* **2008**, *72*, 572–576. [CrossRef] [PubMed]

221. Allen, J.M.; Berg Miller, M.E.; Pence, B.D.; Whitlock, K.; Nehra, V.; Gaskins, H.R.; White, B.A.; Fryer, J.D.; Woods, J.A. Voluntary and forced exercise differentially alters the gut microbiome in C57BL/6J mice. *J. Appl. Physiol.* **2015**, *118*, 1059–1066. [CrossRef] [PubMed]

222. Choi, J.J.; Eum, S.Y.; Rampersaud, E.; Daunert, S.; Abreu, M.T.; Toborek, M. Exercise attenuates PCB-induced changes in the mouse gut microbiome. *Environ. Health Perspect.* **2013**, *121*, 725–730. [CrossRef] [PubMed]

223. Queipo-Ortuno, M.I.; Seoane, L.M.; Murri, M.; Pardo, M.; Gomez-Zumaquero, J.M.; Cardona, F.; Casanueva, F.; Tinahones, F.J. Gut microbiota composition in male rat models under different nutritional status and physical activity and its association with serum leptin and ghrelin levels. *PLoS ONE* **2013**, *8*, e65465.

224. Mika, A.; Van Treuren, W.; Gonzalez, A.; Herrera, J.J.; Knight, R.; Fleshner, M. Exercise is more effective at altering gut microbial composition and producing stable changes in lean mass in juvenile versus adult male F344 rats. *PLoS ONE* **2015**, *10*, e0125889. [CrossRef] [PubMed]

225. Shukla, S.K.; Cook, D.; Meyer, J.; Vernon, S.D.; Le, T.; Clevidence, D.; Robertson, C.E.; Schrodi, S.J.; Yale, S.; Frank, D.N. Changes in gut and plasma microbiome following exercise challenge in myalgic encephalomyelitis/chronic fatigue syndrome (ME/CFS). *PLoS ONE* **2015**, *10*, e0145453. [CrossRef] [PubMed]

226. Cassidy, S.; Thoma, C.; Hallsworth, K.; Parikh, J.; Hollingsworth, K.G.; Taylor, R.; Jakovljevic, D.G.; Trenell, M.I. High intensity intermittent exercise improves cardiac structure and function and reduces liver fat in patients with type 2 diabetes: A randomised controlled trial. *Diabetologia* **2016**, *59*, 56–66. [CrossRef] [PubMed]

227. Hallsworth, K.; Thoma, C.; Hollingsworth, K.G.; Cassidy, S.; Anstee, Q.M.; Day, C.P.; Trenell, M.I. Modified high-intensity interval training reduces liver fat and improves cardiac function in non-alcoholic fatty liver disease: A randomised controlled trial. *Clin. Sci.* **2015**, *129*, 1097–1105. [CrossRef] [PubMed]

228. Schwiertz, A.; Taras, D.; Schafer, K.; Beijer, S.; Bos, N.A.; Donus, C.; Hardt, P.D. Microbiota and SCFA in lean and overweight healthy subjects. *Obesity* **2010**, *18*, 190–195. [CrossRef] [PubMed]

229. Meissner, M.; Lombardo, E.; Havinga, R.; Tietge, U.J.F.; Kuipers, F.; Groen, A.K. Voluntary wheel running increases bile acid as well as cholesterol excretion and decreases atherosclerosis in hypercholesterolemic mice. *Atherosclerosis* **2011**, *218*, 323–329. [CrossRef] [PubMed]

230. Rowell, L.B.; Detry, J.R.; Profant, G.R.; Wyss, C. Splanchnic vasoconstriction in hyperthermic man—Role of falling blood pressure. *J. Appl. Physiol.* **1971**, *31*, 864–869. [PubMed]

International Journal of
Molecular Sciences

MDPI

Review

Diet, Microbiota, Obesity, and NAFLD: A Dangerous Quartet

Mariana Verdelho Machado [1,2] **and Helena Cortez-Pinto** [1,2,*]

1   Departamento de Gastrenterologia, Hospital de Santa Maria, Centro Hospitalar Lisboa Norte (CHLN), 1649-035 Lisbon, Portugal; mverdelhomachado@gmail.com
2   Laboratório de Nutrição, Faculdade de Medicina de Lisboa, Universidade de Lisboa, Alameda da Universidade, 1649-004 Lisboa, Portugal
*   Correspondence: hlcortezpinto@netcabo.pt; Tel.: +351-21-7985-187; Fax: +351-21-7985-142

Academic Editors: Amedeo Lonardo and Giovanni Targher
Received: 29 February 2016; Accepted: 28 March 2016; Published: 1 April 2016

Abstract: Recently, the importance of the gut-liver-adipose tissue axis has become evident. Nonalcoholic fatty liver disease (NAFLD) is the hepatic disease of a systemic metabolic disorder that radiates from energy-surplus induced adiposopathy. The gut microbiota has tremendous influences in our whole-body metabolism, and is crucial for our well-being and health. Microorganisms precede humans in more than 400 million years and our guest flora evolved with us in order to help us face aggressor microorganisms, to help us maximize the energy that can be extracted from nutrients, and to produce essential nutrients/vitamins that we are not equipped to produce. However, our gut microbiota can be disturbed, dysbiota, and become itself a source of stress and injury. Dysbiota may adversely impact metabolism and immune responses favoring obesity and obesity-related disorders such as insulin resistance/diabetes mellitus and NAFLD. In this review, we will summarize the latest evidence of the role of microbiota/dysbiota in diet-induced obesity and NAFLD, as well as the potential therapeutic role of targeting the microbiota in this set.

Keywords: nonalcoholic fatty liver disease; microbiota; diet; obesity; dysbiota; probiotics

---

1. Introduction

Nonalcoholic fatty liver disease (NAFLD) refers to the ectopic accumulation of fat in the liver. In its primary form, NAFLD is the hepatic manifestation of metabolic dysfunction associated with energy surplus-induced adiposopathy. The term adiposopathy has only recently been introduced in the medical lexicon and translates the adipose tissue dysfunction that occurs, in susceptible individuals, as a consequence of chronic positive caloric balance and sedentary lifestyle [1]. The true significance of hepatic steatosis as a contributing player in obesity-induced dysmetabolism and global metabolic and cardiovascular health is still unclear [2]. Regarding liver health, although most patients will present stable, non-progressive disease, the high prevalence of this condition explains why NAFLD is the number one cause of chronic liver disease in Western world and will predictably be the number one cause of end-stage liver disease in the near future [3].

Little more than a decade ago, a major breakthrough linked the gut microbiota to the pathogenesis of obesity and NAFLD [4]. Since then, medical research in the field has flourished exponentially. However, huge gaps in knowledge still preclude us to have effective therapeutic strategies for obesity and NAFLD that act through modulation of gut microbiota.

The gut microbiota comprises 10 to 100 trillion microbes. The gut microbiota is composed by bacteria, archea, virus, and fungi, being dominated by four main phyla of bacteria: Firmicutes, Bacterioidetes, Actinobacteria, and Proteobacteria, which represent more than 95% [5,6]. The collective genome of the gut microbiota, referred to as a microbiome, contains at least 100 times more genes than the human genome [6]. Those extra genes are crucial to maintain our homeostasis. In fact, the gut microbiome is enriched in several genes important for glycans and aminoacids metabolism, xenobiotics metabolism, methanogenesis, and biosynthesis of vitamins [6]. This explains why the gut microbiota contributes to host nutrition, bone mineral density, modulation of the immune system, xenobiotics metabolism, intestinal cell development and proliferation, and protection against pathogens [7].

One important question still not fully answered is if there is a core microbiota common to humans. In fact, although culture-based studies suggest that healthy humans would share the same gut bacterial species, culture-independent studies showed that each individual harbors a unique collection of bacterial strains and species [7,8]. Not only gut microbiota is specific to individual, it is also highly resilient, promptly returning to baseline after perturbation [7,9–11]. However, recovery may be impaired with recurrent perturbation [12]. Interestingly, despite the unique individual gut microbiota, humans share similar functional gene profiles, implying a core functional microbiome [8].

The composition of the gut microbiota is regulated by (a) external factors such as vaginal *versus* cesarean section delivery, breast feeding, antibiotics, pre/probiotics, diet, hygienic habits, and random chance resulting in a colonization cascade; (b) interaction with the host such as genetics, Paneth cell function, mucus composition, secretion of antimicrobial peptides; and (c) interaction between microbes, which can result in competition or cooperation [5,13,14].

In this review, we will summarize the latest research on the interplay between diet, gut microbiota, obesity, and fatty liver disease. We will also discuss the evidence of microbiota-targeting approaches in the treatment of NAFLD.

2. Microbiota and Obesity

The first clue on the role of the microbiota in the pathogenesis of obesity came from Backhed *et al.* [4] studies. They compared body weight gain in germ free mice and conventionally raised mice, and found that the latter gained more weight, with increased adipose tissue and body fat percentage, which could not be explained by different diet intake. Importantly, metabolic status was worse in conventionally raised mice, with higher leptin levels, lower insulin sensitivity and greater fat accumulation in the liver. Further supporting the concept that body weight was regulated by gut microbiota, transplantation of microbiota harvested from conventionally raised mice into germ free mice resulted in an increase in body weight and decrease in insulin sensitivity [4]. Moreover, the same group showed that, not only germ-free mice were leaner than conventionally raised mice, they were also resistant to western-type high-fat diet induced obesity [15]. Lastly, studies on animal models showed us that not all microbiota has the same effect on metabolism, and raised the possibility of an obesity-specific microbiota. In fact, transplantation of microbiota harvested by either genetically-obese ob/ob mice [16] or high-fat diet induced obese mice [17] into germ free mice mimicked the obese insulin resistant phenotype. Supporting the animal data, a small human study in male patients with the metabolic syndrome submitted to autologous or allogenic (from a lean donor) intestinal microbiota via duodenal tube, showed improvement in insulin sensitivity when the donor was lean [18].

Since then, several groups tried to characterize the obese-associated microbiota. Studies in either genetically or diet-induced obese mice showed differences in the microbiota when comparing with lean mice. Obese mice consistently showed a decrease in Bacterioidetes and an increase in Firmicutes (particularly from the class Millicutes) [19–21]. This increase in Firmicutes associated with an increase in enzymes able to breakdown indigestible polysaccharides from diet and producing short chain fatty acids (SCFA) [19]. Obese mice also presented an increase in methanogenic Archea, which associates with a lower hydrogen partial pressure and optimization of bacterial fermentation [19].

Studies in human obesity showed lower microbial diversity and similar differences in the intestinal microbiota as suggested by animal studies [22–24].

In summary, there is an obesity-associated gut microbiota, and obesity can be infectiously transmitted by transplant of that microbiome, suggesting that it is the microbiota itself that promotes obesity. Supporting this concept, a prospective study in children showed that the risk of being overweight at seven years old could be predicted by the composition of gut microbiota at six months old, which associated with lower prevalence of *Bifidobacterium* and higher of *Staphylococcus aureus* [25].

Obese mice waste less energy in the stools as compared to lean mice, and as little as a 20% decrease in fecal Bacterioidetes associates with 150 Kcal decrease in energy harvest from the diet [26]. The microbiota can modulate body weight through several mechanisms. One such mechanism is the differential fermentation of indigestible carbohydrates in SCFA: butyrate, propionate, and acetate [27]. Overall, colonic-derived SCFA account for 10% of harvested energy from the diet, with acetate being the main source of energy [28]. Butyrate and propionate are considered anti-obesogenic, and acetate mainly obesogenic. Interestingly, while acetate and propionate are mainly produced by the phylum Bacterioidetes, butyrate is mainly produced by Firmicutes (the most important belonging to clostridial lusters IV and XIVa: *Faecalibacterium prausnitzii*, *Eubacterium rectale*, and *Rosuberia intestinalis*) [29,30]. Butyrate is a major source of energy for colonocytes, increasing intestinal health and potentially decreasing gut permeability and preventing metabolic endotoxemia [31]. Butyrate also seems to positively affect insulin sensitivity through stimulation of the release of the incretins glucagon-like peptide-1 (GLP-1) and gastric inhibitory polypeptide (GIP) [32]. Both butyrate and propionate can increase the expression of the anorexigenic adipokine leptin [33]. Other beneficial effects of propionate are inhibition of resistin expression by the adipose tissue [34] and inhibition of cholesterol synthesis through inhibition of acetyl-CoA synthetase and via buffering fatty acids to gluconeogenesis in detriment of cholesterol synthesis [27]. On the other hand, acetate is the most substantially absorbed SCFA, and is a substrate for lipogenesis and cholesterol synthesis in the liver and adipose tissue [27]. Finally, SCFA bind to specific receptors in the gut, liver, and adipose tissue, GRP43 and GRP41, which seem to have anti-inflammatory and metabolic actions that protect from obesity [28]. Interestingly, supplementation of oral butyrate in mice fed a Western diet, partially prevented liver steatosis and inflammation, while having no effect on obesity [35].

Gut microbiota can also decrease the intestinal expression of the adipose tissue lipoprotein lipase inhibitor fasting induced adipose factor (Fiaf), also known as angiopoietin-like factor IV (ANGPTL4). The net result is increased uptake of fatty acids in the adipose tissue and liver, favoring expansion of the adipose tissue and hepatic steatosis. Microbiota also prevents the beneficial action of Fiaf in the expression of peroxisome proliferator-activated receptor (PPAR)-1α coactivator (PGC) and fatty acids oxidation [15,36]. Other mechanisms by which gut microbiota promote obesity are an increase in mucosal gut blood flow enhancing nutrients absorption [37]; inhibition of adenosine monophosphate-activated protein kinase AMPK in the liver and muscle, and consequently inhibiting peripheral fatty acids oxidation and insulin resistance [15]; and modulation of the pattern of conjugated bile acids and its function in lipid absorption [38].

Obesity itself may also change the microbiota, independently of the diet. For example, leptin, an adipokine whose levels are increased in obesity, has a direct role regulating the gut microbiota composition, through the modulation of antimicrobial peptides secretion by Paneth cells in the gut [39]. As such, a vicious circle between microbiota and adiposity promotes further worsening of obesity.

3. Microbiota and Nonalcoholic Fatty Liver Disease (NAFLD)/Nonalcoholic Steatohepatitis (NASH)

NAFLD strongly associates with obesity. The aggregate data suggests that the gut microbiota may play a significant role in the pathogenesis of obesity, as such it would be logical to think that the gut microbiota also plays a role in the development of NAFLD and its progressive form, nonalcoholic steatohepatitis (NASH). Indeed, that seems to be the case. Transplanting harvested microbiota from conventionally raised mice to germ free mice, besides increasing body weight, it also increases the fat content in the liver [4]. Furthermore, treatment with antibiotics protected from hepatic steatosis in different dietary and genetic obese rodent models [40,41]. However, the association between gut microbiota and NAFLD goes beyond the association with obesity.

Several studies in animal models and patients with NAFLD or NASH showed an association with small bowel overgrowth and increased intestinal permeability [42–49]. Brun *et al.* [45], compared two strains of genetically obese mice, leptin deficient ob/ob and leptin-resistant db/db, with lean control mice. They found that obese mice had increased intestinal permeability with lower intestinal resistance and profound changes in the cytoskeleton of cells in the intestinal mucosa. In association with increased gut permeability, obese mice, as compared to lean mice, had higher circulating levels of inflammatory cytokines and portal endotoxemia. Finally, hepatic stellate cells from obese mice expressed higher levels of the lipopolysaccharide (LPS) co-receptor CD14, and responded with a more inflammatory and fibrogenic phenotype after stimulation with LPS [45]. Furthermore, a study compared NAFLD patients with healthy subjects, and found that patients with NAFLD had an increased susceptibility to develop increased intestinal permeability after a minor challenge with low dose aspirin [46]. Concordant with those observations, obesity and NAFLD associates with metabolic endotoxemia, *i.e.*, increased blood levels of lipopolysaccharide (LPS), a component of the wall of Gram-negative bacteria that binds to specific receptors, toll like receptor-4 (TLR-4), and can promote hepatic and systemic inflammation [47,49,50]. Verdam *et al.* [51] also showed an increase in plasma antibodies against LPS in patients with NASH as compared to healthy controls, which progressively increased with increased severity of liver disease. The role of LPS is highlighted by the study by Cani *et al.* [50] in which LPS injections in mice simulated the effects of a high-fat diet, in terms of weight gain, insulin resistance, and development of NAFLD. Furthermore, mice deficient in TLR-4 are not only protected from LPS-induced obesity and NAFLD, but also from high-fat diet-induced obesity and NAFLD [50], as well as NAFLD and NASH in different rodent models [47,52–54].

Perturbations in the metabolism of bile acids seem to have a prominent role in the pathogenesis of NAFLD [55]. Bile acids are not only critical in the absorption of fat, they are also signaling molecules with actions in their own metabolism, as well as energy, lipoproteins, and glucose metabolism, through its receptors farsenoid X receptor FXR and TGR5. There is a known mutual influence between bile acids and gut microbiota. Bile acids have potent antimicrobial properties [56]. On the other hand, the gut microbiota increases the diversity of bile acids through the deconjugation, dehydrogenation, and dehydroxylation of primary bile acids. In fact, conventionally raised mice, as compared to germ free mice presented a decrease in tauro-conjugates (which are potent FXR antagonists and hence positive regulators of bile acids synthesis), while maintaining levels of the more toxic cholic acid [57].

Recently, two studies elegantly demonstrated that NAFLD could be a transmissible disease, through gut microbiota. Le Roy *et al.* [58] fed mice with high fat diet for 16 weeks, and while most of the animals developed NAFLD, insulin resistance, and systemic inflammation (dubbed responders), some mice did not develop NAFLD or insulin resistance (dubbed non-responders). When they transplanted germ free mice with microbiota harvested from those animals, they obtained a metabolic and liver phenotype only if the donors were responders. Furthermore, mice with a genetic deficiency of the inflammasome in the gut exhibited a perturbed gut-innate immunity and an abnormal gut microbiota with increased Bacteroidetes (particularly from the family Porphyromondaceae) and decreased Firmicutes. Those mice developed worse liver damage when fed NASH-inducing diets, with increased steatosis, inflammation, and aminotransferases levels, as compared to their wild type counterparts. Interestingly, co-housing those transgenic mice with wild type mice turned the latter more sensitive to the diet-inducing NASH, effect that was abrogated by concomitant treatment with antibiotics [59]. Lastly, de Minicis *et al.* [60] modulated gut microbiota through high-fat diet (which induced an increase in Proteobacteria), before submitting mice to bile duct ligation. Those mice developed worse fibrosis than chow diet fed mice. They simulated the increased susceptibility to fibrosis by transplanting gut microbiota from high-fat diet fed mice, which was even worse when they selectively transplanted Gram-negative bacteria.

The gut microbiota also seems to have a role in NAFLD-associated hepatocarcinogenesis. Yoshimoto *et al.* [61] showed that, in different animal models of obesity, dysbiota associates with increased deoxycholic acid reaching the liver through the enterohepatic circulation. This bile acid was able to produce a senescence phenotype in hepatic stellate cells that induced a secretory profile able to promote inflammation and tumorigenesis.

Several studies in adult patients, have tried to evaluate if the presence of NAFLD associates with a specific dysbiota [62–67] (Table 1). Those are small studies, with different populations and controls and often without histological diagnosis. Furthermore, statistical significance was achieved in different categories in the taxonomic hierarchy. Though NAFLD/NASH seems to share some of the microbiota specificities associated with obesity, at the phylum level, only one study found NASH to be associated with a decreased percentage of Bacterioidetes [63]. The two studies that compared patients with NAFLD with healthy controls found an increase of the genus *Lactobacillus*, and a decrease in the family Ruminococcaceae in NAFLD patients [64,67]. Regarding the association with *Lactobacillus*, it is surprising, since several species from this genus are frequently used as probiotics. *Lactobacillus* are lactic acid bacteria that can inhibit pathogens, enhance the epithelial barrier function, and modulate immune responses [68], actions that would seem protective in the pathogenesis of NAFLD/NASH. However, *Lactobacillus* may associate with the production of volatile organic compounds such as acetate and ethanol [69], which may be important in the pathogenesis of obesity and NAFLD [64]. In fact, the genus *Lactobacillus* comprises over 180 species and a wide variety of organisms; while some can only produce lactic acid from the fermentation of sugars (e.g., *L. acidophilus* and *L. salivarius*), other can also produce ethanol (e.g., *L. casei*, *L. brevis* and *L. plantarum*). Again, the decrease of Ruminococcaceae may also translate to a decrease in the production of SCFA such as butyrate, since many bacteria from that family produce butyrate [70]. A decrease in butyrate-producing bacteria, such as the genus *Faecalibacterium* [70] has also been associated with NASH, as compared to healthy controls [65]. As compared to healthy subjects, patients with NAFLD also showed increased percentage of bacteria from the genera *Escherichia* and pathogenic *Streptococcus*, both known to potentially induce persistent inflammation in the intestinal mucosa, and to be associated with inflammatory bowel disease [71,72]. In accordance, patients with NAFLD exhibited higher expression of proinflammatory cytokines in the intestinal mucosa [67]. Some *Escherichia* species also produce ethanol, which can further increase gut permeability. In fact, children with NASH also displayed increased levels of *Escherichia* bacteria in their stools [73].

Spencer *et al.* [62] evaluated an interaction between choline metabolism and microbiota in the development of NAFLD. They studied 15 inpatient women and submitted them to depletion of choline. They found that differences in two classes of bacteria (decrease in Gammaproteobacteria and increase in Erysipelotrichi), in association with genetic polymorphisms in phosphatidylethanolamine N-methyltransferase (PEMT, a key enzyme in the choline metabolism), could predict the susceptibility to develop NAFLD with choline depletion. This is highly relevant, because the median choline intake in the United States is half the recommended dose (recommended dose: 550 mg per day) [74]. Gut microbiota can further promote choline depletion by hydrolyzing choline to trimethylamine, which can be further metabolized in the liver into the toxic compound trimethylamine N-oxide (TMAO). Interestingly, feeding mice with high fat diet is known to shift the gut microbiota into a choline degradation profile [75].

In patients with NAFLD, the presence of NASH associated with an increase in the genus *Bacteroides* [66]. This skew in favor of *Bacteroides* may translate to an increase in the toxic bile deoxycholic acid, which is known to induce apoptosis in hepatocytes and to be increased in patients with NASH [76,77]. Furthermore, *Bacteroides* has been associated with an increase in branched-chain fatty acids derived from aminoacids fermentation, which have diabetogenic potential [78]. Lastly, in patients with NAFLD, the presence of significant fibrosis also associated with increased content of the genus *Ruminococcus*, which is difficult to interpret, since it is a highly heterogeneous genus including both potentially beneficial and detrimental species [66]. Nevertheless, some species from the *Ruminococcus* genus are pro-inflammatory and able to produce ethanol [79–81], two potential pathogenic mechanisms in the progression of NAFLD.

Table 1. Studies evaluating microbiota in human NAFLD/NASH.

Study	Population	Phyla	Class	Order	Family	Genera	Species
Spencer, M.D., 2011 [62]	15 women with a choline deficient diet and risk for NAFLD	Firmicutes	↑ Erysipelotrichi				
		Proteobacteriaceae	**Gammaproteobacteria**				
Mouzaki, H., 2013 [63]	17 controls biopsy proven: 11 SS 22 NASH	**↓ Bacteriodetes**					
		Firmicutes	Clostridia	Clostridiales	Clostridiaceae	*Clostridium*	↑ *C. coccoide*
		Firmicutes	Bacilli	Lactobacillales	Lactobacillaceae	↑ *Lactobacillus*	
Raman, H., 2013 [64]	30 obese with NAFLD 30 healthy controls	Firmicutes	Clostridia	Clostridiales	↑ Lachnospiraceae	↑ *Robinsoniella* ↑ *Roseburia* ↑ *Dorea*	
					↓ Ruminococeceae	↓ *Oscillibacter*	
		Bacteriodetes	Bacteroidia	Bacteroidales	↑ **Porphyromonadaceae**	↑ *Parabacteroides*	
Wong, V.W.S., 2013 [65]	16 NASH 22 healthy controls	↓ Firmicutes	Clostridia	↓ **Clostridiales**	Clostridiaceae	↓ *Faecalibacterium* ↓ *Anaesporobacter*	
			Negativicutes	Selenomonodales	Veillonellaceae	↑ *Allisonela*	
		Proteobacteria	Gammaproteobacteria	↑ **Aeromonadales**	↑ **Succinivibrionaceae**		
Boursier, J., 2015 [66]	57 patients with NAFLD: 30 F0/F1 27 > F1	Bacteriodetes	Bacteriodia	↑ **Bacteroidales (NASH)**	Ruminococceceae	↑ *Ruminococus* (>F1)	
		Firmicutes	Clostridia	Clostridiales	↓ **Porphyromonadaceae**	↓ *Odoribacter*	
Jiang, W., 2015 [67]	53 NAFLD 32 healthy controls	Bacteriodetes	Bacteriodia	Bacteroidales	Rikenellaceae	↓ *Alistipes*	
					Prevotellaceae	↓ *Prevotella*	
			Bacilli	Lactobacillales	Lactobacillaceae	↑ *Lactobacillus*	
					Streptococcaceae	↑ *Streptococcus*	
		Firmicutes	Clostridia	Clostridiales	Clostridiaceae	↑ *Clostridium*	
					↓ **Ruminococceceae**	↓ *Oscillibacter*	
						↓ *Flavonifractor*	
		Proteobacteriaceae	Gammaproteobacteria	Enterobacteriales	Enterobacteraceae	↑ *Escherichia*	
		↓ Lentisphaerae					

In bold are the associations described. NAFLD, nonalcoholic fatty liver disease; NASH, nonalcoholic steatohepatitis; F0/F1, no or mild fibrosis; >F1, significant fibrosis. Arrows indicate the differences in the studied group as compared to the control group.

NAFLD and particularly NASH also seem to associate with specific changes in the oral microbiota. Yoneda *et al.* [82] studied 150 patients with NAFLD (of those 102 with NASH) and 60 healthy controls, and found that infection with *Porphyromonas gingivalis* (the major cause of periodontitis) tripled the risk for NAFLD and quadrupled the risk for NASH, independent of ge and metabolic syndrome. In 10 patients with NAFLD, treatment of periodontitis prompted an improvement in liver enzymes [82]. Furthermore, in patients with NASH, positive immunohistochemistry for *P. gingivalis* associated with increased fibrosis [83]. In mice fed high-fat diet, infection with *P. gingivalis* associated with endotoxemia and increased blood levels of proinflammatory cytokines, as well as worse liver disease, including worse fibrosis [82,83].

In summary, gut microbiota can contribute to the development and progression of NAFLD via several mechanisms: (a) modulation of energy homeostasis and energy harvested from diet with associated obesity and dysmetabolism [4,26]; (b) modulation of intestinal permeability promoting endotoxemia as well as other microbe products that promote systemic and hepatic inflammation [50]; (c) modulation of the choline metabolism (required for very low density lipoproteins VLDL synthesis and export of lipids from the liver) [75]; (d) generation of endogenous ethanol as well as other toxic products such as TMAO [73,84–86]; and (e) modulation of bile acids homeostasis and FXR function [87,88] (Figure 1).

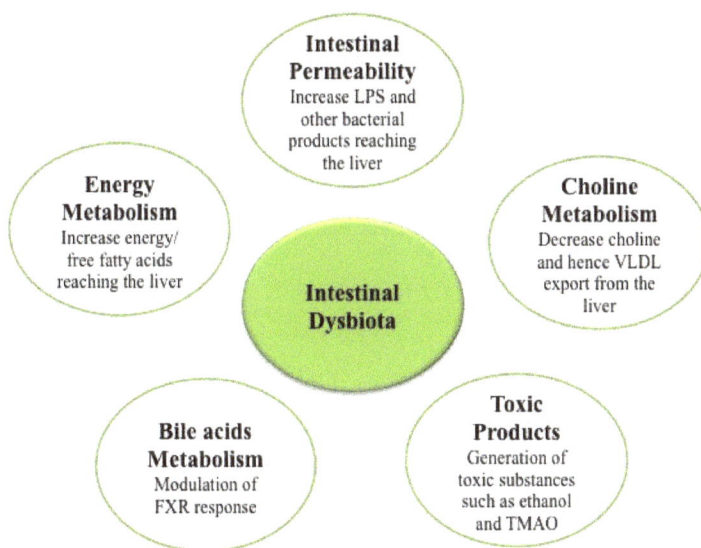

Figure 1. Nonalcoholic fatty liver disease (NAFLD) associated mechanisms of intestinal dysbiota.

4. Diet and Microbiota

Both the quality and quantity of our diet strongly modulate the gut microbiota. Different diets associate with different compositions of the microbiota. De Fillipo *et al.*'s [89] work beautifully translates this concept. They compared the fecal microbiota of European children (who ate a modern Western diet) with children from a rural African village of Burkina Faso (which ate a high-fiber diet, similar to the ancient diet soon after the birth of agriculture). Children from Burkina Faso had a decreased Firmicutes/Bacterioidetes ratio, a higher percentage of bacteria from the genera *Prevotella* and *Xylanibacter* (known to be equipped with enzymes in the degradation of indigestible carbohydrates), and a decrease in the proinflammatory Enterobacteriaceae, *Shigella* and *Escherichia*.

They also had higher amounts of SCFA in the stools. This study suggests that gut microbiota coevolved with the polysaccharide rich diet in order to maximize energy intake from fibers [89].

How quickly can a change in the diet induce differences in the microbiome? In mice, we can induce changes in the gut microbiome after just one single day on a different diet [17]. Studies in humans also showed diet-driven changes in the intestinal microbiota occurring as early as in three to four days [90]. In a clinical study, David *et al.* [91] were able to induce differences in microbiota, that would be metabolically more fit to the type of diet administered, entirely animal or entirely plant products, in just five days. Furthermore, volunteers placed on a three-day high or low-calorie diet, showed that even this short-term increase in energy intake, associated with an increased Firmicutes/Bacterioidetes ratio, correlated with a decrease in the proportion of energy loss in the stools [26]. Indeed, diets enriched in fibers associate with an increase in the fecal loss of energy [92]. However, after stopping the diet, microbiota quickly returned to the basal state, translating the high resilience of our gut flora. Similarly, a dietary intervention in obese or overweight subjects, consisting of administering an energy-restricted high protein diet during six weeks, increased the diversity of species in the gut, along with decreased adiposity, which reverted to basal levels after the diet was stopped [93]. In contrast, long-term diets were able to induce more profound changes in the microbiota than short-term ones [94].

Chronic high-fat diet feeding in mice is known to change gut microbiota with progressive increase in Firmicutes and decrease in Bacterioidetes [20,21]. One important question regarding diet-induced changes in the microbiota is whether it is the composition of the diet or the number of calories ingested that has an effect on gut flora. Also, is diet or obesity itself the important factor for our gut health? Several lines of evidence suggest that both quantity and quality of the diet modulate gut microbiota. Mice deficient in resistin-like molecule β are resistant to high-fat diet induced obesity, however they still shift their gut microbiota with a decrease in Bacterioidetes and increase in Firmicutes as well as Proteobacteria, in response to those diets, in a similar way as their wild type counterparts [95]. This suggests that it is diet and not obesity, the critical factor determining the gut microbiota. On the other hand, when genetically obese leptin resistant mice were pair-fed with wild type mice, they still maintained the same differences in gut microbiota as genetically obese leptin resistant mice fed *ad libitum* [39]. This suggests that leptin itself (and hence the obesity state) may modulate gut microbiota independently of the diet.

Suggesting a critical effect on the composition of the diet, different formulations of high-fat diet, with different percentages of saturated and polyunsaturated fatty acids, seem to have different effects on the gut microbiota. Feeding mice with diets with higher percentage of saturated fatty acids not only seemed to associate with worse weight gain and hepatic steatosis, it also induced more profound changes in the microbiome, with a decrease in diversity and an increase in the Firmicutes/Bacterioidetes ratio [96]. Concordant with the concept of diet composition and gut microbiota crosstalk, mice were fed with either low-fat diet for 35 weeks (remaining lean), high-fat diet for 35 weeks (becoming and remaining obese), low-fat diet for 12 weeks followed by restricted intake of low-fat diet for 23 weeks (to maintain a 20% reduction in body weight), or high-fat diet for 12 weeks followed by restricted intake of high-fat diet for 23 weeks (in order to gain weight and then maintain a 20% reduction in body weight) [97]. The authors found that, regardless of weight status, low-fat diets induced the higher abundance of Firmicutes due to two species from the genus *Allobaculum*, and the high-fat diets induced the higher abundance of non-*Allobaculum* Firmicutes, Bacterioidetes and Mucispirillum. The aggregate animal data suggest a contribution of the quality of the diet *versus* the caloric intake in the composition of the gut microbiota.

Similar conclusions regarding the importance of quality *versus* quantity of the diet, can be taken from a study on obese volunteers that ate one of two isocaloric diets: low carbohydrates/high fat or high carbohydrates/low fat [98]. While the former diet associated with a decrease in fecal SCFA and *Bifidobacterium*, the latter associated with an increase in total anaerobes in fecal samples.

Fava *et al.* [99] studied subjects at increased risk for the metabolic syndrome. Those subjects were given a high saturated fat diet for four weeks and, subsequently, randomized for one of the following diets: high saturated fat diet, high monosaturated fat (MUFA)/high glycemic index diet, high MUFA/low glycemic index diet, high carbohydrate/high glycemic index diet and high carbohydrate/low glycemic index diet. They found that high carbohydrate diets (low fat) increased fecal *Bifidobacterium* and improved glucose metabolism, however if the diet had high glycemic index, it associated with an increase in fecal Bacteroides (which were associated with NASH in patients with NAFLD [66]), and if the glycemic index were lower, it associated with an increase in *Faecalibacterium prausnitzii* (which seems beneficial in protecting from NASH [65]). Furthermore, high saturated fat diets associated with increased fecal SCFA content. In conclusion, the Fava *et al.* [99] study beautifully translates that different compositions of isocaloric diets can modulate the gut microbiota, with potential impact in the risk for the development of the metabolic syndrome and NASH.

Studies in mice showed that high-fat diets could increase fecal content of hydrogen sulfide producing bacteria such as from the family Desulfovibrionaceae. This is a relevant effect since hydrogen sulfide is toxic to colonocytes, perturbing intestinal barrier function and increasing endotoxemia [100]. Another important association was made with *Akkermansia muciniphila*, a specific type of mucin-degrading bacteria that improves intestinal barrier. *Akkermansia muciniphila* levels were shown to decrease after high fat diet [101].

Recently, different groups showed that bariatric surgery might induce weight loss not necessarily by a decrease in food intake and through malabsorption, but also by modulating the gut microbiota. Obese patients submitted to bariatric surgery experienced profound changes in the gut microbiota that correlated with weight loss, including: an increase in diversity, decrease in Firmicutes and methanogenic Archea, with concurrent increases in Bacterioidetes and Gammaproteobacteria, as well as a decrease in lactic acid bacteria such as *Lactobacillus* and *Bifidobacterium* [102–104]. Indeed, causality between modulation of gut microbiota and weight loss was proved by Liou *et al.* [105] Transfering the gut microbiota from mice that underwent bariatric surgery into non-operated germ-free mice, resulted in weight loss, decreased body and liver fat, as compared to germ-free mice receiving gut microbiota from mice submitted to sham surgery.

More recently, bile acids entered the equation between bariatric surgery, altered microbiota and weight loss. In fact, bariatric surgery is known to associate with increased circulating levels of bile acids and FXR signaling [106–109]. Suggesting a role of bile acids through FXR signaling, FXR deficient mice submitted to high-fat diet induced obesity and subsequent bariatric surgery (vertical sleeve gastrectomy), were less prone to sustained weight loss after surgery, with compensatory increase in food intake within three to five weeks [110]. Also, they did not improve glycemic control after surgery. Interestingly, as compared to wild type mice, in FXR deficient mice, bariatric surgery had an attenuated ability to modulate the gut microbiota, with no inhibition of Bacteroides and maintaining a decrease in *Roseburia* (known to also be decreased in human type 2 diabetes mellitus).

5. Microbiota as a Therapeutic Target

We can intervene in order to modulate our gut microbiota either giving commensal organisms known to improve our health status (dubbed probiotics), giving carbohydrates that stimulate the growth of potential beneficial commensals (dubbed prebiotics), or by giving a mix of both (dubbed symbiotics). In this review we will focus on the evidence on probiotics and symbiotics, since data on prebiotics alone are less robust.

Probiotics can potentially be beneficial in the treatment of NAFLD/NASH through several mechanisms: (a) competition with pathogenic species and antimicrobial effect modulating IgA secretion; (b) anti-inflammatory effect with inhibition of pro-inflammatory cytokines production; (c) increased gut satiety signals such as induction of YY peptide and inhibition of orexigenic ghrelin; (d) promotion of intestinal epithelium integrity and improvement of intestinal barrier; (e) decreased harvesting of energy from non-digestible carbohydrates; (f) decreased production of ethanol and other volatile organic compounds; (g) increased production of Fiaf; (h) decreased fatty acid oxidation in the liver; (i) insulin-sensitizing effect via synthesis of GLP-1; (j) modulation of bile acids and cholesterol metabolism; as well as (k) modulation of choline metabolism [13,111,112].

Due to the high resilience of our gut microbiota that easily tends to return to baseline after perturbation, interventions aimed to modulate the gut microbiota are deemed to early relapse to the initial dysbiota state after stopping the intervention, unless long-term approaches are used.

Several pre-clinical studies evaluated the role of probiotics in protecting from obesity and/or the metabolic syndrome, in different rodent models of obesity [113–117]. The studies are difficult to compare because not only are the models used different, the probiotics used are also different. While not all studies achieved a decrease in body weight and adiposity [117], all showed some metabolic benefit. Similarly, clinical studies in obese patients used different probiotics [118–122]. Those studies had small sample sizes and many of them were uncontrolled interventions [118,120,121]. Not all interventions achieved an improvement in body weight [118] or in metabolic profile [119,121]. While small pilot studies on prebiotics applied to obese patients did modify the gut microbiota [123] and improved lipid profile, in general those interventions failed to achieve weight loss or improvement in the glucose metabolism [124–126].

Probiotics have also been studied as a therapeutic tool for NAFLD/NASH. Three preclinical studies in mouse models of NAFLD associated with genetic and/or diet-induced obesity evaluated the role of a probiotic preparation, VSL#3. VSL#3 contains eight bacterial species from the genera *Bifidobacterium*, *Lactobacillus*, and *Streptococcus salivarius* subsp. thermophilus. This intervention improved steatosis, aminotransferases levels, serum lipids and insulin resistance [127–129]. Additionally, mice fed methionine-choline diet, a model of severe NASH not associated with obesity or the metabolic syndrome, developed less liver fibrosis when treated with VSL#3 [130]. Other probiotics also showed beneficial effects in animal models of NAFLD/NASH [131–139].

In humans, only small short-term pilot studies evaluated different probiotic/symbiotic preparations as a therapeutic approach for NAFLD (Table 2) [140–147]. However, the expectations on probiotics as a therapeutic tool in NAFLD are so high, that there are more systematic reviews and meta-analysis [13,112,148–154] on the topic than primary studies itself. Most studies did find a decrease in aminotransferases levels and hepatic steatosis after a short-term intervention. However, in terms of dysmetabolism, these studies failed to show benefit in anthropometric parameters and effect on lipid and glucose metabolism was not consistent among studies. Eslamparast *et al.* [146] noninvasively assessed liver fibrosis with transient elastography, pre- and post-intervention. They performed a randomized clinical trial, compared to placebo in 26 patients with NAFLD in each arm. They used a probiotic mixture that included different species from *Lactobacillus*, *Bifidobacterium*, and *Streptococcus* genera, as well as two different yeasts. After seven months of therapy, they did achieve a difference between probiotic and placebo arms in liver fibrosis, favoring the probiotic arm. One randomized clinical trial, with 36 patients with NASH in the probiotic group and 36 in the control group, performed liver biopsy pre and post-intervention [143]. After six months of treatment with Zirfos (a symbiotic with *B. longum*), patients in the symbiotic group, as compared to the placebo group, profited in terms of hepatic steatosis, but had no advantage in hepatocellular ballooning, liver inflammation, or liver fibrosis.

In summary, though promising, the evidence for the use of probiotics in the treatment of NAFLD/NASH is still insufficient. Studies are small, with short-term interventions, different formulations, different compositions of probiotics/symbiotics, and different durations of treatment. Also, most studies lack liver biopsy. The one study that systematically performed liver biopsy pre- and post-intervention failed to demonstrate significant differences between probiotics and placebo in important histological endpoints such as hepatic inflammation and fibrosis [143].

Table 2. Studies evaluating the therapeutic role of probiotics in human NAFLD/NASH.

Study	Design	Probiotic Composition	Results
Loguercio, C., 2002 [140]	10 patients with NASH No control group Two months intervention	LAB: *L. acidophilus, L. rhamnosus, L. plantarum, L. salivarius, L. casei, L. bulgaricus, B. lactis, B. bifidus, B. breve,* FOS, vitamins	↓ liver enzymes: ALT and γGT ↓ TNF-α levels and oxidative stress Relapse after stopping the intervention
Loguercio, C., 2005 [141]	22 patients with NASH No control group Three months intervention	VSL#3: *B. breve, B. longum, B. infantis, L. acidophilus, L. plantarum, L. paracasei, L. bulgaricus, S. Thermophilus* (2 capsules, twice a day)	↓ liver enzymes ↓ oxidative stress
Aller, R., 2011 [142]	Patients with NAFLD: probiotic group *n* = 15 and control group *n* = 15 Three months intervention	Mixture of 500 million *L. bulgaricus* + *S. thermophilus*	↓ liver enzymes: ALT no difference in anthropometric metrics no difference in lipid/glucose metabolism no difference in IL-6 or TNF-α levels
Malaguarnera, M., 2012 [143]	Patients with NASH: Probiotic group *n* = 34 and control group *n* = 29 Biopsy pre and post-intervention Six months intervention	Zirfos: FOS, *B. longum,* vitamins	↓ liver enzymes: AST ↓ LDL-cholesterol and insulin resistance ↓ TNF-α levels and endotoxemia no difference in anthropometric metrics ↓ steatosis and NAS score no difference in ballooning, inflammation or fibrosis
Wong, V.W.S., 2013 [144]	Patients with NASH: probiotic group *n* = 10 and control group *n* = 10 Six months intervention	Lepicol: *L. desibrueckii, L. acidophilus, L. rhamnosus, B. bifidum*	↓ liver steatosis by H-MRS ↓ liver enzymes: AST no difference in anthropometric metrics no difference in lipid/glucose metabolism
Nabavi, S., 2014 [145]	Patients with NAFLD: probiotic group *n* = 36 and control group *n* = 36 Two months intervention	Probiotic yogurt containing *L. acidophilus* La5 and *B. lactis* Bb12	↓ liver enzymes: ALT and AST ↓ total cholesterol and LDL-cholesterol
Eslamparast, T., 2014 [146]	Patients with NAFLD: Probiotic group *n* = 26 and control group *n* = 26 Fibroscan© pre and post-intervention Seven months intervention	Protexin: *L. plantarum, L. bulgaricus, L. acidophilus, L. casei, B. bifidum, S. thermophilus, S. faecium, Torulopsis* spp. *Aspergillus oryzae*	↓ liver enzymes: AST, ALT and γGT ↓ TNF-α levels ↓ fibrosis assessed by transient elastography
Sepideh, A., 2015 [147]	Patients with NAFLD: probiotic group *n* = 21 and control group *n* = 21 Two months intervention	Lactocare: *L. casei, L. acidophilus, L. rhamnosus, L. bulgaricus, B. breve, B. longum, S. Thermophilus* (2 capsules per day)	↓ insulin resistance and IL-6 no difference in anthropometric metrics no difference in TNF-α levels

ALT, alanine aminotransferase; AST, aspartate aminotransferase; FOS, fructooligosaccharides; γGT, γ-glutamyl transpeptidase; H-MRS, proton magnetic resonance spectroscopy; IL-6, interleukin-6; LDL, low density lipoprotein; NAFLD, nonalcoholic fatty liver disease; NASH, nonalcoholic steatohepatitis; TNF-α, tumor necrosis factor α. Arrows indicate the differences in the intervention group as compared to the control group.

6. Conclusions

Obesity-associated NAFLD is the hepatic pandemic of our century. The gut microbiota has a huge impact in the pathogenesis of obesity and its metabolic complications, as well as in the development and progression of NAFLD. Gut dysbiosis promotes obesity through modulation of the energy harvested from the diet, as well as through direct modulation of adipose tissue and hepatic metabolism. Bacterial products may be toxic, two examples being ethanol and TMAO. Dysbiota may also perturb choline and bile acid metabolism, with detrimental effects in the liver. Furthermore, gut dysbiota can perturb the intestinal barrier, and bacterial products may induce systemic toxicity, including hepatic toxicity, that favors proinflammatory states and liver injury.

Several lines of evidence link NAFLD to dysbiosis; for example NAFLD associates with small bowel bacterial overgrowth, increased intestinal permeability, and endotoxemia. Also, in animal models of NAFLD/NASH, as well as in patients, the composition of the gut microbiota tends to be different from healthy subjects. Lastly, in animal models, NAFLD can be a transmissible disease by fecal microbiota transplantation from donors prone to develop NAFLD.

Taken into consideration the acknowledged role of gut dysbiosis in the pathogenesis of NAFLD/NASH, there are huge expectations on the role of probiotics/symbiotics in modulating the gut microbiota and hence having a therapeutic role in NAFLD. Despite the enthusiasm on the field, the available studies are small, heterogeneous, short-term, and do not properly address hepatic histology/risk for progressive liver disease. Hence, the lack of solid evidence, still precludes us implementing probiotics in the management of NAFLD/NASH. Extensive pre-clinical studies comparing different approaches in different animal models of NASH would be important to better delineate large multicentric well-designed, well-powered studies in patients with NASH. Other strategies for modulating the gut microbiota, such as fecal microbiota transplantation may merit further study.

Conflicts of Interest: The authors declare no conflict of interest.

References

1. Bays, H. Adiposopathy, "sick fat", ockham's razor, and resolution of the obesity paradox. *Curr. Atheroscler. Rep.* **2014**, *16*, 409. [CrossRef] [PubMed]
2. Byrne, C.D.; Targher, G. NAFLD: A multisystem disease. *J. Hepatol.* **2015**, *62*, S47–S64. [CrossRef] [PubMed]
3. Charlton, M.R.; Burns, J.M.; Pedersen, R.A.; Watt, K.D.; Heimbach, J.K.; Dierkhising, R.A. Frequency and outcomes of liver transplantation for nonalcoholic steatohepatitis in the United States. *Gastroenterology* **2011**, *141*, 1249–1253. [CrossRef] [PubMed]
4. Backhed, F.; Ding, H.; Wang, T.; Hooper, L.V.; Koh, G.Y.; Nagy, A.; Semenkovich, C.F.; Gordon, J.I. The gut microbiota as an environmental factor that regulates fat storage. *Proc. Natl. Acad. Sci. USA* **2004**, *101*, 15718–15723. [CrossRef] [PubMed]
5. Lagier, J.C.; Million, M.; Hugon, P.; Armougom, F.; Raoult, D. Human gut microbiota: Repertoire and variations. *Front. Cell. Infect. Microbiol.* **2012**, *2*, 136. [CrossRef] [PubMed]
6. Gill, S.R.; Pop, M.; Deboy, R.T.; Eckburg, P.B.; Turnbaugh, P.J.; Samuel, B.S.; Gordon, J.I.; Relman, D.A.; Fraser-Liggett, C.M.; Nelson, K.E. Metagenomic analysis of the human distal gut microbiome. *Science* **2006**, *312*, 1355–1359. [CrossRef] [PubMed]
7. Seksik, P.; Landman, C. Understanding microbiome data: A primer for clinicians. *Dig. Dis.* **2015**, *33*, 11–16. [CrossRef] [PubMed]
8. Lozupone, C.A.; Stombaugh, J.I.; Gordon, J.I.; Jansson, J.K.; Knight, R. Diversity, stability and resilience of the human gut microbiota. *Nature* **2012**, *489*, 220–230. [CrossRef] [PubMed]
9. Imajo, K.; Yoneda, M.; Ogawa, Y.; Wada, K.; Nakajima, A. Microbiota and nonalcoholic steatohepatitis. *Semin. Immunopathol.* **2014**, *36*, 115–132. [CrossRef] [PubMed]
10. Martinez, I.; Muller, C.E.; Walter, J. Long-term temporal analysis of the human fecal microbiota revealed a stable core of dominant bacterial species. *PLoS ONE* **2013**, *8*, e69621. [CrossRef] [PubMed]

11. Faith, J.J.; Guruge, J.L.; Charbonneau, M.; Subramanian, S.; Seedorf, H.; Goodman, A.L.; Clemente, J.C.; Knight, R.; Heath, A.C.; Leibel, R.L.; *et al.* The long-term stability of the human gut microbiota. *Science* **2013**, *341*, 1237439. [CrossRef] [PubMed]

12. Dethlefsen, L.; Relman, D.A. Incomplete recovery and individualized responses of the human distal gut microbiota to repeated antibiotic perturbation. *Proc. Natl. Acad. Sci. USA* **2011**, *108*, 4554–4561. [CrossRef] [PubMed]

13. Tarantino, G.; Finelli, C. Systematic review on intervention with prebiotics/probiotics in patients with obesity-related nonalcoholic fatty liver disease. *Future Microbiol.* **2015**, *10*, 889–902. [CrossRef] [PubMed]

14. Donaldson, G.P.; Lee, S.M.; Mazmanian, S.K. Gut biogeography of the bacterial microbiota. *Nat. Rev. Microbiol.* **2016**, *14*, 20–32. [CrossRef] [PubMed]

15. Backhed, F.; Manchester, J.K.; Semenkovich, C.F.; Gordon, J.I. Mechanisms underlying the resistance to diet-induced obesity in germ-free mice. *Proc. Natl. Acad. Sci. USA* **2007**, *104*, 979–984. [CrossRef] [PubMed]

16. Turnbaugh, P.J.; Ley, R.E.; Mahowald, M.A.; Magrini, V.; Mardis, E.R.; Gordon, J.I. An obesity-associated gut microbiome with increased capacity for energy harvest. *Nature* **2006**, *444*, 1027–1031. [CrossRef] [PubMed]

17. Turnbaugh, P.J.; Ridaura, V.K.; Faith, J.J.; Rey, F.E.; Knight, R.; Gordon, J.I. The effect of diet on the human gut microbiome: A metagenomic analysis in humanized gnotobiotic mice. *Sci. Transl. Med.* **2009**, *1*, 6ra14. [CrossRef] [PubMed]

18. Vrieze, A.; van Nood, E.; Holleman, F.; Salojarvi, J.; Kootte, R.S.; Bartelsman, J.F.; Dallinga-Thie, G.M.; Ackermans, M.T.; Serlie, M.J.; Oozeer, R.; *et al.* Transfer of intestinal microbiota from lean donors increases insulin sensitivity in individuals with metabolic syndrome. *Gastroenterology* **2012**, *143*, 913–916. [CrossRef] [PubMed]

19. Ley, R.E.; Backhed, F.; Turnbaugh, P.; Lozupone, C.A.; Knight, R.D.; Gordon, J.I. Obesity alters gut microbial ecology. *Proc. Natl. Acad. Sci. USA* **2005**, *102*, 11070–11075. [CrossRef] [PubMed]

20. Murphy, E.F.; Cotter, P.D.; Healy, S.; Marques, T.M.; O'Sullivan, O.; Fouhy, F.; Clarke, S.F.; O'Toole, P.W.; Quigley, E.M.; Stanton, C.; *et al.* Composition and energy harvesting capacity of the gut microbiota: Relationship to diet, obesity and time in mouse models. *Gut* **2010**, *59*, 1635–1642. [CrossRef] [PubMed]

21. Turnbaugh, P.J.; Backhed, F.; Fulton, L.; Gordon, J.I. Diet-induced obesity is linked to marked but reversible alterations in the mouse distal gut microbiome. *Cell Host Microbe* **2008**, *3*, 213–223. [CrossRef] [PubMed]

22. Turnbaugh, P.J.; Hamady, M.; Yatsunenko, T.; Cantarel, B.L.; Duncan, A.; Ley, R.E.; Sogin, M.L.; Jones, W.J.; Roe, B.A.; Affourtit, J.P.; *et al.* A core gut microbiome in obese and lean twins. *Nature* **2009**, *457*, 480–484. [CrossRef] [PubMed]

23. Patil, D.P.; Dhotre, D.P.; Chavan, S.G.; Sultan, A.; Jain, D.S.; Lanjekar, V.B.; Gangawani, J.; Shah, P.S.; Todkar, J.S.; Shah, S.; *et al.* Molecular analysis of gut microbiota in obesity among indian individuals. *J. Biosci.* **2012**, *37*, 647–657. [CrossRef] [PubMed]

24. Ferrer, M.; Ruiz, A.; Lanza, F.; Haange, S.B.; Oberbach, A.; Till, H.; Bargiela, R.; Campoy, C.; Segura, M.T.; Richter, M.; *et al.* Microbiota from the distal guts of lean and obese adolescents exhibit partial functional redundancy besides clear differences in community structure. *Environ. Microbiol.* **2013**, *15*, 211–226. [CrossRef] [PubMed]

25. Kalliomaki, M.; Collado, M.C.; Salminen, S.; Isolauri, E. Early differences in fecal microbiota composition in children may predict overweight. *Am. J. Clin. Nutr.* **2008**, *87*, 534–538. [PubMed]

26. Jumpertz, R.; Le, D.S.; Turnbaugh, P.J.; Trinidad, C.; Bogardus, C.; Gordon, J.I.; Krakoff, J. Energy-balance studies reveal associations between gut microbes, caloric load, and nutrient absorption in humans. *Am. J. Clin. Nutr.* **2011**, *94*, 58–65. [CrossRef] [PubMed]

27. Chakraborti, C.K. New-found link between microbiota and obesity. *World J. Gastrointest. Pathophysiol.* **2015**, *6*, 110–119. [CrossRef] [PubMed]

28. Brahe, L.K.; Astrup, A.; Larsen, L.H. Is butyrate the link between diet, intestinal microbiota and obesity-related metabolic diseases? *Obes. Rev.* **2013**, *14*, 950–959. [CrossRef] [PubMed]

29. Louis, P.; Flint, H.J. Diversity, metabolism and microbial ecology of butyrate-producing bacteria from the human large intestine. *FEMS Microbiol. Lett.* **2009**, *294*, 1–8. [CrossRef] [PubMed]

30. Abdallah Ismail, N.; Ragab, S.H.; Abd Elbaky, A.; Shoeib, A.R.; Alhosary, Y.; Fekry, D. Frequency of firmicutes and bacteroidetes in gut microbiota in obese and normal weight egyptian children and adults. *Arch. Med. Sci.* **2011**, *7*, 501–507. [CrossRef] [PubMed]

31. Roy, C.C.; Kien, C.L.; Bouthillier, L.; Levy, E. Short-chain fatty acids: Ready for prime time? *Nutr. Clin. Pract.* **2006**, *21*, 351–366. [CrossRef] [PubMed]

32. Lin, H.V.; Frassetto, A.; Kowalik, E.J., Jr.; Nawrocki, A.R.; Lu, M.M.; Kosinski, J.R.; Hubert, J.A.; Szeto, D.; Yao, X.; Forrest, G.; *et al.* Butyrate and propionate protect against diet-induced obesity and regulate gut hormones via free fatty acid receptor 3-independent mechanisms. *PLoS ONE* **2012**, *7*, e35240.

33. Xiong, Y.; Miyamoto, N.; Shibata, K.; Valasek, M.A.; Motoike, T.; Kedzierski, R.M.; Yanagisawa, M. Short-chain fatty acids stimulate leptin production in adipocytes through the G protein-coupled receptor GPR41. *Proc. Natl. Acad. Sci. USA* **2004**, *101*, 1045–1050. [CrossRef] [PubMed]

34. Al-Lahham, S.H.; Roelofsen, H.; Priebe, M.; Weening, D.; Dijkstra, M.; Hoek, A.; Rezaee, F.; Venema, K.; Vonk, R.J. Regulation of adipokine production in human adipose tissue by propionic acid. *Eur. J. Clin. Investig.* **2010**, *40*, 401–407. [CrossRef] [PubMed]

35. Jin, C.J.; Sellmann, C.; Engstler, A.J.; Ziegenhardt, D.; Bergheim, I. Supplementation of sodium butyrate protects mice from the development of non-alcoholic steatohepatitis (NASH). *Br. J. Nutr.* **2015**, *114*, 1745–1755. [CrossRef] [PubMed]

36. Aronsson, L.; Huang, Y.; Parini, P.; Korach-Andre, M.; Hakansson, J.; Gustafsson, J.A.; Pettersson, S.; Arulampalam, V.; Rafter, J. Decreased fat storage by lactobacillus paracasei is associated with increased levels of angiopoietin-like 4 protein (ANGPTL4). *PLoS ONE* **2010**, *5*, e13087. [CrossRef] [PubMed]

37. Ding, S.; Chi, M.M.; Scull, B.P.; Rigby, R.; Schwerbrock, N.M.; Magness, S.; Jobin, C.; Lund, P.K. High-fat diet: Bacteria interactions promote intestinal inflammation which precedes and correlates with obesity and insulin resistance in mouse. *PLoS ONE* **2010**, *5*, e12191. [CrossRef] [PubMed]

38. Claus, S.P.; Ellero, S.L.; Berger, B.; Krause, L.; Bruttin, A.; Molina, J.; Paris, A.; Want, E.J.; de Waziers, I.; Cloarec, O.; *et al.* Colonization-induced host-gut microbial metabolic interaction. *MBio* **2011**, *2*, e00271–e00210. [CrossRef] [PubMed]

39. Rajala, M.W.; Patterson, C.M.; Opp, J.S.; Foltin, S.K.; Young, V.B.; Myers, M.G., Jr. Leptin acts independently of food intake to modulate gut microbial composition in male mice. *Endocrinology* **2014**, *155*, 748–757. [CrossRef] [PubMed]

40. Bergheim, I.; Weber, S.; Vos, M.; Kramer, S.; Volynets, V.; Kaserouni, S.; McClain, C.J.; Bischoff, S.C. Antibiotics protect against fructose-induced hepatic lipid accumulation in mice: Role of endotoxin. *J. Hepatol.* **2008**, *48*, 983–992. [CrossRef] [PubMed]

41. Membrez, M.; Blancher, F.; Jaquet, M.; Bibiloni, R.; Cani, P.D.; Burcelin, R.G.; Corthesy, I.; Mace, K.; Chou, C.J. Gut microbiota modulation with norfloxacin and ampicillin enhances glucose tolerance in mice. *FASEB J.* **2008**, *22*, 2416–2426. [CrossRef] [PubMed]

42. Drenick, E.J.; Fisler, J.; Johnson, D. Hepatic steatosis after intestinal bypass—Prevention and reversal by metronidazole, irrespective of protein-calorie malnutrition. *Gastroenterology* **1982**, *82*, 535–548. [PubMed]

43. Nazim, M.; Stamp, G.; Hodgson, H.J. Non-alcoholic steatohepatitis associated with small intestinal diverticulosis and bacterial overgrowth. *Hepatogastroenterology* **1989**, *36*, 349–351. [PubMed]

44. Wigg, A.J.; Roberts-Thomson, I.C.; Dymock, R.B.; McCarthy, P.J.; Grose, R.H.; Cummins, A.G. The role of small intestinal bacterial overgrowth, intestinal permeability, endotoxaemia, and tumour necrosis factor α in the pathogenesis of non-alcoholic steatohepatitis. *Gut* **2001**, *48*, 206–211. [CrossRef] [PubMed]

45. Brun, P.; Castagliuolo, I.; di Leo, V.; Buda, A.; Pinzani, M.; Palu, G.; Martines, D. Increased intestinal permeability in obese mice: New evidence in the pathogenesis of nonalcoholic steatohepatitis. *Am. J. Physiol. Gastrointest. Liver Physiol.* **2007**, *292*, G518–G525. [CrossRef] [PubMed]

46. Farhadi, A.; Gundlapalli, S.; Shaikh, M.; Frantzides, C.; Harrell, L.; Kwasny, M.M.; Keshavarzian, A. Susceptibility to gut leakiness: A possible mechanism for endotoxaemia in non-alcoholic steatohepatitis. *Liver Int.* **2008**, *28*, 1026–1033. [CrossRef] [PubMed]

47. Spruss, A.; Kanuri, G.; Wagnerberger, S.; Haub, S.; Bischoff, S.C.; Bergheim, I. Toll-like receptor 4 is involved in the development of fructose-induced hepatic steatosis in mice. *Hepatology* **2009**, *50*, 1094–1104. [CrossRef] [PubMed]

48. Miele, L.; Valenza, V.; la Torre, G.; Montalto, M.; Cammarota, G.; Ricci, R.; Masciana, R.; Forgione, A.; Gabrieli, M.L.; Perotti, G.; *et al.* Increased intestinal permeability and tight junction alterations in nonalcoholic fatty liver disease. *Hepatology* **2009**, *49*, 1877–1887. [CrossRef] [PubMed]

49. Shanab, A.A.; Scully, P.; Crosbie, O.; Buckley, M.; O'Mahony, L.; Shanahan, F.; Gazareen, S.; Murphy, E.; Quigley, E.M. Small intestinal bacterial overgrowth in nonalcoholic steatohepatitis: Association with toll-like receptor 4 expression and plasma levels of interleukin 8. *Dig. Dis. Sci.* **2011**, *56*, 1524–1534. [CrossRef] [PubMed]

50. Cani, P.D.; Amar, J.; Iglesias, M.A.; Poggi, M.; Knauf, C.; Bastelica, D.; Neyrinck, A.M.; Fava, F.; Tuohy, K.M.; Chabo, C.; *et al.* Metabolic endotoxemia initiates obesity and insulin resistance. *Diabetes* **2007**, *56*, 1761–1772. [CrossRef] [PubMed]

51. Verdam, F.J.; Rensen, S.S.; Driessen, A.; Greve, J.W.; Buurman, W.A. Novel evidence for chronic exposure to endotoxin in human nonalcoholic steatohepatitis. *J. Clin. Gastroenterol.* **2011**, *45*, 149–152. [CrossRef] [PubMed]

52. Poggi, M.; Bastelica, D.; Gual, P.; Iglesias, M.A.; Gremeaux, T.; Knauf, C.; Peiretti, F.; Verdier, M.; Juhan-Vague, I.; Tanti, J.F.; *et al.* C3H/HEJ mice carrying a toll-like receptor 4 mutation are protected against the development of insulin resistance in white adipose tissue in response to a high-fat diet. *Diabetologia* **2007**, *50*, 1267–1276. [CrossRef] [PubMed]

53. Csak, T.; Velayudham, A.; Hritz, I.; Petrasek, J.; Levin, I.; Lippai, D.; Catalano, D.; Mandrekar, P.; Dolganiuc, A.; Kurt-Jones, E.; *et al.* Deficiency in myeloid differentiation factor-2 and toll-like receptor 4 expression attenuates nonalcoholic steatohepatitis and fibrosis in mice. *Am. J. Physiol. Gastrointest. Liver Physiol.* **2011**, *300*, G433–G441. [CrossRef] [PubMed]

54. Ye, D.; Li, F.Y.; Lam, K.S.; Li, H.; Jia, W.; Wang, Y.; Man, K.; Lo, C.M.; Li, X.; Xu, A. Toll-like receptor-4 mediates obesity-induced non-alcoholic steatohepatitis through activation of X-box binding protein-1 in mice. *Gut* **2012**, *61*, 1058–1067. [CrossRef] [PubMed]

55. Yuan, L.; Bambha, K. Bile acid receptors and nonalcoholic fatty liver disease. *World J. Hepatol.* **2015**, *7*, 2811–2818. [CrossRef] [PubMed]

56. Stacey, M.; Webb, M. Studies on the antibacterial properties of the bile acids and some compounds derived from cholanic acid. *Proc. R. Soc. Med.* **1947**, *134*, 523–537. [CrossRef] [PubMed]

57. Sayin, S.I.; Wahlstrom, A.; Felin, J.; Jantti, S.; Marschall, H.U.; Bamberg, K.; Angelin, B.; Hyotylainen, T.; Oresic, M.; Backhed, F. Gut microbiota regulates bile acid metabolism by reducing the levels of tauro-β-muricholic acid, a naturally occurring fxr antagonist. *Cell Metab.* **2013**, *17*, 225–235. [CrossRef] [PubMed]

58. Le Roy, T.; Llopis, M.; Lepage, P.; Bruneau, A.; Rabot, S.; Bevilacqua, C.; Martin, P.; Philippe, C.; Walker, F.; Bado, A.; *et al.* Intestinal microbiota determines development of non-alcoholic fatty liver disease in mice. *Gut* **2013**, *62*, 1787–1794. [CrossRef] [PubMed]

59. Henao-Mejia, J.; Elinav, E.; Jin, C.; Hao, L.; Mehal, W.Z.; Strowig, T.; Thaiss, C.A.; Kau, A.L.; Eisenbarth, S.C.; Jurczak, M.J.; *et al.* Inflammasome-mediated dysbiosis regulates progression of NAFLD and obesity. *Nature* **2012**, *482*, 179–185. [CrossRef] [PubMed]

60. De Minicis, S.; Rychlicki, C.; Agostinelli, L.; Saccomanno, S.; Candelaresi, C.; Trozzi, L.; Mingarelli, E.; Facinelli, B.; Magi, G.; Palmieri, C.; *et al.* Dysbiosis contributes to fibrogenesis in the course of chronic liver injury in mice. *Hepatology* **2014**, *59*, 1738–1749. [CrossRef] [PubMed]

61. Yoshimoto, S.; Loo, T.M.; Atarashi, K.; Kanda, H.; Sato, S.; Oyadomari, S.; Iwakura, Y.; Oshima, K.; Morita, H.; Hattori, M.; *et al.* Obesity-induced gut microbial metabolite promotes liver cancer through senescence secretome. *Nature* **2013**, *499*, 97–101. [CrossRef] [PubMed]

62. Spencer, M.D.; Hamp, T.J.; Reid, R.W.; Fischer, L.M.; Zeisel, S.H.; Fodor, A.A. Association between composition of the human gastrointestinal microbiome and development of fatty liver with choline deficiency. *Gastroenterology* **2011**, *140*, 976–986. [CrossRef] [PubMed]

63. Mouzaki, M.; Comelli, E.M.; Arendt, B.M.; Bonengel, J.; Fung, S.K.; Fischer, S.E.; McGilvray, I.D.; Allard, J.P. Intestinal microbiota in patients with nonalcoholic fatty liver disease. *Hepatology* **2013**, *58*, 120–127. [CrossRef] [PubMed]

64. Raman, M.; Ahmed, I.; Gillevet, P.M.; Probert, C.S.; Ratcliffe, N.M.; Smith, S.; Greenwood, R.; Sikaroodi, M.; Lam, V.; Crotty, P.; *et al.* Fecal microbiome and volatile organic compound metabolome in obese humans with nonalcoholic fatty liver disease. *Clin. Gastroenterol. Hepatol.* **2013**, *11*, 868–875. [CrossRef] [PubMed]

65. Wong, V.W.; Tse, C.H.; Lam, T.T.; Wong, G.L.; Chim, A.M.; Chu, W.C.; Yeung, D.K.; Law, P.T.; Kwan, H.S.; Yu, J.; *et al.* Molecular characterization of the fecal microbiota in patients with nonalcoholic steatohepatitis—A longitudinal study. *PLoS ONE* **2013**, *8*, e62885. [CrossRef] [PubMed]

66. Boursier, J.; Mueller, O.; Barret, M.; Machado, M.; Fizanne, L.; Araujo-Perez, F.; Guy, C.D.; Seed, P.C.; Rawls, J.F.; David, L.A.; *et al.* The severity of NAFLD is associated with gut dysbiosis and shift in the metabolic function of the gut microbiota. *Hepatology* **2016**, *63*, 764–775. [CrossRef] [PubMed]

67. Jiang, W.; Wu, N.; Wang, X.; Chi, Y.; Zhang, Y.; Qiu, X.; Hu, Y.; Li, J.; Liu, Y. Dysbiosis gut microbiota associated with inflammation and impaired mucosal immune function in intestine of humans with non-alcoholic fatty liver disease. *Sci. Rep.* **2015**, *5*, 8096. [CrossRef] [PubMed]

68. Lebeer, S.; Vanderleyden, J.; de Keersmaecker, S.C. Genes and molecules of lactobacilli supporting probiotic action. *Microbiol. Mol. Biol. Rev.* **2008**, *72*, 728–764. [CrossRef] [PubMed]

69. Elshaghabee, F.M.; Bockelmann, W.; Meske, D.; de Vrese, M.; Walte, H.G.; Schrezenmeir, J.; Heller, K.J. Ethanol production by selected intestinal microorganisms and lactic acid bacteria growing under different nutritional conditions. *Front. Microbiol.* **2016**, *7*, 47. [CrossRef] [PubMed]

70. Scott, K.P.; Martin, J.C.; Duncan, S.H.; Flint, H.J. Prebiotic stimulation of human colonic butyrate-producing bacteria and bifidobacteria, *in vitro. FEMS Microbiol. Ecol.* **2014**, *87*, 30–40. [CrossRef] [PubMed]

71. Prorok-Hamon, M.; Friswell, M.K.; Alswied, A.; Roberts, C.L.; Song, F.; Flanagan, P.K.; Knight, P.; Codling, C.; Marchesi, J.R.; Winstanley, C.; *et al.* Colonic mucosa-associated diffusely adherent *afaC + Escherichia coli* expressing *lpfA* and *pks* are increased in inflammatory bowel disease and colon cancer. *Gut* **2014**, *63*, 761–770. [CrossRef] [PubMed]

72. Al-Jashamy, K.; Murad, A.; Zeehaida, M.; Rohaini, M.; Hasnan, J. Prevalence of colorectal cancer associated with streptococcus bovis among inflammatory bowel and chronic gastrointestinal tract disease patients. *Asian Pac. J. Cancer Prev.* **2010**, *11*, 1765–1768. [PubMed]

73. Zhu, L.; Baker, S.S.; Gill, C.; Liu, W.; Alkhouri, R.; Baker, R.D.; Gill, S.R. Characterization of gut microbiomes in nonalcoholic steatohepatitis (NASH) patients: A connection between endogenous alcohol and NASH. *Hepatology* **2013**, *57*, 601–609. [CrossRef] [PubMed]

74. Zeisel, S.H. Choline. *Adv. Nutr.* **2010**, *1*, 46–48. [CrossRef] [PubMed]

75. Dumas, M.E.; Barton, R.H.; Toye, A.; Cloarec, O.; Blancher, C.; Rothwell, A.; Fearnside, J.; Tatoud, R.; Blanc, V.; Lindon, J.C.; *et al.* Metabolic profiling reveals a contribution of gut microbiota to fatty liver phenotype in insulin-resistant mice. *Proc. Natl. Acad. Sci. USA* **2006**, *103*, 12511–12516. [CrossRef] [PubMed]

76. Ferreira, D.M.; Afonso, M.B.; Rodrigues, P.M.; Simao, A.L.; Pereira, D.M.; Borralho, P.M.; Rodrigues, C.M.; Castro, R.E. c-jun N-terminal kinase 1/c-jun activation of the p53/microRNA 34a/sirtuin 1 pathway contributes to apoptosis induced by deoxycholic acid in rat liver. *Mol. Cell. Biol.* **2014**, *34*, 1100–1120. [CrossRef] [PubMed]

77. Aranha, M.M.; Cortez-Pinto, H.; Costa, A.; da Silva, I.B.; Camilo, M.E.; de Moura, M.C.; Rodrigues, C.M. Bile acid levels are increased in the liver of patients with steatohepatitis. *Eur. J. Gastroenterol. Hepatol.* **2008**, *20*, 519–525. [CrossRef] [PubMed]

78. Newgard, C.B. Interplay between lipids and branched-chain amino acids in development of insulin resistance. *Cell Metab.* **2012**, *15*, 606–614. [CrossRef] [PubMed]

79. Png, C.W.; Linden, S.K.; Gilshenan, K.S.; Zoetendal, E.G.; McSweeney, C.S.; Sly, L.I.; McGuckin, M.A.; Florin, T.H. Mucolytic bacteria with increased prevalence in ibd mucosa augment *in vitro* utilization of mucin by other bacteria. *Am. J. Gastroenterol.* **2010**, *105*, 2420–2428. [CrossRef] [PubMed]

80. Sartor, R.B. Key questions to guide a better understanding of host-commensal microbiota interactions in intestinal inflammation. *Mucosal Immunol.* **2011**, *4*, 127–132. [CrossRef] [PubMed]

81. Christopherson, M.R.; Dawson, J.A.; Stevenson, D.M.; Cunningham, A.C.; Bramhacharya, S.; Weimer, P.J.; Kendziorski, C.; Suen, G. Unique aspects of fiber degradation by the ruminal ethanologen ruminococcus albus 7 revealed by physiological and transcriptomic analysis. *BMC Genom.* **2014**, *15*, 1066. [CrossRef] [PubMed]

82. Yoneda, M.; Naka, S.; Nakano, K.; Wada, K.; Endo, H.; Mawatari, H.; Imajo, K.; Nomura, R.; Hokamura, K.; Ono, M.; *et al.* Involvement of a periodontal pathogen, porphyromonas gingivalis on the pathogenesis of non-alcoholic fatty liver disease. *BMC Gastroenterol.* **2012**, *12*, 16. [CrossRef] [PubMed]

83. Furusho, H.; Miyauchi, M.; Hyogo, H.; Inubushi, T.; Ao, M.; Ouhara, K.; Hisatune, J.; Kurihara, H.; Sugai, M.; Hayes, C.N.; *et al.* Dental infection of porphyromonas gingivalis exacerbates high fat diet-induced steatohepatitis in mice. *J. Gastroenterol.* **2013**, *48*, 1259–1270. [CrossRef] [PubMed]

84. Cope, K.; Risby, T.; Diehl, A.M. Increased gastrointestinal ethanol production in obese mice: Implications for fatty liver disease pathogenesis. *Gastroenterology* **2000**, *119*, 1340–1347. [CrossRef] [PubMed]

85. Nair, S.; Cope, K.; Risby, T.H.; Diehl, A.M. Obesity and female gender increase breath ethanol concentration: Potential implications for the pathogenesis of nonalcoholic steatohepatitis. *Am. J. Gastroenterol.* **2001**, *96*, 1200–1204. [CrossRef] [PubMed]

86. Sajjad, A.; Mottershead, M.; Syn, W.K.; Jones, R.; Smith, S.; Nwokolo, C.U. Ciprofloxacin suppresses bacterial overgrowth, increases fasting insulin but does not correct low acylated ghrelin concentration in non-alcoholic steatohepatitis. *Aliment. Pharmacol. Ther.* **2005**, *22*, 291–299. [CrossRef] [PubMed]

87. Swann, J.R.; Want, E.J.; Geier, F.M.; Spagou, K.; Wilson, I.D.; Sidaway, J.E.; Nicholson, J.K.; Holmes, E. Systemic gut microbial modulation of bile acid metabolism in host tissue compartments. *Proc. Natl. Acad. Sci. USA* **2011**, *108*, 4523–4530. [CrossRef] [PubMed]

88. Jiang, C.; Xie, C.; Li, F.; Zhang, L.; Nichols, R.G.; Krausz, K.W.; Cai, J.; Qi, Y.; Fang, Z.Z.; Takahashi, S.; *et al.* Intestinal farnesoid X receptor signaling promotes nonalcoholic fatty liver disease. *J. Clin. Investig.* **2015**, *125*, 386–402. [CrossRef] [PubMed]

89. De Filippo, C.; Cavalieri, D.; di Paola, M.; Ramazzotti, M.; Poullet, J.B.; Massart, S.; Collini, S.; Pieraccini, G.; Lionetti, P. Impact of diet in shaping gut microbiota revealed by a comparative study in children from europe and rural africa. *Proc. Natl. Acad. Sci. USA* **2010**, *107*, 14691–14696. [CrossRef] [PubMed]

90. Walker, A.W.; Ince, J.; Duncan, S.H.; Webster, L.M.; Holtrop, G.; Ze, X.; Brown, D.; Stares, M.D.; Scott, P.; Bergerat, A.; *et al.* Dominant and diet-responsive groups of bacteria within the human colonic microbiota. *ISME J.* **2011**, *5*, 220–230. [CrossRef] [PubMed]

91. David, L.A.; Maurice, C.F.; Carmody, R.N.; Gootenberg, D.B.; Button, J.E.; Wolfe, B.E.; Ling, A.V.; Devlin, A.S.; Varma, Y.; Fischbach, M.A.; *et al.* Diet rapidly and reproducibly alters the human gut microbiome. *Nature* **2014**, *505*, 559–563. [CrossRef] [PubMed]

92. Beyer, P.L.; Flynn, M.A. Effects of high- and low-fiber diets on human feces. *J. Am. Diet. Assoc.* **1978**, *72*, 271–277. [PubMed]

93. Cotillard, A.; Kennedy, S.P.; Kong, L.C.; Prifti, E.; Pons, N.; Le Chatelier, E.; Almeida, M.; Quinquis, B.; Levenez, F.; Galleron, N.; *et al.* Dietary intervention impact on gut microbial gene richness. *Nature* **2013**, *500*, 585–588. [CrossRef] [PubMed]

94. Wu, G.D.; Chen, J.; Hoffmann, C.; Bittinger, K.; Chen, Y.Y.; Keilbaugh, S.A.; Bewtra, M.; Knights, D.; Walters, W.A.; Knight, R.; *et al.* Linking long-term dietary patterns with gut microbial enterotypes. *Science* **2011**, *334*, 105–108. [CrossRef] [PubMed]

95. Hildebrandt, M.A.; Hoffmann, C.; Sherrill-Mix, S.A.; Keilbaugh, S.A.; Hamady, M.; Chen, Y.Y.; Knight, R.; Ahima, R.S.; Bushman, F.; Wu, G.D. High-fat diet determines the composition of the murine gut microbiome independently of obesity. *Gastroenterology* **2009**, *137*, 1716–1724. [CrossRef] [PubMed]

96. De Wit, N.; Derrien, M.; Bosch-Vermeulen, H.; Oosterink, E.; Keshtkar, S.; Duval, C.; de Vogel-van den Bosch, J.; Kleerebezem, M.; Muller, M.; van der Meer, R. Saturated fat stimulates obesity and hepatic steatosis and affects gut microbiota composition by an enhanced overflow of dietary fat to the distal intestine. *Am. J. Physiol. Gastrointest. Liver Physiol.* **2012**, *303*, G589–G599. [CrossRef] [PubMed]

97. Ravussin, Y.; Koren, O.; Spor, A.; LeDuc, C.; Gutman, R.; Stombaugh, J.; Knight, R.; Ley, R.E.; Leibel, R.L. Responses of gut microbiota to diet composition and weight loss in lean and obese mice. *Obesity* **2012**, *20*, 738–747. [CrossRef] [PubMed]

98. Brinkworth, G.D.; Noakes, M.; Clifton, P.M.; Bird, A.R. Comparative effects of very low-carbohydrate, high-fat and high-carbohydrate, low-fat weight-loss diets on bowel habit and faecal short-chain fatty acids and bacterial populations. *Br. J. Nutr.* **2009**, *101*, 1493–1502. [CrossRef] [PubMed]

99. Fava, F.; Gitau, R.; Griffin, B.A.; Gibson, G.R.; Tuohy, K.M.; Lovegrove, J.A. The type and quantity of dietary fat and carbohydrate alter faecal microbiome and short-chain fatty acid excretion in a metabolic syndrome "at-risk" population. *Int. J. Obes.* **2013**, *37*, 216–223. [CrossRef] [PubMed]

100. Zhang, C.; Zhang, M.; Wang, S.; Han, R.; Cao, Y.; Hua, W.; Mao, Y.; Zhang, X.; Pang, X.; Wei, C.; *et al.* Interactions between gut microbiota, host genetics and diet relevant to development of metabolic syndromes in mice. *ISME J.* **2010**, *4*, 232–241. [CrossRef] [PubMed]

101. Everard, A.; Belzer, C.; Geurts, L.; Ouwerkerk, J.P.; Druart, C.; Bindels, L.B.; Guiot, Y.; Derrien, M.; Muccioli, G.G.; Delzenne, N.M.; *et al.* Cross-talk between akkermansia muciniphila and intestinal epithelium controls diet-induced obesity. *Proc. Natl. Acad. Sci. USA* **2013**, *110*, 9066–9071. [CrossRef] [PubMed]

102. Zhang, H.; DiBaise, J.K.; Zuccolo, A.; Kudrna, D.; Braidotti, M.; Yu, Y.; Parameswaran, P.; Crowell, M.D.; Wing, R.; Rittmann, B.E.; *et al.* Human gut microbiota in obesity and after gastric bypass. *Proc. Natl. Acad. Sci. USA* **2009**, *106*, 2365–2370. [CrossRef] [PubMed]

103. Furet, J.P.; Kong, L.C.; Tap, J.; Poitou, C.; Basdevant, A.; Bouillot, J.L.; Mariat, D.; Corthier, G.; Dore, J.; Henegar, C.; *et al.* Differential adaptation of human gut microbiota to bariatric surgery-induced weight loss: Links with metabolic and low-grade inflammation markers. *Diabetes* **2010**, *59*, 3049–3057. [CrossRef] [PubMed]

104. Kong, L.C.; Tap, J.; Aron-Wisnewsky, J.; Pelloux, V.; Basdevant, A.; Bouillot, J.L.; Zucker, J.D.; Dore, J.; Clement, K. Gut microbiota after gastric bypass in human obesity: Increased richness and associations of bacterial genera with adipose tissue genes. *Am. J. Clin. Nutr.* **2013**, *98*, 16–24. [CrossRef] [PubMed]

105. Liou, A.P.; Paziuk, M.; Luevano, J.M., Jr.; Machineni, S.; Turnbaugh, P.J.; Kaplan, L.M. Conserved shifts in the gut microbiota due to gastric bypass reduce host weight and adiposity. *Sci. Transl. Med.* **2013**, *5*, 178ra141. [CrossRef] [PubMed]

106. Patti, M.E.; Houten, S.M.; Bianco, A.C.; Bernier, R.; Larsen, P.R.; Holst, J.J.; Badman, M.K.; Maratos-Flier, E.; Mun, E.C.; Pihlajamaki, J.; *et al.* Serum bile acids are higher in humans with prior gastric bypass: Potential contribution to improved glucose and lipid metabolism. *Obesity* **2009**, *17*, 1671–1677. [CrossRef] [PubMed]

107. Kohli, R.; Bradley, D.; Setchell, K.D.; Eagon, J.C.; Abumrad, N.; Klein, S. Weight loss induced by Roux-en-Y gastric bypass but not laparoscopic adjustable gastric banding increases circulating bile acids. *J. Clin. Endocrinol. Metab.* **2013**, *98*, E708–E712. [CrossRef] [PubMed]

108. Gerhard, G.S.; Styer, A.M.; Wood, G.C.; Roesch, S.L.; Petrick, A.T.; Gabrielsen, J.; Strodel, W.E.; Still, C.D.; Argyropoulos, G. A role for fibroblast growth factor 19 and bile acids in diabetes remission after Roux-en-Y gastric bypass. *Diabetes Care* **2013**, *36*, 1859–1864. [CrossRef] [PubMed]

109. Myronovych, A.; Kirby, M.; Ryan, K.K.; Zhang, W.; Jha, P.; Setchell, K.D.; Dexheimer, P.J.; Aronow, B.; Seeley, R.J.; Kohli, R. Vertical sleeve gastrectomy reduces hepatic steatosis while increasing serum bile acids in a weight-loss-independent manner. *Obesity* **2014**, *22*, 390–400. [CrossRef] [PubMed]

110. Ryan, K.K.; Tremaroli, V.; Clemmensen, C.; Kovatcheva-Datchary, P.; Myronovych, A.; Karns, R.; Wilson-Perez, H.E.; Sandoval, D.A.; Kohli, R.; Backhed, F.; *et al.* Fxr is a molecular target for the effects of vertical sleeve gastrectomy. *Nature* **2014**, *509*, 183–188. [CrossRef] [PubMed]

111. Shen, W.; Gaskins, H.R.; McIntosh, M.K. Influence of dietary fat on intestinal microbes, inflammation, barrier function and metabolic outcomes. *J. Nutr. Biochem.* **2014**, *25*, 270–280. [CrossRef] [PubMed]

112. Ferolla, S.M.; Armiliato, G.N.; Couto, C.A.; Ferrari, T.C. Probiotics as a complementary therapeutic approach in nonalcoholic fatty liver disease. *World J. Hepatol.* **2015**, *7*, 559–565. [CrossRef] [PubMed]

113. Kang, J.H.; Yun, S.I.; Park, M.H.; Park, J.H.; Jeong, S.Y.; Park, H.O. Anti-obesity effect of lactobacillus gasseri BNR17 in high-sucrose diet-induced obese mice. *PLoS ONE* **2013**, *8*, e54617. [CrossRef] [PubMed]

114. Fak, F.; Backhed, F. Lactobacillus reuteri prevents diet-induced obesity, but not atherosclerosis, in a strain dependent fashion in Apoe$^{-/-}$ mice. *PLoS ONE* **2012**, *7*, e46837. [CrossRef] [PubMed]

115. Lee, H.Y.; Park, J.H.; Seok, S.H.; Baek, M.W.; Kim, D.J.; Lee, K.E.; Paek, K.S.; Lee, Y.; Park, J.H. Human originated bacteria, lactobacillus rhamnosus pl60, produce conjugated linoleic acid and show anti-obesity effects in diet-induced obese mice. *Biochim. Biophys. Acta* **2006**, *1761*, 736–744. [CrossRef] [PubMed]

116. An, H.M.; Park, S.Y.; Lee do, K.; Kim, J.R.; Cha, M.K.; Lee, S.W.; Lim, H.T.; Kim, K.J.; Ha, N.J. Antiobesity and lipid-lowering effects of *Bifidobacterium* spp. In high fat diet-induced obese rats. *Lipids Health Dis.* **2011**, *10*, 116. [CrossRef] [PubMed]

117. Andersson, U.; Branning, C.; Ahrne, S.; Molin, G.; Alenfall, J.; Onning, G.; Nyman, M.; Holm, C. Probiotics lower plasma glucose in the high-fat fed C57BL/6J mouse. *Benef. Microbes* **2010**, *1*, 189–196. [CrossRef] [PubMed]

118. Agerholm-Larsen, L.; Raben, A.; Haulrik, N.; Hansen, A.S.; Manders, M.; Astrup, A. Effect of 8 week intake of probiotic milk products on risk factors for cardiovascular diseases. *Eur. J. Clin. Nutr.* **2000**, *54*, 288–297. [CrossRef] [PubMed]

119. Kadooka, Y.; Sato, M.; Imaizumi, K.; Ogawa, A.; Ikuyama, K.; Akai, Y.; Okano, M.; Kagoshima, M.; Tsuchida, T. Regulation of abdominal adiposity by probiotics (*Lactobacillus gasseri* SBT2055) in adults with obese tendencies in a randomized controlled trial. *Eur. J. Clin. Nutr.* **2010**, *64*, 636–643. [CrossRef] [PubMed]

120. Mikirova, N.A.; Casciari, J.J.; Hunninghake, R.E.; Beezley, M.M. Effect of weight reduction on cardiovascular risk factors and CD34-positive cells in circulation. *Int. J. Med. Sci.* **2011**, *8*, 445–452. [CrossRef] [PubMed]

121. Kadooka, Y.; Sato, M.; Ogawa, A.; Miyoshi, M.; Uenishi, H.; Ogawa, H.; Ikuyama, K.; Kagoshima, M.; Tsuchida, T. Effect of *Lactobacillus gasseri* SBT2055 in fermented milk on abdominal adiposity in adults in a randomised controlled trial. *Br. J. Nutr.* **2013**, *110*, 1696–1703. [CrossRef] [PubMed]

122. Sanchez, M.; Darimont, C.; Drapeau, V.; Emady-Azar, S.; Lepage, M.; Rezzonico, E.; Ngom-Bru, C.; Berger, B.; Philippe, L.; Ammon-Zuffrey, C.; *et al.* Effect of lactobacillus rhamnosus cgmcc1.3724 supplementation on weight loss and maintenance in obese men and women. *Br. J. Nutr.* **2014**, *111*, 1507–1519. [CrossRef] [PubMed]

123. Dewulf, E.M.; Cani, P.D.; Claus, S.P.; Fuentes, S.; Puylaert, P.G.; Neyrinck, A.M.; Bindels, L.B.; de Vos, W.M.; Gibson, G.R.; Thissen, J.P.; *et al.* Insight into the prebiotic concept: Lessons from an exploratory, double blind intervention study with inulin-type fructans in obese women. *Gut* **2013**, *62*, 1112–1121. [CrossRef] [PubMed]

124. de Luis, D.A.; de la Fuente, B.; Izaola, O.; Conde, R.; Gutierrez, S.; Morillo, M.; Teba Torres, C. Double blind randomized clinical trial controlled by placebo with an α linoleic acid and prebiotic enriched cookie on risk cardiovascular factor in obese patients. *Nutr. Hosp.* **2011**, *26*, 827–833. [PubMed]

125. De Luis, D.A.; de la Fuente, B.; Izaola, O.; Conde, R.; Gutierrez, S.; Morillo, M.; Teba Torres, C. Randomized clinical trial with a inulin enriched cookie on risk cardiovascular factor in obese patients. *Nutr. Hosp.* **2010**, *25*, 53–59. [PubMed]

126. Balcazar-Munoz, B.R.; Martinez-Abundis, E.; Gonzalez-Ortiz, M. Effect of oral inulin administration on lipid profile and insulin sensitivity in subjects with obesity and dyslipidemia. *Rev. Med. Chile* **2003**, *131*, 597–604. [PubMed]

127. Li, Z.; Yang, S.; Lin, H.; Huang, J.; Watkins, P.A.; Moser, A.B.; Desimone, C.; Song, X.Y.; Diehl, A.M. Probiotics and antibodies to TNF inhibit inflammatory activity and improve nonalcoholic fatty liver disease. *Hepatology* **2003**, *37*, 343–350. [CrossRef] [PubMed]

128. Ma, X.; Hua, J.; Li, Z. Probiotics improve high fat diet-induced hepatic steatosis and insulin resistance by increasing hepatic NKT cells. *J. Hepatol.* **2008**, *49*, 821–830. [CrossRef] [PubMed]

129. Esposito, E.; Iacono, A.; Bianco, G.; Autore, G.; Cuzzocrea, S.; Vajro, P.; Canani, R.B.; Calignano, A.; Raso, G.M.; Meli, R. Probiotics reduce the inflammatory response induced by a high-fat diet in the liver of young rats. *J. Nutr.* **2009**, *139*, 905–911. [CrossRef] [PubMed]

130. Velayudham, A.; Dolganiuc, A.; Ellis, M.; Petrasek, J.; Kodys, K.; Mandrekar, P.; Szabo, G. Vsl#3 probiotic treatment attenuates fibrosis without changes in steatohepatitis in a diet-induced nonalcoholic steatohepatitis model in mice. *Hepatology* **2009**, *49*, 989–997. [PubMed]

131. Xu, R.Y.; Wan, Y.P.; Fang, Q.Y.; Lu, W.; Cai, W. Supplementation with probiotics modifies gut flora and attenuates liver fat accumulation in rat nonalcoholic fatty liver disease model. *J. Clin. Biochem. Nutr.* **2012**, *50*, 72–77. [CrossRef] [PubMed]

132. Bhathena, J.; Martoni, C.; Kulamarva, A.; Tomaro-Duchesneau, C.; Malhotra, M.; Paul, A.; Urbanska, A.M.; Prakash, S. Oral probiotic microcapsule formulation ameliorates non-alcoholic fatty liver disease in Bio F1B Golden Syrian hamsters. *PLoS ONE* **2013**, *8*, e58394. [CrossRef] [PubMed]

133. Endo, H.; Niioka, M.; Kobayashi, N.; Tanaka, M.; Watanabe, T. Butyrate-producing probiotics reduce nonalcoholic fatty liver disease progression in rats: New insight into the probiotics for the gut-liver axis. *PLoS ONE* **2013**, *8*, e63388.

134. Ritze, Y.; Bardos, G.; Claus, A.; Ehrmann, V.; Bergheim, I.; Schwiertz, A.; Bischoff, S.C. Lactobacillus rhamnosus GG protects against non-alcoholic fatty liver disease in mice. *PLoS ONE* **2014**, *9*, e80169.

135. Xin, J.; Zeng, D.; Wang, H.; Ni, X.; Yi, D.; Pan, K.; Jing, B. Preventing non-alcoholic fatty liver disease through lactobacillus johnsonii BS15 by attenuating inflammation and mitochondrial injury and improving gut environment in obese mice. *Appl. Microbiol. Biotechnol.* **2014**, *98*, 6817–6829. [CrossRef] [PubMed]

136. Li, C.; Nie, S.P.; Zhu, K.X.; Ding, Q.; Li, C.; Xiong, T.; Xie, M.Y. Lactobacillus plantarum ncu116 improves liver function, oxidative stress and lipid metabolism in rats with high fat diet induced non-alcoholic fatty liver disease. *Food Funct.* **2014**, *5*, 3216–3223. [CrossRef] [PubMed]

137. Sohn, W.; Jun, D.W.; Lee, K.N.; Lee, H.L.; Lee, O.Y.; Choi, H.S.; Yoon, B.C. Lactobacillus paracasei induces M2-Dominant Kupffer Cell Polarization in a Mouse Model of Nonalcoholic Steatohepatitis. *Dig. Dis. Sci.* **2015**, *60*, 3340–3350. [CrossRef] [PubMed]

138. Ting, W.J.; Kuo, W.W.; Hsieh, D.J.; Yeh, Y.L.; Day, C.H.; Chen, Y.H.; Chen, R.J.; Padma, V.V.; Chen, Y.H.; Huang, C.Y. Heat killed lactobacillus reuteri GMNL-263 reduces fibrosis effects on the liver and heart in high fat diet-hamsters via TGF-β suppression. *Int. J. Mol. Sci.* **2015**, *16*, 25881–25896. [CrossRef] [PubMed]

139. Cortez-Pinto, H.; Borralho, P.; Machado, J.; Lopes, M.T.; Gato, I.V.; Santos, A.M.; Guerreiro, A.S. Microbiota modulation with synbiotic decreases liver fibrosis in a high fat choline deficient diet mice model of nonalcoholic steatohepatitis (NASH). *Port. J. Gastroenterol.* **2016**. in press.

140. Loguercio, C.; de Simone, T.; Federico, A.; Terracciano, F.; Tuccillo, C.; di Chicco, M.; Carteni, M. Gut-liver axis: A new point of attack to treat chronic liver damage? *Am. J. Gastroenterol.* **2002**, *97*, 2144–2146. [CrossRef] [PubMed]

141. Loguercio, C.; Federico, A.; Tuccillo, C.; Terracciano, F.; D'Auria, M.V.; de Simone, C.; del Vecchio Blanco, C. Beneficial effects of a probiotic VSL#3 on parameters of liver dysfunction in chronic liver diseases. *J. Clin. Gastroenterol.* **2005**, *39*, 540–543. [PubMed]

142. Aller, R.; de Luis, D.A.; Izaola, O.; Conde, R.; Gonzalez Sagrado, M.; Primo, D.; de la Fuente, B.; Gonzalez, J. Effect of a probiotic on liver aminotransferases in nonalcoholic fatty liver disease patients: A double blind randomized clinical trial. *Eur. Rev. Med. Pharmacol. Sci.* **2011**, *15*, 1090–1095. [PubMed]

143. Malaguarnera, M.; Vacante, M.; Antic, T.; Giordano, M.; Chisari, G.; Acquaviva, R.; Mastrojeni, S.; Malaguarnera, G.; Mistretta, A.; Li Volti, G.; *et al.* Bifidobacterium longum with fructo-oligosaccharides in patients with non alcoholic steatohepatitis. *Dig. Dis. Sci.* **2012**, *57*, 545–553. [CrossRef] [PubMed]

144. Wong, V.W.; Won, G.L.; Chim, A.M.; Chu, W.C.; Yeung, D.K.; Li, K.C.; Chan, H.L. Treatment of nonalcoholic steatohepatitis with probiotics. A proof-of-concept study. *Ann. Hepatol.* **2013**, *12*, 256–262. [PubMed]

145. Nabavi, S.; Rafraf, M.; Somi, M.H.; Homayouni-Rad, A.; Asghari-Jafarabadi, M. Effects of probiotic yogurt consumption on metabolic factors in individuals with nonalcoholic fatty liver disease. *J. Dairy Sci.* **2014**, *97*, 7386–7393. [CrossRef] [PubMed]

146. Eslamparast, T.; Poustchi, H.; Zamani, F.; Sharafkhah, M.; Malekzadeh, R.; Hekmatdoost, A. Synbiotic supplementation in nonalcoholic fatty liver disease: A randomized, double-blind, placebo-controlled pilot study. *Am. J. Clin. Nutr.* **2014**, *99*, 535–542. [CrossRef] [PubMed]

147. Sepideh, A.; Karim, P.; Hossein, A.; Leila, R.; Hamdollah, M.; Mohammad, E.G.; Mojtaba, S.; Mohammad, S.; Ghader, G.; Seyed Moayed, A. Effects of multistrain probiotic supplementation on glycemic and inflammatory indices in patients with nonalcoholic fatty liver disease: A double-blind randomized clinical trial. *J. Am. Coll.Nutr.* **2015**, 1–6. [CrossRef] [PubMed]

148. Lirussi, F.; Mastropasqua, E.; Orando, S.; Orlando, R. Probiotics for non-alcoholic fatty liver disease and/or steatohepatitis. *Cochrane Database Syst. Rev.* **2007**, CD005165. [CrossRef]

149. Abenavoli, L.; Scarpellini, E.; Rouabhia, S.; Balsano, C.; Luzza, F. Probiotics in non-alcoholic fatty liver disease: Which and when. *Ann. Hepatol.* **2013**, *12*, 357–363. [PubMed]

150. Kelishadi, R.; Farajian, S.; Mirlohi, M. Probiotics as a novel treatment for non-alcoholic fatty liver disease; a systematic review on the current evidences. *Hepat. Mon.* **2013**, *13*, e7233. [CrossRef] [PubMed]

151. Ma, Y.Y.; Li, L.; Yu, C.H.; Shen, Z.; Chen, L.H.; Li, Y.M. Effects of probiotics on nonalcoholic fatty liver disease: A meta-analysis. *World J. Gastroenterol.* **2013**, *19*, 6911–6918. [CrossRef] [PubMed]

152. Eslamparast, T.; Eghtesad, S.; Hekmatdoost, A.; Poustchi, H. Probiotics and nonalcoholic fatty liver disease. *Middle East J. Dig. Dis.* **2013**, *5*, 129–136. [PubMed]

153. Buss, C.; Valle-Tovo, C.; Miozzo, S.; Alves de Mattos, A. Probiotics and synbiotics may improve liver aminotransferases levels in non-alcoholic fatty liver disease patients. *Ann. Hepatol.* **2014**, *13*, 482–488. [PubMed]

154. Gao, X.; Zhu, Y.; Wen, Y.; Liu, G.; Wan, C. Efficacy of probiotics in nonalcoholic fatty liver disease in adult and children: A meta-analysis of randomized controlled trials. *Hepatol. Res.* **2016**. in press. [CrossRef] [PubMed]

International Journal of
Molecular Sciences

MDPI

Article

PNPLA3 Expression Is Related to Liver Steatosis in Morbidly Obese Women with Non-Alcoholic Fatty Liver Disease

Gemma Aragonès [1,†], Teresa Auguet [1,2,†], Sandra Armengol [1], Alba Berlanga [1], Esther Guiu-Jurado [1], Carmen Aguilar [1], Salomé Martínez [3], Fátima Sabench [4], José Antonio Porras [2], Maikel Daniel Ruiz [2], Mercé Hernández [4], Joan Josep Sirvent [3], Daniel Del Castillo [4] and Cristóbal Richart [1,2,*]

1   Group de Recerca GEMMAIR (AGAUR)-Medicina Aplicada, Institut Investigació Sanitària Pere Virgili (IISPV), Departament de Medicina i Cirurgia, Universitat Rovira i Virgili (URV), 43007 Tarragona, Spain; gemma.aragones@iispv.cat (G.A.); tauguet.hj23.ics@gencat.cat (T.A.); sandra.armengol@urv.cat (S.A.); alba.berlanga@urv.cat (A.B.); esther.guiu@urv.cat (E.G.-J.); caguilar.hj23@gencat.cat (C.A.)
2   Servei Medicina Interna, Hospital Universitari Joan XXIII Tarragona, Mallafré Guasch, 4, 43007 Tarragona, Spain; aporras.hj23.ics@gencat.cat (J.A.P.); drgorrin@yahoo.es (M.D.R.)
3   Servei Anatomia Patològica, Hospital Universitari Joan XXIII Tarragona, Mallafré Guasch, 4, 43007 Tarragona, Spain; mgonzalez.hj23.ics@gencat.cat (S.M.); jsirvent.hj23.ics@gencat.cat (J.J.S.)
4   Servei de Cirurgia, Hospital Sant Joan de Reus, Departament de Medicina i Cirurgia, Universitat Rovira i Virgili (URV), IISPV, Avinguda Doctor Josep Laporte, 2, 43204 Tarragona, Spain; fatima.sabench@urv.cat (F.S.); mhernandezg@grupsagessa.com (M.H.); ddelcastillo@grupsagessa.com (D.D.C.)
*   Correspondence: crichart.hj23.ics@gencat.cat; Tel./Fax: +34-977-295-833
†   These authors contributed equally to this work.

Academic Editors: Giovanni Targher and Amedeo Lonardo
Received: 24 February 2016; Accepted: 22 April 2016; Published: 27 April 2016

Abstract: Recent reports suggest a role for the Patatin-like phospholipase domain-containing protein 3 (PNPLA3) in the pathology of non-alcoholic fatty liver disease (NAFLD). Lipid deposition in the liver seems to be a critical process in the pathogenesis of NAFLD. The aim of the present work was to evaluate the association between the liver *PNPLA3* expression, key genes of lipid metabolism, and the presence of NAFLD in morbidly obese women. We used real-time polymerase chain reaction (PCR) analysis to analyze the hepatic expression of *PNPLA3* and lipid metabolism-related genes in 55 morbidly obese subjects with normal liver histology (NL, $n = 18$), simple steatosis (SS, $n = 20$), and non-alcoholic steatohepatitis (NASH, $n = 17$). Liver biopsies were collected during bariatric surgery. We observed that liver *PNPLA3* expression was increased in NAFLD than in NL. It was also upregulated in SS than in NL. Interestingly, we found that the expression of *PNPLA3* was significantly higher in severe than mild SS group. In addition, the expression of the transcription factors *LXRα*, *PPARα*, and *SREBP2* was positively correlated with *PNPLA3* liver expression. Regarding rs738409 polymorphism, GG genotype was positive correlated with the presence of NASH. In conclusion, our results show that PNPLA3 could be related to lipid accumulation in liver, mainly in the development and progression of simple steatosis.

Keywords: PNPLA3; morbid obesity; non-alcoholic fatty liver disease; simple steatosis; fatty acid metabolism; non-alcoholic steatohepatitis

---

1. Introduction

Non-alcoholic fatty liver disease (NAFLD), the most common liver disease in Western countries, is characterized by the accumulation of excess triglycerides (TG) in hepatocytes and is associated with or anticipates the metabolic syndrome and its individual features, including visceral obesity, hyperlipidemia, and type 2 diabetes mellitus (T2DM) [1]. NAFLD includes a range of diseases from simple fatty infiltration (simple steatosis (SS)), fat accumulation, and inflammation (non-alcoholic steatohepatitis (NASH)) to liver fibrosis/cirrhosis [2]. General prevalence of NAFLD is 25.24%, with the highest prevalence in the Middle East and South America. This prevalence is particularly high in obese adults (80%–90%), patients with T2DM (30%–50%), and up to 90% in patients with hyperlipidemia [3]. NAFLD is usually diagnosed by abdominal ultrasonography in subjects without any apparent liver alteration who do not consume excessive alcohol [4]. Some studies have shown that insulin resistance (IR) promotes not only the recruitment of free fatty acids (FAs) in liver from the serum pool, but also the accumulation of intrahepatic FA, which indicates that IR is, among other mechanisms, crucial to the pathogenesis of NAFLD/NASH. In this regard, some authors have attempted to explain the pathophysiology of NAFLD by advancing the "multiple parallel hits hypothesis" [5]. However, the specific process responsible for the development and progression of NAFLD is still an open question. While SS is considered a relatively benign condition with little risk of progression, NASH may progress to cirrhosis and, in a small percentage of patients, to hepatocellular carcinoma (HCC) [6]. In fact, there is increasing evidence to indicate a complex interplay between environmental genetic factors that predispose the progression of NAFLD [7].

Patatin-like phospholipase domain-containing protein 3 (PNPLA3), which is also known as adiponutrin, is mainly expressed in hepatocytes but also in adipocytes [8]. The protein is one of the candidates potentially related to NAFLD susceptibility. Regarding PNPLA3 lipase activity against TG and acylglycerol transacetylase activity, its expression is responsible for energy mobilization and the storage in lipid droplets [9,10]. Additionally, it is highly modulated by nutritional stimuli at transcriptional and posttranscriptional levels [11].

In 2008, Romeo *et al.* [12] reported that a *PNPLA3* single nucleotide polymorphism at residue 148 in the DNA sequence, resulting in a substitution of isoleucine for methionine (I148M, rs738409), was a genetic determinant of NAFLD. Since then, the correlation between the *PNPLA3* 148M variant and NAFLD has been investigated in considerable detail. Multiple studies have demonstrated a link between the *PNPLA3* 148M variant and the development and progression of NAFLD, including liver fibrosis [13–18]. Recently, it has been reported that *PNPLA3* 148M elevates retinyl-palmitate content in human hepatic stellate cells providing evidence for a potential link between the PNPLA3 variant, human hepatic retinoid metabolism, and chronic liver disease [19,20]. All this research indicates that this variant is a potential modifier of NAFLD. Nevertheless, its role in the NAFLD development and the specific molecular mechanisms has not been fully elucidated.

Lipid deposition in the liver seems to be a critical mechanism in the pathogenesis of NAFLD, so its regulatory processes need to be elucidated if the progression of NAFLD is to be controlled. Although these potential regulatory mechanisms are multiple, one of them affecting TG remodeling could be PNPLA3 [21–23].

On the basis of this data, the aim of our work was to study the relationship between the liver expression of *PNPLA3* and the presence of NAFLD in morbidly obese women. Furthermore, as lipid metabolism seems to be involved in the pathogenesis of NAFLD, we investigated the association between the hepatic expression of *PNPLA3* and the expression of the main lipid metabolism-related genes. Finally, in order to explore the impact of the *PNPLA3* genetic variant on the presence of NAFLD, we determined the relationships between the rs738409 polymorphism in the *PNPLA3* gene and the severity of the disease.

2. Results

2.1. General Characteristics of Cohort

Our morbidly obese women (MO) cohort was sub-classified according to liver pathology study into normal liver (NL, *n* = 18), simple steatosis (SS, *n* = 20), and non-alcoholic steatohepatitis

(NASH, n = 17) (Table 1). We found no significant differences regarding age and anthropometrical measurements between the three groups studied. With regard to biochemical analysis, glucose levels were significantly increased in the SS and NASH groups compared to the NL group (p = 0.017 and p = 0.010). Glycosylated hemoglobin (HbA1c) levels were also higher in SS than in NL (p = 0.039). Our results showed that aspartate aminotransferase (AST) and alanine aminotransferase (ALT) activity were higher in the NASH group than in the NL group (p = 0.001 and $p \leqslant 0.001$) and that ALT was increased in NASH compared to SS (p = 0.001).

Table 1. General characteristics of the studied cohort classified according to the liver pathology.

Variables	Morbidly Obese Subjects (n = 55)		
	NL (n = 18)	SS (n = 20)	NASH (n = 17)
	Mean ± SD	Mean ± SD	Mean ± SD
Age (years)	48.6 ± 10.9	50.4 ± 11.0	47.8 ± 13.0
Weight (kg)	120.5 ± 19.3	120.4 ± 18.1	116.6 ± 15.5
BMI (kg/m^2)	50.1 ± 7.6	48.8 ± 8.5	47.0 ± 4.8
WC (cm)	130.0 ± 17.9	129.5 ± 12.9	129.4 ± 12.0
Glucose (mg/dL)	94.2 ± 22.6	133.9 ± 50.6 *	138.7 ± 49.1 *
Insulin (mUI/L)	12.1 ± 7.8	18.6 ± 12.3	20.1 ± 16.4
HbA1c (%)	5.2 ± 0.9	6.5 ± 1.7 *	6.3 ± 1.6
HOMA2-IR	1.6 ± 0.9	2.8 ± 1.4	2.8 ± 2.1
HDL-C (mg/dL)	44.5 ± 9.8	36.8 ± 11.3	37.1 ± 5.9
LDL-C (mg/dL)	99.0 ± 27.3	100.9 ± 29.3	104.4 ± 31.2
Total cholesterol (mg/dL)	173.03 ± 35.53	169.55 ± 34.04	174.81 ± 33.66
Triglycerides (mg/dL)	136.5 ± 58.4	193.1 ± 128.6	174.0 ± 81.1
AST (U/L)	23.5 ± 12.3	40.2 ± 33.9	64.9 ± 35.8 *
ALT (U/L)	22.1 ± 8.5	37.6 ± 22.9	67.0 ± 33.4 *,#
GGT (U/L)	26.6 ± 23.5	27.6 ± 14.8	53.7 ± 59.5
ALP (U/L)	61.9 ± 12.4	74.1 ± 20.3	79.9 ± 29.7

ALP: alkaline phosphatase; ALT: alanine aminotransferase; AST: aspartate aminotransferase; BMI: body mass index; GGT: gamma-glutamyltransferase; HbA1c: glycosylated hemoglobin; HDL-C: high density lipoprotein cholesterol; HOMA2-IR: homeostatic model assessment 2-insulin resistance; LDL-C: low density lipoprotein cholesterol; NASH: morbidly obese subjects with steatohepatitis; NL: morbidly obese subjects with normal liver; SS: morbidly obese subjects with simple steatosis; WC: waist circumference. One-way ANOVA with *post-hoc* Tukey test was used to compare variables between groups. * indicates statistically significant differences respect NL group (p < 0.05); # indicates statistically significant differences respect SS group (p < 0.05). Data are expressed as mean ± SD.

2.2. Determination of Patatin-Like Phospholipase Domain-Containing Protein 3 (PNPLA3) Liver Expression

We analyzed *PNPLA3* liver expression in MO women in relation to the presence of NAFLD. The results showed that *PNPLA3* expression was a significant 72% greater in MO NAFLD women than in MO women with NL (MO NAFLD: 3.6 ± 2.2 and MO NL: 2.1 ± 0.8, p = 0.001). Furthermore, when we classified the MO cohort into NL, SS, and NASH, we observed that the expression of *PNPLA3* was significantly higher in SS than in NL (p = 0.006, Figure 1A). There were no differences between NL or SS and NASH (p = 0.380 and p = 0.170, respectively). It is important to note that, in our work, any patient with steatohepatitis had fibrosis in the liver histology, so we could not perform correlations between fibrosis staging and *PNPLA3* liver expression.

In addition, in order to explore the increased expression of *PNPLA3* in simple steatosis, we classified the SS group into grades: mild (n = 9), moderate (n = 5), or severe SS (n = 6). We found that the expression of *PNPLA3* was significantly increased in the severe group compared to the mild SS group (p = 0.020, Figure 1B).

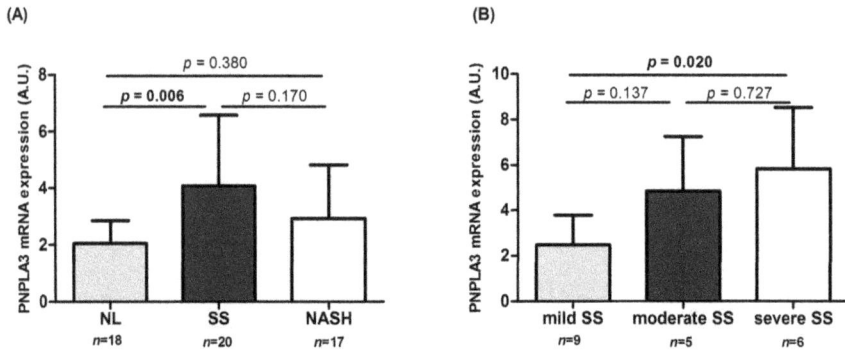

Figure 1. Hepatic expression of *PNPLA3* gene in morbidly obese women according to the liver histopathology (**A**) and subclassifying the SS group into: mild, moderate, or severe SS (**B**). A.U.: arbitrary units; NASH: morbidly obese women with steatohepatitis; NL: morbidly obese women with a normal liver; SS: morbidly obese women with simple steatosis. ANOVA test was used to determinate differences between groups. $p < 0.05$ are considered statistically significant.

2.3. Correlations between the Expression of PNPLA3 and Biochemical Variables, Histopathological Parameters and Genes Involved in Lipid Metabolism and Inflammation in Liver from Morbidly Obese Subjects

When we analyzed the associations between *PNPLA3* expression and parameters related to glucose metabolism and lipid profile, we observed a direct correlation between circulating levels of triglycerides and *PNPLA3* expression in the whole study cohort ($r = 0.272$, $p = 0.046$).

Regarding histopathological features, we only found a direct association between *PNPLA3* expression and degree of steatosis in the total MO group ($r = 0.441$, $p = 0.001$).

In order to clarify whether *PNPLA3* was associated with hepatic lipid metabolism, we studied the correlation between *PNPLA3* expression and lipid metabolism related genes in liver from the MO cohort. In the lipogenic and fatty acid oxidation pathways, hepatic liver X receptor (*LXRα*) and peroxisome-proliferator-activated receptor α (*PPARα*) expression correlated directly with PNPLA3 expression in the total morbidly obese group ($r = 0.671$, $p = 0.008$ and $r = 0.640$, $p = 0.008$; Table 2). We also showed a positive association between *PNPLA3* and both the transcription factor sterol regulatory element binding protein 2 (*SREBP2*) ($r = 0.412$, $p = 0.032$) and lipocalin 2 (*LCN2*) ($r = 0.570$, $p = 0.032$) in the whole population.

Interestingly, when we analyzed the relationship between the expression of these genes in the SS subgroup, we observed that both *LXRα* and *PPARα* correlations were stronger (*LXRα*: $r = 0.806$, $p = 0.016$; *PPARα*: $r = 0.796$, $p = 0.024$).

2.4. rs738409 Genotype Distribution in Morbidly Obese Subjects

The distribution of the studied genetic polymorphism is shown in Table 3, as are comparisons between NL, SS, and NASH patients. The G allele was more frequent (66.6%) than the C allele (33.3%) in the whole population. No individuals were homozygous for the C allele. The genotype frequencies of the rs738409 polymorphism showed significant variations between NL, SS, and NASH patients ($p = 0.021$). In addition, the GG genotype was correlated with the presence of NASH ($r = 0.382$, $p < 0.001$). However, the allele frequencies did not show statistically significant differences ($p = 0.145$). Regarding clinical and biochemical variables, the GG genotype was only associated with increased body mass index (BMI) ($r = 0.300$, $p = 0.032$). There was no association between PNPLA3 genetic variant and its hepatic expression ($p = 0.478$).

Table 2. Correlations between *PNPLA3* expression and genes related to *de novo* lipogenesis, FA oxidation, FA transport and uptake, inflammation, adipocytokines, and cholesterol metabolism in livers from MO women and those sub-classified as SS in the MO cohort.

Variables	MO PNPLA3 (n = 55)		SS PNPLA3 (n = 20)	
	r	*p*-Value *	r	*p*-Value *
De Novo Lipogenesis				
SREBP1c	−0.016	0.920	0.130	0.906
LxRα	**0.671**	**0.008**	**0.806**	**0.016**
ACC1	−0.025	0.920	0.090	0.906
FAS	−0.021	0.920	0.114	0.906
Fatty Acid Oxidation				
PPARα	**0.640**	**0.008**	**0.796**	**0.024**
CPT1α	0.134	0.576	−0.233	0.906
CROT	0.200	0.466	0.098	0.906
Cholesterol Metabolism				
ABCA1	0.016	0.920	−0.189	0.906
SREBP2	**0.412**	**0.032**	0.361	0.784
Transport and Uptake FA				
FABP4	−0.371	0.285	0.464	0.784
ABCG1	0.099	0.713	−0.074	0.906
Inflammation				
IL6	−0.379	0.285	−0.012	0.980
TNFα	0.227	0.576	0.089	0.906
LCN2	**0.570**	**0.032**	0.466	0.784
Adipokines				
RESISTIN	0.209	0.576	0.124	0.906
ADIPOR2	−0.245	0.576	0.491	0.784

ABCA1: ATP-binding cassette transporter A1; ABCG1: ATP-binding cassette transporter G1; ADIPOR2: adiponectin receptor; ACC1: acetyl-coenzyme A carboxylase 1; CROT: carnitine O-octanoyltransferase ; FA: fatty acid; FABP4: fatty acid binding protein 4; FAS: fatty acid synthase; IL6: interleukin 6; LCN2: lipocalin 2; LXRα: liver X receptor; MO: morbidly obese women; PPARα: peroxisome-proliferator-activated receptor α; SREBP1c: sterol regulatory element binding protein 1c; SREBP2: sterol regulatory element binding protein 2; SS: simple steatosis; TNFα: tumor necrosis factor. Bold numbers indicate statistically significant correlations (*p*-value < 0.05). * *p*-Value adjusted by the Benjamini–Hochberg method [24].

Table 3. The distribution of rs738409 polymorphism in morbidly obese women according to liver histology.

Groups	Genotype, n (%)		Allele, n (%)	
	CG	GG	C	G
NL (n = 16)	12 (75)	4 (25)	12 (37.5)	20 (62.5)
SS (n = 18)	15 (83.3)	3 (16.6)	15 (41.7)	21 (58.3)
NASH (n = 17)	7 (41.2)	10 (58.8)	7 (20.6)	27 (79.4)

CG: individuals carrying the genotype (CG); GG: individuals carrying the genotype (GG); C: Allele C; G: Allele G; NASH: morbidly obese subjects with steatohepatitis; NL: morbidly obese subjects with normal liver; SS: morbidly obese subjects with simple steatosis.

3. Discussion

In an own previous work, we demonstrated a downregulation of the lipogenic pathway related to the severity of steatosis in a cohort of women with morbid obesity [25]. As PNPLA3 seems to be related with the accumulation of hepatic TG, in the present study, we examined the relationship between the liver expression levels of *PNPLA3*, the key lipid metabolism-related genes expression, and the clinicopathological factors in a cohort of morbidly obese women with NAFLD. In our study, 36% and 31% of morbidly obese women were diagnosed with SS and NASH, respectively, using the diagnostic *gold standard* liver biopsy. Our findings show that *PNPLA3* liver expression was increased in morbidly obese women with NAFLD. It is important to note that we have demonstrated a clear relationship between *PNPLA3* and the degrees of SS, suggesting a direct correlation between *PNPLA3* and the severity of steatosis.

Nowadays, more than 50 studies on the genotyping of *PNPLA3* have confirmed the association between the 148M variant and the full range of NAFLD, including simple steatosis, steatohepatitis, cirrhosis, and hepatocellular carcinoma. PNPLA3 148M has been shown to be related to an increased risk of NAFLD across multiple ethnic groups [26–34]. The aim of the present work was to compare the hepatic expression of *PNPLA3* in a cohort of morbidly obese women presenting a normal liver or NAFLD. We showed that the hepatic expression of PNPLA3 in morbidly obese women with NAFLD was higher than in MO women with NL. Consistent with our work, Kotronen *et al.* [8] described a direct correlation between *PNPLA3* liver expression and liver fat content measured by magnetic resonance. It is important to note that our study confirms this finding in biopsy-proven NAFLD. Regarding steatosis degree, recent studies observed that a variant of this protein has an association with moderate-to-severe steatosis [35,36]. Although these studies analyzed only a variant of PNPLA3, not its liver expression, their results are in agreement with ours. A recent interesting work by Donati *et al.* [37] has demonstrated that PNPLA3 rs2294918 E434K diminished *PNPLA3* expression and protein levels, lessening the effect of the rs738409 polymorphism on the predisposition to steatosis liver injury. Moreover, the authors suggested that this PNPLA3 variant had a codominant negative effect on TG mobilization from lipid droplets. Regarding non-alcoholic steatohepatitis, a DNA microarray study in human liver revealed an upregulation of *PNPLA3* in NASH *vs.* healthy controls [38]. Nevertheless, Kitamoto *et al.* [39] described lower *PNPLA3* mRNA levels in the liver of patients with an advanced grade of NAFLD (with fibrosis) compared with those with mild NAFLD. However, we were not able to reproduce any of these findings. Perhaps the differences in the groups studied in these works regarding age, gender, BMI, or race can explain these discrepancies.

Because PNPLA3 has previously been reported to influence lipid metabolism in animal models and in *in vitro* studies [40,41], we evaluated the interplay of *PNPLA3* liver expression with the expression of the main lipid metabolism-related genes. In the current first human study in this sense, *PNPLA3* expression positively correlated with *LXRα*, *PPARα*, and *SREBP2* liver expression. All these proteins are transcription factors that relate to response elements found in a various genes that are associated with lipid turnover including their own genes [42]. Specifically, *LXRα* belong to the nuclear hormone receptor superfamily of ligand-activated transcription factors as *SREBP1* which, in liver, serve as lipid sensors and regulate the expression of main genes which modulate the cholesterol and FA metabolism [43]. Regarding NAFLD, interaction between *LXR* and *SREBP1* is a crucial step in the molecular cascade of events characterizing steatogenesis [44]. In this regard, Huang *et al.* [41] determined that the overexpression of the three SREBP family members (*SREBP1a*, *1c*, and *2*) increases liver *PNPLA3* expression in mice. They also found that PNPLA3 expression was regulated by *SREBP1c* and *LXRα*. Similar results were described by Dubuquoy *et al.* [45], who showed that, in the mouse liver, *PNPLA3* gene expression was under the direct transcriptional control of *SREBP1c* in response to insulin. However, at variance with murine studies, we were not able to find any association with *SREBP1*, one of the key genes related to *de novo* lipogenesis. Moreover, Mancina *et al.* [34] conducted a study to evaluate the contribution of *de novo* lipogenesis to liver fat accumulation in the PNPLA3 I148M genetic variant of NAFLD. They showed a dissociation between hepatic *de novo* lipogenesis and liver fat content due to the PNPLA3 148M allele, suggesting that increased *de novo* lipogenesis is not a main feature in all subjects with steatosis. However, these authors have not studied the hepatic expression of *PNPLA3*. Regarding the positive relationship between *PPARα* and PNPLA3, it is known that *PPARα* seems to control the expression of genes regulating peroxisomal/mitochondrial β-oxidation [46]. In this context, perhaps the induction of fatty acid catabolism might act as a defense mechanism, preventing hepatocellular fat accumulation [47]; in other words, it might represent an inefficient physiological response to counteract steatosis by promoting the β-oxidation of fatty acids in the hepatocytes. In our study, the association between *PNPLA3* and *SREBP2* may suggest a novel association with cholesterol metabolism in humans. Currently, experimental and human evidence has related to altered hepatic cholesterol metabolism and free cholesterol accumulation to the pathogenesis of steatosis and liver damage [48]. Specifically, Min *et al.* [49] have demonstrated dysregulated cholesterol metabolism in NAFLD, which may contribute to disease severity through activation of SREBP2 and 3-Hydroxy-3-Methylglutaryl-CoA Reductase (HMGCR).

In the present work, we observed an interesting association between liver PNPLA3 expression and the liver expression of *LCN2* in the severely obese women group, which has not been previously described. In one of our previous studies, we described increased liver *LCN2* expression in NAFLD, and this expression positively correlated with SS [50]. Additionally, in this work, an increased regulation of *LCN2* expression was detected in *in vitro* experiments with HepG2 cells under harmful conditions. Perhaps, as some authors have suggested, *LCN2* is a protective molecule [51]—in this case, against the development of NAFLD.

Moreover, we did not find any relationship between *PNPLA3* liver expression and other adipocytokines studied, probably because the molecular function of PNPLA3 is related to cellular lipid accumulation in the liver more than with inflammation [52]. Unexpectedly, we did not find any relationship with the expression of genes related to transport and the uptake of fatty acids. Perhaps this mechanism of liver accumulation of fatty acids has a lower contribution in humans, as we and other authors have previously shown [25,38].

Finally, to explore the effect of the *PNPLA3* genetic variant with a potential impact on NAFLD, we determined the relationship between the rs738409 polymorphism in the *PNPLA3* gene and the severity of disease. In this sense, we found that the GG genotype, encoding I148M, was directly correlated with the presence of NASH. Our results are similar to recent studies that showed a relationship between this genetic variant and the severity of NAFLD [12,13,15,53]. Consistent with our results, Kotronen *et al.* [8] observed that there were no differences in the hepatic *PNPLA3* mRNA expression between different *PNPLA3* genotype carriers.

We should point out the following drawbacks of our study. The main limitation of this work is an adjusted sample size and the lack of evaluation of protein expression. Additionally, the study is cross-sectional. We could not prove a causal link between *PNPLA3* expression and NALFD development. However, our study cohort of morbidly obese women has revealed clear relationships between the expression of *PNPLA3* and NAFLD, without the interference of gender or age. Thus, our findings cannot be extrapolated to men or other obesity groups such as normal-weight or over-weight women.

4. Materials and Methods

4.1. Subjects

The study was approved by the ethics committee of the Hospital Joan XXIII (23c/2015, Tarragona, Spain), and all subjects gave written informed consent. We included 55 Caucasian MO women (BMI > 40 kg/m^2). Liver biopsies were obtained during planned laparoscopic bariatric surgery and were performed for clinical indications.

The diagnosis of NAFLD was made using the following criteria: (1) liver pathology; (2) an intake of less than 10 g of ethanol/day; and (3) appropriate exclusion of other liver diseases.

The body weight of all women had not fluctuated more than 2% for at least 3 months prior to bariatric surgery. The exclusion criteria were: (1) concurrent use of medications known to produce hepatic steatosis; (2) patients using hypolipemiant treatment; (3) diabetic subjects who were receiving insulin or on medication likely to influence endogenous insulin levels; (4) menopausal or post-menopausal women; (5) women undergoing contraceptive treatment and subjects receiving contraceptive treatment; (6) patients who had an acute illness, current evidence of acute or chronic inflammatory or infectious diseases, or malignant diseases.

4.2. Liver Pathology

Liver samples were processed by two experienced hepatopathologists using methods previously described [54,55]. Simple steatosis (SS) was graded as follows: Grade 1 or mild SS: more than 5% and less than 33% of hepatocytes affected; Grade 2 or moderate SS: 33% to 66% of hepatocytes affected; or Grade 3 or severe SS: more than 66% of hepatocytes affected. Moreover, the minimum criteria for the steatohepatitis diagnosis included the presence of either ballooning cells and lobular inflammation or perisinusoidal/pericellular fibrosis in zone 3 of the hepatic acinus.

According to liver pathology, women were sub-classified into: (1) normal liver (NL) histology (n = 18); (2) simple steatosis (SS) (micro/macrovesicular steatosis without inflammation or fibrosis, n = 20); (3) non-alcoholic steatohepatitis (NASH) (Brunt Grades 1–3, n = 17).

4.3. Biochemical Analyses

Each of our patients was evaluated with a complete physical, anthropometrical, and biochemical assessment. BMI was calculated as body weight divided by height squared (kg/m^2). Fasting glucose, insulin, HbA1c, HDL-C, LDL-C, TG, and transaminases were measured using a conventional automated analyzer after overnight fasting. Insulin resistance was calculated using HOMA2-IR [56].

4.4. RNA Isolation and Real-Time PCR

Liver samples were preserved in RNAlater (Sigma, Barcelona, Spain) for 24 h at 4 °C and then stored at −80 °C. Total RNA was extracted by using an RNeasy mini kit (Qiagen, Barcelona, Spain). And was reverse transcribed by the High Capacity RNA-to-cDNA Kit (Applied Biosystems, Madrid, Spain). Real-time quantitative PCR was carried out with the TaqMan Assay predesigned by Applied Biosystems for the detection of *PNPLA3* (Hs00228747_m1), *ABCA1* (Hs01059118_m1), *ABCG1* (Hs00245154_m1), *ADIPOR2* (Hs00226105_m1), *ACC1* (Hs00167385_m1), *CROT* (Hs00221733_m1), *FABP4* (Hs00609791_m1), *FAS* (Hs00188012_m1), *IL6* (Hs00985639_m1), *LCN2* (Hs00194353_m1), *LXRα* (Hs00173195_m1), *PPARα*(Hs00947538_m1), *RESISTIN* (Hs00220767_m1), *SREBP1c* (Hs01088691_m1), *SREBP2* (Hs01081784_m1), *TNFα*(Hs99999043_m1), and *18S ribosomal RNA* (4352930E), which was used as the housekeeping gene. All reactions were performed in duplicate using the 7900HT Fast Real-Time PCR systems (Applied Biosystems).

4.5. Genotyping

Subjects were genotyped for the rs738409 polymorphism using the TaqMan 5′ allelic discrimination assay (TaqMan SNP Genotyping Assay C 7241 10, Applied Biosystems,). Amplifications were carried out using the 7900HT Sequencing Detection System for continuous fluorescence monitoring.

4.6. Statistical Analysis

We used the SPSS/PC+ statistical package for Windows (version 22.0; SPSS, Chicago, IL, USA). One-way ANOVA with a *post-hoc* Tukey test was carried out to determine differences between groups. The correlations between variables was analyzed using Pearson's method (parametric variables) and Spearman's test (non-parametric variables). Allele and genotype frequencies were evaluated with the χ-squared test. p-Values <0.05 were considered to be statistically significant.

5. Conclusions

The main results of our study show that liver *PNPLA3* expression is increased in NAFLD patients and is particularly associated to severity of steatosis. Moreover, *PNPLA3* expression is correlated with the expression of main cholesterol and hepatic lipid metabolism-related genes. Further human studies are required to confirm these associations.

Acknowledgments: This study was supported by the Fondo de Investigación Sanitaria and Fondo Europeo de Desarrollo Regional (FEDER, grant number PI13/00468, to Teresa Auguet), by funds from Agència de Gestió d'Ajuts Universitaris de Recerca (AGAUR 2009 SGR 959 to Cristóbal Richart) and the Grup de Recerca en Medicina Aplicada-Universitat Rovira Virgili (2015 PFR-URV-B2-72 to Cristóbal Richart), and by the Fundación Biociencia.

Author Contributions: Gemma Aragonès and Teresa Auguet participated in the design of the study and in the analysis and interpretation of data and were involved in the drafting of the manuscript. Teresa Auguet reviewed/edited the manuscript. Sandra Armengol, Alba Berlanga, Esther Guiu-Jurado, and Carmen Aguilar carried out the experimental work. Salomé Martinez and Joan Josep Sirvent are the pathologists. Maikel Daniel Ruiz, Fátima Sabench, Mercé Hernández, José Antonio Porras, and Daniel Del Castillo made substantial contributions to the conception and design of the study, and to the acquisition of the samples. Cristóbal Richart revised the draft and gave the final approval for publication. The authors have all seen the final version.

Conflicts of Interest: The authors declare no conflict of interest.

Abbreviations

ABCA1	ATP-binding cassette transporter A1
ABCG1	ATP-binding cassette transporter G1
ADIPOR	adiponectin receptor
ACC1	acetyl-coenzyme A carboxylase 1
ALT	alanine aminotransaminase
AST	aspartate aminotransaminase
ALP	alkaline phosphatase
BMI	body mass index
CROT	carnitine *O*-octanoyltransferase
FABP4	fatty acid binding protein 4
FAS	fatty acid synthase
18S	18S ribosomal RNA
GGT	γ-glutamyl transferase
HbA1c	glycosylated hemoglobin
HDL-C	high density lipoprotein
HOMA2-IR	homeostasis model assessment of insulin resistance
IL6	interleukin 6
LDL-C	low density lipoprotein
LCN2	lipocalin 2
LXRα	liver X receptor
MO	morbidly obese
NAFLD	non-alcoholic fatty liver disease
NASH	non-alcoholic steatosis
NL	normal liver
PPARα	peroxisome-proliferator-activated receptor α
SREBP1c	sterol regulatory element binding protein 1c
SREBP2	sterol regulatory element binding protein 2
SS	simple steatosis
TG	triglycerides
TNFα	tumor necrosis factor
WC	waist circumference

References

1. Lonardo, A.; Bellentani, S.; Argo, C.K.; Ballestri, S.; Byrne, C.D.; Caldwell, S.H.; Cortez-Pinto, H.; Grieco, A.; Machado, M.V.; Miele, L.; *et al.* Epidemiological modifiers of non-alcoholic fatty liver disease: Focus on high-risk groups. *Dig. Liver Dis.* **2015**, *47*, 997–1006. [CrossRef]

2. Farrell, G.C.; Larter, C.Z. Nonalcoholic fatty liver disease: From steatosis to cirrhosis. *Hepatology* **2006**, *43*, S99–S112. [CrossRef]

3. Younossi, Z.M.; Koenig, A.B.; Abdelatif, D.; Fazel, Y.; Henry, L.; Wymer, M. Global epidemiology of non-alcoholic fatty liver disease-meta-analytic assessment of prevalence, incidence and outcomes. *Hepatology* **2015**. [CrossRef]

4. Ballestri, S.; Romagnoli, D.; Nascimbeni, F.; Francica, G.; Lonardo, A. Role of ultrasound in the diagnosis and treatment of nonalcoholic fatty liver disease and its complications. *Expert Rev. Gastroenterol. Hepatol.* **2015**, *9*, 603–627. [CrossRef]

5. Buzzetti, E.; Pinzani, M.; Tsochatzis, E.A. The multiple-hit pathogenesis of non-alcoholic fatty liver disease (NAFLD). *Metabolism* **2016**, 1–11. [CrossRef]

6. Vernon, G.; Baranova, A.; Younossi, Z.M. Systematic review: The epidemiology and natural history of non-alcoholic fatty liver disease and non-alcoholic steatohepatitis in adults. *Aliment. Pharmacol. Ther.* **2011**, *34*, 274–285. [CrossRef]

7. Daly, A.K.; Ballestri, S.; Carulli, L.; Loria, P.; Day, C.P. Genetic determinants of susceptibility and severity in nonalcoholic fatty liver disease. *Expert Rev. Gastroenterol. Hepatol.* **2011**, *5*, 253–263. [CrossRef]

8. Kotronen, A.; Johansson, L.E.; Johansson, L.M.; Roos, C.; Westerbacka, J.; Hamsten, A.; Bergholm, R.; Arkkila, P.; Arola, J.; Kiviluoto, T.; *et al.* A common variant in PNPLA3, which encodes adiponutrin, is associated with liver fat content in humans. *Diabetologia* **2009**, *52*, 1056–1060. [CrossRef]

9. Sookoian, S.; Pirola, C.J. PNPLA3, the triacylglycerol synthesis/hydrolysis/storage dilemma, and nonalcoholic fatty liver disease. *World J. Gastroenterol.* **2012**, *18*, 6018–6026. [CrossRef]

10. Jenkins, C.M.; Mancuso, D.J.; Yan, W.; Sims, H.F.; Gibson, B.; Gross, R.W. Identification, cloning, expression, and purification of three novel human calcium-independent phospholipase A2 family members possessing triacylglycerol lipase and acylglycerol transacylase activities. *J. Biol. Chem.* **2004**, *279*, 48968–48975. [CrossRef]

11. Lake, A.C.1.; Sun, Y.; Li, J.L.; Kim, J.E.; Johnson, J.W.; Li, D.; Revett, T.; Shih, H.H.; Liu, W.; Paulsen, J.E.; *et al.* Expression, regulation, and triglyceride hydrolase activity of Adiponutrin family members. *J. Lipid Res.* **2005**, *46*, 2477–2487. [CrossRef]

12. Romeo, S.; Kozlitina, J.; Xing, C.; Pertsemlidis, A.; Cox, D.; Pennacchio, L.A.; Boerwinkle, E.; Cohen, J.C.; Hobbs, H.H. Genetic variation in PNPLA3 confers susceptibility to nonalcoholic fatty liver disease. *Nat. Genet.* **2008**, *40*, 1461–1465. [CrossRef]

13. Rotman, Y.; Koh, C.; Zmuda, J.M.; Kleiner, D.E.; Liang, T.J. The association of genetic variability in patatin-like phospholipase domain-containing protein 3 (PNPLA3) with histological severity of nonalcoholic fatty liver disease. *Hepatology* **2010**, *52*, 894–903. [CrossRef]

14. Valenti, L.; Alisi, A.; Galmozzi, E.; Bartuli, A.; Del Menico, B.; Alterio, A.; Dongiovanni, P.; Fargion, S.; Nobili, V. I148M patatin-like phospholipase domain-containing 3 gene variant and severity of pediatric nonalcoholic fatty liver disease. *Hepatology* **2010**, *52*, 1274–1280. [CrossRef]

15. Sookoian, S.; Pirola, C.J. Meta-analysis of the influence of I148M variant of patatin-like phospholipase domain containing 3 gene (*PNPLA3*) on the susceptibility and histological severity of nonalcoholic fatty liver disease. *Hepatology* **2011**, *53*, 1883–1894. [CrossRef]

16. Krawczyk, M.; Grünhage, F.; Zimmer, V.; Lammert, F. Variant adiponutrin (PNPLA3) represents a common fibrosis risk gene: Non-invasive elastography-based study in chronic liver disease. *J. Hepatol.* **2011**, *55*, 299–306. [CrossRef]

17. Valenti, L.; Al-Serri, A.; Daly, A.K.; Galmozzi, E.; Rametta, R.; Dongiovanni, P.; Nobili, V.; Mozzi, E.; Roviaro, G.; Vanni, E.; *et al.* Homozygosity for the patatin-like phospholipase-3/adiponutrin I148M polymorphism influences liver fibrosis in patients with nonalcoholic fatty liver disease. *Hepatology* **2010**, *51*, 1209–1217. [CrossRef]

18. Zain, S.M.; Mohamed, R.; Mahadeva, S.; Cheah, P.L.; Rampal, S.; Basu, R.C.; Mohamed, Z. A multi-ethnic study of a *PNPLA3* gene variant and its association with disease severity in non-alcoholic fatty liver disease. *Hum. Genet.* **2012**, *131*, 1145–1152. [CrossRef] [PubMed]

19. Kovarova, M.; Königsrainer, I.; Königsrainer, A.; Machicao, F.; Häring, H.-U.; Schleicher, E.; Peter, A. The genetic variant I148M in *PNPLA3* is associated with increased hepatic retinyl-palmitate storage in humans. *J. Clin. Endocrinol. Metab.* **2015**, *100*, E1568–E1574. [CrossRef] [PubMed]

20. Pirazzi, C.; Valenti, L.; Motta, B.M.; Pingitore, P.; Hedfalk, K.; Mancina, R.M.; Burza, M.A.; Indiveri, C.; Ferro, Y.; Montalcini, T.; *et al.* PNPLA3 has retinyl-palmitate lipase activity in human hepatic stellate cells. *Hum. Mol. Genet.* **2014**, *23*, 4077–4085. [CrossRef] [PubMed]

21. Chamoun, Z.; Vacca, F.; Parton, R.G.; Gruenberg, J. PNPLA3/adiponutrin functions in lipid droplet formation. *Biol. Cell* **2013**, *105*, 219–233. [CrossRef] [PubMed]

22. Ruhanen, H.; Perttilä, J.; Hölttä-Vuori, M.; Zhou, Y.; Yki-Järvinen, H.; Ikonen, E.; Käkelä, R.; Olkkonen, V.M. PNPLA3 mediates hepatocyte triacylglycerol remodelling. *J. Lipid Res.* **2014**, *55*, 739–746. [CrossRef] [PubMed]

23. Min, H.-K.; Sookoian, S.; Pirola, C.J.; Cheng, J.; Mirshahi, F.; Sanyal, A.J. Metabolic profiling reveals that PNPLA3 induces widespread effects on metabolism beyond triacylglycerol remodeling in Huh-7 hepatoma cells. *Am. J. Physiol. Gastrointest. Liver Physiol.* **2014**, *307*, G66–G76. [CrossRef] [PubMed]

24. Benjamini, Y.; Hochberg, Y. Controlling the false discovery rate: A practical and powerful approach to multiple testing. *J. R. Stat. Soc. B* **1995**, *57*, 289–300.

25. Auguet, T.; Berlanga, A.; Guiu-Jurado, E.; Martinez, S.; Porras, J.A.; Aragonès, G.; Sabench, F.; Hernandez, M.; Aguilar, C.; Sirvent, J.J.; *et al.* Altered fatty acid metabolism-related gene expression in liver from morbidly obese women with non-alcoholic fatty liver disease. *Int. J. Mol. Sci.* **2014**, *15*, 22173–22187. [CrossRef] [PubMed]

26. Lin, Y.-C.; Chang, P.-F.; Chang, M.-H.; Ni, Y.-H. Genetic variants in GCKR and PNPLA3 confer susceptibility to nonalcoholic fatty liver disease in obese individuals. *Am. J. Clin. Nutr.* **2014**, *99*, 869–874. [CrossRef] [PubMed]

27. Wu, P.; Shu, Y.; Guo, F.; Luo, H.; Zhang, G.; Tan, S. [Association between patatin-like phospholipase domain-containing protein 3 gene rs738409 polymorphism and non-alcoholic fatty liver disease susceptibility: A meta-analysis]. *Zhonghua Liu Xing Bing Xue Za Zhi* **2015**, *36*, 78–82. [PubMed]

28. Xu, R.; Tao, A.; Zhang, S.; Deng, Y.; Chen, G. Association between patatin-like phospholipase domain containing 3 gene (PNPLA3) polymorphisms and nonalcoholic fatty liver disease: A HuGE review and meta-analysis. *Sci. Rep.* **2015**, *5*, 9284. [CrossRef] [PubMed]

29. Zhang, L.; You, W.; Zhang, H.; Peng, R.; Zhu, Q.; Yao, A.; Li, X.; Zhou, Y.; Wang, X.; Pu, L.; *et al.* PNPLA3 polymorphisms (rs738409) and non-alcoholic fatty liver disease risk and related phenotypes: A meta-analysis. *J. Gastroenterol. Hepatol.* **2015**, *30*, 821–829. [CrossRef] [PubMed]

30. León-Mimila, P.; Vega-Badillo, J.; Gutiérrez-Vidal, R.; Villamil-Ramírez, H.; Villareal-Molina, T.; Larrieta-Carrasco, E.; López-Contreras, B.E.; Kauffer, L.R.M.; Maldonado-Pintado, D.G.; Méndez-Sánchez, N.; *et al.* A genetic risk score is associated with hepatic triglyceride content and non-alcoholic steatohepatitis in Mexicans with morbid obesity. *Exp. Mol. Pathol.* **2015**, *98*, 178–183. [CrossRef] [PubMed]

31. Zhang, Y.; Cai, W.; Song, J.; Miao, L.; Zhang, B.; Xu, Q.; Zhang, L.; Yao, H. Association between the PNPLA3 I148M polymorphism and non-alcoholic fatty liver disease in the Uygur and Han ethnic groups of northwestern China. *PLoS ONE* **2014**, *9*, e108381. [CrossRef] [PubMed]

32. Tai, C.-M.; Huang, C.-K.; Tu, H.-P.; Hwang, J.-C.; Chang, C.-Y.; Yu, M.-L. PNPLA3 genotype increases susceptibility of nonalcoholic steatohepatitis among obese patients with nonalcoholic fatty liver disease. *Surg. Obes. Relat. Dis.* **2014**, *11*, 888–894. [CrossRef] [PubMed]

33. Lee, S.S.; Byoun, Y.-S.; Jeong, S.-H.; Woo, B.H.; Jang, E.S.; Kim, J.-W.; Kim, H.Y. Role of the PNPLA3 I148M polymorphism in nonalcoholic fatty liver disease and fibrosis in Korea. *Dig. Dis. Sci.* **2014**, *59*, 2967–2974. [CrossRef] [PubMed]

34. Margherita Mancina, R.; Matikainen, N.; Maglio, C.; Söderlund, S.; Lundbom, N.; Hakkarainen, A.; Rametta, R.; Mozzi, E.; Fargion, S.; Valenti, L.; *et al.* Paradoxical dissociation between hepatic fat content and *de novo* lipogenesis due to PNPLA3 sequence variant. *J. Clin. Endocrinol. Metab.* **2015**, *100*, E821–E825. [CrossRef] [PubMed]

35. Shang, X.R.; Song, J.Y.; Liu, F.H.; Ma, J.; Wang, H.J. GWAS-identified common variants with nonalcoholic fatty liver disease in chinese children. *J. Pediatr. Gastroenterol. Nutr.* **2015**, *60*, 669–674. [CrossRef] [PubMed]

36. Nobili, V.; Liccardo, D.; Bedogni, G.; Salvatori, G.; Gnani, D.; Bersani, I.; Alisi, A.; Valenti, L.; Raponi, M. Influence of dietary pattern, physical activity, and I148M PNPLA3 on steatosis severity in at-risk adolescents. *Genes Nutr.* **2014**, *9*, 392. [CrossRef] [PubMed]

37. Donati, B.; Motta, B.M.; Pingitore, P.; Meroni, M.; Pietrelli, A.; Alisi, A.; Petta, S.; Xing, C.; Dongiovanni, P.; del Menico, B.; *et al.* The rs2294918 E434K variant modulates patatin-like phospholipase domain-containing 3 expression and liver damage. *Hepatology* **2016**, *63*, 787–798. [CrossRef] [PubMed]

38. Arendt, B.M.; Comelli, E.M.; Ma, D.W.L.; Lou, W.; Teterina, A.; Kim, T.; Fung, S.K.; Wong, D.K.H.; McGilvray, I.; Fischer, S.E.; *et al.* Altered hepatic gene expression in nonalcoholic fatty liver disease is associated with lower hepatic n-3 and n-6 polyunsaturated fatty acids. *Hepatology* **2015**, *61*, 1565–1578. [CrossRef]

39. Kitamoto, T.; Kitamoto, A.; Ogawa, Y.; Honda, Y.; Imajo, K.; Saito, S.; Yoneda, M.; Nakamura, T.; Nakajima, A.; Hotta, K. Targeted-bisulfite sequence analysis of the methylation of CpG islands in genes encoding PNPLA3, SAMM50, and PARVB of patients with non-alcoholic fatty liver disease. *J. Hepatol.* **2015**, *63*, 494–502. [CrossRef] [PubMed]

40. Hao, L.; Ito, K.; Huang, K.H.; Sae-tan, S.; Lambert, J.D.; Ross, A.C. Shifts in dietary carbohydrate-lipid exposure regulate expression of the non-alcoholic fatty liver disease-associated gene PNPLA3/adiponutrin in mouse liver and HepG2 human liver cells. *Metabolism* **2014**, *63*, 1352–1362. [CrossRef] [PubMed]

41. Huang, Y.; He, S.; Li, J.Z.; Seo, Y.-K.; Osborne, T.F.; Cohen, J.C.; Hobbs, H.H. A feed-forward loop amplifies nutritional regulation of PNPLA3. *Proc. Natl. Acad. Sci. USA* **2010**, *107*, 7892–7897. [CrossRef] [PubMed]

42. Bechmann, L.P.; Hannivoort, R.A.; Gerken, G.; Hotamisligil, G.S.; Trauner, M.; Canbay, A. The interaction of hepatic lipid and glucose metabolism in liver diseases. *J. Hepatol.* **2012**, *56*, 952–964. [CrossRef] [PubMed]

43. Zhang, X.; Liu, J.; Su, W.; Wu, J.; Wang, C.; Kong, X.; Gustafsson, J.-Å.; Ding, J.; Ma, X.; Guan, Y. Liver X receptor activation increases hepatic fatty acid desaturation by the induction of SCD1 expression through an LXRα-SREBP1c-dependent mechanism. *J. Diabetes* **2014**, *6*, 212–220. [CrossRef] [PubMed]

44. Ballestri, S.; Nascimbeni, F.; Romagnoli, D.; Baldelli, E.; Lonardo, A. The role of nuclear receptors in the pathophysiology, natural course, and drug treatment of NAFLD in humans. *Adv. Ther.* **2016**, *33*, 291–319. [CrossRef] [PubMed]

45. Dubuquoy, C.; Robichon, C.; Lasnier, F.; Langlois, C.; Dugail, I.; Foufelle, F.; Girard, J.; Burnol, A.F.; Postic, C.; Moldes, M. Distinct regulation of adiponutrin/PNPLA3 gene expression by the transcription factors ChREBP and SREBP1c in mouse and human hepatocytes. *J. Hepatol.* **2011**, *55*, 145–153. [CrossRef] [PubMed]

46. Pawlak, M.; Lefebvre, P.; Staels, B. Molecular mechanism of PPARα action and its impact on lipid metabolism, inflammation and fibrosis in non-alcoholic fatty liver disease. *J. Hepatol.* **2015**, *62*, 720–733. [CrossRef] [PubMed]

47. Dongiovanni, P.; Valenti, L. Peroxisome proliferator-activated receptor genetic polymorphisms and nonalcoholic Fatty liver disease: Any role in disease susceptibility? *PPAR Res.* **2013**, *2013*, 452061. [CrossRef] [PubMed]

48. Musso, G.; Gambino, R.; Cassader, M. Cholesterol metabolism and the pathogenesis of non-alcoholic steatohepatitis. *Prog. Lipid Res.* **2013**, *52*, 175–191. [CrossRef] [PubMed]

49. Min, H.-K.; Kapoor, A.; Fuchs, M.; Mirshahi, F.; Zhou, H.; Maher, J.; Kellum, J.; Warnick, R.; Contos, M.J.; Sanyal, A.J. Increased hepatic synthesis and dysregulation of cholesterol metabolism is associated with the severity of nonalcoholic fatty liver disease. *Cell Metab.* **2012**, *15*, 665–674. [CrossRef] [PubMed]

50. Auguet, T.; Terra, X.; Quintero, Y.; Martínez, S.; Manresa, N.; Porras, J.A.; Aguilar, C.; Orellana-Gavaldà, J.M.; Hernández, M.; Sabench, F.; *et al.* Liver lipocalin 2 expression in severely obese women with non alcoholic fatty liver disease. *Exp. Clin. Endocrinol. Diabetes* **2013**, *121*, 119–124. [CrossRef] [PubMed]

51. Lee, E.-K.; Kim, H.-J.; Lee, K.-J.; Lee, H.-J.; Lee, J.-S.; Kim, D.-G.; Hong, S.-W.; Yoon, Y.; Kim, J.-S. Inhibition of the proliferation and invasion of hepatocellular carcinoma cells by lipocalin 2 through blockade of JNK and PI3K/Akt signaling. *Int. J. Oncol.* **2011**, *38*, 325–333. [CrossRef] [PubMed]

52. Kumari, M.; Schoiswohl, G.; Chitraju, C.; Paar, M.; Rangrez, A.Y.; Wongsiriroj, N.; Nagy, H.M.; Pavlina, T.; Scott, S.A.; Knittelfelder, O.; *et al.* Adiponutrin functions as a nutritionally regulated lysophosphatidic acid acyltransferase. *Cell Metab.* **2012**, *15*, 691–702. [CrossRef] [PubMed]

53. Chen, L.Z.; Xin, Y.N.; Geng, N.; Jiang, M.; Zhang, D.D.; Xuan, S.Y. PNPLA3 I148M variant in nonalcoholic fatty liver disease: Demographic and ethnic characteristics and the role of the variant in nonalcoholic fatty liver fibrosis. *World J. Gastroenterol.* **2015**, *21*, 794–802. [PubMed]

54. Kleiner, D.E.; Brunt, E.M.; Van Natta, M.; Behling, C.; Contos, M.J.; Cummings, O.W.; Ferrell, L.D.; Liu, Y.-C.; Torbenson, M.S.; Unalp-Arida, A.; *et al.* Design and validation of a histological scoring system for nonalcoholic fatty liver disease. *Hepatology* **2005**, *41*, 1313–1321. [CrossRef] [PubMed]

55. Brunt, E.M.; Janney, C.G.; Di Bisceglie, A.M.; Neuschwander-Tetri, B.A.; Bacon, B.R. Nonalcoholic steatohepatitis: A proposal for grading and staging the histological lesions. *Am. J. Gastroenterol.* **1999**, *94*, 2467–2474. [CrossRef] [PubMed]

56. Terra, X.; Quintero, Y.; Auguet, T.; Porras, J.A.; Hernández, M.; Sabench, F.; Aguilar, C.; Luna, A.M.; Del Castillo, D.; Richart, C. FABP 4 is associated with inflammatory markers and metabolic syndrome in morbidly obese women. *Eur. J. Endocrinol.* **2011**, *164*, 539–547. [CrossRef] [PubMed]

International Journal of
Molecular Sciences

MDPI

Review

Definitions of Normal Liver Fat and the Association of Insulin Sensitivity with Acquired and Genetic NAFLD—A Systematic Review

Elina M. Petäjä [1,2,*] and Hannele Yki-Järvinen [1,2]

1   Minerva Foundation Institute for Medical Research, 00290 Helsinki, Finland;
    hannele.yki-jarvinen@helsinki.fi
2   Department of Medicine, University of Helsinki and Helsinki University Central Hospital,
    00290 Helsinki, Finland
*   Correspondence: elina.petaja@helsinki.fi; Tel./Fax: +358-9-471-71967

Academic Editors: Amedeo Lonardo and Giovanni Targher
Received: 3 March 2016; Accepted: 20 April 2016; Published: 27 April 2016

Abstract: Non-alcoholic fatty liver disease (NAFLD) covers a spectrum of disease ranging from simple steatosis (NAFL) to non-alcoholic steatohepatitis (NASH) and fibrosis. "Obese/Metabolic NAFLD" is closely associated with obesity and insulin resistance and therefore predisposes to type 2 diabetes and cardiovascular disease. NAFLD can also be caused by common genetic variants, the patatin-like phospholipase domain-containing 3 (PNPLA3) or the transmembrane 6 superfamily member 2 (TM6SF2). Since NAFL, irrespective of its cause, can progress to NASH and liver fibrosis, its definition is of interest. We reviewed the literature to identify data on definition of normal liver fat using liver histology and different imaging tools, and analyzed whether NAFLD caused by the gene variants is associated with insulin resistance. Histologically, normal liver fat content in liver biopsies is most commonly defined as macroscopic steatosis in less than 5% of hepatocytes. In the population-based Dallas Heart Study, the upper 95th percentile of liver fat measured by proton magnetic spectroscopy (^{1}H-MRS) in healthy subjects was 5.6%, which corresponds to approximately 15% histological liver fat. When measured by magnetic resonance imaging (MRI)-based techniques such as the proton density fat fraction (PDFF), 5% macroscopic steatosis corresponds to a PDFF of 6% to 6.4%. In contrast to "Obese/metabolic NAFLD", NAFLD caused by genetic variants is not associated with insulin resistance. This implies that NAFLD is heterogeneous and that "Obese/Metabolic NAFLD" but not NAFLD due to the PNPLA3 or TM6SF2 genetic variants predisposes to type 2 diabetes and cardiovascular disease.

Keywords: insulin resistance; liver fat; obesity; PNPLA3; TM6SF2

1. Introduction

Non-alcoholic fatty liver disease (NAFLD) is defined as steatosis not caused by excess alcohol intake (>30 g/day in men and >20 g/day in women), hepatitis B or C, autoimmune hepatitis, iron overload, drugs or toxins [1]. It covers a spectrum from simple steatosis (NAFL) to non-alcoholic steatohepatitis (NASH) and cirrhosis [1,2]. NASH is characterized, in addition to steatosis, by ballooning necrosis, mild inflammation and possibly fibrosis, and can only be diagnosed using a liver biopsy [3].

Several longitudinal studies have shown that NAFLD increases the risk of and mortality from type 2 diabetes and cardiovascular disease [4]. Fibrosis stage is considered to be the most important histological feature predicting advanced liver disease [5,6]. It has been recently shown, however, that NAFL defined as macroscopic steatosis in more than 5% of hepatocytes progresses to

NASH and fibrosis [7–9], as hypothesized by earlier indirect evidence [10]. Thus, NAFL predicts both metabolic and liver complications of NAFLD. It is therefore of interest to define normal liver fat content in humans.

Although NAFLD commonly coexists with obesity, insulin resistance and type 2 diabetes [11], common genetic causes also exist. A variant in patatin-like phospholipase domain-containing 3 (PNPLA3) (rs738409 [G], encoding I148M) confers susceptibility to NAFL, NASH and fibrosis ("PNPLA3 NAFLD") [12]. Genetic variation in transmembrane 6 superfamily member 2 (TM6SF2) (rs58542926 [T], encoding E167K) is also increases liver fat and the risk of NASH ("TM6SF2 NAFLD") [13]. These two conditions do not appear to be characterized by insulin resistance, although both genetic and metabolic causes of NAFLD may exist in the same person [14]. If so, then these types of NAFLD would not predispose to type 2 diabetes and cardiovascular disease.

The ensuing review will focus on defining normal liver fat content and discussing how liver fat content is related to insulin sensitivity in "Obese/Metabolic NAFLD" and the common genetic forms of NAFLD.

2. Definitions of Normal Liver Fat

2.1. Biochemical and Histologic Definitions

The biochemical standard for normal triglyceride content in the human liver is 5.5% of triglyceride of wet liver tissue weight [15,16]. Histologically, the liver is considered steatotic when ⩾5% of hepatocytes in a tissue section stained with hematoxylin and eosin contain macrovesicular steatosis [17–20]. Steatosis is graded by the pathologist from 0 to 3 based on its severity: grade 0 (normal) = <5%, grade 1 (mild) = 5%–33%, grade 2 (moderate) = 34%–66%, and grade 3 (severe) = ⩾67% of hepatocytes characterized by macroscopic steatosis [17]. As discussed below, these percentages seem quite different from those obtained by proton magnetic resonance spectroscopy (^{1}H-MRS) (Table 1).

Table 1. Definitions of normal liver fat using different approaches.

Study	Year	N	Subjects	Normal Value
			Biochemical	
Laurell S [21]	1971	3	Healthy subjects	2.0 g/100 g of dry tissue weight
Donhoffer H [15]	1974	107	Unselected cadavers	5.5 g/100 g of wet tissue weight
			Histology	
Kleiner DE [17]	2005	576 + 162	Adults and children	Macroscopic fat in <5% of hepatocytes
Brunt EM [3]	2011	976	Adults	Macroscopic fat in <5% of hepatocytes
Bedossa P [19]	2012	679	Morbidly obese adults	Macroscopic fat in <5% of hepatocytes
			CT	
Piekarski J [22]	1980	100	Healthy subjects	50–57 HU or 8–10 HU higher than spleen
			^{1}H-MRS	
Szczepaniak LS [23]	2005	345	Population-based, healthy subjects	<5.56%
Petersen KF [24]	2006	170	Healthy subjects	<3.0%
			MRI-PDFF	
Fishbein MH [25]	1998	28	Healthy subjects	<9.0%
			US	
Joseph AE [26]	1978	60	Adults referred to gastroenterologist	Absense of echogenicity or brightness of the liver
Saveymuttu SH [27]	1985	490	Adults referred to gastroenterologist	Absense of echogenicity or brightness of the liver

^{1}H-MRS, proton magnetic resonance spectroscopy; CT, computed tomography; HU, Houndsfield Unit; MRI-PDFF, magnetic resonance imaging-determined proton density fat fraction; US, ultrasound.

2.2. Proton Magnetic Resonance Spectroscopy (^{1}H-MRS)

Steatosis can most accurately be measured using ^{1}H-MRS [28]. This technique enables sampling of a large volume fraction of the liver compared to a biopsy [29,30] and provides an accurate and reproducible measurement of liver fat content [30]. However, ^{1}H-MRS is expensive, as it requires use of magnetic resonance imaging (MRI) scanner and special expertise to perform proton magnetic resonance spectroscopy (^{1}H-MRS) at the time of MRI scanning. ^{1}H-MRS has been used in one population-based study, the Dallas Heart Study (DHS), to define normal liver fat content [23]. In this study, ^{1}H-MRS was performed on 2349 subjects, of which 345 were considered healthy based on the following criteria: no history of liver disease or risk factors for hepatic steatosis (alcohol consumption $\leqslant$30 g/day in men, $\leqslant$20 g/day in women, body mass index (BMI) <25 kg/m^2, normal fasting serum glucose, non-diabetic and normal serum alanine aminotransferase (ALT) ($\leqslant$30 IU/L in men, $\leqslant$19 IU/L in women)). The upper limit of normal liver fat content was defined based on the upper 95th percentile in the healthy subjects and was 5.56% [23].

The ^{1}H-MRS studies determine the hepatic triglyceride content rather than the percentage of hepatocytes with macroscopic lipid droplets. The relationship between ^{1}H-MRS and histological liver fat content has been analyzed in two small studies, which included 13 [31], 12 [32] and 50 [33] subjects. In the first two studies, the ^{1}H-MRS-determined normal liver fat in the DHS, *i.e.*, the 5.56% value corresponded to 15.7% [31] and 13.9% [32] of hepatocytes with macroscopic steatosis. On the third study, histological grade 1 (5%–33% macroscopic liver fat) corresponded to 11% (7%–14%), grade 2 (33%–66%) to 18% (14%–23%) and grade 3 (>66%) to 25% (10%–28%) ^{1}H-MRS liver fat [33]. ^{1}H-MRS-measured liver fat corresponds well to triglyceride content measured in a liver biopsy ($r = 0.90$, $p < 0.001$) [34]. These data show that the technique used to define normal liver fat influences the normal value.

2.3. Magnetic Resonance Imaging (MRI)

Hepatic steatosis can be diagnosed with MRI using an out-of-phase and in-phase imaging technique developed by Dixon WT *et al.* [35]. This method involves acquisition of MR images at echo times in which fat proton and water proton signals are either out-of-phase (water and fat signals cancel) or in-phase (water and fat signals add up) [35–37]. Once the out-of-phase and in-phase images are acquired by using constant calibration and other scanner settings, a quantitative fat signal fraction can be calculated from the hepatic signal [38]. Modified versions of the early Dixon method have been introduced. These include the hepatic fat fraction by Fishbein MH *et al.* which uses fast gradient echo techniques [25,39] and correlates well with histological liver fat content ($r = 0.77$, $p < 0.001$). The newer MRI-determined proton density fat fraction (PDFF) technique provides a quantitative, standardized and objective MRI measurement of hepatic fat based upon inherent tissue properties [40,41]. The MRI-PDFF method is reproducible and correlates closely with ^{1}H-MRS ($r = 0.99$) [33,42] and liver histology (8.9%–9.4% at grade 1, 15.8%–16.3% at grade 2, and 22.1%–25.0% at grade 3, $p < 0.0001$) [33,43,44]. With this technique, the 5% macroscopic liver fat determined by histology corresponds to a PDFF value of 6% to 6.4% [45,46].

2.4. Ultrasound (US)

Ultrasound (US) is an inexpensive and widely available tool to visualize the liver and its fat content. Hepatic steatosis appears as a diffuse increase in parenchymal brightness and echogenicity on US images, and is often compared to hypoechogenity of the kidney cortex. Most studies score steatosis semiquantitatively as "mild", "moderate" and "severe" based upon the visual assessment of hepatic echogenicity [27,47–49]. Lack of standardization precludes accurate comparison of data acquired by different machines and investigators. US lacks sensitivity in obese subjects [50] and in subjects with low liver fat content [51]. The sensitivity of diagnosing fatty liver increases from 55% to 80% when liver fat increases from 10%–20% to over 30% [51]. A recent study [52] suggested that the optimum sensitivity for US was achieved at a ^{1}H-MRS-measured liver fat content greater than 12.5%. A meta-analysis of 44 studies comprising 4720 subjects concluded that US has a sensitivity of 85% and a specificity of 94% for detecting 20%–30% macroscopic steatosis [53]. The sensitivity and specificity were 65% and 81% for detecting 0%–5% steatosis and 93% and 88%, respectively, for detecting >10% steatosis.

Xia MF *et al.* created an equation for accurate quantification of liver fat content using US in Chinese subjects [54]. A tissue-mimicking phantom was used as a standard and the US hepatic/renal ratio was measured to calculate liver fat content in 127 subjects, in whom liver fat was also measured using ^{1}H-MRS. The adjusted R^2 for the model was 80%. The optimal cut-off for the US-measured liver fat content to diagnose hepatic steatosis was 9.15%, which yielded a sensitivity and specificity of 95% and 100%, respectively. The utility of this technique in other ethnic groups which are more obese than the Chinese in the face of a similar amount of liver fat [55,56] remains to be tested.

2.5. Computed Tomography (CT)

Hepatic steatosis can also be assessed by using computed tomography (CT) by comparing attenuation of the liver parenchyma to that of the spleen [57]. Tissue fat deposition lowers attenuation, hence fatty areas are less dense and appear darker than the non-fatty tissues [22]. The attenuation value in the healthy liver is 50 to 57 Houndsfield Units (HU) and 8 to 10 HU higher than that of spleen [22]. It decreases by 1.6 HU for every 1 mg of triglycerides per gram of liver tissue [58]. In subjects with steatosis, the mean attenuation value of the liver is lower than that of the spleen, and the liver appears darker than the spleen. Attenuation values less than 40 HU in the liver or 10 HU less in the liver than in the spleen are indicative of marked hepatic steatosis (>30%). Smaller fractions of fatty infiltration cannot be accurately and reliably assessed [59,60].

3. Non-Alcoholic Fatty Liver Disease (NAFLD) and Insulin Sensitivity

3.1. Insulin Resistance in "Obese/Metabolic NAFLD"

In subjects with NAFLD and the metabolic syndrome (MetS), *i.e.*, in "Obese/Metabolic NAFLD", liver fat is closely correlated with direct measures of insulin resistance such as the inability of insulin to suppress hepatic glucose production [61], and indirect measures such as fasting serum insulin and the product of fasting insulin and glucose (Homeostasis model assessment for insulin resistance [HOMA-IR]) [62]. Indeed, liver fat correlates better with fasting insulin than with liver enzymes such as serum ALT and aspartate aminotransferase (AST) [63,64]. This close association between fasting insulin and liver fat is physiologically feasible as the main action of insulin after an overnight fast is to restrain hepatic glucose production. The inability of insulin to suppress hepatic glucose production increases fasting glucose, which stimulates insulin secretion leading to hyperglycemia and hyperinsulinemia.

Lipolysis is the main source of fatty acids used for synthesis of intrahepatocellular triglycerides [65,66]. Liver fat is closely correlated with the ability of insulin to suppress lipolysis [67,68]. The ability of insulin to suppress very low density lipoprotein (VLDL) production is also impaired in NAFLD, which contributes to hypertriglyceridemia and a low high density lipoprotein (HDL) cholesterol concentration. Damaged hepatocytes release increased amounts of C-reactive protein (CRP) and coagulation factors, which could contribute to increased risk of cardiovascular disease and atherothrombotic vascular disease (Figure 1).

Any obese person with NAFLD and features of the MetS can be considered to have "Obese/Metabolic NAFLD" irrespective of genetic risk factors. The most recent proposal defines the MetS in 10 different ways [69]. The presence of any three out of five features (hypertriglyceridemia, low HDL cholesterol, hyperglycemia, hypertension, increased waist circumference) is required for diagnosis of the MetS [69]. For clinical practice, this definition still remains the best tool to diagnose insulin resistance, although the extent to which the 10 different definitions increase the risk of endpoints such as type 2 diabetes and cardiovascular disease is unclear. Measurement of fasting insulin and glucose concentrations and their calculation of their product HOMA-IR might seem more attractive direct tools to measure insulin sensitivity in subjects with NAFLD. The problem with this approach is that insulin assays are not internationally standardized and give highly variable results [70].

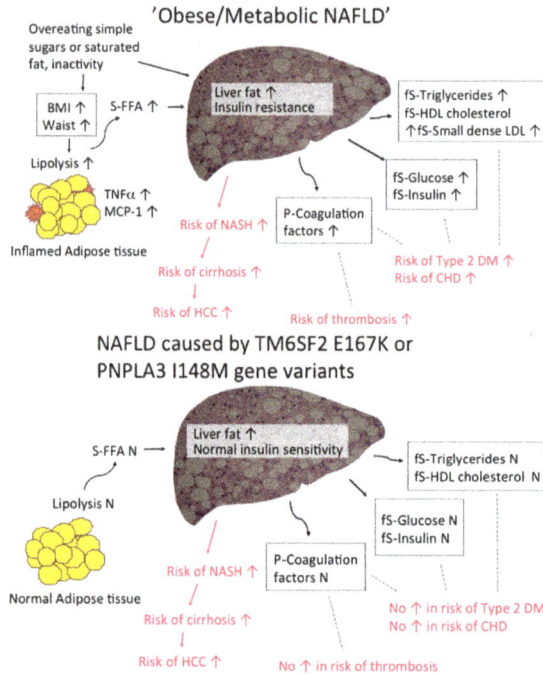

Figure 1. Schematic representation of causes and consequences of "Obese/Metabolic NAFLD" (**top**) and "TM6SF2 NAFLD" and "PNPLA3 NAFLD" (**bottom**). Abbreviations: BMI, body mass index; CHD, coronary heart disease; DM, diabetes mellitus; FFA, free fatty acids; fS, fasting serum; HCC, hepatocellular carcinoma; HDL, high density lipoprotein; MCP-1, monocyte chemoattractant protein-1; NAFLD, non-alcoholic fatty liver disease; NASH, non-alcoholic steatohepatits; LDL, low density lipoprotein; P, plasma; PNPLA3, patatin-like phospholipase domain-containing 3; S, serum; TM6SF2, transmembrane 6 superfamily member 2; TNF-α, tumor necrosis factor-α.

3.2. "Patatin-Like Phospholipase Domain-Containing 3 (PNPLA3) NAFLD" and Insulin Sensitivity

Approximately 30% of Europids and several other ethnic groups carry the PNPLA3 I148M variant [12]. The association between the PNPLA3 gene variant and NAFLD [12] has been replicated in over 50 studies, including eight genome wide association studies [71–73]. In a meta-analysis carriers of the I148M variant had 73% more liver fat, a 3.2-fold higher risk of necro-inflammation and a 3.2-fold greater risk of developing fibrosis than the non-carriers [71]. In a meta-analysis comprising 12 Asian studies, the risk of NAFLD was 1.9-fold increased in carriers compared to non-carriers [72]. Recent meta-analyses have also shown that this gene variant increases the risk of cirrhosis by 1.9-fold [74] and hepatocellular carcinoma (HCC) by 1.8-fold [75].

In vitro, the PNPLA3 I148M gene variant abolishes intrahepatocellular lipolysis [76,77] and by acting as a lysophosphatidic acid acyl transferase stimulates triglyceride synthesis from long unsaturated fatty acids containing coenzyme A (CoA) more than from saturated fatty acid CoAs [78]. The contribution of each these mechanisms to function of the PNPLA3 gene variant in the human liver is uncertain. It is clear, however, that the human liver lipidome markedly differs between

"Obese/Metabolic NAFLD" and "PNPLA3 NAFLD" [14]. The increase in liver fat in the carriers of the PNPLA3 I148M gene variant is due to polyunsaturated triglycerides, whereas in "Obese/Metabolic NAFLD" the concentration of saturated triglycerides and insulin resistance-inducing ceramides is increased [14].

Table 2 summarizes the 14 studies that include data on insulin sensitivity in carriers and non-carriers of the I148M variant [12,79–91]. Carriers of the PNPLA3 I148M variant had more liver fat in their liver than non-carriers. Insulin sensitivity as evaluated by HOMA-IR [62], the hyperinsulinemic clamp technique, fasting or post-glucose insulin and glucose concentrations did not, however, differ between carriers and non-carriers of the gene variant. These studies included obese and non-obese, diabetic and non-diabetic as well as pediatric cohorts. Serum triglycerides were either similar or lower in variant allele carriers as compared to non-carriers, consistent with lack of insulin resistance (Table 2).

3.3. "Transmembrane 6 Superfamily Member 2 (TM6SF2) NAFLD" and Insulin Sensitivity

Approximately 7% of all subjects carry the TM6SF2 E167K variant. This gene variant increases the risk of NAFLD, independent of genetic variation in PNPLA3 at rs738409, obesity and alcohol intake [92]. A recent meta-analysis reported that carriers of the TM6SF2 E167K gene variant have a 2.1-fold higher risk of NAFLD than non-carriers [93]. They also had lower circulating total and low density lipoprotein (LDL) cholesterol, and triglyceride concentrations than non-carriers [93].

Four *in vitro* studies have examined the mechanism by which the TM6SF2 E167K gene variant could increase liver fat. Recombinant adeno-associated viral vectors expressing short hairpin RNAs were used to reduce *Tm6sf2* transcripts in the mouse liver, which increased hepatic triglyceride content three-fold [92]. TM6SF2 knock-out mice developed hepatic steatosis and had a three-fold reduced plasma VLDL triglyceride levels due to decreased lipidation [94]. In another study, TM6SF2 small interfering RNA inhibition also decreased export of triglyceride-rich lipoproteins and lipid droplet content in human hepatoma cell lines (Huh7 and HepG2) [95]. Overexpression of TM6SF2 in Huh7 cells reduced cellular triglyceride content [96]. Transient overexpression of human TM6SF2 in mice using a liver-targeting adenovirus containing the human TM6SF2 coding region increased, while knockdown of endogenous TM6SF2 decreased circulating total cholesterol [96]. In the latter study, no change in hepatic fat content was observed. This was hypothetized to be due to the transient exposure, compared to the lifetime exposure of humans carrying the gene variant [96].

Table 3 summarizes seven studies that have reported data on liver fat content and insulin sensitivity in carriers and non-carriers of TM6SF2 E167K gene variant [13,81,92,97–100]. In all but one of these studies, carriers had a significantly higher liver fat content as determined by ^{1}H-MRS, MRI, histology or US [13,92,97–100] than non-carriers. Insulin sensitivity, as determined by HOMA-IR or from oral glucose tolerance test measures did not differ between carriers and non-carriers. Triglyceride concentrations were either lower [81,98,100] or similar [13,97,99] but also in one study higher [92] in TM6SF2 E167K variant allele carriers compared to non-carriers.

Table 2. Insulin sensitivity in studies comparing liver fat between PNPLA3 I148M carriers and non-carriers.

Cohort	N	BMI (kg/m²)			Liver Fat			Insulin Sensitivity (HOMA-IR)			S-Triglycerides (mmol/L)		
		I148II	I148IM	I148MM	I148II	I148IM	I148MM	I148II	I148IM	I148MM	I148II	I148IM	I148MM
Multiethnic [1] [12]	2111	30.4	31.1	30.0	3.7%ᵃ	4.6%ᵃ	7.7%***,ᵃ	3.3	3.5	3.3	1.32	1.35	1.41
		31.6	32.0	32.2	3.1%	4.8%	4.8%***	3.3	3.3	4.4	0.97	0.97	1.02
		29.2	28.8	28.8	3.5%	3.7%	3.5%***	2.3	2.4	2.0	1.25	1.21	0.90
Germany [79]	330	29.9	29.1	28.7	5.4%ᵃ	6.0%ᵃ	7.2%***,ᵃ	12.6ʸ,ᶻ	12.9ʸ,ᶻ	12.9ʸ,ᶻ	NA	NA	NA
Finnish [80]	291	30.5	30.0	32.2	9.0%ᵃ	10.4%*,ᵃ	14.1%**,ᵃ	72ʸ,ᶻ	70ʸ,ᶻ	74ʸ,ᶻ	1.82	1.60	1.52
British [81]	98	34.6	33.2	31.7	26.7%ᵃ	28.8%ᵃ	33.5%ᵃ	2.4	3.1	2.6	1.60	1.70	1.40
Multiethnic [2] [82]	1214	NAˣ	NAˣ	NAˣ	57ᵇ / 55	55ᵇ / 51	46***,ᵇ / 47***	NAˣ	NAˣ	NAˣ	NAˣ	NAˣ	NAˣ
Dutch [83]	470	37.7	37.6	37.6	66%ᶜ	78%ᶜ	100%***,ᶜ	2.7	2.8	2.9	1.42	1.47	1.46
Italian [84]	61	25.7	25.9		16%ᵈ	32%*,ᵈ		3.4	4.7		1.13	1.15	
Italian [85]	253	30.7	30.7	29.8	44%ᶜ	48%ᶜ	63%***,ᶜ	3.9	4	5.2	1.64	1.85	1.79
Italian [86]	211	32.1	30.4	31.7	4ᵉ	4ᵉ	4ᵉ	3.5	3.5	2.8	1.77	1.59	1.26**
Taiwanese [87]	879	23.3	23.6	23.6	13%ᶠ	19%ᶠ	23%*,ᶠ	1.4	1.5	1.5	1.11	1.16	1.38*
South Korean [88]	1363	24.7	24.4	23.9**	38%ᶠ	45%ᶠ	54%*,ᶠ	2.3	2.1	1.6**	1.54	1.38	1.31**
Taiwanese, pediatric [89]	520	26.3	26.2	25.9	21%ᶠ	13%ᶠ	30%**,ᶠ	2.4	2.5	1.7	1.11	1.03	0.94
Italian, pediatric [90]	475	NA	NA	NA	13%ᶠ	19%ᶠ	41%*,ᶠ	3.3	3.0	3.0	0.56	0.56	0.53
Italian, pediatric [91]	149	95.2°	95.0°	94.1°	70%ᵍ / 30% / 0%	7%ᵍ / 78% / 15%	4%***,ᵍ / 4% / 92%	2.5	2.7	2.4	1.28	1.19	1.39

BMI, body mass index; CT, computed tomography; HOMA-IR, Homeostasis model assessment of insulin resistance [62]; HU, Houndsfield Unit; MRI, magnetic resonance imaging; NA, not available; OGTT, oral glucose tolerance test; US, ultrasound. * Significant difference between groups in ANOVA or *t* test. * *p* < 0.05; ** *p* < 0.01, *** *p* < 0.0001. Data are presented as mean or median. [1] Caucasian, African and Hispanic Americans; [2] Hispanic and African Americas. ° BMI centiles; ᵃ ¹H-MRS (liver fat content,%); ᵇ CT (liver density, HU); ᶜ Histology (prevalence of steatosis, %); ᵈ Histology (% hepatocytes steatotic); ᵉ US (severity of steatosis by Hamaguchi score, 3–4 = moderate); ᶠ US (prevalence of steatosis, %); ᵍ Histology (severity of steatosis, grade 1/2/3); ʸ OGTT (arbitrary unit); ʸ fasting serum insulin (pmol/L); ᶻ hyperinsulinemic clamp was also performed, data not shown in the table; ˣ Data not shown, but it was reported that genetic variation at rs738409 did not correlate with HOMA-IR, insulin sensitivity index, BMI or S-triglycerides.

Table 3. Insulin sensitivity in studies comparing liver fat between TM6SF2 E167K carriers and non-carriers.

Cohort	N	BMI (kg/m^2)		Liver Fat		Insulin Sensitivity (HOMA-IR)		S-Triglycerides (mmol/L)	
		EE	EK + KK	EE	EK + KK	EE	EK + KK	EE	EK + KK
Multiethnic [1] [92]	4587	29.6	28.5/31.8	3.5% [a]	4.4%/15.7% ***,[a]	3.0	2.9/4.6	1.39	1.33/1.47 *
Finns [97]	300	33.7	32.5	6.8% [a]	11.2% *,[a]	3.0	2.9	1.40	1.50
British [81]	98	32.6	35.4	28.5% [a]	29.0% [a]	2.7	4.0	1.60 *	1.50 *
Argentineans [13]	361	29.8	30.2	NA	NA	3.1	3.0	1.87	1.31
Multiethnic [2] [98]	502	32.2	31.2/30.8	S0: 3% [b] S1: 50% S2: 27% S3: 20%	S0: 0%/0% [b] S1: 35%/45% S2: 40%/20% S3: 25%/35% *	3.5	2.8/2.8	1.70	1.36/1.08 **
Multiethnic [1], pediatric [99]	957 ^	33.0	32.6	6.7% [c],^	11.1% **,[c],^	1.9 [x]	2.0 [x]	1.20	1.21
Italian, pediatric [100]	1010	2.9 °	2.9 °	47% [d]	89% ***,[d]	5.6	4.6	1.12	1.02 *

BMI, body mass index; BMI-SDS, body mass index standard deviation score; HOMA-IR, Homeostasis model assessment of insulin resistance [62]; MRI-PDFF, magnetic resonance imaging-measured proton density fat fraction; NA, not available; OGTT, oral glucose tolerance test; US, ultrasound; WBISI, whole body insulin sensitivity index. Significant difference between groups in ANOVA or t test, * $p < 0.05$; ** $p < 0.01$; *** $p < 0.0001$. Data are presented as mean or median. [1] Caucasian, African and Hispanic Americans; [2] Caucasian, Asian, Hispanic; International Liver Disease Genetics Consortium; ^ Liver fat content available on 454 subjects, BMI, insulin sensitivity and S-triglycerides on 957 subjects; ° BMI-SDS; [a] ^{1}H-MRS (liver fat content, %); [b] Histology, prevalence of each steatosis grade; [c] MRI-PDFF, liver fat, %, (n = 454); [d] US (prevalence of steatosis, %); [x] OGTT (WBISI).

4. Materials and Methods

We performed a systematic search using PubMed and Medline on two topics. For definitions of normal liver fat, we used the following search terms and their combinations: "normal liver fat", "liver histology", "liver biopsy" and "liver triglycerides", "liver H-MRS", "liver MRI", "liver MRI-PDFF", "liver CT", "liver ultrasound" and received 526 matches. Thirty-three studies included data on normal liver fat content or compared liver fat measured using different techniques. To review the association between insulin resistance and genetic NAFLD, we searched for studies using the following search terms: "PNPLA3" or "TM6SF2" and "insulin resistance", "euglycemic (hyperinsulinemic) clamp", "fasting glucose", "fasting insulin", "HOMA-IR", "oral glucose tolerance test" and included studies which compared results between carriers and non-carriers of PNPLA3 I148M or TM6SF2 E167K gene variants. A total of 124 matched were found. Of these, 22 studies were informative with respect to liver fat content and insulin resistance between genotypes, and were thus included.

5. Conclusions

Normal liver fat content based on liver histology can be defined as macroscopic steatosis in less than 5% of hepatocytes. With ^{1}H-MRS, normal liver fat in the population-based DHS was defined as less or equal than 5.56% [23], which corresponds to histologic liver fat of approximately 15% [31,32]. Definitions of normal liver fat content thus depend on the method used. There is also no prospective evidence that these normal values are of clinical relevance with respect to the development of liver fibrosis.

Although NAFLD has often been regarded simply as the hepatic manifestation of the MetS, it is now clear that NAFLD is heterogeneous. While "Obese/Metabolic NAFLD" is associated with NAFLD and features of the MetS and an increased risk of type 2 diabetes and cardiovascular disease, NAFLD caused by I148M variant in PNPLA3 and the E167K variant in TM6SF2 is not accompanied by insulin resistance. Thus, lack of insulin resistance does not exclude NAFLD and not all patients with NAFLD are at increased risk of type 2 diabetes and cardiovascular disease. Given that both the MetS and the genetic variants in PNPLA3 and TM6SF2 are common, there are also many individuals with "double trouble NAFLD" [14].

Future Research and Uncertainties

Although NAFL defined as macroscopic steatosis affecting >5% of hepatocytes predicts fibrosis [7–9], it is unknown how various degrees of steatosis predict liver outcomes. Such information would help the clinician to decide which patients to refer to the hepatologist. The same applies to the non-invasive markers of NAFL proposed to be used by the recent European NAFLD guideline if imaging tools are not available [101]. This guideline also recommended testing for the I148M gene variant in "selected cases and in clinical trials". The latter might be helpful in identifying patients with NAFLD who are at risk for advanced liver disease but who lack features of the MetS and are therefore not at risk for cardiovascular disease or type 2 diabetes. A cost–benefit analysis of this suggestion is warranted.

Acknowledgments: This study was supported by research grants from the Academy of Finland (Hannele Yki-Järvinen), EU H2020 EPoS 634413 (Hannele Yki-Järvinen), the Sigrid Juselius (Hannele Yki-Järvinen), State Research Funding (EVO) (Hannele Yki-Järvinen), the Novo Nordisk (Hannele Yki-Järvinen) Foundations and personal grants from the Finnish Medical Association (Elina M. Petäjä) and the Paulo Foundation (Elina M. Petäjä).

Author Contributions: Elina M. Petäjä and Hannele Yki-Järvinen have reviewed the literature and written the review.

Conflicts of Interest: The authors declare no conflict of interest.

Abbreviations

^{1}H-MRS	proton magnetic resonance spectroscopy
ALT	alanine aminotransferase
AST	aspartate aminotransferase
BMI	body mass index
BMI-SDS	body mass index standard deviation score
CHD	coronary heart disease
CoA	coenzyme A
CT	computed tomography
DM	diabetes mellitus
DHS	Dallas Heart Study
FFA	free fatty acids
fS	fasting serum
HDL	high density lipoprotein
MCP-1	monocyte chemoattractant protein-1
HCC	hepatocellular carcinoma
HDL	high density lipoprotein
HOMA-IR	homeostasis model assessment for insulin resistance
LDL	low density lipoprotein
MetS	metabolic syndrome
MRI	magnetic resonance imaging
NAFL	non-alcoholic fatty liver
NAFLD	non-alcoholic fatty liver disease
NASH	non-alcoholic steatohepatitis
OGTT	oral glucose tolerance test
P	plasma
PDFF	proton density fat fraction
PNPLA3	patatin-like phospholipase domain-containing 3
TM6SF2	transmembrane 6 superfamily member 2
TNF-α	tumor necrosis factor-α
US	ultrasound
VLDL	very low density lipoprotein

References

1. Chalasani, N.; Younossi, Z.; Lavine, J.E.; Diehl, A.M.; Brunt, E.M.; Cusi, K.; Charlton, M.; Sanyal, A.J. The diagnosis and management of non-alcoholic fatty liver disease: Practice guideline by the American Association for the Study of Liver Diseases, American College of Gastroenterology, and the American Gastroenterological Association. *Am. J. Gastroenterol.* **2012**, *107*, 811–826. [CrossRef] [PubMed]
2. Neuschwander-Tetri, B.A. Hepatic lipotoxicity and the pathogenesis of nonalcoholic steatohepatitis: The central role of nontriglyceride fatty acid metabolites. *Hepatology* **2010**, *52*, 774–788. [CrossRef] [PubMed]
3. Brunt, E.M.; Kleiner, D.E.; Wilson, L.A.; Belt, P.; Neuschwander-Tetri, B.A. The NAS and the histopathologic diagnosis in NAFLD: Distinct clinicopathologic meanings. *Hepatology* **2011**, *53*, 810–820. [CrossRef] [PubMed]
4. Anstee, Q.M.; Day, C.P. Progression of NAFLD to diabetes mellitus, cardiovascular disease or cirrhosis. *Nat. Rev. Gastroenterol. Hepatol.* **2013**, *10*, 330–344. [CrossRef] [PubMed]
5. Angulo, P.; Kleiner, D.E.; Dam-Larsen, S.; Adams, L.A.; Bjornsson, E.S.; Charatcharoenwitthaya, P.; Mills, P.R.; Keach, J.C.; Lafferty, H.D.; Stahler, A.; *et al.* Liver fibrosis, but no other histologic features, is associated with long-term outcomes of patients with nonalcoholic fatty liver disease. *Gastroenterology* **2015**, *149*, 389–397. [CrossRef] [PubMed]
6. Ekstedt, M.; Hagstrom, H.; Nasr, P.; Fredrikson, M.; Stal, P.; Kechagias, S.; Hultcrantz, R. Fibrosis stage is the strongest predictor for disease-specific mortality in NAFLD after up to 33 years of follow-up. *Hepatology* **2015**, *61*, 1547–1554. [CrossRef] [PubMed]

7. McPherson, S.; Hardy, T.; Henderson, E.; Burt, A.D.; Day, C.P.; Anstee, Q.M. Evidence of NAFLD progression from steatosis to fibrosing-steatohepatitis using paired biopsies: Implications for prognosis and clinical management. *J. Hepatol.* **2015**, *62*, 1148–1155. [CrossRef] [PubMed]

8. Pais, R.; Charlotte, F.; Fedchuk, L.; Bedossa, P.; Lebray, P.; Poynard, T.; Ratziu, V.; LIDO Study Group. A systematic review of follow-up biopsies reveals disease progression in patients with non-alcoholic fatty liver. *J. Hepatol.* **2013**, *59*, 550–556. [CrossRef] [PubMed]

9. Wong, V.W.-S.; Wong, G.L.-H.; Choi, P.C.-L.; Chan, A.W.-H.; Li, M.K.-P.; Chan, H.-Y.; Chim, A.M.-L.; Yu, J.; Sung, J.J.-Y.; Chan, H.L.-Y. Disease progression of non-alcoholic fatty liver disease: A prospective study with paired liver biopsies at 3 years. *Gut* **2010**, *59*, 969–974. [CrossRef] [PubMed]

10. Tarantino, G.; Conca, P.; Riccio, A.; Tarantino, M.; di Minno, M.N.; Chianese, D.; Pasanisi, F.; Contaldo, F.; Scopacasa, F.; Capone, D. Enhanced serum concentrations of transforming growth factor-beta1 in simple fatty liver: Is it really benign? *J. Transl. Med.* **2008**, *6*. [CrossRef] [PubMed]

11. Yki-Järvinen, H. Non-alcoholic fatty liver disease as a cause and a consequence of metabolic syndrome. *Lancet Diabetes Endocrinol.* **2014**, *2*, 901–910. [CrossRef]

12. Romeo, S.; Kozlitina, J.; Xing, C.; Pertsemlidis, A.; Cox, D.; Pennacchio, L.A.; Boerwinkle, E.; Cohen, J.C.; Hobbs, H.H. Genetic variation in PNPLA3 confers susceptibility to nonalcoholic fatty liver disease. *Nat. Genet.* **2008**, *40*, 1461–1465. [CrossRef] [PubMed]

13. Sookoian, S.; Castaño, G.O.; Scian, R.; Mallardi, P.; Fernández Gianotti, T.; Burgueño, A.L.; San Martino, J.; Pirola, C.J. Genetic variation in transmembrane 6 superfamily member 2 and the risk of nonalcoholic fatty liver disease and histological disease severity. *Hepatology* **2015**, *61*, 515–525. [CrossRef] [PubMed]

14. Luukkonen, P.K.; Zhou, Y.; Sädevirta, S.; Leivonen, M.; Arola, J.; Orešič, M.; Hyötyläinen, T.; Yki-Järvinen, H. Hepatic ceramides dissociate steatosis and insulin resistance in patients with non-alcoholic fatty liver disease. *J. Hepatol.* **2016**, *64*, 1167–1175. [CrossRef] [PubMed]

15. Donhoffer, H. Quantitative estimation of lipids in needle biopsy sized specimens of cadaver liver. *Acta Med. Acad. Sci. Hung* **1974**, *31*, 47–49. [PubMed]

16. Hoyumpa, D.A.M., Jr.; Greene, H.L.; Dunn, G.D.; Schenker, S. Fatty liver: Biochemical and clinical considerations. *Dig. Dis. Sci.* **1975**, *20*, 1142–1170. [CrossRef]

17. Kleiner, D.E.; Brunt, E.M.; van Natta, M.; Behling, C.; Contos, M.J.; Cummings, O.W.; Ferrell, L.D.; Liu, Y.-C.; Torbenson, M.S.; Unalp-Arida, A.; *et al.* Nonalcoholic steatohepatitis clinical research network design and validation of a histological scoring system for nonalcoholic fatty liver disease. *Hepatology* **2005**, *41*, 1313–1321. [CrossRef] [PubMed]

18. Brunt, E.M.; Tiniakos, D.G. Histopathology of nonalcoholic fatty liver disease. *World J. Gastroenterol.* **2010**, *16*, 5286–5296. [CrossRef] [PubMed]

19. Bedossa, P.; Poitou, C.; Veyrie, N.; Bouillot, J.-L.; Basdevant, A.; Paradis, V.; Tordjman, J.; Clément, K. Histopathological algorithm and scoring system for evaluation of liver lesions in morbidly obese patients. *Hepatology* **2012**, *56*, 1751–1759. [CrossRef] [PubMed]

20. Korenblat, K.M.; Fabbrini, E.; Mohammed, B.S.; Klein, S. Liver, muscle, and adipose tissue insulin action is directly related to intrahepatic triglyceride content in obese subjects. *Gastroenterology* **2008**, *134*, 1369–1375. [CrossRef] [PubMed]

21. Laurell, S.; Lundquist, A. Lipid composition of human liver biopsy specimens. *Acta Med. Scand.* **1971**, *189*, 65–68. [CrossRef] [PubMed]

22. Piekarski, J.; Goldberg, H.I.; Royal, S.A.; Axel, L.; Moss, A.A. Difference between liver and spleen CT numbers in the normal adult: Its usefulness in predicting the presence of diffuse liver disease. *Radiology* **1980**, *137*, 727–729. [CrossRef] [PubMed]

23. Szczepaniak, L.S.; Nurenberg, P.; Leonard, D.; Browning, J.D.; Reingold, J.S.; Grundy, S.; Hobbs, H.H.; Dobbins, R.L. Magnetic resonance spectroscopy to measure hepatic triglyceride content: Prevalence of hepatic steatosis in the general population. *Am. J. Physiol. Endocrinol. Metab.* **2005**, *288*, E462–E468. [CrossRef] [PubMed]

24. Petersen, K.F.; Dufour, S.; Feng, J.; Befroy, D.; Dziura, J.; Dalla Man, C.; Cobelli, C.; Shulman, G.I. Increased prevalence of insulin resistance and nonalcoholic fatty liver disease in Asian-Indian men. *Proc. Natl. Acad. Sci. USA* **2006**, *103*, 18273–18277. [CrossRef] [PubMed]

25. Fishbein, M.H.; Gardner, K.G.; Potter, C.J.; Schmalbrock, P.; Smith, M.A. Introduction of fast MR imaging in the assessment of hepatic steatosis. *Magn. Reson. Imaging* **1997**, *15*, 287–293. [CrossRef]

26. Joseph, A.E.A.; Dewbury, K.C.; McGuire, P.G. Ultrasound in the detection of chronic liver disease (the "bright liver"). *Br. J. Radiol.* **1978**, *52*, 184–188. [CrossRef] [PubMed]

27. Saverymuttu, S.H.; Joseph, A.E.; Maxwell, J.D. Ultrasound scanning in the detection of hepatic fibrosis and steatosis. *Br. Med. J. (Clin. Res. Ed.)* **1986**, *292*, 13–15. [CrossRef]

28. Bohte, A.E.; van Werven, J.R.; Bipat, S.; Stoker, J. The diagnostic accuracy of US, CT, MRI and 1H-MRS for the evaluation of hepatic steatosis compared with liver biopsy: A meta-analysis. *Eur. Radiol.* **2011**, *21*, 87–97. [CrossRef] [PubMed]

29. Longo, R.; Ricci, C.; Masutti, F.; Vidimari, R.; Crocé, L.S.; Bercich, L.; Tiribelli, C.; Dalla Palma, L. Fatty infiltration of the liver: Quantification by 1H localized magnetic resonance spectroscopy and comparison with computed tomography. *Investig. Radiol.* **1993**, *28*, 297–302. [CrossRef]

30. Szczepaniak, L.S.; Babcock, E.E.; Schick, F.; Dobbins, R.L.; Garg, A.; Burns, D.K.; McGarry, J.D.; Stein, D.T. Measurement of intracellular triglyceride stores by H spectroscopy: Validation *in vivo*. *Am. J. Physiol. Endocrinol. Metab.* **1999**, *276*, E977–E989.

31. Kotronen, A.; Vehkavaara, S.; Seppälä-Lindroos, A.; Bergholm, R.; Yki-Järvinen, H. Effect of liver fat on insulin clearance. *Am. J. Physiol. Endocrinol. Metab.* **2007**, *293*, E1709–E1715. [CrossRef] [PubMed]

32. Cowin, G.J.; Jonsson, J.R.; Bauer, J.D.; Ash, S.; Ali, A.; Osland, E.J.; Purdie, D.M.; Clouston, A.D.; Powell, E.E.; Galloway, G.J. Magnetic resonance imaging and spectroscopy for monitoring liver steatosis. *J. Magn. Reson. Imaging* **2008**, *28*, 937–945. [CrossRef] [PubMed]

33. Noureddin, M.; Lam, J.; Peterson, M.R.; Middleton, M.; Hamilton, G.; Le, T.-A.; Bettencourt, R.; Changchien, C.; Brenner, D.A.; Sirlin, C.; *et al.* Utility of magnetic resonance imaging *versus* histology for quantifying changes in liver fat in nonalcoholic fatty liver disease trials. *Hepatology* **2013**, *58*, 1930–1940. [CrossRef] [PubMed]

34. Thomsen, C.; Becker, U.; Winkler, K.; Christoffersen, P.; Jensen, M.; Henriksen, O. Quantification of liver fat using magnetic resonance spectroscopy. *Magn. Reson. Imaging* **1994**, *12*, 487–495. [CrossRef]

35. Dixon, W.T. Simple proton spectroscopic imaging. *Radiology* **1984**, *153*, 189–194. [CrossRef] [PubMed]

36. Rofsky, N.M.; Weinreb, J.C.; Ambrosino, M.M.; Safir, J.; Krinsky, G. Comparison between in-phase and opposed-phase T1-weighted breath-hold FLASH sequences for hepatic imaging. *J. Comput. Assist. Tomogr.* **1996**, *20*, 230–235. [CrossRef] [PubMed]

37. Cassidy, F.H.; Yokoo, T.; Aganovic, L.; Hanna, R.F.; Bydder, M.; Middleton, M.S.; Hamilton, G.; Chavez, A.D.; Schwimmer, J.B.; Sirlin, C.B. Fatty liver disease: MR Imaging techniques for the detection and quantification of liver steatosis1. *Radiographics* **2009**, *29*, 231–260. [CrossRef] [PubMed]

38. Hussain, H.K.; Chenevert, T.L.; Londy, F.J.; Gulani, V.; Swanson, S.D.; McKenna, B.J.; Appelman, H.D.; Adusumilli, S.; Greenson, J.K.; Conjeevaram, H.S. Hepatic fat fraction: MR imaging for quantitative measurement and display—Early experience 1. *Radiology* **2005**, *237*, 1048–1055. [CrossRef] [PubMed]

39. Fishbein, M.H.; Stevens, W.R. Rapid MRI using a modified Dixon technique: A non-invasive and effective method for detection and monitoring of fatty metamorphosis of the liver. *Pediatr. Radiol.* **2001**, *31*, 806–809. [CrossRef] [PubMed]

40. Hines, C.D.G.; Frydrychowicz, A.; Hamilton, G.; Tudorascu, D.L.; Vigen, K.K.; Yu, H.; McKenzie, C.A.; Sirlin, C.B.; Brittain, J.H.; Reeder, S.B. T_1 independent, T_2^* corrected chemical shift based fat-water separation with multi-peak fat spectral modeling is an accurate and precise measure of hepatic steatosis. *J. Magn. Reson. Imaging* **2011**, *33*, 873–881. [CrossRef] [PubMed]

41. Meisamy, S.; Hines, C.D.G.; Hamilton, G.; Sirlin, C.B.; McKenzie, C.A.; Yu, H.; Brittain, J.H.; Reeder, S.B. Quantification of hepatic steatosis with T1-independent, T2*-corrected MR imaging with spectral modeling of fat: blinded comparison with MR spectroscopy. *Radiology* **2011**, *258*, 767–775. [CrossRef] [PubMed]

42. Kang, G.H.; Cruite, I.; Shiehmorteza, M.; Wolfson, T.; Gamst, A.C.; Hamilton, G.; Bydder, M.; Middleton, M.S.; Sirlin, C.B. Reproducibility of MRI-determined proton density fat fraction across two different MR scanner platforms. *J. Magn. Reson. Imaging* **2011**, *34*, 928–934. [CrossRef] [PubMed]

43. Permutt, Z.; Le, T.A.; Peterson, M.R.; Seki, E.; Brenner, D.A.; Sirlin, C.; Loomba, R. Correlation between liver histology and novel magnetic resonance imaging in adult patients with non-alcoholic fatty liver disease—MRI accurately quantifies hepatic steatosis in NAFLD. *Aliment. Pharmacol. Ther.* **2012**, *36*, 22–29. [CrossRef] [PubMed]

44. Patel, N.S.; Peterson, M.R.; Brenner, D.A.; Heba, E.; Sirlin, C.; Loomba, R. Association between novel MRI-estimated pancreatic fat and liver histology-determined steatosis and fibrosis in non-alcoholic fatty liver disease. *Aliment. Pharmacol. Ther.* **2013**, *37*, 630–639. [CrossRef] [PubMed]

45. Idilman, I.S.; Aniktar, H.; Idilman, R.; Kabacam, G.; Savas, B. Hepatic steatosis: Quantification by proton density fat fraction with MR imaging *versus* liver biopsy. *Radiology* **2013**, *267*, 767–775. [CrossRef] [PubMed]

46. Tang, A.; Tan, J.; Sun, M.; Hamilton, G.; Bydder, M.; Wolfson, T.; Gamst, A.C.; Middleton, M.; Brunt, E.M.; Loomba, R.; *et al.* Nonalcoholic fatty liver disease: MR imaging of liver proton density fat fraction to assess hepatic steatosis. *Radiology* **2013**, *267*, 422–431. [CrossRef] [PubMed]

47. Needleman, L.; Kurtz, A.B.; Rifkin, M.D.; Cooper, H.S.; Pasto, M.E.; Goldberg, B.B. Sonography of diffuse benign liver-disease—Accuracy of pattern-recognition and grading. *Am. J. Roentgenol.* **1986**, *146*, 1011–1015. [CrossRef] [PubMed]

48. Joseph, A.E.A.; Saverymuttu, S.H.; Al-Sam, S.; Cook, M.G.; Maxwell, J.D. Comparison of liver histology with ultrasonography in assessing diffuse parenchymal liver disease. *Clin. Radiol.* **1991**, *43*, 26–31. [CrossRef]

49. Foster, K.J.; Dewbury, K.C.; Griffith, A.H.; Wright, R. The accuracy of ultrasound in the detection of fatty infiltration of the liver. *Br. J. Radiol.* **1979**, *53*, 440–442. [CrossRef] [PubMed]

50. Mottin, C.C.; Moretto, M.; Padoin, A.V.; Swarowsky, A.M.; Toneto, M.G.; Glock, L.; Repetto, G. The role of ultrasound in the diagnosis of hepatic steatosis in morbidly obese patients. *Obes. Surg.* **2004**, *14*, 635–637. [CrossRef] [PubMed]

51. Ryan, C.K.; Johnson, L.A.; Germin, B.I.; Marcos, A. One hundred consecutive hepatic biopsies in the workup of living donors for right lobe liver transplantation. *Liver Transpl.* **2002**, *8*, 1114–1122. [CrossRef] [PubMed]

52. Bril, F.; Ortiz Lopez, C.; Lomonaco, R.; Orsak, B.; Freckleton, M.; Chintapalli, K.; Hardies, J.; Lai, S.; Solano, F.; Tio, F.; *et al.* Clinical value of liver ultrasound for the diagnosis of nonalcoholic fatty liver disease in overweight and obese patients. *Liver Int.* **2015**, *35*, 2139–2146. [CrossRef] [PubMed]

53. Hernaez, R.; Lazo, M.; Bonekamp, S.; Kamel, I.; Brancati, F.L.; Guallar, E.; Clark, J.M. Diagnostic accuracy and reliability of ultrasonography for the detection of fatty liver: A meta-analysis. *Hepatology* **2011**, *54*, 1082–1090. [CrossRef] [PubMed]

54. Xia, M.F.; Yan, H.M.; He, W.Y.; Li, X.M.; Li, C.L.; Yao, X.Z.; Li, R.K.; Zeng, M.S.; Gao, X. Standardized ultrasound hepatic/renal ratio and hepatic attenuation rate to quantify liver fat content: An improvement method. *Obesity (Silver Spring)* **2012**, *20*, 444–452. [CrossRef] [PubMed]

55. Loomba, R.; Sanyal, A.J. The global NAFLD epidemic. *Nat. Rev. Gastroenterol. Hepatol.* **2013**, *10*, 686–690. [CrossRef] [PubMed]

56. Wong, R.J.; Ahmed, A. Obesity and non-alcoholic fatty liver disease: Disparate associations among Asian populations. *World J. Hepatol.* **2014**, *6*, 263–273. [CrossRef] [PubMed]

57. Schwenzer, N.F.; Springer, F.; Schraml, C.; Stefan, N.; Machann, J.; Schick, F. Non-invasive assessment and quantification of liver steatosis by ultrasound, computed tomography and magnetic resonance. *J. Hepatol.* **2009**, *51*, 433–445. [CrossRef] [PubMed]

58. Bydder, G.M.; Chapman, R.W.G.; Harry, D.; Bassan, L.; Sherlock, S.; Kreel, L. Computed tomography attenuation values in fatty liver. *J. Comput. Tomogr.* **1981**, *5*, 33–35. [CrossRef]

59. Park, S.H.; Kim, P.N.; Kim, K.W.; Lee, S.W.; Yoon, S.E.; Park, S.W.; Ha, H.K.; Lee, M.-G.; Hwang, S.; Lee, S.-G.; *et al.* Macrovesicular hepatic steatosis in living liver donors: Use of CT for quantitative and qualitative assessment1. *Radiology* **2006**, *239*, 105–112. [CrossRef] [PubMed]

60. Kodama, Y.; Ng, C.S.; Wu, T.T.; Ayers, G.D.; Curley, S.A.; Abdalla, E.K.; Vauthey, J.N.; Charnsangavej, C. Comparison of CT methods for determining the fat content of the liver. *AJR Am. J. Roentgenol.* **2007**, *188*, 1307–1312. [CrossRef] [PubMed]

61. Seppälä-Lindroos, A.; Vehkavaara, S.; Häkkinen, A.-M.; Goto, T.; Westerbacka, J.; Sovijärvi, A.; Halavaara, J.; Yki-Järvinen, H. Fat accumulation in the liver is associated with defects in insulin suppression of glucose production and serum free fatty acids independent of obesity in normal men. *J. Clin. Endocrinol. Metab.* **2002**, *87*, 3023–3028. [CrossRef] [PubMed]

62. Matthews, D.R.; Hosker, J.P.; Rudenski, A.S.; Naylor, B.A.; Treacher, D.F.; Turner, R.C. Homeostasis model assessment: Insulin resistance and beta-cell function from fasting plasma glucose and insulin concentrations in man. *Diabetologia* **1985**, *28*, 412–419. [CrossRef] [PubMed]

63. Kotronen, A.; Westerbacka, J.; Bergholm, R.; Yki-Järvinen, H. Liver fat in the metabolic syndrome. *J. Clin. Endocrinol. Metab.* **2007**, *92*, 3490–3497. [CrossRef] [PubMed]

64. Gastaldelli, A.; Kozakova, M.; Højlund, K.; Flyvbjerg, A.; Favuzzi, A.; Mitrakou, A.; Balkau, B. Fatty liver is associated with insulin resistance, risk of coronary heart disease, and early atherosclerosis in a large European population. *Hepatology* **2009**, *49*, 1537–1544. [CrossRef] [PubMed]

65. Donnelly, K.L.; Smith, C.I.; Schwarzenberg, S.J.; Jessurun, J.; Boldt, M.D.; Parks, E.J. Sources of fatty acids stored in liver and secreted via lipoproteins in patients with nonalcoholic fatty liver disease. *J. Clin. Investig.* **2005**, *115*, 1343–1351. [CrossRef] [PubMed]

66. Lambert, J.E.; Ramos-Roman, M.A.; Browning, J.D.; Parks, E.J. Increased *de novo* lipogenesis is a distinct characteristic of individuals with nonalcoholic fatty liver disease. *Gastroenterology* **2014**, *146*, 726–735. [CrossRef] [PubMed]

67. Kotronen, A.; Vehkavaara, S.; Yki-Järvinen, H. Increased liver fat, impaired insulin clearance, and hepatic and adipose tissue insulin resistance in type 2 diabetes. *Gastroenterology* **2008**, *135*, 122–130. [CrossRef] [PubMed]

68. Gastaldelli, A.; Cusi, K.; Pettiti, M.; Hardies, J.; Miyazaki, Y.; Berria, R.; Buzzigoli, E.; Sironi, A.M.; Cersosimo, E.; Ferrannini, E.; *et al.* Relationship between hepatic/visceral fat and hepatic insulin resistance in nondiabetic and type 2 diabetic subjects. *Gastroenterology* **2007**, *133*, 496–506. [CrossRef] [PubMed]

69. Alberti, K.G.M.M.; Eckel, R.H.; Grundy, S.M.; Zimmet, P.Z.; Cleeman, J.I.; Donato, K.A.; Fruchart, J.-C.; James, W.P.T.; Loria, C.M.; Smith, S.C.; *et al.* Harmonizing the metabolic syndrome: A joint interim statement of the international diabetes federation task force on epidemiology and prevention; national heart, lung, and blood institute; American heart association; world heart federation; international atherosclerosis society; and international association for the study of obesity. *Circulation* **2009**, *120*, 1640–1645. [PubMed]

70. Manley, S.E.; Stratton, I.M.; Clark, P.M.; Luzio, S.D. Comparison of 11 human insulin assays: Implications for clinical investigation and research. *Clin. Chem.* **2007**, *53*, 922–932. [CrossRef] [PubMed]

71. Sookoian, S.; Pirola, C.J. Meta-analysis of the influence of I148M variant of patatin-like phospholipase domain containing 3 gene (PNPLA3) on the susceptibility and histological severity of nonalcoholic fatty liver disease. *Hepatology* **2011**, *53*, 1883–1894. [CrossRef] [PubMed]

72. Zhang, L.; You, W.; Zhang, H.; Peng, R.; Zhu, Q.; Yao, A.; Li, X.; Zhou, Y.; Wang, X.; Pu, L.; *et al.* PNPLA3 polymorphisms (rs738409) and non-alcoholic fatty liver disease risk and related phenotypes: A meta-analysis. *J. Gastroenterol. Hepatol.* **2015**, *30*, 821–829. [CrossRef] [PubMed]

73. Xu, R.; Tao, A.; Zhang, S.; Deng, Y.; Chen, G. Association between patatin-like phospholipase domain containing 3 gene (PNPLA3) polymorphisms and nonalcoholic fatty liver disease: A HuGE review and meta-analysis. *Sci. Rep.* **2015**, *5*. [CrossRef]

74. Shen, J.-H.; Li, Y.-L.; Li, D.; Wang, N.-N.; Jing, L.; Huang, Y.-H. The rs738409 (I148M) variant of the PNPLA3 gene and cirrhosis: A meta-analysis. *J. Lipid Res.* **2015**, *56*, 167–175. [CrossRef]

75. Trépo, E.; Nahon, P.; Bontempi, G.; Valenti, L.; Falleti, E.; Nischalke, H.D.; Hamza, S.; Corradini, S.G.; Burza, M.A.; Guyot, E.; *et al.* Association between the PNPLA3 (rs738409 C>G) variant and hepatocellular carcinoma: Evidence from a meta-analysis of individual participant data. *Hepatology* **2014**, *59*, 2170–2177. [CrossRef]

76. He, S.; McPhaul, C.; Li, J.Z.; Garuti, R.; Kinch, L.; Grishin, N.V.; Hobbs, H.H. A sequence variation (I148M) in PNPLA3 associated with nonalcoholic fatty liver disease disrupts triglyceride hydrolysis. *J. Biol. Chem.* **2010**, *285*, 6706–6715. [CrossRef]

77. Huang, Y.; Cohen, J.C.; Hobbs, H.H. Expression and characterization of a PNPLA3 protein isoform (I148M) associated with nonalcoholic fatty liver disease. *J. Biol. Chem.* **2011**, *286*, 37085–37093. [CrossRef] [PubMed]

78. Kumari, M.; Schoiswohl, G.; Chitraju, C.; Paar, M.; Cornaciu, I.; Rangrez, A.Y.; Wongsiriroj, N.; Nagy, H.M.; Ivanova, P.T.; Scott, S.A.; *et al.* Adiponutrin functions as a nutritionally regulated lysophosphatidic acid acyltransferase. *Cell Metab.* **2012**, *15*, 691–702. [CrossRef] [PubMed]

79. Kantartzis, K.; Peter, A.; Machicao, F.; Machann, J.; Wagner, S.; Königsrainer, I.; Königsrainer, A.; Schick, F.; Fritsche, A.; Haring, H.-U.; *et al.* Dissociation between fatty liver and insulin resistance in humans carrying a variant of the patatin-like phospholipase 3 gene. *Diabetes* **2009**, *58*, 2616–2623. [CrossRef] [PubMed]

80. Kotronen, A.; Johansson, L.E.; Johansson, L.M.; Roos, C.; Westerbacka, J.; Hamsten, A.; Bergholm, R.; Arkkila, P.; Arola, J.; Kiviluoto, T.; *et al.* A common variant in PNPLA3, which encodes adiponutrin, is associated with liver fat content in humans. *Diabetologia* **2009**, *52*, 1056–1060. [CrossRef] [PubMed]

81. Scorletti, E.; West, A.L.; Bhatia, L.; Hoile, S.P.; McCormick, K.G.; Burdge, G.C.; Lillycrop, K.A.; Clough, G.F.; Calder, P.C.; Byrne, C.D. Treating liver fat and serum triglyceride levels in NAFLD, effects of PNPLA3 and TM6SF2 genotypes: Results from the WELCOME trial. *J. Hepatol.* **2015**, *63*, 1476–1483. [CrossRef] [PubMed]
82. Wagenknecht, L.E.; Palmer, N.D.; Bowden, D.W.; Rotter, J.I.; Norris, J.M.; Ziegler, J.; Chen, Y.D.I.; Haffner, S.; Scherzinger, A.; Langefeld, C.D. Association of PNPLA3 with non-alcoholic fatty liver disease in a minority cohort: The insulin resistance atherosclerosis family study. *Liver Int.* **2011**, *31*, 412–416. [CrossRef] [PubMed]
83. Verrijken, A.; Beckers, S.; Francque, S.; Hilden, H.; Caron, S.; Zegers, D.; Ruppert, M.; Hubens, G.; Marck, E.; Michielsen, P.; *et al.* A gene variant of PNPLA3, but not of APOC3, is associated with histological parameters of NAFLD in an obese population. *Obesity (Silver Spring)* **2013**, *21*, 2138–2145. [CrossRef] [PubMed]
84. Musso, G.; Cassader, M.; Gambino, R. PNPLA3 rs738409 and TM6SF2 rs58542926 gene variants affect renal disease and function in nonalcoholic fatty liver disease. *Hepatology* **2015**, *62*, 658–659. [CrossRef] [PubMed]
85. Valenti, L.; Al-Serri, A.; Daly, A.K.; Galmozzi, E.; Rametta, R.; Dongiovanni, P.; Nobili, V.; Mozzi, E.; Roviaro, G.; Vanni, E.; *et al.* Homozygosity for the patatin-like phospholipase-3/adiponutrin I148M polymorphism influences liver fibrosis in patients with nonalcoholic fatty liver disease. *Hepatology* **2010**, *51*, 1209–1217. [CrossRef] [PubMed]
86. Del Ben, M.; Polimeni, L.; Brancorsini, M.; di Costanzo, A.; D'Erasmo, L.; Baratta, F.; Loffredo, L.; Pastori, D.; Pignatelli, P.; Violi, F.; *et al.* Non-alcoholic fatty liver disease, metabolic syndrome and patatin-like phospholipase domain-containing protein3 gene variants. *Eur. J. Intern. Med.* **2014**, *25*, 566–570. [CrossRef] [PubMed]
87. Wang, C.W.; Lin, H.Y.; Shin, S.J.; Yu, M.-L.; Lin, Z.-Y.; Dai, C.-Y.; Huang, J.-F.; Chen, S.-C.; Li, S.S.L.; Chuang, W.-L. The PNPLA3 I148M polymorphism is associated with insulin resistance and nonalcoholic fatty liver disease in a normoglycaemic population. *Liver Int.* **2011**, *31*, 1326–1331. [CrossRef] [PubMed]
88. Park, J.H.; Cho, B.; Kwon, H.; Prilutsky, D.; Yun, J.M.; Choi, H.C.; Hwang, K.B.; Lee, I.H.; Kim, J.I.; Kong, S.W. I148M variant in PNPLA3 reduces central adiposity and metabolic disease risks while increasing nonalcoholic fatty liver disease. *Liver Int.* **2015**, *35*, 2537–2546. [CrossRef] [PubMed]
89. Lin, Y.-C.; Chang, P.-F.; Hu, F.-C.; Yang, W.-S.; Chang, M.-H.; Ni, Y.-H. A Common variant in the PNPLA3 gene is a risk factor for Non-alcoholic fatty liver disease in obese Taiwanese children. *J. Pediatr.* **2011**, *158*, 740–744. [CrossRef] [PubMed]
90. Romeo, S.; Sentinelli, F.; Cambuli, V.M.; Incani, M.; Congiu, T.; Matta, V.; Pilia, S.; Huang-Doran, I.; Cossu, E.; Loche, S.; *et al.* The 148M allele of the PNPLA3 gene is associated with indices of liver damage early in life. *J. Hepatol.* **2010**, *53*, 335–338. [CrossRef] [PubMed]
91. Valenti, L.; Alisi, A.; Galmozzi, E.; Bartuli, A.; del Menico, B.; Alterio, A.; Dongiovanni, P.; Fargion, S.; Nobili, V. I148M patatin-like phospholipase domain-containing 3 gene variant and severity of pediatric nonalcoholic fatty liver disease. *Hepatology* **2010**, *52*, 1274–1280. [CrossRef] [PubMed]
92. Kozlitina, J.; Smagris, E.; Stender, S.; Nordestgaard, B.G.; Zhou, H.H.; Tybjærg-Hansen, A.; Vogt, T.F.; Hobbs, H.H.; Cohen, J.C. Exome-wide association study identifies a TM6SF2 variant that confers susceptibility to nonalcoholic fatty liver disease. *Nat. Genet.* **2014**, *46*, 352–356. [CrossRef] [PubMed]
93. Pirola, C.J.; Sookoian, S. The dual and opposite role of the TM6SF2-rs58542926 variant in protecting against cardiovascular disease and conferring risk for nonalcoholic fatty liver: A meta-analysis. *Hepatology* **2015**, *62*, 1742–1756. [CrossRef] [PubMed]
94. Smagris, E.; Gilyard, S.; BasuRay, S.; Cohen, J.C.; Hobbs, H.H. Inactivation of TM6SF2, a gene defective in fatty liver disease, impairs lipidation but not secretion of very low density lipoproteins. *J. Biol. Chem.* **2016**. [CrossRef] [PubMed]
95. Mahdessian, H.; Taxiarchis, A.; Popov, S.; Silveira, A.; Franco-Cereceda, A.; Hamsten, A.; Eriksson, P.; van't Hooft, F. TM6SF2 is a regulator of liver fat metabolism influencing triglyceride secretion and hepatic lipid droplet content. *Proc. Natl. Acad. Sci. USA* **2014**, *111*, 8913–8918. [CrossRef] [PubMed]
96. Holmen, O.L.; Zhang, H.; Fan, Y.; Hovelson, D.H.; Schmidt, E.M.; Zhou, W.; Guo, Y.; Zhang, J.; Langhammer, A.; Løchen, M.-L.; *et al.* Systematic evaluation of coding variation identifies a candidate causal variant in TM6SF2 influencing total cholesterol and myocardial infarction risk. *Nat. Genet.* **2014**, *46*, 345–351. [CrossRef] [PubMed]
97. Zhou, Y.; Llauradó, G.; Orešič, M.; Hyötyläinen, T.; Orho-Melander, M.; Yki-Järvinen, H. Circulating triacylglycerol signatures and insulin sensitivity in NAFLD associated with the E167K variant in TM6SF2. *J. Hepatol.* **2015**, *62*, 657–663. [CrossRef] [PubMed]

98. Eslam, M.; Mangia, A.; Berg, T.; Chan, H.L.-Y.; Irving, W.L.; Dore, G.J.; Abate, M.L.; Bugianesi, E.; Adams, L.A.; Najim, M.A.M.; *et al.* Diverse impacts of the rs58542926 E167K variant in TM6SF2 on viral and metabolic liver disease phenotypes. *Hepatology* **2016**. [CrossRef] [PubMed]

99. Goffredo, M.; Caprio, S.; Feldstein, A.E.; D'Adamo, E.; Shaw, M.M.; Pierpont, B.; Savoye, M.; Zhao, H.; Bale, A.E.; Santoro, N. Role of TM6SF2 rs58542926 in the pathogenesis of nonalcoholic pediatric fatty liver disease: A multiethnic study. *Hepatology* **2016**, *63*, 117–125. [CrossRef] [PubMed]

100. Grandone, A.; Cozzolino, D.; Marzuillo, P.; Cirillo, G.; di Sessa, A.; Ruggiero, L.; di Palma, M.R.; Perrone, L.; Miraglia del Giudice, E. TM6SF2 Glu167Lys polymorphism is associated with low levels of LDL-cholesterol and increased liver injury in obese children. *Pediatr. Obes.* **2016**, *11*, 115–119. [CrossRef] [PubMed]

101. European Association for the Study of the Liver (EASL); European Association for the Study of Diabetes (EASD); European Association for the Study of Obesity (EASO). EASL-EASD-EASO Clinical Practice Guidelines for the management of non-alcoholic fatty liver disease. *Diabetologia* **2016**, *9*, 65–90.

International Journal of
Molecular Sciences

MDPI

Review

Vascular Damage in Patients with Nonalcoholic Fatty Liver Disease: Possible Role of Iron and Ferritin

Giuseppina Pisano, Rosa Lombardi and Anna Ludovica Fracanzani *

Department of Pathophysiology and Transplantation, Ca' Granda IRCCS Foundation, Policlinico Hospital, University of Milan, Centre of the Study of Metabolic and Liver Diseases, Via Francesco Sforza 35, 20122 Milan, Italy; pinaz81@hotmail.com (G.P.); rosalombardi@hotmail.it (R.L.)
* Correspondence: anna.fracanzani@unimi.it; Tel.: +39-02-5503-3302

Academic Editors: Amedeo Lonardo and Giovanni Targher
Received: 3 March 2016; Accepted: 26 April 2016; Published: 5 May 2016

Abstract: Non Alcoholic Fatty Liver Disease (NAFLD) is the most common chronic liver disease in Western countries. Recent data indicated that NAFLD is a risk factor by itself contributing to the development of cardiovascular disease independently of classical known risk factors. Hyperferritinemia and mild increased iron stores are frequently observed in patients with NAFLD and several mechanisms have been proposed to explain the role of iron, through oxidative stress and interaction with insulin metabolism, in the development of vascular damage. Moreover, iron depletion has been shown to decrease atherogenesis in experimental models and in humans. This review presents the recent evidence on epidemiology, pathogenesis, and the possible explanation of the role of iron and ferritin in the development of cardiovascular damage in patients with NAFLD, and discusses the possible interplay between metabolic disorders associated with NAFLD and iron in the development of cardiovascular disease.

Keywords: NAFLD; ferritin; iron; cardiovascular disease; metabolic syndrome

1. Introduction

Non Alcoholic Fatty Liver Disease (NAFLD), the most common chronic liver disease in Western countries, was previously indicated as the hepatic expression of the metabolic syndrome (MetS) having shared many similar clinical manifestations [1]. More recently it has been proposed that NAFLD precedes the development of type 2 diabetes and metabolic syndrome [2], significantly increasing the risk of incident type 2 diabetes [3] even in non-overweight subjects [4]. Recent evidence links NAFLD to increases of cardiovascular risk, and further studies reveal that the first causes of death in NAFLD patients are cardiovascular disease (CVD) [5–8] and cancer [5,9–11], and not just liver diseases. NAFLD is also considered by recent studies to be a risk factor in itself to the development of CVD independently of classical known risk factors [12]. Increased ferritin and body iron stores are frequently observed in patients with NAFLD [13,14]. Iron, through oxidative stress and interaction with insulin metabolism [15], can promote the development of vascular damage. Moreover, iron depletion has been reported to decrease atherogenesis in experimental models and in humans [16,17].

2. Ferritin, Insulin Resistance, Metabolic Syndrome, and NAFLD

Growing evidence proposes a correlation between serum ferritin, insulin resistance, and NAFLD [18,19]. Several studies reported a link between high ferritin levels and MetS [20], and its single components [21], with a linear increase with the increasing number of MetS components [20]. Liver fat accumulation is considered to be one of the first pieces of evidence in the development of insulin resistance, and a strong association between NAFLD, insulin resistance, and MetS features has been demonstrated [19,22,23]. The association between ferritin and components of the MetS has been suggested to be related to an undiagnosed NAFLD. Zelber-Sagi *et al.* [24] demonstrated that insulin was the strongest predictor of increased serum ferritin levels and, *vice versa*, ferritin has been proposed as a marker of insulin resistance [25].

The evidence that increased ferritin levels precede the development of diabetes was demonstrated in prospective studies [26,27], however, it is not well defined if increased ferritin (expression of body iron accumulation) could induce metabolic alteration. In chronic liver disease hyperferritinemia may be caused by an augmented release of the protein from injured hepatocytes. Pro-inflammatory cytokines, in fact, stimulate the synthesis of ferritin, which is an acute phase reactant [28]. In patients with NAFLD (in whom ferritin and body iron are frequently increased [13,29]) inflammation, metabolic alterations, and hepatocytes necrosis may coexist with a mild iron overload, all leading to hyperferritinemia [30,31]. In addition, even a small amount of hepatic iron accumulation combined with other cofactors can increase oxidative stress responsible for liver cell necrosis, activation of hepatic stellate cells, and fibrosis [19,32], implying that iron could also play a role in the progression from "benign" fatty liver to non-alcoholic steatohepatitis (NASH). The same mechanisms determining liver damage might act in the vessel walls.

Epidemiological studies indicated that ferritin not only is a marker of insulin resistance but also is one of the strongest risk factors for the progression of carotid atherosclerosis [33,34]. Confirming this observation, the removal of iron by phlebotomy was found to improve insulin resistance, liver function tests [13,35], and atherosclerosis [36]; however, mainly due to the small sample size of the studies, the impact of phlebotomy in NAFLD is still debated [37].

3. Iron and Atherosclerosis

The role of iron in the development and progression of atherosclerosis has been reported in several papers. Iron deposition, especially in macrophages of arterial walls, is increased in atherosclerotic lesions [14,38], and has been proposed as a marker of cardiovascular risk [16]. The role that iron plays in atherosclerosis has been hypothesized to be an increase in vascular oxidative stress and acceleration of arterial thrombosis [39]; this could be caused by the induction of oxidative stress catalysis, promotion of insulin resistance [15], decreased plasma antioxidant activity, increased low-density lipoprotein (LDL) oxidation [40], and enhanced macrophage activation determining oxidized LDL uptake [41].

Iron depletion in experimental models has been shown to decrease atherogenesis [17], while, in humans, blood donation has been associated with decreased risk for myocardial infarction [26], and phlebotomy has been suggested to decrease the progression of peripheral vascular disease [42].

A worse cognitive performance in patients with metabolic alterations—as a potential consequence of vascular damage, or directly as a neurodegenerative alteration—has been described in relation to iron status in animal models, and more recently in humans as well [43]. In insulin resistant obese patients a worse cognitive performance was found related with brain iron load in the caudate, lenticular nucleus, hypothalamus, and hippocampus (by magnetic resonance imaging (RMI)) and with increased hepatic iron concentration. It is possible to hypothesize that in presence of insulin resistance, the excess of iron, being highly reactive and promoting the generation of hydroxyl radicals, may cause both metabolic distress in the liver and alterations in some target brain areas [44].

4. Iron and Carotid Plaques: Arterial Iron Promotes Plaque Instability

Through the use of electron paramagnetic resonance spectroscopy Stadler *et al.* [45] were able to quantify iron in *ex vivo* carotid lesions and in healthy human arteries and, in doing so, found that iron in the carotid lesions was higher than in healthy subjects. They also found a correlation between cholesterols and iron accumulation in the lesions.

Lapenna *et al.* [14] in studying *ex vivo* carotid endo-arterectomy specimens found a significant correlation between serum ferritin and low molecular weight iron. Yuan *et al.* and Li *et al.* [46,47] suggested that iron found in atherosclerotic vascular tissue, generated mostly by erythrophagocytosis, could interact with lipoproteins in macrophages and be responsible for increased oxidative stress and their transformation into foam cells in the presence of an atherogenic environment. Thus the increase of iron in macrophages might contribute to vulnerability of human atheroma. Moreover, Li *et al.* reported, in *ex vivo* human carotid atherosclerotic lesions [48], the positive correlation of transferrin receptor 1 (TfR1) expression and macrophage infiltration, ectopic lysosomal cathepsin L, and ferritin expression and they suggested that the expression of TfR1 and ferritin in CD68 positive macrophages was correlated with the severity of human carotid plaques.

5. Ferritin and Atherosclerosis

Ferritin is considered a marker of atherosclerosis progression [33] and a relationship has been proposed between its levels and carotid atherosclerosis [34] in epidemiological studies. Moreover, ferritin was found associated with carotid intima-media thickness (IMT), and with the presence of carotid plaques in a large cohort of NAFLD patients [49]. In this paper the authors described a stronger association of ferritin with plaques rather than with increased IMT, hypothesizing that iron, by favoring endothelial damage and thrombosis [39], can promote the development of atherosclerotic complications. In NAFLD ferritin can reflect oxidative stress, inflammation, and hepatic necrosis. This protein has been found strongly associated not only with parameters influencing iron stores, such as sex, age, alcohol, and genetic factors (*i.e.*, *HFE* mutations), but also with metabolic alterations defining the metabolic syndrome. However, a correlation was described between ferritin and vascular damage that was independent from factors associated with metabolic syndrome [50–52].

These data were recently confirmed in a Chinese population study in which serum ferritin was found significantly increased in patients with abnormal glucose metabolism and related with IMT progression [53].

6. *HFE* Gene Mutations in NAFLD and Atherosclerosis

Several studies analyzed the role of HFE mutations in patients with NAFLD and iron overload. Valenti *et al.* [29] demonstrated that carriers of the C282Y mutation have lower insulin release and develop NAFLD in the presence of less severe metabolic abnormalities. This suggests that heterozygosis for the HFE mutation (responsible for mild iron overload) may trigger the clinical NAFLD manifestation [29]. More controversial is the role of HFE mutations in the development of atherosclerotic damage. In fact, while the atherogenetic role of iron has been reported (as observed in macrophages of arterial walls in atherosclerotic lesions [40,41] and in the beneficial effect of iron depletion on vascular damage [17], a lack of association between HFE mutations with vascular damage has been reported [54]. A faster clearance of iron from arterial lesions could be caused by a decrease of Hepcidin, which could facilitate iron export from macrophages [49].

7. Hepcidin, Macrophage Iron, and Vascular Damage

Hepcidin, mainly produced in the liver, is defined as the key hormone regulating iron balance [55]. Hepcidin provides a defense mechanism against pathogens during inflammation by inhibiting iron recycling from macrophages and iron absorption from enterocytes. Also, in patients with metabolic disease, such as NAFLD, the deregulation of hepcidin expression/activity contributes to increased iron stores [56]. Subclinical inflammation and obesity can induce Hepcidin [57] and cause iron trapping in macrophages [58] in the presence of an atherogenic environment. Excessive iron in macrophages could be responsible for increased oxidative stress and transformation into foam cells. Sullivan *et al.* [16] suggested that increased hepcidin may generate iron induced atherogenesis and cardiovascular damages (Figure 1).

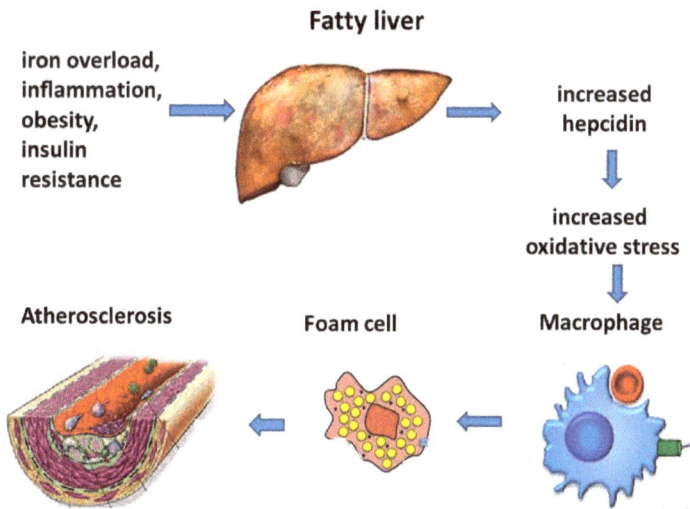

Figure 1. Simplified pathophysiological mechanisms of iron induced vascular damage through fatty liver.

Experimental Models

Findings from animal models of atherosclerosis and from studies of human atherosclerotic plaques provide evidence that elevated arterial iron levels may cause atherosclerosis. Both animal studies and clinical evidence indicate that in the presence of iron deficiency (*i.e.*, anemia) that iron can be mobilized from arterial plaques to be used in erythropoiesis with consequent iron reduction in the plaques.

Valenti *et al.* [59] reported the effect of the manipulation of intracellular iron on the release of atherogenic cytokines in human differentiating monocytes of patients with NAFLD, with Metabolic Syndrome, and with mild iron overload by treatment cells with iron salts or with hepcidin. Macrophages, but also the smooth muscle and the endothelial cells treated with iron salts, increased the release of the macrophage chemo attractant protein (MCP-1), an atherogenic chemokine that plays an important role in both the initiation and progression of atherosclerosis. Moreover, the iron salt treatment increased the IL-6 a proinflammatory cytokine involved in the acute phase response, independently of oxidative stress. IL-6 serum levels have been reported to correlate with vascular risk and with the inflammation within atherosclerotic plaques [60]. In addition it has been found that higher MCP-1 represents a negative prognostic factor in acute coronary syndromes [61]. The effect of hepcidin on MCP-1 release was similar to that of iron salts as it blocked cellular iron export. Furthermore, in patients with NAFLD and MetS, the iron-dependent induction of MCP-1 and IL-6 was found associated with the severity of vascular damage as it promoted macrophage activation by iron and may be involved in the pathogenesis of vascular damage progression. These results have also been observed in monocytes of healthy subjects in which iron treatment determined the induction of MCP-1 transcription and release, suggesting that this depicted a physiological response to increased intracellular iron availability [49].

8. Iron Depletion and Atherosclerosis

It has been reported that iron depletion decreases atherogenesis in experimental models [17]. In addition, iron reduction by frequent blood donations was found to be associated with decreased intima-media thickness [36] and decreased risk of myocardial infarction [26]. Thus, iron reduction potentially offers a benefit in atherosclerotic vascular disease acting as an anti-inflammatory process. However, the role of blood donation on cardiovascular diseases is not yet defined. The Nebraska Diet

Heart Study [62], has established a relationship between blood donation and risk of cardiovascular events. This study evaluated the cardiovascular events in 655 individuals who had donated at least one unit of blood in the preceding 10 years and in 3200 who had not. The results indicated that, compared to non-donors, the blood donors showed a significant reduction of events such as myocardial infarction, angina, or stroke. They also had fewer cardiovascular procedures and less use of nitroglycerin. Nevertheless, it is not possible to rule out that blood donors have less cardiovascular events in connection to them being in apparently good enough health to be eligible to donate blood. The beneficial effect of blood donations on cardiovascular disease has been debated in a number of epidemiological studies [13,35–37]. Interestingly, Zacharski *et al.* [42], in a multicenter prospective trial conducted in veteran participants with peripheral arterial disease, showed that the beneficial effect of phlebotomy was present only in younger patients. This suggests that levels of body iron stores might be operative in the early phase of atherosclerosis, while hypercoagulability and diabetes mellitus in later-stages of the diseases. Low body iron may protect against atherosclerotic CVD through different ways: (1) limiting oxidation of LDL cholesterol [63]; (2) decreasing the clinical activity of myeloperoxidase [64]; (3) increasing high density lipoprotein (HDL) and apolipoprotein A (ApoA) [65]; (4) improving nitric-oxide mediated, endothelium-dependent vasodilation [66], and, finally, improving insulin sensitivity [67].

In addition, iron depletion has been demonstrated to improve insulin resistance [13] in NAFLD, while more controversial is the beneficial effect on liver histology in NASH [68,69]. About one third of patients with NAFLD and MetS have been reported to have dysmetabolic iron overload syndrome [70], and both venesection therapy (in the absence of weight loss) and dietary treatment have been shown to improve ferritin, metabolic parameters, and liver enzymes [70,71].

An imbalance of the homoeostatic mechanisms—including the interaction of iron with hepcidin, ferritin, insulin, and with adipokines and pro-inflammatory molecules—causes parenchymal siderosis that contributes to organ damage such as pancreatic β-cell dysfunction, liver fibrosis, and atherosclerotic plaque growth and instability. *Vice versa*, iron depletion could exert beneficial effects, not only in NAFLD patients with mild iron overload but also in healthy frequent blood donors [72].

9. Dietary Iron, Microbiota, and CVD

Elements such as dietary macronutrients, particularly the types of fats and carbohydrates, are known factors in the etiology of type 2 diabetes, a metabolic disease closely related with NAFLD, while more controversial is the effect of dietary iron. Iron is a transitional metal, strong pro-oxidant, and catalyzer of several cellular reactions that result in the production of reactive oxygen species, thereby consequently increasing the level of oxidative stress. Graham *et al.* [73] reported an increase in liver cholesterol biosynthesis in mice caused by high dietary iron, showing how iron could influence cholesterol levels and cause the development of fatty liver disease. In addition, the high dietary cholesterol promotes the development of fatty liver in guinea pigs which in turn leads to the dysregulation of iron metabolism because of damaged liver [74]. Iron dextran increased oxidative stress, which was associated with the altered expression of genes related to lipid metabolism and therefore contributing to hyperlipidemia [75]. The observations, obtained in animal models, that iron can modulate lipid metabolism and therefore be associated with liver and vascular damage are very promising but not yet consolidated in humans. Also, the effect of dietary iron is not well established [76] in humans, although the intake of heme iron before and during pregnancy has been reported to correlate with the onset of diabetes, a well-known risk factor for CVD [77]. Interestingly, iron deficiency also has been reported to be associated with increased CVD risk. Iron deficiency is associated with thrombocytosis due to the lack of inhibition of thrombopoiesis with consequent increases of thrombotic complications as reported in iron-deficient children and adults [78]. In addition iron deficiency (causing anemia) increases the risk of heart failure by causing tissue ischemia with consequent increased oxidative stress, which could damage myocardial cells [79].

An updated review of cross-sectional, longitudinal, and intervention studies [79] evaluating the relation between iron and cardiovascular risk indicated that concentrations of iron within normal ranges does not have dangerous effects. In contrast, elevated amounts of non-protein-bound iron (free Fe), which has been reported to increase circulating homocysteine [80–82], seems to play a role in atherosclerosis. Free Fe catalyzes the formation of oxygen free radicals and oxidized low-density lipoprotein, which are well-established risk factors for vascular damage, thereby supporting the hypothesis that circulating homocysteine could be in part a surrogate marker for free Fe [83]. However, different iron types might act differently on the cardiovascular risk. Higher dietary intake of heme iron was found to be associated with increased cardiovascular risk; this association was not observed with non-heme and total iron intake [84]. De Oliveira Otto *et al.* [85] in a population study analyzing diet micronutrients indicated that dietary intake of non-heme iron was inversely associated with homocysteine, whereas high red meat intake (a predominant source of heme iron) was found to be associated with C-reactive protein. In addition, it is possible that the intake of nutrients containing non-heme iron (which is found in vegetables, cereals, and fruits) is more common in individuals with a healthy lifestyle (e.g., non-smokers and physically active individuals), while heme iron (abundant in red meat), which was found to be associated with insulin resistance, increased oxidative stress and CVD (Figure 2). In addition, red meat is also rich in choline and carnitine, both processed by enteric microbiota, and found to be related with atherosclerosis [86,87]. Dose-response analyses revealed a 7% increase in the risk of cardiovascular disease for each 1 mg/day increase in dietary heme iron [84].

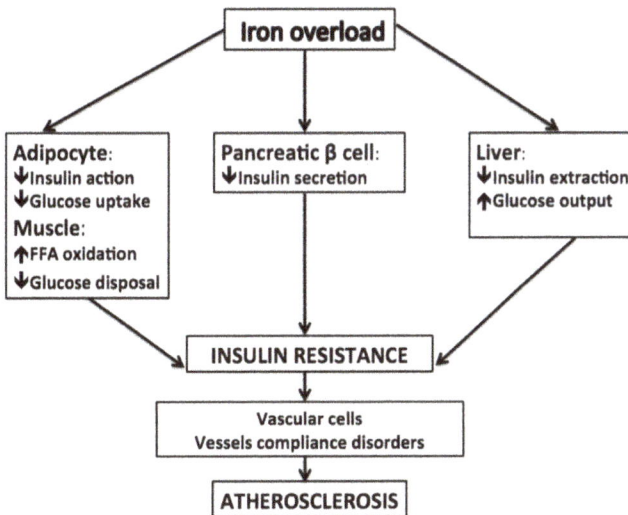

Figure 2. Effect of dietary iron overload on metabolic alterations, insulin resistance, and atherosclerosis. The downward arrows mean decrease and upward arrows mean increase. FFA: free fatty acid.

A clinically important association between bacterial infection and CVD has been reported [88]. One of the possible mechanisms in the pathogenesis of atherosclerosis could be represented by the host immunological response of extravascular tissues and/or vascular walls to bacterial agents. It is known that gut microbiota may interfere with the host metabolism by promoting multiple functions, from development of the intestinal immune system to hepatic and energy metabolism. More recently it has been reported that specific forms of gut microbiota are present in the blood of patients with diabetes and atherosclerotic plaques, thus gut microbiota could represent an environmental risk factor for CVD [89]. Gut microbiota could have a direct proatherogenic influence in atherosclerosis plaque colonization through the bloodstream after events that affect the gut barrier. Both aberrant microbiota profiles and the flux of metabolites derived from gut microbial metabolism of choline, phosphatidylcholine, and L-carnitine have been found to be associated with metabolic disease, and contribute directly to cardiovascular diseases. However, although recent data on the role of microbiota in the development of NAFLD and progression to NASH are promising, particularly in animal models, conclusive results in humans on the effect of microbiota are still missing. Oral iron intake or food rich in heme iron could alter gut microbial composition and function providing one explanation for increased vascular disease risk [90].

10. Conclusions

In patients with NAFLD, hyperferritin and mild increases in body iron store are frequently detected and associated with vascular damage. Different mechanisms have been proposed to explain the atherogenic role of iron leading to increases in vascular oxidative stress and the acceleration of arterial thrombosis. Inflammation, metabolic alterations, and hepatocytes necrosis may coexist with a mild iron overload, all leading to hyperferritinemia, which is considered to be an independent predictor of cardiovascular damage. Iron depletion, achieved by phlebotomy, has been reported to improve insulin resistance and to reduce cardiovascular risk and damage. Finally, dietary strategies, which modulate the gut microbiota and different metabolic activities, could represent efficacious tools for reducing cardiovascular risk.

Acknowledgments: The authors wish to thank Associazione Malattie Metaboliche Fegato O.N.L.U.S. for all the needed support.

Author Contributions: Giuseppina Pisano drafted the manuscript; Rosa Lombardi collected and reviewed literature; Anna Ludovica Fracanzani contributed to drafting the manuscript and provided critical revisions.

Conflicts of Interest: The authors declare no conflict of interest.

References

1. Yki-Jarvinen, H. Non-alcoholic fatty liver disease as a cause and a consequence of metabolic syndrome. *Lancet Diabetes Endocrinol.* **2014**, *2*, 901–910. [CrossRef]
2. Lonardo, A.; Ballestri, S.; Marchesini, G.; Angulo, P.; Loria, P. Nonalcoholic fatty liver disease: A precursor of the metabolic syndrome. *Dig. Liver Dis.* **2015**, *47*, 181–190. [CrossRef] [PubMed]
3. Ballestri, S.; Lonardo, A.; Bonapace, S.; Byrne, C.D.; Loria, P.; Targher, G. Risk of cardiovascular, cardiac and arrhythmic complications in patients with non-alcoholic fatty liver disease. *World J. Gstroenterol.* **2014**, *20*, 1724–1745. [CrossRef] [PubMed]
4. Fukuda, T.; Hamaguchi, M.; Kojima, T.; Hashimoto, Y.; Ohbora, A.; Kato, T.; Nakamura, N.; Fukui, M. The impact of non-alcoholic fatty liver disease on incident type 2 diabetes mellitus in non-overweight individuals. *Liver Int.* **2016**, *36*, 275–283. [CrossRef] [PubMed]
5. Ekstedt, M.; Franzen, L.E.; Mathiesen, U.L.; Thorelius, L.; Holmqvist, M.; Bodemar, G.; Kechagias, S. Long-term follow-up of patients with NAFLD and elevated liver enzymes. *Hepatology* **2006**, *44*, 865–873. [CrossRef] [PubMed]
6. Bhatia, L.S.; Curzen, N.P.; Calder, P.C.; Byrne, C.D. Non-alcoholic fatty liver disease: A new and important cardiovascular risk factor? *Eur. Heart J.* **2012**, *33*, 1190–1200. [CrossRef] [PubMed]
7. Pacana, T.; Fuchs, M. The cardiovascular link to nonalcoholic fatty liver disease: A critical analysis. *Clin. Liver Dis.* **2012**, *16*, 599–613. [CrossRef] [PubMed]
8. Lu, H.; Liu, H.; Hu, F.; Zou, L.; Luo, S.; Sun, L. Independent association between nonalcoholic fatty liver disease and cardiovascular disease: A systematic review and meta-analysis. *Int. J. Endocrinol.* **2013**, *2013*, 124958. [CrossRef] [PubMed]
9. Ascha, M.S.; Hanouneh, I.A.; Lopez, R.; Tamimi, T.A.; Feldstein, A.F.; Zein, N.N. The incidence and risk factors of hepatocellular carcinoma in patients with nonalcoholic steatohepatitis. *Hepatology* **2010**, *51*, 1972–1978. [CrossRef] [PubMed]

10. Younossi, Z.M.; Koenig, A.B.; Abdelatif, D.; Fazel, Y.; Henry, L.; Wymer, M. Global epidemiology of non-alcoholic fatty liver disease-meta-analytic assessment of prevalence, incidence and outcomes. *Hepatology* **2015**. [CrossRef] [PubMed]

11. Reeves, H.L.; Zaki, M.Y.; Day, C.P. Hepatocellular carcinoma in obesity, type 2 diabetes, and NAFLD. *Dig. Dis. Sci.* **2016**, *61*, 1234–1245. [CrossRef] [PubMed]

12. Targher, G.; Day, C.P.; Bonora, E. Risk of cardiovascular disease in patients with nonalcoholic fatty liver disease. *N. Engl. J. Med.* **2010**, *363*, 1341–1350. [CrossRef] [PubMed]

13. Valenti, L.; Fracanzani, A.L.; Dongiovanni, P.; Bugianesi, E.; Marchesini, G.; Manzini, P.; Vanni, E.; Fargion, S. Iron depletion by phlebotomy improves insulin resistance in patients with nonalcoholic fatty liver disease and hyperferritinemia: Evidence from a case-control study. *Am. J. Gastroenterol.* **2007**, *102*, 1251–1258. [CrossRef] [PubMed]

14. Lapenna, D.; Pierdomenico, S.D.; Ciofani, G.; Ucchino, S.; Neri, M.; Giamberardino, M.A.; Cuccurullo, F. Association of body iron stores with low molecular weight iron and oxidant damage of human atherosclerotic plaques. *Free Radic. Biol. Med.* **2007**, *42*, 492–498. [CrossRef] [PubMed]

15. Dongiovanni, P.; Valenti, L.; Ludovicxp a Fracanzani, A.; Gatti, S.; Cairo, G.; Fargion, S. Iron depletion by deferoxamine up-regulates glucose uptake and insulin signaling in hepatoma cells and in rat liver. *Am. J. Pathol.* **2008**, *172*, 738–747. [CrossRef] [PubMed]

16. Sullivan, J.L. Macrophage iron, hepcidin, and atherosclerotic plaque stability. *Exp. Biol. Med.* **2007**, *232*, 1014–1020. [CrossRef] [PubMed]

17. Lee, T.S.; Shiao, M.S.; Pan, C.C.; Chau, L.Y. Iron-deficient diet reduces atherosclerotic lesions in apoe-deficient mice. *Circulation* **1999**, *99*, 1222–1229. [CrossRef] [PubMed]

18. Trombini, P.; Piperno, A. Ferritin, metabolic syndrome and NAFLD: Elective attractions and dangerous liaisons. *J. Hepatol.* **2007**, *46*, 549–552. [CrossRef] [PubMed]

19. Ballestri, S.; Nascimbeni, F.; Romagnoli, D.; Lonardo, A. The independent predictors of NASH and its individual histological features. Insulin resistance, serum uric acid, metabolic syndrome, ALT and serum total cholesterol are a clue to pathogenesis and candidate targets for treatment. *Hepatol. Res.* **2016**. [CrossRef] [PubMed]

20. Bozzini, C.; Girelli, D.; Olivieri, O.; Martinelli, N.; Bassi, A.; De Matteis, G.; Tenuti, I.; Lotto, V.; Friso, S.; Pizzolo, F.; *et al.* Prevalence of body iron excess in the metabolic syndrome. *Diabetes Care* **2005**, *28*, 2061–2063. [CrossRef] [PubMed]

21. Piperno, A.; Trombini, P.; Gelosa, M.; Mauri, V.; Pecci, V.; Vergani, A.; Salvioni, A.; Mariani, R.; Mancia, G. Increased serum ferritin is common in men with essential hypertension. *J. Hypertens.* **2002**, *20*, 1513–1518. [CrossRef] [PubMed]

22. Neuschwander-Tetri, B.A. Nonalcoholic steatohepatitis and the metabolic syndrome. *Am. J. Med. Sci.* **2005**, *330*, 326–335. [CrossRef] [PubMed]

23. Non-alcoholic Fatty Liver Disease Study Group; Lonardo, A.; Bellentani, S.; Argo, C.K.; Ballestri, S.; Byrne, C.D.; Caldwell, S.H.; Cortez-Pinto, H.; Grieco, A.; Machado, M.V.; *et al.* Epidemiological modifiers of non-alcoholic fatty liver disease: Focus on high-risk groups. *Dig. Liver Dis.* **2015**, *47*, 997–1006.

24. Zelber-Sagi, S.; Nitzan-Kaluski, D.; Halpern, Z.; Oren, R. NAFLD and hyperinsulinemia are major determinants of serum ferritin levels. *J. Hepatol.* **2007**, *46*, 700–707. [CrossRef] [PubMed]

25. Fernandez-Real, J.M.; Ricart-Engel, W.; Arroyo, E.; Balanca, R.; Casamitjana-Abella, R.; Cabrero, D.; Fernandez-Castaner, M.; Soler, J. Serum ferritin as a component of the insulin resistance syndrome. *Diabetes Care* **1998**, *21*, 62–68. [CrossRef] [PubMed]

26. Salonen, J.T.; Tuomainen, T.P.; Nyyssonen, K.; Lakka, H.M.; Punnonen, K. Relation between iron stores and non-insulin dependent diabetes in men: Case-control study. *BMJ* **1998**, *317*, 727. [CrossRef] [PubMed]

27. Jiang, R.; Manson, J.E.; Meigs, J.B.; Ma, J.; Rifai, N.; Hu, F.B. Body iron stores in relation to risk of type 2 diabetes in apparently healthy women. *JAMA* **2004**, *291*, 711–717. [CrossRef] [PubMed]

28. Harrison, P.M.; Arosio, P. The ferritins: Molecular properties, iron storage function and cellular regulation. *Biochim. Biophys. Acta* **1996**, *1275*, 161–203. [CrossRef]

29. Valenti, L.; Dongiovanni, P.; Fracanzani, A.L.; Santorelli, G.; Fatta, E.; Bertelli, C.; Taioli, E.; Fiorelli, G.; Fargion, S. Increased susceptibility to nonalcoholic fatty liver disease in heterozygotes for the mutation responsible for hereditary hemochromatosis. *Dig. Liver Dis.* **2003**, *35*, 172–178. [CrossRef]

30. Fargion, S.; Mattioli, M.; Fracanzani, A.L.; Sampietro, M.; Tavazzi, D.; Fociani, P.; Taioli, E.; Valenti, L.; Fiorelli, G. Hyperferritinemia, iron overload, and multiple metabolic alterations identify patients at risk for nonalcoholic steatohepatitis. *Am. J. Gastroenterol.* **2001**, *96*, 2448–2455. [CrossRef] [PubMed]

31. Bugianesi, E.; Manzini, P.; D'Antico, S.; Vanni, E.; Longo, F.; Leone, N.; Massarenti, P.; Piga, A.; Marchesini, G.; Rizzetto, M. Relative contribution of iron burden, hfe mutations, and insulin resistance to fibrosis in nonalcoholic fatty liver. *Hepatology* **2004**, *39*, 179–187. [CrossRef] [PubMed]

32. Rakha, E.A.; Adamson, L.; Bell, E.; Neal, K.; Ryder, S.D.; Kaye, P.V.; Aithal, G.P. Portal inflammation is associated with advanced histological changes in alcoholic and non-alcoholic fatty liver disease. *J. Clin. Pathol.* **2010**, *63*, 790–795. [CrossRef] [PubMed]

33. Kiechl, S.; Willeit, J.; Egger, G.; Poewe, W.; Oberhollenzer, F. Body iron stores and the risk of carotid atherosclerosis: Prospective results from the bruneck study. *Circulation* **1997**, *96*, 3300–3307. [CrossRef] [PubMed]

34. Wolff, B.; Volzke, H.; Ludemann, J.; Robinson, D.; Vogelgesang, D.; Staudt, A.; Kessler, C.; Dahm, J.B.; John, U.; Felix, S.B. Association between high serum ferritin levels and carotid atherosclerosis in the study of health in pomerania (SHIP). *Stroke J. Cereb. Circ.* **2004**, *35*, 453–457.

35. Aigner, E.; Theurl, I.; Theurl, M.; Lederer, D.; Haufe, H.; Dietze, O.; Strasser, M.; Datz, C.; Weiss, G. Pathways underlying iron accumulation in human nonalcoholic fatty liver disease. *Am. J. Clin. Nutr.* **2008**, *87*, 1374–1383. [PubMed]

36. Engberink, M.F.; Geleijnse, J.M.; Durga, J.; Swinkels, D.W.; de Kort, W.L.; Schouten, E.G.; Verhoef, P. Blood donation, body iron status and carotid intima-media thickness. *Atherosclerosis* **2008**, *196*, 856–862. [CrossRef] [PubMed]

37. Adams, L.A.; Crawford, D.H.; Stuart, K.; House, M.J.; St Pierre, T.G.; Webb, M.; Ching, H.L.; Kava, J.; Bynevelt, M.; MacQuillan, G.C.; *et al.* The impact of phlebotomy in nonalcoholic fatty liver disease: A prospective, randomized, controlled trial. *Hepatology* **2015**, *61*, 1555–1564. [CrossRef] [PubMed]

38. Nagy, E.; Eaton, J.W.; Jeney, V.; Soares, M.P.; Varga, Z.; Galajda, Z.; Szentmiklosi, J.; Mehes, G.; Csonka, T.; Smith, A.; *et al.* Red cells, hemoglobin, heme, iron, and atherogenesis. *Arterioscler. Thromb. Vasc. Biol.* **2010**, *30*, 1347–1353. [CrossRef] [PubMed]

39. Day, S.M.; Duquaine, D.; Mundada, L.V.; Menon, R.G.; Khan, B.V.; Rajagopalan, S.; Fay, W.P. Chronic iron administration increases vascular oxidative stress and accelerates arterial thrombosis. *Circulation* **2003**, *107*, 2601–2606. [CrossRef] [PubMed]

40. Valenti, L.; Valenti, G.; Como, G.; Burdick, L.; Santorelli, G.; Dongiovanni, P.; Rametta, R.; Bamonti, F.; Novembrino, C.; Fracanzani, A.L.; *et al.* HFE gene mutations and oxidative stress influence serum ferritin, associated with vascular damage, in hemodialysis patients. *Am. J. Nephrol.* **2007**, *27*, 101–107. [CrossRef] [PubMed]

41. Kraml, P.J.; Klein, R.L.; Huang, Y.; Nareika, A.; Lopes-Virella, M.F. Iron loading increases cholesterol accumulation and macrophage scavenger receptor I expression in THP-1 mononuclear phagocytes. *Metabolism* **2005**, *54*, 453–459. [CrossRef] [PubMed]

42. Zacharski, L.R.; Chow, B.K.; Howes, P.S.; Shamayeva, G.; Baron, J.A.; Dalman, R.L.; Malenka, D.J.; Ozaki, C.K.; Lavori, P.W. Reduction of iron stores and cardiovascular outcomes in patients with peripheral arterial disease: A randomized controlled trial. *JAMA* **2007**, *297*, 603–610. [CrossRef] [PubMed]

43. Schroder, N.; Figueiredo, L.S.; de Lima, M.N. Role of brain iron accumulation in cognitive dysfunction: Evidence from animal models and human studies. *J. Alzheimers Dis.* **2013**, *34*, 797–812. [PubMed]

44. Blasco, G.; Puig, J.; Daunis, I.E.J.; Molina, X.; Xifra, G.; Fernandez-Aranda, F.; Pedraza, S.; Ricart, W.; Portero-Otin, M.; Fernandez-Real, J.M. Brain iron overload, insulin resistance, and cognitive performance in obese subjects: A preliminary MRI case-control study. *Diabetes Care* **2014**, *37*, 3076–3083. [CrossRef] [PubMed]

45. Stadler, N.; Lindner, R.A.; Davies, M.J. Direct detection and quantification of transition metal ions in human atherosclerotic plaques: Evidence for the presence of elevated levels of iron and copper. *Arterioscler. Thromb. Vasc. Biol.* **2004**, *24*, 949–954. [CrossRef] [PubMed]

46. Yuan, X.M.; Li, W. The iron hypothesis of atherosclerosis and its clinical impact. *Ann. Med.* **2003**, *35*, 578–591. [CrossRef] [PubMed]

47. Li, W.; Ostblom, M.; Xu, L.H.; Hellsten, A.; Leanderson, P.; Liedberg, B.; Brunk, U.T.; Eaton, J.W.; Yuan, X.M. Cytocidal effects of atheromatous plaque components: The death zone revisited. *FASEB J.* **2006**, *20*, 2281–2290. [CrossRef] [PubMed]

48. Li, W.; Xu, L.H.; Forssell, C.; Sullivan, J.L.; Yuan, X.M. Overexpression of transferrin receptor and ferritin related to clinical symptoms and destabilization of human carotid plaques. *Exp. Biol. Med.* **2008**, *233*, 818–826. [CrossRef] [PubMed]

49. Valenti, L.; Swinkels, D.W.; Burdick, L.; Dongiovanni, P.; Tjalsma, H.; Motta, B.M.; Bertelli, C.; Fatta, E.; Bignamini, D.; Rametta, R.; *et al.* Serum ferritin levels are associated with vascular damage in patients with nonalcoholic fatty liver disease. *Nutr. Metab. Cardiovasc. Dis.* **2011**, *21*, 568–575. [CrossRef] [PubMed]

50. Forouhi, N.G.; Harding, A.H.; Allison, M.; Sandhu, M.S.; Welch, A.; Luben, R.; Bingham, S.; Khaw, K.T.; Wareham, N.J. Elevated serum ferritin levels predict new-onset type 2 diabetes: Results from the epic-norfolk prospective study. *Diabetologia* **2007**, *50*, 949–956. [CrossRef] [PubMed]

51. Wrede, C.E.; Buettner, R.; Bollheimer, L.C.; Scholmerich, J.; Palitzsch, K.D.; Hellerbrand, C. Association between serum ferritin and the insulin resistance syndrome in a representative population. *Eur. J. Endocrinol.* **2006**, *154*, 333–340. [CrossRef] [PubMed]

52. Kim, C.H.; Kim, H.K.; Bae, S.J.; Park, J.Y.; Lee, K.U. Association of elevated serum ferritin concentration with insulin resistance and impaired glucose metabolism in korean men and women. *Metabolism* **2011**, *60*, 414–420. [CrossRef] [PubMed]

53. Zhou, F.L.; Gao, Y.; Tian, L.; Yan, F.F.; Chen, T.; Zhong, L.; Tian, H.M. Serum ferritin is associated with carotid atherosclerotic plaques but not intima-media thickness in patients with abnormal glucose metabolism. *Clin. Chim. Acta* **2015**, *450*, 190–195. [CrossRef] [PubMed]

54. Engberink, M.F.; Povel, C.M.; Durga, J.; Swinkels, D.W.; de Kort, W.L.; Schouten, E.G.; Verhoef, P.; Geleijnse, J.M. Hemochromatosis (HFE) genotype and atherosclerosis: Increased susceptibility to iron-induced vascular damage in c282y carriers? *Atherosclerosis* **2010**, *211*, 520–525. [CrossRef] [PubMed]

55. Pietrangelo, A. Hemochromatosis: An endocrine liver disease. *Hepatology* **2007**, *46*, 1291–1301. [CrossRef] [PubMed]

56. Barisani, D.; Pelucchi, S.; Mariani, R.; Galimberti, S.; Trombini, P.; Fumagalli, D.; Meneveri, R.; Nemeth, E.; Ganz, T.; Piperno, A. Hepcidin and iron-related gene expression in subjects with dysmetabolic hepatic iron overload. *J. Hepatol.* **2008**, *49*, 123–133. [CrossRef] [PubMed]

57. Bekri, S.; Gual, P.; Anty, R.; Luciani, N.; Dahman, M.; Ramesh, B.; Iannelli, A.; Staccini-Myx, A.; Casanova, D.; Ben Amor, I.; *et al.* Increased adipose tissue expression of hepcidin in severe obesity is independent from diabetes and NASH. *Gastroenterology* **2006**, *131*, 788–796. [CrossRef] [PubMed]

58. Theurl, I.; Theurl, M.; Seifert, M.; Mair, S.; Nairz, M.; Rumpold, H.; Zoller, H.; Bellmann-Weiler, R.; Niederegger, H.; Talasz, H.; *et al.* Autocrine formation of hepcidin induces iron retention in human monocytes. *Blood* **2008**, *111*, 2392–2399. [CrossRef] [PubMed]

59. Valenti, L.; Dongiovanni, P.; Motta, B.M.; Swinkels, D.W.; Bonara, P.; Rametta, R.; Burdick, L.; Frugoni, C.; Fracanzani, A.L.; Fargion, S. Serum hepcidin and macrophage iron correlate with MCP-1 release and vascular damage in patients with metabolic syndrome alterations. *Arterioscler. Thromb. Vasc. Biol.* **2011**, *31*, 683–690. [CrossRef] [PubMed]

60. Luc, G.; Bard, J.M.; Juhan-Vague, I.; Ferrieres, J.; Evans, A.; Amouyel, P.; Arveiler, D.; Fruchart, J.C.; Ducimetiere, P.; Group, P.S. C-reactive protein, interleukin-6, and fibrinogen as predictors of coronary heart disease: The prime study. *Arterioscler. Thromb. Vasc. Biol.* **2003**, *23*, 1255–1261. [CrossRef] [PubMed]

61. Amasyali, B.; Kose, S.; Kursaklioglu, H.; Barcin, C.; Kilic, A. Monocyte chemoattractant protein-1 in acute coronary syndromes: Complex vicious interaction. *Int. J. Cardiol.* **2009**, *136*, 356–357. [CrossRef] [PubMed]

62. Meyers, D.G.; Strickland, D.; Maloley, P.A.; Seburg, J.K.; Wilson, J.E.; McManus, B.F. Possible association of a reduction in cardiovascular events with blood donation. *Heart* **1997**, *78*, 188–193. [CrossRef] [PubMed]

63. Meyers, D.G.; Jensen, K.C.; Menitove, J.E. A historical cohort study of the effect of lowering body iron through blood donation on incident cardiac events. *Transfusion* **2002**, *42*, 1135–1139. [CrossRef] [PubMed]

64. Sullivan, J.L. Stored iron and vascular reactivity. *Arterioscler. Thromb. Vasc. Biol.* **2005**, *25*, 1532–1535. [CrossRef] [PubMed]

65. Jialal, I. Evolving lipoprotein risk factors: Lipoprotein(a) and oxidized low-density lipoprotein. *Clin. Chem.* **1998**, *44*, 1827–1832. [PubMed]

66. Duffy, S.J.; Biegelsen, E.S.; Holbrook, M.; Russell, J.D.; Gokce, N.; Keaney, J.F., Jr.; Vita, J.A. Iron chelation improves endothelial function in patients with coronary artery disease. *Circulation* **2001**, *103*, 2799–2804. [CrossRef] [PubMed]
67. Fernandez-Real, J.M.; Lopez-Bermejo, A.; Ricart, W. Iron stores, blood donation, and insulin sensitivity and secretion. *Clin. Chem.* **2005**, *51*, 1201–1205. [CrossRef] [PubMed]
68. Beaton, M.D.; Chakrabarti, S.; Levstik, M.; Speechley, M.; Marotta, P.; Adams, P. Phase II clinical trial of phlebotomy for non-alcoholic fatty liver disease. *Aliment. Pharmacol. Ther.* **2013**, *37*, 720–729. [CrossRef] [PubMed]
69. Valenti, L.; Fracanzani, A.L.; Dongiovanni, P.; Rovida, S.; Rametta, R.; Fatta, E.; Pulixi, E.A.; Maggioni, M.; Fargion, S. A randomized trial of iron depletion in patients with nonalcoholic fatty liver disease and hyperferritinemia. *World J. Gstroenterol.* **2014**, *20*, 3002–3010. [CrossRef] [PubMed]
70. Dongiovanni, P.; Fracanzani, A.L.; Fargion, S.; Valenti, L. Iron in fatty liver and in the metabolic syndrome: A promising therapeutic target. *J. Hepatol.* **2011**, *55*, 920–932. [CrossRef] [PubMed]
71. Piperno, A.; Vergani, A.; Salvioni, A.; Trombini, P.; Vigano, M.; Riva, A.; Zoppo, A.; Boari, G.; Mancia, G. Effects of venesections and restricted diet in patients with the insulin-resistance hepatic iron overload syndrome. *Liver Int.* **2004**, *24*, 471–476. [CrossRef] [PubMed]
72. Fernandez-Real, J.M.; Manco, M. Effects of iron overload on chronic metabolic diseases. *Lancet Diabetes Endocrinol.* **2014**, *2*, 513–526. [CrossRef]
73. Graham, R.M.; Chua, A.C.; Carter, K.W.; Delima, R.D.; Johnstone, D.; Herbison, C.E.; Firth, M.J.; O'Leary, R.; Milward, E.A.; Olynyk, J.K.; *et al.* Hepatic iron loading in mice increases cholesterol biosynthesis. *Hepatology* **2010**, *52*, 462–471. [CrossRef] [PubMed]
74. Ye, P.; Cheah, I.K.; Halliwell, B. A high-fat and cholesterol diet causes fatty liver in guinea pigs. The role of iron and oxidative damage. *Free Radic. Res.* **2013**, *47*, 602–613. [CrossRef] [PubMed]
75. Silva, M.; da Costa Guerra, J.F.; Sampaio, A.F.; de Lima, W.G.; Silva, M.E.; Pedrosa, M.L. Iron dextran increases hepatic oxidative stress and alters expression of genes related to lipid metabolism contributing to hyperlipidaemia in murine model. *BioMed Res. Int.* **2015**, *2015*, 272617. [CrossRef] [PubMed]
76. Munoz-Bravo, C.; Gutierrez-Bedmar, M.; Gomez-Aracena, J.; Garcia-Rodriguez, A.; Navajas, J.F. Iron: Protector or risk factor for cardiovascular disease? Still controversial. *Nutrients* **2013**, *5*, 2384–2404. [CrossRef] [PubMed]
77. Qiu, C.; Zhang, C.; Gelaye, B.; Enquobahrie, D.A.; Frederick, I.O.; Williams, M.A. Gestational diabetes mellitus in relation to maternal dietary heme iron and nonheme iron intake. *Diabetes Care* **2011**, *34*, 1564–1569. [CrossRef] [PubMed]
78. Franchini, M.; Targher, G.; Montagnana, M.; Lippi, G. Iron and thrombosis. *Ann. Hematol.* **2008**, *87*, 167–173. [CrossRef] [PubMed]
79. Lapice, E.; Masulli, M.; Vaccaro, O. Iron deficiency and cardiovascular disease: An updated review of the evidence. *Curr. Atheroscler. Rep.* **2013**, *15*. [CrossRef] [PubMed]
80. Wang, X.; Qin, X.; Demirtas, H.; Li, J.; Mao, G.; Huo, Y.; Sun, N.; Liu, L.; Xu, X. Efficacy of folic acid supplementation in stroke prevention: A meta-analysis. *Lancet* **2007**, *369*, 1876–1882. [CrossRef]
81. Smulders, Y.M.; Blom, H.J. The homocysteine controversy. *J. Inherit. Metab. Dis.* **2011**, *34*, 93–99. [CrossRef] [PubMed]
82. Debreceni, B.; Debreceni, L. Why do homocysteine-lowering B vitamin and antioxidant E vitamin supplementations appear to be ineffective in the prevention of cardiovascular diseases? *Cardiovasc. Ther.* **2012**, *30*, 227–233. [CrossRef] [PubMed]
83. Baggott, J.E.; Tamura, T. Homocysteine, iron and cardiovascular disease: A hypothesis. *Nutrients* **2015**, *7*, 1108–1118. [CrossRef] [PubMed]
84. Fang, X.; An, P.; Wang, H.; Wang, X.; Shen, X.; Li, X.; Min, J.; Liu, S.; Wang, F. Dietary intake of heme iron and risk of cardiovascular disease: A dose-response meta-analysis of prospective cohort studies. *Nutr. Metab. Cardiovasc. Dis.* **2015**, *25*, 24–35. [CrossRef] [PubMed]
85. De Oliveira Otto, M.C.; Alonso, A.; Lee, D.H.; Delclos, G.L.; Jenny, N.S.; Jiang, R.; Lima, J.A.; Symanski, E.; Jacobs, D.R., Jr.; Nettleton, J.A. Dietary micronutrient intakes are associated with markers of inflammation but not with markers of subclinical atherosclerosis. *J. Nutr.* **2011**, *141*, 1508–1515. [CrossRef] [PubMed]

86. Koeth, R.A.; Wang, Z.; Levison, B.S.; Buffa, J.A.; Org, E.; Sheehy, B.T.; Britt, E.B.; Fu, X.; Wu, Y.; Li, L.; *et al.* Intestinal microbiota metabolism of L-carnitine, a nutrient in red meat, promotes atherosclerosis. *Nat. Med.* **2013**, *19*, 576–585. [CrossRef] [PubMed]

87. Wang, Z.; Klipfell, E.; Bennett, B.J.; Koeth, R.; Levison, B.S.; Dugar, B.; Feldstein, A.E.; Britt, E.B.; Fu, X.; Chung, Y.M.; *et al.* Gut flora metabolism of phosphatidylcholine promotes cardiovascular disease. *Nature* **2011**, *472*, 57–63. [CrossRef] [PubMed]

88. Budzynski, J.; Wisniewska, J.; Ciecierski, M.; Kedzia, A. Association between bacterial infection and peripheral vascular disease: A review. *Int. J. Angiol.* **2016**, *25*, 3–13. [PubMed]

89. Stock, J. Gut microbiota: An environmental risk factor for cardiovascular disease. *Atherosclerosis* **2013**, *229*, 440–442. [CrossRef] [PubMed]

90. Goldsmith, J.R.; Sartor, R.B. The role of diet on intestinal microbiota metabolism: Downstream impacts on host immune function and health, and therapeutic implications. *J. Gastroenterol.* **2014**, *49*, 785–798. [CrossRef] [PubMed]

International Journal of
Molecular Sciences

MDPI

Review

Role of Hedgehog Signaling Pathway in NASH

Mariana Verdelho Machado [1,2,*] **and Anna Mae Diehl** [1,*]

1   Division of Gastroenterology, Department of Medicine, Duke University Medical Center,
    Durham, NC 27710, USA
2   Gastroenterology Department, Hospital de Santa Maria, Centro Hospitalar Lisboa Norte (CHLN),
    Lisboa 1649-035, Portugal
*   Correspondence: mverdelhomachado@gmail.com (M.V.M.); diehl004@mc.duke.edu or
    annamae.diehl@dm.duke.edu (A.M.D.); Tel.: +1-919-684-2366 (A.M.D.)

Academic Editors: Amedeo Lonardo and Giovanni Targher
Received: 22 March 2016; Accepted: 26 May 2016; Published: 1 June 2016

Abstract: Non-alcoholic fatty liver disease (NAFLD) is the number one cause of chronic liver disease in the Western world. Although only a minority of patients will ultimately develop end-stage liver disease, it is not yet possible to efficiently predict who will progress and, most importantly, effective treatments are still unavailable. Better understanding of the pathophysiology of this disease is necessary to improve the clinical management of NAFLD patients. Epidemiological data indicate that NAFLD prognosis is determined by an individual's response to lipotoxic injury, rather than either the severity of exposure to lipotoxins, or the intensity of liver injury. The liver responds to injury with a synchronized wound-healing response. When this response is abnormal, it leads to pathological scarring, resulting in progressive fibrosis and cirrhosis, rather than repair. The hedgehog pathway is a crucial player in the wound-healing response. In this review, we summarize the pre-clinical and clinical evidence, which demonstrate the role of hedgehog pathway dysregulation in NAFLD pathogenesis, and the preliminary data that place the hedgehog pathway as a potential target for the treatment of this disease.

Keywords: nonalcoholic fatty liver disease; hedgehog pathway; wound-healing response

1. Introduction

Nonalcoholic fatty liver disease (NAFLD), the ectopic accumulation of fat in the liver that is unrelated to excessive alcohol consumption, is the liver pandemic of our century. NAFLD affects roughly one billion subjects worldwide [1]. When steatosis is accompanied by cell death and inflammation it is dubbed nonalcoholic steatohepatitis (NASH). The main risk factors for NAFLD/NASH are obesity and its associated metabolic disorders, such as type 2 diabetes mellitus and the metabolic syndrome [2]. Energy surplus overcomes the reservoir capacity of the adipose tissue, leading to ectopic accumulation of fat in the cardiovascular system, the pancreas and the liver [3]. The majority of individuals affected with NAFLD have non-progressive, isolated steatosis; about a quarter will develop NASH, and fewer than 10% will progress to liver cirrhosis and end-stage liver disease [4]. However, due to the high prevalence of NAFLD, it is already the second cause of liver transplantation in the US [5], and the most rapidly growing cause of liver transplantation in patients with hepatocellular carcinoma [6]. These epidemiological data have huge implications for the management of NAFLD: To follow and/or treat all individuals with NAFLD would be impractical and pointless. On the other hand, we clearly need to identify those at risk for severe liver-related morbidity and mortality. Our aim should be to identify this high-risk subpopulation in an effective, non-invasive, simple, and inexpensive way. Ideally, we should also have an effective treatment to apply. Recent epidemiological studies have demonstrated that neither the severity of steatosis, nor the presence of hepatocellular injury (*i.e.*, NASH), independently predict which NAFLD patients will develop bad liver outcomes [7–9]. On the other hand, NAFLD prognosis strongly correlates with the presence and severity of liver fibrosis [7,8]. Liver fibrosis is a manifestation of defective regeneration and thus, whether or not liver injury is repaired effectively is a better determinant of liver outcome than the severity of the insult (steatosis), or the severity of the injury (hepatocellular ballooning and NASH), *per se*. Lipotoxic insults that damage the liver trigger a wound-healing response to regenerate normal hepatic architecture and function. This process involves coordinated actions of different cell types, such as epithelial cells, progenitor cells, matrix-producing cells, endothelial cells and inflammatory cells, which collaborate to restrain toxicity and match the increased metabolic demands required to remodel the matrix, replace lost liver cells, and regenerate functional liver mass. Inability to assemble a wound-healing response may lead to liver failure. However, an overly exuberant response leads to excessive fibrogenesis and promotes scarring that may progress to cirrhosis and its complications. In fact, a study evaluating hepatic gene expression in patients with NAFLD showed that the most important difference between patients with mild NAFLD and NAFLD with advanced fibrosis was up-regulation of several genes in tissue repair and regeneration [10]. Therefore, understanding the mechanisms governing the wound-healing response is critical to develop therapeutic strategies that optimize liver repair to permit full recovery from fatty liver damage. The hedgehog pathway is a pivotal maestro of the wound-healing response, and its actions are conserved across different organs, including the skin [11], lung [12], kidney [13], pancreas [14] and liver [15]. Because hedgehog is the best characterized pathway that mediates liver fibrosis in NAFLD, we will summarize the role of hedgehog in the pathogenesis and progression of NAFLD, in this review.

2. The Hedgehog Signaling Pathway

The hedgehog (Hh) pathway was first identified by Nüsslein-Volhard and Wirschaus, in a genetic screen in *Drosophila melanogaster* [16]. Flies deficient in Hh had developmental defects in the cuticle, displaying a layer of disorganized hair-liked bristles that resembled the mammal hedgehog. Hh is a morphogen, and as such, its effect on cell fate depends on its local concentration. Hh diffuses to the extracellular matrix and thus, cells closer to the Hh-producing cells are exposed to high concentrations of Hh ligands [17]. Hh ligands (Sonic hedgehog, Shh; Indian hedgehog, Ihh; and Desert hedgehog, Dhh) are produced as 45 kDa precursor proteins, and undergo autocatalytic cleavage. The resultant N-terminal fragment has intrinsic cholesterol transferase activity, which promotes cholesterol lipidation of the active N-terminal fragment. Cholesterol modification is very important for Hh activity, promoting its retention in plasma membrane lipid rafts where Hh ligands interact with other lipids. A member of the membrane-bound O-acyltransferase (MBOAT) protein family, skinny hedgehog (SKI), mediates a second lipidation with palmitic acid. Palmitoylation is necessary for full ligand activity, as well as for long-distance movement [18]. Release of Hh from producing cells occurs in one of three ways: a process facilitated by the protein Dispatched, through assembly in very low-density lipoproteins (VLDL), or through exosomes [18].

All three mammalian Hh ligands have similar affinity for Hh binding proteins. They are equipotent in some but not all cell types, denoting overlap but also some specificity in their action [19]. Shh and Ihh are expressed widely, though Shh is the predominant ligand in the proximal gut, and Ihh in the hindgut. Dhh expression, however, is restricted to the nervous tissue and testis [20].

The cellular receptor for Hh is the 12-transmembranar protein Patched (Ptch). Ptch exists in two isoforms: Ptch-1, which is the one definitely involved in the activation of the Hh pathway, and Ptch-2, which seems to be expressed independently of pathway activity [21]. Three co-receptors enhance ligand-receptor interaction: CAM-related down-regulated by oncogenes (Cdo), brother of Cdo (Boc), and growth arrest-specific (GAS)-1 [17].

Cells in the resting state express Ptch that exerts a repressing effect on Smoothened (Smo). When Hh ligand binds to Ptch, it eliminates the repressing effect on Smo, allowing activation of the hedgehog pathway, through regulation of the processing and stability of Gli transcription factors. In short, when Smo is inactive, Gli factors are either degraded or processed in inactive forms. In contrast, when Smo is active, full-length Gli factors (or processed active forms) are stabilized and can accumulate/translocate to the nucleus, where they act as transcription factors.

In the absence of Hh ligand, Gli couples to a suppressor protein complex composed by fused kinase (Fu), suppressor of Fused (Sufu) and Costal-2 (Cos) [20,22]. This complex sequesters Gli in the cytoplasm promoting its sequential serine phosphorylations by protein kinase A (PKA), glycogen synthase kinase (GSK)-3β, and members of casein kinase-1 (CK1) family. Phosphorylation enhances binding of Gli to β-transducin repeat-containing protein (βTrCp), which targets Gli for ubiquitination and subsequent proteasome degradation. Partial degradation generates an inhibitor Gli-peptide that can translocate to the nucleus and repress transcription. Active Smo allows dissociation of Sufu from Gli [23]. Full-length Gli-protein can then translocate to the nucleus, where it acts as a transcription factor. Important known target genes are: vascular endothelial growth factor (VEGF), angiopoietin-1 and -2 (in endothelial cells); snail, twist-2, FoxF1, α-smooth muscle actin (α-SMA), vimentin, interleukin (IL)-6 (in fibroblasts/myofibroblasts); and Sox-2, Sox-9 and Nanog (in stem/progenitor cells) [20].

Gli proteins belong to the Kruppel-like family of transcription factors with highly conserved zinc finger DNA-binding domain [21]. Mammals have three Gli proteins: Gli-1, Gli-2 and Gli-3, which behave differently. Gli-1 and Gli-2 transcription profiles overlap, but are not identical [21]. Unlike the other Gli factors, Gli-1 is not proteolytically processed to a repressor form. Gli-1 is also a direct transcriptional target of Gli-2 [24]. Gli-3 acts mainly as a transcription repressor, with very efficient proteolytic processing, whereas Gli-2 acts mainly as a transcription activator, with an extremely inefficient proteolytic processing [25].

The activation of Hh signaling through Smo seems to require the presence of primary cilia. Primary cilia are small, immotile cilia, elaborated in interphase by most quiescent, differentiated cells [26]. Primary cilia are made of polymerized tubulin, and consist of the basal body (that derives from the mother centriole at the end of cell division), and the filamentous axoneme that protrudes into the extracellular space.

In resting cells, Smo resides in intracytoplasmic vesicles outside of the primary cilia. Hh binding removes Ptch from the primary cilia, allowing Smo to accumulate in the cilia membrane. Smo can then move along the cilia from the base to the tip, in a kinesin motor protein-based transport system, which is facilitated by the ciliary Bardet-Biedl syndrome proteins (BBS) and intraflagellar transport proteins (IFP). At the tip of the cilia, Smo enables removal of Gli from the inhibitor complex with Sufu. Free Gli then moves along the cilia in a retrograde fashion via a dynein motor protein-based transport system, which is facilitated by BBS, IFP and Kif7. Full length Gli ultimately translocates from the cytoplasm to the nucleus, where it acts as a transcription factor [20] (Figure 1).

The Hh pathway has several intrinsic mechanisms of negative regulation that limit sustained activation. For example, Gli, the main effector in the Hh pathway, increases the expression of important inhibitors of the pathway. In fact, three direct Gli-target genes are Ptch, hedgehog-interacting protein (Hip) and Foxa2, all of them can inhibit Hh pathway activity. Ptch constitutively suppresses Smo, Hip binds to Hh and prevents ligand from engaging Ptch so that Smo cannot be de-repressed; and Foxa2 suppresses Gli-2 transcription, thereby depleting cells of the factor that drives transcription of Gli-1, the main activator of Hh target gene expression [27].

In addition to the aforementioned "canonical" Hh signaling pathway, two types of non-canonical Hh signaling have been described: type 1 is Ptch-dependent (but Smo-independent) and type 2 is Smo-dependent (but does not require Hh interaction with Ptch) [21,22]. In type 1 signaling, binding of Hh ligand to Ptch prevents Ptch from directly interacting with, and activating, caspases [28], and thus has an anti-apoptotic effect. In addition, the interaction promotes proliferation by preventing Ptch from blocking cyclin B translocation into the nucleus [29,30]. In type 2 signaling, Smo behaves as a 7-transmembrane protein that has a G-protein-coupled receptor (GPCR)-like function and acts independently of Gli and of the primary cilia [31]. The GPCR-like functions of Smo engage a calcium-AMP kinase axis that induces a Warburg-like glycolytic metabolic reprogramming in muscle and adipose tissue [32]. Smo GPCR-like activity also stimulates small GTPases that promote cytoskeletal rearrangement allowing migration of fibroblasts, and tubulogenesis in endothelial cells [33–35].

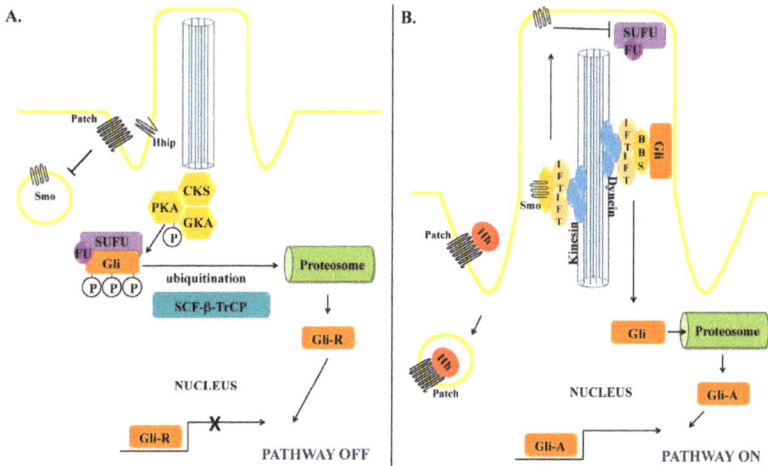

Figure 1. Hedgehog signaling pathway and the primary cilia. (**A**) In the absence of Hedgehog (Hh) ligand, Gli localizes in the cytoplasm as part of an inhibitory complex with Fused kinase (Fu) and Suppressor of Fused (SuFu), which allows the sequential phosphorylation by several kinases: Protein kinase A (PKA), glycogen synthase-3β (GSK3β) and casein kinase-1 (CK1). Thereafter, ubiquitination by Skip-Cullin-F-box (SCF) protein/β-Transducing repeat Containing Protein (TrCP) primes the phosphorylated Gli to limited proteosomic degradation, exposing the N-terminal repressor domain (GliR), which translocates to the nucleus and represses; (**B**) When Hh ligand binds to Ptch, it releases the inhibitory effect of Ptch on Smo that localizes in cytoplasmic vesicles. Smo then undergoes anterograde movement along the cilia, directed by kinesin and facilitated by the ciliary proteins Bardet-Biedl syndrome proteins (BBS) and intraflagellar transport proteins (IFP). At the tip of the cilia, Smo releases Gli from the suppressor complex, allowing it to move along the cilia, directed by dynein proteins. Unphosphorylated Gli undergoes limited proteosomal degradation, exposing the C-terminal activator domain (GliA), which translocates to the nucleus promoting gene transcription.

Finally, Gli-2 transcription/activation can be induced by Hedgehog-ligand independent pathways, including transforming growth factor (TGF)-β, phosphatydilinositol 3-kinase (PI3K)/AKT, Ras and mitogen-activated protein kinases (MAPK)/extracellular signal-regulated kinases (ERK) [22]. Osteopontin, besides being a target gene of Gli, also inhibits GSK3β, thereby promoting Gli activation [36].

3. Hedgehog Pathway and the Wound Healing Response

The Hh pathway is a recognized maestro of the wound healing response [37]. The wound-healing response is a coordinated reaction to liver injury that aims to overcome the loss of hepatic structure and function that results when liver cells die. Injured or fatty hepatocytes cannot mount an adequate proliferative response to replace these cells [38], and hence progenitor cells are crucial for sick livers to regenerate. Progenitors in the liver (similar to other populations of stem/progenitor cells [39]) are sensitive to Hh [40–43]. Indeed, Hh activation enhances progenitor cell viability and proliferation, whereas Hh inhibition promotes progenitor differentiation or cell death by apoptosis [40,44]. Another conserved wound healing response that occurs after liver injury is the development of an inflammatory reaction, which is also strongly regulated by the Hh pathway. For example, hepatic NKT cells respond to Hh with improved viability and proliferation, and acquire a profibrogenic phenotype that includes up-regulating their expression of IL-13 [45]. Hh also directly induces M2 pro-fibrogenic polarization of macrophages/Kupffer cells, further crafting a pro-fibrogenic liver microenvironment [46]. Another important player in the wound healing response is the hepatic stellate cell (HSC), the main source of myofibroblasts in the liver [47]. HSC not only produce the extracellular matrix necessary to maintain hepatic architecture during injury, they are a rich source of paracrine trophic substances that act on all other cell types involved in the healing response [37], and have recently been shown to function as progenitor cells themselves [48]. Excessive HSC activation may lead to anomalous matrix deposition that causes progressive fibrosis. Hh enhances HSC survival by inhibiting apoptosis, promotes HSC proliferation, and stimulates HSC to undergo an epithelial to mesenchymal-like transition in order to acquire a myofibroblastic phenotype [49]. Lastly, liver sinusoidal endothelial cells respond to Hh with capillarisation of hepatic sinusoids and vascular remodeling; perpetuation of this response favors the development of portal hypertension [50].

Whereas in the healthy liver the expression of Hh ligands is barely detected [40], Hh pathway activation increases proportionally to the severity and duration of the liver insult [42,51]. During injury, several cell types up-regulate expression of Hh ligands. For example, Hh production is virtually absent in healthy hepatocytes, but injured ballooned hepatocytes are a major source of Hh ligands in NAFLD [51–53]. Other sources of Hh ligands during a regenerative/repair response in the liver are inflammatory cells [45,46], activated ductular/progenitor cells [54] and HSC [49,55,56].

Although the hedgehog pathway seems important in wound-healing response/regeneration in different systems besides the liver, such as kidney, skin, cardiovascular system [57], a recent report in the lung showed that the hedgehog pathway may be important in maintaining adult lung quiescence and is down-regulated in response to epithelial injury [58]. These data demonstrate how complex this exciting pathway is, and further research is needed to clarify its function in liver health and repair.

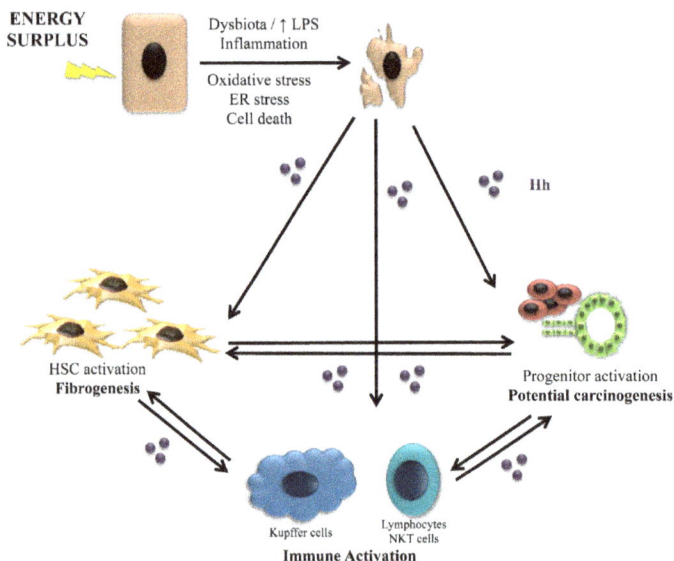

Figure 2. The role of Hedgehog on the wound-healing response. Energy surplus leads to fat accumulation in the hepatocytes, which promote oxidative stress, endoplasmic reticulum (ER) stress and cell death. The injury of hepatocytes is promoted by an inflammatory state, among other factors, favored by a deregulated gut microbiota and increase in lipopolysaccharide (LPS). Injured and dying hepatocytes release hedgehog ligands (Hh) that act on the immune system increasing inflammation, in stellate cells and progenitors cells activating them and inducing fibrogenesis and pathways of hepatocarcinogenesis. Once started, the regenerative/repair response perpetuates through crosstalk between the different cell types involved.

In summary, the wound-healing response depends on coordinated cross-talk among different cell types. Injured hepatocytes produce Hh ligands that attract and activate inflammatory cells. Infiltrating inflammatory cells, in turn, up-regulate their expression of Hh ligands and begin to produce profibrogenic cytokines, such as IL-13 and transforming growth factor (TGF)-β. These factors, not only activate myofibroblasts, but also are toxic to hepatocytes, further increasing hepatocyte injury and Hh ligand production [43]. Hh ligands also activate progenitor cells, inducing a ductular reaction. Activated ductular/progenitor cells up-regulate expression of chemokines/cytokines such as CXCL16 and platelet-derived growth factor (PDGF), which recruit more inflammatory cells and promote accumulation of myofibroblasts [59,60]. Hh ligands also activate HSC, causing their transdifferentiation into myofibroblasts and thus, promoting a fibrogenic response. If this initially adaptive response is not appropriately constrained, excessive activation of HSC/myofibroblasts promotes progressive fibrosis, and excessive proliferation of relatively immature liver epithelial cells represses regeneration of fully functional hepatocytes, leading to liver failure and carcinogenesis (Figure 2).

4. The Role of Hedgehog in Animal Models of NASH

Activation of the Hh pathway is a conserved feature of chronic liver disease, and NAFLD/NASH is no exception. Different rodent animal models of NAFLD show activation of the Hh pathway, demonstrated by increased expression of Hh ligands and Hh-producing cells, with accumulation of nuclear Gli-2 positive cells and increased expression of Gli-target genes such as osteopontin [42,53,61–65]. Furthermore, the activation of the Hh pathway is proportional to liver injury, namely to hepatocyte injury/apoptosis, ductular reaction and, most importantly, fibrosis [42,53,65].

Lipotoxic dying hepatocytes are a main source of Hh ligands that can trigger the repair response during NAFLD/NASH. *In vitro* models of lipotoxicity demonstrated up-regulation of Hh ligands in hepatocytes incubated with saturated fatty acids and lysophospholipid [65,66]. The mechanism leading to Hh ligand expression has not been clearly demonstrated. However, agents that can induce endoplasmic reticulum stress or activation of the NFkB pathway mimic the lipotoxic phenotype [52,67].

In animal models of NASH, the Hh-responsive progenitor population expands, and Hh-stimulated HSC undergo epithelial-to-mesenchymal transdifferentiation into myofibroblasts acquiring a pro-fibrogenic phenotype [42,61]. Activated ductular progenitor cells and myofibroblasts, in turn, up-regulate their production of Hh ligands, and release pro-inflammatory and chemotactic cytokines, such as osteopontin and CXCL-16 [60,63]. Immune cells are recruited, namely NKT cells, which have a pivotal role in NASH pathogenesis. Active NKT cells, in its turn, secrete more Hh ligands and profibrogenic cytokines, such as IL-13, perpetuating the disease progression [62,68].

Genetically modified mice, with heterozygous deficiency of Ptch (Ptch$^{+/-}$), which display an overly active Hh pathway, develop worse liver disease when submitted to a NASH-inducing diet [61–63]. In contrast, genetically modified mice with conditional liver-specific inhibition of Smo, were protected from liver injury and liver fibrosis in different dietary models of NASH, despite similar accumulation of ectopic fat in the liver [37,69]. A recent study took advantage of a transgenic mouse with transposon encoding Shh hydrodinamically delivered to the liver to extend knowledge about hedgehog's role in NASH progression. Although this approach achieve expression of Shh in only 2%–5% of hepatocytes, it was sufficient to induce spontaneous liver fibrosis after 6 months and hepatocellular carcinoma after 13 months [70]. Hh ligands stimulate and increase proliferation of progenitor cells, as well as immune cells and hepatic stellate cells. As such, ductular progenitor cells, immune and hepatic stellate cells are Gli-2-positive (*i.e.*, Hh-responsive). Remarkably, 30%–50% of hepatocytes also exhibited nuclear Gli-2 expression. This finding challenges current dogma in the field, which posits that healthy hepatocytes cannot respond to Hh because they do not express primary cilia.

Different laboratories, studying different rodent models of diet-induced NASH, showed that pharmacological inhibition of Smo (vismodebig or LDE225) decreased activation of hedgehog pathway and consistently improved liver inflammation and fibrosis [61,69,71]. Those results place the Hh pathway as a potential therapeutic target in NASH.

5. The Hegdehog Pathway in Human NASH

The prevalence of human NAFLD is increasing worldwide in association with globalization of western lifestyles characterized by physical inactivity and overfeeding with predilection to sugar and fat enriched food. Roughly one fourth of the U.S. population has hepatic steatosis, however only a minority (2%–5%) will progress to NAFLD-related liver cirrhosis and end-stage liver disease [4]. Importantly, we still lack an effective treatment for this disease, which explains why NASH-related cirrhosis has become the second leading cause for liver transplantation in the US [5]. Liver prognosis is dictated by the fidelity of the wound healing response, with deregulated wound-healing promoting development of progressive fibrosis [7,8]. Hh is a crucial factor involved in this abnormal response to injury. Not only is Hh the best characterized fibrogenic pathway in animal models of NASH, but there is also strong human data that highlight its role in the pathogenesis of human cirrhosis.

Although isolated steatosis does not stimulate Hh pathway activation, steatohepatitis-related hepatocyte injury triggers Hh ligand production, and in human NASH the intensity of activation of the Hh pathway parallels the severity of liver disease. Hh pathway activity has been demonstrated to correlate with portal inflammation, hepatocellular ballooning, and markers of liver repair (e.g., numbers of hepatic progenitor cells and myofibroblasts) in NAFLD patients. More importantly, Hh activation correlates with the severity of fibrosis [51,61]. The major source of Hh ligands seems to be injured ballooned hepatocytes. In fact, the number of Shh expressing ballooned hepatocytes strongly correlates with fibrosis severity [51,72]. Furthermore, the number of Shh expressing ballooned hepatocytes also correlates with the severity of the ductular reaction, which strongly associates with fibrogenesis and carcinogenesis [73,74].

In the pediatric population, NAFLD can occur with a similar histology as in adults, or it can present a unique histology that is characterized by less hepatocellular ballooning but a predominantly portal phenotype, *i.e.*, intense ductular proliferation, portal inflammation and fibrosis. A tremendous increase in the number of portal Gli-2 positive cells has been demonstrated in this pediatric pattern of NASH [75] and it occurs most often in pre-pubertal children, paralleling the kinetics of hepatic Hh expression, which is high in children and falls after adolescence [76].

Recently, a *post hoc* evaluation of the PIVENS (Pioglitazone, Vitamin E for Non-alcoholic Steatohepatitis) trial, analyzed pre- and post-treatment liver biopsies from 30 patients randomized to vitamin E and 29 to placebo [77]. Loss of Shh expressing hepatocytes strongly correlated with treatment response in terms of aminotransferases levels, hepatocyte ballooning, ductular reaction, presence of NASH and, most importantly, fibrosis stage [77]. This evidence linking reduced Hh activity with improvement of NASH in humans complements and extends the aforementioned work in preclinical models which showed that pharmacological strategies that directly decreased Hh activity abrogated NASH progression.

The roles of canonical and non-canonical pathways in liver disease in general and NASH in particular is still a matter of debate. Whereas progenitor cells clearly express primary cilia and thus can engage the canonical Hh pathway, it has been suggested that HSC, immune cells and hepatocytes do not express primary cilia, and hence Gli-2 activation/Gli-1 expression would be the result of non-canonical pathways [78,79]. In addition, type 2 non-canonical Smo-dependent RhoA/Rho kinase activation of HSC has been suggested to play a role in hepatic fibrogenesis [80]. Further research is needed to clarify the relevance of these different signaling cascades to better delineate a treatment strategy. To date, the most studied inhibitors of the Hh pathway *in vitro* and in animal models of NASH are cyclopamine and vismodegib, both strong Smo antagonists, which bind Smo and inhibit of its ciliary localization [81]. Interestingly, although HSC are sensitive to factors that induce non-canonical Hh pathway activation, they are also highly responsive to Hh ligands, antibodies against Hh and to both cyclopamine and vismodegib [49,55,56]. Furthermore, while healthy hepatocytes do not respond to cyclopamine, murine hepatocytes isolated after partial hepatectomy respond to cyclopamine with increased proliferation [82]. This suggests that the presence of a primary cilium may be a dynamic event, depending on the cell cycle phase and maybe in response to injury [83].

The aggregate data in animal models and human NASH strongly suggest that modulation of the Hh pathway may be a treatment for NASH that prevents fibrosis progression. As such, patients that would most benefit from treatment would be the ones that already have liver fibrosis to prevent progression to cirrhosis and its complications. This approach is particularly appealing because several Hh inhibitors have already been approved by the FDA to treat other diseases such as basal cell carcinoma [84] and, thus, the time lag between preclinical/clinical research and treatment of actual NASH patients should be short.

6. Conclusions

NASH-associated cirrhosis occurs when the liver reacts to lipotoxicity with a deregulated wound-healing response that is maladaptive. The liver must repair and regenerate when confronted with injury or death will ensue, just as Prometheus' survival depended upon his liver's ability to regenerate after being eaten by Zeus' eagle. When the eagle repeatedly eats the liver or when the repair/regenerative response cannot be shut down even when the satiated eagle stops eating the liver, the protracted wound-healing response leads to progressive fibrosis and carcinogenesis. The Hh pathway is a known maestro orchestrating an integrated regenerative response by the different cellular players involved in wound-healing. The Hh pathway is hibernating in the normal liver, but it wakens during injury, and the intensity of its activation is a reflection of the severity of liver injury. Data from animal models and human NASH have consistently confirmed that Hh pathway activation correlates with the severity of liver disease. More importantly, direct pharmacological inhibition of the Hh pathway prevents disease progression in different rodent models of NASH and Hh pathway activity decreases with improvement of NASH in humans. These findings position the Hh pathway as a potential therapeutic target in NASH, the hepatic pandemic of our century for which development of an effective treatment is a priority for hepatologists worldwide.

Acknowledgments: This research is supported by NIH DK0077794, DK053792 and R37 AA010154 (Diehl A.M.), and Duke Endowment: The Florence McAlister Professorship (Diehl A.M.).

Author Contributions: Mariana Verdelho Machado and Anna Mae Diehl wrote the paper.

Conflicts of Interest: There are no conflicts of interest to state.

Abbreviations

BBS	Bardet-Biedl syndrome proteins
Boc	brother of Cdo
Cdo	CAM-related downregulated by oncogenes
Cos	Costal-2
CK1	casein kinase-1
Dhh	Desert hedgehog
Fu	fused kinase
GAS-1	growth arrest-specific-1
GPCR	G-protein-coupled receptor
GSK	glycogen synthase kinase
Hh	hedgehog
Hip	hedgehog-interacting protein
HSC	hepatic stellate cell
IFP	intraflagellar transport proteins
Ihh	Indian hedgehog
IL	interleukin
MBOAT	membrane-bound O-acyltransferase
NAFLD	nonalcoholic fatty liver disease
NASH	nonalcoholic steatohepatitis
PDGF	platelet-derived growth factor
PKA	protein kinase A
Ptch	Ptched
Shh	Sonic hedgehog
SKI	skinny hedgehog

SMA	smooth muscle actin
Smo	smoothened
Sufu	suppressor of fused
TGF	transforming growth factor
TrCp	transducing repeat-containing protein
VEGF	vascular endothelial growth factor
VLDL	very low-density lipoproteins

References

1. Loomba, R.; Sanyal, A.J. The global nafld epidemic. *Nat. Rev. Gastroenterol. Hepatol.* **2013**, *10*, 686–690. [CrossRef] [PubMed]
2. Lonardo, A.; Bellentani, S.; Argo, C.K.; Ballestri, S.; Byrne, C.D.; Caldwell, S.H.; Cortez-Pinto, H.; Grieco, A.; Machado, M.V.; Miele, L.; *et al.* Epidemiological modifiers of non-alcoholic fatty liver disease: Focus on high-risk groups. *Dig. Liver Dis.* **2015**, *47*, 997–1006. [CrossRef] [PubMed]
3. Machado, M.V.; Diehl, A.M. Pathogenesis of nonalcoholic steatohepatitis. *Gastroenterology* **2006**, *40*, S17–S29. [CrossRef] [PubMed]
4. Machado, M.V.; Cortez-Pinto, H. Non-alcoholic fatty liver disease: What the clinician needs to know. *World J. Gastroenterol.* **2014**, *20*, 12956–12980. [CrossRef] [PubMed]
5. Wong, R.J.; Aguilar, M.; Cheung, R.; Perumpail, R.B.; Harrison, S.A.; Younossi, Z.M.; Ahmed, A. Nonalcoholic steatohepatitis is the second leading etiology of liver disease among adults awaiting liver transplantation in the united states. *Gastroenterology* **2015**, *148*, 547–555. [CrossRef] [PubMed]
6. Wong, R.J.; Cheung, R.; Ahmed, A. Nonalcoholic steatohepatitis is the most rapidly growing indication for liver transplantation in patients with hepatocellular carcinoma in the U.S. *Hepatology* **2014**, *59*, 2188–2195. [CrossRef] [PubMed]
7. Angulo, P.; Kleiner, D.E.; Dam-Larsen, S.; Adams, L.A.; Bjornsson, E.S.; Charatcharoenwitthaya, P.; Mills, P.R.; Keach, J.C.; Lafferty, H.D.; Stahler, A.; *et al.* Liver fibrosis, but no other histologic features, is associated with long-term outcomes of patients with nonalcoholic fatty liver disease. *Gastroenterology* **2015**, *149*, 389–397.e10. [CrossRef] [PubMed]
8. Ekstedt, M.; Hagstrom, H.; Nasr, P.; Fredrikson, M.; Stal, P.; Kechagias, S.; Hultcrantz, R. Fibrosis stage is the strongest predictor for disease-specific mortality in nafld after up to 33 years of follow-up. *Hepatology* **2015**, *61*, 1547–1554. [CrossRef] [PubMed]
9. Singh, S.; Allen, A.M.; Wang, Z.; Prokop, L.J.; Murad, M.H.; Loomba, R. Fibrosis progression in nonalcoholic fatty liver vs nonalcoholic steatohepatitis: A systematic review and meta-analysis of paired-biopsy studies. *Clin. Gastroenterol. Hepatol.* **2015**, *13*, 643–654, e641–649; quiz e639–640. [CrossRef] [PubMed]
10. Moylan, C.A.; Pang, H.; Dellinger, A.; Suzuki, A.; Garrett, M.E.; Guy, C.D.; Murphy, S.K.; Ashley-Koch, A.E.; Choi, S.S.; Michelotti, G.A.; *et al.* Hepatic gene expression profiles differentiate presymptomatic patients with mild *versus* severe nonalcoholic fatty liver disease. *Hepatology* **2014**, *59*, 471–482. [CrossRef] [PubMed]
11. Horn, A.; Palumbo, K.; Cordazzo, C.; Dees, C.; Akhmetshina, A.; Tomcik, M.; Zerr, P.; Avouac, J.; Gusinde, J.; Zwerina, J.; *et al.* Hedgehog signaling controls fibroblast activation and tissue fibrosis in systemic sclerosis. *Arthritis Rheum.* **2012**, *64*, 2724–2733. [CrossRef] [PubMed]
12. Kugler, M.C.; Joyner, A.L.; Loomis, C.A.; Munger, J.S. Sonic hedgehog signaling in the lung. From development to disease. *Am. J. Respir. Cell Mol. Biol.* **2015**, *52*, 1–13. [CrossRef] [PubMed]
13. Fabian, S.L.; Penchev, R.R.; St-Jacques, B.; Rao, A.N.; Sipila, P.; West, K.A.; McMahon, A.P.; Humphreys, B.D. Hedgehog-gli pathway activation during kidney fibrosis. *Am. J. Pathol.* **2012**, *180*, 1441–1453. [CrossRef] [PubMed]
14. Wang, L.W.; Lin, H.; Lu, Y.; Xia, W.; Gao, J.; Li, Z.S. Sonic hedgehog expression in a rat model of chronic pancreatitis. *World J. Gastroenterol.* **2014**, *20*, 4712–4717. [CrossRef] [PubMed]
15. Choi, S.S.; Omenetti, A.; Syn, W.K.; Diehl, A.M. The role of hedgehog signaling in fibrogenic liver repair. *Int. J. Biochem. Cell Biol.* **2011**, *43*, 238–244. [CrossRef] [PubMed]
16. Nusslein-Volhard, C.; Wieschaus, E. Mutations affecting segment number and polarity in drosophila. *Nature* **1980**, *287*, 795–801. [CrossRef] [PubMed]
17. Briscoe, J.; Therond, P.P. The mechanisms of hedgehog signalling and its roles in development and disease. *Nat. Rev. Mol. Cell Biol.* **2013**, *14*, 416–429. [CrossRef] [PubMed]

18. Farzan, S.F.; Singh, S.; Schilling, N.S.; Robbins, D.J. The adventures of sonic hedgehog in development and repair. III. Hedgehog processing and biological activity. *Am. J. Physiol. Gastrointest. Liver Physiol.* **2008**, *294*, G844–G849. [CrossRef] [PubMed]

19. Pathi, S.; Pagan-Westphal, S.; Baker, D.P.; Garber, E.A.; Rayhorn, P.; Bumcrot, D.; Tabin, C.J.; Blake Pepinsky, R.; Williams, K.P. Comparative biological responses to human sonic, indian, and desert hedgehog. *Mech. Dev.* **2001**, *106*, 107–117. [CrossRef]

20. Merchant, J.L.; Saqui-Salces, M. Inhibition of hedgehog signaling in the gastrointestinal tract: Targeting the cancer microenvironment. *Cancer Treat. Rev.* **2014**, *40*, 12–21. [CrossRef] [PubMed]

21. Hu, L.; Lin, X.; Lu, H.; Chen, B.; Bai, Y. An overview of hedgehog signaling in fibrosis. *Mol. Pharmacol.* **2015**, *87*, 174–182. [CrossRef] [PubMed]

22. Teperino, R.; Aberger, F.; Esterbauer, H.; Riobo, N.; Pospisilik, J.A. Canonical and non-canonical hedgehog signalling and the control of metabolism. *Semin. Cell Dev. Biol.* **2014**, *33*, 81–92. [CrossRef] [PubMed]

23. Jia, J.; Kolterud, A.; Zeng, H.; Hoover, A.; Teglund, S.; Toftgard, R.; Liu, A. Suppressor of fused inhibits mammalian hedgehog signaling in the absence of cilia. *Dev. Biol.* **2009**, *330*, 452–460. [CrossRef] [PubMed]

24. Ikram, M.S.; Neill, G.W.; Regl, G.; Eichberger, T.; Frischauf, A.M.; Aberger, F.; Quinn, A.; Philpott, M. Gli2 is expressed in normal human epidermis and bcc and induces Gli1 expression by binding to its promoter. *J. Investig. Dermatol.* **2004**, *122*, 1503–1509. [CrossRef] [PubMed]

25. Pan, Y.; Bai, C.B.; Joyner, A.L.; Wang, B. Sonic hedgehog signaling regulates Gli2 transcriptional activity by suppressing its processing and degradation. *Mol. Cell. Biol.* **2006**, *26*, 3365–3377. [CrossRef] [PubMed]

26. Roy, S. Cilia and hedgehog: When and how was their marriage solemnized? *Differentiation* **2012**, *83*, S43–S48. [CrossRef] [PubMed]

27. Peterson, K.A.; Nishi, Y.; Ma, W.; Vedenko, A.; Shokri, L.; Zhang, X.; McFarlane, M.; Baizabal, J.M.; Junker, J.P.; van Oudenaarden, A.; *et al.* Neural-specific Sox2 input and differential Gli-binding affinity provide context and positional information in Shh-directed neural patterning. *Genes Dev.* **2012**, *26*, 2802–2816. [CrossRef] [PubMed]

28. Chinchilla, P.; Xiao, L.; Kazanietz, M.G.; Riobo, N.A. Hedgehog proteins activate pro-angiogenic responses in endothelial cells through non-canonical signaling pathways. *Cell Cycle* **2010**, *9*, 570–579. [CrossRef] [PubMed]

29. Pasca di Magliano, M.; Hebrok, M. Hedgehog signalling in cancer formation and maintenance. *Nat. Rev. Cancer* **2003**, *3*, 903–911. [CrossRef] [PubMed]

30. Barnes, E.A.; Kong, M.; Ollendorff, V.; Donoghue, D.J. Patched1 interacts with cyclin B1 to regulate cell cycle progression. *EMBO J.* **2001**, *20*, 2214–2223. [CrossRef] [PubMed]

31. Polizio, A.H.; Chinchilla, P.; Chen, X.; Manning, D.R.; Riobo, N.A. Sonic hedgehog activates the gtpases rac1 and rhoa in a Gli-independent manner through coupling of smoothened to G_i proteins. *Sci. Signal.* **2011**, *4 Pt 7*. [CrossRef] [PubMed]

32. Teperino, R.; Amann, S.; Bayer, M.; McGee, S.L.; Loipetzberger, A.; Connor, T.; Jaeger, C.; Kammerer, B.; Winter, L.; Wiche, G.; *et al.* Hedgehog partial agonism drives warburg-like metabolism in muscle and brown fat. *Cell* **2012**, *151*, 414–426. [CrossRef] [PubMed]

33. Bijlsma, M.F.; Borensztajn, K.S.; Roelink, H.; Peppelenbosch, M.P.; Spek, C.A. Sonic hedgehog induces transcription-independent cytoskeletal rearrangement and migration regulated by arachidonate metabolites. *Cell Signal.* **2007**, *19*, 2596–2604. [CrossRef] [PubMed]

34. Polizio, A.H.; Chinchilla, P.; Chen, X.; Kim, S.; Manning, D.R.; Riobo, N.A. Heterotrimeric G_i proteins link hedgehog signaling to activation of rho small gtpases to promote fibroblast migration. *J. Biol. Chem.* **2011**, *286*, 19589–19596. [CrossRef] [PubMed]

35. Razumilava, N.; Gradilone, S.A.; Smoot, R.L.; Mertens, J.C.; Bronk, S.F.; Sirica, A.E.; Gores, G.J. Non-canonical hedgehog signaling contributes to chemotaxis in cholangiocarcinoma. *J. Hepatol.* **2014**, *60*, 599–605. [CrossRef] [PubMed]

36. Das, S.; Samant, R.S.; Shevde, L.A. Nonclassical activation of hedgehog signaling enhances multidrug resistance and makes cancer cells refractory to smoothened-targeting hedgehog inhibition. *J. Biol. Chem.* **2013**, *288*, 11824–11833. [CrossRef] [PubMed]

37. Michelotti, G.A.; Xie, G.; Swiderska, M.; Choi, S.S.; Karaca, G.; Kruger, L.; Premont, R.; Yang, L.; Syn, W.K.; Metzger, D.; *et al.* Smoothened is a master regulator of adult liver repair. *J. Clin. Investig.* **2013**, *123*, 2380–2394. [CrossRef] [PubMed]

38. Sommerfeld, A.; Reinehr, R.; Haussinger, D. Free fatty acids shift insulin-induced hepatocyte proliferation towards CD95-dependent apoptosis. *J. Biol. Chem.* **2015**, *290*, 4398–4409. [CrossRef] [PubMed]

39. Mooney, C.J.; Hakimjavadi, R.; Fitzpatrick, E.; Kennedy, E.; Walls, D.; Morrow, D.; Redmond, E.M.; Cahill, P.A. Hedgehog and resident vascular stem cell fate. *Stem Cells Int.* **2015**, *2015*, 468428. [CrossRef] [PubMed]

40. Sicklick, J.K.; Li, Y.X.; Melhem, A.; Schmelzer, E.; Zdanowicz, M.; Huang, J.; Caballero, M.; Fair, J.H.; Ludlow, J.W.; McClelland, R.E.; *et al.* Hedgehog signaling maintains resident hepatic progenitors throughout life. *Am. J. Physiol. Gastrointest. Liver Physiol.* **2006**, *290*, G859–G870. [CrossRef] [PubMed]

41. Jung, Y.; Witek, R.P.; Syn, W.K.; Choi, S.S.; Omenetti, A.; Premont, R.; Guy, C.D.; Diehl, A.M. Signals from dying hepatocytes trigger growth of liver progenitors. *Gut* **2010**, *59*, 655–665. [CrossRef] [PubMed]

42. Fleig, S.V.; Choi, S.S.; Yang, L.; Jung, Y.; Omenetti, A.; VanDongen, H.M.; Huang, J.; Sicklick, J.K.; Diehl, A.M. Hepatic accumulation of hedgehog-reactive progenitors increases with severity of fatty liver damage in mice. *Lab. Investig.* **2007**, *87*, 1227–1239. [CrossRef] [PubMed]

43. Jung, Y.; Brown, K.D.; Witek, R.P.; Omenetti, A.; Yang, L.; Vandongen, M.; Milton, R.J.; Hines, I.N.; Rippe, R.A.; Spahr, L.; *et al.* Accumulation of hedgehog-responsive progenitors parallels alcoholic liver disease severity in mice and humans. *Gastroenterology* **2008**, *134*, 1532–1543. [CrossRef] [PubMed]

44. Hirose, Y.; Itoh, T.; Miyajima, A. Hedgehog signal activation coordinates proliferation and differentiation of fetal liver progenitor cells. *Exp. Cell Res.* **2009**, *315*, 2648–2657. [CrossRef] [PubMed]

45. Syn, W.K.; Witek, R.P.; Curbishley, S.M.; Jung, Y.; Choi, S.S.; Enrich, B.; Omenetti, A.; Agboola, K.M.; Fearing, C.M.; Tilg, H.; *et al.* Role for hedgehog pathway in regulating growth and function of invariant NKT cells. *Eur. J. Immunol.* **2009**, *39*, 1879–1892. [CrossRef] [PubMed]

46. Pereira, T.A.; Xie, G.; Choi, S.S.; Syn, W.K.; Voieta, I.; Lu, J.; Chan, I.S.; Swiderska, M.; Amaral, K.B.; Antunes, C.M.; *et al.* Macrophage-derived hedgehog ligands promotes fibrogenic and angiogenic responses in human schistosomiasis mansoni. *Liver Int.* **2013**, *33*, 149–161. [CrossRef] [PubMed]

47. Iwaisako, K.; Brenner, D.A.; Kisseleva, T. What's new in liver fibrosis? The origin of myofibroblasts in liver fibrosis. *J. Gastroenterol. Hepatol.* **2012**, *27* (Suppl. 2), 65–68. [CrossRef] [PubMed]

48. Swiderska-Syn, M.; Syn, W.K.; Xie, G.; Kruger, L.; Machado, M.V.; Karaca, G.; Michelotti, G.A.; Choi, S.S.; Premont, R.T.; Diehl, A.M. Myofibroblastic cells function as progenitors to regenerate murine livers after partial hepatectomy. *Gut* **2013**. [CrossRef] [PubMed]

49. Yang, L.; Wang, Y.; Mao, H.; Fleig, S.; Omenetti, A.; Brown, K.D.; Sicklick, J.K.; Li, Y.X.; Diehl, A.M. Sonic hedgehog is an autocrine viability factor for myofibroblastic hepatic stellate cells. *J. Hepatol.* **2008**, *48*, 98–106. [CrossRef] [PubMed]

50. Xie, G.; Choi, S.S.; Syn, W.K.; Michelotti, G.A.; Swiderska, M.; Karaca, G.; Chan, I.S.; Chen, Y.; Diehl, A.M. Hedgehog signalling regulates liver sinusoidal endothelial cell capillarisation. *Gut* **2013**, *62*, 299–309. [CrossRef] [PubMed]

51. Guy, C.D.; Suzuki, A.; Zdanowicz, M.; Abdelmalek, M.F.; Burchette, J.; Unalp, A.; Diehl, A.M.; Nash, C.R.N. Hedgehog pathway activation parallels histologic severity of injury and fibrosis in human nonalcoholic fatty liver disease. *Hepatology* **2012**, *55*, 1711–1721. [CrossRef] [PubMed]

52. Rangwala, F.; Guy, C.D.; Lu, J.; Suzuki, A.; Burchette, J.L.; Abdelmalek, M.F.; Chen, W.; Diehl, A.M. Increased production of sonic hedgehog by ballooned hepatocytes. *J. Pathol.* **2011**, *224*, 401–410. [CrossRef] [PubMed]

53. Machado, M.V.; Michelotti, G.A.; Pereira Tde, A.; Boursier, J.; Kruger, L.; Swiderska-Syn, M.; Karaca, G.; Xie, G.; Guy, C.D.; Bohinc, B.; *et al.* Reduced lipoapoptosis, hedgehog pathway activation and fibrosis in caspase-2 deficient mice with non-alcoholic steatohepatitis. *Gut* **2015**, *64*, 1148–1157. [CrossRef] [PubMed]

54. Omenetti, A.; Porrello, A.; Jung, Y.; Yang, L.; Popov, Y.; Choi, S.S.; Witek, R.P.; Alpini, G.; Venter, J.; Vandongen, H.M.; *et al.* Hedgehog signaling regulates epithelial-mesenchymal transition during biliary fibrosis in rodents and humans. *J. Clin. Investig.* **2008**, *118*, 3331–3342. [CrossRef] [PubMed]

55. Sicklick, J.K.; Li, Y.X.; Choi, S.S.; Qi, Y.; Chen, W.; Bustamante, M.; Huang, J.; Zdanowicz, M.; Camp, T.; Torbenson, M.S.; *et al.* Role for hedgehog signaling in hepatic stellate cell activation and viability. *Lab. Investig.* **2005**, *85*, 1368–1380. [CrossRef] [PubMed]

56. Lin, N.; Tang, Z.; Deng, M.; Zhong, Y.; Lin, J.; Yang, X.; Xiang, P.; Xu, R. Hedgehog-mediated paracrine interaction between hepatic stellate cells and marrow-derived mesenchymal stem cells. *Biochem. Biophys. Res. Commun.* **2008**, *372*, 260–265. [CrossRef] [PubMed]

57. Kramann, R.; Schneider, R.K.; DiRocco, D.P.; Machado, F.; Fleig, S.; Bondzie, P.A.; Henderson, J.M.; Ebert, B.L.; Humphreys, B.D. Perivascular Gli1+ progenitors are key contributors to injury-induced organ fibrosis. *Cell Stem Cell* **2015**, *16*, 51–66. [CrossRef] [PubMed]

58. Peng, T.; Frank, D.B.; Kadzik, R.S.; Morley, M.P.; Rathi, K.S.; Wang, T.; Zhou, S.; Cheng, L.; Lu, M.M.; Morrisey, E.E. Hedgehog actively maintains adult lung quiescence and regulates repair and regeneration. *Nature* **2015**, *526*, 578–582. [CrossRef] [PubMed]

59. Omenetti, A.; Popov, Y.; Jung, Y.; Choi, S.S.; Witek, R.P.; Yang, L.; Brown, K.D.; Schuppan, D.; Diehl, A.M. The hedgehog pathway regulates remodelling responses to biliary obstruction in rats. *Gut* **2008**, *57*, 1275–1282. [CrossRef] [PubMed]

60. Omenetti, A.; Syn, W.K.; Jung, Y.; Francis, H.; Porrello, A.; Witek, R.P.; Choi, S.S.; Yang, L.; Mayo, M.J.; Gershwin, M.E.; *et al.* Repair-related activation of hedgehog signaling promotes cholangiocyte chemokine production. *Hepatology* **2009**, *50*, 518–527. [CrossRef] [PubMed]

61. Syn, W.K.; Jung, Y.; Omenetti, A.; Abdelmalek, M.; Guy, C.D.; Yang, L.; Wang, J.; Witek, R.P.; Fearing, C.M.; Pereira, T.A.; *et al.* Hedgehog-mediated epithelial-to-mesenchymal transition and fibrogenic repair in nonalcoholic fatty liver disease. *Gastroenterology* **2009**, *137*, 1478–1488.e8. [CrossRef] [PubMed]

62. Syn, W.K.; Oo, Y.H.; Pereira, T.A.; Karaca, G.F.; Jung, Y.; Omenetti, A.; Witek, R.P.; Choi, S.S.; Guy, C.D.; Fearing, C.M.; *et al.* Accumulation of natural killer T cells in progressive nonalcoholic fatty liver disease. *Hepatology* **2010**, *51*, 1998–2007. [CrossRef] [PubMed]

63. Syn, W.K.; Choi, S.S.; Liaskou, E.; Karaca, G.F.; Agboola, K.M.; Oo, Y.H.; Mi, Z.; Pereira, T.A.; Zdanowicz, M.; Malladi, P.; *et al.* Osteopontin is induced by hedgehog pathway activation and promotes fibrosis progression in nonalcoholic steatohepatitis. *Hepatology* **2011**, *53*, 106–115. [CrossRef] [PubMed]

64. Pazzaglia, S.; Cifaldi, L.; Saran, A.; Nobili, V.; Fruci, D.; Alisi, A. Hedgehog/hyaluronic acid interaction network in nonalcoholic fatty liver disease, fibrosis, and hepatocellular carcinoma. *Hepatology* **2012**, *56*, 1589. [CrossRef] [PubMed]

65. Machado, M.V.; Michelotti, G.A.; Xie, G.; Almeida Pereira, T.; Boursier, J.; Bohnic, B.; Guy, C.D.; Diehl, A.M. Mouse models of diet-induced nonalcoholic steatohepatitis reproduce the heterogeneity of the human disease. *PLoS ONE* **2015**, *10*, e0127991. [CrossRef] [PubMed]

66. Kakisaka, K.; Cazanave, S.C.; Werneburg, N.W.; Razumilava, N.; Mertens, J.C.; Bronk, S.F.; Gores, G.J. A hedgehog survival pathway in 'undead' lipotoxic hepatocytes. *J. Hepatol.* **2012**, *57*, 844–851. [CrossRef] [PubMed]

67. Nakashima, H.; Nakamura, M.; Yamaguchi, H.; Yamanaka, N.; Akiyoshi, T.; Koga, K.; Yamaguchi, K.; Tsuneyoshi, M.; Tanaka, M.; Katano, M. Nuclear factor-kappab contributes to hedgehog signaling pathway activation through sonic hedgehog induction in pancreatic cancer. *Cancer Res.* **2006**, *66*, 7041–7049. [CrossRef] [PubMed]

68. Syn, W.K.; Agboola, K.M.; Swiderska, M.; Michelotti, G.A.; Liaskou, E.; Pang, H.; Xie, G.; Philips, G.; Chan, I.S.; Karaca, G.F.; *et al.* Nkt-associated hedgehog and osteopontin drive fibrogenesis in non-alcoholic fatty liver disease. *Gut* **2012**, *61*, 1323–1329. [CrossRef] [PubMed]

69. Kwon, H.; Song, K.; Han, C.; Chen, W.; Wang, Y.; Dash, S.; Lim, K.; Wu, T. Inhibition of hedgehog signaling ameliorates hepatic inflammation in mice with nonalcoholic fatty liver disease. *Hepatology* **2015**. [CrossRef] [PubMed]

70. Chung, S.I.; Moon, H.; Ju, H.L.; Cho, K.J.; Kim, D.Y.; Han, K.H.; Eun, J.W.; Nam, S.W.; Ribback, S.; Dombrowski, F.; *et al.* Hepatic expression of sonic hedgehog induces liver fibrosis and promotes hepatocarcinogenesis in a transgenic mouse model. *J. Hepatol.* **2015**, *64*, 618–627. [CrossRef] [PubMed]

71. Hirsova, P.; Ibrahim, S.H.; Bronk, S.F.; Yagita, H.; Gores, G.J. Vismodegib suppresses trail-mediated liver injury in a mouse model of nonalcoholic steatohepatitis. *PLoS ONE* **2013**, *8*, e70599. [CrossRef] [PubMed]

72. Machado, M.V.; Michelotti, G.A.; Pereira, T.A.; Xie, G.; Premont, R.; Cortez-Pinto, H.; Diehl, A.M. Accumulation of duct cells with activated yap parallels fibrosis progression in non-alcoholic fatty liver disease. *J. Hepatol.* **2015**, *63*, 962–970. [CrossRef] [PubMed]

73. Richardson, M.M.; Jonsson, J.R.; Powell, E.E.; Brunt, E.M.; Neuschwander-Tetri, B.A.; Bhathal, P.S.; Dixon, J.B.; Weltman, M.D.; Tilg, H.; Moschen, A.R.; *et al.* Progressive fibrosis in nonalcoholic steatohepatitis: Association with altered regeneration and a ductular reaction. *Gastroenterology* **2007**, *133*, 80–90. [CrossRef] [PubMed]

74. Ye, F.; Jing, Y.Y.; Guo, S.W.; Yu, G.F.; Fan, Q.M.; Qu, F.F.; Gao, L.; Yang, Y.; Wu, D.; Meng, Y.; *et al.* Proliferative ductular reactions correlate with hepatic progenitor cell and predict recurrence in hcc patients after curative resection. *Cell Biosci.* **2014**, *4*, 50. [CrossRef] [PubMed]

75. Swiderska-Syn, M.; Suzuki, A.; Guy, C.D.; Schwimmer, J.B.; Abdelmalek, M.F.; Lavine, J.E.; Diehl, A.M. Hedgehog pathway and pediatric nonalcoholic fatty liver disease. *Hepatology* **2013**, *57*, 1814–1825. [CrossRef] [PubMed]

76. Omenetti, A.; Bass, L.M.; Anders, R.A.; Clemente, M.G.; Francis, H.; Guy, C.D.; McCall, S.; Choi, S.S.; Alpini, G.; Schwarz, K.B.; *et al.* Hedgehog activity, epithelial-mesenchymal transitions, and biliary dysmorphogenesis in biliary atresia. *Hepatology* **2011**, *53*, 1246–1258. [CrossRef] [PubMed]

77. Guy, C.D.; Suzuki, A.; Abdelmalek, M.F.; Burchette, J.L.; Diehl, A.M.; NASH CRN. Treatment response in the pivens trial is associated with decreased hedgehog pathway activity. *Hepatology* **2015**, *61*, 98–107. [CrossRef] [PubMed]

78. Grzelak, C.A.; Martelotto, L.G.; Sigglekow, N.D.; Patkunanathan, B.; Ajami, K.; Calabro, S.R.; Dwyer, B.J.; Tirnitz-Parker, J.E.; Watkins, D.N.; Warner, F.J.; *et al.* The intrahepatic signalling niche of hedgehog is defined by primary cilia positive cells during chronic liver injury. *J. Hepatol.* **2014**, *60*, 143–151. [CrossRef] [PubMed]

79. Matz-Soja, M.; Gebhardt, R. The many faces of hedgehog signalling in the liver: Recent progress reveals striking cellular diversity and the importance of microenvironments. *J. Hepatol.* **2014**, *61*, 1449–1450. [CrossRef] [PubMed]

80. Uschner, F.E.; Ranabhat, G.; Choi, S.S.; Granzow, M.; Klein, S.; Schierwagen, R.; Raskopf, E.; Gautsch, S.; van der Ven, P.F.; Furst, D.O.; *et al.* Statins activate the canonical hedgehog-signaling and aggravate non-cirrhotic portal hypertension, but inhibit the non-canonical hedgehog signaling and cirrhotic portal hypertension. *Sci. Rep.* **2015**, *5*, 14573. [CrossRef] [PubMed]

81. Corbit, K.C.; Aanstad, P.; Singla, V.; Norman, A.R.; Stainier, D.Y.; Reiter, J.F. Vertebrate smoothened functions at the primary cilium. *Nature* **2005**, *437*, 1018–1021. [CrossRef] [PubMed]

82. Ochoa, B.; Syn, W.K.; Delgado, I.; Karaca, G.F.; Jung, Y.; Wang, J.; Zubiaga, A.M.; Fresnedo, O.; Omenetti, A.; Zdanowicz, M.; *et al.* Hedgehog signaling is critical for normal liver regeneration after partial hepatectomy in mice. *Hepatology* **2010**, *51*, 1712–1723. [CrossRef] [PubMed]

83. Lim, Y.C.; McGlashan, S.R.; Cooling, M.T.; Long, D.S. Culture and detection of primary cilia in endothelial cell models. *Cilia* **2015**, *4*, 11. [CrossRef] [PubMed]

84. Guha, M. Hedgehog inhibitor gets landmark skin cancer approval, but questions remain for wider potential. *Nat. Rev. Drug Discov.* **2012**, *11*, 257–258. [CrossRef] [PubMed]

International Journal of
Molecular Sciences

MDPI

Review

Molecular Pathogenesis of NASH

Alessandra Caligiuri, Alessandra Gentilini and Fabio Marra *

Dipartimento di Medicina Sperimentale e Clinica, Università degli Studi di Firenze, Firenze 50121, Italy;
alessandra.caligiuri@unifi.it (A.C.); alessandra.gentilini@unifi.it (A.G.)
* Correspondence: fabio.marra@unifi.it; Tel.: +39-055-7945425; Fax: +39-055-2758099

Academic Editors: Giovanni Targher and Amedeo Lonardo
Received: 14 July 2016; Accepted: 7 September 2016; Published: 20 September 2016

Abstract: Nonalcoholic steatohepatitis (NASH) is the main cause of chronic liver disease in the Western world and a major health problem, owing to its close association with obesity, diabetes, and the metabolic syndrome. NASH progression results from numerous events originating within the liver, as well as from signals derived from the adipose tissue and the gastrointestinal tract. In a fraction of NASH patients, disease may progress, eventually leading to advanced fibrosis, cirrhosis and hepatocellular carcinoma. Understanding the mechanisms leading to NASH and its evolution to cirrhosis is critical to identifying effective approaches for the treatment of this condition. In this review, we focus on some of the most recent data reported on the pathogenesis of NASH and its fibrogenic progression, highlighting potential targets for treatment or identification of biomarkers of disease progression.

Keywords: fibrosis; inflammation; chemokines; genetics; microbiota; pattern-recognition receptors; nuclear receptors; hepatic stellate cells; macrophages

1. Introduction

Nonalcoholic fatty liver disease (NAFLD) is an expanding health problem, which varies in prevalence among ethnic groups, occurring with an estimated global prevalence of 25% [1]. NAFLD associates with obesity, insulin resistance or type 2 diabetes and other metabolic abnormalities, such as dyslipidemia and hypertension, collectively termed metabolic syndrome. In high risk populations, the prevalence of NAFLD may be as high as 70%–90% [2,3]. NAFLD covers a spectrum of pathological abnormalities. Although most patients have simple steatosis, around 7%–30% develop nonalcoholic steatohepatitis (NASH), that in at least a third of cases progresses to advanced fibrosis or cirrhosis. The tendency to develop hepatic steatosis differs among ethnic groups, with African-Americans having a lower (24%) and Hispanics a higher (45%) frequency of the disease than Americans of European descent (33%). The causes for these ethnic differences in prevalence of hepatic steatosis and liver injury are not entirely understood.

NASH is characterized by hepatocellular damage, inflammation and fibrosis [4,5]. In general, simple steatosis is considered a less severe form of NAFLD, although recent data indicate a possible risk of progression [6,7]. In contrast, NASH is a significant risk factor for the development of cirrhosis and hepatocellular carcinoma [8–10]. Although NASH was first documented more than 30 years ago [11], its pathogenesis is still not fully elucidated. Initially, a two-hit hypothesis, based on appearance of steatosis (first hit), followed by a second hit leading to inflammation, hepatocyte damage, and fibrosis, was proposed by Day and James [12]. While accumulation of triglycerides is necessary for the development of NASH, they may actually have a protective role against hepatocytes lipotoxicity, which is mainly induced by fatty acids and derived metabolites such as diacylgycerols, acylcarnitines or ceramides [13,14]. In addition, it is still unclear whether NASH develops sequentially, on the grounds of a fatty liver, or it is rather a de novo response to a lipotoxic environment. The multiparallel hypothesis proposed more recently [15] suggests that NASH is the result of numerous conditions acting in parallel, including genetic predisposition, abnormal lipid metabolism, oxidative stress, lipotoxicity, mitochondrial dysfunction, altered production of cytokines and adipokines, gut dysbiosis and endoplasmic reticulum stress. According to this hypothesis, hepatic inflammation in NASH may even precede steatosis. As more contributing factors are continuously identified, a more complex picture of NASH pathogenesis is emerging [16] (Figure 1).

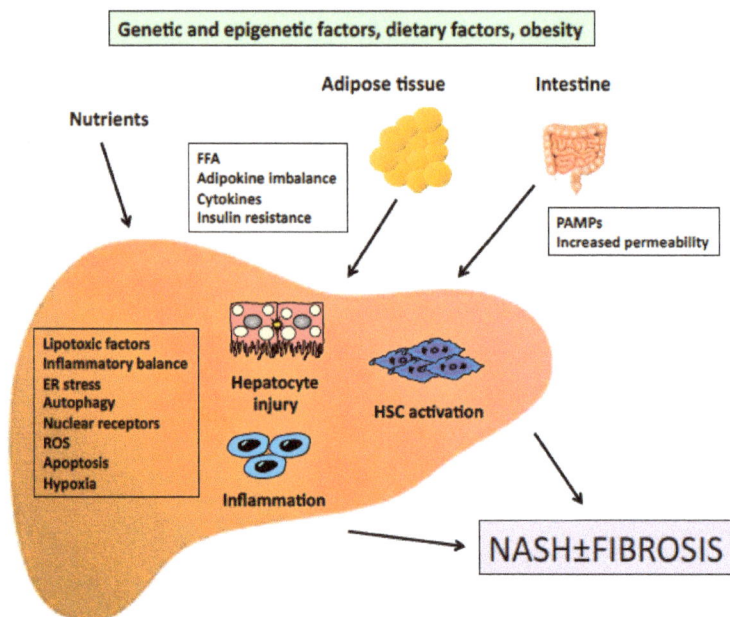

Figure 1. Outline of the pathogenesis of NASH. Signals generated inside the liver as a consequence of increased lipid accumulation, together with signals derived from extrahepatic organs cooperate to induce inflammation and fibrosis. FFA, free fatty acids; PAMPs, pathogen-associated molecular patterns; ER, endoplasmic reticulum; ROS, reactive oxygen species; HSC, hepatic stellate cell.

2. Genetic Factors

The relevance of genetic factor in the context of NASH has been recently and elegantly outlined by twin studies [17]. A long list of genes potentially implicated in NAFLD appearance and progression has been reported, and these data have been the subject of a recent review [18].

A significant association with a SNP was identified in patatin-like phospholipase domain-containing 3 (*PNPLA3*) on chromosome 22. The variant (rs738409 c.444 C>G, p.I148M), a non-synonymous cytosine to guanine mutation resulting in isoleucine to methionine conversion, correlates with increased hepatic lipid content and predisposes to fatty liver-associated liver disease, from simple steatosis to steatohepatitis, fibrosis and hepatocellular carcinoma [19,20]. *PNPLA3* encodes for a 481 amino acid protein, whose role has not been fully elucidated. It appears to function as acylglycerol hydrolase, acting on triacylglycerol, diacylglycerol, and monoacylglycerol [21,22]. Additional evidence indicates that PNPLA3 also acts as lysophosphatidic acid acetyltransferase [23,24]. Overexpression of the I148M variant in mouse liver promotes accumulation of triacylglycerol, increased synthesis of fatty acids and impaired hydrolysis of triacylglycerol [25]. Moreover, the *PNPLA3* genotype has been reported to influence liver storage of retinol and retinol serum levels in obese subjects [26], suggesting a potential role of PNPLA3 in regulating retinol metabolism and hepatic stellate cell (HSC) biology [27]. Remarkably, PNPLA3 has been recently shown to be expressed in hepatic stellate cells [28]. Interestingly, the prevalence of the *PNPLA3* I148M allele varies considerably among different ethnic groups, with the highest frequency in Hispanics (0.49), and lower frequencies in European Americans (0.23) and African-Americans (0.17) [20]. This is in agreement with the different prevalence of NAFLD in the three ethnic groups.

Carriage of a non-synonymous genetic variant in *TM6SF2* (rs58542926 c.449 C>T, p.E167K) on chromosome 19 (19p13.11) has been reported to correlate with steatosis and increased risk of advanced fibrosis in NAFLD patients [29,30], independently of other factors, including diabetes, obesity, or *PNPLA3* genotype. The minor allele frequency in one of the NAFLD populations tested was 0.12, compared to a frequency of 0.07 in a reference population. TM6SF2, is a transmembrane protein localized in endoplasmic reticulum (ER) and ER–Golgi compartments and functions as a lipid transporter [31]. The amino acid change E167K causes loss of function of TM6SF2 protein. Studies performed in cell lines showed that downregulation of *TM6SF2* reduces lipoproteins and apolipoprotein B (APOB) levels, and increases hepatic deposition of triglycerides and the amount and size of lipid droplets. In contrast, the size and number of lipid droplets diminishes when TM6SF2 is overexpressed, indicating that TM6SF2 plays a role in regulating hepatic lipid efflux [29,31].

A broad spectrum of other genes has been associated with NAFLD. Polymorphism was reported in genes involved in carbohydrate and lipid metabolism, insulin-induced pathways, as well as inflammatory response, oxidative stress and fibrogenesis. A study by Dongiovanni et al. reported that non-synonymous SNPs in ectoenzyme nucleotide pyrophosphate phosphodiesterase 1 (*ENPP1* or *PC1*) (rs1044498, K121Q) and insulin receptor substrate-1 (*IRS1*) (rs1801278, Q972R), are associated with insulin resistance, through impairment of insulin receptor-mediated pathways, such as reduced AKT activation, and promote fibrosis in NAFLD patients [32].

A functional non-synonymous variant (rs1260326, P446L) of glucokinase regulatory protein (GCKR) has also been associated with NAFLD [33]. This variant produces a GCKR with defective inhibitory function, leading to increased glucokinase activity and hepatic glucose uptake [34]. The resultant unimpeded hepatic glycolysis reduces glucose levels, inducing malonyl-CoA synthesis, a substrate for lipogenesis that causes liver fat deposition and impairs mitochondrial β-oxidation. A polymorphism in the solute carrier family 2 member 1 gene (*SLC2A1*), a glucose transporter, has been reported in NAFLD subjects. SLC2A1 downregulation in hepatocytes results in lipid accumulation and oxidative stress [35].

Several genes involved in oxidative stress have been investigated. Two reports correlated the C282Y variant in hemochromatosis gene (HFE) with NASH and higher susceptibility to more severe disease, as fibrosis or cirrhosis [36,37]. However, these findings have not been confirmed by other studies [38–40]. Very recently, the rs641738 genotype at the *MBOAT7-TMC4* locus, encoding for the membrane bound O-acyltransferase domain-containing 7 was associated with more severe liver damage and increased risk of fibrosis in patients with NAFLD. This effect has been ascribed to changes in remodeling of the hepatic phosphatidylinositol acyl-chain [41].

3. Epigenetics

Epigenetic changes consist in modifications at the transcriptional level affecting gene expression and phenotype. A number of epigenetic aberrations have been associated with NAFLD pathogenesis, causing alterations in lipid metabolism, insulin resistance (IR), dysfunction of endoplasmic reticulum (ER) and mitochondria, oxidative stress and inflammation [42]. The different epigenetic pathways potentially involved in NAFLD are summarized in Figure 2.

Aberrant DNA methylation is a major epigenetic process in NAFLD development and progression to NASH [43]. It occurs through methyltransferases (DNMTs) that catalyze the conversion of cytosine to 5-methylcytosine [44], leading to gene silencing. It has been reported that mice fed with a methyl-deficient diet show reduced levels of hepatic *S*-adenosylmethionine (SAM), associated with methylation of genes involved in DNA damage and repair, lipid and glucose metabolism and fibrosis progression [45]. In agreement, food-derived methyl donors, such as folate, betaine and choline, responsible for SAM synthesis, counteract DNA methylation [46] whereas folate deficiency correlates with enhanced fatty acid synthesis and hepatic accumulation of triglycerides (TG) via DNA methylation [47]. Methyl donor supplementation reverts liver lipid deposition induced by high fat/high sucrose-diet, lowering global hepatic DNA methylation and methylation levels of the promoter regions of different regulatory factors [48]. Betaine has been demonstrated to diminish the methylation levels of the promoter of microsomal triglyceride transfer protein (MTP), enhancing hepatic TG export and ameliorating liver steatosis in mice administered a high-fat diet (HFD) [43]. In addition, epigenetic changes of peroxisome proliferator-activated receptor gamma (PPARγ) in the liver of NAFLD patients seems to promote IR [49].

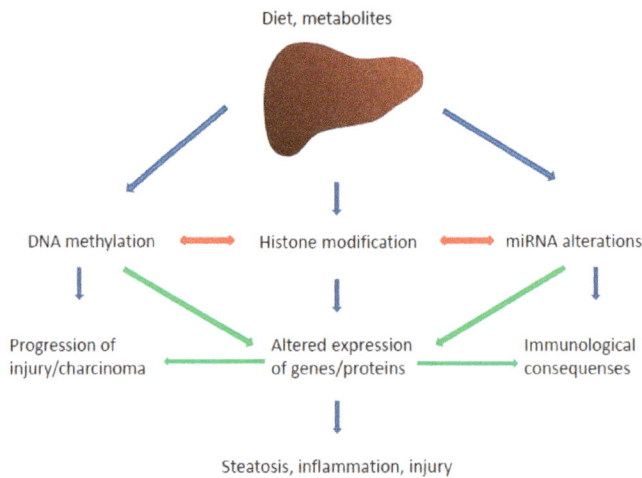

Figure 2. Epigenetic pathways implicated in the pathogenesis of NASH. The major pathways and their main effectors are depicted.

Although most epigenetic alterations are transient, DNA methylation can be inherited from parents [50]. It has been reported that maternal Western diet during prenatal time can increase the susceptibility to NAFLD of male progeny [51]. Novel evidence indicates that mitochondrial DNA (mtDNA) methylation may also play a role in NAFLD pathogenesis [52,53]. Liver methylation of *NADH dehydrogenase 6* (*MT-ND6*) correlates with NAFLD severity, resulting in significantly lower expression of MT-ND6 mRNA in NASH than in patients with simple steatosis [54].

Histone acetylation, regulated by histone acetyltransferases (HATs) and histone deacetylases (HDACs), has been extensively associated with NAFLD [55,56]. High-fat maternal diet was shown to lead to depletion of fetal hepatic HDAC1, suggesting that diet-induced maternal obesity can alter fetal chromatin via histone modifications [55]. Carbohydrate-responsive element-binding protein (ChREBP), an activator of lipogenic and glycolytic pathways involved in NAFLD progression, is regulated by the HAT activator p300. Glucose-activated p300 induces ChREBP hyperacetylation, stimulating its transcriptional activity and hepatic lipogenesis in mice, and p300 overexpression is associated with steatosis and IR [56].

NAFLD has been also correlated with histone methylation. Lipid accumulation in the liver of HFD mice has been associated with H3K4 and H3K9 histone trimethylation of peroxisome proliferator-activated receptor alpha (PPARα) and lipolysis-related genes [57]. In addition, trans-generational changes in histone methylation promote lipogenesis and ER stress, acting on endoplasmic reticulum oxidoreductin 1α (ERO1α) and liver X receptor α (LXRα) [58].

Sirtuins (SIRTs) belong to the silent information regulator-2 family. SIRT1 deacetylation has been recognized as a regulatory mechanism for several proteins involved in NAFLD pathogenesis [59] and low SIRT1 expression has been observed in NAFLD models [60]. In addition, SIRT1-mediated regulation of fetal metabolome and epigenome has been reported under maternal HFD [61]. SIRT3 is localized in mitochondria and regulates fatty acid oxidation. SIRT3 knockout mice fed HFD develop hepatic steatosis and IR [62].

MicroRNAs (miRNAs) modulate gene expression via post-transcriptional mechanisms, regulating the main cellular processes, such as lipid metabolism, inflammation, apoptosis, cell growth and differentiation. In the last few years, aberrant miRNA expression has been reported in a number of diseases including metabolic disorders [63,64], whereas an increasing number of dysregulated miRNAs, implicated in fatty acid synthesis, uptake and storage of triglycerides or oxidation, have been recently identified in NAFLD [65] (Table 1). Among these, miR-122, which negatively regulates hepatic lipogenesis, is reduced in NASH patients [66] whereas miR-34a, that induces β-oxidation and inhibits synthesis of fatty acids via a sirtuin1/5′ adenosine monophosphate-activated protein kinase/3-hydroxy-3-methylglutaryl-CoA reductase (SIRT1-AMPK-HMGCR) mechanism, is upregulated in NAFLD patients [67]. miRNA-33a has been recently reported to participate in NASH development, counteracting cholesterol 7alpha-hydroxylase (CYP7A1). Sterol response element-binding protein 2 (SREBP2) binds to its own gene promoter to induce miR-33a, which leads to a decrease in cholesterol efflux to HDL and bile acid synthesis in Cyp7a1-tg mice [68]. In addition, miR-33a inhibits CYP7A1 and bile acid synthesis to inhibit cholesterol catabolism.

Table 1. Modulation of miRNA expression relevant to NAFLD/NASH. Δ indicates up- (↑) or downregulation (↓). CYP7A1: cholesterol 7α1-hydroxylase; SREBP2: sterol response element-binding protein 2; SIRT1: sirtuin1; AMPK: 5′ adenosine monophosphate-activated protein kinase; HMGCR: 3-hydroxy-3-methylglutaryl-CoA reductase; FAS: fatty acid synthase; ACC: Acetyl-CoA carboxylase; mTOR: mammalian target of rapamycin; ROS: reactive oxygen species; RAC1: Ras-related C3 botulinum toxin substrate 1; ?: mechanism and/or target unknown.

miR	Δ	Disease	Model	Role	Validated/ Predicted Target	Reference
33a	↑	NASH	Mouse Liver	Cholesterol and bile acid homeostasis	CYP7A1, SREPB2	[68]
34a	↑	NAFLD/NASH	Human Biopsies	Lipid homeostasis	SIRT1-AMPK-HMGCR	[67,69]
103a2	↑	NAFLD	Human Biopsies	Insulin signaling, metabolism, inflammation	?	[30,70]
160b	↑	NAFLD	Human Biopsies	Insulin signaling	?	[30]
122	↓	NASH	HFD mice/ Human Biopsies	Lipid and cholesterol metabolism	HMGCR, FAS, SREBP1/2, ACC	[66,71]
301a-3p	↑	Steatosis/ NAFLD/NASH	Human Biopsies	?	?	[69]
375	↓	NAFLD/NASH/ Cirrhosis	Human Biopsies	?	?	[69]
576-5p	↑	NAFLD	Human Biopsies	Insulin signaling, metabolic homeostasis, inflammation	mTOR signaling, ephrin B signaling, ROS production, RAC1	[70]
892a	↑	NAFLD	Human Biopsies	Kupffer cell activation ?	?	[70]
I137	↑	NAFLD	Human Biopsies	?	?	[70]
1282	↓	NAFLD	Human Biopsies	Insulin signaling, metabolism, inflammation	?	[70]
3663-5p	↑	NAFLD	Human Biopsies	Insulin signaling, metabolism, inflammation	?	[70]
3924	↑	NAFLD	Human Biopsies	Insulin signaling, metabolism, inflammation	?	[70]

More recently, other dysregulated miRNAs have been identified in NAFLD livers [70]. Among these, the most significantly upregulated (miR-103a-2, miR-106b, miR-576-5p, miRPlus-I137, miR-892a, miR-1282, miR-3663-5p, and miR-3924) play critical roles in insulin signaling, metabolism homeostasis, inflammation and cancer. In particular, miR-576-5p influences multiple pathways implied in NAFLD, including mammalian target of rapamycin (mTOR), a kinase modulated by insulin that induces hepatic lipogenesis through a PPARγ-dependent mechanism [72]. miR-576-5p also regulates eukaryotic translation initiation factor 4 (eIF4), p70S6 kinase (p70S6K) and phosphatidylinositol-4,5-bisphosphate 3-kinase (PI3K), pathways associated with insulin action and metabolic control. Moreover, a direct target of miR-576-5p is the small GTPase RAC1, which promotes lipotoxicity via c-Jun N-terminal kinase (JNK) activation. RAC1 is negatively modulated by miR-576-5p, triggering a protective effect against NAFLD progression [72]. Finally, in a study conducted in biopsy-staged NAFLD patients, increased miR-301a-3p and miR-34a-5p and decreased miR-375 significantly correlated with disease progression [69].

4. Dietary Factors

Lifestyle changes focusing on weight loss remain the keystone of NAFLD and NASH treatment [73]. Recent reports indicate that lifestyle modifications based on decreased energy intake and/or increased physical activity during 6–12 months cause improvement in biochemical and metabolic parameters and reduce steatosis and inflammation [74]. Conversely, increased consumption of sugar-sweetened food and beverages has been associated with NAFLD development and progression. High intake of fructose, used as food and drink sweetener, is implicated in NAFLD pathogenesis through several mechanisms. In addition, a fructose-enriched diet contributes to induce liver fibrosis in animal models of NASH [75]. Via the portal vein, dietary fructose reaches the liver in high concentrations, exerting a lipogenic action by activation of the transcription factors SREBP1 and ChREBP and subsequent induction of acetyl-CoA carboxylase (ACC) 1, fatty acid synthase (FAS) and stearoyl-CoA desaturase 1 (SCD1) [76]. These effects persist in liver-specific insulin receptor knockout mice, indicating that fructose stimulates lipogenesis independently of insulin signaling [77]. Fructose-induced de novo lipogenesis (DNL), enhancing malonyl-CoA concentration, inhibits mitochondrial β-oxidation and decreases mitochondrial ATP production [78]. In addition, fructose stimulates lipogenesis by inducing ER stress and subsequently activating the transcription factor X-box binding protein 1 (XBP1), which, in turn, upregulates lipogenic enzymes, as demonstrated in mice fed with a 60% fructose diet [79]. In concomitance, phosphorylation of fructose to fructose-1-phosphate leads to depletion of hepatic ATP and increase in ADP and inosine monophosphate (IMP), which is converted to uric acid [80], that promotes steatosis inducing mitochondrial oxidative stress [81]. Generation of reactive oxygen species (ROS) is also induced by fructose metabolism [82], and nutrient-derived ROS have been associated with enhanced steatosis via insulin-independent PI3K pathway [83]. Moreover, upregulating ketohexokinase, fructose potentiates its own metabolism and ketohexokinase inhibition leads to decreased fatty liver and reduced liver inflammation in high-fat/high-sucrose fed mice [84]. Finally, fructose-induced metabolic disorders can be mediated by epigenetic changes, such as alterations in genomic or mitochondrial DNA (mtDNA) methylation [85,86].

Dietary iron overload has been recently implicated in NASH pathogenesis. A study by Handa et al. [87] shows that dietary iron excess leads to a severe NASH phenotype in an obese, diabetogenic mouse model characterized by oxidative stress, inflammation and ballooning. Different molecular mechanisms are involved, including upregulation of cytokines (interleukin 6, IL-6, tumor necrosis factor α, TNFα) and immune mediators (Toll-like receptor 4, TLR4, inducible nitric oxide synthase, NOS, interferon gamma, IFNγ), and induction of inflammasome related factors (NOD like receptor 3, NLRP3, interleukin 18, IL-18) and genes associated with lipid metabolism. Moreover, emerging evidence indicates that hepatic copper (Cu) deficiency is associated with NAFLD development and progression. In an experimental rat model, a Cu deficient diet coupled with high sucrose intake provoked NASH, even in the absence of obesity or severe steatosis. Rats fed low-Cu/high-sucrose diet displayed enhanced liver expression of lipogenic enzymes, such as ATP citrate lyase (ACLY) and FAS, and of inflammatory and pro-fibrogenic factors (TNFα, C–C motif chemokine CCL2, CCL3), together with hepatic stellate cell activation. While low Cu alone promotes lipid peroxidation, as indicated by increased levels of malondialdehyde (MDA), its combination with high sucrose (or fructose), that causes a further reduction of hepatic Cu, causes insulin resistance and liver damage, with hepatocyte ballooning and occurrence of Mallory-Denk bodies. In addition, Cu deficiency influences Fe retention and partitioning in animals as well as in NAFLD patients [88].

Several lines of evidence correlate hepatic free fatty acids (FFAs) and free cholesterol (FC) accumulation to NAFLD pathogenesis. Dysregulation of lipid homeostasis plays an essential role in NAFLD pathogenesis, induced by a surplus of dietary free fatty acids, enhanced DNL and augmented lipolysis [89]. Rather than total hepatic fat content, the role of specific lipid classes in the development and progression of NAFLD is emerging [90]. In particular, accumulation of different lipids as well as upregulation of distinct enzymes mediating DNL was found to be associated with macrovesicular or microvesicular steatosis, the latter correlating with mitochondrial dysfunction and NAFLD [91]. Among toxic lipids, saturated fatty acids have been shown to be elevated in NASH patients [92] and induce inflammation and hepatocyte apoptosis by activating JNK and mitochondrial pathways. Other lipids having a role in NAFLD include ceramide, diacylglycerol (DAG) and sphingosine [90,93–96]. In particular, DAG and ceramide impair insulin capability to stimulate glycogen synthesis and suppress gluconeogenesis, through protein kinase-C epsilon (PKCε) activation [97]. In contrast, unsaturated fatty acids do not affect cell viability and an increase in their content leads to enhanced hepatic synthesis of TG. In turn, TG accumulation is not toxic but may protect the liver from the excessive deposition of toxic TG precursors [98,99]. Omega-3 polyunsaturated fatty acids (PUFAs) plasma levels are reduced in patients with NASH. However, pharmacologic supplementation did not induce an amelioration of the histologic picture of NASH [100], and in an experimental model it was even associated with more severe damage [101].

Emerging evidence underscores the role of cholesterol as a prominent risk factor for the pathogenesis of NAFLD/NASH. In humans a progressive increase in hepatic FC during NAFLD progression to NASH has been observed [102,103]. In experimental models increase in dietary cholesterol has been shown to promote hepatic inflammation and fibrosis [104–106], whereas a cholesterol-free diet ameliorates NASH [107]. The molecular mechanisms underlying FC accumulation during NASH development are multiple and only partially elucidated. Current data indicate that cholesterol homeostasis is dysregulated in NAFLD, due to an increase in cholesterol synthesis and uptake or dysfunction in cholesterol metabolism. Accordingly, the activity of two key regulators of cholesterol synthesis, HMGCR and SREBP2, is elevated in NASH patients [103,108,109]. Similarly, expression analysis of genes involved in cholesterol metabolism reveals a number of altered pathways in individuals with NASH [108].

Cholesterol uptake from lipoproteins is mediated by different proteins, including the low density lipoprotein receptor (LDLR) and the scavenger receptor class B type I (SR-BI) [110]. Hepatic uptake of LDL-cholesterol occurs via the scavenger receptor pathway in unrestrained manner, leading to deposition of cholesterol crystals in hepatocytes and generation of foamy Kupffer cells, two critical features of NASH [111,112]. Intracellular accumulation of free cholesterol represents a key event for inflammasome activation and inflammatory response [112] and sensitizes cells to transforming growth factor beta (TGF-β), TNF-α and Fas, leading to liver damage and disease progression [104,113]. Moreover, LDL cholesterol can be oxidized to oxidized low-density lipoprotein (oxLDL) cholesterol, which has been found in high concentrations in the plasma of NASH patients [114] and induces proinflammatory cytokine secretion accumulating in lysosomes of Kupffer cells [111,112]. Recently, a reduced efflux of FC has been observed in injured (foam) hepatocytes of NAFLD patients, associated with reduced expression of ATP-binding cassette sub-family G member 8 (ABCG8), which regulates cholesterol excretion trough the bile [108]. In addition, decreased expression of CYP7A1 and CYP27A responsible for cholesterol transformation into bile acids (BA) has been found in human NAFLD/NASH [108], as well as in a rat model of NASH induced by dietary cholesterol overload [115].

Oxysterols, the oxidative products of cholesterol generated during bile acid synthesis, have been described to induce liver damage through mitochondrial impairment. A study by Bellanti et al. [116] shows that mice fed high fat/high cholesterol (HF/HC) exhibit high levels of toxic oxysterols, such as triol, and oxidative stress and mitochondrial dysfunction associated with NASH. Accordingly, Huh7 and primary rat hepatocytes co-exposed to triol and palmitic or oleic acid, undergo apoptosis, mediated by impaired mitochondrial respiratory chain [116]. Finally, besides the effects on liver, cholesterol contributes to NASH pathogenesis also by stimulating inflammatory reactions in other tissues, such as adipose tissue and arterial wall, representing a key factor in the multiparallel scenario concurring to NASH [117,118].

5. Mitochondrial Dysfunction and Apoptosis

Oxidative stress has been recognized as a major factor in the pathogenesis of NASH. Based on the evidence that a high amount of intracellular ROS are generated in mitochondria and ROS overproduction is elicited in the presence of respiratory chain disruption, mitochondrial impairment has been suggested as a main event in NASH development [83,119,120]. Along these lines, structural and functional defects in mitochondria have been reported in patients with NASH [121,122].

Several mechanisms contribute to mitochondrial impairment and subsequent hepatic cell injury during NASH, mainly associated with lipotoxicity. It has been shown that, following lipid accumulation, water and calcium influx in mitochondria is increased, due to lower phosphorylation of the voltage dependent anion channel (VDAC) in the mitochondrial outer membrane, resulting in cytochrome c release and cell death [123]. Lipotoxic effects in mitochondria are also mediated by JNK; high concentrations of palmitate cause mitochondrial dysfunction and apoptosis through phosphorylation of Sab (SH3BP5), a mitochondrial outer membrane substrate of JNK [124], whereas free cholesterol accumulation in the liver of NASH mice induces mitochondrial permeability, ROS production and apoptosis through JNK1. An emerging role for NAD^+ in mitochondrial stress induction during NASH development has been recently shown. Gariani et al. demonstrated that mice fed high-fat/high-sucrose exhibit impaired mitochondrial function associated with lower hepatic NAD^+ levels [125]. Conversely, NAD^+ repletion displays a protective effect against NAFLD, probably mediated by the induction of mitochondrial unfolded protein response (UPRmt), an adaptive mechanism dependent on the histone deacetylases SIRT1 and SIRT3, aimed to enhance mitochondrial activity and hepatic β-oxidation [126]. Furthermore, recent studies have suggested a role for coenzyme Q (CoQ), which is essential for mitochondrial respiration, in NAFLD development and progression to NASH [127–130]. Abnormal concentrations of CoQ have been found in plasma and liver of NAFLD patients [131] and perturbation in CoQ metabolism was observed in experimental NAFLD during disease progression [132,133].

Other key inducers of mitochondrial dysfunction are lysosomal permeabilization, which is frequently observed in NAFLD patients and associated with caspase activation [134], and ROS generation. CYP2E1 promotes oxidative stress, inflammation and protein modifications, by hydrolyzing molecules such as fatty acids and ethanol into toxic metabolites, including ROS, which cause respiratory chain disruption and mitochondrial damage [135], resulting in hepatocyte injury and progression to NASH [136].

6. Necroptosis

Necroptosis is a recently described cell death mechanism, morphologically comparable to necrosis, but consisting in definite biochemical pathways that occur in a programmed mode [137] and are potentially involved in inflammatory disorders, including liver diseases. Necroptosis can be initiated by activation of multiple signals, such as toll-like receptors, death receptors and others, which lead to the assembly of the necrosome, a multiprotein complex consisting in caspase-8,

Fas-Associated protein with Death Domain (FADD), cellular FLICE/caspase 8-like inhibitory protein (cFLIP), and receptor-interacting proteins 1 and 3 (RIP1 and RIP3) [138]. RIP1–RIP3 interaction initiates necroptotic signaling [139]; RIP3 phosphorylates mixed lineage kinase domain-like protein (MLKL), which oligomerizes and translocates to the plasma membrane causing irreversible membrane damage and consequent cell death [140]. In specific cell setting, RIP3 can mediate necroptosis independently of RIP1 [141–143]. In other cell contexts, a RIP3 dependent ROS production may play an additional role [144,145].

Recently, necroptosis has been proposed as a novel mechanism in the pathogenesis of NAFLD both in humans and experimental models. Gautheron et al. found that RIP3 was overexpressed and mediated liver inflammation, activation of hepatic progenitor cells/cholangiocytes and liver fibrosis in NASH patients and in the methionine/choline-deficient (MCD) mouse model of steatohepatitis. They observed that RIP3 induces JNK activation, leading to release of pro-inflammatory mediators, such as CCL2, that further sustain RIP3-dependent signaling, cell death, and liver fibrosis. RIP3-induced pathways were blocked by caspase-8. [146]. A study by Afonso et al. [147] confirmed that hepatic levels of RIP3 are significantly augmented in steatohepatitis and showed that RIP3-dependent MLKL activation is increased in the liver of NAFLD patients as well as in MCD-induced experimental NASH. Moreover, lack of RIP3 ameliorates liver injury, steatosis, inflammation and fibrosis in experimental NASH.

7. Endoplasmic Reticulum Stress

ER stress has been implicated in a number of liver diseases, including NASH. ER dysfunction, ATP depletion or other stimuli induce the unfolded protein response (UPR), an adaptive mechanism directed to avoid luminal accumulation of defective proteins and apoptosis initiation. In NAFLD, a cross-talk between insulin signaling and UPR has been reported, involving XBP–1/PI3K interaction and consequent XBP-1 nuclear translocation [148]. Other pathways activated by cellular response to ER stress involve JNK, an activator of inflammation and apoptosis implicated in NAFLD progression to NASH [90] and SREBP-1c, which induces liver fat accumulation, worsening ER stress [149]. In vitro studies show that exposure of hepatic cells to a lipotoxic concentration of palmitate, a saturated fatty acid (SFA), is associated with ER calcium depletion, ROS accumulation and apoptosis [92,150,151]. In fact, increased SFA incorporation in ER membrane, as well as altered phosphatidylcholine/phosphatidylethanolamine ratio, induces disruption of ER membrane and impairment of sarcoendoplasmic reticulum calcium ATPase (SERCA) function, causing a net calcium efflux from ER stores and its subsequent translocation to the mitochondria, with dysregulation of mitochondrial metabolism and oxidative stress. Accordingly SERCA activity is impaired in obese livers [152] and overexpression of SERCA in obese mice improve hepatic ER stress, indicating that SERCA plays a crucial role in lipotoxic-induced ER stress and, indirectly, in mitochondrial dysfunction [152].

8. Hypoxia

In experimental NASH, hypoxia causes alterations in lipid homeostasis, upregulating genes involved in lipogenesis, such as SREBP-1c, PPARγ, ACC1 or 2 and downregulating genes implied in lipid metabolism, such as PPARα and carnitine palmitoyltransferase-1 (CPT-1) [153]. Besides lipid metabolism, insulin signaling is also affected and under hypoxic conditions hepatic upregulation of inflammatory cytokines and profibrogenic genes was observed [154]. Moreover, reduced oxygen availability induces secretion of adipokines and inflammatory cytokines in adipose tissue [155], contributing to alter lipid metabolism and glucose homeostasis [156,157]. These effects are mediated by hypoxia-inducible transcription factors (HIF-1α and HIF-2α) that regulate cellular response to oxygen deficiency and can be also activated by other stimuli, including oxidative stress or inflammatory signals [158]. In particular, HIF-1α transcription is induced by nuclear factor kappa-B (NF-κB), and NF-κB activity is crucial for HIF-1α accumulation under oxygen deprivation [159]. Furthermore, hypoxia has been reported to modulate inflammation by regulating TLR expression and function through HIF-1 [160,161]. Along these lines, it is conceivable that the proinflammatory state observed in obese NAFLD patients may be enhanced by hypoxia, due to a positive feedback mechanism involving HIF-1α and NF-κB, explaining the exacerbation of liver injury in NAFLD subjects in the presence of obstructive sleep apnea-hypopnea syndrome (OSAHS) [162].

9. Inflammation

Inflammation represents a crucial aspect in NASH pathogenesis. Overload of toxic lipids, mainly FFA, causes cellular stress and induces specific signals that trigger hepatocyte apoptosis, the prevailing mechanism of cell death in NASH, correlating with the degree of liver inflammation and fibrosis [163]. Signaling pathways induced by key death receptors, such as TNF-related apoptosis-inducing ligand (TRAIL-R), Fas and tumor necrosis factor receptor (TNFR), are upregulated in NASH, indicating they may have a role in promoting inflammation and chemokine secretion. Although the precise role of Fas and TNFR in NASH in vivo is still controversial, it has been shown that lack of TRAIL-R is protective, as TRAIL-R-deficient mice display reduced steatosis, inflammation and fibrosis in association with lower hepatocyte apoptosis [164]. Moreover, prolonged ER stress and mitochondrial dysfunction, two critical events in NAFLD, have been reported to induce apoptosis through TRAIL-R/caspase 8 [165].

Different types of immune cells are recruited and/or activated to the site of injury, contributing to NAFLD development and progression. Kupffer Cell (KC) activation is critical in NASH and precedes the recruitment of other cells [166]. Lanthier et al. [167] have shown that KC depletion increases insulin sensitivity and ameliorates inflammation and fibrosis. Depending on the settings, different polarization forms have been described for KCs, mainly classified in two phenotypes: M1, pro-inflammatory and M2, considered primarily immunoregulatory [168]. However, markers of both M1 and M2 forms can be expressed at once [169]. Differentiation of KCs towards a M1 phenotype is principally driven by pathogen-associated molecular patterns (PAMPs) that, interacting with TLRs, induce the secretion of various cytokines, such as IL-1β, IL-12, TNF-α, CCL2 and CCL5, concurring to further hepatocyte damage and release of damage-associated molecular patterns (DAMPs). DAMPs, in turn, act on TLRs amplifying KCs activation and inflammation. In addition, some cytokines (i.e., CCL2 and CCL5), induce HSC activation, initiating a fibrogenic response [170]. Activation of KCs in NAFLD is also triggered by toxic lipids, that upregulate TLRs and augment the response to lipopolysaccharide (LPS) [171]. KCs displaying the M2 phenotype produce several factors with anti-inflammatory properties, as IL-4, IL-10, IL-13 and TGF-α [168,169], but different subtypes have been identified with diverse actions. Although it has been reported that induction of peroxisome proliferator-activated receptor delta (PPARδ) drives KCs toward the M2 form, reducing obesity-induced insulin resistance in mice [172], the role of M2 KCs in NAFLD is still not elucidated [168].

Despite potent antimicrobial and phagocytic properties, neutrophils display scarce specificity. Excess of neutrophil recruitment in NASH crucially contributes to hepatocyte damage, inflammation and fibrosis, through the release of different factors [173,174], including cytotoxic enzymes as myeloperoxidase and elastase. Myeloperoxidase-deficient mice show moderated NASH, associated with lower hepatic secretion of inflammatory cytokines [175]. Similarly, deletion of neutrophil elastase attenuates liver inflammation in experimental NAFLD [176].

Dendritic Cells (DCs) counteract sterile inflammation acting as antigen-presenting cells and eliminating cell debris and apoptotic cells. Studies aimed to establish DCs' function in NASH have shown controversial results [177]. An anti-inflammatory and antifibrotic role of DCs in NASH is suggested by the fact that liver depletion of these cells exacerbates inflammation and fibrosis. According to the study by Henning et al liver infiltrating DCs activate and secrete IL-6, TNF-α and CCL2 [178]. In contrast, other findings report that avoiding the accumulation of DCs subtypes expressing high levels of inflammatory factors limits liver injury in experimental NASH [179].

Natural Killer (NK) cells in the liver are stimulated through several receptors upon interaction with other hepatic cells. In NASH, activation of NK can be achieved by a broad number of ligands and cytokines, but the role of these cells in NAFLD pathogenesis is still controversial [180,181]. Two different phenotypes of NKT cells have been recently associated with liver disease, acting in opposite modes during sterile inflammation: proinflammatory type I and protective type II cells [182]. Although NKT type I cells can be activated by lipids, suggesting their possible involvement in NAFLD, NKT-deficient mice fed HFD are more prone to steatosis and weight gain than wild type mice [183]. In addition, adoptive transfer of NKT cells in leptin-deficient mice ameliorates glucose metabolism and diminishes fatty liver [184]. Furthermore, depletion of NKT can result in activation of KC and secretion of IL-12 [184]. Conversely, clinical studies performed in patients with different stages of NAFLD demonstrate that NKT cells tend to increase in the liver during disease progression [185]. According to these data, NKT cells seem to be depleted in early NAFLD to enhance in the later phases, participating in inflammation and fibrosis [186].

10. Hedgehog

Hedgehog (Hh) is a well-characterized factor implied in the fibrogenic process of several organs, including the liver. Hh pathway activation is proportional to the severity and persistence of injury [187], induces a cascade of events concurring to wound healing response and involves various cell types, including damaged ballooned hepatocytes, inflammatory cells (mainly NKT cells and macrophages), ductular/progenitor cells and HSCs [188].

The Hh pathway was associated with severe NASH in a gene profiling study where patients with different severity of the disease were included [189]. In experimental NASH, the Hh pathway leads to proliferation and activation of ductular progenitor cells and HSC, that, in turn, produce Hh ligands and, consequently, soluble mediators such as osteopontin and CXCL-16, responsible for immune cells recruitment and damage progression [190,191]. Moreover, Patched-heterozygous deficient mice, characterized by hyperactivation of the Hh pathway, show exacerbation of the disease following a NASH-inducing diet, whereas liver-specific inhibition of Smo prevents diet-induced liver damage and fibrosis, despite hepatic lipid accumulation [190].

Caspase-2 has been recently identified as a critical factor in NASH pathogenesis, mediating hepatocyte lipoapoptosis. Hepatic caspase-2 was found to be increased both in human and experimental NASH, in association with profibrogenic factors, such as Hh-related genes. When challenged with a HF diet or fed a MCD diet, caspase-2 knockout mice showed lipid-induced hepatic apoptosis, together with decreased activation of Hh signaling and fibrosis [192].

In NAFLD patients, Hh activity and Hh ligands' expression correlates with the degree of fibrosis [193] and elevated Hh activation is associated with hepatocyte ballooning, high presence of progenitor cells and myofibroblasts and portal inflammation [187]. In agreement with these findings, the Pioglitazone vs. Vitamin E vs. Placebo for treatment of NASH (PIVENS) trial demonstrated that amelioration of NASH in response to treatment was associated with a marked decrease of Sonic Hh ligand (Shh) expressing hepatocytes [194].

11. Nuclear Receptors

Nuclear receptors are ligand-dependent transcription factors that regulate glucose and lipid metabolism in the liver. Nuclear receptors are divided into seven subfamilies named as NR0-NR6 [195] and NR1 subfamily is of particular importance in NAFLD. This latter group of nuclear receptors is retained in the nucleus and heterodimerizes with the retinoid X receptor (RXRα) [195,196] and includes: NR1C1-3 (the peroxisome proliferator-activated receptors, PPARα, β, γ), NR1H2-3 (the liver X receptors, LXRα, β), NR1H4 (the farnesoid X receptor, FXRα), NR1I2 (the constitutive androstane receptor, CAR), and NR1I3 (the pregnane X receptor, PXR). PPARs inhibit inflammation in the obese state acting on NF-κB and AP1 transcription factor and regulate metabolism by inducing transcription of adiponectin (PPARγ) and fibroblast growth factor-21 (FGF21) (PPARα and FXR) [195].

PPARα regulates β-oxidation and cholesterol removal during the fasting state or when metabolism increases in adipose and/or muscle tissues [195]. Hepatic PPARα expression decreases in NAFLD leading to steatosis, but is enhanced following diet and exercise [197,198].

In animal models of steatosis and steatohepatitis, the use of PPARα activators improves the disease [199,200]. In addition, several studies in mice suggest that induction of both PPARβ/δ and PPARγ ameliorates steatosis [201,202]. Indeed, animals treated with PPARα activators show less weight gain than controls, lower levels of epididymal fat, and are protected from atherosclerosis [203]. PPAR activation may also ameliorate fibrosis, since NASH patients treated with pioglitazone (a PPARγ agonist) had improved fibrosis biomarkers [204]. Recent studies show that PPARγ downregulates adipocyte endothelial nitric oxide synthase (eNOS), a molecule that contributes to IR and development of NASH [205]. Since the use of selective PPARα agonists has proven quite ineffective against NAFLD [197] the use of mixed receptor agonists (PPARα and PPARβ/γ) is underway in the therapy for NASH patients and recent results have been reported [206].

PXR, expressed in many tissues but mainly in the liver [207], is released not only by hepatocytes, but also by Kupffer and stellate cells [208]. Two polymorphisms of this gene have been associated with augmented severity of NAFLD: rs7643645/G and rs2461823 [209], whereas a variant encoding a short dominant negative PXR isoform, which inhibits the full-length isoform activity, has been recently described [210]. PXR regulates various genes involved in xenobiotic and drug metabolism, including enzymes [211] that play a role in the oxidative metabolism of lipophilic compounds such as steroids, fatty acids, bile acids, drugs, retinoids, and xenobiotics. PXR activation has been associated with increased severity of steatosis, obesity, insulin resistance and hypercholesterolemia as it enhances hepatic fatty acid uptake and lipogenesis, while it decreases β-oxidation [212,213]. The role of PXR in experimental NAFLD is more complex. While PXR knockout mice are resistant to obesity, they show impaired glucose tolerance, hyperleptinemia and hypoadiponectinemia, together with elevated fasting glucose levels [212]. Recently, it was shown that PXR activation inhibits the production of many NF-κB target genes and increases the production of secreted interleukin-1 receptor antagonist (IL-1RA), reducing the effects of LPS-induced inflammation [214].

Human CAR1-3, expressed mainly in liver and intestine and to a lower extent in other tissues [215], is implicated in protection against toxic food or contaminants [216]. CAR is also associated with lipid metabolism and inflammation in NAFLD. CAR increases in the liver in the fed state, reducing hepatic steatosis, inflammation, insulin resistance and hypercholesterolemia [217]. In animal models, treatment with an agonist of CAR ameliorates diet-induced obesity, hepatic steatosis and diabetes [218]. Moreover, in knockout mice for the low density lipoprotein receptor (LDLR), activation of CAR reduces triglycerides and cholesterol plasma levels [219]. Recently, it has been reported that activated CAR translocates into the nucleus and functions as an adaptor protein to recruit PGC1α to the Cullin1 E3 ligase complex for ubiquitination. The interaction between CAR and PGC1α also induces the degradation of PGC1α and suppression of gluconeogenesis both in vitro and in vivo [220]. CAR can induce carcinogenesis in mice, although this effect has not observed in humans [221]. Indeed, CAR activation in humans may have antiproliferative effects, as demonstrated by a recent report showing that CAR-deficient HepaRG cells have increased expression of proliferative genes [222].

FXR, highly expressed in liver, kidney, intestine, and adrenals, inhibits the expression of CYP7A1 and sterol 12-α-hydroxylase (CYP8B1), genes involved in bile acid synthesis from cholesterol. Besides its central role in bile acid metabolism, FXR activation also regulates the expression of various genes involved in glucose, lipid, and lipoprotein metabolism, crucial in NAFLD [223]. Hepatic FXR inhibits fatty acid synthesis and uptake and upregulates beta oxidation, regulating lipid homeostasis [224]. In NAFLD patients and in animal models, activation of FXR by obeticholic acid (OCA) decreases both steatosis and obesity [225,226]. In HF/HC diet-treated mice, the FXR agonist GW4064 decreased the expression of the hepatic lipid transporter CD36, reducing hepatic steatosis and weight gain [227]. FXR can regulate insulin resistance as recently demonstrated in

NASH patients treated with OCA, which improves insulin sensitivity [228]. Similarly, OCA treatment in Zucker (fa/fa) rats improves insulin sensitivity, and GW4064 treatment, in HF/HC diet mice, reduces hyperinsulinemia and hyperglycemia [226]. Besides OCA and GW4064, further potential novel therapeutic targets in NASH are currently in phase II clinical development [229].

Intestinal activation of FXR reduces weight gain, liver glucose production and steatosis, stimulating human fibroblast growth factor-19 (FGF19). This factor inhibits CYP7A1 resulting in an inhibition of liver bile acid synthesis. Indeed, administration of FGF19 in mice and rats animal models increases fat oxidation and decreases liver triglycerides and glucose levels [230,231]. Recent studies show that activation of intestinal FXR by feraxamine inhibits weight gain induced by diet, hepatic glucose production and steatosis. These effects are mediated by fibroblast growth factor-15 signaling, without interfering with hepatic FXR activation [232]. Intestinal FXR agonism promotes adipose tissue browning and reduces obesity and insulin resistance, suggesting that tissue-specific activation of FXR may be a novel approach to treat NAFLD. Activation of intestinal FXR affords hepatoprotection by restoring hepatic homeostasis, regulating cellular proliferation and decreasing hepatic fibrosis and inflammation [233].

12. Pattern Recognition Receptors and the Inflammasomes

Toll-like receptors are highly conserved receptors that recognize endogenous danger signals, such as molecules released by damaged cells (damage-associated molecular patterns, DAMPs) or exogenous danger signals, as gut-derived pathogen-associated molecules (pathogen-associated molecular patterns, PAMPs) [234,235]. Due to the high liver exposure to danger signals via the portal system, TLR-induced pathways play a central role in activation of hepatic cells, primarily Kupffer cells, but also hepatocytes and HSC. As pattern recognition receptors (PRR), TLRs act as defense mechanism, but are also implicated in the pathogenesis of NASH [236,237]. Among NAFLD-related TLRs, TLR2 interacts with a broad range of PAMPs, including peptidoglycan, a surface component of Gram-positive bacteria [238], which appears to be increased in NAFLD [239]. Importantly, inhibition of TLR2 signaling prevents insulin resistance in HFD mice [240], whereas TLR2-deficient mice fed HFD display reduced levels of inflammatory cytokines and do not develop NASH [241].

The role of TLR5 in NAFLD pathogenesis is still unclear, as only a correlation with dysbiosis and metabolic syndrome has been reported [242,243]. TLR9, an intracellular receptor, is activated by unmethylated DNA, typically express in viruses and bacteria but rare in mammalian cells. TLR9 downstream signaling involves IL-1, and is associated with NASH severity and fibrosis [244]. A study conducted in an experimental model of colitis, with high portal levels of LPS, shows increased TLR9 liver expression, associated with hepatic steatosis, inflammation, and fibrosis [245].

The crucial role of TLR4 in NAFLD pathogenesis has been demonstrated in TLR4-deficient mice, that display lower levels of inflammatory mediators and fail to develop NAFLD or insulin resistance [246]. TLR4 plays a major role in linking innate immunity with inflammatory response and the function of TLR4 in Kupffer cells is well characterized [247]. TLR4 is primarily activated by Gram-negative bacterial lipopolysaccharides (LPS), leading to overexpression of cytokines, chemokines and antimicrobial molecules [248,249]. LPS/TLR4 interaction, that requires LPS-binding protein and two co-receptors (CD14 and myeloid differentiation protein 2, MD2), activates downstream pathways in a myeloid differentiation factor (MyD)88-dependent or independent fashion [250]. The MyD88-dependent pathway signals through IκB kinase (IKK)/NF-κB and mitogen activated protein kinase (MAPK)/AP-1, inducing the expression of pro-inflammatory cytokines (TNF-α, IL-1β, IL-6 and IL-12) and genes implicated in the immune response [250]. The MyD88-independent cascade involves IFNs [250]. ROS production and subsequent activation of the unfolded protein response are also induced in TLR4-activated Kupffer cells, representing an additional mechanism triggered by TLRs in NAFLD progression [251].

Besides Kupffer cells, TLR4 is expressed by other hepatic cells, including HSCs, hepatocytes and cholangiocytes and LPS/TLR4 axis plays a critical role in the pathogenesis and progression of fatty liver diseases, as demonstrated by increased levels of portal endotoxins and TLR4 hepatic expression in experimental NASH [252,253]. Based on its expression in HSC, a direct role of TLR4 in liver fibrogenesis has been suggested. According to this hypothesis, the expression of chemokines and adhesion molecules, as well as TGF-β-mediated signaling, are positively modulated by TLR4 [254], while two TLR4 polymorphisms, protective against fibrosis, are associated with a lower apoptotic threshold for HSC [255].

TLR4-mediated inflammatory response can also be elicited by DAMPs released by necrotic cells, such as high mobility group box 1 (HMGB1) or phospholipids. These molecules stimulate monocyte and Kupffer cells to secrete inflammatory mediators (Figure 3). It is noteworthy that, in the presence of high glucose, TLR4 activation and downstream signaling can be triggered by FFA [256], clarifying, at least in part, the mechanism by which saturated fatty acids, frequently enhanced in plasma of obese patients, have toxic effects [257].

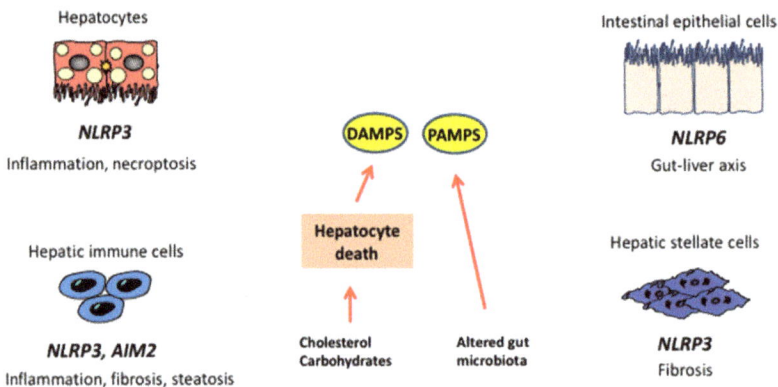

Figure 3. Inflammasomes and the liver. In steatosis, hepatic damage leads to generation of damage-associated molecular pattern (DAMPs), while alterations in microbiota lead to increased availability of pathogen-associated molecular patterns (PAMPs). DAMPs and PAMPs act on receptors localized on liver cells leading to activation of different inflammasomes and release of cytokines implicated in NASH. NLRP3: NOD-like receptor family, pyrin domain containing 3; AIM2: Absent in melanoma 2.

An important role in NASH pathogenesis has been recently ascribed to the nucleotide oligomerization domain (NOD)-like receptors (NLRs). NLR activation in response to DAMPs or PAMPs leads to the assembly of inflammasome, a multiprotein complex required for caspase-1 activity and initiation of inflammatory signals. Full activation of inflammasome, mediated by PRRs via NF-κB, can be induced by a broad spectrum of signals, such as uric acid, ROS, ATP [258] and mitochondrial DNA [259], and results in secretion of mature IL-1 and IL-18 [260,261]. These cytokines, acting on different cell types, elicit inflammatory signals in liver as well as in the adipose tissue and intestine, triggering steatosis, insulin resistance, inflammation and cell death [262]. A role for inflammasomes in NAFLD development and progression to NASH has been shown both in humans and animal models [263,264]. Activation of NLRP3 inflammasome has been reported in MCD diet-induced steatohepatitis [265], as well following protracted HF/HC/HS feeding [266]. Moreover, NLRP3 gain of function correlates with liver fibrosis. Conversely, absence of this receptor appears to improve metabolic activity [267] and diet-induced steatohepatitis [268], although a study by Henao-Mejia et al. [269] demonstrated that lack of NLP3 promotes gut dysbiosis and chronic inflammation. Activation of NLRP3 inflammasome has been associated with hepatocyte pyroptosis, a recently described, inflammasome-mediated cell death mechanism [268,270].

Hepatocyte damage leads to secretion of intracellular molecules, DAMPs, acting as danger signals capable to recruit and/or activate immune cells and initiate an inflammatory response in the absence of pathogens, a mechanism referred as sterile inflammation [271,272]. Several DAMPs have been identified, including nuclear and mitochondrial DNA, purine nucleotides (ATP, UTP), nuclear factors as HMGB1 and uric acid [180,273]. Besides mitochondrial DNA, which activates TLR9, a number of mitochondrial components have been shown to play a part in sterile inflammation [274,275], including formyl-peptides, ATP and ROS, that act by inducing inflammasome activation [276–278]. High concentrations of extracellular ATP, as a consequence of cell death, result in inflammasome activation and IL-1β production, via P2X7 receptor [279]. As binding of ATP to P2X7 provokes pore formation in the plasma membrane, allowing bacterial products to enter the cells, ATP plays a role also in pathogen-associated molecular pattern-induced inflammation [280].

HMGB1 is a constitutively expressed nuclear protein that induces transcriptional activation [281], and is released in response to different stimuli, such as PAMPs and DAMPs [282,283]. HMGB1 interacts with a broad spectrum of receptors (TLR4, TLR2, TLR9, and RAGE) exerting proinflammatory actions in complex with other factors, as single stranded DNA, LPS and IL-1β [284].

In its crystal form, uric acid induce inflammatory response by inflammasome activation in a receptor-independent manner, causing phagosome burst and spill of cytosolic proteases [285]. In some settings, DAMPs can be also secreted independently of apoptosis. HMGB1 production can occur by activated macrophages in response to LPS, TNF, and TGFβ [286]. Moreover, secondary necrosis, due to impaired efferocytosis, may contribute to release of intracellular components amplifying the inflammatory response.

13. Adipokines

Adipose tissue is recognized as an endocrine organ that secretes adipokines, which are peptides with autocrine, paracrine and endocrine functions, controlling systemic metabolism and energy homeostasis [287]. Among these, leptin and adiponectin are involved in the pathogenesis of NAFLD and progression to NASH, leptin being identified as a profibrogenic adipokine [285,288]. Adipose tissue also produces other molecules (including classical cytokines), mostly released by endothelial or immune cells, such as TNF-α and IL-6 [289]. Adiponectin has in general a beneficial impact on NAFLD [290], while others, as resistin, TNF-α and IL-6 possibly have an adverse impact. In particular, adiponectin reduces IR and shows anti-steatotic and anti-inflammatory properties, while TNF-α increases IR and displays pro-inflammatory effects [291,292]. In physiologic conditions, cytokine-adipokine interplay is finely regulated, but in some setting, such as increased adipose tissue mass, the critical balance between cytokines and adipokines is compromised, leading to chronic inflammation, IR and NAFLD [292]. Leptin, an adipokine which plays a major role in energy homeostasis, is mainly produced by adipose tissue, but it is also synthesized in other organs [293]. Consequent to an increase in adipose tissue mass, leptin is upregulated, acting as compensatory factor in preserving insulin sensitivity and exerting anti-steatotic effects. Nevertheless, if adipose tissue continues to augment, the compensatory mechanism fails, with a sustained rise in IR and hepatic steatosis [294]. Leptin-mediated dual action has been demonstrated in experimental NAFLD, as in early disease leptin exerts a protective effect by inhibiting hepatic glucose production and de novo lipogenesis through stimulation of fatty acid oxidation, while as NAFLD proceeds, it acts as a pro-fibrogenic and inflammatory factor [294]. Novel evidence indicates that leptin-mediated nicotinamide adenine dinucleotide phosphate (NADPH) oxidase increases the levels of miR21, which is a key regulator of TGF-β signaling. The rise in miR21 increases TGF-β and SMAD2/3-SMAD4 nuclear colocalizations, whilst repressing SMAD7 [295]. In addition, leptin reduces PPAR-γ expression in HSCs, promoting hepatic fibrosis [296]. A recent study, conducted by Heinrich et al., shows that leptin resistance contributes to obesity in null mice mutated for carcinoembryonic antigen cell adhesion molecule 1 (CEACAM1) [297]. CEACAM1 is a molecule that induces insulin clearance [298] and reduces fatty acid synthesis in liver in the presence of insulin resistance, hepatic steatosis and visceral obesity [299]. Furthermore, $(Cc1^{-/-})$ mice develop hyperleptinemia, firstly related to the augmented visceral obesity, followed by hyperphagia and reduced physical activity. These effects are possibly due to leptin resistance and elevated hypothalamic fatty acid synthase activity, that could, in turn, be mediated by both central and peripheral factors [297].

Adiponectin is one of the most abundant adipokines, and is also produced by hepatocytes in response to liver injury [300]. It exhibits anti-steatotic and antiapoptotic actions on hepatocytes and exerts anti-inflammatory and anti-fibrotic effects acting on HSC, Kupffer and sinusoidal cells [301]. Adiponectin amounts drop when adipose mass increases, but the underlying mechanism is not completely elucidated. It may involve adipose tissue hypoxia, oxidative stress [155,302] and increased inflammatory mediator levels [303]. Another potential factor linking adipocyte hypertrophy to reduced adiponectin synthesis is mitochondrial dysfunction [304]. Recent reports show that 11β-hydroxysteroid dehydrogenase type1 (11β-HSD1) expression increases in hypertrophic adipocytes and this could be responsible for mitochondrial dysfunction and reduced adiponectin synthesis.

After NASH progression towards cirrhosis, circulating adiponectin seems to increase [305], probably due to two main mechanisms: a decrease in hepatic clearance of adiponectin and/or a compensatory mechanism aimed to buffer the hyper-secretion of inflammatory cytokines. Recent studies show that in the compensated late stage of NASH, circulating adiponectin is associated with hepatic lipid loss [306]. These data reinforce the theory that adiponectin may be involved in the "burnt-out NASH", characterized by the loss of hepatic lipids, often observed in advanced fibrosis and cirrhosis.

Adipose tissue (mainly visceral) and liver (mainly hepatocytes) are the principal producers of chemerin [307]. Chemerin concentrations, which are generally higher in obesity and IR and drop after weight loss, may modulate insulin resistance and inflammatory responses [308]. Animal models of obesity and IR (*ob/ob* and *db/db* mice) display increased chemerin expression [309,310]. A recent study conducted in NAFLD subjects show that circulating levels of chemerin positively correlate with body mass index (BMI) and are also higher in individuals with impaired glucose tolerance (IGT) or type 2 diabetes. In MCD-induced NASH, hepatic levels of chemerin tend to increase. In human NASH, liver chemerin mRNA is upregulated in respect to healthy controls, but similar levels have been found also in steatosis [311].

14. Microbiota

Accumulating evidence indicates that dysregulation of microbiota components are involved in various liver diseases, including NAFLD and NASH, through obesity predisposition, metabolic alterations and liver inflammation. Gut microbiota produces extra energy for the host, processing polysaccharides to short-chain fatty acids (mainly acetate, propionate, and butyrate) [312] and stimulating lipogenesis. A potential role of specific gut microbiome has been suggested in the pathogenesis of NAFLD, as obese mouse models host 50% less *Bacteroides* and more *Firmicutes* compared to lean control [313], and germ-free mice show significantly greater increase in body fat following colonization with an "obese microbiome" [313]. Conversely, a recently described bacterium, *Akkermansia muciniphila*, has been associated with a non-obese phenotype both in humans and animal models, and HFD mice administered with *Akkermansia* show reduced adipose tissue inflammation and increased glucose tolerance [314,315]. The intestinal microflora produces enzymes that metabolize dietary choline, a cell membrane component regulating lipid transport in liver, into methylamines, toxic compounds responsible for inflammation and liver injury [316]. Aberrant microbiota could induce triglyceride accumulation and promote NASH both reducing choline and increasing methylamines [317].

Alterations in bile acid metabolism have been reported during NAFLD development. Intestinal bacteria can modify bile acid pool through the conversion of cholic and chenodeoxycholic acid into secondary bile acids, influencing lipid and glucose homeostasis. In addition, abnormal microbiota can impair bile acid receptor signaling, such as FXR and the G-protein-coupled bile acid-activated receptor TGR5 [318,319], affecting hepatic de novo lipogenesis and very low-density lipoprotein VLDL export [320] as well as glucose metabolism [321,322].

Int. J. Mol. Sci. **2016**, *17*, 1575

Endogenous ethanol is produced by several microbiome species. Ethanol induces hepatotoxicity stimulating Kupffer cells to produce nitric acid and cytokines, whereas ethanol metabolites promote triglyceride accumulation and oxidative stress in the liver. In addition, ethanol impairs gut mucosal permeability inducing endotoxemia. Enhanced breath ethanol content was found in *ob/ob* mice and it was abolished by antibiotic treatment [323]. Increased ethanol levels were also detected in obese individuals and in children with NASH [324].

The gut microflora plays an important role in the development and function of the host immune system [325]. Through the portal circulation, liver is directly exposed to gut-derived products, being the first line of defense against bacterial toxins. Enhanced levels of circulating LPS and endotoxins have been detected in rodents with diet-induced NAFLD and in NASH patients, respectively. LPS, the active component of endotoxins, interacts with LPS-binding protein and the CD14 receptor, activating TLRs and, consequently, the inflammatory cascade that involves stress-activated protein kinases, JNK, p38, interferon regulatory factor-3 (IRF-3) and NF-κB, pathways implicated in insulin resistance and triglycerides synthesis [252,325].

Finally, a correlation between small intestinal bacterial overgrowth (SIBO) and NAFLD has been observed in clinical and experimental studies [237,326,327]. Bacterial overgrowth in the small intestine, as well as qualitative microbiome abnormalities can impair the barrier functions of the intestinal mucosa, leading to enhanced mucosa permeability and subsequent translocation of endotoxin to the bloodstream [328,329]. Therefore, increased gut permeability represents an additional mechanism in NASH pathogenesis, acting through the accumulation of endotoxin and bacterial metabolites in liver and subsequent induction of inflammatory responses, via activation of pattern recognition receptors.

15. Perspectives

Extensive information has accumulated in the past few years on the molecular mechanisms underlying the development of steatohepatitis. This has been paralleled by a number of clinical trials exploring novel approaches, in part derived from preclinical data. Continuing research in this field will be instrumental in providing new targets and biomarkers for the management of this very prevalent condition.

Acknowledgments: Work on steatohepatitis in Marra's laboratory is supported by grants from the Italian Ministry for Research (Projects PRIN and FIRB), the European Community (projects FLIP and EPoS), and the CARIPLO Foundation.

Author Contributions: Alessandra Caligiuri and Alessandra Gentilini searched the literature, contributed to manuscript organization and wrote the text. Fabio Marra defined manuscript organization and reviewed the final version of the manuscript.

Conflicts of Interest: The authors declare no conflict of interest.

References

1. Satapathy, S.K.; Sanyal, A.J. Epidemiology and natural history of nonalcoholic fatty liver disease. *Semin. Liver Dis.* **2015**, *35*, 221–235. [CrossRef] [PubMed]
2. Vernon, G.; Baranova, A.; Younossi, Z.M. Systematic review: The epidemiology and natural history of non-alcoholic fatty liver disease and non-alcoholic steatohepatitis in adults. *Aliment. Pharmacol. Ther.* **2011**, *34*, 274–285. [CrossRef] [PubMed]
3. Williams, C.D.; Stengel, J.; Asike, M.I.; Torres, D.M.; Shaw, J.; Contreras, M.; Landt, C.L.; Harrison, S.A. Prevalence of nonalcoholic fatty liver disease and nonalcoholic steatohepatitis among a largely middle-aged population utilizing ultrasound and liver biopsy: A prospective study. *Gastroenterology* **2011**, *140*, 124–131. [CrossRef] [PubMed]
4. Browning, J.D.; Horton, J.D. Molecular mediators of hepatic steatosis and liver injury. *J. Clin. Investig.* **2004**, *114*, 147–152. [CrossRef] [PubMed]

5. Brunt, E.M.; Kleiner, D.E.; Wilson, L.A.; Belt, P.; Neuschwander-Tetri, B.A.; Network, N.C.R. Nonalcoholic fatty liver disease (NAFLD) activity score and the histopathologic diagnosis in NAFLD: Distinct clinicopathologic meanings. *Hepatology* **2011**, *53*, 810–820. [CrossRef] [PubMed]

6. Pais, R.; Charlotte, F.; Fedchuk, L.; Bedossa, P.; Lebray, P.; Poynard, T.; Ratziu, V. A systematic review of follow-up biopsies reveals disease progression in patients with non-alcoholic fatty liver. *J. Hepatol.* **2013**, *59*, 550–556. [CrossRef] [PubMed]

7. McPherson, S.; Hardy, T.; Henderson, E.; Burt, A.D.; Day, C.P.; Anstee, Q.M. Evidence of NAFLD progression from steatosis to fibrosing-steatohepatitis using paired biopsies: Implications for prognosis and clinical management. *J. Hepatol.* **2015**, *62*, 1148–1155. [CrossRef] [PubMed]

8. Angulo, P. Long-term mortality in nonalcoholic fatty liver disease: Is liver histology of any prognostic significance? *Hepatology* **2010**, *51*, 373–375. [CrossRef] [PubMed]

9. Ekstedt, M.; Franzen, L.E.; Mathiesen, U.L.; Thorelius, L.; Holmqvist, M.; Bodemar, G.; Kechagias, S. Long-term follow-up of patients with NAFLD and elevated liver enzymes. *Hepatology* **2006**, *44*, 865–873. [CrossRef] [PubMed]

10. Adams, L.A.; Lymp, J.F.; St Sauver, J.; Sanderson, S.O.; Lindor, K.D.; Feldstein, A.; Angulo, P. The natural history of nonalcoholic fatty liver disease: A population-based cohort study. *Gastroenterology* **2005**, *129*, 113–121. [CrossRef] [PubMed]

11. Ludwig, J.; Viggiano, T.R.; McGill, D.B.; Oh, B.J. Nonalcoholic steatohepatitis: Mayo clinic experiences with a hitherto unnamed disease. *Mayo Clin. Proc.* **1980**, *55*, 434–438. [PubMed]

12. Day, C.P.; James, O.F. Steatohepatitis: A tale of two "hits"? *Gastroenterology* **1998**, *114*, 842–845. [CrossRef]

13. Cusi, K. Role of obesity and lipotoxicity in the development of nonalcoholic steatohepatitis: Pathophysiology and clinical implications. *Gastroenterology* **2012**, *142*, 711–725. [CrossRef] [PubMed]

14. Neuschwander-Tetri, B.A. Hepatic lipotoxicity and the pathogenesis of nonalcoholic steatohepatitis: The central role of nontriglyceride fatty acid metabolites. *Hepatology* **2010**, *52*, 774–788. [CrossRef] [PubMed]

15. Tilg, H.; Moschen, A.R. Evolution of inflammation in nonalcoholic fatty liver disease: The multiple parallel hits hypothesis. *Hepatology* **2010**, *52*, 1836–1846. [CrossRef] [PubMed]

16. Marra, F.; Lotersztajn, S. Pathophysiology of NASH: Perspectives for a targeted treatment. *Curr. Pharm. Des.* **2013**, *19*, 5250–5269. [CrossRef] [PubMed]

17. Loomba, R.; Schork, N.; Chen, C.H.; Bettencourt, R.; Bhatt, A.; Ang, B.; Nguyen, P.; Hernandez, C.; Richards, L.; Salotti, J.; et al. Heritability of hepatic fibrosis and steatosis based on a prospective twin study. *Gastroenterology* **2015**, *149*, 1784–1793. [CrossRef] [PubMed]

18. Anstee, Q.M.; Seth, D.; Day, C.P. Genetic factors that affect risk of alcoholic and nonalcoholic fatty liver disease. *Gastroenterology* **2016**, *150*, 1728–1744. [CrossRef] [PubMed]

19. Dongiovanni, P.; Donati, B.; Fares, R.; Lombardi, R.; Mancina, R.M.; Romeo, S.; Valenti, L. PNPLA3 I148M polymorphism and progressive liver disease. *World J. Gastroenterol.* **2013**, *19*, 6969–6978. [CrossRef] [PubMed]

20. Romeo, S.; Kozlitina, J.; Xing, C.; Pertsemlidis, A.; Cox, D.; Pennacchio, L.A.; Boerwinkle, E.; Cohen, J.C.; Hobbs, H.H. Genetic variation in PNPLA3 confers susceptibility to nonalcoholic fatty liver disease. *Nat. Genet.* **2008**, *40*, 1461–1465. [CrossRef] [PubMed]

21. Speliotes, E.K.; Butler, J.L.; Palmer, C.D.; Voight, B.F.; Consortium, G.; Consortium, M.I.; Nash, C.R.N.; Hirschhorn, J.N. PNPLA3 variants specifically confer increased risk for histologic nonalcoholic fatty liver disease but not metabolic disease. *Hepatology* **2010**, *52*, 904–912. [CrossRef] [PubMed]

22. Pirazzi, C.; Adiels, M.; Burza, M.A.; Mancina, R.M.; Levin, M.; Stahlman, M.; Taskinen, M.R.; Orho-Melander, M.; Perman, J.; Pujia, A.; et al. Patatin-like phospholipase domain-containing 3 (PNPLA3) I148M (RS738409) affects hepatic VLDL secretion in humans and in vitro. *J. Hepatol.* **2012**, *57*, 1276–1282. [CrossRef] [PubMed]

23. Kumari, M.; Schoiswohl, G.; Chitraju, C.; Paar, M.; Cornaciu, I.; Rangrez, A.Y.; Wongsiriroj, N.; Nagy, H.M.; Ivanova, P.T.; Scott, S.A.; et al. Adiponutrin functions as a nutritionally regulated lysophosphatidic acid acyltransferase. *Cell Metab.* **2012**, *15*, 691–702. [CrossRef] [PubMed]

24. Chen, W.; Chang, B.; Li, L.; Chan, L. Patatin-like phospholipase domain-containing 3/adiponutrin deficiency in mice is not associated with fatty liver disease. *Hepatology* **2010**, *52*, 1134–1142. [CrossRef] [PubMed]

25. Smagris, E.; BasuRay, S.; Li, J.; Huang, Y.; Lai, K.M.; Gromada, J.; Cohen, J.C.; Hobbs, H.H. PNPLA3 I148M knockin mice accumulate PNPLA3 on lipid droplets and develop hepatic steatosis. *Hepatology* **2015**, *61*, 108–118. [CrossRef] [PubMed]

26. Mondul, A.; Mancina, R.M.; Merlo, A.; Dongiovanni, P.; Rametta, R.; Montalcini, T.; Valenti, L.; Albanes, D.; Romeo, S. *PNPLA3* I148M variant influences circulating retinol in adults with nonalcoholic fatty liver disease or obesity. *J. Nutr.* **2015**, *145*, 1687–1691. [CrossRef] [PubMed]

27. Kovarova, M.; Konigsrainer, I.; Konigsrainer, A.; Machicao, F.; Haring, H.U.; Schleicher, E.; Peter, A. The genetic variant I148M in *PNPLA3* is associated with increased hepatic retinyl-palmitate storage in humans. *J. Clin. Endocrinol. Metab.* **2015**, *100*, E1568–E1574. [CrossRef] [PubMed]

28. Pirazzi, C.; Valenti, L.; Motta, B.M.; Pingitore, P.; Hedfalk, K.; Mancina, R.M.; Burza, M.A.; Indiveri, C.; Ferro, Y.; Montalcini, T.; et al. PNPLA3 has retinyl-palmitate lipase activity in human hepatic stellate cells. *Hum. Mol. Genet.* **2014**, *23*, 4077–4085. [CrossRef] [PubMed]

29. Kozlitina, J.; Smagris, E.; Stender, S.; Nordestgaard, B.G.; Zhou, H.H.; Tybjaerg-Hansen, A.; Vogt, T.F.; Hobbs, H.H.; Cohen, J.C. Exome-wide association study identifies a *TM6SF2* variant that confers susceptibility to nonalcoholic fatty liver disease. *Nat. Genet.* **2014**, *46*, 352–356. [CrossRef] [PubMed]

30. Liu, Y.L.; Reeves, H.L.; Burt, A.D.; Tiniakos, D.; McPherson, S.; Leathart, J.B.; Allison, M.E.; Alexander, G.J.; Piguet, A.C.; Anty, R.; et al. TM6SF2 RS58542926 influences hepatic fibrosis progression in patients with non-alcoholic fatty liver disease. *Nat. Commun.* **2014**, *5*. [CrossRef] [PubMed]

31. Mahdessian, H.; Taxiarchis, A.; Popov, S.; Silveira, A.; Franco-Cereceda, A.; Hamsten, A.; Eriksson, P.; van't Hooft, F. TM6SF2 is a regulator of liver fat metabolism influencing triglyceride secretion and hepatic lipid droplet content. *Proc. Natl. Acad. Sci. USA* **2014**, *111*, 8913–8918. [CrossRef] [PubMed]

32. Dongiovanni, P.; Valenti, L.; Rametta, R.; Daly, A.K.; Nobili, V.; Mozzi, E.; Leathart, J.B.; Pietrobattista, A.; Burt, A.D.; Maggioni, M.; et al. Genetic variants regulating insulin receptor signalling are associated with the severity of liver damage in patients with non-alcoholic fatty liver disease. *Gut* **2010**, *59*, 267–273. [CrossRef] [PubMed]

33. Beer, N.L.; Tribble, N.D.; McCulloch, L.J.; Roos, C.; Johnson, P.R.; Orho-Melander, M.; Gloyn, A.L. The P446L variant in *GCKR* associated with fasting plasma glucose and triglyceride levels exerts its effect through increased glucokinase activity in liver. *Hum. Mol. Genet.* **2009**, *18*, 4081–4088. [CrossRef] [PubMed]

34. Santoro, N.; Zhang, C.K.; Zhao, H.; Pakstis, A.J.; Kim, G.; Kursawe, R.; Dykas, D.J.; Bale, A.E.; Giannini, C.; Pierpont, B.; et al. Variant in the glucokinase regulatory protein (GCKR) gene is associated with fatty liver in obese children and adolescents. *Hepatology* **2012**, *55*, 781–789. [CrossRef] [PubMed]

35. Tonjes, A.; Scholz, M.; Loeffler, M.; Stumvoll, M. Association of Pro12Ala polymorphism in peroxisome proliferator-activated receptor γ with pre-diabetic phenotypes: Meta-analysis of 57 studies on nondiabetic individuals. *Diabetes Care* **2006**, *29*, 2489–2497. [CrossRef] [PubMed]

36. Nelson, J.E.; Bhattacharya, R.; Lindor, K.D.; Chalasani, N.; Raaka, S.; Heathcote, E.J.; Miskovsky, E.; Shaffer, E.; Rulyak, S.J.; Kowdley, K.V. HFE C282Y mutations are associated with advanced hepatic fibrosis in caucasians with nonalcoholic steatohepatitis. *Hepatology* **2007**, *46*, 723–729. [CrossRef] [PubMed]

37. Bugianesi, E.; Manzini, P.; D'Antico, S.; Vanni, E.; Longo, F.; Leone, N.; Massarenti, P.; Piga, A.; Marchesini, G.; Rizzetto, M. Relative contribution of iron burden, HFE mutations, and insulin resistance to fibrosis in nonalcoholic fatty liver. *Hepatology* **2004**, *39*, 179–187. [CrossRef] [PubMed]

38. Valenti, L.; Fracanzani, A.L.; Bugianesi, E.; Dongiovanni, P.; Galmozzi, E.; Vanni, E.; Canavesi, E.; Lattuada, E.; Roviaro, G.; Marchesini, G.; et al. *HFE* genotype, parenchymal iron accumulation, and liver fibrosis in patients with nonalcoholic fatty liver disease. *Gastroenterology* **2010**, *138*, 905–912. [CrossRef] [PubMed]

39. Raszeja-Wyszomirska, J.; Kurzawski, G.; Lawniczak, M.; Miezynska-Kurtycz, J.; Lubinski, J. Nonalcoholic fatty liver disease and *HFE* gene mutations: A polish study. *World J. Gastroenterol.* **2010**, *16*, 2531–2536. [CrossRef] [PubMed]

40. Al-Serri, A.; Anstee, Q.M.; Valenti, L.; Nobili, V.; Leathart, J.B.; Dongiovanni, P.; Patch, J.; Fracanzani, A.; Fargion, S.; Day, C.P.; et al. The *SOD2* C47T polymorphism influences NAFLD fibrosis severity: Evidence from case-control and intra-familial allele association studies. *J. Hepatol.* **2012**, *56*, 448–454. [CrossRef] [PubMed]

41. Mancina, R.M.; Dongiovanni, P.; Petta, S.; Pingitore, P.; Meroni, M.; Rametta, R.; Boren, J.; Montalcini, T.; Pujia, A.; Wiklund, O.; et al. The *MBOAT7-TMC4* variant rs641738 increases risk of nonalcoholic fatty liver disease in individuals of European descent. *Gastroenterology* **2016**, *150*, 1219–1230. [CrossRef] [PubMed]

42. Sun, C.; Fan, J.G.; Qiao, L. Potential epigenetic mechanism in non-alcoholic fatty liver disease. *Int. J. Mol. Sci.* **2015**, *16*, 5161–5179. [CrossRef] [PubMed]

43. Wang, L.J.; Zhang, H.W.; Zhou, J.Y.; Liu, Y.; Yang, Y.; Chen, X.L.; Zhu, C.H.; Zheng, R.D.; Ling, W.H.; Zhu, H.L. Betaine attenuates hepatic steatosis by reducing methylation of the *MTTP* promoter and elevating genomic methylation in mice fed a high-fat diet. *J. Nutr. Biochem.* **2014**, *25*, 329–336. [CrossRef] [PubMed]
44. Iacobazzi, V.; Castegna, A.; Infantino, V.; Andria, G. Mitochondrial DNA methylation as a next-generation biomarker and diagnostic tool. *Mol. Genet. Metab.* **2013**, *110*, 25–34. [CrossRef] [PubMed]
45. Tryndyak, V.P.; Han, T.; Muskhelishvili, L.; Fuscoe, J.C.; Ross, S.A.; Beland, F.A.; Pogribny, I.P. Coupling global methylation and gene expression profiles reveal key pathophysiological events in liver injury induced by a methyl-deficient diet. *Mol. Nutr. Food Res.* **2011**, *55*, 411–418. [CrossRef] [PubMed]
46. Kalhan, S.C.; Edmison, J.; Marczewski, S.; Dasarathy, S.; Gruca, L.L.; Bennett, C.; Duenas, C.; Lopez, R. Methionine and protein metabolism in non-alcoholic steatohepatitis: Evidence for lower rate of transmethylation of methionine. *Clin. Sci.* **2011**, *121*, 179–189. [CrossRef] [PubMed]
47. Zivkovic, A.M.; Bruce German, J.; Esfandiari, F.; Halsted, C.H. Quantitative lipid metabolomic changes in alcoholic micropigs with fatty liver disease. *Alcohol. Clin. Exp. Res.* **2009**, *33*, 751–758. [CrossRef] [PubMed]
48. Cordero, P.; Campion, J.; Milagro, F.I.; Martinez, J.A. Transcriptomic and epigenetic changes in early liver steatosis associated to obesity: Effect of dietary methyl donor supplementation. *Mol. Genet. Metab.* **2013**, *110*, 388–395. [CrossRef] [PubMed]
49. Sookoian, S.; Rosselli, M.S.; Gemma, C.; Burgueno, A.L.; Fernandez Gianotti, T.; Castano, G.O.; Pirola, C.J. Epigenetic regulation of insulin resistance in nonalcoholic fatty liver disease: Impact of liver methylation of the peroxisome proliferator-activated receptor γ coactivator 1α promoter. *Hepatology* **2010**, *52*, 1992–2000. [CrossRef] [PubMed]
50. Wolff, G.L.; Kodell, R.L.; Moore, S.R.; Cooney, C.A. Maternal epigenetics and methyl supplements affect *agouti* gene expression in A^{vy}/a mice. *FASEB J.* **1998**, *12*, 949–957. [PubMed]
51. Pruis, M.G.; Lendvai, A.; Bloks, V.W.; Zwier, M.V.; Baller, J.F.; de Bruin, A.; Groen, A.K.; Plosch, T. Maternal western diet primes non-alcoholic fatty liver disease in adult mouse offspring. *Acta Physiol.* **2014**, *210*, 215–227. [CrossRef] [PubMed]
52. Chen, G.; Broseus, J.; Hergalant, S.; Donnart, A.; Chevalier, C.; Bolanos-Jimenez, F.; Gueant, J.L.; Houlgatte, R. Identification of master genes involved in liver key functions through transcriptomics and epigenomics of methyl donor deficiency in rat: Relevance to nonalcoholic liver disease. *Mol. Nutr. Food Res.* **2015**, *59*, 293–302. [CrossRef] [PubMed]
53. Carabelli, J.; Burgueno, A.L.; Rosselli, M.S.; Gianotti, T.F.; Lago, N.R.; Pirola, C.J.; Sookoian, S. High fat diet-induced liver steatosis promotes an increase in liver mitochondrial biogenesis in response to hypoxia. *J. Cell. Mol. Med.* **2011**, *15*, 1329–1338. [CrossRef] [PubMed]
54. Pirola, C.J.; Gianotti, T.F.; Burgueno, A.L.; Rey-Funes, M.; Loidl, C.F.; Mallardi, P.; Martino, J.S.; Castano, G.O.; Sookoian, S. Epigenetic modification of liver mitochondrial DNA is associated with histological severity of nonalcoholic fatty liver disease. *Gut* **2013**, *62*, 1356–1363. [CrossRef] [PubMed]
55. Aagaard-Tillery, K.M.; Grove, K.; Bishop, J.; Ke, X.; Fu, Q.; McKnight, R.; Lane, R.H. Developmental origins of disease and determinants of chromatin structure: Maternal diet modifies the primate fetal epigenome. *J. Mol. Endocrinol.* **2008**, *41*, 91–102. [CrossRef] [PubMed]
56. Bricambert, J.; Miranda, J.; Benhamed, F.; Girard, J.; Postic, C.; Dentin, R. Salt-inducible kinase 2 links transcriptional coactivator p300 phosphorylation to the prevention of ChREBP-dependent hepatic steatosis in mice. *J. Clin. Investig.* **2010**, *120*, 4316–4331. [CrossRef] [PubMed]
57. Jun, H.J.; Kim, J.; Hoang, M.H.; Lee, S.J. Hepatic lipid accumulation alters global histone H3 Lysine 9 and 4 trimethylation in the peroxisome proliferator-activated receptor α network. *PLoS ONE* **2012**, *7*, e44345. [CrossRef]
58. Li, J.; Huang, J.; Li, J.S.; Chen, H.; Huang, K.; Zheng, L. Accumulation of endoplasmic reticulum stress and lipogenesis in the liver through generational effects of high fat diets. *J. Hepatol.* **2012**, *56*, 900–907. [CrossRef] [PubMed]
59. Colak, Y.; Yesil, A.; Mutlu, H.H.; Caklili, O.T.; Ulasoglu, C.; Senates, E.; Takir, M.; Kostek, O.; Yilmaz, Y.; Yilmaz Enc, F.; et al. A potential treatment of non-alcoholic fatty liver disease with SIRT1 activators. *J. Gastrointest. Liver Dis.* **2014**, *23*, 311–319.
60. Colak, Y.; Ozturk, O.; Senates, E.; Tuncer, I.; Yorulmaz, E.; Adali, G.; Doganay, L.; Enc, F.Y. SIRT1 as a potential therapeutic target for treatment of nonalcoholic fatty liver disease. *Med. Sci. Monit.* **2011**, *17*, HY5–HY9. [CrossRef] [PubMed]

61. Suter, M.A.; Chen, A.; Burdine, M.S.; Choudhury, M.; Harris, R.A.; Lane, R.H.; Friedman, J.E.; Grove, K.L.; Tackett, A.J.; Aagaard, K.M. A maternal high-fat diet modulates fetal SIRT1 histone and protein deacetylase activity in nonhuman primates. *FASEB J.* **2012**, *26*, 5106–5114. [CrossRef] [PubMed]

62. Hirschey, M.D.; Shimazu, T.; Jing, E.; Grueter, C.A.; Collins, A.M.; Aouizerat, B.; Stancakova, A.; Goetzman, E.; Lam, M.M.; Schwer, B.; et al. SIRT3 deficiency and mitochondrial protein hyperacetylation accelerate the development of the metabolic syndrome. *Mol. Cell* **2011**, *44*, 177–190. [CrossRef] [PubMed]

63. Rottiers, V.; Naar, A.M. MicroRNAs in metabolism and metabolic disorders. *Nat. Rev. Mol. Cell Biol.* **2012**, *13*, 239–250. [CrossRef] [PubMed]

64. Williams, M.D.; Mitchell, G.M. MicroRNAs in insulin resistance and obesity. *Exp. Diabetes Res.* **2012**, *2012*. [CrossRef] [PubMed]

65. Ferreira, D.M.; Simao, A.L.; Rodrigues, C.M.; Castro, R.E. Revisiting the metabolic syndrome and paving the way for microRNAs in non-alcoholic fatty liver disease. *FEBS J.* **2014**, *281*, 2503–2524. [CrossRef] [PubMed]

66. Cheung, O.; Puri, P.; Eicken, C.; Contos, M.J.; Mirshahi, F.; Maher, J.W.; Kellum, J.M.; Min, H.; Luketic, V.A.; Sanyal, A.J. Nonalcoholic steatohepatitis is associated with altered hepatic MicroRNA expression. *Hepatology* **2008**, *48*, 1810–1820. [CrossRef] [PubMed]

67. Castro, R.E.; Ferreira, D.M.; Afonso, M.B.; Borralho, P.M.; Machado, M.V.; Cortez-Pinto, H.; Rodrigues, C.M. miR-34a/SIRT1/p53 is suppressed by ursodeoxycholic acid in the rat liver and activated by disease severity in human non-alcoholic fatty liver disease. *J. Hepatol.* **2013**, *58*, 119–125. [CrossRef] [PubMed]

68. Li, T.; Francl, J.M.; Boehme, S.; Chiang, J.Y. Regulation of cholesterol and bile acid homeostasis by the cholesterol 7α-hydroxylase/steroid response element-binding protein 2/microRNA-33a axis in mice. *Hepatology* **2013**, *58*, 1111–1121. [CrossRef] [PubMed]

69. Guo, Y.; Xiong, Y.; Sheng, Q.; Zhao, S.; Wattacheril, J.; Flynn, C.R. A micro-RNA expression signature for human NAFLD progression. *J. Gastroenterol.* **2016**. [CrossRef] [PubMed]

70. Soronen, J.; Yki-Jarvinen, H.; Zhou, Y.; Sadevirta, S.; Sarin, A.P.; Leivonen, M.; Sevastianova, K.; Perttila, J.; Laurila, P.P.; Sigruener, A.; et al. Novel hepatic microRNAs upregulated in human nonalcoholic fatty liver disease. *Physiol. Rep.* **2016**, *4*. [CrossRef] [PubMed]

71. Esau, C.; Davis, S.; Murray, S.F.; Yu, X.X.; Pandey, S.K.; Pear, M.; Watts, L.; Booten, S.L.; Graham, M.; McKay, R.; et al. miR-122 regulation of lipid metabolism revealed by in vivo antisense targeting. *Cell Metab.* **2006**, *3*, 87–98. [CrossRef] [PubMed]

72. Li, Z.; Xu, G.; Qin, Y.; Zhang, C.; Tang, H.; Yin, Y.; Xiang, X.; Li, Y.; Zhao, J.; Mulholland, M.; et al. Ghrelin promotes hepatic lipogenesis by activation of mtor-PPARγ signaling pathway. *Proc. Natl. Acad. Sci. USA* **2014**, *111*, 13163–13168. [CrossRef] [PubMed]

73. Promrat, K.; Kleiner, D.E.; Niemeier, H.M.; Jackvony, E.; Kearns, M.; Wands, J.R.; Fava, J.L.; Wing, R.R. Randomized controlled trial testing the effects of weight loss on nonalcoholic steatohepatitis. *Hepatology* **2010**, *51*, 121–129. [CrossRef] [PubMed]

74. Wong, V.W.; Chan, R.S.; Wong, G.L.; Cheung, B.H.; Chu, W.C.; Yeung, D.K.; Chim, A.M.; Lai, J.W.; Li, L.S.; Sea, M.M.; et al. Community-based lifestyle modification programme for non-alcoholic fatty liver disease: A randomized controlled trial. *J. Hepatol.* **2013**, *59*, 536–542. [CrossRef] [PubMed]

75. Charlton, M.; Krishnan, A.; Viker, K.; Sanderson, S.; Cazanave, S.; McConico, A.; Masuoko, H.; Gores, G. Fast food diet mouse: Novel small animal model of nash with ballooning, progressive fibrosis, and high physiological fidelity to the human condition. *Am. J. Physiol. Gastrointest. Liver Physiol.* **2011**, *301*, G825–G834. [CrossRef] [PubMed]

76. Garbow, J.R.; Doherty, J.M.; Schugar, R.C.; Travers, S.; Weber, M.L.; Wentz, A.E.; Ezenwajiaku, N.; Cotter, D.G.; Brunt, E.M.; Crawford, P.A. Hepatic steatosis, inflammation, and ER stress in mice maintained long term on a very low-carbohydrate ketogenic diet. *Am. J. Physiol. Gastrointest. Liver Physiol.* **2011**, *300*, G956–G967. [CrossRef] [PubMed]

77. Haas, J.T.; Miao, J.; Chanda, D.; Wang, Y.; Zhao, E.; Haas, M.E.; Hirschey, M.; Vaitheesvaran, B.; Farese, R.V., Jr.; Kurland, I.J.; et al. Hepatic insulin signaling is required for obesity-dependent expression of SREBP-1c mRNA but not for feeding-dependent expression. *Cell Metab.* **2012**, *15*, 873–884. [CrossRef] [PubMed]

78. Schmid, A.I.; Szendroedi, J.; Chmelik, M.; Krssak, M.; Moser, E.; Roden, M. Liver ATP synthesis is lower and relates to insulin sensitivity in patients with type 2 diabetes. *Diabetes Care* **2011**, *34*, 448–453. [CrossRef] [PubMed]

79. Lee, A.H.; Scapa, E.F.; Cohen, D.E.; Glimcher, L.H. Regulation of hepatic lipogenesis by the transcription factor XBP1. *Science* **2008**, *320*, 1492–1496. [CrossRef] [PubMed]

80. Nakagawa, T.; Hu, H.; Zharikov, S.; Tuttle, K.R.; Short, R.A.; Glushakova, O.; Ouyang, X.; Feig, D.I.; Block, E.R.; Herrera-Acosta, J.; et al. A causal role for uric acid in fructose-induced metabolic syndrome. *Am. J. Physiol. Ren. Physiol.* **2006**, *290*, F625–F631. [CrossRef] [PubMed]

81. Lanaspa, M.A.; Sanchez-Lozada, L.G.; Choi, Y.J.; Cicerchi, C.; Kanbay, M.; Roncal-Jimenez, C.A.; Ishimoto, T.; Li, N.; Marek, G.; Duranay, M.; et al. Uric acid induces hepatic steatosis by generation of mitochondrial oxidative stress: Potential role in fructose-dependent and -independent fatty liver. *J. Biol. Chem.* **2012**, *287*, 40732–40744. [CrossRef] [PubMed]

82. Lim, J.S.; Mietus-Snyder, M.; Valente, A.; Schwarz, J.M.; Lustig, R.H. The role of fructose in the pathogenesis of NAFLD and the metabolic syndrome. *Nat. Rev. Gastroenterol. Hepatol.* **2010**, *7*, 251–264. [CrossRef] [PubMed]

83. Kohli, R.; Pan, X.; Malladi, P.; Wainwright, M.S.; Whitington, P.F. Mitochondrial reactive oxygen species signal hepatocyte steatosis by regulating the phosphatidylinositol 3-kinase cell survival pathway. *J. Biol. Chem.* **2007**, *282*, 21327–21336. [CrossRef] [PubMed]

84. Ishimoto, T.; Lanaspa, M.A.; Rivard, C.J.; Roncal-Jimenez, C.A.; Orlicky, D.J.; Cicerchi, C.; McMahan, R.H.; Abdelmalek, M.F.; Rosen, H.R.; Jackman, M.R.; et al. High-fat and high-sucrose (western) diet induces steatohepatitis that is dependent on fructokinase. *Hepatology* **2013**, *58*, 1632–1643. [CrossRef] [PubMed]

85. Ohashi, K.; Munetsuna, E.; Yamada, H.; Ando, Y.; Yamazaki, M.; Taromaru, N.; Nagura, A.; Ishikawa, H.; Suzuki, K.; Teradaira, R.; et al. High fructose consumption induces DNA methylation at PPARα and CPT1A promoter regions in the rat liver. *Biochem. Biophys. Res. Commun.* **2015**, *468*, 185–189. [CrossRef] [PubMed]

86. Yamazaki, M.; Munetsuna, E.; Yamada, H.; Ando, Y.; Mizuno, G.; Murase, Y.; Kondo, K.; Ishikawa, H.; Teradaira, R.; Suzuki, K.; et al. Fructose consumption induces hypomethylation of hepatic mitochondrial DNA in rats. *Life Sci.* **2016**, *149*, 146–152. [CrossRef] [PubMed]

87. Handa, P.; Morgan-Stevenson, V.; Maliken, B.D.; Nelson, J.E.; Washington, S.; Westerman, M.; Yeh, M.M.; Kowdley, K.V. Iron overload results in hepatic oxidative stress, immune cell activation, and hepatocellular ballooning injury, leading to nonalcoholic steatohepatitis in genetically obese mice. *Am. J. Physiol. Gastrointest. Liver Physiol.* **2016**, *310*, G117–G127. [CrossRef] [PubMed]

88. Tallino, S.; Duffy, M.; Ralle, M.; Cortes, M.P.; Latorre, M.; Burkhead, J.L. Nutrigenomics analysis reveals that copper deficiency and dietary sucrose up-regulate inflammation, fibrosis and lipogenic pathways in a mature rat model of nonalcoholic fatty liver disease. *J. Nutr. Biochem.* **2015**, *26*, 996–1006. [CrossRef] [PubMed]

89. Peverill, W.; Powell, L.W.; Skoien, R. Evolving concepts in the pathogenesis of nash: Beyond steatosis and inflammation. *Int. J. Mol. Sci.* **2014**, *15*, 8591–8638. [CrossRef] [PubMed]

90. Puri, P.; Mirshahi, F.; Cheung, O.; Natarajan, R.; Maher, J.W.; Kellum, J.M.; Sanyal, A.J. Activation and dysregulation of the unfolded protein response in nonalcoholic fatty liver disease. *Gastroenterology* **2008**, *134*, 568–576. [CrossRef] [PubMed]

91. Tandra, S.; Yeh, M.M.; Brunt, E.M.; Vuppalanchi, R.; Cummings, O.W.; Unalp-Arida, A.; Wilson, L.A.; Chalasani, N.; Network, N.C.R. Presence and significance of microvesicular steatosis in nonalcoholic fatty liver disease. *J. Hepatol.* **2011**, *55*, 654–659. [CrossRef] [PubMed]

92. Leamy, A.K.; Egnatchik, R.A.; Young, J.D. Molecular mechanisms and the role of saturated fatty acids in the progression of non-alcoholic fatty liver disease. *Prog. Lipid Res.* **2013**, *52*, 165–174. [CrossRef] [PubMed]

93. Cheung, O.; Sanyal, A.J. Abnormalities of lipid metabolism in nonalcoholic fatty liver disease. *Semin. Liver Dis.* **2008**, *28*, 351–359. [CrossRef] [PubMed]

94. Alkhouri, N.; Dixon, L.J.; Feldstein, A.E. Lipotoxicity in nonalcoholic fatty liver disease: Not all lipids are created equal. *Expert Rev. Gastroenterol. Hepatol.* **2009**, *3*, 445–451. [CrossRef] [PubMed]

95. Pagadala, M.; Kasumov, T.; McCullough, A.J.; Zein, N.N.; Kirwan, J.P. Role of ceramides in nonalcoholic fatty liver disease. *Trends Endocrinol. Metab.* **2012**, *23*, 365–371. [CrossRef] [PubMed]

96. Brenner, C.; Galluzzi, L.; Kepp, O.; Kroemer, G. Decoding cell death signals in liver inflammation. *J. Hepatol.* **2013**, *59*, 583–594. [CrossRef] [PubMed]

97. Chaurasia, B.; Summers, S.A. Ceramides—Lipotoxic inducers of metabolic disorders. *Trends Endocrinol. Metab.* **2015**, *26*, 538–550. [CrossRef] [PubMed]

98. Yamaguchi, K.; Yang, L.; McCall, S.; Huang, J.; Yu, X.X.; Pandey, S.K.; Bhanot, S.; Monia, B.P.; Li, Y.X.; Diehl, A.M. Inhibiting triglyceride synthesis improves hepatic steatosis but exacerbates liver damage and fibrosis in obese mice with nonalcoholic steatohepatitis. *Hepatology* **2007**, *45*, 1366–1374. [CrossRef] [PubMed]

99. McClain, C.J.; Barve, S.; Deaciuc, I. Good fat/bad fat. *Hepatology* **2007**, *45*, 1343–1346. [CrossRef] [PubMed]

100. Sanyal, A.J. Reply: To PMID 24818764. *Gastroenterology* **2015**, *148*, 262–263. [CrossRef] [PubMed]

101. Provenzano, A.; Milani, S.; Vizzutti, F.; Delogu, W.; Navari, N.; Novo, E.; Maggiora, M.; Maurino, V.; Laffi, G.; Parola, M.; et al. N-3 polyunsaturated fatty acids worsen inflammation and fibrosis in experimental nonalcoholic steatohepatitis. *Liver Int.* **2014**, *34*, 918–930. [CrossRef] [PubMed]

102. Puri, P.; Baillie, R.A.; Wiest, M.M.; Mirshahi, F.; Choudhury, J.; Cheung, O.; Sargeant, C.; Contos, M.J.; Sanyal, A.J. A lipidomic analysis of nonalcoholic fatty liver disease. *Hepatology* **2007**, *46*, 1081–1090. [CrossRef] [PubMed]

103. Caballero, F.; Fernandez, A.; De Lacy, A.M.; Fernandez-Checa, J.C.; Caballeria, J.; Garcia-Ruiz, C. Enhanced free cholesterol, SREBP-2 and star expression in human nash. *J. Hepatol.* **2009**, *50*, 789–796. [CrossRef] [PubMed]

104. Mari, M.; Caballero, F.; Colell, A.; Morales, A.; Caballeria, J.; Fernandez, A.; Enrich, C.; Fernandez-Checa, J.C.; Garcia-Ruiz, C. Mitochondrial free cholesterol loading sensitizes to TNF- and FAS-mediated steatohepatitis. *Cell Metab.* **2006**, *4*, 185–198. [CrossRef] [PubMed]

105. Savard, C.; Tartaglione, E.V.; Kuver, R.; Haigh, W.G.; Farrell, G.C.; Subramanian, S.; Chait, A.; Yeh, M.M.; Quinn, L.S.; Ioannou, G.N. Synergistic interaction of dietary cholesterol and dietary fat in inducing experimental steatohepatitis. *Hepatology* **2013**, *57*, 81–92. [CrossRef] [PubMed]

106. Van Rooyen, D.M.; Larter, C.Z.; Haigh, W.G.; Yeh, M.M.; Ioannou, G.; Kuver, R.; Lee, S.P.; Teoh, N.C.; Farrell, G.C. Hepatic free cholesterol accumulates in obese, diabetic mice and causes nonalcoholic steatohepatitis. *Gastroenterology* **2011**, *141*, 1393–1403. [CrossRef] [PubMed]

107. Wouters, K.; van Gorp, P.J.; Bieghs, V.; Gijbels, M.J.; Duimel, H.; Lutjohann, D.; Kerksiek, A.; van Kruchten, R.; Maeda, N.; Staels, B.; et al. Dietary cholesterol, rather than liver steatosis, leads to hepatic inflammation in hyperlipidemic mouse models of nonalcoholic steatohepatitis. *Hepatology* **2008**, *48*, 474–486. [CrossRef] [PubMed]

108. Min, H.K.; Kapoor, A.; Fuchs, M.; Mirshahi, F.; Zhou, H.; Maher, J.; Kellum, J.; Warnick, R.; Contos, M.J.; Sanyal, A.J. Increased hepatic synthesis and dysregulation of cholesterol metabolism is associated with the severity of nonalcoholic fatty liver disease. *Cell Metab.* **2012**, *15*, 665–674. [CrossRef] [PubMed]

109. Simonen, P.; Kotronen, A.; Hallikainen, M.; Sevastianova, K.; Makkonen, J.; Hakkarainen, A.; Lundbom, N.; Miettinen, T.A.; Gylling, H.; Yki-Jarvinen, H. Cholesterol synthesis is increased and absorption decreased in non-alcoholic fatty liver disease independent of obesity. *J. Hepatol.* **2011**, *54*, 153–159. [CrossRef] [PubMed]

110. Cortes, V.A.; Busso, D.; Maiz, A.; Arteaga, A.; Nervi, F.; Rigotti, A. Physiological and pathological implications of cholesterol. *Front. Biosci.* **2014**, *19*, 416–428. [CrossRef]

111. Walenbergh, S.M.; Koek, G.H.; Bieghs, V.; Shiri-Sverdlov, R. Non-alcoholic steatohepatitis: The role of oxidized low-density lipoproteins. *J. Hepatol.* **2013**, *58*, 801–810. [CrossRef] [PubMed]

112. Hendrikx, T.; Walenbergh, S.M.; Hofker, M.H.; Shiri-Sverdlov, R. Lysosomal cholesterol accumulation: Driver on the road to inflammation during atherosclerosis and non-alcoholic steatohepatitis. *Obes. Rev.* **2014**, *15*, 424–433. [CrossRef] [PubMed]

113. Tomita, K.; Teratani, T.; Suzuki, T.; Shimizu, M.; Sato, H.; Narimatsu, K.; Okada, Y.; Kurihara, C.; Irie, R.; Yokoyama, H.; et al. Free cholesterol accumulation in hepatic stellate cells: Mechanism of liver fibrosis aggravation in nonalcoholic steatohepatitis in mice. *Hepatology* **2014**, *59*, 154–169. [CrossRef] [PubMed]

114. Chalasani, N.; Younossi, Z.; Lavine, J.E.; Diehl, A.M.; Brunt, E.M.; Cusi, K.; Charlton, M.; Sanyal, A.J. The diagnosis and management of non-alcoholic fatty liver disease: Practice guideline by the American association for the study of liver diseases, American college of gastroenterology, and the American gastroenterological association. *Hepatology* **2012**, *55*, 2005–2023. [CrossRef] [PubMed]

115. Spolding, B.; Connor, T.; Wittmer, C.; Abreu, L.L.; Kaspi, A.; Ziemann, M.; Kaur, G.; Cooper, A.; Morrison, S.; Lee, S.; et al. Rapid development of non-alcoholic steatohepatitis in psammomys obesus (Israeli Sand Rat). *PLoS ONE* **2014**, *9*, e92656. [CrossRef] [PubMed]

116. Bellanti, F.; Mitarotonda, D.; Tamborra, R.; Blonda, M.; Iannelli, G.; Petrella, A.; Sanginario, V.; Iuliano, L.; Vendemiale, G.; Serviddio, G. Oxysterols induce mitochondrial impairment and hepatocellular toxicity in non-alcoholic fatty liver disease. *Free Radic. Biol. Med.* **2014**, *75*, S16–S17. [CrossRef] [PubMed]

117. Tall, A.R.; Yvan-Charvet, L. Cholesterol, inflammation and innate immunity. *Nat. Rev. Immunol.* **2015**, *15*, 104–116. [CrossRef] [PubMed]

118. Chung, S.; Cuffe, H.; Marshall, S.M.; McDaniel, A.L.; Ha, J.H.; Kavanagh, K.; Hong, C.; Tontonoz, P.; Temel, R.E.; Parks, J.S. Dietary cholesterol promotes adipocyte hypertrophy and adipose tissue inflammation in visceral, but not in subcutaneous, fat in monkeys. *Arterioscler. Thromb. Vasc. Biol.* **2014**, *34*, 1880–1887. [CrossRef] [PubMed]

119. Serviddio, G.; Bellanti, F.; Vendemiale, G.; Altomare, E. Mitochondrial dysfunction in nonalcoholic steatohepatitis. *Expert Rev. Gastroenterol. Hepatol.* **2011**, *5*, 233–244. [CrossRef] [PubMed]

120. Tessari, P.; Coracina, A.; Cosma, A.; Tiengo, A. Hepatic lipid metabolism and non-alcoholic fatty liver disease. *Nutr. Metab. Cardiovasc. Dis.* **2009**, *19*, 291–302. [CrossRef] [PubMed]

121. Nassir, F.; Ibdah, J.A. Role of mitochondria in nonalcoholic fatty liver disease. *Int. J. Mol. Sci.* **2014**, *15*, 8713–8742. [CrossRef] [PubMed]

122. Mailloux, R.J.; Florian, M.; Chen, Q.; Yan, J.; Petrov, I.; Coughlan, M.C.; Laziyan, M.; Caldwell, D.; Lalande, M.; Patry, D.; et al. Exposure to a northern contaminant mixture (NCM) alters hepatic energy and lipid metabolism exacerbating hepatic steatosis in obese JCR rats. *PLoS ONE* **2014**, *9*, e106832. [CrossRef] [PubMed]

123. Martel, C.; Allouche, M.; Esposti, D.D.; Fanelli, E.; Boursier, C.; Henry, C.; Chopineau, J.; Calamita, G.; Kroemer, G.; Lemoine, A.; et al. Glycogen synthase kinase 3-mediated voltage-dependent anion channel phosphorylation controls outer mitochondrial membrane permeability during lipid accumulation. *Hepatology* **2013**, *57*, 93–102. [CrossRef] [PubMed]

124. Win, S.; Than, T.A.; Le, B.H.; Garcia-Ruiz, C.; Fernandez-Checa, J.C.; Kaplowitz, N. Sab (Sh3bp5) dependence of JNK mediated inhibition of mitochondrial respiration in palmitic acid induced hepatocyte lipotoxicity. *J. Hepatol.* **2015**, *62*, 1367–1374. [CrossRef] [PubMed]

125. Penke, M.; Larsen, P.S.; Schuster, S.; Dall, M.; Jensen, B.A.; Gorski, T.; Meusel, A.; Richter, S.; Vienberg, S.G.; Treebak, J.T.; et al. Hepatic nad salvage pathway is enhanced in mice on a high-fat diet. *Mol. Cell. Endocrinol.* **2015**, *412*, 65–72. [CrossRef] [PubMed]

126. Gariani, K.; Menzies, K.J.; Ryu, D.; Wegner, C.J.; Wang, X.; Ropelle, E.R.; Moullan, N.; Zhang, H.; Perino, A.; Lemos, V.; et al. Eliciting the mitochondrial unfolded protein response by nicotinamide adenine dinucleotide repletion reverses fatty liver disease in mice. *Hepatology* **2016**, *63*, 1190–1204. [CrossRef] [PubMed]

127. Bentinger, M.; Brismar, K.; Dallner, G. The antioxidant role of coenzyme Q. *Mitochondrion* **2007**, *7*, S41–S50. [CrossRef] [PubMed]

128. Nowicka, B.; Kruk, J. Occurrence, biosynthesis and function of isoprenoid quinones. *Biochim. Biophys. Acta* **2010**, *1797*, 1587–1605. [CrossRef] [PubMed]

129. Laredj, L.N.; Licitra, F.; Puccio, H.M. The molecular genetics of coenzyme Q biosynthesis in health and disease. *Biochimie* **2014**, *100*, 78–87. [CrossRef] [PubMed]

130. Bentinger, M.; Tekle, M.; Dallner, G. Coenzyme Q—Biosynthesis and functions. *Biochem. Biophys. Res. Commun.* **2010**, *396*, 74–79. [CrossRef] [PubMed]

131. Yesilova, Z.; Yaman, H.; Oktenli, C.; Ozcan, A.; Uygun, A.; Cakir, E.; Sanisoglu, S.Y.; Erdil, A.; Ates, Y.; Aslan, M.; et al. Systemic markers of lipid peroxidation and antioxidants in patients with nonalcoholic fatty liver disease. *Am. J. Gastroenterol.* **2005**, *100*, 850–855. [CrossRef] [PubMed]

132. Huertas, J.R.; Battino, M.; Lenaz, G.; Mataix, F.J. Changes in mitochondrial and microsomal rat liver coenzyme Q9 and Q10 content induced by dietary fat and endogenous lipid peroxidation. *FEBS Lett.* **1991**, *287*, 89–92. [CrossRef]

133. Bravo, E.; Palleschi, S.; Rossi, B.; Napolitano, M.; Tiano, L.; D'Amore, E.; Botham, K.M. Coenzyme Q metabolism is disturbed in high fat diet-induced non-alcoholic fatty liver disease in rats. *Int. J. Mol. Sci.* **2012**, *13*, 1644–1657. [CrossRef] [PubMed]

134. Feldstein, A.E.; Werneburg, N.W.; Canbay, A.; Guicciardi, M.E.; Bronk, S.F.; Rydzewski, R.; Burgart, L.J.; Gores, G.J. Free fatty acids promote hepatic lipotoxicity by stimulating TNF-α expression via a lysosomal pathway. *Hepatology* **2004**, *40*, 185–194. [CrossRef] [PubMed]

135. Aubert, J.; Begriche, K.; Knockaert, L.; Robin, M.A.; Fromenty, B. Increased expression of cytochrome P450 2E1 in nonalcoholic fatty liver disease: Mechanisms and pathophysiological role. *Clin. Res. Hepatol. Gastroenterol.* **2011**, *35*, 630–637. [CrossRef] [PubMed]

136. Abdelmegeed, M.A.; Banerjee, A.; Yoo, S.H.; Jang, S.; Gonzalez, F.J.; Song, B.J. Critical role of cytochrome P450 2E1 (CYP2E1) in the development of high fat-induced non-alcoholic steatohepatitis. *J. Hepatol.* **2012**, *57*, 860–866. [CrossRef] [PubMed]

137. Guicciardi, M.E.; Malhi, H.; Mott, J.L.; Gores, G.J. Apoptosis and necrosis in the liver. *Compr. Physiol.* **2013**, *3*, 977–1010. [PubMed]

138. Hirsova, P.; Gores, G.J. Death receptor-mediated cell death and proinflammatory signaling in nonalcoholic steatohepatitis. *Cell. Mol. Gastroenterol. Hepatol.* **2015**, *1*, 17–27. [CrossRef] [PubMed]

139. Li, J.; McQuade, T.; Siemer, A.B.; Napetschnig, J.; Moriwaki, K.; Hsiao, Y.S.; Damko, E.; Moquin, D.; Walz, T.; McDermott, A.; et al. The RIP1/RIP3 necrosome forms a functional amyloid signaling complex required for programmed necrosis. *Cell* **2012**, *150*, 339–350. [CrossRef] [PubMed]

140. Wang, H.; Sun, L.; Su, L.; Rizo, J.; Liu, L.; Wang, L.F.; Wang, F.S.; Wang, X. Mixed lineage kinase domain-like protein MLKL causes necrotic membrane disruption upon phosphorylation by RIP3. *Mol. Cell* **2014**, *54*, 133–146. [CrossRef] [PubMed]

141. Zhang, D.W.; Shao, J.; Lin, J.; Zhang, N.; Lu, B.J.; Lin, S.C.; Dong, M.Q.; Han, J. RIP3, an energy metabolism regulator that switches TNF-induced cell death from apoptosis to necrosis. *Science* **2009**, *325*, 332–336. [CrossRef] [PubMed]

142. Upton, J.W.; Kaiser, W.J.; Mocarski, E.S. Virus inhibition of RIP3-dependent necrosis. *Cell Host Microbe* **2010**, *7*, 302–313. [CrossRef] [PubMed]

143. Moujalled, D.M.; Cook, W.D.; Okamoto, T.; Murphy, J.; Lawlor, K.E.; Vince, J.E.; Vaux, D.L. TNF can activate RIPK3 and cause programmed necrosis in the absence of RIPK1. *Cell Death Dis.* **2013**, *4*. [CrossRef] [PubMed]

144. Degterev, A.; Huang, Z.; Boyce, M.; Li, Y.; Jagtap, P.; Mizushima, N.; Cuny, G.D.; Mitchison, T.J.; Moskowitz, M.A.; Yuan, J. Chemical inhibitor of nonapoptotic cell death with therapeutic potential for ischemic brain injury. *Nat. Chem. Biol.* **2005**, *1*, 112–119. [CrossRef] [PubMed]

145. Zhao, J.; Jitkaew, S.; Cai, Z.; Choksi, S.; Li, Q.; Luo, J.; Liu, Z.G. Mixed lineage kinase domain-like is a key receptor interacting protein 3 downstream component of TNF-induced necrosis. *Proc. Natl. Acad. Sci. USA* **2012**, *109*, 5322–5327. [CrossRef] [PubMed]

146. Gautheron, J.; Vucur, M.; Reisinger, F.; Cardenas, D.V.; Roderburg, C.; Koppe, C.; Kreggenwinkel, K.; Schneider, A.T.; Bartneck, M.; Neumann, U.P.; et al. A positive feedback loop between RIP3 and JNK controls non-alcoholic steatohepatitis. *EMBO Mol. Med.* **2014**, *6*, 1062–1074. [CrossRef] [PubMed]

147. Afonso, M.B.; Rodrigues, P.M.; Carvalho, T.; Caridade, M.; Borralho, P.; Cortez-Pinto, H.; Castro, R.E.; Rodrigues, C.M. Necroptosis is a key pathogenic event in human and experimental murine models of non-alcoholic steatohepatitis. *Clin. Sci.* **2015**, *129*, 721–739. [CrossRef] [PubMed]

148. Park, S.W.; Zhou, Y.; Lee, J.; Lu, A.; Sun, C.; Chung, J.; Ueki, K.; Ozcan, U. The regulatory subunits of PI3K, p85α and p85β, interact with XBP-1 and increase its nuclear translocation. *Nat. Med.* **2010**, *16*, 429–437. [CrossRef] [PubMed]

149. Kapoor, A.; Sanyal, A.J. Endoplasmic reticulum stress and the unfolded protein response. *Clin. Liver Dis.* **2009**, *13*, 581–590. [CrossRef] [PubMed]

150. Padilla, A.; Descorbeth, M.; Almeyda, A.L.; Payne, K.; de Leon, M. Hyperglycemia magnifies Schwann cell dysfunction and cell death triggered by PA-induced lipotoxicity. *Brain Res.* **2011**, *1370*, 64–79. [CrossRef] [PubMed]

151. Wei, Y.; Wang, D.; Topczewski, F.; Pagliassotti, M.J. Saturated fatty acids induce endoplasmic reticulum stress and apoptosis independently of ceramide in liver cells. *Am. J. Physiol. Endocrinol. Metab.* **2006**, *291*, E275–E281. [CrossRef] [PubMed]

152. Fu, S.; Yang, L.; Li, P.; Hofmann, O.; Dicker, L.; Hide, W.; Lin, X.; Watkins, S.M.; Ivanov, A.R.; Hotamisligil, G.S. Aberrant lipid metabolism disrupts calcium homeostasis causing liver endoplasmic reticulum stress in obesity. *Nature* **2011**, *473*, 528–531. [CrossRef] [PubMed]

153. Arias-Loste, M.T.; Fabrega, E.; Lopez-Hoyos, M.; Crespo, J. The crosstalk between hypoxia and innate immunity in the development of obesity-related nonalcoholic fatty liver disease. *BioMed Res. Int.* **2015**, *2015*. [CrossRef] [PubMed]

154. Qu, A.; Taylor, M.; Xue, X.; Matsubara, T.; Metzger, D.; Chambon, P.; Gonzalez, F.J.; Shah, Y.M. Hypoxia-inducible transcription factor 2α promotes steatohepatitis through augmenting lipid accumulation, inflammation, and fibrosis. *Hepatology* **2011**, *54*, 472–483. [CrossRef] [PubMed]

155. Ye, J.; Gao, Z.; Yin, J.; He, Q. Hypoxia is a potential risk factor for chronic inflammation and adiponectin reduction in adipose tissue of *ob/ob* and dietary obese mice. *Am. J. Physiol. Endocrinol. Metab.* **2007**, *293*, E1118–E1128. [CrossRef] [PubMed]

156. Hodson, L. Adipose tissue oxygenation: Effects on metabolic function. *Adipocyte* **2014**, *3*, 75–80. [CrossRef] [PubMed]

157. Hodson, L.; Humphreys, S.M.; Karpe, F.; Frayn, K.N. Metabolic signatures of human adipose tissue hypoxia in obesity. *Diabetes* **2013**, *62*, 1417–1425. [CrossRef] [PubMed]

158. Eltzschig, H.K.; Carmeliet, P. Hypoxia and inflammation. *N. Engl. J. Med.* **2011**, *364*, 656–665. [PubMed]

159. Rius, J.; Guma, M.; Schachtrup, C.; Akassoglou, K.; Zinkernagel, A.S.; Nizet, V.; Johnson, R.S.; Haddad, G.G.; Karin, M. NF-κB links innate immunity to the hypoxic response through transcriptional regulation of HIF-1α. *Nature* **2008**, *453*, 807–811. [CrossRef] [PubMed]

160. Kuhlicke, J.; Frick, J.S.; Morote-Garcia, J.C.; Rosenberger, P.; Eltzschig, H.K. Hypoxia inducible factor (HIF)-1 coordinates induction of toll-like receptors TLR2 and TLR6 during hypoxia. *PLoS ONE* **2007**, *2*, e1364. [CrossRef] [PubMed]

161. Kim, S.Y.; Choi, Y.J.; Joung, S.M.; Lee, B.H.; Jung, Y.S.; Lee, J.Y. Hypoxic stress up-regulates the expression of toll-like receptor 4 in macrophages via hypoxia-inducible factor. *Immunology* **2010**, *129*, 516–524. [CrossRef] [PubMed]

162. Aron-Wisnewsky, J.; Minville, C.; Tordjman, J.; Levy, P.; Bouillot, J.L.; Basdevant, A.; Bedossa, P.; Clement, K.; Pepin, J.L. Chronic intermittent hypoxia is a major trigger for non-alcoholic fatty liver disease in morbid obese. *J. Hepatol.* **2012**, *56*, 225–233. [CrossRef] [PubMed]

163. Feldstein, A.E.; Canbay, A.; Angulo, P.; Taniai, M.; Burgart, L.J.; Lindor, K.D.; Gores, G.J. Hepatocyte apoptosis and FAS expression are prominent features of human nonalcoholic steatohepatitis. *Gastroenterology* **2003**, *125*, 437–443. [CrossRef]

164. Idrissova, L.; Malhi, H.; Werneburg, N.W.; LeBrasseur, N.K.; Bronk, S.F.; Fingas, C.; Tchkonia, T.; Pirtskhalava, T.; White, T.A.; Stout, M.B.; et al. Trail receptor deletion in mice suppresses the inflammation of nutrient excess. *J. Hepatol.* **2015**, *62*, 1156–1163. [CrossRef] [PubMed]

165. Lu, M.; Lawrence, D.A.; Marsters, S.; Acosta-Alvear, D.; Kimmig, P.; Mendez, A.S.; Paton, A.W.; Paton, J.C.; Walter, P.; Ashkenazi, A. Opposing unfolded-protein-response signals converge on death receptor 5 to control apoptosis. *Science* **2014**, *345*, 98–101. [CrossRef] [PubMed]

166. Gadd, V.L.; Skoien, R.; Powell, E.E.; Fagan, K.J.; Winterford, C.; Horsfall, L.; Irvine, K.; Clouston, A.D. The portal inflammatory infiltrate and ductular reaction in human nonalcoholic fatty liver disease. *Hepatology* **2014**, *59*, 1393–1405. [CrossRef] [PubMed]

167. Lanthier, N. Targeting Kupffer cells in non-alcoholic fatty liver disease/non-alcoholic steatohepatitis: Why and how? *World J. Hepatol.* **2015**, *7*, 2184–2188. [CrossRef] [PubMed]

168. Dixon, L.J.; Barnes, M.; Tang, H.; Pritchard, M.T.; Nagy, L.E. Kupffer cells in the liver. *Compr. Physiol.* **2013**, *3*, 785–797. [PubMed]

169. Tacke, F.; Zimmermann, H.W. Macrophage heterogeneity in liver injury and fibrosis. *J. Hepatol.* **2014**, *60*, 1090–1096. [CrossRef] [PubMed]

170. Marra, F.; Tacke, F. Roles for chemokines in liver disease. *Gastroenterology* **2014**, *147*, 577–594. [CrossRef] [PubMed]

171. Leroux, A.; Ferrere, G.; Godie, V.; Cailleux, F.; Renoud, M.L.; Gaudin, F.; Naveau, S.; Prevot, S.; Makhzami, S.; Perlemuter, G.; et al. Toxic lipids stored by Kupffer cells correlates with their pro-inflammatory phenotype at an early stage of steatohepatitis. *J. Hepatol.* **2012**, *57*, 141–149. [CrossRef] [PubMed]

172. Chinetti-Gbaguidi, G.; Staels, B. Macrophage polarization in metabolic disorders: Functions and regulation. *Curr. Opin. Lipidol.* **2011**, *22*, 365–372. [CrossRef] [PubMed]

173. Xu, R.; Huang, H.; Zhang, Z.; Wang, F.S. The role of neutrophils in the development of liver diseases. *Cell. Mol. Immunol.* **2014**, *11*, 224–231. [CrossRef] [PubMed]

174. Ibusuki, R.; Uto, H.; Arima, S.; Mawatari, S.; Setoguchi, Y.; Iwashita, Y.; Hashimoto, S.; Maeda, T.; Tanoue, S.; Kanmura, S.; et al. Transgenic expression of human neutrophil peptide-1 enhances hepatic fibrosis in mice fed a choline-deficient, l-amino acid-defined diet. *Liver Int.* **2013**, *33*, 1549–1556. [CrossRef] [PubMed]

175. Rensen, S.S.; Bieghs, V.; Xanthoulea, S.; Arfianti, E.; Bakker, J.A.; Shiri-Sverdlov, R.; Hofker, M.H.; Greve, J.W.; Buurman, W.A. Neutrophil-derived myeloperoxidase aggravates non-alcoholic steatohepatitis in low-density lipoprotein receptor-deficient mice. *PLoS ONE* **2012**, *7*, e52411. [CrossRef] [PubMed]

176. Talukdar, S.; Oh da, Y.; Bandyopadhyay, G.; Li, D.; Xu, J.; McNelis, J.; Lu, M.; Li, P.; Yan, Q.; Zhu, Y.; et al. Neutrophils mediate insulin resistance in mice fed a high-fat diet through secreted elastase. *Nat. Med.* **2012**, *18*, 1407–1412. [CrossRef] [PubMed]

177. Tacke, F.; Yoneyama, H. From NAFLD to NASH to fibrosis to HCC: Role of dendritic cell populations in the liver. *Hepatology* **2013**, *58*, 494–496. [CrossRef] [PubMed]

178. Henning, J.R.; Graffeo, C.S.; Rehman, A.; Fallon, N.C.; Zambirinis, C.P.; Ochi, A.; Barilla, R.; Jamal, M.; Deutsch, M.; Greco, S.; et al. Dendritic cells limit fibroinflammatory injury in nonalcoholic steatohepatitis in mice. *Hepatology* **2013**, *58*, 589–602. [CrossRef] [PubMed]

179. Sutti, S.; Locatelli, I.; Bruzzi, S.; Jindal, A.; Vacchiano, M.; Bozzola, C.; Albano, E. CX3CR1-expressing inflammatory dendritic cells contribute to the progression of steatohepatitis. *Clin. Sci.* **2015**, *129*, 797–808. [CrossRef] [PubMed]

180. Ganz, M.; Szabo, G. Immune and inflammatory pathways in NASH. *Hepatol. Int.* **2013**, *7*, 771–781. [CrossRef] [PubMed]

181. Tian, Z.; Chen, Y.; Gao, B. Natural killer cells in liver disease. *Hepatology* **2013**, *57*, 1654–1662. [CrossRef] [PubMed]

182. Kumar, V. NKT-cell subsets: Promoters and protectors in inflammatory liver disease. *J. Hepatol.* **2013**, *59*, 618–620. [CrossRef] [PubMed]

183. Martin-Murphy, B.V.; You, Q.; Wang, H.; De La Houssaye, B.A.; Reilly, T.P.; Friedman, J.E.; Ju, C. Mice lacking natural killer T cell are more susceptible to metabolic alterations following high fat diet feeding. *PLoS ONE* **2014**, *9*, e80949. [CrossRef] [PubMed]

184. Kremer, M.; Thomas, E.; Milton, R.J.; Perry, A.W.; van Rooijen, N.; Wheeler, M.D.; Zacks, S.; Fried, M.; Rippe, R.A.; Hines, I.N. Kupffer cell and interleukin-12-dependent loss of natural killer T cell in hepatosteatosis. *Hepatology* **2010**, *51*, 130–141. [CrossRef] [PubMed]

185. Syn, W.K.; Oo, Y.H.; Pereira, T.A.; Karaca, G.F.; Jung, Y.; Omenetti, A.; Witek, R.P.; Choi, S.S.; Guy, C.D.; Fearing, C.M.; et al. Accumulation of natural killer T cells in progressive nonalcoholic fatty liver disease. *Hepatology* **2010**, *51*, 1998–2007. [CrossRef] [PubMed]

186. Tajiri, K.; Shimizu, Y. Role of NKT cells in the pathogenesis of NAFLD. *Int. J. Hepatol.* **2012**, *2012*. [CrossRef] [PubMed]

187. Guy, C.D.; Suzuki, A.; Zdanowicz, M.; Abdelmalek, M.F.; Burchette, J.; Unalp, A.; Diehl, A.M.; Nash, C.R.N. Hedgehog pathway activation parallels histologic severity of injury and fibrosis in human nonalcoholic fatty liver disease. *Hepatology* **2012**, *55*, 1711–1721. [CrossRef] [PubMed]

188. Verdelho Machado, M.; Diehl, A.M. Role of Hedgehog Signaling Pathway in NASH. *Int. J. Mol. Sci.* **2016**, *17*. [CrossRef] [PubMed]

189. Moylan, C.A.; Pang, H.; Dellinger, A.; Suzuki, A.; Garrett, M.E.; Guy, C.D.; Murphy, S.K.; Ashley-Koch, A.E.; Choi, S.S.; Michelotti, G.A.; et al. Hepatic gene expression profiles differentiate presymptomatic patients with mild versus severe nonalcoholic fatty liver disease. *Hepatology* **2014**, *59*, 471–482. [CrossRef] [PubMed]

190. Kwon, H.; Song, K.; Han, C.; Chen, W.; Wang, Y.; Dash, S.; Lim, K.; Wu, T. Inhibition of hedgehog signaling ameliorates hepatic inflammation in mice with nonalcoholic fatty liver disease. *Hepatology* **2015**, *63*, 1155–1169. [CrossRef] [PubMed]

191. Syn, W.K.; Choi, S.S.; Liaskou, E.; Karaca, G.F.; Agboola, K.M.; Oo, Y.H.; Mi, Z.; Pereira, T.A.; Zdanowicz, M.; Malladi, P.; et al. Osteopontin is induced by hedgehog pathway activation and promotes fibrosis progression in nonalcoholic steatohepatitis. *Hepatology* **2011**, *53*, 106–115. [CrossRef] [PubMed]

192. Machado, M.V.; Michelotti, G.A.; Pereira, T.; Boursier, J.; Swiderska-Syn, M.; Karaca, G.; Xie, G.; Guy, C.D.; Bohinc, B.; Lindblom, K.R.; et al. Reduced lipoapoptosis, hedgehog pathway activation and fibrosis in caspase-2 deficient mice with non-alcoholic steatohepatitis. *Gut* **2015**, *64*, 1148–1157. [CrossRef] [PubMed]

193. Machado, M.V.; Michelotti, G.A.; Pereira, T.A.; Xie, G.; Premont, R.; Cortez-Pinto, H.; Diehl, A.M. Accumulation of duct cell with activated YAP parallels fibrosis progression in non-alcoholic fatty liver disease. *J. Hepatol.* **2015**, *63*, 962–970. [CrossRef] [PubMed]

194. Guy, C.D.; Suzuki, A.; Abdelmalek, M.F.; Burchette, J.L.; Diehl, A.M. Treatment response in the PIVENS trial is associated with decreased hedgehog pathway activity. *Hepatology* **2015**, *61*, 98–107. [CrossRef] [PubMed]

195. Evans, R.M.; Mangelsdorf, D.J. Nuclear receptors, RXR, and the big bang. *Cell* **2014**, *157*, 255–266. [CrossRef] [PubMed]

196. Fuchs, C.D.; Traussnigg, S.A.; Trauner, M. Nuclear receptor modulation for the treatment of nonalcoholic fatty liver disease. *Semin. Liver Dis.* **2016**, *36*, 69–86. [CrossRef] [PubMed]

197. Tailleux, A.; Wouters, K.; Staels, B. Roles of PPARs in NAFLD: Potential therapeutic targets. *Biochim. Biophys. Acta* **2012**, *1821*, 809–818. [CrossRef] [PubMed]

198. Francque, S.; Verrijken, A.; Caron, S.; Prawitt, J.; Paumelle, R.; Derudas, B.; Lefebvre, P.; Taskinen, M.R.; Van Hul, W.; Mertens, I.; et al. PPARα gene expression correlates with severity and histological treatment response in patients with non-alcoholic steatohepatitis. *J. Hepatol.* **2015**, *63*, 164–173. [CrossRef] [PubMed]

199. Reddy, J.K.; Rao, M.S. Lipid metabolism and liver inflammation. II. Fatty liver disease and fatty acid oxidation. *Am. J. Physiol. Gastrointest. Liver Physiol.* **2006**, *290*, G852–G858. [CrossRef] [PubMed]

200. Ip, E.; Farrell, G.; Hall, P.; Robertson, G.; Leclercq, I. Administration of the potent PPARα agonist, Wy-14,643, reverses nutritional fibrosis and steatohepatitis in mice. *Hepatology* **2004**, *39*, 1286–1296. [CrossRef] [PubMed]

201. Shan, W.; Nicol, C.J.; Ito, S.; Bility, M.T.; Kennett, M.J.; Ward, J.M.; Gonzalez, F.J.; Peters, J.M. Peroxisome proliferator-activated receptor-β/δ protects against chemically induced liver toxicity in mice. *Hepatology* **2008**, *47*, 225–235. [CrossRef] [PubMed]

202. Kawaguchi, K.; Sakaida, I.; Tsuchiya, M.; Omori, K.; Takami, T.; Okita, K. Pioglitazone prevents hepatic steatosis, fibrosis, and enzyme-altered lesions in rat liver cirrhosis induced by a choline-deficient L-amino acid-defined diet. *Biochem. Biophys. Res. Commun.* **2004**, *315*, 187–195. [CrossRef] [PubMed]

203. Stienstra, R.; Duval, C.; Muller, M.; Kersten, S. PPARs, obesity, and inflammation. *PPAR Res.* **2007**, *2007*. [CrossRef] [PubMed]

204. Lutchman, G.; Modi, A.; Kleiner, D.E.; Promrat, K.; Heller, T.; Ghany, M.; Borg, B.; Loomba, R.; Liang, T.J.; Premkumar, A.; et al. The effects of discontinuing pioglitazone in patients with nonalcoholic steatohepatitis. *Hepatology* **2007**, *46*, 424–429. [CrossRef] [PubMed]

205. Yamada, Y.; Eto, M.; Ito, Y.; Mochizuki, S.; Son, B.K.; Ogawa, S.; Iijima, K.; Kaneki, M.; Kozaki, K.; Toba, K.; et al. Suppressive role of PPARγ-regulated endothelial nitric oxide synthase in adipocyte lipolysis. *PLoS ONE* **2015**, *10*, e0136597. [CrossRef] [PubMed]

206. Ratziu, V.; Harrison, S.A.; Francque, S.; Bedossa, P.; Lehert, P.; Serfaty, L.; Romero-Gomez, M.; Boursier, J.; Abdelmalek, M.; Caldwell, S.; et al. Elafibranor, an agonist of the peroxisome proliferator-activated receptor-α and -β, induces resolution of nonalcoholic steatohepatitis without fibrosis worsening. *Gastroenterology* **2016**, *150*, 1147–1159. [CrossRef] [PubMed]

207. Lamba, V.; Yasuda, K.; Lamba, J.K.; Assem, M.; Davila, J.; Strom, S.; Schuetz, E.G. PXR (NR1I2): Splice variants in human tissues, including brain, and identification of neurosteroids and nicotine as PXR activators. *Toxicol. Appl. Pharmacol.* **2004**, *199*, 251–265. [CrossRef] [PubMed]

208. Haughton, E.L.; Tucker, S.J.; Marek, C.J.; Durward, E.; Leel, V.; Bascal, Z.; Monaghan, T.; Koruth, M.; Collie-Duguid, E.; Mann, D.A.; et al. Pregnane X receptor activators inhibit human hepatic stellate cell transdifferentiation in vitro. *Gastroenterology* **2006**, *131*, 194–209. [CrossRef] [PubMed]

209. Sookoian, S.; Castano, G.O.; Burgueno, A.L.; Gianotti, T.F.; Rosselli, M.S.; Pirola, C.J. The nuclear receptor PXR gene variants are associated with liver injury in nonalcoholic fatty liver disease. *Pharmacogenet. Genom.* **2010**, *20*, 1–8. [CrossRef] [PubMed]

210. Breuker, C.; Planque, C.; Rajabi, F.; Nault, J.C.; Couchy, G.; Zucman-Rossi, J.; Evrard, A.; Kantar, J.; Chevet, E.; Bioulac-Sage, P.; et al. Characterization of a novel PXR isoform with potential dominant-negative properties. *J. Hepatol.* **2014**, *61*, 609–616. [CrossRef] [PubMed]

211. Monostory, K.; Dvorak, Z. Steroid regulation of drug-metabolizing cytochromes P450. *Curr. Drug Metab.* **2011**, *12*, 154–172. [CrossRef] [PubMed]

212. Spruiell, K.; Richardson, R.M.; Cullen, J.M.; Awumey, E.M.; Gonzalez, F.J.; Gyamfi, M.A. Role of pregnane X receptor in obesity and glucose homeostasis in male mice. *J. Biol. Chem.* **2014**, *289*, 3244–3261. [CrossRef] [PubMed]

213. Li, L.; Li, H.; Garzel, B.; Yang, H.; Sueyoshi, T.; Li, Q.; Shu, Y.; Zhang, J.; Hu, B.; Heyward, S.; et al. SLC13A5 is a novel transcriptional target of the pregnane X receptor and sensitizes drug-induced steatosis in human liver. *Mol. Pharmacol.* **2015**, *87*, 674–682. [CrossRef] [PubMed]

214. Sun, M.; Cui, W.; Woody, S.K.; Staudinger, J.L. Pregnane X receptor modulates the inflammatory response in primary cultures of hepatocytes. *Drug Metab. Dispos.* **2015**, *43*, 335–343. [CrossRef] [PubMed]

215. Nishimura, M.; Naito, S.; Yokoi, T. Tissue-specific mRNA expression profiles of human nuclear receptor subfamilies. *Drug Metab. Pharmacokinet.* **2004**, *19*, 135–149. [CrossRef] [PubMed]

216. Beilke, L.D.; Aleksunes, L.M.; Holland, R.D.; Besselsen, D.G.; Beger, R.D.; Klaassen, C.D.; Cherrington, N.J. Constitutive androstane receptor-mediated changes in bile acid composition contributes to hepatoprotection from lithocholic acid-induced liver injury in mice. *Drug Metab. Dispos.* **2009**, *37*, 1035–1045. [CrossRef] [PubMed]

217. Fisher, C.D.; Lickteig, A.J.; Augustine, L.M.; Ranger-Moore, J.; Jackson, J.P.; Ferguson, S.S.; Cherrington, N.J. Hepatic cytochrome P450 enzyme alterations in humans with progressive stages of nonalcoholic fatty liver disease. *Drug Metab. Dispos.* **2009**, *37*, 2087–2094. [CrossRef] [PubMed]

218. Gao, J.; He, J.; Zhai, Y.; Wada, T.; Xie, W. The constitutive androstane receptor is an anti-obesity nuclear receptor that improves insulin sensitivity. *J. Biol. Chem.* **2009**, *284*, 25984–25992. [CrossRef] [PubMed]

219. Sberna, A.L.; Assem, M.; Xiao, R.; Ayers, S.; Gautier, T.; Guiu, B.; Deckert, V.; Chevriaux, A.; Grober, J.; Le Guern, N.; et al. Constitutive androstane receptor activation decreases plasma apolipoprotein B-containing lipoproteins and atherosclerosis in low-density lipoprotein receptor-deficient mice. *Arterioscler. Thromb. Vasc. Biol.* **2011**, *31*, 2232–2239. [CrossRef] [PubMed]

220. Gao, J.; Yan, J.; Xu, M.; Ren, S.; Xie, W. CAR suppresses hepatic gluconeogenesis by facilitating the ubiquitination and degradation of PGC1α. *Mol. Endocrinol.* **2015**, *29*, 1558–1570. [CrossRef] [PubMed]

221. Dong, B.; Lee, J.S.; Park, Y.Y.; Yang, F.; Xu, G.; Huang, W.; Finegold, M.J.; Moore, D.D. Activating CAR and β-catenin induces uncontrolled liver growth and tumorigenesis. *Nat. Commun.* **2015**, *6*. [CrossRef] [PubMed]

222. Li, D.; Mackowiak, B.; Brayman, T.G.; Mitchell, M.; Zhang, L.; Huang, S.M.; Wang, H. Genome-wide analysis of human constitutive androstane receptor (CAR) transcriptome in wild-type and CAR-knockout HepaRG cells. *Biochem. Pharmacol.* **2015**, *98*, 190–202. [CrossRef] [PubMed]

223. Kunne, C.; Acco, A.; Duijst, S.; de Waart, D.R.; Paulusma, C.C.; Gaemers, I.; Oude Elferink, R.P. FXR-dependent reduction of hepatic steatosis in a bile salt deficient mouse model. *Biochim. Biophys. Acta* **2014**, *1842*, 739–746. [CrossRef] [PubMed]

224. Pineda Torra, I.; Claudel, T.; Duval, C.; Kosykh, V.; Fruchart, J.C.; Staels, B. Bile acids induce the expression of the human peroxisome proliferator-activated receptor α gene via activation of the farnesoid X receptor. *Mol. Endocrinol.* **2003**, *17*, 259–272. [CrossRef] [PubMed]

225. Neuschwander-Tetri, B.A.; Loomba, R.; Sanyal, A.J.; Lavine, J.E.; van Natta, M.L.; Abdelmalek, M.F.; Chalasani, N.; Dasarathy, S.; Diehl, A.M.; Hameed, B.; et al. Farnesoid X nuclear receptor ligand obeticholic acid for non-cirrhotic, non-alcoholic steatohepatitis (FLINT): A multicentre, randomised, placebo-controlled trial. *Lancet* **2015**, *385*, 956–965. [CrossRef]

226. Cipriani, S.; Mencarelli, A.; Palladino, G.; Fiorucci, S. FXR activation reverses insulin resistance and lipid abnormalities and protects against liver steatosis in zucker (FA/FA) obese rats. *J. Lipid Res.* **2010**, *51*, 771–784. [CrossRef] [PubMed]

227. Ma, Y.; Huang, Y.; Yan, L.; Gao, M.; Liu, D. Synthetic FXR agonist GW4064 prevents diet-induced hepatic steatosis and insulin resistance. *Pharm. Res.* **2013**, *30*, 1447–1457. [CrossRef] [PubMed]

228. Mudaliar, S.; Henry, R.R.; Sanyal, A.J.; Morrow, L.; Marschall, H.U.; Kipnes, M.; Adorini, L.; Sciacca, C.I.; Clopton, P.; Castelloe, E.; et al. Efficacy and safety of the farnesoid x receptor agonist obeticholic acid in patients with type 2 diabetes and nonalcoholic fatty liver disease. *Gastroenterology* **2013**, *145*, 574–582. [CrossRef] [PubMed]

229. Jahn, D.; Rau, M.; Wohlfahrt, J.; Hermanns, H.M.; Geier, A. Non-alcoholic steatohepatitis: From pathophysiology to novel therapies. *Dig. Dis.* **2016**, *34*, 356–363. [CrossRef] [PubMed]

230. Tomlinson, E.; Fu, L.; John, L.; Hultgren, B.; Huang, X.; Renz, M.; Stephan, J.P.; Tsai, S.P.; Powell-Braxton, L.; French, D.; et al. Transgenic mice expressing human fibroblast growth factor-19 display increased metabolic rate and decreased adiposity. *Endocrinology* **2002**, *143*, 1741–1747. [CrossRef] [PubMed]

231. Fu, L.; John, L.M.; Adams, S.H.; Yu, X.X.; Tomlinson, E.; Renz, M.; Williams, P.M.; Soriano, R.; Corpuz, R.; Moffat, B.; et al. Fibroblast growth factor 19 increases metabolic rate and reverses dietary and leptin-deficient diabetes. *Endocrinology* **2004**, *145*, 2594–2603. [CrossRef] [PubMed]

232. Fang, S.; Suh, J.M.; Reilly, S.M.; Yu, E.; Osborn, O.; Lackey, D.; Yoshihara, E.; Perino, A.; Jacinto, S.; Lukasheva, Y.; et al. Intestinal FXR agonism promotes adipose tissue browning and reduces obesity and insulin resistance. *Nat. Med.* **2015**, *21*, 159–165. [CrossRef] [PubMed]

233. Degirolamo, C.; Modica, S.; Vacca, M.; Di Tullio, G.; Morgano, A.; D'Orazio, A.; Kannisto, K.; Parini, P.; Moschetta, A. Prevention of spontaneous hepatocarcinogenesis in farnesoid X receptor-null mice by intestinal-specific farnesoid x receptor reactivation. *Hepatology* **2015**, *61*, 161–170. [CrossRef] [PubMed]

234. Seki, E.; Brenner, D.A. Toll-like receptors and adaptor molecules in liver disease: Update. *Hepatology* **2008**, *48*, 322–335. [CrossRef] [PubMed]

235. Strowig, T.; Henao-Mejia, J.; Elinav, E.; Flavell, R. Inflammasomes in health and disease. *Nature* **2012**, *481*, 278–286. [CrossRef] [PubMed]

236. Vanni, E.; Bugianesi, E. The gut-liver axis in nonalcoholic fatty liver disease: Another pathway to insulin resistance? *Hepatology* **2009**, *49*, 1790–1792. [CrossRef] [PubMed]

237. Miele, L.; Valenza, V.; La Torre, G.; Montalto, M.; Cammarota, G.; Ricci, R.; Masciana, R.; Forgione, A.; Gabrieli, M.L.; Perotti, G.; et al. Increased intestinal permeability and tight junction alterations in nonalcoholic fatty liver disease. *Hepatology* **2009**, *49*, 1877–1887. [CrossRef] [PubMed]

238. Akira, S.; Uematsu, S.; Takeuchi, O. Pathogen recognition and innate immunity. *Cell* **2006**, *124*, 783–801. [CrossRef] [PubMed]

239. Raman, M.; Ahmed, I.; Gillevet, P.M.; Probert, C.S.; Ratcliffe, N.M.; Smith, S.; Greenwood, R.; Sikaroodi, M.; Lam, V.; Crotty, P.; et al. Fecal microbiome and volatile organic compound metabolome in obese humans with nonalcoholic fatty liver disease. *Clin. Gastroenterol. Hepatol.* **2013**, *11*, 868–875. [CrossRef] [PubMed]

240. Douhara, A.; Moriya, K.; Yoshiji, H.; Noguchi, R.; Namisaki, T.; Kitade, M.; Kaji, K.; Aihara, Y.; Nishimura, N.; Takeda, K.; et al. Reduction of endotoxin attenuates liver fibrosis through suppression of hepatic stellate cell activation and remission of intestinal permeability in a rat non-alcoholic steatohepatitis model. *Mol. Med. Rep.* **2015**, *11*, 1693–1700. [CrossRef] [PubMed]

241. Ehses, J.A.; Meier, D.T.; Wueest, S.; Rytka, J.; Boller, S.; Wielinga, P.Y.; Schraenen, A.; Lemaire, K.; Debray, S.; van Lommel, L.; et al. Toll-like receptor 2-deficient mice are protected from insulin resistance and β cell dysfunction induced by a high-fat diet. *Diabetologia* **2010**, *53*, 1795–1806. [CrossRef] [PubMed]

242. Vijay-Kumar, M.; Aitken, J.D.; Carvalho, F.A.; Cullender, T.C.; Mwangi, S.; Srinivasan, S.; Sitaraman, S.V.; Knight, R.; Ley, R.E.; Gewirtz, A.T. Metabolic syndrome and altered gut microbiota in mice lacking toll-like receptor 5. *Science* **2010**, *328*, 228–231. [CrossRef] [PubMed]

243. Al-Daghri, N.M.; Clerici, M.; Al-Attas, O.; Forni, D.; Alokail, M.S.; Alkharfy, K.M.; Sabico, S.; Mohammed, A.K.; Cagliani, R.; Sironi, M. A nonsense polymorphism (R392X) in TLR5 protects from obesity but predisposes to diabetes. *J. Immunol.* **2013**, *190*, 3716–3720. [CrossRef] [PubMed]

244. Miura, K.; Kodama, Y.; Inokuchi, S.; Schnabl, B.; Aoyama, T.; Ohnishi, H.; Olefsky, J.M.; Brenner, D.A.; Seki, E. Toll-like receptor 9 promotes steatohepatitis by induction of interleukin-1β in mice. *Gastroenterology* **2010**, *139*, 323–334. [CrossRef] [PubMed]

245. Gabele, E.; Dostert, K.; Hofmann, C.; Wiest, R.; Scholmerich, J.; Hellerbrand, C.; Obermeier, F. DSS induced colitis increases portal LPS levels and enhances hepatic inflammation and fibrogenesis in experimental NASH. *J. Hepatol.* **2011**, *55*, 1391–1399. [CrossRef] [PubMed]

246. Csak, T.; Velayudham, A.; Hritz, I.; Petrasek, J.; Levin, I.; Lippai, D.; Catalano, D.; Mandrekar, P.; Dolganiuc, A.; Kurt-Jones, E.; et al. Deficiency in myeloid differentiation factor-2 and toll-like receptor 4 expression attenuates nonalcoholic steatohepatitis and fibrosis in mice. *Am. J. Physiol. Gastrointest. Liver Physiol.* **2011**, *300*, G433–G441. [CrossRef] [PubMed]

247. Dolganiuc, A.; Norkina, O.; Kodys, K.; Catalano, D.; Bakis, G.; Marshall, C.; Mandrekar, P.; Szabo, G. Viral and host factors induce macrophage activation and loss of toll-like receptor tolerance in chronic HCV infection. *Gastroenterology* **2007**, *133*, 1627–1636. [CrossRef] [PubMed]

248. Beutler, B. Inferences, questions and possibilities in toll-like receptor signalling. *Nature* **2004**, *430*, 257–263. [CrossRef] [PubMed]

249. Kawasaki, T.; Kawai, T. Toll-like receptor signaling pathways. *Front. Immunol.* **2014**, *5*. [CrossRef] [PubMed]

250. Guo, J.; Friedman, S.L. Toll-like receptor 4 signaling in liver injury and hepatic fibrogenesis. *Fibrogenes. Tissue Repair* **2010**, *3*. [CrossRef] [PubMed]

251. Ye, D.; Li, F.Y.; Lam, K.S.; Li, H.; Jia, W.; Wang, Y.; Man, K.; Lo, C.M.; Li, X.; Xu, A. Toll-like receptor-4 mediates obesity-induced non-alcoholic steatohepatitis through activation of X-box binding protein-1 in mice. *Gut* **2012**, *61*, 1058–1067. [CrossRef] [PubMed]

252. Rivera, C.A.; Adegboyega, P.; van Rooijen, N.; Tagalicud, A.; Allman, M.; Wallace, M. Toll-like receptor-4 signaling and Kupffer cells play pivotal roles in the pathogenesis of non-alcoholic steatohepatitis. *J. Hepatol.* **2007**, *47*, 571–579. [CrossRef] [PubMed]

253. Szabo, G.; Bala, S. Alcoholic liver disease and the gut-liver axis. *World J. Gastroenterol.* **2010**, *16*, 1321–1329. [CrossRef] [PubMed]

254. Seki, E.; de Minicis, S.; Osterreicher, C.H.; Kluwe, J.; Osawa, Y.; Brenner, D.A.; Schwabe, R.F. TLR4 enhances TGF-β signaling and hepatic fibrosis. *Nat. Med.* **2007**, *13*, 1324–1332. [CrossRef] [PubMed]

255. Guo, J.; Loke, J.; Zheng, F.; Hong, F.; Yea, S.; Fukata, M.; Tarocchi, M.; Abar, O.T.; Huang, H.; Sninsky, J.J.; et al. Functional linkage of cirrhosis-predictive single nucleotide polymorphisms of toll-like receptor 4 to hepatic stellate cell responses. *Hepatology* **2009**, *49*, 960–968. [CrossRef] [PubMed]

256. Dasu, M.R.; Jialal, I. Free fatty acids in the presence of high glucose amplify monocyte inflammation via toll-like receptors. *Am. J. Physiol. Endocrinol. Metab.* **2011**, *300*, E145–E154. [CrossRef] [PubMed]

257. Shi, H.; Kokoeva, M.V.; Inouye, K.; Tzameli, I.; Yin, H.; Flier, J.S. TLR4 links innate immunity and fatty acid-induced insulin resistance. *J. Clin. Investig.* **2006**, *116*, 3015–3025. [CrossRef] [PubMed]

258. Dostert, C.; Petrilli, V.; van Bruggen, R.; Steele, C.; Mossman, B.T.; Tschopp, J. Innate immune activation through NALP3 inflammasome sensing of asbestos and silica. *Science* **2008**, *320*, 674–677. [CrossRef] [PubMed]

259. Shimada, K.; Crother, T.R.; Karlin, J.; Dagvadorj, J.; Chiba, N.; Chen, S.; Ramanujan, V.K.; Wolf, A.J.; Vergnes, L.; Ojcius, D.M.; et al. Oxidized mitochondrial DNA activates the NLRP3 inflammasome during apoptosis. *Immunity* **2012**, *36*, 401–414. [CrossRef] [PubMed]

260. Martinon, F.; Burns, K.; Tschopp, J. The inflammasome: A molecular platform triggering activation of inflammatory caspases and processing of proIL-β. *Mol. Cell* **2002**, *10*, 417–426. [CrossRef]

261. Szabo, G.; Csak, T. Inflammasomes in liver diseases. *J. Hepatol.* **2012**, *57*, 642–654. [CrossRef] [PubMed]

262. Dixon, L.J.; Flask, C.A.; Papouchado, B.G.; Feldstein, A.E.; Nagy, L.E. Caspase-1 as a central regulator of high fat diet-induced non-alcoholic steatohepatitis. *PLoS ONE* **2013**, *8*, e56100. [CrossRef] [PubMed]

263. Stienstra, R.; Joosten, L.A.; Koenen, T.; van Tits, B.; van Diepen, J.A.; van den Berg, S.A.; Rensen, P.C.; Voshol, P.J.; Fantuzzi, G.; Hijmans, A.; et al. The inflammasome-mediated caspase-1 activation controls adipocyte differentiation and insulin sensitivity. *Cell Metab.* **2010**, *12*, 593–605. [CrossRef] [PubMed]

264. Membrez, M.; Ammon-Zufferey, C.; Philippe, D.; Aprikian, O.; Monnard, I.; Mace, K.; Darimont, C. Interleukin-18 protein level is upregulated in adipose tissue of obese mice. *Obesity* **2009**, *17*, 393–395. [CrossRef] [PubMed]

265. Csak, T.; Pillai, A.; Ganz, M.; Lippai, D.; Petrasek, J.; Park, J.K.; Kodys, K.; Dolganiuc, A.; Kurt-Jones, E.A.; Szabo, G. Both bone marrow-derived and non-bone marrow-derived cells contribute to AIM2 and NLRP3 inflammasome activation in a MyD88-dependent manner in dietary steatohepatitis. *Liver Int.* **2014**, *34*, 1402–1413. [CrossRef] [PubMed]

266. Ganz, M.; Bukong, T.N.; Csak, T.; Saha, B.; Park, J.K.; Ambade, A.; Kodys, K.; Szabo, G. Progression of non-alcoholic steatosis to steatohepatitis and fibrosis parallels cumulative accumulation of danger signals that promote inflammation and liver tumors in a high fat-cholesterol-sugar diet model in mice. *J. Transl. Med.* **2015**, *13*. [CrossRef] [PubMed]

267. Vandanmagsar, B.; Youm, Y.H.; Ravussin, A.; Galgani, J.E.; Stadler, K.; Mynatt, R.L.; Ravussin, E.; Stephens, J.M.; Dixit, V.D. The NLRP3 inflammasome instigates obesity-induced inflammation and insulin resistance. *Nat. Med.* **2011**, *17*, 179–188. [CrossRef] [PubMed]

268. Wree, A.; McGeough, M.D.; Pena, C.A.; Schlattjan, M.; Li, H.; Inzaugarat, M.E.; Messer, K.; Canbay, A.; Hoffman, H.M.; Feldstein, A.E. NLRP3 inflammasome activation is required for fibrosis development in NAFLD. *J. Mol. Med.* **2014**, *92*, 1069–1082. [CrossRef] [PubMed]

269. Henao-Mejia, J.; Elinav, E.; Jin, C.; Hao, L.; Mehal, W.Z.; Strowig, T.; Thaiss, C.A.; Kau, A.L.; Eisenbarth, S.C.; Jurczak, M.J.; et al. Inflammasome-mediated dysbiosis regulates progression of NAFLD and obesity. *Nature* **2012**, *482*, 179–185. [CrossRef] [PubMed]

270. Wree, A.; Eguchi, A.; McGeough, M.D.; Pena, C.A.; Johnson, C.D.; Canbay, A.; Hoffman, H.M.; Feldstein, A.E. NLRP3 inflammasome activation results in hepatocyte pyroptosis, liver inflammation, and fibrosis in mice. *Hepatology* **2014**, *59*, 898–910. [CrossRef] [PubMed]

271. Seki, E.; Schwabe, R.F. Hepatic inflammation and fibrosis: Functional links and key pathways. *Hepatology* **2015**, *61*, 1066–1079. [CrossRef] [PubMed]

272. Luedde, T.; Kaplowitz, N.; Schwabe, R.F. Cell death and cell death responses in liver disease: Mechanisms and clinical relevance. *Gastroenterology* **2014**, *147*, 765–783. [CrossRef] [PubMed]

273. Huebener, P.; Pradere, J.P.; Hernandez, C.; Gwak, G.Y.; Caviglia, J.M.; Mu, X.; Loike, J.D.; Jenkins, R.E.; Antoine, D.J.; Schwabe, R.F. The HMGB1/RAGE axis triggers neutrophil-mediated injury amplification following necrosis. *J. Clin. Investig.* **2015**, *125*, 539–550. [CrossRef] [PubMed]

274. Zhang, Q.; Raoof, M.; Chen, Y.; Sumi, Y.; Sursal, T.; Junger, W.; Brohi, K.; Itagaki, K.; Hauser, C.J. Circulating mitochondrial damps cause inflammatory responses to injury. *Nature* **2010**, *464*, 104–107. [CrossRef] [PubMed]

275. Tschopp, J. Mitochondria: Sovereign of inflammation? *Eur. J. Immunol.* **2011**, *41*, 1196–1202. [CrossRef] [PubMed]

276. Carp, H. Mitochondrial N-formylmethionyl proteins as chemoattractants for neutrophils. *J. Exp. Med.* **1982**, *155*, 264–275. [CrossRef] [PubMed]

277. Iyer, S.S.; Pulskens, W.P.; Sadler, J.J.; Butter, L.M.; Teske, G.J.; Ulland, T.K.; Eisenbarth, S.C.; Florquin, S.; Flavell, R.A.; Leemans, J.C.; et al. Necrotic cells trigger a sterile inflammatory response through the NLRP3 inflammasome. *Proc. Natl. Acad. Sci. USA* **2009**, *106*, 20388–20393. [CrossRef] [PubMed]

278. Nakahira, K.; Haspel, J.A.; Rathinam, V.A.; Lee, S.J.; Dolinay, T.; Lam, H.C.; Englert, J.A.; Rabinovitch, M.; Cernadas, M.; Kim, H.P.; et al. Autophagy proteins regulate innate immune responses by inhibiting the release of mitochondrial DNA mediated by the NALP3 inflammasome. *Nat. Immunol.* **2011**, *12*, 222–230. [CrossRef] [PubMed]

279. Coddou, C.; Yan, Z.; Obsil, T.; Huidobro-Toro, J.P.; Stojilkovic, S.S. Activation and regulation of purinergic P2X receptor channels. *Pharmacol. Rev.* **2011**, *63*, 641–683. [CrossRef] [PubMed]

280. Di Virgilio, F. Liaisons dangereuses: P2X$_7$ and the inflammasome. *Trends Pharmacol. Sci.* **2007**, *28*, 465–472. [CrossRef] [PubMed]

281. Stros, M. HMGB proteins: Interactions with DNA and chromatin. *Biochim. Biophys. Acta* **2010**, *1799*, 101–113. [CrossRef] [PubMed]

282. Scaffidi, P.; Misteli, T.; Bianchi, M.E. Release of chromatin protein HMGB1 by necrotic cells triggers inflammation. *Nature* **2002**, *418*, 191–195. [CrossRef] [PubMed]

283. Tsung, A.; Klune, J.R.; Zhang, X.; Jeyabalan, G.; Cao, Z.; Peng, X.; Stolz, D.B.; Geller, D.A.; Rosengart, M.R.; Billiar, T.R. HMGB1 release induced by liver ischemia involves toll-like receptor 4 dependent reactive oxygen species production and calcium-mediated signaling. *J. Exp. Med.* **2007**, *204*, 2913–2923. [CrossRef] [PubMed]

284. Bianchi, M.E. HMGB1 loves company. *J. Leukoc. Biol.* **2009**, *86*, 573–576. [CrossRef] [PubMed]

285. Hornung, V.; Bauernfeind, F.; Halle, A.; Samstad, E.O.; Kono, H.; Rock, K.L.; Fitzgerald, K.A.; Latz, E. Silica crystals and aluminum salts activate the NALP3 inflammasome through phagosomal destabilization. *Nat. Immunol.* **2008**, *9*, 847–856. [CrossRef] [PubMed]

286. Lotze, M.T.; Tracey, K.J. High-mobility group box 1 protein (HMGB1): Nuclear weapon in the immune arsenal. *Nat. Rev. Immunol.* **2005**, *5*, 331–342. [CrossRef] [PubMed]

287. Bluher, M. Clinical relevance of adipokines. *Diabetes Metab. J.* **2012**, *36*, 317–327. [CrossRef] [PubMed]

288. Marra, F.; Bertolani, C. Adipokines in liver diseases. *Hepatology* **2009**, *50*, 957–969. [CrossRef] [PubMed]

289. Polyzos, S.A.; Kountouras, J.; Zavos, C. Nonalcoholic fatty liver disease: The pathogenetic roles of insulin resistance and adipocytokines. *Curr. Mol. Med.* **2009**, *9*, 299–314. [CrossRef] [PubMed]

290. Polyzos, S.A.; Kountouras, J.; Zavos, C.; Tsiaousi, E. The role of adiponectin in the pathogenesis and treatment of non-alcoholic fatty liver disease. *Diabetes Obes. Metab.* **2010**, *12*, 365–383. [CrossRef] [PubMed]

291. Polyzos, S.A.; Kountouras, J.; Zavos, C. The multi-hit process and the antagonistic roles of tumor necrosis factor-α and adiponectin in non alcoholic fatty liver disease. *Hippokratia* **2009**, *13*, 127. [PubMed]

292. Tilg, H.; Hotamisligil, G.S. Nonalcoholic fatty liver disease: Cytokine-adipokine interplay and regulation of insulin resistance. *Gastroenterology* **2006**, *131*, 934–945. [CrossRef] [PubMed]

293. Moon, H.S.; Dalamaga, M.; Kim, S.Y.; Polyzos, S.A.; Hamnvik, O.P.; Magkos, F.; Paruthi, J.; Mantzoros, C.S. Leptin's role in lipodystrophic and nonlipodystrophic insulin-resistant and diabetic individuals. *Endocr. Rev.* **2013**, *34*, 377–412. [CrossRef] [PubMed]

294. Polyzos, S.A.; Kountouras, J.; Mantzoros, C.S. Leptin in nonalcoholic fatty liver disease: A narrative review. *Metabolism* **2015**, *64*, 60–78. [CrossRef] [PubMed]

295. Dattaroy, D.; Pourhoseini, S.; Das, S.; Alhasson, F.; Seth, R.K.; Nagarkatti, M.; Michelotti, G.A.; Diehl, A.M.; Chatterjee, S. Micro-RNA 21 inhibition of SMAD7 enhances fibrogenesis via leptin-mediated NADPH oxidase in experimental and human nonalcoholic steatohepatitis. *Am. J. Physiol. Gastrointest. Liver Physiol.* **2015**, *308*, G298–G312. [CrossRef] [PubMed]

296. Zhou, Q.; Guan, W.; Qiao, H.; Cheng, Y.; Li, Z.; Zhai, X.; Zhou, Y. Gata binding protein 2 mediates leptin inhibition of PPARγ1 expression in hepatic stellate cells and contributes to hepatic stellate cell activation. *Biochim. Biophys. Acta* **2014**, *1842*, 2367–2377. [CrossRef] [PubMed]

297. Heinrich, G.; Russo, L.; Castaneda, T.R.; Pfeiffer, V.; Ghadieh, H.E.; Ghanem, S.S.; Wu, J.; Faulkner, L.D.; Ergun, S.; McInerney, M.F.; et al. Leptin resistance contributes to obesity in mice with null mutation of carcinoembryonic antigen-related cell adhesion molecule 1. *J. Biol. Chem.* **2016**, *291*, 11124–11132. [CrossRef] [PubMed]

298. Poy, M.N.; Yang, Y.; Rezaei, K.; Fernstrom, M.A.; Lee, A.D.; Kido, Y.; Erickson, S.K.; Najjar, S.M. CEACAM1 regulates insulin clearance in liver. *Nat. Genet.* **2002**, *30*, 270–276. [CrossRef] [PubMed]

299. DeAngelis, A.M.; Heinrich, G.; Dai, T.; Bowman, T.A.; Patel, P.R.; Lee, S.J.; Hong, E.G.; Jung, D.Y.; Assmann, A.; Kulkarni, R.N.; et al. Carcinoembryonic antigen-related cell adhesion molecule 1: A link between insulin and lipid metabolism. *Diabetes* **2008**, *57*, 2296–2303. [CrossRef] [PubMed]

300. Yoda-Murakami, M.; Taniguchi, M.; Takahashi, K.; Kawamata, S.; Saito, K.; Choi-Miura, N.H.; Tomita, M. Change in expression of GBP28/adiponectin in carbon tetrachloride-administrated mouse liver. *Biochem. Biophys. Res. Commun.* **2001**, *285*, 372–377. [CrossRef] [PubMed]

301. Heiker, J.T.; Kosel, D.; Beck-Sickinger, A.G. Molecular mechanisms of signal transduction via adiponectin and adiponectin receptors. *Biol. Chem.* **2010**, *391*, 1005–1018. [CrossRef] [PubMed]

302. Jiang, C.; Qu, A.; Matsubara, T.; Chanturiya, T.; Jou, W.; Gavrilova, O.; Shah, Y.M.; Gonzalez, F.J. Disruption of hypoxia-inducible factor 1 in adipocytes improves insulin sensitivity and decreases adiposity in high-fat diet-fed mice. *Diabetes* **2011**, *60*, 2484–2495. [CrossRef] [PubMed]

303. Otani, H. Oxidative stress as pathogenesis of cardiovascular risk associated with metabolic syndrome. *Antioxid. Redox Signal.* **2011**, *15*, 1911–1926. [CrossRef] [PubMed]

304. Kusminski, C.M.; Scherer, P.E. Mitochondrial dysfunction in white adipose tissue. *Trends Endocrinol. Metab.* **2012**, *23*, 435–443. [CrossRef] [PubMed]

305. Polyzos, S.A.; Kountouras, J.; Zavos, C. Nonlinear distribution of adiponectin in patients with nonalcoholic fatty liver disease limits its use in linear regression analysis. *J. Clin. Gastroenterol.* **2010**, *44*, 229–230. [CrossRef] [PubMed]

306. Van der Poorten, D.; Samer, C.F.; Ramezani-Moghadam, M.; Coulter, S.; Kacevska, M.; Schrijnders, D.; Wu, L.E.; McLeod, D.; Bugianesi, E.; Komuta, M.; et al. Hepatic fat loss in advanced nonalcoholic steatohepatitis: Are alterations in serum adiponectin the cause? *Hepatology* **2013**, *57*, 2180–2188. [CrossRef] [PubMed]

307. Bozaoglu, K.; Bolton, K.; McMillan, J.; Zimmet, P.; Jowett, J.; Collier, G.; Walder, K.; Segal, D. Chemerin is a novel adipokine associated with obesity and metabolic syndrome. *Endocrinology* **2007**, *148*, 4687–4694. [CrossRef] [PubMed]

308. Sell, H.; Divoux, A.; Poitou, C.; Basdevant, A.; Bouillot, J.L.; Bedossa, P.; Tordjman, J.; Eckel, J.; Clement, K. Chemerin correlates with markers for fatty liver in morbidly obese patients and strongly decreases after weight loss induced by bariatric surgery. *J. Clin. Endocrinol. Metab.* **2010**, *95*, 2892–2896. [CrossRef] [PubMed]

309. Ernst, M.C.; Issa, M.; Goralski, K.B.; Sinal, C.J. Chemerin exacerbates glucose intolerance in mouse models of obesity and diabetes. *Endocrinology* **2010**, *151*, 1998–2007. [CrossRef] [PubMed]

310. Yoshimura, T.; Oppenheim, J.J. Chemerin reveals its chimeric nature. *J. Exp. Med.* **2008**, *205*, 2187–2190. [CrossRef] [PubMed]

311. Krautbauer, S.; Wanninger, J.; Eisinger, K.; Hader, Y.; Beck, M.; Kopp, A.; Schmid, A.; Weiss, T.S.; Dorn, C.; Buechler, C. Chemerin is highly expressed in hepatocytes and is induced in non-alcoholic steatohepatitis liver. *Exp. Mol. Pathol.* **2013**, *95*, 199–205. [CrossRef] [PubMed]

312. Topping, D.L.; Clifton, P.M. Short-chain fatty acids and human colonic function: Roles of resistant starch and nonstarch polysaccharides. *Physiol. Rev.* **2001**, *81*, 1031–1064. [PubMed]

313. Turnbaugh, P.J.; Ley, R.E.; Mahowald, M.A.; Magrini, V.; Mardis, E.R.; Gordon, J.I. An obesity-associated gut microbiome with increased capacity for energy harvest. *Nature* **2006**, *444*, 1027–1031. [CrossRef] [PubMed]

314. Shin, N.R.; Lee, J.C.; Lee, H.Y.; Kim, M.S.; Whon, T.W.; Lee, M.S.; Bae, J.W. An increase in the *Akkermansia* spp. population induced by metformin treatment improves glucose homeostasis in diet-induced obese mice. *Gut* **2014**, *63*, 727–735. [CrossRef] [PubMed]

315. Karlsson, C.L.; Onnerfalt, J.; Xu, J.; Molin, G.; Ahrne, S.; Thorngren-Jerneck, K. The microbiota of the gut in preschool children with normal and excessive body weight. *Obesity* **2012**, *20*, 2257–2261. [CrossRef] [PubMed]

316. Zeisel, S.H.; Wishnok, J.S.; Blusztajn, J.K. Formation of methylamines from ingested choline and lecithin. *J. Pharmacol. Exp. Ther.* **1983**, *225*, 320–324. [PubMed]

317. Spencer, M.D.; Hamp, T.J.; Reid, R.W.; Fischer, L.M.; Zeisel, S.H.; Fodor, A.A. Association between composition of the human gastrointestinal microbiome and development of fatty liver with choline deficiency. *Gastroenterology* **2011**, *140*, 976–986. [CrossRef] [PubMed]

318. Sinal, C.J.; Tohkin, M.; Miyata, M.; Ward, J.M.; Lambert, G.; Gonzalez, F.J. Targeted disruption of the nuclear receptor FXR/BAR impairs bile acid and lipid homeostasis. *Cell* **2000**, *102*, 731–744. [CrossRef]

319. Hylemon, P.B.; Zhou, H.; Pandak, W.M.; Ren, S.; Gil, G.; Dent, P. Bile acids as regulatory molecules. *J. Lipid Res.* **2009**, *50*, 1509–1520. [CrossRef] [PubMed]

320. Tremaroli, V.; Backhed, F. Functional interactions between the gut microbiota and host metabolism. *Nature* **2012**, *489*, 242–249. [CrossRef] [PubMed]

321. Prawitt, J.; Abdelkarim, M.; Stroeve, J.H.; Popescu, I.; Duez, H.; Velagapudi, V.R.; Dumont, J.; Bouchaert, E.; van Dijk, T.H.; Lucas, A.; et al. Farnesoid X receptor deficiency improves glucose homeostasis in mouse models of obesity. *Diabetes* **2011**, *60*, 1861–1871. [CrossRef] [PubMed]

322. Thomas, C.; Gioiello, A.; Noriega, L.; Strehle, A.; Oury, J.; Rizzo, G.; Macchiarulo, A.; Yamamoto, H.; Mataki, C.; Pruzanski, M.; et al. TGR5-mediated bile acid sensing controls glucose homeostasis. *Cell Metab.* **2009**, *10*, 167–177. [CrossRef] [PubMed]

323. Cope, K.; Risby, T.; Diehl, A.M. Increased gastrointestinal ethanol production in obese mice: Implications for fatty liver disease pathogenesis. *Gastroenterology* **2000**, *119*, 1340–1347. [CrossRef] [PubMed]

324. Zhu, L.; Baker, S.S.; Gill, C.; Liu, W.; Alkhouri, R.; Baker, R.D.; Gill, S.R. Characterization of gut microbiomes in nonalcoholic steatohepatitis (NASH) patients: A connection between endogenous alcohol and NASH. *Hepatology* **2013**, *57*, 601–609. [CrossRef] [PubMed]

325. Noverr, M.C.; Huffnagle, G.B. Does the microbiota regulate immune responses outside the gut? *Trends Microbiol.* **2004**, *12*, 562–568. [CrossRef] [PubMed]

326. Sabate, J.M.; Jouet, P.; Harnois, F.; Mechler, C.; Msika, S.; Grossin, M.; Coffin, B. High prevalence of small intestinal bacterial overgrowth in patients with morbid obesity: A contributor to severe hepatic steatosis. *Obes. Surg.* **2008**, *18*, 371–377. [CrossRef] [PubMed]

327. Wigg, A.J.; Roberts-Thomson, I.C.; Dymock, R.B.; McCarthy, P.J.; Grose, R.H.; Cummins, A.G. The role of small intestinal bacterial overgrowth, intestinal permeability, endotoxaemia, and tumour necrosis factor α in the pathogenesis of non-alcoholic steatohepatitis. *Gut* **2001**, *48*, 206–211. [CrossRef] [PubMed]

328. Minemura, M.; Shimizu, Y. Gut microbiota and liver diseases. *World J. Gastroenterol.* **2015**, *21*, 1691–1702. [CrossRef] [PubMed]

329. Fukui, H. Gut-liver axis in liver cirrhosis: How to manage leaky gut and endotoxemia. *World J. Hepatol.* **2015**, *7*, 425–442. [CrossRef] [PubMed]

International Journal of
Molecular Sciences

MDPI

Article

Liver Fat Measured by MR Spectroscopy: Estimate of Imprecision and Relationship with Serum Glycerol, Caeruloplasmin and Non-Esterified Fatty Acids

Michael France [1,*], See Kwok [2], Handrean Soran [3], Steve Williams [4], Jan Hoong Ho [3,*], Safwaan Adam [4], Dexter Canoy [5], Yifen Liu [6] and Paul N. Durrington [6]

[1] Department of Clinical Biochemistry, Cobbett House, Central Manchester Foundation Trust, Oxford Road, Manchester M13 9WL, UK
[2] Cardiovascular Trials Unit, The Old St Mary's Hospital, Hathersage Road, Oxford Road, Manchester M13 9WL, UK; sk7@doctors.org.uk
[3] Department of Medicine, Central Manchester Foundation Trust, Oxford Road, Manchester M13 9WL, UK; hsoran@aol.com
[4] Department of Imaging Science, University of Manchester, Oxford Road, Manchester M13 9PT, UK; steve.williams@manchester.ac.uk (S.W.); s.adam@doctors.org.uk (S.A.)
[5] Cancer Epidemiology Unit, University of Oxford, Richard Doll Building, Roosevelt Drive, Oxford OX3 7LF, UK; dexter.canoy@ceu.ox.ac.uk
[6] School of Biomedicine, 3rd floor, Core Technology Facility, 46 Grafton Street, Manchester M13 9NT, UK; yifen.liu@manchester.ac.uk (Y.L.); paul.durrington@manchester.ac.uk (P.N.D.)
* Correspondence: michael.france@cmft.nhs.uk (M.F.); jan.ho@doctors.org.uk (J.H.H.); Tel.: +44-161-276-4284 (M.F.); +44-780-966-9984 (J.H.H.)

Academic Editors: Amedeo Lonardo and Giovanni Targher
Received: 21 May 2016; Accepted: 30 June 2016; Published: 8 July 2016

Abstract: Magnetic resonance spectroscopy (MRS) is a non-invasive method for quantitative estimation of liver fat. Knowledge of its imprecision, which comprises biological variability and measurement error, is required to design therapeutic trials with measurement of change. The role of adipocyte lipolysis in ectopic fat accumulation remains unclear. We examined the relationship between liver fat content and indices of lipolysis, and determine whether lipolysis reflects insulin resistance or metabolic liver disease. Imprecision of measurement of liver fat was estimated from duplicate measurements by MRS at one month intervals. Patients provided fasting blood samples and we examined the correlation of liver fat with indices of insulin resistance, lipolysis and metabolic liver disease using Kendall Tau statistics. The coefficient of variation of liver fat content was 14.8%. Liver fat was positively related to serum insulin (T = 0.48, $p = 0.042$), homeostasis model assessment (HOMA)-B% (T = -0.48, $p = 0.042$), and body mass index (BMI) (T = 0.59, $p = 0.012$); and inversely related to HOMA-S% (T = -0.48, $p = 0.042$), serum glycerol (T = -0.59, $p = 0.014$), and serum caeruloplasmin (T = 0.055, $p = 0.047$). Our estimate of total variability in liver fat content (14.8%) is nearly twice that of the reported procedural variability (8.5%). We found that liver fat content was significantly inversely related to serum glycerol but not to non-esterified fatty acids (NEFA), suggesting progressive suppression of lipolysis. Reduction of caeruloplasmin with increasing liver fat may be a consequence or a cause of hepatic steatosis.

Keywords: fatty liver; NEFA; glycerol; lipolysis; insulin; magnetic resonance spectroscopy

1. Introduction

Nonalcoholic fatty liver disease (NAFLD) is associated with the histological finding of hepatic steatosis or steatohepatitis and has a number of causes [1–4]. Steatosis is defined as a liver fat content of greater than 5% [3,5], and may be detected by ultrasonography in patients investigated for abnormal serum transaminase levels. It is a common finding in patients with hypertriglyceridaemia and is frequently accompanied by insulin resistance and other features of metabolic syndrome. Although the condition is usually benign, 10% of patients do progress to nonalcoholic steatohepatitis (NASH), of whom 25% may proceed to cirrhosis [2].

Magnetic resonance spectroscopy (MRS) is a non-invasive and effective method in assessment of hepatic fat accumulation with high diagnostic accuracy and correspondence with histopathologic grade being demonstrated [6]. Imprecision in the measurement of liver fat content by MRS comprises biological variability and measurement error. It is an important consideration in the design of therapeutic trials aiming to measure change in liver fat content. We estimated imprecision from duplicate measurements at an interval of one month and compared our estimate with variability reported after immediate repetition of MRS in 10 individuals with similar characteristics. Although it has been suggested that accumulation of liver fat in metabolic syndrome is driven by increased hepatic fatty acid delivery due to adipocyte insulin resistance [7], raised levels of non-esterified fatty acids (NEFA) are not always found in hepatic steatosis [8]. We investigated the relationship between liver fat and indices of lipolysis and metabolic liver disease as these have the potential to influence biological variability.

2. Results

The distribution of differences between duplicate liver fat measurements was sufficiently normal (Shapiro–Wilk 0.7612) to calculate imprecision from the differences, with coefficient of variation 14.8%. The median body mass index (BMI) was 30.8 kg/m^2 (range 20.2–40.4) with 2 patients having a BMI <25 kg/m^2. MR image of the abdomen and a spectrum from the liver from one patient are shown in Figure 1. Both water and triglyceride signals are visible at high signal-to-noise. Median liver fat content was 44 g·kg^{-1} water (range, 10–332). Triglycerides were greater than 1.7 mmol·L^{-1} in 10 out of 11 patients. Hyperinsulinaemia was present in all patients although only one had a fasting plasma glucose in the impaired glucose tolerance range >6.1 mmol·L^{-1} and one in the diabetes range at 7.5 mmol·L^{-1}. Nine patients had supra-normal β cell function with (homeostasis model assessment (HOMA)-B% >100%) and all patients had impaired insulin sensitivity (HOMA-S% < 100%, median 43.9% and range 13.3–91.9). Table 1 shows the correlation of metabolic parameters related to insulin resistance, alcohol intake, ferritin, iron studies, α-1 antitrypsin (A1AT), and caeruloplasmin with the average of the two liver fat measurements.

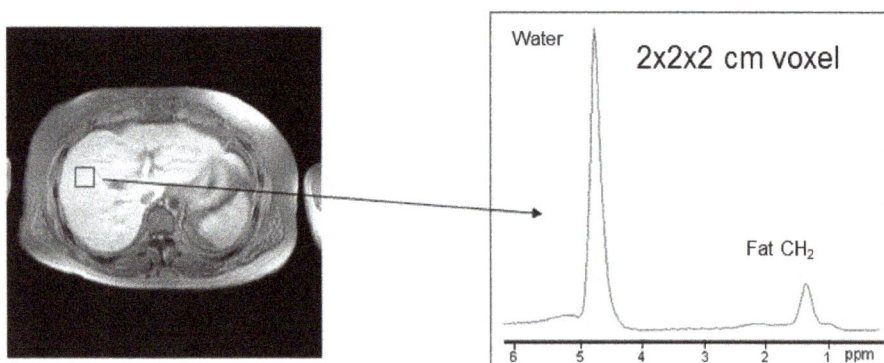

Figure 1. Transverse magnetic resonance (MR) image through the abdomen and localised MR spectrum recorded from the 2 × 2 × 2 cm voxel placed over the liver. The frequency axis of the spectrum is expressed in parts per million (ppm).

Table 1. Kendall Tau rank correlation between liver fat and metabolic parameters.

Measurement	Tau	*p* Value
BMI kg· m^{-2}	0.59	0.012
NEFA umol· L^{-1}	−0.22	0.3
Glycerol umol· L^{-1}	−0.59	0.014
Glucose mmol· L^{-1}	0.13	0.5
Insulin mU· L^{-1}	0.48	0.042
HOMA-S%	−0.48	0.042
HOMA-B%	0.48	0.042
Triglyceride mmol· L^{-1}	0.37	0.1
Caeruloplasmin g· L^{-1}	−0.55	0.047
Iron umol· L^{-1}	0.15	0.5
TIBC umol· L^{-1}	0.24	0.3
Iron % saturation of TIBC	0.31	0.2
Ferritin μg· L^{-1}	0.4	0.1
Alcohol units/week	−0.17	0.5
A1AT g· L^{-1}	−0.22	0.3

BMI: body mass index, NEFA: non-esterified fatty acids, HOMA-S%: homeostatic model assessment—insulin sensitivity, HOMA-B%: homeostatic model assessment—β cell function, TIBC: total iron binding capacity, A1AT: α-1 antitrypsin.

The correlations between insulin, glycerol, and caeruloplasmin and liver fat are illustrated in Figure 2. Insulin (Figure 2a) and HOMA-B% were positively related to liver fat whereas HOMA-S% was inversely related (these are identical because insulin concentration is a component of all three and the ranked pairs of observations in this small series, by chance, are the same). NEFA and glycerol (Figure 2b) were inversely related to liver fat, but this inverse correlation was only significant for glycerol. The median NEFA was 302 umol· L^{-1} with range 138–491 umol· L^{-1}, and all were in the lower half of the reference range (130–1050 umol· L^{-1}). Glycerol (reference range 27–37 umol· L^{-1}) had a wider range of 10–210 umol· L^{-1} and median 90 umol· L^{-1} reflecting suppression with high liver fat and high levels with low liver fat. Glucose, triglycerides, alcohol intake, ferritin, iron, % iron binding capacity, and A1AT were not related to liver fat but caeruloplasmin (Figure 2c) was inversely related. One patient had a caeruloplasmin level below the lower reference interval but Wilson's disease was excluded by follow-up studies. There were no differences in liver fat content between the following groups: "untreated with statins or fibrates", "statin monotherapy" or "fibrate monotherapy" (*p* = 0.5), or between groups either taking or not taking Omacor (*p* = 0.2).

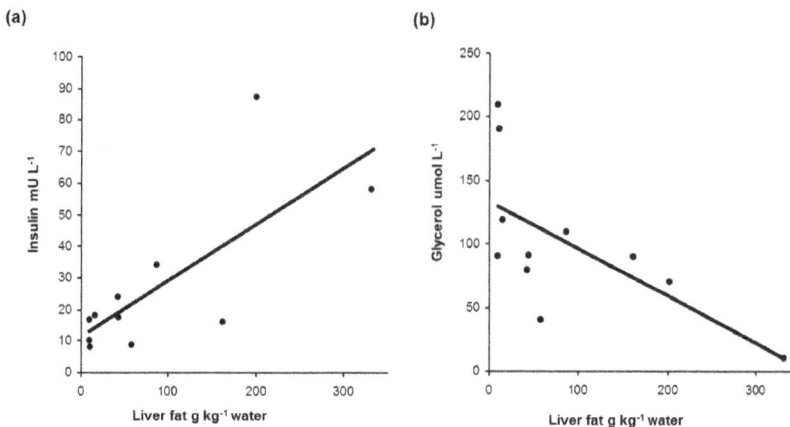

(a)

(b)

Figure 2. *Cont.*

(c)

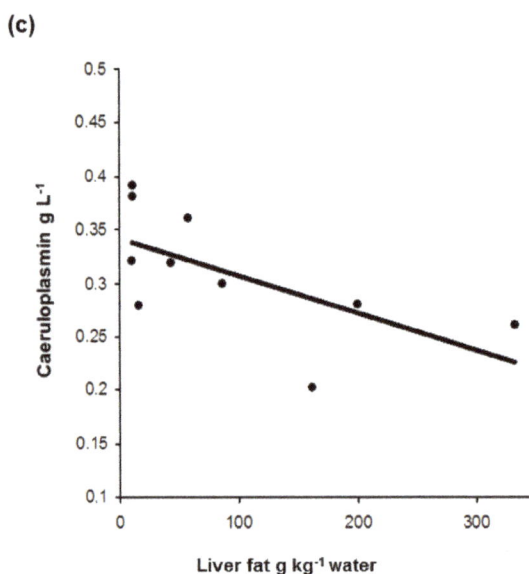

Figure 2. Relationship of insulin (**a**); glycerol (**b**); and caeruloplasmin (**c**) with liver fat content.

3. Discussion

Our data on repeat MRS at one month intervals showed a coefficient of variation of 14.8%, which is higher than the coefficient of variation of 8.5% observed between repeat MRS taken at 10 min intervals [5]. This difference likely reflects the technical challenge of repositioning the subject and reproducing conditions of the scan after one month. This would also have been contributed by alterations in hepatic adiposity in the subjects during the time period. It is important to take account of the overall imprecision of repeated measurements of liver fat in the design of therapeutic trials. Duplicate measurements improved the estimate of liver fat content in this study.

In this group of patients, we found no evidence of increased lipolysis despite increasing insulin resistance with increasing liver fat content. Higher liver fat content was significantly associated with lower serum glycerol but not NEFA. Glycerol was suppressed to quite low levels with increasing liver fat. In fact, in the subject with liver fat >30 g·kg^{-1} water, glycerol was almost completely suppressed. NEFA levels are in the lower half of the reference range with a downward trend as liver fat increased. It is interesting that the relationship between liver fat and glycerol is stronger than that of NEFA. Glycerol is regarded as a better reflection of adipocyte lipolysis than NEFA because, unlike NEFA, once released it cannot be taken up by the adipocyte again [9]. Our findings, therefore, do not accord with the hypothesis that increased delivery of NEFA secondary to adipocyte insulin resistance causes ectopic hepatic fat accumulation [1]. Indeed, the role of increased lipolysis in ectopic fat accumulation has been questioned in a previous study [8], with an alternative mechanism of diversion of chylomicron fatty acid to ectopic storage sites due to dysfunctional adipose tissue being proposed. It is suggested that this occurs with down regulation of NEFA trafficking and preservation of serum NEFA. Furthermore, obese subjects have been shown to have a reduction in NEFA release per unit of adipose tissue with no difference in NEFA levels compared with lean controls, and have reduced adipose tissue lipolysis [10].

The range of liver fat found in our subjects was similar to that found in the Dallas Heart Study [5]. Despite fatty liver having been reported by ultrasonography, 6 patients had a level of liver fat below the 95th centile of 5.6 g·kg^{-1} water cut-off established in a sub-set of the Dallas Heart Study's population without risk factors for fatty liver and normal serum transaminase levels. This may reflect the qualitative nature of hepatic ultrasound assessment of liver fat but may also reflect variability in liver fat content, particularly at near normal levels. Our subjects were not required to fast for the MRS because this has been shown not to contribute to variability [5].

The observed negative relationship of caeruloplasmin with hepatic steatosis is unexplained. Transferrin, A1AT, and caeruloplasmin are acute phase proteins, all of which increases with inflammation. Decreasing caeruloplasmin is, therefore, unlikely to reflect the inflammatory component of steatohepatitis. The decrease in caeruloplasmin could reflect reduced secretion of holoprotein due to failure to incorporate copper, an occurrence similar to that in Wilson's disease, decreased synthesis, and increased catabolism. Our results are consistent with a recent report demonstrating reduced hepatic copper related to the severity of steatosis in patients with NAFLD [11]. Furthermore, a reduction in caeruloplasmin measured as copper oxidase activity has been noted in alcoholic liver disease implying reduced incorporation of copper into caeruloplasmin [12]. The role of hepatic copper in steatosis remains undefined. One of our patients had a false positive caeruloplasmin test for Wilson's disease with a value below the lower limit of the reference range, suggesting a potential need to adjust the cut-off in the context of NAFLD.

4. Materials and Methods

4.1. Subjects

We recruited eleven patients (10 males and 1 female) attending the lipid outpatient clinic who had elevated serum alanine transaminase (ALT) levels and established hepatic steatosis demonstrated by ultrasonography. Their baseline characteristics are shown in Table 2.

Table 2. Baseline characteristics of study participants.

Population Characteristics	Median (Range)	Reference Range
Gender (n = 11)	10 males/1 female	-
Age	51 (32–67)	-
BMI kg·m^{-2}	29.6 (20.2–40.4)	<25% *
Alcohol (units)	3 (Male)	0–24
	5 (Female)	0–14
TC mmol·L^{-1}	5.7 (4.6–8.5)	<4.0 *
HDL mmol·L^{-1}	Female 1.26	Female > 1.2 *
	Male 1.34 (0.2–1.49)	Male > 1.0 *
TG mmol·L^{-1}	2.7 (0.6–6.0)	<1.7 *
NEFA umol·L^{-1}	302 (138–491)	130–1050
Glycerol umol·L^{-1}	90 (10–210)	27–137
Insulin mU·L^{-1}	17.2 (8.3–87.4)	3.4–6.4 **
Glucose mmol·L^{-1}	5.6 (5.0–7.5)	<6.1
HOMA-S%	43.9 (13.3–91.9)	100%
HOMA-B%	126.4 (92.6–254.5)	100%
Liver fat g·kg^{-1} water	44.0 (10.0–332.0)	<5.6 (95th centile)
ALT U·L^{-1}	56 (19–119)	5–40
Iron umol·L^{-1}	20.2 (10.2–28.1)	7–29
TIBC umol·L^{-1}	65 (50–74)	45–70
Iron % of TIBC	33 (17.6–49.4)	<50% ***
Ferritin μg·L^{-1}	187 (41.4–549.7)	15–200
Caeruloplasmin g·L^{-1}	0.31 (0.2–0.39)	0.25–0.63
A1AT g·L^{-1}	1.32 (1.07–1.95)	1.0–2.0

BMI: body mass index; TC: total cholesterol; HDL: high density cholesterol; TG: triglyceride; NEFA: non-esterified fatty acids; HOMA-S%: homeostatic model assessment—insulin sensitivity; HOMA-B%: homeostatic model assessment—β cell function; ALT: alanine transaminase; TIBC: total iron binding capacity; A1AT: α-1 antitrypsin; Reference ranges are 95th % confidence intervals unless otherwise indicated. * Clinic target levels; ** Interquartile range; *** British Society for Haematology Guideline 2000 on screening for haemochromatosis.

A diagnosis of fatty liver was made by exclusion. The presence of biliary obstruction or other structural abnormalities were excluded on ultrasonography. Autoimmune liver disease, chronic hepatitis and metabolic liver disease were excluded by the presence of normal immunoglobulin levels, absence of autoantibody markers, negative serological tests for hepatitis B and C, and measurements of serum ferritin, iron saturation, caeruloplasmin, and α-1 antitrypsin (A1AT). No patient had any clinical manifestations of Wilson's disease. Excess alcohol consumption (greater than 24 units per week for men and 14 units per week for women) was excluded on detailed history. Patients treated with hypoglycaemic agents were excluded. The study was restricted to subjects with ALT levels less than three times the upper limit of normal (120 U·L^{-1}). All patients were following a cardioprotective diet and were also provided with advice regarding recommended levels of physical activity which comprises 150 min of moderate intensity aerobic physical activity or 75 min of high intensity aerobic physical activity per week in combination with muscle-strengthening activities for at least 2 days a week. Drug treatment was unchanged for six months prior to and during the study. Daily drug treatment was targeted at treatment of combined dyslipidaemia and consisted of no treatment ($N = 3$), statin monotherapy (Simvastatin 10 mg o.d., Simvastatin 40 mg o.d. and Atorvastatin 80 mg o.d.) ($N = 3$), statin in combination with Omacor (Atorvastatin 80 mg o.d. with Omacor 2 g per day) ($N = 1$), fibrate monotherapy (Fenofibrate 160 mg o.d. and 200 mg o.d.) ($N = 2$), fibrate in combination with Omacor (Fenofibrate 267 mg o.d. with Omacor 2 g per day) ($N = 1$), and Omacor monotherapy (4 g per day) ($N = 1$). None of the patients were on thyroxine, β blockers, thiazolidinediones or thiazide diuretics. All patients provided blood samples in clinic following a minimum of 12 h fasting and had their height and weight measured, which was used to calculate their body mass index (BMI) as weight (kg) × height (m^{-2}).

4.2. Laboratory Methods

Serum total cholesterol, high density lipoprotein cholesterol (HDL), triglycerides, iron, total iron binding capacity (TIBC), % iron saturation of TIBC, and fluoride oxalate plasma glucose were measured routinely using the standard laboratory protocols of the Department of Clinical Biochemistry at the Central Manchester University Hospital NHS Foundation Trust (CMFT) using a Roche Modular P Analyzer. Serum caeruloplasmin was measured by a nephelometric assay on the Beckman Array Analyser using a Beckman calibrator. Serum ferritin was measured using the standard laboratory protocol of the Department of Clinical Haematology at CMFT on a Beckman Access Analyser with reagents supplied by Beckman Coulter. Serum glycerol was measured using Sigma Aldrich GPO PAP reagents and serum NEFA were measured using Wako NEFA C ACS-ACOD reagents (Wako Chemicals GmbH, Neuss, Germany) on a Roche Cobas Mira analyzer (Roche, Basel, Switzerland). Serum insulin was measured by an "in house" method using a polyclonal anti-porcine insulin, raised in guinea-pig obtained from Diagnostics Scotland, Carluke, Scotland, UK and using ^{125}I labeled Insulin (DSL-1620, 185kBq, DSL Ltd.) obtained through Oxford Bio-Innovation Ltd., Bicester, UK. HOMA-S% and HOMA-B% were calculated using the Oxford University Calculator HOMA2 2004 [13].

4.3. Estimation of Liver Fat

Two MRS of the liver were performed, at one month intervals, in each patient using a Philips 1.5 Tesla *Achieva* MR scanner (Amsterdam, The Netherlands). After subjects were positioned to allow access to an area free of blood vessels, fully relaxed (repetition time, TR = 6 s) and localised ^{1}H MR spectra were obtained from a 2 × 2 × 2 cm volume using PRESS localization without water suppression (echo time, TE = 23 ms, 32 averages). T$_2$ relaxation times (the time constant for decay of transverse components of magnetisation (M$_{xy}$)) for water and fat were estimated from a series of 5 spectra recorded in each session (8 averages, TR = 1600) at TE values of 23, 50, 100, 150, and 200 ms. Analysis of the spectra was performed using the AMARES routine in the jMRUI deconvolution software (MRUI consortium) [14], which provided a ratio of intracellular triglyceride to water. The ratio was corrected for T$_2$ relaxation time differences between water and fat [15,16]. In order to provide

Int. J. Mol. Sci. **2016**, *17*, 1089

consistency between serial scans, the second scan performed after a one month interval was obtained in a similar position with the aid of the first scan. The MRS procedure was well tolerated with only one patient experiencing claustrophobia.

4.4. Statistical Methods

The standard deviation of MRS estimates of liver fat was calculated from the differences between the two scans as $\sqrt{[\sum (\text{differences}^2)/22]}$. The normality of the distribution of differences was assessed using the Shapiro–Wilk W test. All other data are expressed as median (range) because of their non-parametric distribution. Correlation between variables was calculated as the Kendall Tau rank statistic with a 2 tailed probability of <0.05 being regarded as significant. The Kruskal Wallace one way analysis of variance test was used to assess the differences in liver fat content between 3 groups defined by drug treatment as: "no statin or fibrate treatment", "statin monotherapy", and "fibrate monotherapy", which were mutually exclusive, and between 2 groups defined as "Omacor treated" or "not Omacor treated".

The study was designed to estimate the variability of sequential measures of liver fat to inform power calculation for future studies. The estimate was considered sufficiently robust after 11 patients, after review by our statistician.

5. Main Messages

Variability of repeat scans performed one month apart is nearly twice that observed with immediate repetition, and should be taken into account in the design of interventional trials with liver fat content as the endpoint. Glycerol is inversely related to liver fat content suggesting down regulation of fatty acid trafficking consistent with the new paradigm for the pathogenesis of fatty liver. Caeruloplasmin is inversely related to liver fat content, which is as yet unexplained.

Acknowledgments: Support from the Manchester Wellcome Trust Clinical Research Facility and the National Institute of Health Research (NIHR) Biomedical Research Centre is acknowledged.

Author Contributions: Michael France, See Kwok and Paul N. Durrington were involved in the design of the study. Michael France, See Kwok, Handrean Soran, Yifen Liu, Safwaan Adam and Jan Hoong Ho wrote the first draft and all authors were involved in production of the final manuscript. Dexter Canoy advised on and critically appraised the statistical analysis. Steve Williams designed the magnetic resonance protocol and supervised the liver scans.

Conflicts of Interest: The authors declare no conflict of interest.

References

1.   Kopec, K.L.; Burns, D. Nonalcoholic fatty liver disease: A review of the spectrum of disease, diagnosis, and therapy. *Nutr. Clin. Pract.* **2011**, *26*, 565–576. [CrossRef] [PubMed]
2.   Cheung, O.; Sanyal, A.J. Recent advances in nonalcoholic fatty liver disease. *Curr. Opin. Gastroenterol.* **2010**, *26*, 202–208. [CrossRef] [PubMed]
3.   Tessari, P.; Coracina, A.; Cosma, A.; Tiengo, A. Hepatic lipid metabolism and non-alcoholic fatty liver disease. *Nutr. Metab. Cardiovasc. Dis.* **2009**, *19*, 291–302. [CrossRef] [PubMed]
4.   Mehta, S.R. Advances in the treatment of nonalcoholic fatty liver disease. *Ther. Adv. Endocrinol. Metab.* **2010**, *1*, 101–115. [CrossRef] [PubMed]
5.   Szczepaniak, L.S.; Nurenberg, P.; Leonard, D.; Browning, J.D.; Reingold, J.S.; Grundy, S.; Hobbs, H.H.; Dobbins, R.L. Magnetic resonance spectroscopy to measure hepatic triglyceride content: Prevalence of hepatic steatosis in the general population. *Am. J. Physiol. Endocrinol. Metab.* **2005**, *288*, E462–E468. [CrossRef] [PubMed]
6.   Georgoff, P.; Thomasson, D.; Louie, A.; Fleischman, E.; Dutcher, L.; Mani, H.; Kottilil, S.; Morse, C.; Dodd, L.; Kleiner, D.; et al. Hydrogen-1 MR spectroscopy for measurement and diagnosis of hepatic steatosis. *AJR Am. J. Roentgenol.* **2012**, *199*, 2–7. [CrossRef] [PubMed]

7.   Baldeweg, S.E.; Golay, A.; Natali, A.; Balkau, B.; del Prato, S.; Coppack, S.W. Insulin resistance, lipid and fatty acid concentrations in 867 healthy Europeans. European Group for the Study of Insulin Resistance (EGIR). *Eur. J. Clin. Investig.* **2000**, *30*, 45–52. [CrossRef]

8.   McQuaid, S.E.; Hodson, L.; Neville, M.J.; Dennis, A.L.; Cheeseman, J.; Humphreys, S.M.; Ruge, T.; Gilbert, M.; Fielding, B.A.; Frayn, K.N.; et al. Downregulation of adipose tissue fatty acid trafficking in obesity: A driver for ectopic fat deposition? *Diabetes* **2011**, *60*, 47–55. [CrossRef] [PubMed]

9.   Galton, D.J.; Wallis, S. The regulation of adipose cell metabolism. *Proc. Nutr. Soc.* **1982**, *41*, 167–173. [CrossRef] [PubMed]

10. Kolditz, C.I.; Langin, D. Adipose tissue lipolysis. *Curr. Opin. Clin. Nutr. Metab. Care* **2010**, *13*, 377–381. [CrossRef] [PubMed]

11. Aigner, E.; Strasser, M.; Haufe, H.; Sonnweber, T.; Hohla, F.; Stadlmayr, A.; Solioz, M.; Tilg, H.; Patsch, W.; Weiss, G.; et al. A role for low hepatic copper concentrations in nonalcoholic Fatty liver disease. *Am. J. Gastroenterol.* **2010**, *105*, 1978–1985. [CrossRef] [PubMed]

12. Uhlikova, E.; Kupcova, V.; Szantova, M.; Turecky, L. Plasma copper and ceruloplasmin in patients with alcoholic liver steatosis. *Bratisl. Lek. List.* **2008**, *109*, 431–433.

13. Levy, J.C.; Matthews, D.R.; Hermans, M.P. Correct homeostasis model assessment (HOMA) evaluation uses the computer program. *Diabetes Care* **1998**, *21*, 2191–2192. [CrossRef] [PubMed]

14. Vanhamme, L.; van den Boogaart, A.; van Huffel, S. Improved method for accurate and efficient quantification of MRS data with use of prior knowledge. *J. Magn. Reson.* **1997**, *129*, 35–43. [CrossRef] [PubMed]

15. Stefan, D.; di Cesare, F.; Andrasescu, A.; Popa, E.; Lazariev, A.; Vescovo, E.; Strbak, O.; Williams, S.; Starcuk, Z.; Cabanas, M.; et al. Quantitation of magnetic resonance spectroscopy signals: The jMRUI software package. *Meas. Sci. Technol.* **2010**, *20*, 104035–104044. [CrossRef]

16. Thomas, E.L.; Saeed, N.; Hajnal, J.V.; Brynes, A.; Goldstone, A.P.; Frost, G.; Bell, J.D. Magnetic resonance imaging of total body fat. *J. Appl. Physiol.* **1998**, *85*, 1778–1785. [PubMed]

International Journal of
Molecular Sciences

MDPI

Review

Pathophysiology of Non Alcoholic Fatty Liver Disease

Salvatore Petta [1], Amalia Gastaldelli [2], Eleni Rebelos [3], Elisabetta Bugianesi [4], Piergiorgio Messa [5], Luca Miele [6], Gianluca Svegliati-Baroni [7], Luca Valenti [8] and Ferruccio Bonino [3,9,*]

[1]   Gastroenterology, Di.Bi.M.I.S Policlinic Paolo Giaccone Hospital, University of Palermo, PC 90127 Palermo, Italy; petsa@inwind.it
[2]   Cardiometabolic Risk Unit—Institute of Clinical Physiology, CNR, PC 56124 Pisa, Italy; amalia@ifc.cnr.it
[3]   Department of Clinical and Experimental Medicine, University of Pisa, PC 56122 Pisa, Italy; elenirebelos@gmail.com
[4]   Gastroenterology and Hepatology, Department of Medical Sciences, Città della, Salute e della Scienza di Torino Hospital, University of Turin, PC 10122 Turin, Italy; ebugianesi@yahoo.it
[5]   Department of Nephrology, Urology and Renal Transplant—Fondazione IRCCS Ca', Granda, PC 20122 Milano, Italy; pmessa@policlinico.mi.it
[6]   Institute of Internal Medicine, Gastroenterology and Liver Diseases Unit, Fondazione Policlinico Gemelli, Catholic University of Rome, PC 00168 Rome, Italy; luca.miele@policlinicogemelli.it
[7]   Department of Gastroenterology 1 and Obesity 2, Polytechnic University of Marche, PC 60121 Ancona, Italy; gsvegliati@gmail.com
[8]   Metabolic Liver Diseases—Università degli Studi Milano-Fondazione IRCCS Ca', Granda via F Sforza 35, PC 20122 Milano, Italy; luca.valenti@unimi.it
[9]   Institute for Health, PC 53042 Chianciano Terme, Italy
*   Correspondence: ferruccio.bonino@unipi.it; Tel.: +39-337-221-762

Academic Editors: Amedeo Lonardo and Giovanni Targher
Received: 22 September 2016; Accepted: 1 December 2016; Published: 11 December 2016

Abstract: The physiopathology of fatty liver and metabolic syndrome are influenced by diet, life style and inflammation, which have a major impact on the severity of the clinicopathologic outcome of non-alcoholic fatty liver disease. A short comprehensive review is provided on current knowledge of the pathophysiological interplay among major circulating effectors/mediators of fatty liver, such as circulating lipids, mediators released by adipose, muscle and liver tissues and pancreatic and gut hormones in relation to diet, exercise and inflammation.

Keywords: fatty liver; insulin resistance; free fatty acids; cholesterol; adiponectin; leptin; insulin; glucagon; glucagon-like peptide 1; ghrelin; irisin; selenoprotein P

1. Introduction

Nonalcoholic fatty liver disease (NAFLD) is associated with a wide pathological spectrum, ranging from indolent liver fat storage, associated with an asymptomatic benign clinical course, to progressive cardiovascular, metabolic and/or liver and kidney diseases with higher cancer risks. Insulin resistance (IR) plays a pivotal role in the pathogenic switch of fatty liver. IR as a hallmark of metabolic syndrome stems from the complex dimensional interplay among inflammation and key circulating mediators, organs and tissues, genetic background and major conditioning factors, such as lifestyle (i.e., diet and physical activity). Here, we review the current knowledge on the dynamics of major circulating effectors/mediators of fatty liver, such as circulating lipids, released compounds from adipose, muscle and liver tissues and pancreatic and gut hormones in relation to lifestyle (i.e., diet and exercise) and inflammation. As renal function is frequently altered in patients with NAFLD, contributing to organ damage progression, the interplay with renal pathophysiology has also been addressed for circulating effectors/mediators other than pancreatic hormones.

2. Circulating Lipids

2.1. Free Fatty Acids (FFA)

Circulating FFA, which represent the major source of hepatic fat accumulation in patients with NAFLD, are mainly derived from adipose tissue lipolysis and partly from lipoprotein spill over and are the major fuel substrate for all tissues, except brain during fasting. Thus, their plasma levels are high during fasting and decline after feeding because of the anti-lipolytic action of insulin. In the presence of adipose tissue insulin resistance, FFA levels are high, despite high levels of circulating insulin, because of the resistance to the anti-lipolytic action of this hormone [1,2]. FFAs are involved in the pathogenesis of different metabolic disorders associated with insulin resistance, and different forms of FFA have different implications in cardio-metabolic disorders, ranging from protective to harmful effects [3–7]. Plasma FFAs are reabsorbed in various organs where, if not oxidized, they accumulate under the form of triglycerides within intra-cytoplasmic lipid droplets, and some lipid intermediates, such as or diacyl-glycerols (DAG), promote cell lipotoxicity and mitochondrial dysfunction (Figure 1). Hepatic FFAs can be exported as very low density lipoproteins (VLDL), which can contribute to high circulating triglycerides and low density lipoproteins (LDL), reduced high density lipoproteins (HDL) and an increased risk of atherosclerosis [8].

2.1.1. FFA and Diet

Consistent with the above evidence is that a higher saturated fatty acid (SFA) intake was associated with increased cardiovascular risk [9], whereas a higher intake of polyunsaturated fatty acids (PUFA) showed a protective effect [10], even if contradictory data arose from studies assessing the impact of PUFA supplementation on cardiovascular outcomes [11]. From a practical point of view, a recommended diet should be rich in PUFA and low in SFA.

2.1.2. FFA and Exercise

FFA mobilization and oxidation are higher during low and prolonged versus short and high intensity exercise [12]. In fact, during high intensity exercise, most energy is derived from glucose, while the highest use of FFA as a substrate occurs during low intensity exercise (25% of VO_2 max).

2.1.3. FFA and Inflammation

Elevated plasma FFA levels, affected also by diet and exercise and resulting from obesity or high-fat feeding, can cause insulin resistance, as well as low-grade inflammation [13]. Recently, the activation of the c-Jun terminal kinase (JNK) pathway by SFA was demonstrated in in vivo investigations [14], contributing to the development of hepatic steatosis and insulin resistance, as well as activation of pro-inflammatory M1 macrophages. Other in vitro studies showed that palmitate may induce endoplasmatic reticulum (ER) and oxidative stress in hepatocytes [15] and trigger the inflammasome via the activation of macrophages through TLR2/1 dimerization [16]. On the contrary, the contribution of unsaturated fatty acids (e.g., oleate, linoleate) to insulin resistance is still debated; they seem unable to affect the cell, but can impact TG storage [17]. Finally, FFAs are the source of diacyl glycerol (DAG), triglycerides and other metabolites, such as ceramides, which are synthesized in the ER of hepatocytes from long-chain SFA, as a substrate [18]. Ceramides were shown to be lipotoxic to pancreatic cells and involved in hepatic insulin resistance [19], but direct evidence of their pro-apoptotic role on hepatocytes is missing [20]. Increased hepatic ceramides and saturated TG and FFA were found in patients with NAFLD [21]. ER stress contributes to NASH progression, and saturated FFAs were shown to induce an ER stress response in hepatocytes and increased levels of ER stress in patients with NAFLD/NASH [22].

2.1.4. FFA and Nonalcoholic Fatty Liver Disease (NAFLD)

The above-mentioned effect of FFA on insulin resistance and low grade inflammation can explain the link between FFA and NAFLD/NASH. Recent in vitro and in vivo studies support the hypothesis that FFAs, which are not esterified and compartmentalized in lipid droplets, may induce irreversible cell damage and trigger pro-inflammatory signaling pathways (lipotoxicity), either alone or in combination with other lipid metabolites [23–25]. In addition, other in vitro and in vivo studies have shown that inhibiting hepatic TG synthesis results in an amelioration of hepatic steatosis, but exacerbates liver cell damage due to an increased intra-hepatic accumulation of FFAs [26]. All together, these observations suggest a possible protective role for increased hepatic TG synthesis against FFA-mediated cell toxicity.

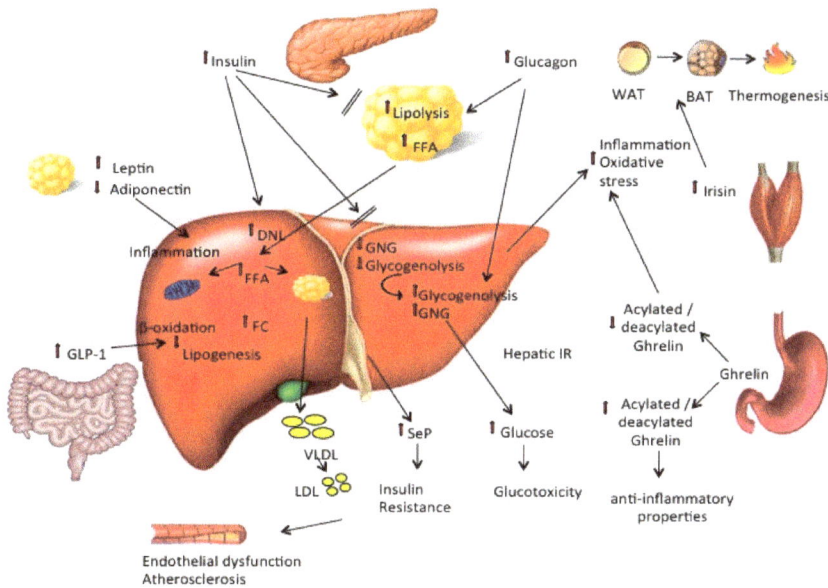

Figure 1. The key metabolic players and the major pathogenic pathways involved in NAFLD. Fatty liver is considered to be the hepatic component of metabolic syndrome. Systemic insulin resistance reduces adiponectin and increases leptin concentrations, while adipose tissue lipolysis is not suppressed (as shown with the "//" symbol), despite high circulating insulin levels, and plasma FFA concentration is increased. Increased glucagon levels have also been reported in NAFLD patients. The altered insulin/glucagon ratio promotes DNL, glycogenolysis and gluconeogenesis in the liver, thus increasing hepatic glucose production and hepatic insulin resistance. Several hormones secreted by the gastrointestinal tract regulate glucose/lipid metabolism, as well as food intake and, thus, might be implicated in the development of NAFLD. Impaired GLP-1 secretion and decreased levels of GLP-1 receptors have been reported in the liver of subjects with NAFLD, which further impair hepatic glucose and lipid metabolism. Ghrelin modulates appetite and insulin secretion, and an increased acylated/deacylated ghrelin ratio exerts anti-inflammatory properties.The liver secretes several hepatokines, including SeP, which further enhance insulin resistance, increase the production of small LDL particles that induce atherosclerosis and promote oxidative stress. Adipose tissues secrete adipokine-like leptin and adiponectin that are involved in the modulation of inflammation, fatty acid oxidation and energy expenditure, insulin resistance and insulin secretion. Myokines can also affect glucose and lipid metabolism, e.g., irisin, of which secretion is stimulated by exercise and induces thermogenesis, although its role has not yet been completely elucidated. Small red arrows versus the top: indicate increased concentrations; small red arrows versus the bottom: indicate reduced concentrations.

2.1.5. FFA and Kidney

The same mechanisms advocating FFA in the pathogenesis of NAFLD/NASH could also be involved in chronic kidney disease (CKD), where the lipotoxicity of FFAs in kidney cells, and in particular on podocytes [27], via ER stress, could explain the pathogenic role of obesity in CKD. Additionally in CKD, although polyunsaturated FAs (such as linoleic acid) probably play a protective role on the kidneys, saturated FFAs, such as palmitic acid, are responsible for intracellular lipotoxicity [28,29].

2.2. Cholesterol

Cholesterol is a major lipotoxic molecule, critical in the development of experimental and human metabolic disorders, such as atherosclerosis [30,31]. Different lines of evidence have reported that the accumulation of LDL in vessels make macrophages and smooth muscle cells able to convert esterified cholesterol into cholesterol [31–33]. When intra- and extra-cellular accumulation of cholesterol cannot be removed HDL mediated mechanisms, this leads to the generation of cholesterol crystals that, in turn, promote cell death, intima injury and atherosclerotic plaque destabilization [31]. The Seven Countries Study clearly reported a strong link between circulating total cholesterol levels, cardiovascular mortality and diet, with a higher intake of both refined sugar and fat being associated with poor outcomes [31], while dietary fibers have a protective effect [33,34].

2.2.1. Cholesterol and Diet

The influence of cholesterol-free diets on cholesterol serum levels is controversial, in spite of the very large number of different cholesterol-free diet programs [35]. One major reason for this may be the fact that the impact of different diet components on plasma lipid composition is mediated by gut microbiota [36]. The interactions between gut microbiota and dietary lipids in regulating liver and plasma lipid composition, liver gene expression and hepatic cholesterol metabolism were recently shown in germ-free and normally-raised mice [36]. In a study on mice fed lard, gut microbiota increased hepatic, but not serum, levels of cholesterol and cholesteryl esters, while, in mice fed fish oil, neither hepatic nor serum levels of cholesterol and cholesteryl esters were affected [36].

2.2.2. Cholesterol and Exercise

Considering the effect of exercise on cholesterol levels [37], available evidence suggests the particular effectiveness of higher-intensity aerobic exercise [38] and moderate-intensity resistance training [39], with a dose-response relationship between activity levels and increases in HDL cholesterol. However, in order to observe a reduction in plasma cholesterol with exercise training, a reduction in caloric intake and dietary fat during the exercise training program, resulting in a decrease in body weight/body fat, is important [40].

2.2.3. Cholesterol and Inflammation

Cholesterol accumulation in macrophages leads to the induction and secretion of two major inflammatory cytokines, tumor necrosis factor-α (TNF-α) and interleukin-6 (IL-6), which induce inflammation via NLRP3 (nucleotide-binding domain, leucine-rich-containing family, pyrin domain-containing-3) activation and the production of IL1-β and C-reactive protein, suggesting that excess ER cholesterol triggers endogenous cellular events. This proinflammatory activity can explain the link between high cholesterol levels, cholesterol deposition in atherosclerotic plaques and vascular damage [41].

2.2.4. Cholesterol and NAFLD

Lipidomic analyses of NAFLD have demonstrated that, apart from triglycerides, there is also an accumulation of free cholesterol (FC) without a similar increase in cholesterol esters (CE) in both

NAFLD and NASH [42] (Figure 1). Again, the above-mentioned cholesterol-related proinflammatory mechanisms, involved in vascular damage, have been also linked to cholesterol-mediated liver damage in NASH [31–33]. Along this line, multiple and complex alterations occur in the pathways of cholesterol homeostasis in both NAFLD and NASH [43]. Consistently, statin use has been associated with possible protection from hepatic damage and fibrosis in NAFLD [44].

2.2.5. Cholesterol and Kidney

Several findings suggest the role of systemic and renal lipids in kidney disease development and progression [45]. In fact, lipid loaded cells (i.e., foam cells) are frequently observed in many progressive nephropathies, such as in experimental diabetic kidney disease (DKD) and in focal segmental glomerular sclerosis (FSGS) or minimal change nephropathy in humans [46–48]. Secondly, the high prevalence, in African American subjects, of genetic variants of the APOL1 gene, encoding apolipoprotein L1 (a component of HDL), may explain the high susceptibility to nephropathy, in particular to FSGS, of this ethnic group [49]. Finally, some interventions that interfere with lipid accumulation in glomerular cells (podocytes) are effective in reducing kidney damage in some experimental kidney diseases [50]. Although no clear benefit of statin use on chronic kidney disease (CKD) occurrence and/or progression has been demonstrated in a clinical setting [51], the mechanism(s) by which cholesterol might play a causal role in CKD may be more complex than that which is only related to serum cholesterol concentration; again, involving its ability to activate pro-inflammatory mechanisms already involved in atherosclerosis and NASH [45].

3. Adipose Tissue Released Compounds

3.1. Adiponectin

Adiponectin is a cytokine that is mostly produced by adipocytes, its expression being primarily determined by adipocyte size and insulin sensitivity, with larger, insulin-resistant adipocytes being less productive [52,53]. It is a "protective" adipocytokine, involved in the regulation of glucose and lipid metabolism, as well as in inflammation inhibiting NF-κB and TNF-α production in macrophages; consistent with these data, its serum concentrations are inversely related to obesity and diabetes [54]. Adiponectin levels are inversely related to insulin resistance and are lower in obese subjects and patients with established insulin resistance, e.g., in type 2 diabetes, NAFLD/NASH and hypertension.

3.1.1. Adiponectin and Diet

High-fat, but not low fat, diets were associated with increased adiponectin levels, whereas a modest increase was reported with n-3 polyunsaturated fatty acids (PUFA) supplementation [55]; however, on the contrary, conjugated linoleic acid supplementation showed a reduction in adiponectin levels [55]. In mice, a high-carbohydrate diet was shown to increase adiponectin levels [56], and in humans, Rezvani et al. reported a significant increase of adiponectin levels during the consumption of glucose, but not fructose [57]. Some evidence suggests that adiponectin production by adipocytes is regulated via insulin-stimulated glucose utilization [58].

3.1.2. Adiponectin and Exercise

Mild or moderate physical activity does not change adiponectin levels, though a positive effect was reported with longer exercise [59]. Consistently, increased serum adiponectin levels paralleled the improvement of carotid vascular function in obese individuals undergoing intense exercise and moderate caloric restriction [60].

3.1.3. Adiponectin and Inflammation

While the impact of diet and exercise on adiponectin is controversial, the anti-inflammatory activity of this adipokine, able to inhibit NF-κB and TNF-α production in macrophages, is well established (Figure 1); consistent with these data, its serum concentrations are inversely related to obesity and chronic metabolic disorders, such as insulin resistance and diabetes. In contrast, adiponectin levels are elevated in classic chronic inflammatory/autoimmune diseases unrelated to increased adipose tissue, such as rheumatoid arthritis, systemic lupus erythematosus (SEL), inflammatory bowel disease, type 1 diabetes (T1D) and cystic fibrosis [61].

3.1.4. Adiponectin and NAFLD

Due to the above-mentioned insulin sensitizing and anti-inflammatory activity of adiponectin, its plasma levels are decreased in patients with NAFLD and are associated with fat content [62]. After treatment with thiazolidinediones, adiponectin values increase in NASH as a sign of improvement of hepatic steatosis, necroinflammation and, most importantly, fibrosis [63].

3.1.5. Adiponectin and Kidney

Adiponectin, due to its insulin sensitizing and anti-inflammatory activities, has a protective role on the kidney [64]. In fact, low adiponectin levels were associated with increased albumin urinary excretion and histological evidence of kidney damage, both in experimental and clinical studies [65–67]. At odds with these findings, in CKD, the levels of adiponectin are often increased. Whether this finding represents a compensatory phenomenon or just the consequence of the reduced renal clearance of a relatively small molecule (30 kD) and/or of an altered signaling at cellular levels is still a matter of debate [68–70].

3.2. Leptin

Leptin is a cytokine that is primarily secreted from adipose tissue, with a critical role in the regulation of body weight and fat mass. In obese mice, leptin causes weight loss, increasing energy expenditure and fatty acid oxidation, reducing appetite and triglyceride synthesis and counteracting the lipogenic action of insulin [71]. Its role in humans is less clear-cut; only patients with lipodystrophy have a beneficial effect when treated with leptin, while obese subjects do not lose weight. Circulating leptin is strongly associated with both subcutaneous and visceral fat [72], and different studies have hypothesized that obesity might induce a state of leptin resistance. High leptin levels are associated with reduced insulin secretion, increased gluconeogenesis and reduced glucose uptake, leading to hyperglycemia and ultimately contributing to increased insulin resistance [73–75] (Figure 1). Leptin may negatively affect the cardiovascular system by exerting potential atherogenic, thrombotic and angiogenic activities, as well as, even if with contrasting data, leading to cardiac hypertrophy [76].

3.2.1. Leptin and Diet

A higher energy storage is directly related to serum leptin levels [71]. Considering different types of fatty acids: SFAs are associated with increased leptin levels, whereas MUFA and PUFA have an opposite effect [71]. Finally, fiber and higher protein intake increase leptin sensitivity, which induces central satiety [71].

3.2.2. Leptin and Exercise

Available evidence suggests that, while acute and short-term physical activity do not affect leptin levels, longer exercise (at least 60 min) is associated with increased energy expenditure that could lead to leptin decrease [59]. Accordingly, the adiponectin/leptin ratio results as an independent predictor of carotid intima-media thickness (CIMT) alterations [77].

3.2.3. Leptin and Inflammation

Leptin may exert pro-inflammatory activity by the impairment of NO-related vassal relaxation, via increased oxidative stress, and by increased endothelin expression [54,78], by potentiating the effect of angiotensin II, which, in turn, increases leptin synthesis by inducing pro-inflammatory cytokines (e.g., TNF-α, IL-6 and MCP-1 receptor) by increasing the expression of adhesion molecules (e.g., VCAM-1, ICAM-1 and E-selectin). These features could explain why hyperleptinemia is observed in many chronic inflammatory diseases [79,80], such as atherosclerosis, and how it can participate in damage.

3.2.4. Leptin and NAFLD

A recent meta-analysis indicates that circulating leptin levels are higher in patients with NAFLD than in controls, and higher serum leptin levels were associated with an increased severity of NAFLD [81]. This is in agreement with the above-mentioned evidence of inflammatory-mediated damage related to leptin and potential involvement in NASH pathogenesis.

3.2.5. Leptin and Kidney

Leptin is cleared from circulation by glomerular filtration and metabolic degradation in renal tubules, which accounts for the elevated levels of leptin in CKD patients [79]. Given its anoxygenic and pro-inflammatory activities, leptin might contribute to malnutrition and inflammation, often observed in CKD patients, and a consistently higher risk of cardio-vascular morbidity and mortality [80,82,83]. Again, common inflammatory pathways could account for the role of leptin in kidney damage.

4. Pancreatic Hormones and NAFLD

4.1. Insulin

Insulin is secreted by the pancreas in response to changes in glucose concentrations that occur after a meal or after hormone release, such as catecholamines or glucagon [2]. Insulin tightly regulates glucose metabolism and plasma concentrations, on the one hand, by promoting glucose uptake in skeletal muscle and liver (for glucose oxidation or glycogen storage), in adipose tissue (where glucose is utilized for triglyceride synthesis) and, on the other hand, by suppressing hepatic glucose production. Insulin also acts on lipid metabolism, as it promotes fatty acid re-esterification into triglycerides in adipose tissue and liver, but also inhibits peripheral adipose tissue lipolysis (Figure 1). Thus, the role of insulin in the development of NAFLD is crucial. In the presence of insulin resistance, the pancreas is stimulated to increase insulin secretion to overcome the defect in peripheral glucose uptake and to decrease hepatic glucose production. Since the pancreas releases secreted insulin into the portal vein and the liver clears most of it, the amount of insulin that reaches the liver is much higher than in the periphery. Thus, when hepatic glucose production rates are high in the presence of high insulin values, it is recognized as a sign of hepatic insulin resistance [84]. Insulin mainly acts in suppressing hepatic glycogenolysis, rather than gluconeogenesis; however, until "hepatic autoregulation" is maintained, fasting glucose concentrations remain within normal ranges (Figure 1). When hepatic autoregulation is lost, both components of hepatic glucose production (i.e., glycogenolysis and gluconeogenesis) are increased and assist in the development of fasting hyperglycemia and type 2 diabetes [85]. Finally, different evidence supports a bidirectional link between insulin resistance and chronic inflammation. However, this topic is not the main goal of the present paper, while being the object of a huge debate in the literature, as reported in different reviews [86–88].

4.1.1. Insulin and Diet

A carbohydrate-rich diet (with a high glycemic index) determines higher glucose excursion and triggers a higher insulin secretion rate. Moreover, both lipids and amino acids determine increased insulin secretion; oral amino acids elicit a stronger and sustained insulin secretion, as compared to amino acids given intravenously [89]. In addition, lipids have an incretin effect, and a diet high in saturated fats determines insulin resistance and a higher glucose-stimulated insulin secretion (GSIS) [90]. A sustained increase in plasma free fatty acids by long-term intralipid infusion increases GSIS, but this response was found to be impaired in non-diabetic subjects, genetically predisposed to develop type 2 diabetes [91].

4.1.2. Insulin and NAFLD

Insulin promotes de novo lipogenesis (DNL) and glyceroneogenesis [25] (Figure 1). Both pathways are increased in NAFLD, even in non-diabetic patients, contributing to the synthesis of hepatic triglycerides and the promotion of hepatic steatosis [92]. In addition, patients with NAFLD have increased hepatic synthesis of palmitate through DNL, and this increases the risk of lipotoxicity and cell damage [25,93]. Finally, insulin, in the context of insulin resistance, prompts fibrogenesis by stellate cells [94,95]. Most patients with NAFLD have normal fasting glucose concentrations, but high levels of fasting insulin and high hepatic insulin resistance. Thus, it is not surprising that NAFLD is a major risk factor for the development of type 2 diabetes.

4.1.3. Insulin and Exercise

Exercise increases the demand of glucose in the periphery (muscle), and thus, there is a demand for increased endogenous glucose production (EGP). However, since glucose is immediately used by the muscle to produce ATP, glucose concentrations are usually stable, and thus, there is no stimulus for an increase in insulin secretion. However, other hormones, such as glucagon and catecholamine, are increased during exercise and stimulate EGP [12,96].

4.2. Glucagon

Glucagon is produced and secreted from alpha cells located in clusters of endocrine cells, in the islets of Langerhans, distributed throughout the pancreas [97]. Glucagon secretion is found to be increased, not only in diabetes, but also in several insulin resistant states, including NAFLD [98]. The role of glucagon is opposite that of insulin (Figure 1); glucagon stimulates glucose production via activation of hepatic glycogenolysis and gluconeogenesis by inhibition of glycolysis [98]. It also regulates fatty acid metabolism via stimulation of peripheral lipolysis, reduction of malonyl-CoA and stimulation of fatty acid oxidation [99]. However, the most recent data indicate that glucagon is also involved in amino acid metabolism, both because amino acids can stimulate glucagon secretion and because glucagon can stimulate protein metabolism [98].

4.2.1. Glucagon and Diet

Glucose is the most important regulator of pancreatic glucagon secretion. In normal glucose tolerant (NGT) subjects, when glucose concentrations are high, glucagon secretion is suppressed, and when there are low glucose concentrations, glucagon secretion is increased, securing an essential supply of energy (i.e., glucose) to the central nervous system and muscles. In patients with diabetes, glucagon concentrations are elevated in the fasting state and fail to decrease appropriately, or even increase, during an oral glucose tolerance test (OGTT) or after ingestion of a mixed meal [100–102]. Certain amino acids, such as glutamine, alanine and arginine, are also important glucagon secretors, with the latter being the most potent stimulatory amino acid [103,104]. Fat intake also increases glucagon secretion [105].

4.2.2. Glucagon and NAFLD

Since glucagon stimulates lipolysis and reduces lipogenesis [99], glucagon was proposed as a therapy option for hepatic steatosis [106]. Similarly, it was thought that the reduction of glucagon signaling, i.e., via the use of glucagon receptor antagonists, might lead to the accumulation of lipids in the liver [107]. However, more recent studies [108] have shown that glucagon receptor knockout mice have reduced hepatic lipid contents compared with wild-type mice. The impact of glucagon on NAFLD has not been elucidated. Junker and colleagues [109] have shown that patients with NAFLD have fasting hyperglucagonemia, independent of their glucose tolerance status. According to the authors, this finding suggests that NAFLD might be involved in the generation of hyperglucagonemia in T2D, which is supported by several animal studies [110].

4.2.3. Glucagon and Exercise

Exercise induces an increase in glucagon secretion in order to increase hepatic glucose production and gluconeogenesis. However, although pancreatic hormones are important in the stimulation of EGP during low or moderate intensity exercise, during strenuous exercise (i.e., 80% VO_2 max), EGP is increased, mainly because of increased catecholamine, while changes in glucagon and insulin are not necessary to stimulate the increase in Ra [96].

4.2.4. Glucagon and Inflammation

Patients with trauma, burns or sepsis normally exhibit increased plasma levels of glucagon, in order to promote gluconeogenesis, increase circulating glucose and compensate for the energetic demand of the body during these extreme situations [111]. Interestingly, significant increases of both glucagon and inflammatory mediators occur after a high fat high carbohydrate meal, as compared with an American Heart Association-recommended meal [112]. Plasma IL-6, a pro-inflammatory cytokine, is elevated in physiological and pathophysiological settings where glucagon is also elevated, such as exercise [113], diabetes [114] and inflammatory stress [115]. Tweedell et al. have demonstrated that IL-6-deficient (IL-6-KO) mice have a blunted glucagon response to acute inflammation compared with their wild-type littermates, while glucagon response is completely rescued by intravenous replacement of IL-6 [116]. Consistent with this, Ortega and colleagues demonstrated that, in patients with altered glucose tolerance, but not in NGT subjects, circulating glucagon levels were associated with inflammatory mediators, such as IL-6 [111].

5. Gut Released Hormones

5.1. GLP-1

Glucagon-like peptide 1 (GLP-1) is an incretin hormone produced mainly by the L-cells of the gut in response to food intake. GLP-1 has an important role in the regulation of glucose metabolism, since it potentiates insulin secretion and inhibits glucagon release [117,118] (Figure 1). GLP-1 exerts its effect through binding to GLP-1 receptors, which are mainly expressed in the pancreas and brain, but also in the heart, liver, colon and kidney [117]. Other effects of GLP-1 include the central suppression of appetite and the induction of satiety by delaying gastric emptying [117,119]. Other than these classical activities, GLP-1 seems to be able to modulate the function of different key organs by interacting with GLP-1 receptors present in the lung, stomach, liver, colon, kidney and heart. Consistent with these data, growing evidence suggests a direct protective effect of GLP-1 on the cardiovascular system [117,119].

5.1.1. GLP-1 and Diet

GLP-1 release can be stimulated by mixed meals or individual nutrients, including glucose and other sugars, fatty acids, essential amino acids and dietary fiber. Oral, but not intravenous, glucose administration stimulates GLP-1 secretion in humans [120].

5.1.2. GLP-1 and Exercise

Exercise-related studies have shown that healthy people have increased levels of incretin hormones, such as GLP-1, after physical activity [121]. Lee et al. showed higher GLP-1 levels after high intensity vs. low intensity exercise, with matched energy expenditures [122].

5.1.3. GLP-1 and Inflammation

GLP-1 receptor agonists (GLP-1RAS) have anti-inflammatory effects in different cell types, including human umbilical vein endothelial cells, glomerular endothelial cells, monocytes and macrophages [123,124]. GLP-1 levels decreased for a mean duration of 7.5 months in a retrospective analysis of 110 obese patients with T2D who were treated with liraglutide [125]. Consistently, TNF-α induced systemic inflammation and reduced GLP-1 concentrations, thereby reducing the suppression of endogenous glucose production (EGP) during GLP-1 infusion [126].

5.1.4. GLP-1 and NAFLD

In vitro studies have shown that human hepatocytes express the GLP-1 receptor [127,128]. In liver tissue, the expression of GLP-1 receptors is controversial [117], but Svegliati-Baroni was able to demonstrate that, in human livers of subjects with NASH, both the expression and protein content of GLP-1R were decreased compared to subjects without NASH [128]. In subjects with hepatic steatosis, open-label studies have shown that exenatide may improve liver enzymes and decrease steatosis when assessed by magnetic resonance spectroscopy (MRS) [129,130] and even improve histology [131]. A recent study by Armstrong et al. has shown that, after 48 months of double blind treatment with liraglutide vs. placebo (the LEAN study), 39% of patients receiving liraglutide vs. 9% of those receiving placebo had a resolution of definite non-alcoholic steatohepatitis with no worsening in fibrosis [132]. Among the mechanisms that lead to the improvement in liver histology were significant weight loss, reduced FFA flux to the liver, reduced de novo hepatic DNL and the above-mentioned anti-inflammatory activities [133] (Figure 1). All in all, these findings qualify GLP-1RA as a potential candidate for the treatment of NAFLD.

5.1.5. GLP-1 and Kidney

The effects of GLP-1 on glucose metabolism and inflammation, again, can indirectly benefit the kidney. Furthermore, incretin may also have direct renal effects, since its specific receptors have been described both in renal tubular and in glomerular cells [123,134]. One potential mechanism by which GLP-1 may play a nephro-protective role is its natriuretic activity, due to the direct inhibition of two key sodium transporters (Na-hydrogen exchanger-3 and sodium-glucose co-transporter-2) at the tubular level [124]. Furthermore, GLP-1 might also have a positive hemodynamic effect on the kidney by its stimulating and inhibitory effects on atrial natriuretic peptide (ANP) and angiotensin 2, respectively [125].

5.2. Ghrelin

Ghrelin is a hormone that is mainly derived from the stomach and duodenum, with a key role in growth hormone release and in food intake control by inducing appetite and controlling energy expenditure [135]. Ghrelin molecules are present as two major endogenous forms, an acylated form, which is the biologically-active form of ghrelin (AG), and a de-acylated form (DeAG) that does not bind to ghrelin receptors [136]. AG is secreted before a meal and disappears more rapidly from plasma than total ghrelin, with an elimination half-life of 9–13 vs. 27–31 min. The main organ that secretes ghrelin is the stomach, where 65%–90% of the circulating ghrelin is synthesized, followed by the small bowel, and in small amounts by other organs, including liver, pancreas, hypothalamus, kidney, liver, fat, muscle and heart (Figure 1). Ghrelin *O*-acyltransferase (GOAT), the enzyme responsible for acylation, was found to be involved in glucose metabolism, insulin resistance, lipid metabolism dysfunction and inflammation [137,138]. GOAT is expressed in several organs, mainly in the gastrointestinal tract, but also in the central nervous system, pancreas, heart, kidney, muscle, tongue, testis, thymus and adipose tissue, but not in the liver.

5.2.1. Ghrelin and Diet

Ghrelin levels (both AG and DeAG) increase with prolonged food deprivation and prior to meal time, while decreases in weight gain, adiposity and in the post-prandial phase with a magnitude proportional to caloric intake and macronutrient content [135,139,140]. GOAT expression and activity and, thus, the availability of AG are modified by dietary lipids, in particular by the availability of short and medium chain fatty acids [138]. Specifically, in a trial using isocaloric beverages, mostly containing fat or carbohydrates or proteins, the lipid drink was the least effective, and the protein drink was the most effective in lowering ghrelin levels, while the carbohydrate drink induced the largest drop in ghrelin levels and was then followed by a significant rebound [141]. Van Name et al. studied the AG response to glucose and fructose beverage in lean and obese adolescents (IS or IR). They found that AG levels were suppressed after either glucose or fructose consumption in lean subjects. In obese IS subjects, AG suppression was higher after glucose as compared to fructose consumption, whereas in obese IR subjects, suppression of AG was blunted following fructose consumption [142]. Thus, it would appear that, in addition to obesity in adolescents, the presence of insulin resistance further limits the capacity of fructose to suppress this key orexigenic hormone and may continue to promote hunger and overconsumption of fructose (or other calories), particularly in obese adolescents who are insulin resistant.

5.2.2. Ghrelin and Exercise

Contradictory results exist on the effect of physical activity on ghrelin levels. Short-term running, cycling or rowing exercise do not alter plasma total ghrelin [143–145]. On the other hand, Mackelvie et al. showed that daily exercise for five consecutive days (1-h sessions of aerobic exercise) is associated with an increase in plasma concentrations of AG, independent of the acute effect of exercise and from changes in weight or markers of insulin sensitivity. In addition, the increase in AG was more pronounced in normal weights compared with overweight subjects and was associated with an increase in markers of appetite [146]. However, Shiiya et al. report that plasma AG, but not DeAG levels, are suppressed during acute moderate exercise (cycle exercise for 60 minutes at 50% of VO_2 max) [146]. From a clinical point of view, this seems more reasonable since exercise increases appetite and exercise is associated with an increase in ghrelin levels (total or acylated form). However, more studies are needed to address the links between different forms of exercise, type, intensity and duration and ghrelin yield.

5.2.3. Ghrelin and Inflammation

Ghrelin, and especially AG, exert anti-inflammatory activity by reducing the production of pro-inflammatory cytokines, such as IL-1, IL-6 and TNF-α, via suppression of NF-κB [137]. The anti-inflammatory properties of ghrelin are consistent with the evidence from murine models that ghrelin prevents diabetes [139] and has a protective cardiovascular effect. These anti-inflammatory properties of ghrelin prompt the ghrelin-GOAT system as a promising new target for the treatment of NASH [137]. AG can improve cardiac function by increasing cardiac output, ameliorating cardiac contractility, acting on cardiac remodeling, reducing pulmonary hypertension, reducing fatal arrhythmia after myocardial infarction and leading to vasodilation [139,147–150].

5.2.4. Ghrelin and NAFLD

Whether ghrelin levels are altered in NAFLD is still controversial, as Marchesini et al. [151] reported low total ghrelin levels, while Mykhalchyshyn et al. [152] found high serum levels of AG in NAFLD compared to controls. However, the above-mentioned effects of ghrelin on energy and lipid metabolism, IR, inflammation and apoptotic cell death, which are common to both obesity and NAFLD, highly suggest its interplay with NAFLD/NASH pathogenesis [137].

5.2.5. Ghrelin and Kidney

In CKD, increased levels of total ghrelin, but not of AG, are frequently observed, due to the reduced metabolic clearance of the total (mainly DeAG) by failed kidneys. The consequently-reduced AG/DeAG ratio might contribute to inflammatory and malnutrition status, which is typical in many CKD patients [153,154].

6. Muscle Released Compounds

6.1. Irisin

Irisin is a recently-discovered myokine, encoded by the *FNDC5* gene; it is implicated in the regulation of energy homeostasis and metabolism and the interactions between skeletal muscle and other tissues (Figure 1). Irisin can induce the differentiation of white adipose into brown adipocytes, along with upregulation of uncoupling protein 1 (UCP1) expression and an increase in heat production [155,156]. Accordingly, circulating irisin can increase total energy expenditure, thus reducing obesity and insulin resistance [155,156].

6.1.1. Irisin and Diet

Results of studies on the effect of diet on irisin concentrations are not unanimous. Some studies report that irisin is not affected by food intake [157], while others indicate that irisin levels are positively associated with increasing fruit intake and negatively associated with meat consumption [158]. Finally, an inverse association between irisin and higher caloric intake has been shown [159].

6.1.2. Irisin and Exercise

The reported relationship between irisin and exercise are also contradictory. Some reports have claimed increased irisin serum levels in subjects who exercise [156], while a recent meta-analysis reported that chronic exercise training leads to significantly-decreased circulating irisin levels in randomized controlled trials only, with evidence remaining inconclusive in some other studies [160].

6.1.3. Irisin, NAFLD and Inflammation

To the best of our knowledge, there is only one study in which lower irisin levels were independently associated with higher intrahepatic triglyceride content, as assessed by 1H magnetic resonance spectroscopy [161]. However, in a recent study by Polyzos and colleagues [162], irisin levels were slightly higher in patients with NAFLD and significantly higher in NAFLD patients with portal inflammation, as compared to those without portal inflammation. Contrasting data on higher or lower serum irisin levels in relation with metabolic disorders, diet and exercise are worth further investigation and could be mostly due to the inaccuracy and lack of standardization of commercially-available ELISA assays. Mechanisms underlying the protective metabolic effects of irisin are not well understood and seem to be mostly related to higher induced energy expenditure and not to anti-inflammatory activities, such as NF-κB inactivation [157–159].

6.1.4. Irisin and Kidney

CKD patients have been reported to have lower, normal or higher energy expenditures than normal healthy people. The discrepancy among the different studies may be due to many factors related to the type of CKD stage, different therapies and also other, as of yet, unrecognized factors [163,164]. In this complex picture, a recent paper reported an inverse relationship between serum irisin levels and intima-media thickness in dialysis patients [165]. It is also well known that malnourished CKD patients have a worse outcome compared, not only with normally-nourished, but even obese CKD patients. Irisin levels have been found to be lower in CKD patients, and its concentrations were directly dependent on renal function and were related to the components of metabolic syndrome [166,167]. Furthermore, higher irisin levels were associated with sarcopenia in peritoneal dialysis patients [165]. On the basis of these considerations, irisin has been suggested as a candidate for the malnutrition status, often found in the more advanced stages of CKD. However, as for liver diseases, the role and the mechanisms by which irisin affects CKD remain to be further investigated.

7. Liver-Released Compounds

7.1. Selenoprotein P

Selenoprotein P (SeP; encoded by *SEPP1* in humans) is a secretory protein produced mainly by the liver [168,169] that functions as a selenium transporter from the liver to the rest of the body [170,171]. SeP functions as a hepatokine that contributes to insulin resistance in type 2 diabetes [172] (Figure 1). Importantly, the RNA interference-mediated knockdown of SeP improves insulin resistance and hyperglycemia in a mouse model of type 2 diabetes, suggesting the suppression of SeP production in the liver [173].

7.1.1. Selenoprotein P and Diet

SeP serum levels are directly correlated with the selenium (Se) diet supply (up to 0.1 mg/kg), and Se plays a pivotal role in homeostasis, with its inextricable U-shaped link with health status. Additional selenium intake may benefit people with low levels, whereas it may adversely affect those with adequate-to-high selenium levels. Individuals with serum or plasma selenium concentration of 122 μg/L or higher should not be supplemented with selenium [174].

7.1.2. Selenoprotein P and Exercise

SeP serum levels represent the biologically-active body Se-pool that was shown to slowly decrease during basic training in both trained and untrained individuals [175].

7.1.3. Selenoprotein P and Inflammation

SeP acts as an intracellular antioxidant in phagocytes, modulating inflammatory response via switching macrophage differentiation from M1 to M2 and, of consequence, limiting pathogenicity and oxidative damage [176,177]. On the other hand, SeP serum levels were shown to be lowered by acute-phase inflammatory response [178,179]. A systemic inflammatory response produces cytokines, inhibiting the expression of SEPP1 and reducing selenium levels; pro-inflammatory cytokines, downregulating the SELP promoter in vitro, can, overall, reduce the anti-inflammatory effects of SeP [180]. The interplay between SeP and inflammation may be the link of such a molecule with atherosclerosis, and some controversial epidemiologic data in type 2 diabetes exist [181]. Higher serum levels, inversely related to adiponectin and hepatic SeP concentrations, were reported in patients with type 2 diabetes, with a direct and independent link between SeP and both serum C-reactive protein levels and carotid intima-media thickness, while lower SeP expression was observed in murine adipocytes [173,182,183]. Differences in diabetes-related inflammation and the U-shaped association between SeP and type 2 diabetes risk, mimicking the U-shaped link of Se with health status, might explain some of the apparently contradictory epidemiologic findings. All of these data are worthy of further studies and validation, but indicate the key role of SeP in inflammatory-related cardiovascular alterations.

7.1.4. Selenoprotein P and NAFLD

SeP was found to be increased in NAFLD patients after correction for confounding factors [184]. However, the role of SeP in NAFLD remains to be well elucidated, even if they are able to act, as mentioned earlier, by their ability to modulate inflammatory response and insulin resistance.

In addition, different evidence suggests that metformin improves systemic insulin sensitivity through the regulation of SeP production, suggesting a novel potential therapeutic approach to treating type 2 diabetes [185].

7.1.5. Selenoprotein P and Kidney

SeP is the major carrier transporting selenium to target tissues and organs, including kidneys, were it is taken up by mechanisms, which are dependent, by specific receptor-related proteins [186]. According to Reinhardt and colleagues, in patients with CKD, SeP concentrations increase with impaired renal function (even after correction for age and CRP concentrations), whereas SeP concentrations are significantly lower in dialysis patients [187]. The reasons for the discrepant SeP concentrations among the stages of chronic renal failure are not yet completely defined, though the increased inflammatory status in dialysis patients [188] could play an important pathogenic role.

7.2. Fetuin-A

Human Fetuin-A/a2-Heremans-Schmid glycoprotein is an abundant 59-kDa serum glycoprotein, produced principally by the liver (thus, it can be classified as a "hepatokine"), and adipose tissue [189]. It works as a natural inhibitor of insulin receptors in the liver and skeletal muscle [190] and also exerts pro-adipogenic effects and suppresses adiponectin release [191]. Deletion of Fetuin-A improves insulin resistance and dyslipidemia and enhances glucose clearance in mice [192], whereas with genetic variants in humans, Fetuin-A has been associated with type 2 diabetes [193] and is linked with insulin action in adipocytes [194]. Serum Fetuin-A levels have been shown to correlate with metabolic syndrome and its main features [191].

7.2.1. Fetuin-A and Diet

In the general population, circulating Fetuin-A was decreased by alcohol intake and milk/dairy product intake, whereas meat and fish had no effect [195]. Resveratrol and curcumin intake may decrease Fetuin-A release [196].

7.2.2. Fetuin-A and Exercise

Short-term exercise training has been shown to reduce Fetuin-A levels, contributing to improvement in hepatic insulin sensitivity, especially in patients with NAFLD [197], although evidence concerning other exercise regimens is still controversial [198].

7.2.3. Fetuin-A and Inflammation

Fetuin-A does not seem to be directly regulated by inflammation, and no correlation was observed between hepatic inflammation and serum levels in patients with NAFLD [199].

7.2.4. Fetuin-A and NAFLD

Increased Fetuin-A has been reported in obese children and lean adults with NAFLD [199,200]. In patients with NAFLD, Fetuin-A levels were associated with the severity of steatosis, were influenced by genetic risk factors for hepatic fat accumulation and also correlated with insulin resistance and metabolic syndrome features [199]. Consistent with the above-mentioned lack of interplay between Fetuin-A and inflammatory response, no correlation was observed between hepatic inflammation and serum Fetuin-A levels in patients with NAFLD [189]. Fetuin-A could affect NAFLD/NASH because it is implicated in the development of insulin resistance and accelerated atherogenesis associated with fatty liver [199,201].

7.2.5. Fetuin-A and Kidney

Fetuin-A is also an inhibitor of vascular calcification, is progressively reduced in patients with renal failure and may modulate the progression of atherosclerosis in patients with chronic kidney disease [202].

8. Conclusions

Recent years have brought a great deal of new insights into the complex and dynamic interplay among the multiple effectors/mediators of fatty liver disease. Genomic, meta-genomic and metabolic profiling technologies and other top-down systems biology approaches are well suited for studies of metabolic syndrome and fatty liver disease. The appropriate analysis and interpretation of the physiopathological signatures require a new system of approaches to study and stratify the multifaceted clinical profiles of fatty liver and metabolic syndromes. Bio-statistical modeling will help to identify and combine genomic and meta-genomic determinants of the metabolic pathways and protein interaction networks. Similarly, the systems approach will help to stratify and re-define clinical phenotypes assessing the multiple nature of disease susceptibility and progression. The integration of metabolomic with genomic and meta-genomic markers will improve the understanding of metabolic syndrome and fatty liver disease, and the combined molecular and clinic-pathologic stratification of individuals with metabolic syndrome will allow redefining risks and prognoses, as well as identifying new diagnostic criteria, new markers of disease progression and new endpoints of clinical trials for specific groups of individuals with fatty liver.

Author Contributions: All authors contributed in preparing the draft; All authors revised the draft; All authors approved the final version of the manuscript.

Conflicts of Interest: The authors declare no conflicts of interest.

Abbreviations

AG	acylated ghrelin
AMPK	adenosine monophosphate-activated protein kinase
ANP	atrial natriuretic peptide
BAT	brown adipose tissue
BMI	body mass index
CIMT	carotid intima-media thickness
CKD	chronic kidney disease
CRP	C-reactive protein
DAG	diacyl glycerol
DeAG	des-acylated ghrelin
DKD	diabetic kidney disease
DNL	de novo lipogenesis
ELISA	enzyme-linked immunosorbent assay
FC	free cholesterol
FFA	free fatty acid
FNDC5	fibronectin type III domain-containing protein 5
FoxO3a	forkhead box O3a
FSGS	focal segmental glomerular sclerosis
GLP-1	glucagon-like peptide 1
GLP-1R	glucagon-like peptide 1 receptor
GNG	gluconeogenesis
GOAT	ghrelin-ghrelin *O*-acyltransferase
(Oct)-1	organic cation transporter
IR	insulin resistance
IS	insulin sensitive
JNK	c-Jun terminal kinase
LDL	low density lipoprotein
MRS	magnetic resonance spectroscopy
MS	metabolic syndrome
MUFA	monounsaturated fatty acids
NAFLD	non-alcoholic fatty liver disease
NASH	non-alcoholic steatohepatitis

NF-κB	nuclear factor kappa-light-chain-enhancer of activated B cells
NGT	normal glucose tolerance
NLRP3	nucleotide-binding domain, leucine-rich-containing family, pyrin domain-containing-3
NO	nitric oxide
OGTT	oral glucose tolerance test
PUFA	polyunsaturated fatty acids
SC	subcutaneous
Se	selenium
SeP	selenoprotein P
SEPP1	selenoprotein P, plasma 1
SFA	saturated fatty acids
T2D	type 2 diabetes
TLR	toll like receptors
TNF-α	tumor necrosis factor-α
UCP1	uncoupling protein 1
VS	visceral
VLDL	very low density lipoprotein
WAT	white adipose tissue

References

1. Groop, L.C.; Bonadonna, R.C.; DelPrato, S.; Ratheiser, K.; Zyck, K.; Ferrannini, E.; DeFronzo, R.A. Glucose and free fatty acid metabolism in non-insulin-dependent diabetes mellitus. Evidence for multiple sites of insulin resistance. *J. Clin. Investig.* **1989**, *84*, 205–213. [CrossRef] [PubMed]

2. Bugianesi, E.; Gastaldelli, A.; Vanni, E.; Gambino, R.; Cassader, M.; Baldi, S.; Ponti, V.; Pagano, G.; Ferrannini, E.; Rizzetto, M. Insulin resistance in non-diabetic patients with non-alcoholic fatty liver disease: Sites and mechanisms. *Diabetologia* **2005**, *48*, 634–642. [CrossRef] [PubMed]

3. Lafontan, M.; Langin, D. Lipolysis and lipid mobilization in human adipose tissue. *Prog. Lipid Res.* **2009**, *48*, 275–297. [CrossRef] [PubMed]

4. Ferrannini, E.; Camastra, S.; Coppack, S.W.; Fliser, D.; Golay, A.; Mitrakou, A. Insulin action and non-esterified fatty acids. The European Group for the Study of Insulin Resistance (EGIR). *Proc. Nutr. Soc.* **1997**, *56*, 753–761. [CrossRef] [PubMed]

5. Legrand-Poels, S.; Esser, N.; L'Homme, L.; Scheen, A.; Paquot, N.; Piette, J. Free fatty acids as modulators of the NLRP3 inflammasome in obesity/type 2 diabetes. *Biochem. Pharmacol.* **2014**, *92*, 131–141. [CrossRef] [PubMed]

6. Rocha, D.M.; Caldas, A.P.; Oliveira, L.L.; Bressan, J.; Hermsdorff, H.H. Saturated fatty acids trigger TLR4-mediated inflammatory response. *Atherosclerosis* **2016**, *244*, 211–215. [CrossRef] [PubMed]

7. Moreira, A.P.; Texeira, T.F.; Ferreira, A.B.; Peluzio Mdo, C.; Alfenas Rde, C. Influence of a high-fat diet on gut microbiota, intestinal permeability and metabolic endotoxaemia. *Br. J. Nutr.* **2012**, *108*, 801–809. [CrossRef] [PubMed]

8. Mittendorfer, B.; Yoshino, M.; Patterson, B.W.; Klein, S. VLDL triglyceride kinetics in lean, overweight, and obese men and women. *J. Clin. Endocrinol. Metab.* **2016**, *101*, 4151–4160. [CrossRef] [PubMed]

9. De Souza, R.J.; Mente, A.; Maroleanu, A.; Cozma, A.I.; Ha, V.; Kishibe, T.; Uleryk, E.; Budylowski, P.; Schunemann, H.; Beyene, J.; et al. Intake of saturated and trans unsaturated fatty acids and risk of all cause mortality, cardiovascular disease, and type 2 diabetes: Systematic review and meta-analysis of observational studies. *BMJ* **2015**, *351*, h3978. [CrossRef] [PubMed]

10. Patterson, E.; Wall, R.; Fitzgerald, G.F.; Ross, R.P.; Stanton, C. Health implications of high dietary omega-6 polyunsaturated Fatty acids. *J. Nutr. Metab.* **2012**, *2012*, 539426. [CrossRef] [PubMed]

11. Maehre, H.K.; Jensen, I.J.; Elvevoll, E.O.; Eilertsen, K.E. Omega-3 fatty acids and cardiovascular diseases: Effects, mechanisms and dietary relevance. *Int. J. Mol. Sci.* **2015**, *16*, 22636–22661. [CrossRef] [PubMed]

12. Romijn, J.A.; Coyle, E.F.; Sidossis, L.S.; Gastaldelli, A.; Horowitz, J.F.; Endert, E.; Wolfe, R.R. Regulation of endogenous fat and carbohydrate metabolism in relation to exercise intensity and duration. *Am. J. Physiol.* **1993**, *265*, E380–E391. [PubMed]

13. Boden, G. Fatty acid-induced inflammation and insulin resistance in skeletal muscle and liver. *Curr. Diabetes Rep.* **2006**, *6*, 177–181. [CrossRef]

14. Gadang, V.; Kohli, R.; Myronovych, A.; Hui, D.Y.; Perez-Tilve, D.; Jaeschke, A. MLK3 promotes metabolic dysfunction induced by saturated fatty acid-enriched diet. *Am. J. Physiol. Endocrinol. Metab.* **2013**, *305*, E549–E556. [CrossRef] [PubMed]

15. Leamy, A.K.; Egnatchik, R.A.; Shiota, M.; Ivanova, P.T.; Myers, D.S.; Brown, H.A.; Young, J.D. Enhanced synthesis of saturated phospholipids is associated with ER stress and lipotoxicity in palmitate treated hepatic cells. *J. Lipid Res.* **2014**, *55*, 1478–1488. [CrossRef] [PubMed]

16. Snodgrass, R.G.; Huang, S.; Choi, I.W.; Rutledge, J.C.; Hwang, D.H. Inflammasome-mediated secretion of IL-1β in human monocytes through TLR2 activation; modulation by dietary fatty acids. *J. Immunol.* **2013**, *191*, 4337–4347. [CrossRef] [PubMed]

17. Das, S.K.; Mondal, A.K.; Elbein, S.C. Distinct gene expression profiles characterize cellular responses to palmitate and oleate. *J. Lipid Res.* **2010**, *51*, 2121–2131. [CrossRef] [PubMed]

18. Yang, G.; Badeanlou, L.; Bielawski, J.; Roberts, A.J.; Hannun, Y.A.; Samad, F. Central role of ceramide biosynthesis in body weight regulation, energy metabolism, and the metabolic syndrome. *Am. J. Physiol. Endocrinol. Metab.* **2009**, *297*, E211–E224. [CrossRef] [PubMed]

19. Ussher, J.R.; Koves, T.R.; Cadete, V.J.; Zhang, L.; Jaswal, J.S.; Swyrd, S.J.; Lopaschuk, D.G.; Proctor, S.D.; Keung, W.; Muoio, D.M.; et al. Inhibition of de novo ceramide synthesis reverses diet-induced insulin resistance and enhances whole-body oxygen consumption. *Diabetes* **2010**, *59*, 2453–2464. [CrossRef] [PubMed]

20. Wei, Y.; Wang, D.; Topczewski, F.; Pagliassotti, M.J. Saturated fatty acids induce endoplasmic reticulum stress and apoptosis independently of ceramide in liver cells. *Am. J. Physiol. Endocrinol. Metab.* **2006**, *291*, E275–E281. [CrossRef] [PubMed]

21. Luukkonen, P.K.; Zhou, Y.; Sadevirta, S.; Leivonen, M.; Arola, J.; Oresic, M.; Hyotylainen, T.; Yki-Jarvinen, H. Hepatic ceramides dissociate steatosis and insulin resistance in patients with non-alcoholic fatty liver disease. *J. Hepatol.* **2016**, *64*, 1167–1175. [CrossRef] [PubMed]

22. Gregor, M.F.; Yang, L.; Fabbrini, E.; Mohammed, B.S.; Eagon, J.C.; Hotamisligil, G.S.; Klein, S. Endoplasmic reticulum stress is reduced in tissues of obese subjects after weight loss. *Diabetes* **2009**, *58*, 693–700. [CrossRef] [PubMed]

23. Mantzaris, M.D.; Tsianos, E.V.; Galaris, D. Interruption of triacylglycerol synthesis in the endoplasmic reticulum is the initiating event for saturated fatty acid-induced lipotoxicity in liver cells. *FEBS J.* **2011**, *278*, 519–530. [CrossRef] [PubMed]

24. Listenberger, L.L.; Han, X.; Lewis, S.E.; Cases, S.; Farese, R.V., Jr.; Ory, D.S.; Schaffer, J.E. Triglyceride accumulation protects against fatty acid-induced lipotoxicity. *Proc. Natl. Acad. Sci. USA* **2003**, *100*, 3077–3082. [CrossRef] [PubMed]

25. Saponaro, C.; Gaggini, M.; Carli, F.; Gastaldelli, A. The subtle balance between lipolysis and lipogenesis: A critical point in metabolic homeostasis. *Nutrients* **2015**, *7*, 9453–9474. [CrossRef] [PubMed]

26. Yamaguchi, K.; Yang, L.; McCall, S.; Huang, J.; Yu, X.X.; Pandey, S.K.; Bhanot, S.; Monia, B.P.; Li, Y.X.; Diehl, A.M. Inhibiting triglyceride synthesis improves hepatic steatosis but exacerbates liver damage and fibrosis in obese mice with nonalcoholic steatohepatitis. *Hepatology* **2007**, *45*, 1366–1374. [CrossRef] [PubMed]

27. Sieber, J.; Jehle, A.W. Free fatty acids and their metabolism affect function and survival of podocytes. *Front. Endocrinol.* **2014**, *5*, 186. [CrossRef] [PubMed]

28. Lennon, R.; Pons, D.; Sabin, M.A.; Wei, C.; Shield, J.P.; Coward, R.J.; Tavare, J.M.; Mathieson, P.W.; Saleem, M.A.; Welsh, G.I. Saturated fatty acids induce insulin resistance in human podocytes: Implications for diabetic nephropathy. *Nephrol. Dial. Transplant.* **2009**, *24*, 3288–3296. [CrossRef] [PubMed]

29. Sieber, J.; Lindenmeyer, M.T.; Kampe, K.; Campbell, K.N.; Cohen, C.D.; Hopfer, H.; Mundel, P.; Jehle, A.W. Regulation of podocyte survival and endoplasmic reticulum stress by fatty acids. *Am. J. Physiol. Ren. Physiol.* **2010**, *299*, F821–F829. [CrossRef] [PubMed]

30. Ioannou, G.N. The role of cholesterol in the pathogenesis of NASH. *Trends Endocrinol. Metab.* **2016**, *27*, 84–95. [CrossRef] [PubMed]

31. Janoudi, A.; Shamoun, F.E.; Kalavakunta, J.K.; Abela, G.S. Cholesterol crystal induced arterial inflammation and destabilization of atherosclerotic plaque. *Eur. Heart J.* **2016**, *37*, 1959–1967. [CrossRef] [PubMed]

32. Tall, A.R.; Yvan-Charvet, L. Cholesterol, inflammation and innate immunity. *Nat. Rev. Immunol.* **2015**, *15*, 104–116. [CrossRef] [PubMed]

33. Keys, A. Coronary heart disease, serum cholesterol, and the diet. *Acta Med. Scand.* **1980**, *207*, 153–160. [CrossRef] [PubMed]

34. Franklin, B.A.; Durstine, J.L.; Roberts, C.K.; Barnard, R.J. Impact of diet and exercise on lipid management in the modern era. *Best Pract. Res. Clin. Endocrinol. Metab.* **2014**, *28*, 405–421. [CrossRef] [PubMed]

35. Virtanen, J.K.; Mursu, J.; Virtanen, H.E.; Fogelholm, M.; Salonen, J.T.; Koskinen, T.T.; Voutilainen, S.; Tuomainen, T.P. Associations of egg and cholesterol intakes with carotid intima-media thickness and risk of incident coronary artery disease according to apolipoprotein E phenotype in men: The Kuopio Ischaemic Heart Disease Risk Factor Study. *Am. J. Clin. Nutr.* **2016**, *103*, 895–901. [CrossRef] [PubMed]

36. Caesar, R.; Nygren, H.; Oresic, M.; Backhed, F. Interaction between dietary lipids and gut microbiota regulates hepatic cholesterol metabolism. *J. Lipid Res.* **2016**, *57*, 474–481. [CrossRef] [PubMed]

37. Mann, S.; Beedie, C.; Jimenez, A. Differential effects of aerobic exercise, resistance training and combined exercise modalities on cholesterol and the lipid profile: Review, synthesis and recommendations. *Sports Med.* **2014**, *44*, 211–221. [CrossRef] [PubMed]

38. O'Donovan, G.; Owen, A.; Bird, S.R.; Kearney, E.M.; Nevill, A.M.; Jones, D.W.; Woolf-May, K. Changes in cardiorespiratory fitness and coronary heart disease risk factors following 24 wk of moderate- or high-intensity exercise of equal energy cost. *J. Appl. Physiol.* **2005**, *98*, 1619–1625. [CrossRef] [PubMed]

39. Lira, F.S.; Yamashita, A.S.; Uchida, M.C.; Zanchi, N.E.; Gualano, B.; Martins, E., Jr.; Caperuto, E.C.; Seelaender, M. Low and moderate, rather than high intensity strength exercise induces benefit regarding plasma lipid profile. *Diabetol. Metab. Syndr.* **2010**, *2*, 31. [CrossRef] [PubMed]

40. Katzmarzyk, P.T.; Leon, A.S.; Rankinen, T.; Gagnon, J.; Skinner, J.S.; Wilmore, J.H.; Rao, D.C.; Bouchard, C. Changes in blood lipids consequent to aerobic exercise training related to changes in body fatness and aerobic fitness. *Metabolism* **2001**, *50*, 841–848. [CrossRef] [PubMed]

41. Li, Y.; Schwabe, R.F.; Devries-Seimon, T.; Yao, P.M.; Gerbod-Giannone, M.C.; Tall, A.R.; Davis, R.J.; Flavell, R.; Brenner, D.A.; Tabas, I. Free cholesterol-loaded macrophages are an abundant source of tumor necrosis factor-α and interleukin-6: Model of NF-κB and map kinase-dependent inflammation in advanced atherosclerosis. *J. Biol. Chem.* **2005**, *280*, 21763–21772. [CrossRef] [PubMed]

42. Puri, P.; Baillie, R.A.; Wiest, M.M.; Mirshahi, F.; Choudhury, J.; Cheung, O.; Sargeant, C.; Contos, M.J.; Sanyal, A.J. A lipidomic analysis of nonalcoholic fatty liver disease. *Hepatology* **2007**, *46*, 1081–1090. [CrossRef] [PubMed]

43. Min, H.K.; Kapoor, A.; Fuchs, M.; Mirshahi, F.; Zhou, H.; Maher, J.; Kellum, J.; Warnick, R.; Contos, M.J.; Sanyal, A.J. Increased hepatic synthesis and dysregulation of cholesterol metabolism is associated with the severity of nonalcoholic fatty liver disease. *Cell Metab.* **2012**, *15*, 665–674. [CrossRef] [PubMed]

44. Dongiovanni, P.; Petta, S.; Maglio, C.; Fracanzani, A.L.; Pipitone, R.; Mozzi, E.; Motta, B.M.; Kaminska, D.; Rametta, R.; Grimaudo, S.; et al. Transmembrane 6 superfamily member 2 gene variant disentangles nonalcoholic steatohepatitis from cardiovascular disease. *Hepatology* **2015**, *61*, 506–514. [CrossRef] [PubMed]

45. Wahl, P.; Ducasa, G.M.; Fornoni, A. Systemic and renal lipids in kidney disease development and progression. *Am. J. Physiol. Ren. Physiol.* **2016**, *310*, F433–F445. [CrossRef] [PubMed]

46. Lee, H.S.; Kruth, H.S. Accumulation of cholesterol in the lesions of focal segmental glomerulosclerosis. *Nephrology* **2003**, *8*, 224–223. [CrossRef] [PubMed]

47. Fornoni, A.; Merscher, S.; Kopp, J.B. Lipid biology of the podocyte—New perspectives offer new opportunities. *Nat. Rev. Nephrol.* **2014**, *10*, 379–388. [CrossRef] [PubMed]

48. Wang, X.X.; Jiang, T.; Shen, Y.; Caldas, Y.; Miyazaki-Anzai, S.; Santamaria, H.; Urbanek, C.; Solis, N.; Scherzer, P.; Lewis, L.; et al. Diabetic nephropathy is accelerated by farnesoid X receptor deficiency and inhibited by farnesoid X receptor activation in a type 1 diabetes model. *Diabetes* **2010**, *59*, 2916–2927. [CrossRef] [PubMed]

49. Kopp, J.B.; Smith, M.W.; Nelson, G.W.; Johnson, R.C.; Freedman, B.I.; Bowden, D.W.; Oleksyk, T.; McKenzie, L.M.; Kajiyama, H.; Ahuja, T.S.; et al. MYH9 is a major-effect risk gene for focal segmental glomerulosclerosis. *Nat. Genet.* **2008**, *40*, 1175–1184. [CrossRef] [PubMed]

50. Kiss, E.; Kranzlin, B.; Wagenblabeta, K.; Bonrouhi, M.; Thiery, J.; Grone, E.; Nordstrom, V.; Teupser, D.; Gretz, N.; Malle, E.; et al. Lipid droplet accumulation is associated with an increase in hyperglycemia-induced renal damage: Prevention by liver X receptors. *Am. J. Pathol.* **2013**, *182*, 727–741. [CrossRef] [PubMed]

51. Agarwal, R. Effects of statins on renal function. *Am. J. Cardiol.* **2006**, *97*, 748–755. [CrossRef] [PubMed]

52. Nigro, E.; Scudiero, O.; Monaco, M.L.; Palmieri, A.; Mazzarella, G.; Costagliola, C.; Bianco, A.; Daniele, A. New insight into adiponectin role in obesity and obesity-related diseases. *BioMed Res. Int.* **2014**, *2014*, 658913. [CrossRef] [PubMed]

53. Scherer, P.E. The multifaceted roles of adipose tissue-therapeutic targets for diabetes and beyond: The 2015 banting lecture. *Diabetes* **2016**, *65*, 1452–1461. [CrossRef] [PubMed]

54. Freitas Lima, L.C.; Braga, V.A.; do Socorro de Franca Silva, M.; Cruz, J.C.; Sousa Santos, S.H.; de Oliveira Monteiro, M.M.; Balarini, C.M. Adipokines, diabetes and atherosclerosis: An inflammatory association. *Front. Physiol.* **2015**, *6*, 304. [CrossRef] [PubMed]

55. Von Frankenberg, A.D.; Silva, F.M.; de Almeida, J.C.; Piccoli, V.; do Nascimento, F.V.; Sost, M.M.; Leitao, C.B.; Remonti, L.L.; Umpierre, D.; Reis, A.F.; et al. Effect of dietary lipids on circulating adiponectin: A systematic review with meta-analysis of randomised controlled trials. *Br. J. Nutr.* **2014**, *112*, 1235–1250. [CrossRef] [PubMed]

56. Kamari, Y.; Grossman, E.; Oron-Herman, M.; Peleg, E.; Shabtay, Z.; Shamiss, A.; Sharabi, Y. Metabolic stress with a high carbohydrate diet increases adiponectin levels. *Horm. Metab. Res.* **2007**, *39*, 384–388. [CrossRef] [PubMed]

57. Rezvani, R.; Cianflone, K.; McGahan, J.P.; Berglund, L.; Bremer, A.A.; Keim, N.L.; Griffen, S.C.; Havel, P.J.; Stanhope, K.L. Effects of sugar-sweetened beverages on plasma acylation stimulating protein, leptin and adiponectin: Relationships with metabolic outcomes. *Obesity* **2013**, *21*, 2471–2480. [CrossRef] [PubMed]

58. Swarbrick, M.M.; Havel, P.J. Physiological, pharmacological, and nutritional regulation of circulating adiponectin concentrations in humans. *Metab. Syndr. Relat. Disord.* **2008**, *6*, 87–102. [CrossRef] [PubMed]

59. Golbidi, S.; Laher, I. Exercise induced adipokine changes and the metabolic syndrome. *J. Diabetes Res.* **2014**, *2014*, 726861. [CrossRef] [PubMed]

60. Ahmadi, N.; Eshaghian, S.; Huizenga, R.; Sosnin, K.; Ebrahimi, R.; Siegel, R. Effects of intense exercise and moderate caloric restriction on cardiovascular risk factors and inflammation. *Am. J. Med.* **2011**, *124*, 978–982. [CrossRef] [PubMed]

61. Fantuzzi, G. Adiponectin and inflammation: Consensus and controversy. *J. Allergy Clin. Immunol.* **2008**, *121*, 326–330. [CrossRef] [PubMed]

62. Bugianesi, E.; Pagotto, U.; Manini, R.; Vanni, E.; Gastaldelli, A.; de Iasio, R.; Gentilcore, E.; Natale, S.; Cassader, M.; Rizzetto, M.; et al. Plasma adiponectin in nonalcoholic fatty liver is related to hepatic insulin resistance and hepatic fat content, not to liver disease severity. *J. Clin. Endocrinol. Metab.* **2005**, *90*, 3498–3504. [CrossRef] [PubMed]

63. Gastaldelli, A.; Harrison, S.; Belfort-Aguiar, R.; Hardies, J.; Balas, B.; Schenker, S.; Cusi, K. Pioglitazone in the treatment of NASH: The role of adiponectin. *Aliment. Pharmacol. Ther.* **2010**, *32*, 769–775. [CrossRef] [PubMed]

64. Kadowaki, T.; Yamauchi, T. Adiponectin and adiponectin receptors. *Endocr. Rev.* **2005**, *26*, 439–451. [CrossRef] [PubMed]

65. Yano, Y.; Hoshide, S.; Ishikawa, J.; Hashimoto, T.; Eguchi, K.; Shimada, K.; Kario, K. Differential impacts of adiponectin on low-grade albuminuria between obese and nonobese persons without diabetes. *J. Clin. Hypertens.* **2007**, *9*, 775–782. [CrossRef]

66. Ohashi, K.; Iwatani, H.; Kihara, S.; Nakagawa, Y.; Komura, N.; Fujita, K.; Maeda, N.; Nishida, M.; Katsube, F.; Shimomura, I.; et al. Exacerbation of albuminuria and renal fibrosis in subtotal renal ablation model of adiponectin-knockout mice. *Arterioscler. Thromb. Vasc. Biol.* **2007**, *27*, 1910–1917. [CrossRef] [PubMed]

67. Sharma, K.; Ramachandrarao, S.; Qiu, G.; Usui, H.K.; Zhu, Y.; Dunn, S.R.; Ouedraogo, R.; Hough, K.; McCue, P.; Chan, L.; et al. Adiponectin regulates albuminuria and podocyte function in mice. *J. Clin. Investig.* **2008**, *118*, 1645–1656. [CrossRef] [PubMed]

68. Iwashima, Y.; Horio, T.; Kumada, M.; Suzuki, Y.; Kihara, S.; Rakugi, H.; Kawano, Y.; Funahashi, T.; Ogihara, T. Adiponectin and renal function, and implication as a risk of cardiovascular disease. *Am. J. Cardiol.* **2006**, *98*, 1603–1608. [CrossRef] [PubMed]

69. Ignacy, W.; Chudek, J.; Adamczak, M.; Funahashi, T.; Matsuzawa, Y.; Kokot, F.; Wiecek, A. Reciprocal association of plasma adiponectin and serum C-reactive protein concentration in haemodialysis patients with end-stage kidney disease—A follow-up study. *Nephron Clin. Pract.* **2005**, *101*, c18–c24. [CrossRef] [PubMed]

70. Marchlewska, A.; Stenvinkel, P.; Lindholm, B.; Danielsson, A.; Pecoits-Filho, R.; Lonnqvist, F.; Schalling, M.; Heimburger, O.; Nordfors, L. Reduced gene expression of adiponectin in fat tissue from patients with end-stage renal disease. *Kidney Int.* **2004**, *66*, 46–50. [CrossRef] [PubMed]

71. Izadi, V.; Saraf-Bank, S.; Azadbakht, L. Dietary intakes and leptin concentrations. *ARYA Atheroscler.* **2014**, *10*, 266–272. [PubMed]

72. Gastaldelli, A.; Sironi, A.M.; Ciociaro, D.; Positano, V.; Buzzigoli, E.; Giannessi, D.; Lombardi, M.; Mari, A.; Ferrannini, E. Visceral fat and beta cell function in non-diabetic humans. *Diabetologia* **2005**, *48*, 2090–2096. [CrossRef] [PubMed]

73. Maffei, M.; Halaas, J.; Ravussin, E.; Pratley, R.E.; Lee, G.H.; Zhang, Y.; Fei, H.; Kim, S.; Lallone, R.; Ranganathan, S.; et al. Leptin levels in human and rodent: Measurement of plasma leptin and ob RNA in obese and weight-reduced subjects. *Nat. Med.* **1995**, *1*, 1155–1161. [CrossRef] [PubMed]

74. Adya, R.; Tan, B.K.; Randeva, H.S. Differential effects of leptin and adiponectin in endothelial angiogenesis. *J. Diabetes Res.* **2015**, *2015*, 648239. [CrossRef] [PubMed]

75. Martin, L.J.; Siliart, B.; Lutz, T.A.; Biourge, V.; Nguyen, P.; Dumon, H.J. Postprandial response of plasma insulin, amylin and acylated ghrelin to various test meals in lean and obese cats. *Br. J. Nutr.* **2010**, *103*, 1610–1619. [CrossRef] [PubMed]

76. Hall, M.E.; Harmancey, R.; Stec, D.E. Lean heart: Role of leptin in cardiac hypertrophy and metabolism. *World J. Cardiol.* **2015**, *7*, 511–524. [PubMed]

77. Masquio, D.C.; de Piano, A.; Sanches, P.L.; Corgosinho, F.C.; Campos, R.M.; Carnier, J.; da Silva, P.L.; Caranti, D.A.; Tock, L.; Oyama, L.M.; et al. The effect of weight loss magnitude on pro-/anti-inflammatory adipokines and carotid intima-media thickness in obese adolescents engaged in interdisciplinary weight loss therapy. *Clin. Endocrinol.* **2013**, *79*, 55–64. [CrossRef] [PubMed]

78. La Cava, A.; Matarese, G. The weight of leptin in immunity. *Nat. Rev. Immunol.* **2004**, *4*, 371–379. [CrossRef] [PubMed]

79. Cumin, F.; Baum, H.P.; de Gasparo, M.; Levens, N. Removal of endogenous leptin from the circulation by the kidney. *Int. J. Obes. Relat. Metab. Disord.* **1997**, *21*, 495–504. [CrossRef] [PubMed]

80. Stenvinkel, P.; Lindholm, B.; Lonnqvist, F.; Katzarski, K.; Heimburger, O. Increases in serum leptin levels during peritoneal dialysis are associated with inflammation and a decrease in lean body mass. *J. Am. Soc. Nephrol.* **2000**, *11*, 1303–1309. [PubMed]

81. Polyzos, S.A.; Aronis, K.N.; Kountouras, J.; Raptis, D.D.; Vasiloglou, M.F.; Mantzoros, C.S. Circulating leptin in non-alcoholic fatty liver disease: A systematic review and meta-analysis. *Diabetologia* **2016**, *59*, 30–43. [CrossRef] [PubMed]

82. Mak, R.H.; Cheung, W.; Cone, R.D.; Marks, D.L. Leptin and inflammation-associated cachexia in chronic kidney disease. *Kidney Int.* **2006**, *69*, 794–797. [CrossRef] [PubMed]

83. Carrero, J.J.; Nakashima, A.; Qureshi, A.R.; Lindholm, B.; Heimburger, O.; Barany, P.; Stenvinkel, P. Protein-energy wasting modifies the association of ghrelin with inflammation, leptin, and mortality in hemodialysis patients. *Kidney Int.* **2011**, *79*, 749–756. [CrossRef] [PubMed]

84. Gastaldelli, A.; Cusi, K.; Pettiti, M.; Hardies, J.; Miyazaki, Y.; Berria, R.; Buzzigoli, E.; Sironi, A.M.; Cersosimo, E.; Ferrannini, E.; et al. Relationship between hepatic/visceral fat and hepatic insulin resistance in nondiabetic and type 2 diabetic subjects. *Gastroenterology* **2007**, *133*, 496–506. [CrossRef] [PubMed]

85. Gastaldelli, A.; Baldi, S.; Pettiti, M.; Toschi, E.; Camastra, S.; Natali, A.; Landau, B.R.; Ferrannini, E. Influence of obesity and type 2 diabetes on gluconeogenesis and glucose output in humans: A quantitative study. *Diabetes* **2000**, *49*, 1367–1373. [CrossRef] [PubMed]

86. Khodabandehloo, H.; Gorgani-Firuzjaee, S.; Panahi, G.; Meshkani, R. Molecular and cellular mechanisms linking inflammation to insulin resistance and β-cell dysfunction. *Transl. Res.* **2016**, *167*, 228–256. [CrossRef] [PubMed]

87. Keane, K.N.; Cruzat, V.F.; Carlessi, R.; de Bittencourt, P.I., Jr.; Newsholme, P. Molecular events linking oxidative stress and inflammation to insulin resistance and β-cell dysfunction. *Oxid. Med. Cell. Longev.* **2015**, *2015*, 181643. [CrossRef] [PubMed]

88. Chen, L.; Chen, R. Mechanisms linking inflammation to insulin resistance. *Int. J. Endocrinol.* **2015**, *2015*, 508409. [CrossRef] [PubMed]

89. Lindgren, O.; Pacini, G.; Tura, A.; Holst, J.J.; Deacon, C.F.; Ahren, B. Incretin effect after oral amino acid ingestion in humans. *J. Clin. Endocrinol. Metab.* **2015**, *100*, 1172–1176. [CrossRef] [PubMed]

90. Dobbins, R.L.; Szczepaniak, L.S.; Myhill, J.; Tamura, Y.; Uchino, H.; Giacca, A.; McGarry, J.D. The composition of dietary fat directly influences glucose-stimulated insulin secretion in rats. *Diabetes* **2002**, *51*, 1825–1833. [CrossRef] [PubMed]

91. Kashyap, S.; Belfort, R.; Gastaldelli, A.; Pratipanawatr, T.; Berria, R.; Pratipanawatr, W.; Bajaj, M.; Mandarino, L.; DeFronzo, R.; Cusi, K. A sustained increase in plasma free fatty acids impairs insulin secretion in nondiabetic subjects genetically predisposed to develop type 2 diabetes. *Diabetes* **2003**, *52*, 2461–2474. [CrossRef] [PubMed]

92. Hyotylainen, T.; Jerby, L.; Petaja, E.M.; Mattila, I.; Jantti, S.; Auvinen, P.; Gastaldelli, A.; Yki-Jarvinen, H.; Ruppin, E.; Oresic, M. Genome-scale study reveals reduced metabolic adaptability in patients with non-alcoholic fatty liver disease. *Nat. Commun.* **2016**, *7*, 8994. [CrossRef] [PubMed]

93. Donnelly, K.L.; Smith, C.I.; Schwarzenberg, S.J.; Jessurun, J.; Boldt, M.D.; Parks, E.J. Sources of fatty acids stored in liver and secreted via lipoproteins in patients with nonalcoholic fatty liver disease. *J. Clin. Investig.* **2005**, *115*, 1343–1351. [CrossRef] [PubMed]

94. Paradis, V.; Perlemuter, G.; Bonvoust, F.; Dargere, D.; Parfait, B.; Vidaud, M.; Conti, M.; Huet, S.; Ba, N.; Buffet, C.; et al. High glucose and hyperinsulinemia stimulate connective tissue growth factor expression: A potential mechanism involved in progression to fibrosis in nonalcoholic steatohepatitis. *Hepatology* **2001**, *34*, 738–744. [CrossRef] [PubMed]

95. Svegliati-Baroni, G.; Ridolfi, F.; Di Sario, A.; Casini, A.; Marucci, L.; Gaggiotti, G.; Orlandoni, P.; Macarri, G.; Perego, L.; Benedetti, A.; et al. Insulin and insulin-like growth factor-1 stimulate proliferation and type I collagen accumulation by human hepatic stellate cells: Differential effects on signal transduction pathways. *Hepatology* **1999**, *29*, 1743–1751. [CrossRef] [PubMed]

96. Coggan, A.R.; Raguso, C.A.; Gastaldelli, A.; Williams, B.D.; Wolfe, R.R. Regulation of glucose production during exercise at 80% of VO$_2$ peak in untrained humans. *Am. J. Physiol.* **1997**, *273*, E348–E354. [PubMed]

97. Cabrera, O.; Berman, D.M.; Kenyon, N.S.; Ricordi, C.; Berggren, P.O.; Caicedo, A. The unique cytoarchitecture of human pancreatic islets has implications for islet cell function. *Proc. Natl. Acad. Sci. USA* **2006**, *103*, 2334–2339. [CrossRef] [PubMed]

98. Wewer Albrechtsen, N.J.; Kuhre, R.E.; Pedersen, J.; Knop, F.K.; Holst, J.J. The biology of glucagon and the consequences of hyperglucagonemia. *Biomark. Med.* **2016**, *10*, 1141–1151. [CrossRef] [PubMed]

99. Unger, R.H. Glucagon physiology and pathophysiology in the light of new advances. *Diabetologia* **1985**, *28*, 574–578. [CrossRef] [PubMed]

100. Gromada, J.; Franklin, I.; Wollheim, C.B. α-Cells of the endocrine pancreas: 35 years of research but the enigma remains. *Endocr. Rev.* **2007**, *28*, 84–116. [CrossRef] [PubMed]

101. Mitrakou, A.; Ryan, C.; Veneman, T.; Mokan, M.; Jenssen, T.; Kiss, I.; Durrant, J.; Cryer, P.; Gerich, J. Hierarchy of glycemic thresholds for counterregulatory hormone secretion, symptoms, and cerebral dysfunction. *Am. J. Physiol.* **1991**, *260*, E67–E74. [PubMed]

102. Bagger, J.I.; Knop, F.K.; Lund, A.; Holst, J.J.; Vilsboll, T. Glucagon responses to increasing oral loads of glucose and corresponding isoglycaemic intravenous glucose infusions in patients with type 2 diabetes and healthy individuals. *Diabetologia* **2014**, *57*, 1720–1725. [CrossRef] [PubMed]

103. Rocha, D.M.; Faloona, G.R.; Unger, R.H. Glucagon-stimulating activity of 20 amino acids in dogs. *J. Clin. Investig.* **1972**, *51*, 2346–2351. [CrossRef] [PubMed]

104. Palmer, J.P.; Benson, J.W.; Walter, R.M.; Ensinck, J.W. Arginine-stimulated acute phase of insulin and glucagon secretion in diabetic subjects. *J. Clin. Investig.* **1976**, *58*, 565–570. [CrossRef] [PubMed]

105. Radulescu, A.; Gannon, M.C.; Nuttall, F.Q. The effect on glucagon, glucagon-like peptide-1, total and acyl-ghrelin of dietary fats ingested with and without potato. *J. Clin. Endocrinol. Metab.* **2010**, *95*, 3385–3391. [CrossRef] [PubMed]

106. Hippen, A.R. Glucagon as a potential therapy for ketosis and fatty liver. *Vet. Clin. N. Am. Food Anim. Pract.* **2000**, *16*, 267–282. [CrossRef]

107. Jiang, G.; Zhang, B.B. Glucagon and regulation of glucose metabolism. *Am. J. Physiol. Endocrinol. Metab.* **2003**, *284*, E671–E678. [CrossRef] [PubMed]

108. Conarello, S.L.; Jiang, G.; Mu, J.; Li, Z.; Woods, J.; Zycband, E.; Ronan, J.; Liu, F.; Roy, R.S.; Zhu, L.; et al. Glucagon receptor knockout mice are resistant to diet-induced obesity and streptozotocin-mediated beta cell loss and hyperglycaemia. *Diabetologia* **2007**, *50*, 142–150. [CrossRef] [PubMed]

109. Junker, A.E.; Gluud, L.; Holst, J.J.; Knop, F.K.; Vilsboll, T. Diabetic and nondiabetic patients with nonalcoholic fatty liver disease have an impaired incretin effect and fasting hyperglucagonaemia. *J. Intern. Med.* **2016**, *279*, 485–493. [CrossRef] [PubMed]

110. Liang, Y.; Osborne, M.C.; Monia, B.P.; Bhanot, S.; Gaarde, W.A.; Reed, C.; She, P.; Jetton, T.L.; Demarest, K.T. Reduction in glucagon receptor expression by an antisense oligonucleotide ameliorates diabetic syndrome in *db/db* mice. *Diabetes* **2004**, *53*, 410–417. [CrossRef] [PubMed]

111. Ortega, F.J.; Moreno-Navarrete, J.M.; Sabater, M.; Ricart, W.; Fruhbeck, G.; Fernandez-Real, J.M. Circulating glucagon is associated with inflammatory mediators in metabolically compromised subjects. *Eur. J. Endocrinol.* **2011**, *165*, 639–645. [CrossRef] [PubMed]

112. Dandona, P.; Ghanim, H.; Abuaysheh, S.; Green, K.; Batra, M.; Dhindsa, S.; Makdissi, A.; Patel, R.; Chaudhuri, A. Decreased insulin secretion and incretin concentrations and increased glucagon concentrations after a high-fat meal when compared with a high-fruit and -fiber meal. *Am. J. Physiol. Endocrinol. Metab.* **2015**, *308*, E185–E191. [CrossRef] [PubMed]

113. Pedersen, B.K.; Steensberg, A.; Schjerling, P. Exercise and interleukin-6. *Curr. Opin. Hematol.* **2001**, *8*, 137–141. [CrossRef] [PubMed]

114. Bastard, J.P.; Maachi, M.; Van Nhieu, J.T.; Jardel, C.; Bruckert, E.; Grimaldi, A.; Robert, J.J.; Capeau, J.; Hainque, B. Adipose tissue IL-6 content correlates with resistance to insulin activation of glucose uptake both in vivo and in vitro. *J. Clin. Endocrinol. Metab.* **2002**, *87*, 2084–2089. [CrossRef] [PubMed]

115. Hirano, T. Interleukin 6 in autoimmune and inflammatory diseases: A personal memoir. *Proc. Jpn. Acad. Ser. B Phys. Biol. Sci.* **2010**, *86*, 717–730. [CrossRef] [PubMed]

116. Tweedell, A.; Mulligan, K.X.; Martel, J.E.; Chueh, F.Y.; Santomango, T.; McGuinness, O.P. Metabolic response to endotoxin in vivo in the conscious mouse: Role of interleukin-6. *Metabolism* **2011**, *60*, 92–98. [CrossRef] [PubMed]

117. Campbell, J.E.; Drucker, D.J. Pharmacology, physiology, and mechanisms of incretin hormone action. *Cell Metab.* **2013**, *17*, 819–837. [CrossRef] [PubMed]

118. Holst, J.J. Enteroendocrine secretion of gut hormones in diabetes, obesity and after bariatric surgery. *Curr. Opin. Pharmacol.* **2013**, *13*, 983–988. [CrossRef] [PubMed]

119. Fava, S. Glucagon-like peptide 1 and the cardiovascular system. *Curr. Diabetes Rev.* **2014**, *10*, 302–310. [CrossRef] [PubMed]

120. Unger, R.H.; Ohneda, A.; Valverde, I.; Eisentraut, A.M.; Exton, J. Characterization of the responses of circulating glucagon-like immunoreactivity to intraduodenal and intravenous administration of glucose. *J. Clin. Investig.* **1968**, *47*, 48–65. [CrossRef] [PubMed]

121. McAlpine, C.S.; Bowes, A.J.; Werstuck, G.H. Diabetes, hyperglycemia and accelerated atherosclerosis: Evidence supporting a role for endoplasmic reticulum (ER) stress signaling. *Cardiovasc. Hematol. Disord. Drug Targets* **2010**, *10*, 151–157. [CrossRef] [PubMed]

122. Lee, S.S.; Yoo, J.H.; So, Y.S. Effect of the low- versus high-intensity exercise training on endoplasmic reticulum stress and GLP-1 in adolescents with type 2 diabetes mellitus. *J. Phys. Ther. Sci.* **2015**, *27*, 3063–3068. [CrossRef] [PubMed]

123. Kodera, R.; Shikata, K.; Kataoka, H.U.; Takatsuka, T.; Miyamoto, S.; Sasaki, M.; Kajitani, N.; Nishishita, S.; Sarai, K.; Hirota, D.; et al. Glucagon-like peptide-1 receptor agonist ameliorates renal injury through its anti-inflammatory action without lowering blood glucose level in a rat model of type 1 diabetes. *Diabetologia* **2011**, *54*, 965–978. [CrossRef] [PubMed]

124. Arakawa, M.; Mita, T.; Azuma, K.; Ebato, C.; Goto, H.; Nomiyama, T.; Fujitani, Y.; Hirose, T.; Kawamori, R.; Watada, H. Inhibition of monocyte adhesion to endothelial cells and attenuation of atherosclerotic lesion by a glucagon-like peptide-1 receptor agonist, exendin-4. *Diabetes* **2010**, *59*, 1030–1037. [CrossRef] [PubMed]

125. Varanasi, A.; Patel, P.; Makdissi, A.; Dhindsa, S.; Chaudhuri, A.; Dandona, P. Clinical use of liraglutide in type 2 diabetes and its effects on cardiovascular risk factors. *Endocr. Pract.* **2012**, *18*, 140–145. [CrossRef] [PubMed]

126. Lehrskov-Schmidt, L.; Lehrskov-Schmidt, L.; Nielsen, S.T.; Holst, J.J.; Moller, K.; Solomon, T.P. The effects of TNF-α on GLP-1-stimulated plasma glucose kinetics. *J. Clin. Endocrinol. Metab.* **2015**, *100*, E616–E622. [CrossRef] [PubMed]

127. Gupta, N.A.; Mells, J.; Dunham, R.M.; Grakoui, A.; Handy, J.; Saxena, N.K.; Anania, F.A. Glucagon-like peptide-1 receptor is present on human hepatocytes and has a direct role in decreasing hepatic steatosis in vitro by modulating elements of the insulin signaling pathway. *Hepatology* **2010**, *51*, 1584–1592. [CrossRef] [PubMed]

128. Svegliati-Baroni, G.; Saccomanno, S.; Rychlicki, C.; Agostinelli, L.; de Minicis, S.; Candelaresi, C.; Faraci, G.; Pacetti, D.; Vivarelli, M.; Nicolini, D.; et al. Glucagon-like peptide-1 receptor activation stimulates hepatic lipid oxidation and restores hepatic signalling alteration induced by a high-fat diet in nonalcoholic steatohepatitis. *Liver Int.* **2011**, *31*, 1285–1297. [CrossRef] [PubMed]

129. Klonoff, D.C.; Buse, J.B.; Nielsen, L.L.; Guan, X.; Bowlus, C.L.; Holcombe, J.H.; Wintle, M.E.; Maggs, D.G. Exenatide effects on diabetes, obesity, cardiovascular risk factors and hepatic biomarkers in patients with type 2 diabetes treated for at least 3 years. *Curr. Med. Res. Opin.* **2008**, *24*, 275–286. [CrossRef] [PubMed]

130. Cuthbertson, D.J.; Irwin, A.; Gardner, C.J.; Daousi, C.; Purewal, T.; Furlong, N.; Goenka, N.; Thomas, E.L.; Adams, V.L.; Pushpakom, S.P.; et al. Improved glycaemia correlates with liver fat reduction in obese, type 2 diabetes, patients given glucagon-like peptide-1 (GLP-1) receptor agonists. *PLoS ONE* **2012**, *7*, e50117. [CrossRef] [PubMed]

131. Kenny, P.R.; Brady, D.E.; Torres, D.M.; Ragozzino, L.; Chalasani, N.; Harrison, S.A. Exenatide in the treatment of diabetic patients with non-alcoholic steatohepatitis: A case series. *Am. J. Gastroenterol.* **2010**, *105*, 2707–2709. [CrossRef] [PubMed]

132. Armstrong, M.J.; Gaunt, P.; Aithal, G.P.; Barton, D.; Hull, D.; Parker, R.; Hazlehurst, J.M.; Guo, K.; LEAN trial team; Abouda, G.; et al. Liraglutide safety and efficacy in patients with non-alcoholic steatohepatitis (LEAN): A multicentre, double-blind, randomised, placebo-controlled phase 2 study. *Lancet* **2015**, *387*, 679–690. [CrossRef]

133. Gastaldelli, A.; Marchesini, G. Time for Glucagon like peptide-1 receptor agonists treatment for patients with NAFLD? *J. Hepatol.* **2016**, *64*, 262–264. [CrossRef] [PubMed]

134. Jendle, J.; Nauck, M.A.; Matthews, D.R.; Frid, A.; Hermansen, K.; During, M.; Zdravkovic, M.; Strauss, B.J.; Garber, A.J.; LEAD-2 and LEAD-3 Study Groups. Weight loss with liraglutide, a once-daily human glucagon-like peptide-1 analogue for type 2 diabetes treatment as monotherapy or added to metformin, is primarily as a result of a reduction in fat tissue. *Diabetes Obes. Metab.* **2009**, *11*, 1163–1172. [CrossRef] [PubMed]

135. Muller, T.D.; Nogueiras, R.; Andermann, M.L.; Andrews, Z.B.; Anker, S.D.; Argente, J.; Batterham, R.L.; Benoit, S.C.; Bowers, C.Y.; Broglio, F.; et al. Ghrelin. *Mol. Metab.* **2015**, *4*, 437–460. [CrossRef] [PubMed]

136. Buscher, A.K.; Buscher, R.; Hauffa, B.P.; Hoyer, P.F. Alterations in appetite-regulating hormones influence protein-energy wasting in pediatric patients with chronic kidney disease. *Pediatr. Nephrol.* **2010**, *25*, 2295–2301. [CrossRef] [PubMed]

137. Zhang, S.R.; Fan, X.M. Ghrelin-ghrelin *O*-acyltransferase system in the pathogenesis of nonalcoholic fatty liver disease. *World J. Gastroenterol.* **2015**, *21*, 3214–3222. [PubMed]

138. Al Massadi, O.; Tschop, M.H.; Tong, J. Ghrelin acylation and metabolic control. *Peptides* **2011**, *32*, 2301–2308. [CrossRef] [PubMed]

139. Cummings, D.E.; Frayo, R.S.; Marmonier, C.; Aubert, R.; Chapelot, D. Plasma ghrelin levels and hunger scores in humans initiating meals voluntarily without time- and food-related cues. *Am. J. Physiol. Endocrinol. Metab.* **2004**, *287*, E297–E304. [CrossRef] [PubMed]

140. Rodriguez, A. Novel molecular aspects of ghrelin and leptin in the control of adipobiology and the cardiovascular system. *Obes. Facts* **2014**, *7*, 82–95. [CrossRef] [PubMed]

141. Foster-Schubert, K.E.; Overduin, J.; Prudom, C.E.; Liu, J.; Callahan, H.S.; Gaylinn, B.D.; Thorner, M.O.; Cummings, D.E. Acyl and total ghrelin are suppressed strongly by ingested proteins, weakly by lipids, and biphasically by carbohydrates. *J. Clin. Endocrinol. Metab.* **2008**, *93*, 1971–1979. [CrossRef] [PubMed]

142. Van Name, M.; Giannini, C.; Santoro, N.; Jastreboff, A.M.; Kubat, J.; Li, F.; Kursawe, R.; Savoye, M.; Duran, E.; Dziura, J.; et al. Blunted suppression of acyl-ghrelin in response to fructose ingestion in obese adolescents: The role of insulin resistance. *Obesity* **2015**, *23*, 653–661. [CrossRef] [PubMed]

143. Muller, T.D.; Tschop, M.H.; Jarick, I.; Ehrlich, S.; Scherag, S.; Herpertz-Dahlmann, B.; Zipfel, S.; Herzog, W.; de Zwaan, M.; Burghardt, R.; et al. Genetic variation of the ghrelin activator gene ghrelin *O*-acyltransferase (GOAT) is associated with anorexia nervosa. *J. Psychiatr. Res.* **2011**, *45*, 706–711. [CrossRef] [PubMed]

144. Burns, S.F.; Broom, D.R.; Miyashita, M.; Mundy, C.; Stensel, D.J. A single session of treadmill running has no effect on plasma total ghrelin concentrations. *J. Sports Sci.* **2007**, *25*, 635–642. [CrossRef] [PubMed]

145. Schmidt, A.; Maier, C.; Schaller, G.; Nowotny, P.; Bayerle-Eder, M.; Buranyi, B.; Luger, A.; Wolzt, M. Acute exercise has no effect on ghrelin plasma concentrations. *Horm. Metab. Res.* **2004**, *36*, 174–177. [PubMed]

146. Mackelvie, K.J.; Meneilly, G.S.; Elahi, D.; Wong, A.C.; Barr, S.I.; Chanoine, J.P. Regulation of appetite in lean and obese adolescents after exercise: Role of acylated and desacyl ghrelin. *J. Clin. Endocrinol. Metab.* **2007**, *92*, 648–654. [CrossRef] [PubMed]

147. Athinarayanan, S.; Wei, R.; Zhang, M.; Bai, S.; Traber, M.G.; Yates, K.; Cummings, O.W.; Molleston, J.; Liu, W.; Chalasani, N. Genetic polymorphism of cytochrome P450 4F2, vitamin E level and histological response in adults and children with nonalcoholic fatty liver disease who participated in PIVENS and TONIC clinical trials. *PLoS ONE* **2014**, *9*, e95366. [CrossRef] [PubMed]

148. Prodam, F.; Filigheddu, N. Ghrelin gene products in acute and chronic inflammation. *Arch. Immunol. Ther. Exp.* **2014**, *62*, 369–384. [CrossRef] [PubMed]

149. Delhanty, P.J.; Huisman, M.; Baldeon-Rojas, L.Y.; van den Berge, I.; Grefhorst, A.; Abribat, T.; Leenen, P.J.; Themmen, A.P.; van der Lely, A.J. Des-acyl ghrelin analogs prevent high-fat-diet-induced dysregulation of glucose homeostasis. *FASEB J.* **2013**, *27*, 1690–1700. [CrossRef] [PubMed]

150. Tokudome, T.; Kishimoto, I.; Miyazato, M.; Kangawa, K. Ghrelin and the cardiovascular system. *Front. Horm. Res.* **2014**, *43*, 125–133. [PubMed]

151. Marchesini, G.; Pagotto, U.; Bugianesi, E.; de Iasio, R.; Manini, R.; Vanni, E.; Pasquali, R.; Melchionda, N.; Rizzetto, M. Low ghrelin concentrations in nonalcoholic fatty liver disease are related to insulin resistance. *J. Clin. Endocrinol. Metab.* **2003**, *88*, 5674–5679. [CrossRef] [PubMed]

152. Mykhalchyshyn, G.; Kobyliak, N.; Bodnar, P. Diagnostic accuracy of acyl-ghrelin and it association with non-alcoholic fatty liver disease in type 2 diabetic patients. *J. Diabetes Metab. Disord.* **2015**, *14*, 44. [CrossRef] [PubMed]

153. Gunta, S.S.; Mak, R.H. Ghrelin and leptin pathophysiology in chronic kidney disease. *Pediatr. Nephrol.* **2013**, *28*, 611–616. [CrossRef] [PubMed]

154. Suneja, M.; Murry, D.J.; Stokes, J.B.; Lim, V.S. Hormonal regulation of energy-protein homeostasis in hemodialysis patients: An anorexigenic profile that may predispose to adverse cardiovascular outcomes. *Am. J. Physiol. Endocrinol. Metab.* **2011**, *300*, E55–E64. [CrossRef] [PubMed]

155. Raschke, S.; Eckel, J. Adipo-myokines: Two sides of the same coin—Mediators of inflammation and mediators of exercise. *Mediat. Inflamm.* **2013**, *2013*, 320724. [CrossRef] [PubMed]

156. Arias-Loste, M.T.; Ranchal, I.; Romero-Gomez, M.; Crespo, J. Irisin, a link among fatty liver disease, physical inactivity and insulin resistance. *Int. J. Mol. Sci.* **2014**, *15*, 23163–23178. [CrossRef] [PubMed]

157. Anastasilakis, A.D.; Polyzos, S.A.; Saridakis, Z.G.; Kynigopoulos, G.; Skouvaklidou, E.C.; Molyvas, D.; Vasiloglou, M.F.; Apostolou, A.; Karagiozoglou-Lampoudi, T.; Siopi, A.; et al. Circulating irisin in healthy, young individuals: Day-night rhythm, effects of food intake and exercise, and associations with gender, physical activity, diet, and body composition. *J. Clin. Endocrinol. Metab.* **2014**, *99*, 3247–3255. [CrossRef] [PubMed]

158. Ko, B.J.; Park, K.H.; Shin, S.; Zaichenko, L.; Davis, C.R.; Crowell, J.A.; Joung, H.; Mantzoros, C.S. Diet quality and diet patterns in relation to circulating cardiometabolic biomarkers. *Clin. Nutr.* **2016**, *35*, 484–490. [CrossRef] [PubMed]

159. Schlogl, M.; Piaggi, P.; Votruba, S.B.; Walter, M.; Krakoff, J.; Thearle, M.S. Increased 24-hour ad libitum food intake is associated with lower plasma irisin concentrations the following morning in adult humans. *Appetite* **2015**, *90*, 154–159. [CrossRef] [PubMed]

160. Qiu, S.; Cai, X.; Sun, Z.; Schumann, U.; Zugel, M.; Steinacker, J.M. Chronic exercise training and circulating irisin in adults: A meta-analysis. *Sports Med.* **2015**, *45*, 1577–1588. [CrossRef] [PubMed]

161. Zhang, H.J.; Zhang, X.F.; Ma, Z.M.; Pan, L.L.; Chen, Z.; Han, H.W.; Han, C.K.; Zhuang, X.J.; Lu, Y.; Li, X.J.; et al. Irisin is inversely associated with intrahepatic triglyceride contents in obese adults. *J. Hepatol.* **2013**, *59*, 557–562. [CrossRef] [PubMed]

162. Polyzos, S.A.; Kountouras, J.; Anastasilakis, A.D.; Geladari, E.V.; Mantzoros, C.S. Irisin in patients with nonalcoholic fatty liver disease. *Metabolism* **2014**, *63*, 207–217. [CrossRef] [PubMed]

163. Zurlo, F.; Larson, K.; Bogardus, C.; Ravussin, E. Skeletal muscle metabolism is a major determinant of resting energy expenditure. *J. Clin. Investig.* **1990**, *86*, 1423–1427. [CrossRef] [PubMed]

164. Panesar, A.; Agarwal, R. Resting energy expenditure in chronic kidney disease: Relationship with glomerular filtration rate. *Clin. Nephrol.* **2003**, *59*, 360–366. [CrossRef] [PubMed]

165. Lee, M.J.; Lee, S.A.; Nam, B.Y.; Park, S.; Lee, S.H.; Ryu, H.J.; Kwon, Y.E.; Kim, Y.L.; Park, K.S.; Oh, H.J.; et al. Irisin, a novel myokine is an independent predictor for sarcopenia and carotid atherosclerosis in dialysis patients. *Atherosclerosis* **2015**, *242*, 476–482. [CrossRef] [PubMed]

166. Wen, M.S.; Wang, C.Y.; Lin, S.L.; Hung, K.C. Decrease in irisin in patients with chronic kidney disease. *PLoS ONE* **2013**, *8*, e64025. [CrossRef] [PubMed]

167. Ebert, T.; Focke, D.; Petroff, D.; Wurst, U.; Richter, J.; Bachmann, A.; Lossner, U.; Kralisch, S.; Kratzsch, J.; Beige, J.; et al. Serum levels of the myokine irisin in relation to metabolic and renal function. *Eur. J. Endocrinol.* **2014**, *170*, 501–506. [CrossRef] [PubMed]

168. Burk, R.F.; Hill, K.E. Selenoprotein P: An extracellular protein with unique physical characteristics and a role in selenium homeostasis. *Annu. Rev. Nutr.* **2005**, *25*, 215–235. [CrossRef] [PubMed]

169. Carlson, B.A.; Novoselov, S.V.; Kumaraswamy, E.; Lee, B.J.; Anver, M.R.; Gladyshev, V.N.; Hatfield, D.L. Specific excision of the selenocysteine tRNA[Ser]Sec (*Trsp*) gene in mouse liver demonstrates an essential role of selenoproteins in liver function. *J. Biol. Chem.* **2004**, *279*, 8011–8017. [CrossRef] [PubMed]

170. Hill, K.E.; Zhou, J.; McMahan, W.J.; Motley, A.K.; Atkins, J.F.; Gesteland, R.F.; Burk, R.F. Deletion of selenoprotein P alters distribution of selenium in the mouse. *J. Biol. Chem.* **2003**, *278*, 13640–13646. [CrossRef] [PubMed]

171. Schomburg, L.; Schweizer, U.; Holtmann, B.; Flohe, L.; Sendtner, M.; Kohrle, J. Gene disruption discloses role of selenoprotein P in selenium delivery to target tissues. *Biochem. J.* **2003**, *370*, 397–402. [CrossRef] [PubMed]

172. Misu, H.; Takamura, T.; Takayama, H.; Hayashi, H.; Matsuzawa-Nagata, N.; Kurita, S.; Ishikura, K.; Ando, H.; Takeshita, Y.; Ota, T.; et al. A liver-derived secretory protein, selenoprotein P, causes insulin resistance. *Cell Metab.* **2010**, *12*, 483–495. [CrossRef] [PubMed]

173. Misu, H.; Ishikura, K.; Kurita, S.; Takeshita, Y.; Ota, T.; Saito, Y.; Takahashi, K.; Kaneko, S.; Takamura, T. Inverse correlation between serum levels of selenoprotein P and adiponectin in patients with type 2 diabetes. *PLoS ONE* **2012**, *7*, e34952. [CrossRef] [PubMed]

174. Yang, J.G.; Hill, K.E.; Burk, R.F. Dietary selenium intake controls rat plasma selenoprotein P concentration. *J. Nutr.* **1989**, *119*, 1010–1012. [PubMed]

175. Falnoga, I.; Kobal, A.B.; Stibilj, V.; Horvat, M. Selenoprotein P in subjects exposed to mercury and other stress situations such as physical load or metal chelation treatment. *Biol. Trace Elem. Res.* **2002**, *89*, 25–33. [CrossRef]

176. Huang, Z.; Rose, A.H.; Hoffmann, P.R. The role of selenium in inflammation and immunity: From molecular mechanisms to therapeutic opportunities. *Antioxid. Redox Signal.* **2012**, *16*, 705–743. [CrossRef] [PubMed]

177. Mattmiller, S.A.; Carlson, B.A.; Sordillo, L.M. Regulation of inflammation by selenium and selenoproteins: Impact on eicosanoid biosynthesis. *J. Nutr. Sci.* **2013**, *2*, e28. [PubMed]

178. Nichol, C.; Herdman, J.; Sattar, N.; O'Dwyer, P.J.; St, J.O.R.D.; Littlejohn, D.; Fell, G. Changes in the concentrations of plasma selenium and selenoproteins after minor elective surgery: Further evidence for a negative acute phase response? *Clin. Chem.* **1998**, *44*, 1764–1766. [PubMed]

179. Hesse-Bahr, K.; Dreher, I.; Kohrle, J. The influence of the cytokines Il-1beta and INFgamma on the expression of selenoproteins in the human hepatocarcinoma cell line HepG2. *Biofactors* **2000**, *11*, 83–85. [CrossRef] [PubMed]

180. Dreher, I.; Jakobs, T.C.; Kohrle, J. Cloning and characterization of the human selenoprotein P promoter. Response of selenoprotein P expression to cytokines in liver cells. *J. Biol. Chem.* **1997**, *272*, 29364–29371. [CrossRef] [PubMed]

181. Rayman, M.P. Selenium and human health. *Lancet* **2012**, *379*, 1256–1268. [CrossRef]

182. Yang, S.J.; Hwang, S.Y.; Choi, H.Y.; Yoo, H.J.; Seo, J.A.; Kim, S.G.; Kim, N.H.; Baik, S.H.; Choi, D.S.; Choi, K.M. Serum selenoprotein P levels in patients with type 2 diabetes and prediabetes: Implications for insulin resistance, inflammation, and atherosclerosis. *J. Clin. Endocrinol. Metab.* **2011**, *96*, E1325–E1329. [CrossRef] [PubMed]

183. Rose, A.H.; Hoffmann, P.R. Selenoproteins and cardiovascular stress. *Thromb. Haemost.* **2015**, *113*, 494–504. [CrossRef] [PubMed]

184. Choi, H.Y.; Hwang, S.Y.; Lee, C.H.; Hong, H.C.; Yang, S.J.; Yoo, H.J.; Seo, J.A.; Kim, S.G.; Kim, N.H.; Baik, S.H.; et al. Increased selenoprotein p levels in subjects with visceral obesity and nonalcoholic Fatty liver disease. *Diabetes Metab. J.* **2013**, *37*, 63–71. [CrossRef] [PubMed]

185. Takayama, H.; Misu, H.; Iwama, H.; Chikamoto, K.; Saito, Y.; Murao, K.; Teraguchi, A.; Lan, F.; Kikuchi, A.; Saito, R.; et al. Metformin suppresses expression of the selenoprotein P gene via an AMP-activated kinase (AMPK)/FoxO3a pathway in H4IIEC3 hepatocytes. *J. Biol. Chem.* **2014**, *289*, 335–345. [CrossRef] [PubMed]

186. Burk, R.F.; Hill, K.E. Regulation of selenium metabolism and transport. *Annu. Rev. Nutr.* **2015**, *35*, 109–134. [CrossRef] [PubMed]

187. Reinhardt, W.; Dolff, S.; Benson, S.; Broecker-Preuss, M.; Behrendt, S.; Hog, A.; Fuhrer, D.; Schomburg, L.; Kohrle, J. Chronic kidney disease distinctly affects relationship between selenoprotein P status and serum thyroid hormone parameters. *Thyroid* **2015**, *25*, 1091–1096. [CrossRef] [PubMed]

188. Meyer, T.W.; Hostetter, T.H. Uremia. *N. Engl. J. Med.* **2007**, *357*, 1316–1325. [CrossRef] [PubMed]

189. Denecke, B.; Graber, S.; Schafer, C.; Heiss, A.; Woltje, M.; Jahnen-Dechent, W. Tissue distribution and activity testing suggest a similar but not identical function of fetuin-B and fetuin-A. *Biochem. J.* **2003**, *376*, 135–145. [CrossRef] [PubMed]

190. Mathews, S.T.; Chellam, N.; Srinivas, P.R.; Cintron, V.J.; Leon, M.A.; Goustin, A.S.; Grunberger, G. α2-HSG, a specific inhibitor of insulin receptor autophosphorylation, interacts with the insulin receptor. *Mol. Cell. Endocrinol.* **2000**, *164*, 87–98. [CrossRef]

191. Stefan, N.; Hennige, A.M.; Staiger, H.; Machann, J.; Schick, F.; Krober, S.M.; Machicao, F.; Fritsche, A.; Haring, H.U. α2-Heremans-Schmid glycoprotein/fetuin-A is associated with insulin resistance and fat accumulation in the liver in humans. *Diabetes Care* **2006**, *29*, 853–857. [CrossRef] [PubMed]

192. Mathews, S.T.; Singh, G.P.; Ranalletta, M.; Cintron, V.J.; Qiang, X.; Goustin, A.S.; Jen, K.L.; Charron, M.J.; Jahnen-Dechent, W.; Grunberger, G. Improved insulin sensitivity and resistance to weight gain in mice null for the Ahsg gene. *Diabetes* **2002**, *51*, 2450–2458. [CrossRef] [PubMed]

193. Siddiq, A.; Lepretre, F.; Hercberg, S.; Froguel, P.; Gibson, F. A synonymous coding polymorphism in the α2-Heremans-schmid glycoprotein gene is associated with type 2 diabetes in French Caucasians. *Diabetes* **2005**, *54*, 2477–2481. [CrossRef] [PubMed]

194. Dahlman, I.; Eriksson, P.; Kaaman, M.; Jiao, H.; Lindgren, C.M.; Kere, J.; Arner, P. α2-Heremans-Schmid glycoprotein gene polymorphisms are associated with adipocyte insulin action. *Diabetologia* **2004**, *47*, 1974–1979. [CrossRef] [PubMed]

195. Nimptsch, K.; Janke, J.; Pischon, T.; Linseisen, J. Association between dietary factors and plasma fetuin-A concentrations in the general population. *Br. J. Nutr.* **2015**, *114*, 1278–1285. [CrossRef] [PubMed]

196. Seyithanoglu, M.; Oner-Iyidogan, Y.; Dogru-Abbasoglu, S.; Tanrikulu-Kucuk, S.; Kocak, H.; Beyhan-Ozdas, S.; Kocak-Toker, N. The effect of dietary curcumin and capsaicin on hepatic fetuin-A expression and fat accumulation in rats fed on a high-fat diet. *Arch. Physiol. Biochem.* **2016**, *122*, 94–102. [CrossRef] [PubMed]

197. Malin, S.K.; Mulya, A.; Fealy, C.E.; Haus, J.M.; Pagadala, M.R.; Scelsi, A.R.; Huang, H.; Flask, C.A.; McCullough, A.J.; Kirwan, J.P. Fetuin-A is linked to improved glucose tolerance after short-term exercise training in nonalcoholic fatty liver disease. *J. Appl. Physiol.* **2013**, *115*, 988–994. [CrossRef] [PubMed]

198. Yang, S.J.; Hong, H.C.; Choi, H.Y.; Yoo, H.J.; Cho, G.J.; Hwang, T.G.; Baik, S.H.; Choi, D.S.; Kim, S.M.; Choi, K.M. Effects of a three-month combined exercise programme on fibroblast growth factor 21 and fetuin-A levels and arterial stiffness in obese women. *Clin. Endocrinol.* **2011**, *75*, 464–469. [CrossRef] [PubMed]

199. Rametta, R.; Ruscica, M.; Dongiovanni, P.; Macchi, C.; Fracanzani, A.L.; Steffani, L.; Fargion, S.; Magni, P.; Valenti, L. Hepatic steatosis and PNPLA3 I148M variant are associated with serum Fetuin-A independently of insulin resistance. *Eur. J. Clin. Investig.* **2014**, *44*, 627–633. [CrossRef] [PubMed]

200. Yilmaz, Y.; Yonal, O.; Kurt, R.; Ari, F.; Oral, A.Y.; Celikel, C.A.; Korkmaz, S.; Ulukaya, E.; Ozdogan, O.; Imeryuz, N.; et al. Serum fetuin A/α2HS-glycoprotein levels in patients with non-alcoholic fatty liver disease: Relation with liver fibrosis. *Ann. Clin. Biochem.* **2010**, *47*, 549–553. [CrossRef] [PubMed]

201. Ou, H.Y.; Yang, Y.C.; Wu, H.T.; Wu, J.S.; Lu, F.H.; Chang, C.J. Increased fetuin-A concentrations in impaired glucose tolerance with or without nonalcoholic fatty liver disease, but not impaired fasting glucose. *J. Clin. Endocrinol. Metab.* **2012**, *97*, 4717–4723. [CrossRef] [PubMed]

202. Cottone, S.; Palermo, A.; Arsena, R.; Riccobene, R.; Guarneri, M.; Mule, G.; Tornese, F.; Altieri, C.; Vaccaro, F.; Previti, A.; et al. Relationship of fetuin-A with glomerular filtration rate and endothelial dysfunction in moderate-severe chronic kidney disease. *J. Nephrol.* **2010**, *23*, 62–69. [PubMed]

International Journal of
Molecular Sciences

MDPI

Review

Relationship between Non-Alcoholic Fatty Liver Disease and Psoriasis: A Novel Hepato-Dermal Axis?

Alessandro Mantovani [1], Paolo Gisondi [2], Amedeo Lonardo [3] and Giovanni Targher [1,*]

[1]   Section of Endocrinology, Diabetes and Metabolism, Department of Medicine,
      University and Azienda Ospedaliera Universitaria Integrata of Verona, Piazzale Stefani, 1,
      Verona 37126, Italy; alessandro.mantovani24@gmail.com
[2]   Section of Dermatology, Department of Medicine, University and Azienda Ospedaliera Universitaria
      Integrata of Verona, Piazzale Stefani, 1, Verona 37126, Italy; paolo.gisondi@univr.it
[3]   Outpatient Liver Clinic and Division of Internal Medicine—Department of Biomedical,
      Metabolic and Neural Sciences, NOCSAE, University of Modena and Reggio Emilia and
      Azienda USL Modena, Baggiovara, Modena 41126, Italy; a.lonardo@libero.it
*   Correspondence: giovanni.targher@univr.it; Tel.: +39-045-812-3110; Fax: +39-045-802-7314

Academic Editor: Johannes Haybaeck
Received: 19 January 2016; Accepted: 2 February 2016; Published: 5 February 2016

Abstract: Over the past 10 years, it has become increasingly evident that nonalcoholic fatty liver disease (NAFLD) is a multisystem disease that affects multiple extra-hepatic organ systems and interacts with the regulation of several metabolic and immunological pathways. In this review we discuss the rapidly expanding body of clinical and epidemiological evidence supporting a strong association between NAFLD and chronic plaque psoriasis. We also briefly discuss the possible biological mechanisms underlying this association, and discuss treatment options for psoriasis that may influence NAFLD development and progression. Recent observational studies have shown that the prevalence of NAFLD (as diagnosed either by imaging or by histology) is remarkably higher in psoriatic patients (occurring in up to 50% of these patients) than in matched control subjects. Notably, psoriasis is associated with NAFLD even after adjusting for metabolic syndrome traits and other potential confounding factors. Some studies have also suggested that psoriatic patients are more likely to have the more advanced forms of NAFLD than non-psoriatic controls, and that psoriatic patients with NAFLD have more severe psoriasis than those without NAFLD. In conclusion, the published evidence argues for more careful evaluation and surveillance of NAFLD among patients with psoriasis.

Keywords: nonalcoholic fatty liver disease; NAFLD; nonalcoholic steatohepatitis; management; psoriasis

---

1. Introduction

Psoriasis is a chronic, immune-mediated, inflammatory skin disease that affects approximately 2%–3% of the adults in the general population of Western countries [1,2]. This disease is known for its typical cutaneous manifestations; described as well-demarcated, erythematous oval plaques with adherent silvery scales. However, recent studies have also linked psoriasis with multiple comorbid conditions, including arthritis, uveitis, inflammatory bowel diseases, depression, osteoporosis, cardiovascular disease and metabolic syndrome [3].

In parallel, nonalcoholic fatty liver disease (NAFLD) is the most frequent liver disease worldwide, affecting an estimated 30% of the adult population in developed countries [4,5]. NAFLD and the metabolic syndrome are mutually and bi-directionally associated, as these two pathologic conditions share insulin resistance as a common pathophysiological mechanism [6–8]. NAFLD encompasses a spectrum of pathologic conditions ranging from simple steatosis to nonalcoholic steatohepatitis ((NASH) featuring steatosis associated with inflammatory changes, hepatocellular ballooning and pericellular fibrosis), to advanced fibrosis and cirrhosis. NAFLD is projected to become the most common indication for liver transplantation in the United States by 2030 [5,9]. However, over the past 10 years, it has become increasingly clear that NAFLD is not only associated with increased liver-related mortality or morbidity, but also is a multisystem disease affecting a variety of extra-hepatic organ systems, including the heart and the vascular system [9,10]. Cardiovascular disease represents the primary cause of mortality in NAFLD patients [9,10].

In this updated review we will discuss the clinical evidence supporting a link between NAFLD and chronic plaque psoriasis, and the putative mechanisms underlying this association. We will also briefly discuss some of the therapeutic options for psoriasis that may influence NAFLD development and progression. We extensively searched PubMed database to identify original articles published through December 31st 2015, using the following key-words "nonalcoholic fatty liver disease" or "NAFLD" combined with "chronic plaque psoriasis", "psoriasis" or "psoriatic treatment".

2. Epidemiology, Clinical Manifestations and Pathogenesis of Psoriasis

Psoriasis is a chronic, recurrent, immune-mediated inflammatory disease of the skin, affecting approximately 2%–3% of the general adult population in many parts of the world [1]. The prevalence of this disease in adults ranges from approximately 1% (United States) to 8.5% (Norway). The incidence estimate varies from approximately 80/100,000 person-years (United States) to 230/100,000 person-years (Italy) [1]. Epidemiological studies suggest that the prevalence of psoriasis varies according to increasing age and is more common in countries more distant from the equator [1]. However, additional studies are needed to better understand the epidemiology of psoriasis and trends in incidence over time.

Psoriasis manifests as raised, irregularly round and well-demarcated erythematous lesions that are usually covered by silver scales (Figure 1).

Psoriatic lesions are distributed symmetrically on the scalp, elbows, knees, lumbo-sacral area and in the body folds. Psoriatic lesions are frequently symptomatic with pruritus by far the most bothersome skin symptom reported by the patients, even for those with limited disease, followed by scaling and flaking. Psoriasis may have a negative impact on the physical, emotional and psychosocial wellbeing of affected patients. About one third of patients have symptoms of arthritis, which might be very disabling in the more severe cases [11]. Psoriasis is also frequently associated with multiple metabolic co-morbidities, including abdominal overweight or obesity, type 2 diabetes, metabolic syndrome and NAFLD [3,12,13].

The exact aetiology of psoriasis is largely unknown. However, strong evidence indicates that psoriasis is a chronic inflammatory skin disease, occurring against a predisposing genetic background. The pathogenesis of psoriasis is complex, with a combination of genetic and environmental factors playing an integrated role [2]. The contribution of genetic factors to the pathogenesis of psoriasis is extensive, with the human leukocyte antigen (HLA)-C*06 showing the most significant association, although genome-wide association studies have identified more than 35 psoriasis risk gene regions primarily involved in innate and adaptive immunity [14]. A deregulated cytokine network occurs in psoriasis, leading to the release of multiple pro-inflammatory mediators from immune cells, which in turn induce increased keratinocyte proliferation [15]. Psoriasis is thought to be a T cell-driven disease, with the Th1 and Th17 cell populations playing a major role. These immune cells produce a variety of pro-inflammatory cytokines, including tumour necrosis factor (TNF)-α, interleukin (IL)-6, IL-17, IL-22 and interferon-gamma, resulting in abnormal differentiation and proliferation of keratinocytes, blood vessels dilatation and inflammatory infiltration of leukocytes into the dermis and epidermis [15,16]. A number of environmental factors have been also identified as possible triggers of psoriasis, including physical traumas (known as Koebner's phenomenon), bacterial infections, stressful life events or use of some drugs, such as interferon α and lithium salts [2,15]. However, more precise identification of genetic and environmental factors that are potentially involved in the development of psoriasis will help to better elucidate the pathogenesis of this disease and identify new targets for a more specific and effective treatment.

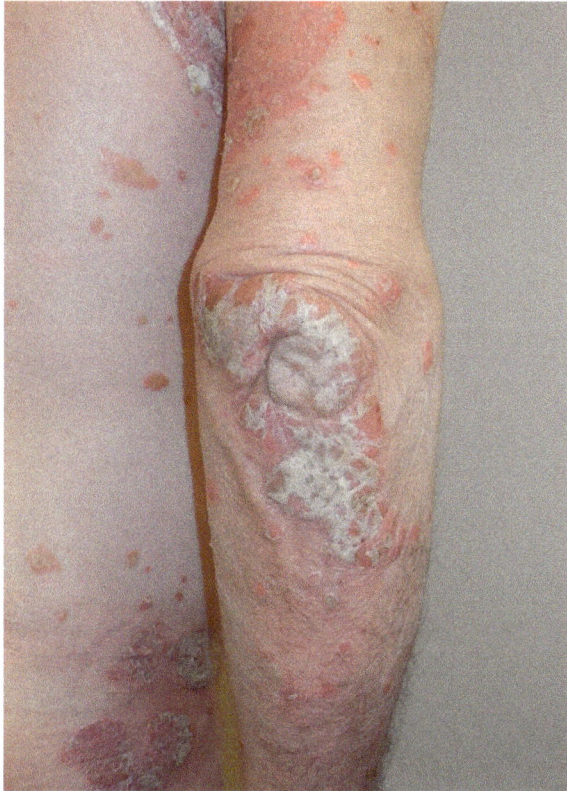

Figure 1. Psoriatic lesions on the elbows.

3. Epidemiological Evidence Linking Nonalcoholic Fatty Liver Disease (NAFLD) to Psoriasis

Given the strong relationship of the metabolic syndrome with both psoriasis [3,12,13] and NAFLD [4–6], it is perhaps not surprising that these two latter diseases may coexist within the same individual.

In a case report published in 2001 Lonardo *et al.* [17] were the first to describe three cases of concurrent psoriasis vulgaris and NASH, diagnosed on biopsy. All patients were obese and had other features of the metabolic syndrome. Similarly, Matsumoto *et al.* [18] described a case of a young obese psoriatic man with NASH that improved after hypocaloric diet.

As detailed in Table 1, after these pioneering case reports, multiple observational (cross-sectional and case-control) studies have recently assessed whether NAFLD (as diagnosed either by ultrasonography or by histology) is associated with psoriasis [19–27].

Table 1. Principal studies examining the relationship between NAFLD and psoriasis (ordered by publication year).

Authors, Year (Reference)	Study Characteristics	NAFLD Diagnosis	Main Findings
Gisondi *et al.* 2009 [19]	Cross-sectional: 130 consecutive Italian patients with chronic plaque psoriasis and 260 healthy controls matched for age, sex and BMI	Ultrasonography	Prevalence of NAFLD was remarkably higher in psoriatic patients than in matched controls (47% *vs.* 28%; *p* < 0.001). Patients with psoriasis and NAFLD were more likely to have metabolic syndrome and had higher serum C-reactive protein concentrations and greater severity of psoriasis according to PASI score than those with psoriasis alone. At multivariate linear regression analysis, NAFLD was associated with higher PASI score (standardized β coefficient 0.19, *p* = 0.03), independent of age, sex, BMI, psoriasis duration and alcohol consumption
Miele *et al.* 2009 [20]	Retrospective, case-control: 142 Italian patients with psoriasis and 125 non-psoriatic patients with biopsy-proven NAFLD comparable for age and BMI	Ultrasonography and biopsy	Prevalence of NAFLD was 59.2% in the cohort of psoriatic patients. In these patients NAFLD was significantly associated with metabolic syndrome and psoriatic arthritis. Compared with the non-psoriatic NAFLD cohort, psoriatic patients with NAFLD were likely to have more severe NAFLD reflected by either non-invasive NAFLD Fibrosis score or AST/ALT ratio >1
Madanagobalane *et al.* 2012 [21]	Cross-sectional: 333 Indian psoriatic patients and 330 controls matched for age, sex and BMI	Ultrasonography and liver enzymes	Prevalence of NAFLD was higher in psoriatic patients than in matched controls (17.4% *vs.* 7.9%; *p* < 0.005). Psoriatic patients with NAFLD had more severe psoriasis than those without NAFLD. In a subset of participants, psoriatic patients had more severe forms of NAFLD than non-psoriatic patients with NAFLD (as estimated by non-invasive fibrosis markers)
van der Voort *et al.* 2014 [22]	Cross-sectional: population-based cohort of 2292 Dutch elderly participants (the Rotterdam Study)	Ultrasonography	Prevalence of psoriasis was 5.1% (by a validated algorithm). Prevalence of NAFLD was higher in psoriatic patients than in participants without psoriasis (46.2% *vs.* 33.3%, *p* = 0.005). Psoriasis was associated with NAFLD (OR 1.70, 95% CI 1.1–2.6, *p* = 0.01), independent of age, sex, alcohol consumption, pack-years and smoking status, metabolic syndrome, and serum ALT levels
van der Voort *et al.* 2015 [23]	Cross-sectional: population-based cohort of 1535 elderly participants (the Rotterdam Study) of whom 74 (4.7%) had psoriasis	Ultrasonography and transient elastography (Fibroscan)	Prevalence of NAFLD was higher in subjects with psoriasis than in those without psoriasis (44.3% *vs.* 34%, *p* < 0.05). Moreover, prevalence of advanced liver fibrosis was 8.1% in psoriatic patients compared with 3.6% in the control group (*p* < 0.05). Multivariate logistic regression analysis revealed that the risk of advanced liver fibrosis remained higher in psoriatic patients after adjustment for age, sex, alcohol consumption, serum ALT levels, presence of metabolic syndrome and hepatic steatosis (OR 2.57, 95% CI 1.0–6.6)
Gisondi *et al.* 2015 [24]	Cross-sectional: 124 Italian patients with psoriasis and 79 healthy controls	Ultrasonography	Prevalence of NAFLD was higher in psoriatic patients than in controls (44% *vs.* 26%, *p* < 0.001). NAFLD fibrosis score was also higher in psoriatic patients (*p* < 0.001). Multivariate regression analysis revealed that psoriasis was associated with higher NAFLD fibrosis score, independent of age, sex, BMI, hypertension and pre-existing diabetes
Abedini *et al.* 2015 [25]	Cross-sectional: 123 Iranian patients with psoriasis and 123 healthy controls matched by age, sex and BMI	Ultrasonography	Prevalence of NAFLD was higher in psoriatic patients than in matched controls (65.6% *vs.* 35%, *p* < 0.01). Multivariate logistic regression analysis revealed that PASI score, waist circumference, hypertension and serum aminotransferase levels independently predicted the ultrasonographic severity of NAFLD
Roberts *et al.* 2015 [26]	Cross-sectional: 103 United States adult patients with a diagnosis of psoriasis or psoriatic arthritis	Ultrasonography and biopsy (available in a subgroup of 52 patients)	The overall prevalence of NAFLD was 47%. The prevalence of NASH was 22% in those who underwent liver biopsy. Psoriatic patients with NAFLD had higher mean PASI scores than those without NAFLD
Candia *et al.* 2015 [27]	Systematic review and meta-analysis: 7 case-control studies included	Ultrasonography and liver enzymes	Psoriatic patients had an increased risk of prevalent NAFLD compared with control subjects (6 studies, *n* = 267,761 patients, OR 2.15, 95% CI 1.6–2.9, *p* < 0.05). The risk of prevalent NAFLD was higher in patients with psoriatic arthritis (3 studies, *n* = 505 patients, OR 2.25, 95% CI 1.4–3.7, *p* < 0.05) and in those with moderate-to-severe psoriasis compared with patients with mild psoriasis (2 studies, *n* = 51,930 patients, OR 2.07, 95% CI 1.6–2.7, *p* < 0.05)

Abbreviations: ALT, alanine aminotransferase; AST, aspartate aminotransferase; BMI, body mass index; CI, confidence interval; NAFLD, nonalcoholic fatty liver disease; NASH, nonalcoholic steatohepatitis; PASI, psoriasis area and severity index; OR, odds ratio.

For instance, in a case-control study involving 130 consecutive patients with chronic plaque psoriasis (none of whom treated with methotrexate or other potentially hepato-toxic drugs) and 260 matched healthy controls, Gisondi *et al.* [19] have documented that NAFLD prevalence was almost two times higher among psoriatic patients than among control individuals (47% *vs.* 28%, *p* < 0.001). This difference remained significant (37% *vs.* 21%; *p* < 0.01), even after excluding subjects with mild-moderate alcohol consumption (*i.e.*, those who drank less than 30 grams of alcohol per day). Patients with psoriasis and NAFLD were also more likely to have higher circulating levels of C-reactive protein, IL-6 and lower adiponectin levels than those without NAFLD. Furthermore, NAFLD was associated with a greater clinical severity of psoriasis as estimated by the Psoriasis Area and Severity Index (PASI) score after adjusting for many cardio-metabolic risk factors [19]. This score measures the severity of psoriatic lesions (evaluating the degree of erythema, thickness, and scaling of psoriatic plaques in four separate body areas) based on area coverage and plaque appearance.

In another retrospective study Miele *et al.* [20] found a NAFLD prevalence of 59.2% in an outpatient cohort of 142 adults with psoriasis. Although there were no differences in PASI score between psoriatic patients with or without NAFLD, those with NAFLD were more likely to have psoriatic arthritis and more severe NAFLD as estimated non-invasively with the NAFLD fibrosis score. Unfortunately, data on liver biopsy were available only for five psoriatic patients, but revealed that three of these patients had histologically proven NASH.

Interestingly, in a large population-based cohort study which included 2292 elderly individuals of whom 5.1% had psoriasis, van der Voort *et al.* [22] documented that the prevalence of NAFLD on ultrasonography was greater among psoriatic patients than among the reference group without psoriasis (46.2% *vs.* 33.3%, *p* = 0.005). Notably, multivariate regression analysis revealed that psoriatic participants were 70% more likely to have NAFLD than those without psoriasis (odds ratio (OR) 1.70, 95% confidence interval (CI) 1.1–2.6, *p* = 0.01), independent of metabolic syndrome and other common NAFLD risk factors. In a subsequent analysis of the same cohort, the authors have also reported that the prevalence of advanced hepatic fibrosis, as detected by transient elastography, was greater among those with psoriasis than among those without this disease (8.1% *vs.* 3.6%, *p* < 0.05), and that psoriatic patients were twice as likely to have advanced hepatic fibrosis, irrespective of common risk factors (adjusted-OR 2.57, 95% CI 1.0–6.6) [23]. Similarly, in a smaller case-control study, Gisondi *et al.* [24] reported that the NAFLD fibrosis score (*i.e.*, a non-invasive scoring system that identifies advanced hepatic fibrosis) was higher in psoriatic patients than in control subjects, and psoriasis predicted advanced liver fibrosis, independently of coexisting metabolic syndrome features and other potential confounding factors.

Recently, in a cross-sectional study involving 103 United States middle-aged adult patients with psoriasis or psoriatic arthritis recruited over a 24-month period, Roberts *et al.* [26] found that the prevalence of ultrasound-diagnosed NAFLD was 47%, whereas that of NASH was 22% among those (*n* = 52) who underwent liver biopsy. Moreover, similarly to previous studies, the authors also found that psoriatic patients with NAFLD had significantly higher PASI scores than those without this disease.

Finally, a recent systematic review and meta-analysis of seven case-control studies confirmed that psoriatic patients had a two-fold increased rate of prevalent NAFLD compared with non-psoriatic control individuals, and that this risk was higher among those with either more severe psoriasis or psoriatic arthritis. Interestingly, the significant relationship between psoriasis and NAFLD was consistent in all studies included in this meta-analysis and was maintained even when the studies of lower methodological quality (due to poorly documented diagnosis of NAFLD or insufficient adjustment for potential confounding variables) were excluded from the analysis [27]. However, it is important to note that the cross-sectional nature of the above-mentioned studies does not permit to ascertain the temporality and causality of the association between NAFLD and psoriasis [19–27]. Future follow-up studies are required to improve our understanding of this topic.

That said, the data available to date show that NAFLD prevalence is very high in patients with psoriasis (affecting up to 50% of these patients), independent of coexisting metabolic syndrome components. In addition, the relatively advanced stage of NASH revealed by the biopsies from psoriatic patients suggests the possibility of an increased risk of long-term liver-related complications in this patient population. Thus, the current evidence argues for more careful monitoring and evaluation of the presence of NAFLD in people with chronic plaque psoriasis.

4. Potential Biological Mechanisms Linking Psoriasis and NAFLD

To date, the underlying mechanisms linking NAFLD to psoriasis are complex and not fully understood. However, identification of the pathophysiological mechanisms linking these two diseases is of clinical relevance because it may offer the promise for novel pharmacological approaches.

Psoriasis and NAFLD share multiple inflammatory and cytokine-mediated mechanisms and are part of an intriguing network of genetic, clinical and pathophysiological features. Indeed, it is possible to assume that the mechanisms underlying the association between NAFLD and psoriasis are multifactorial (involving both genetic and environmental factors) and often overlap with metabolic abnormalities, which frequently coexist in psoriatic patients.

The schematic Figure 2 shows the possible links between expanded visceral adipose tissue, steatotic liver and psoriatic skin, and the signals passing between these three organs.

Although the liver is a key regulator of glucose metabolism, and is the leading source of multiple inflammatory and coagulation factors [5,9,28], the close inter-relationships of psoriasis and NAFLD with visceral obesity and insulin resistance make it very difficult to distinguish the individual contribution of NAFLD to the inflammatory and metabolic manifestations of psoriasis. Although the studies available in the literature do not allow to clearly determine the directionality of the association between NAFLD and psoriasis, it is conceivable that several pro-inflammatory cytokines (e.g., IL-6, IL-17, TNF-α) that are locally over-produced by lymphocytes and keratinocytes into the skin of psoriatic patients may contribute, at least in part, to the pathogenesis of systemic insulin resistance [29,30], and that psoriatic patients with greater insulin resistance are the ones who get NAFLD. Undoubtedly, an expanded and inflamed (dysfunctional) visceral adipose tissue plays a key role in the development of insulin resistance, chronic inflammation and NAFLD, possibly through the secretion of multiple factors, such as increased release of non-esterified fatty acids, increased production of various hormones and pro-inflammatory adipocytokines (including also TNF-α, IL-6, leptin, visfatin, and resistin), and decreased production of adiponectin [9,31–34]. In the presence of obesity and insulin resistance, there is an increased influx of non-esterified fatty acids to the liver. There is now substantial evidence that non-esterified fatty acids play a key role in directly promoting liver injury by increasing intra-hepatic oxidative stress and by activating inflammatory pathways [9,31–34]. The central role of hepatocyte cytokine production in NAFLD progression is supported by studies showing that cytokines may replicate all of the histological features associated with NASH, including neutrophil chemotaxis, hepatocyte necrosis and stellate cell activation [9,31–34]. It is possible to assume that the increased release of non-esterified free fatty acids from the expanded and dysfunctional adipose tissue, in presence of insulin resistance, may also exert a deleterious impact on inflammatory skin lesions in psoriasis. However, to our knowledge, there are currently no reliable data regarding a direct pathogenic role of non-esterified fatty acids in the pathogenesis of psoriasis. Further studies are required to better elucidate this topic.

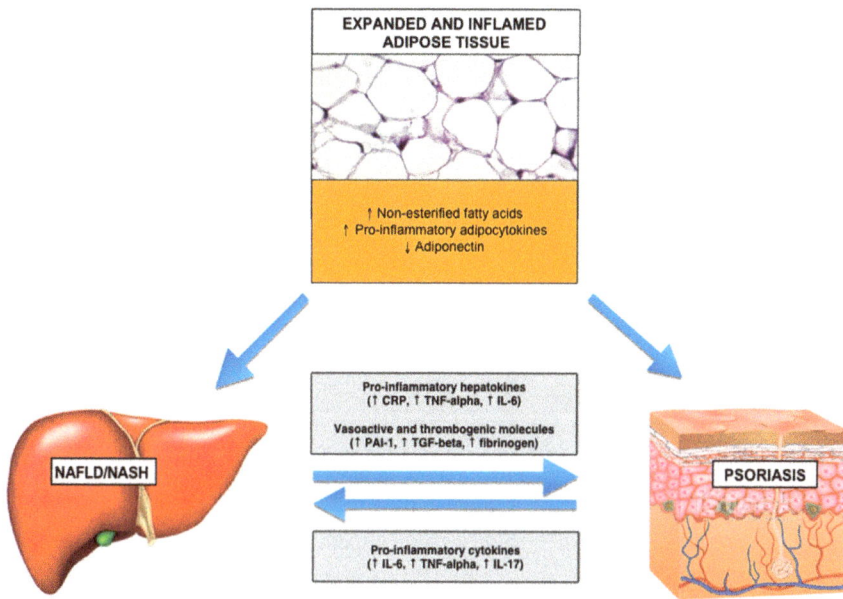

Figure 2. Possible mechanisms linking expanded and inflamed (dysfunctional) visceral adipose tissue, psoriasis and nonalcoholic fatty liver disease. Abbreviations: CRP, C-reactive protein; IL-6, interleukin-6; IL-17, interleukin-17; NAFLD, nonalcoholic fatty liver disease; NASH, nonalcoholic steatohepatitis; PAI-1, plasminogen activator inhibitor-1; TGF-β, transforming growth factor-β; TNF-α, tumor necrosis factor-α.

To date, accumulating evidence indicates that NAFLD, especially its necro-inflammatory and progressive form (NASH), may exacerbate insulin resistance, predisposes to atherogenic dyslipidemia and releases a myriad of pro-inflammatory, pro-coagulant, pro-oxidant and pro-fibrogenic mediators (e.g., C-reactive protein, IL-6, fibrinogen, plasminogen activator inhibitor-1, transforming growth factor-β) that may play important roles in the pathophysiology of psoriasis [5,9,31,35]. It is possible to hypothesize that the release of these pro-inflammatory, pro-oxidant and pro-atherogenic mediators from the steatotic and inflamed liver (which is also one of the most important mechanisms by which fatty liver directly contributes to the development of cardiovascular disease and type 2 diabetes [5,9,36]) may adversely influence the severity of psoriasis by increased keratinocyte proliferation, increased inflammation, and up-regulation of various vascular adhesion molecules. Experimentally, it has been also shown that induction of oxazolone-induced skin inflammation is more evident in NAFLD mice than in normal mice; oxazolone challenge significantly increases ear thickness, ear weight, nuclear factor-κB activity, and histological features of skin inflammation in NAFLD mice as compared to normal mice [37]. The oxazolone-induced skin inflammation model is not specifically designed to study the pathogenesis of psoriasis. Nevertheless, this simple mouse model of NAFLD-enhanced skin inflammation might be used to evaluate new therapeutic strategies for treatment of NAFLD with associated skin inflammation and also to understand the nexus between these two co-morbidities.

5. Treatment for Psoriasis and Its Potential Implications for NAFLD

Detailed discussion of treatment options for psoriasis is beyond the scope of this review and have been recently discussed elsewhere [38]. There are numerous treatment options against psoriasis and they are classified as topical, systemic or phototherapy. Systemic drugs such as methotrexate, cyclosporine and acitretin are indicated for moderate-to-severe psoriasis, especially when the disease is either widespread or resistant to topical therapy. In the case of intolerance, inefficacy or contraindication to either phototherapy or conventional systemic treatments, patients with psoriasis are eligible for newer biological agents, which include TNF-α antagonists (etanercept, adalimumab and infliximab), the anti-IL-2/23 monoclonal antibody ustekinumab, and the anti-IL-17 monoclonal antibodies secukinumab and ixekizumab [38].

From a clinical perspective, understanding whether psoriatic patients have underlying metabolic comorbidities, including NAFLD, is important to ensure that treatment is safe [38,39]. Indeed, while phototherapy or topical treatments are not expected to cause significant changes in metabolic parameters and liver function tests, some pharmacological treatments may negatively influence metabolic comorbidities (including NAFLD) or exert interactions with drugs that are commonly used to treat them [39].

In particular, methotrexate should be administered with caution in the presence of obesity, type 2 diabetes or NAFLD because of the increased risk of drug-induced hepatic fibrosis [40–42]. Indeed, psoriatic patients with type 2 diabetes or obesity are at higher risk of developing hepatic fibrosis during methotrexate treatment compared with those without such metabolic comorbidities [39]. The liver injury induced by methotrexate appears to mimic NAFLD histologically. So, drug induced liver injury should be always considered in a patient with hepatic steatosis who has been previously treated with methotrexate [40,41]. Similarly, cyclosporine should be used cautiously among psoriatic patients with coexisting metabolic syndrome. This drug may worsen type 2 diabetes, exacerbate arterial hypertension and predispose to atherogenic dyslipidemia and hyperuricemia [38,43]. Moreover, the drug interaction between cyclosporine and statins may also increase the risk of rhabdomyolysis [44]. In some cases, cyclosporine may induce liver injury and cholestasis with increased levels of serum aminotransferases, bilirubin and alkaline phosphatase [38,43]. However, cyclosporine-induced hepatitis is a relatively rare event that is less common than nephrotoxicity and occurs more frequently among liver-transplant patients. Acitretin is a vitamin A derivative that has been used to treat psoriasis since the early 1980s. The use of acitretin is limited by its potential adverse effects (e.g., muco-cutaneous effects, dyslipidemia and hepatotoxicity). These effects may be reduced by using lower doses of acitretin or in combination with other therapies [43,45].

Biologic drugs represent a major advancement in the treatment of psoriasis [38]. Generally, biologic agents do not seem to negatively affect metabolic parameters and serum liver enzyme levels as conventional systemic treatments can. Indeed, the drug survival of biologics is higher than that of conventional treatments because they are better tolerated in the longer term. Although the effects of TNF-α inhibitors on insulin sensitivity are a matter of intense debate [38,43,46], preliminary evidence suggests that treatment with etanercept (*i.e.*, a TNF-α inhibitor) may improve both plasma glucose levels and insulin resistance indices [47], and that patients with psoriasis or rheumatoid arthritis receiving TNF-α inhibitors exhibit a lower risk of new-onset type 2 diabetes compared with those receiving other non-biological disease-modifying anti-rheumatic drugs [48]. Clinically meaningful dyslipidemia has been rarely reported in patients receiving etanercept or other TNF-α antagonists, so that it is not a serious concern in routine clinical practice [49]. A significant body weight gain, mainly due to increased fat mass, has been also documented among psoriatic patients receiving TNF-α antagonists [38,39,43], whereas it is not observed among those receiving the anti-IL-12/23 monoclonal antibody ustekinumab [50]. Mild to moderate elevations in serum transaminases may be observed in some patients receiving TNF-α antagonists (especially infliximab [51]), but they usually return to normal after discontinuation of the drug [38,43,52]. In a small clinical trial, Campanati *et al.* [53] have recently compared the effect of a 24-week treatment with etanercept *versus* phototherapy on serum markers of hepatic fibrosis in 89 overweight patients with psoriasis and NAFLD. Notably, they found that there were significant improvements in the aspartate aminotransferase-to-alanine aminotransferase ratio, serum C-reactive protein levels and insulin resistance indices only among psoriatic patients receiving etanercept. This finding suggests that etanercept is more efficacious to reduce the risk of hepatic fibrosis than phototherapy, and that this effect might be mainly dependent on its metabolic and anti-inflammatory properties. However, additional studies with more accurate and direct measures of hepatic fibrosis are needed to further examine this topic. Recently, preliminary evidence has suggested that NAFLD might also be a side effect of TNF-α inhibitor treatment in some cases, and that previous methotrexate exposure and patatin-like phospholipase domain-containing protein-3 (PNPLA3) genotype might be the most important risk factors [54]. Even though only few cases have been reported in the literature, TNF-α inhibitors may induce autoimmune hepatitis, granulomatous hepatitis, and reactivation of viral hepatitis [38,52].

Finally, similarly to patients with NAFLD, lifestyle interventions (hypocaloric diet, exercise and avoiding alcohol consumption) are the mainstay treatment for the majority of psoriatic patients because they may also improve the response to pharmacological treatments for psoriasis [38,39,43]. It is known that the risk of psoriasis and its clinical severity are closely associated with the degree of overweight/obesity of this patient population. Although weight loss alone may be insufficient for maintaining skin disease remission in obese patients with psoriasis [55], some recent intervention trials have demonstrated that treatment with a low-energy diet showed a trend towards significant improvement in PASI scores among overweight or obese patients with psoriasis, and that body weight reduction in psoriatic patients receiving either low-dose cyclosporine or biologics increased the efficacy of these drugs [56–58]. A recent systematic review and meta-analysis including four small randomized clinical trials with either pioglitazone or rosiglitazone that examined the efficacy of glitazones on psoriasis severity has concluded that pioglitazone may exert some positive effect on psoriasis [59]. However, the clinical significance of this effect and role of this drug in management of psoriatic patients deserve further study.

There are as yet few proven therapies available for patients with NAFLD and NASH, and current therapeutic strategies are specifically directed towards improving features of the metabolic syndrome [5,9,36]. Pioglitazone has the best evidence-based data for NASH treatment. To date, however, lifestyle changes are the more effective therapeutic option that is sharable between patients with NAFLD and those with psoriasis. To our knowledge, no randomized clinical trials have specifically examined the effects of chronic treatment with the newer biologic agents on histologic features of NAFLD. Therefore, additional studies are required to evaluate the best approach to management of NAFLD among patients with psoriasis.

6. Conclusions

Although the published evidence is restricted to observational (cross-sectional and case-control) studies [17–27], a growing body of clinical evidence suggests a strong relationship between NAFLD and psoriasis. Published studies indicate that NAFLD is a very frequent condition among adult patients with psoriasis (affecting up to 50% of these patients) and that patients with psoriasis and NAFLD are more likely to have metabolic syndrome and a more severe degree of skin disease than their counterparts without NAFLD. In addition, psoriatic patients are at higher risk of developing the more severe forms of NAFLD (*i.e.*, about a quarter of these patients may develop NASH during the course of the disease). However, further research is required to ascertain whether NAFLD is merely an epiphenomen of coexisting metabolic syndrome features, or is an independent risk factor for the development and progression of psoriasis. Additional studies are also needed to better elucidate the putative biological mechanisms linking NAFLD with psoriasis. Specific mediators of this novel "hepato-dermal axis" need to be further investigated in order to discover innovative drugs and treatments.

In the meantime, given the strong association between NAFLD and psoriasis, we believe that health care providers following psoriatic patients should be mindful of this potentially progressive liver disease that is commonly observed among psoriatic patients. The presence of NAFLD should be also taken into consideration when choosing pharmacological treatment, as some conventional drugs for psoriasis are potentially hepatotoxic.

These findings imply that psoriatic patients should be routinely screened for NAFLD and that consideration should be given to referring these patients to a hepatologist for further evaluation. The optimal method of screening is presently unknown. However, given the intrinsic limitations of serum liver enzyme levels as initial screening test for NAFLD, we think liver ultrasound and transient elastography combined with the use of the NAFLD fibrosis score or other non-invasive fibrosis scoring systems are useful as first-line options in identifying patients with suspected NASH to submit to biopsy among those with psoriasis [60–62]. Moreover, all these patients should be followed regularly to monitor the development of liver-related, metabolic and cardiovascular complications [63].

Acknowledgments: Acknowledgments: Giovanni Targher is supported in part by grants from the University School of Medicine of Verona.

Author Contributions: Author Contributions: Alessandro Mantovani and Giovanni Targher conceived the study and researched the data. Paolo Gisondi and Amedeo Lonardo contributed to discussion and reviewed/edited the manuscript. Giovanni Targher wrote the manuscript.

Conflicts of Interest: Conflicts of Interest: The authors declare no conflict of interest.

References

1. Parisi, R.; Symmons, D.P.; Griffiths, C.E.; Ashcroft, D.M. Global epidemiology of psoriasis: A systematic review of incidence and prevalence. *J. Investig. Dermatol.* **2013**, *133*, 377–385. [CrossRef] [PubMed]
2. Griffiths, C.E.; Barker, J.N. Pathogenesis and clinical features of psoriasis. *Lancet* **2007**, *370*, 263–271. [CrossRef]
3. Gottlieb, A.B.; Chao, C.; Dann, F. Psoriasis comorbidities. *J. Dermatol. Treat.* **2008**, *19*, 5–21. [CrossRef] [PubMed]
4. Non-alcoholic fatty liver disease (NAFLD) Study Group, dedicated to the memory of Prof. Paola Loria; Lonardo, A.; Bellentani, S.; Argo, C.K.; Ballestri, S.; Byrne, C.D.; Caldwell, S.H.; Cortez-Pinto, H.; Grieco, A.; Machado, M.V.; *et al.* Epidemiological modifiers of non-alcoholic fatty liver disease: Focus on high-risk groups. *Dig. Liver Dis.* **2015**, *47*, 997–1006.
5. Anstee, Q.M.; Targher, G.; Day, C.P. Progression of NAFLD to diabetes mellitus, cardiovascular disease or cirrhosis. *Nat. Rev. Gastroenterol. Hepatol.* **2013**, *10*, 330–344. [CrossRef] [PubMed]
6. Lonardo, A.; Ballestri, S.; Marchesini, G.; Angulo, P.; Loria, P. Nonalcoholic fatty liver disease: A precursor of the metabolic syndrome. *Dig. Liver Dis.* **2015**, *47*, 181–190. [CrossRef] [PubMed]
7. Zhang, Y.; Zhang, T.; Zhang, C.; Tang, F.; Zhong, N.; Li, H.; Song, X.; Lin, H.; Liu, Y.; Xue, F. Identification of reciprocal causality between non-alcoholic fatty liver disease and metabolic syndrome by a simplified Bayesian network in a Chinese population. *BMJ Open* **2015**, *5*. [CrossRef] [PubMed]
8. Ballestri, S.; Zona, S.; Targher, G.; Romagnoli, D.; Baldelli, E.; Nascimbeni, F.; Roverato, A.; Guaraldi, G.; Lonardo, A. Nonalcoholic fatty liver disease is associated with an almost two-fold increased risk of incident type 2 diabetes and metabolic syndrome. Evidence from a systematic review and meta-analysis. *J. Gastroenterol. Hepatol.* **2015**. [CrossRef] [PubMed]
9. Byrne, C.D.; Targher, G. NAFLD: A multisystem disease. *J. Hepatol.* **2015**, *62*, S47–S64. [CrossRef] [PubMed]
10. Ballestri, S.; Lonardo, A.; Bonapace, S.; Byrne, C.D.; Loria, P.; Targher, G. Risk of cardiovascular, cardiac and arrhythmic complications in patients with non-alcoholic fatty liver disease. *World J. Gastroenterol.* **2014**, *20*, 1724–1745. [CrossRef] [PubMed]
11. Ogdie, A.; Gelfand, J.M. Clinical risk factors for the development of psoriatic arthritis among patients with psoriasis: A review of available evidence. *Curr. Rheumatol. Rep.* **2015**, *17*. [CrossRef] [PubMed]
12. Sommer, D.M.; Jenisch, S.; Suchan, M.; Christophers, E.; Weichenthal, M. Increased prevalence of the metabolic syndrome in patients with moderate to severe psoriasis. *Arch. Dermatol. Res.* **2006**, *298*, 321–328. [CrossRef] [PubMed]
13. Gisondi, P.; Tessari, G.; Conti, A.; Piaserico, S.; Schianchi, S.; Peserico, A.; Giannetti, A.; Girolomoni, G. Prevalence of metabolic syndrome in patients with psoriasis: A hospital-based case-control study. *Br. J. Dermatol.* **2007**, *157*, 68–73. [CrossRef] [PubMed]
14. Chandra, A.; Ray, A.; Senapati, S.; Chatterjee, R. Genetic and epigenetic basis of psoriasis pathogenesis. *Mol. Immunol.* **2015**, *64*, 313–323. [CrossRef] [PubMed]

15. Lowes, M.A.; Suarez-Farinas, M.; Krueger, J.G. Immunology of psoriasis. *Annu. Rev. Immunol.* **2014**, *32*, 227–255. [CrossRef] [PubMed]
16. Durham, L.E.; Kirkham, B.W.; Taams, L.S. Contribution of the IL-17 pathway to psoriasis and psoriatic arthritis. *Curr. Rheumatol. Rep.* **2015**, *17*. [CrossRef] [PubMed]
17. Lonardo, A.; Loria, P.; Carulli, N. Concurrent non-alcoholic steatohepatitis and psoriasis. Report of three cases from the POLI.ST.E.N.A. Study. *Dig. Liver Dis.* **2001**, *33*, 86–87. [CrossRef]
18. Matsumoto, T.; Suziki, N.; Watanabe, H.; Irie, M.; Iwata, K.; Anan, A.; Nakane, H.; Yoshikane, M.; Nishizawa, S.; Sohda, T.; *et al.* Nonalcoholic steatohepatitis associated with psoriasis vulgaris. *J. Gastroenterol.* **2004**, *39*, 1102–1110. [CrossRef] [PubMed]
19. Gisondi, P.; Targher, G.; Zoppini, G.; Girolomoni, G. Non-alcoholic fatty liver disease in patients with chronic plaque psoriasis. *J. Hepatol.* **2009**, *51*, 758–764. [CrossRef] [PubMed]
20. Miele, L.; Vallone, S.; Cefalo, C.; la Torre, G.; di Stasi, C.; Vecchio, F.M.; D'Agostino, M.; Gabrieli, M.L.; Vero, V.; Biolato, M.; *et al.* Prevalence, characteristics and severity of non-alcoholic fatty liver disease in patients with chronic plaque psoriasis. *J. Hepatol.* **2009**, *51*, 778–786. [CrossRef] [PubMed]
21. Madanagobalane, S.; Anandan, S. The increased prevalence of non-alcoholic fatty liver disease in psoriatic patients: A study from South India. *Australas. J. Dermatol.* **2012**, *53*, 190–197. [CrossRef] [PubMed]
22. Van der Voort, E.A.; Koehler, E.M.; Dowlatshahi, E.A.; Hofman, A.; Stricker, B.H.; Janssen, H.L.; Schouten, J.N.; Nijsten, T. Psoriasis is independently associated with nonalcoholic fatty liver disease in patients 55 years old or older: Results from a population-based study. *J. Am. Acad. Dermatol.* **2014**, *70*, 517–524. [CrossRef] [PubMed]
23. Van der Voort, E.A.; Koehler, E.M.; Nijsten, T.; Stricker, B.H.; Hofman, A.; Janssen, H.L.; Schouten, J.N.; Wakkee, M. Increased prevalence of advanced liver fibrosis in patients with psoriasis: A cross-sectional analysis from the Rotterdam study. *Acta Derm. Venereol.* **2015**. [CrossRef] [PubMed]
24. Gisondi, P.; Barba, E.; Girolomoni, G. Non-alcoholic fatty liver disease fibrosis score in patients with psoriasis. *J. Eur. Acad. Dermatol. Venereol.* **2015**, *30*, 282–287. [CrossRef] [PubMed]
25. Abedini, R.; Salehi, M.; Lajevardi, V.; Beygi, S. Patients with psoriasis are at a higher risk of developing nonalcoholic fatty liver disease. *Clin. Exp. Dermatol.* **2015**, *40*, 722–727. [CrossRef] [PubMed]
26. Roberts, K.K.; Cochet, A.E.; Lamb, P.B.; Brown, P.J.; Battafarano, D.F.; Brunt, E.M.; Harrison, S.A. The prevalence of NAFLD and NASH among patients with psoriasis in a tertiary care dermatology and rheumatology clinic. *Aliment. Pharmacol. Ther.* **2015**, *41*, 293–300. [CrossRef] [PubMed]
27. Candia, R.; Ruiz, A.; Torres-Robles, R.; Chávez-Tapia, N.; Méndez-Sánchez, N.; Arrese, M. Risk of non-alcoholic fatty liver disease in patients with psoriasis: A systematic review and meta-analysis. *J. Eur. Acad. Dermatol. Venereol.* **2015**, *29*, 656–662. [CrossRef] [PubMed]
28. Birkenfeld, A.L.; Shulman, G.I. Nonalcoholic fatty liver disease, hepatic insulin resistance, and type 2 diabetes. *Hepatology* **2014**, *59*, 713–723. [CrossRef] [PubMed]
29. Shoelson, S.E.; Lee, J.; Goldfine, A.B. Inflammation and insulin resistance. *J. Clin. Investig.* **2006**, *116*, 1793–1801. [CrossRef] [PubMed]
30. Ucak, S.; Ekmekci, T.; Basat, O. Comparison of various insulin sensitivity indices in psoriatic patients and their relationship with types of psoriasis. *J. Eur. Acad. Dermatol. Venereol.* **2006**, *20*, 517–522. [CrossRef] [PubMed]
31. Byrne, C.D.; Targher, G. Ectopic fat, insulin resistance, and nonalcoholic fatty liver disease: Implications for cardiovascular disease. *Arterioscler. Thromb. Vasc. Biol.* **2014**, *34*, 1155–1161. [CrossRef] [PubMed]
32. Loria, P.; Carulli, L.; Bertolotti, M.; Lonardo, A. Endocrine and liver interaction: The role of endocrine pathways in NASH. *Nat. Rev. Gastroenterol. Hepatol.* **2009**, *6*, 236–247. [CrossRef] [PubMed]
33. Shulmann, G.I. Ectopic fat in insulin resistance, dyslipidemia, and cardiometabolic disease. *N. Engl. J. Med.* **2014**, *371*, 1131–1141. [CrossRef] [PubMed]
34. Hunter, C.A.; Jones, S.A. IL-6 as a keystone cytokine in health and disease. *Nat. Immunol.* **2015**, *16*, 448–457. [CrossRef] [PubMed]
35. Stefan, N.; Häring, H.U. The role of hepatokines in metabolism. *Nat. Rev. Endocrinol.* **2013**, *9*, 144–152. [CrossRef] [PubMed]
36. Targher, G.; Day, C.P.; Bonora, E. Risk of cardiovascular disease in patients with nonalcoholic fatty liver disease. *N. Engl. J. Med.* **2010**, *363*, 1341–1350.

37. Kulkarni, N.M.; Jaji, M.S.; Shetty, P.; Kurhe, Y.V.; Chaudhary, S.; Vijaykant, G.; Raghul, J.; Vishwakarma, S.L.; Rajesh, B.N.; Mookkan, J.; *et al.* A novel animal model of metabolic syndrome with non-alcoholic fatty liver disease and skin inflammation. *Pharm. Biol.* **2015**, *53*, 1110–1117. [CrossRef] [PubMed]

38. Nast, A.; Gisondi, P.; Ormerod, A.D.; Saiag, P.; Smith, C.; Spuls, P.I.; Arenberger, P.; Bachelez, H.; Barker, J.; Dauden, E.; *et al.* European S3-Guidelines on the systemic treatment of psoriasis vulgaris—Update 2015—Short version—EDF in cooperation with EADV and IPC. *J. Eur. Acad. Dermatol. Venereol.* **2015**, *29*, 2277–2294. [CrossRef] [PubMed]

39. Gisondi, P.; Galvan, A.; Idolazzi, L.; Girolomoni, G. Management of moderate to severe psoriasis in patients with metabolic comorbidities. *Front. Med.* **2015**, *2*. [CrossRef] [PubMed]

40. Kalb, R.E.; Strober, B.; Weinstein, G.; Lebwohl, M. Methotrexate and psoriasis: 2009 National psoriasis foundation consensus conference. *J. Am. Acad. Dermatol.* **2009**, *60*, 824–837. [CrossRef] [PubMed]

41. Hardwick, R.N.; Clarke, J.D.; Lake, A.D.; Canet, M.J.; Anumol, T.; Street, S.M.; Merrell, M.D.; Goedken, M.J.; Snyder, S.A.; Cherrington, N.J. Increased susceptibility to methotrexate-induced toxicity in nonalcoholic steatohepatitis. *Toxicol. Sci.* **2014**, *142*, 45–55. [CrossRef] [PubMed]

42. Rosenberg, P.; Urwitz, H.; Johannesson, A.; Ros, A.M.; Lindholm, J.; Kinnman, N.; Hultcrantz, R. Psoriasis patients with diabetes type 2 are at high risk of developing liver fibrosis during methotrexate treatment. *J. Hepatol.* **2007**, *46*, 1111–1118. [CrossRef] [PubMed]

43. Gisondi, P.; Cazzaniga, S.; Chimenti, S.; Giannetti, A.; Maccarone, M.; Picardo, M.; Girolomoni, G.; Naldi, L. Psocare Study Group. Metabolic abnormalities associated with initiation of systemic treatment for psoriasis: Evidence from the Italian Psocare Registry. *J. Eur. Acad. Dermatol. Venereol.* **2013**, *27*, e30–e41. [CrossRef] [PubMed]

44. Neuvonen, P.J.; Niemi, M.; Backman, J.T. Drug interactions with lipid-lowering drugs: Mechanisms and clinical relevance. *Clin. Pharmacol. Ther.* **2006**, *80*, 565–581. [CrossRef] [PubMed]

45. Dunn, L.K.; Gaar, L.R.; Yentzer, B.A.; O'Neill, J.L.; Feldman, S.R. Acitretin in dermatology: A review. *J. Drugs Dermatol.* **2011**, *10*, 772–782. [PubMed]

46. Martinez Abundis, E.; Reynoso-von, D.C.; Hernandez-Salazar, E.; Gonzalez-Ortiz, M. Effect of etanercept on insulin secretion and insulin sensitivity in a randomized trial with psoriatic patients at risk for developing type 2 diabetes mellitus. *Arch. Dermatol. Res.* **2007**, *299*, 461–465. [CrossRef] [PubMed]

47. Stanley, T.L.; Zanni, M.V.; Johnsen, S.; Rasheed, S.; Makimura, H.; Lee, H.; Khor, V.K.; Ahima, R.S.; Grinspoon, S.K. TNF-α antagonism with etanercept decreases glucose and increases the proportion of high molecular weight adiponectin in obese subjects with features of the metabolic syndrome. *J. Clin. Endocrinol. Metab.* **2011**, *96*, E146–E150. [CrossRef] [PubMed]

48. Solomon, D.H.; Massarotti, E.; Garg, R.; Liu, J.; Canning, C.; Schneeweiss, S. Association between disease-modifying anti-rheumatic drugs and diabetes risk in patients with rheumatoid arthritis and psoriasis. *JAMA* **2011**, *305*, 2525–2531. [CrossRef] [PubMed]

49. Lestre, S.; Diamantino, F.; Veloso, L.; Fidalgo, A.; Ferreira, A. Effects of etanercept treatment on lipid profile in patients with moderate-to-severe chronic plaque psoriasis: A retrospective cohort study. *Eur. J. Dermatol.* **2011**, *21*, 916–920. [PubMed]

50. Gisondi, P.; Conti, A.; Galdo, G.; Piaserico, S.; de Simone, C.; Girolomoni, G. Ustekinumab does not increase body mass index in patients with chronic plaque psoriasis: A prospective cohort study. *Br. J. Dermatol.* **2013**, *168*, 1124–1127. [CrossRef] [PubMed]

51. Tobon, G.J.; Cañas, C.; Jaller, J.J.; Restrepo, J.C.; Anaya, J.M. Serious liver disease induced by infliximab. *Clin. Rheumatol.* **2007**, *26*, 578–581. [CrossRef] [PubMed]

52. Tan, K.W.; Griffiths, C.E. Novel systemic therapies for the treatment of psoriasis. *Expert. Opin. Pharmacother.* **2016**, *17*, 79–92. [CrossRef] [PubMed]

53. Campanati, A.; Ganzetti, G.; di Sario, A.; Damiani, A.; Sandroni, L.; Rosa, L.; Benedetti, A.; Offidani, A. The effect of etanercept on hepatic fibrosis risk in patients with non-alcoholic fatty liver disease, metabolic syndrome, and psoriasis. *J. Gastroenterol.* **2013**, *48*, 839–846. [CrossRef] [PubMed]

54. Feagins, L.A.; Flores, A.; Arriens, C.; Park, C.; Crook, T.; Reimold, A.; Brown, G. Nonalcoholic fatty liver disease: A potential consequence of tumor necrosis factor-inhibitor therapy. *Eur. J. Gastroenterol. Hepatol.* **2015**, *27*, 1154–1160. [CrossRef] [PubMed]

55. Del Giglio, M.; Gisondi, P.; Tessari, G.; Girolomoni, G. Weight reduction alone may not be sufficient to maintain disease remission in obese patients with psoriasis: A randomized, investigator-blinded study. *Dermatology* **2012**, *224*, 31–37. [CrossRef] [PubMed]
56. Jensen, P.; Zachariae, C.; Christensen, R.; Geiker, N.R.; Schaadt, B.K.; Stender, S.; Hansen, P.R.; Astrup, A.; Skov, L. Effect of weight loss on the severity of psoriasis: A randomized clinical study. *JAMA Dermatol.* **2013**, *149*, 795–801. [CrossRef] [PubMed]
57. Gisondi, P.; del Giglio, M.; di Francesco, V.; Zamboni, M.; Girolomoni, G. Weight loss improves the response of obese patients with moderate-to-severe chronic plaque psoriasis to low-dose cyclosporine therapy: A randomized, controlled, investigator-blinded clinical trial. *Am. J. Clin. Nutr.* **2008**, *88*, 1242–1247. [PubMed]
58. Al-Mutairi, N.; Nour, T. The effect of weight reduction on treatment outcomes in obese patients with psoriasis on biologic therapy: A randomized controlled prospective trial. *Expert Opin. Biol. Ther.* **2014**, *14*, 749–756. [CrossRef] [PubMed]
59. Malhotra, A.; Shafiq, N.; Rajagopalan, S.; Dogra, S.; Malhotra, S. Thiazolidinediones for plaque psoriasis: A systematic review and meta-analysis. *Evid. Based Med.* **2012**, *17*, 171–176. [CrossRef] [PubMed]
60. Nascimbeni, F.; Pais, R.; Bellentani, S.; Day, C.P.; Ratziu, V.; Loria, P.; Lonardo, A. From NAFLD in clinical practice to answers from guidelines. *J. Hepatol.* **2013**, *59*, 859–871. [CrossRef] [PubMed]
61. Castera, L.; Vilgrain, V.; Angulo, P. Noninvasive evaluation of NAFLD. *Nat. Rev. Gastroenterol. Hepatol.* **2013**, *10*, 666–675. [CrossRef] [PubMed]
62. Ballestri, S.; Romagnoli, D.; Nascimbeni, F.; Francica, G.; Lonardo, A. Role of ultrasound in the diagnosis and treatment of nonalcoholic fatty liver disease and its complications. *Expert Rev. Gastroenterol. Hepatol.* **2015**, *9*, 603–627. [CrossRef] [PubMed]
63. Lonardo, A.; Ballestri, S.; Targher, G.; Loria, P. Diagnosis and management of cardiovascular risk in nonalcoholic fatty liver disease. *Expert Rev. Gastroenterol. Hepatol.* **2015**, *9*, 629–650. [CrossRef] [PubMed]

International Journal of
Molecular Sciences

MDPI

Review

Bidirectional Relationships and Disconnects between NAFLD and Features of the Metabolic Syndrome

Patrick Wainwright [1] and Christopher D. Byrne [2,3,*]

1   Clinical Biochemistry, University Hospital Southampton, Tremona Road, Southampton SO16 6YD, UK;
    patrick.wainwright@uhs.nhs.uk
2   Nutrition and Metabolism, Faculty of Medicine, University of Southampton, Tremona Road,
    Southampton SO16 6YD, UK
3   Southampton National Institute for Health Research Biomedical Research Centre,
    University Hospital Southampton, Tremona Road, Southampton SO16 6YD, UK
*   Correspondence: C.D.Byrne@soton.ac.uk; Tel.: +44-023-8120-5006

Academic Editors: Amedeo Lonardo and Giovanni Targher
Received: 16 February 2016; Accepted: 7 March 2016; Published: 11 March 2016

Abstract: Non-alcoholic fatty liver disease (NAFLD) represents a wide spectrum of liver disease from simple steatosis, to steatohepatitis, (both with and without liver fibrosis), cirrhosis and end-stage liver failure. NAFLD also increases the risk of hepatocellular carcinoma (HCC) and both HCC and end stage liver disease may markedly increase risk of liver-related mortality. NAFLD is increasing in prevalence and is presently the second most frequent indication for liver transplantation. As NAFLD is frequently associated with insulin resistance, central obesity, dyslipidaemia, hypertension and hyperglycaemia, NAFLD is often considered the hepatic manifestation of the metabolic syndrome. There is growing evidence that this relationship between NAFLD and metabolic syndrome is bidirectional, in that NAFLD can predispose to metabolic syndrome features, which can in turn exacerbate NAFLD or increase the risk of its development in those without a pre-existing diagnosis. Although the relationship between NAFLD and metabolic syndrome is frequently bidirectional, recently there has been much interest in genotype/phenotype relationships where there is a disconnect between the liver disease and metabolic syndrome features. Such potential examples of genotypes that are associated with a dissociation between liver disease and metabolic syndrome are patatin-like phospholipase domain-containing protein-3 (PNPLA3) (I148M) and transmembrane 6 superfamily member 2 protein (TM6SF2) (E167K) genotypes. This review will explore the bidirectional relationship between metabolic syndrome and NAFLD, and will also discuss recent insights from studies of PNPLA3 and TM6SF2 genotypes that may give insight into how and why metabolic syndrome features and liver disease are linked in NAFLD.

Keywords: NAFLD; metabolic syndrome; insulin resistance; PNPLA3

---

1. Introduction

Non-alcoholic fatty liver disease (NAFLD) is a considerable public health concern, and is the commonest cause for chronic liver disease in the developed world [1,2]. Worldwide prevalence of NAFLD is estimated to be in the region of 20% in the general population [3]. NAFLD represents a disease spectrum ranging from hepatic steatosis, to non-alcoholic steatohepatitis, to cirrhosis, end-stage liver failure and hepatocellular carcinoma. The accepted definition of NAFLD is a hepatic triglyceride content of greater than 5.5%, as determined from analysis of the Dallas Heart Study cohort [4]. The metabolic syndrome is a collection of underlying risk factors for cardiovascular disease with an estimated prevalence in the USA of 34% [5].

The relationship between NAFLD, obesity, insulin resistance and type 2 diabetes is a complex one. NAFLD has traditionally been considered to be the hepatic manifestation of the metabolic syndrome, due to the close association between NAFLD and the various component features of the metabolic syndrome such as abdominal obesity, hypertension, elevated fasting plasma glucose, raised serum triglycerides and low high-density lipoprotein cholesterol (HDL-C) concentrations. Many epidemiological studies have demonstrated an association between NAFLD and the metabolic syndrome [6–8].

There is now a growing body of evidence supporting the idea that there is a bidirectional relationship between NAFLD and features of the metabolic syndrome, with insulin resistance being the central pathophysiological process common to both conditions. As such there currently exists and "chicken and egg" debate in the literature regarding the temporal relationship between NAFLD and the metabolic syndrome, with no clear consensus about which is considered to generally occur first. A recent study has demonstrated a reciprocal causality between NAFLD and metabolic syndrome in a Chinese population, with metabolic syndrome being found to have a greater effect on incident NAFLD in terms of causality than NAFLD does on incident metabolic syndrome [9].

In addition to this there are recognised situations whereby there is an apparent disconnect between NAFLD and insulin resistance/metabolic syndrome features, and these generally arise as a result of particular genetic polymorphisms such as in the patatin-like phospholipase domain-containing protein-3 (PNPLA3) gene.

This review will attempt to review the available evidence regarding the bidirectional relationship between NAFLD and components of the metabolic syndrome, as well as to explore the potential disconnects that may exist between the two due to genetic variability and inherited metabolic disease.

2. Association between NAFLD and Components of the Metabolic Syndrome

There have been various diagnostic criteria available for the diagnosis of metabolic syndrome, and these have changed subtly over recent years. The most commonly used criteria are those published by the International Diabetes Federation in 2009. It should be noted that these most recent criteria advocate using population- and country- specific definitions for abdominal obesity [10]. Table 1 outlines the various diagnostic criteria available.

NAFLD can occur in individuals who are not obese [11,12], however this is more unusual and generally NAFLD is closely related to increased central adiposity. NAFLD is commonly associated with all of the component features of the metabolic syndrome, and nearly two thirds of people with obesity and type 2 diabetes demonstrate hepatic steatosis [13,14]. One study identified hepatic steatosis via ultrasonography in 50% of patients with hyperlipidaemia [15]. NAFLD is also associated with arterial hypertension and cross-sectional studies have demonstrated that approximately 50% of people with essential hypertension also have NAFLD [16,17]. Importantly, in those people with NAFLD the presence of multiple features of the metabolic syndrome is associated with more severe liver disease and a higher likelihood of progression to NASH and cirrhosis [18,19].

Table 1. Diagnostic criteria available for metabolic syndrome.

Criteria	WHO (1999)	NCEP (2001)	IDF (2005)	IDF (2009)
Required	Insulin resistance	Nil	Waist circumference ≥94 cm in men, ≥80 cm in women	Nil
Number of features	≥2 of:	≥3 of:	≥2 of:	≥3 of:
Obesity	Waist/hip ratio of >0.9 in men, >0.85 in women or BMI ≥ 30	Waist circumference ≥ 102 cm in men, ≥88 cm in women		Waist circumference—population specific definitions
Triglycerides	≥150 mg/dL (1.7 mmol/L)	≥150 mg/dL (1.7 mmol/L)	≥150 mg/dL (1.7 mmol/L)	≥150 mg/dL (1.7 mmol/L)
HDL-cholesterol	<40 mg/dL (1 mmol/L) in men, <50 mg/dL (1.3 mmol/L) in women	<40 mg/dL (1 mmol/L) in men, <50 mg/dL (1.3 mmol/L) in women	<40 mg/dL (1 mmol/L) in men, <50 mg/dL (1.3 mmol/L) in women	<40 mg/dL (1 mmol/L) in men, <50 mg/dL (1.3 mmol/L) in women
Hypertension	≥140/90 mmHg	≥135/85 mmHg	≥135/85 mmHg	≥135/85 mmHg
Glucose	110 mg/dL (6.1 mmol/L)	110 mg/dL (6.1 mmol/L)	100 mg/dL (5.6 mmol/L)	100 mg/dL (5.6 mmol/L)
Microalbuminuria	Albumin/creatinine ratio > 30 mg/g; albumin excretion rate > 20 mcg/min			

WHO, World Health Organisation; NCEP, National Cholesterol Education Program; IDF, international diabetes federation.

3. NAFLD as a Risk Factor for and Precursor to the Metabolic Syndrome

There is evidence to suggest that NAFLD, rather than being simply the hepatic manifestation of the metabolic syndrome, may in fact be a necessary first step in its development.

When the link between NAFLD and insulin resistance was initially described by Day et al, it was proposed as part of a "two hit hypothesis" [20]. Here, the "first hit" was increased triglyceride accumulation as a result of insulin resistance and increased delivery of free fatty acids to the liver, followed by a "second hit" of hepatic oxidative stress resulting in increased lipid peroxidation. This was said to then lead inexorably to hepatocyte injury, inflammation and fibrosis, with the potential for progressive liver damage. It has subsequently been suggested that pathogenesis of NAFLD may in fact reflect "multiple parallel hits" which all contribute to an environment of hepatic inflammation with the involvement of cytokines and adipokines from extrahepatic tissues such as the gut and adipose tissue [21].

From a basic science perspective, there is reason to believe that hepatic lipid accumulation could be a cause and a perpetuating factor for the development of insulin resistance. There is currently much interest in fully elucidating the role that protein kinase C-ε (PKC-ε) may play in this relationship. An elegant study conducted by Samuel et al investigated PKC-ε and how it may link NAFLD and insulin resistance [22]. They observed that rats that were fed a 3 day high-fat diet developed marked hepatic steatosis and hepatic insulin resistance as determined by hyperinsulinaemic-euglycaemic clamp studies. Here, PKC-ε was activated but other forms of PKC were not. Crucially, the authors then went on to attenuate the expression of PKC-ε using an anti-sense oligonucelotide directed at PKC-ε and they noted that this protected the rats from steatosis-induced hepatic insulin resistance and also reversed defects that they had observed in insulin receptor signalling function. It should be noted that both hepatic diacylglycerol and triacylglycerol content were not affected by this intervention suggesting that the hepatic lipid accumulation is a prerequisite for insulin resistance. This relationship has also been investigated in humans, in a study of 37 obese non-diabetic individuals awaiting bariatric surgery [23]. Here it was observed that hepatic diacylglycerol content from liver biopsy specimens was the strongest predictor of insulin resistance and accounted for 64% of the variability in insulin sensitivity. Hepatic diacylglycerol content was strongly correlated with activation of PKC-ε. Given this evidence, a model has emerged whereby increases in liver diacylglycerol content result in activation of PKC-ε, translocation of PKC-ε in the cell membrane, inhibition of hepatic insulin signalling and the resulting generation and maintenance of hepatocyte insulin resistance.

More recently there has been interest in the hepatokine, fetuin B. This compound has been shown to be increased in obese rodents [24]. It has also been shown that overnutrition in experimental mice results in hepatic steatosis, and this alters the hepatocyte protein secretion profile leading to increased secretion of fetuin B [25]. The authors of this study went on to further study the effects of fetuin B *in vivo* and observed that injecting recombinant fetuin B intraperitoneally into mice significantly impaired glucose tolerance when compared with controls. In addition to this, silencing fetuin B gene expression using short hairpin RNA was found to increase glucose tolerance. As such, fetuin B provides an example of how hepatic steatosis can be linked to the development of insulin resistance and thus the metabolic syndrome. Other hepatokines such as FGF21 and selenoprotein P are thought to be play a role in the pathophysiology of insulin resistance with action on the liver and other tissues, however it is less clear how they fit into the relationship between hepatic steatosis and the metabolic syndrome.

It is known that most people with NAFLD also have insulin resistance, however most do not exhibit all of the features of the metabolic syndrome [26]. This could indicate that hepatic steatosis is required as a prerequisite for the development of further metabolic disease such as altered glucose and lipid metabolism. There is now a significant body of clinical evidence for NAFLD preceding, and being a strong risk factor for, development of the metabolic syndrome and its various components. A large prospective cohort study looked at 17,920 individuals from a Han Chinese population and followed them up over a 6 years period [27]. These individuals did not have metabolic syndrome at baseline, and the authors identified NAFLD as an independent risk factor for its development with an adjusted hazard ratio of 1.55 (95% confidence intervals 1.39–1.72). This observation of NAFLD as an independent risk factor for the development of the metabolic syndrome has also been made in a variety of other populations such as North American [28], western Australian [29], Korean [30], Japanese [31] and south Indian [32].

A large prospective cohort study of over 22,000 Korean men demonstrated that NAFLD is an independent risk factor for incident arterial hypertension, and that risk increases with severity of NAFLD [33]. This study replicated the findings of an earlier, smaller prospective study which demonstrated that NAFLD was an independent risk factor for the development of prehypertension [34]. Another prospective cohort study examined 1521 people and stratified them on the basis of their fatty liver index score (a surrogate marker of hepatic steatosis) [35]. It was observed that NAFLD, as diagnosed using fatty liver index score, was an independent risk factor for incident arterial hypertension. Finally, a retrospective cohort study of 11,448 individuals without hypertension revealed that the development of incident fatty liver disease over a five years period was associated with increased risk of incident hypertension [36].

A retrospective study of a Korean occupational cohort of 13,218 individuals observed that development of new fatty liver was associated with incident diabetes [37]. There are many prospective studies in the literature that demonstrate that NAFLD, and the surrogate markers with which it is associated, is a key risk factor and precursor for the development of type 2 diabetes [29,38–46]. Table 2 summarises the characteristics of these key studies.

Of particular interest is a longitudinal cohort study in which the authors followed up 358 individuals (109 with NAFLD, 249 without NAFLD) over an 11 years period [29]. After excluding those who had type 2 diabetes at baseline, they observed that those with NAFLD were significantly more likely to develop diabetes during the follow up period than those without. Similarly, they observed the same regarding who would go on to develop the metabolic syndrome. Also, a retrospective study of a Korean occupational cohort of 12,853 individuals demonstrated that the clustering of insulin resistance, overweight/obesity and hepatic steatosis markedly increased risk of incident type 2 diabetes [47]. The fully adjusted odds ratio for those with all 3 factors and risk of incident diabetes at 5 years follow-up was 14.13 (95% confidence intervals 8.99–22.21).

In addition to this, a meta-analysis has been performed recently which concluded that the presence of NAFLD doubles an individual's risk of developing type 2 diabetes in later life [48]. It would seem that there may be subsets of patients with NAFLD that have different levels of risk of type 2 diabetes, with one small study suggesting that the presence of biopsy-proven NASH is a greater risk factor than steatosis alone [41]. This is consistent with the accepted notion that individuals with nonalcoholic steatohepatitis (NASH) will tend to have a greater burden of metabolic disease.

Table 2. Characteristics of prospective studies linking hepatic steatosis to the development of type 2 diabetes.

Study	Country/Population	Sample Size	NAFLD Diagnostic Method/Surrogate Marker Used	Duration of Follow-Up	Key Findings	Limitations of Study
Vozarova 2002 [38]	Pima Indians aged 18–50	173 women, 278 men	ALT, AST and GGT concentrations	6.9 years average	High baseline ALT associated with increased risk of incident DM	Only surrogate markers used, no control for alcohol/hep C
Lee 2003 [39]	Korean men aged 25–55	4088 men	GGT concentration	4 years	Strong relationship between baseline GGT and risk of incident DM	Only studied men, only used surrogate marker
Hanley 2005 [40]	USA non-Hispanic whites and African American adults	910 women, 715 men	ALT, AST and ALP concentrations	5.2 years average	ALT and ALP in upper quartile at baseline significantly increased risk of metabolic syndrome	Only surrogate markers used for NAFLD diagnosis
Ekstedt 2006 [41]	Swedish NAFLD patients	87 men, 42 women	Biopsy-proven NAFLD	13.7 years average	Marked increase in proportion of patients with DM over period of study	No control group, no baseline glycaemic data to compare
Monami 2008 [42]	Florence aged 40–75	3124 total	ALT, AST and GGT concentrations	40 months average	Baseline GGT near upper limit of normal predicts incident DM	Study population participated in screening programme for diabetes, may not be representative
Goessling 2008 [43]	New England adults, all white	1575 women, 1237 men	ALT and AST concentrations	20 years	Increased ALT associated with higher risk of DM and metabolic syndrome, increased AST associated with incident DM risk	Homogenous study population, only surrogate markers used
Adams 2009 [29]	Western Australian adults	115 women, 243 men	NAFLD diagnosed with ALT after exclusion of other causes	11 years	NAFLD associated with higher risk of incident diabetes	Not an independent predictor if adjusted for WC, hypertension or insulin resistance
Ryu 2010 [44]	Korean men aged 30–65	9148 men	GGT concentrations	4.1 years average	Increase in GGT during study period predicted incident metabolic syndrome	Did not use accepted criteria for diagnosis of metabolic syndrome
Balkau 2010 [45]	Western France, aged 30–65	1950 women, 1861 men	NAFLD diagnosed using fatty liver index (FLI) score	9 years	Higher FLI score at baseline predicted incident DM	Used FLI rather than formal diagnostic methods
Sung 2011 [46]	Korean adults	7236 men, 3855 women	NAFLD diagnosed with ultrasound scan	5 years	Presence of fatty liver on ultrasound strongly predicted incident DM	Ultrasound relatively insensitive for diagnosis

ALT, alanine aminotransferase; AST, aspartate aminotransferase; GGT, gamma-glutamyl transferase; DM, diabetes mellitus; ALP, alkaline Phosphatase; NAFLD, non-alcoholic fatty liver disease; WC, waist circumference.

4. Metabolic Syndrome as an Initiating or Aggravating Factor for Liver Disease

In addition to the evidence from the literature that NAFLD may predispose individuals to developing or worsening insulin resistance and the metabolic syndrome, there is also growing evidence that insulin resistance may contribute to progressive liver damage.

Of particular interest is the role played by plasminogen activator inhibitor 1 [49]. PAI-1 is a member of the serine protease inhibitor family, and acts as a key mediator in the fibrinolytic system. In tissues with a significant degree of fibrosis, concentrations of PAI-1 are elevated leading to an inhibition of tissue proteolytic activities, a decreased rate of collagen degradation and increased tissue fibrogenesis [49]. Increased PAI-1 levels are associated with obesity, insulin resistance, type 2 diabetes and dyslipidaemia [50,51]. Specifically it has been shown that PAI-1 concentrations measured in subcutaneous adipose tissue biopsy samples from individuals with nascent metabolic syndrome are significantly higher than those in control samples [52]. It has also been observed in a human hepatocyte cell line that tumour necrosis factor α (TNF-α) is able to induce the expression of PAI-1, leading to increased hepatic fibrosis and atherosclerosis in insulin-resistant individuals [53]. There is also a wealth of evidence in the literature regarding the role of PAI-1 in initiating and perpetuating hepatic fibrosis [49]. As such this provides evidence of a causative role for insulin resistance and obesity in the generation of ongoing hepatic fibrosis.

In addition to this, there is evidence that other inflammatory cytokines originating from white adipose tissue as a result of obesity and insulin resistance may play a significant role in hepatic fibrosis and inflammation. It has been known for some time that white adipose tissue is not metabolically inert but is a complex organ that can become active in the obese, insulin-resistant state leading to the production of various pro-inflammatory cytokines [54,55]. These cytokines include interleukin-1β (IL-1β), interleukin-6 (IL-6), interleukin-8 (IL-8), interleukin-18 (IL-18), complement component 3 (C3), TNF-α, PAI-1, adiponectin, leptin, resistin, apelin, vaspin and visfatin. There is evidence that these inflammatory mediators could play a role in the progression of liver disease from "simple" steatosis to NASH [56,57], and also that they may stimulate the differentiation of stellate cells in the liver into myofibroblast-like cells resulting in a more fibrogenic environment [58]. IL-1β, IL-6 and TNF-α are traditionally considered to be pro-inflammatory cytokines, and are all thought to play a role in the pathogenesis of NASH and its associated fibrosis [59,60]. More recently it has been suggested that the balance of pro- and anti-inflammatory mediators can lead to alterations in the gut microbiota and that this may have a significant impact on the progression of hepatic steatosis to NASH [61]. It has also been suggested that apoptosis of hepatocytes could be an important factor in liver damage and specifically progression to NASH [62,63]. Recent findings indicate that patients with a higher degree of insulin resistance exhibit greater evidence for apoptosis of hepatocytes in liver biopsy specimens of morbidly obese individuals, and it has been speculated that this may be mediated by inflammatory cytokines [64]. These studies all provide evidence for a causative link between insulin resistance and hepatic damage mediated in part by inflamed, endocrinologically-active adipose tissue.

There is also clinical evidence that insulin resistance and the metabolic syndrome can cause a worsening of liver disease. A retrospective study of 103 individuals with NAFLD examined histological findings from paired liver biopsy specimens with an average interval of 3 years [65]. The authors observed marked variability in the progression of histological features of NAFLD between the 2 time points, but noted that those individuals with diabetes were at higher risk than non-diabetic people for progression of fibrosis. It is also established in the literature that metabolic syndrome and type 2 diabetes are strongly associated with severe liver disease such as cirrhosis and hepatocellular carcinoma [66–69]. It appears from the literature that individuals with type 2 diabetes and NAFLD combined are at markedly greater risk of more severe liver disease than those with NAFLD alone, and their liver-related mortality is greater.

There are a variety of cross-sectional studies available that demonstrate that metabolic syndrome and its components are associated with an increased risk of NAFLD in a variety of populations including North American [70], Mexican [71], Taiwanese [72] and Japanese [26]. However, given the cross-sectional nature of these studies they do not provide real evidence of a causative link. Of interest is a recent longitudinal prospective cohort study of 15,791 Han Chinese individuals followed up over a 6 years period [73]. They observed 3913 new cases of NAFLD in this population, and risk of incident NAFLD was markedly higher in those with metabolic syndrome. After adjusting for possible confounding factors such as age, diet, sex, smoking status and level of physical activity, the hazard ratio for incident NAFLD was found to be 1.94 (95% confidence intervals 1.78–2.13). The authors also observed that hazard ratios for incident NAFLD increased the more components of the metabolic syndrome were present at baseline, reaching 3.51 (95% confidence intervals 3.15–3.91) when 3 components were present as compared with individuals who exhibited no metabolic syndrome components. Figure 1 summarises the bidirectional relationship between hepatic steatosis and the metabolic syndrome with regards to the various aspects described above.

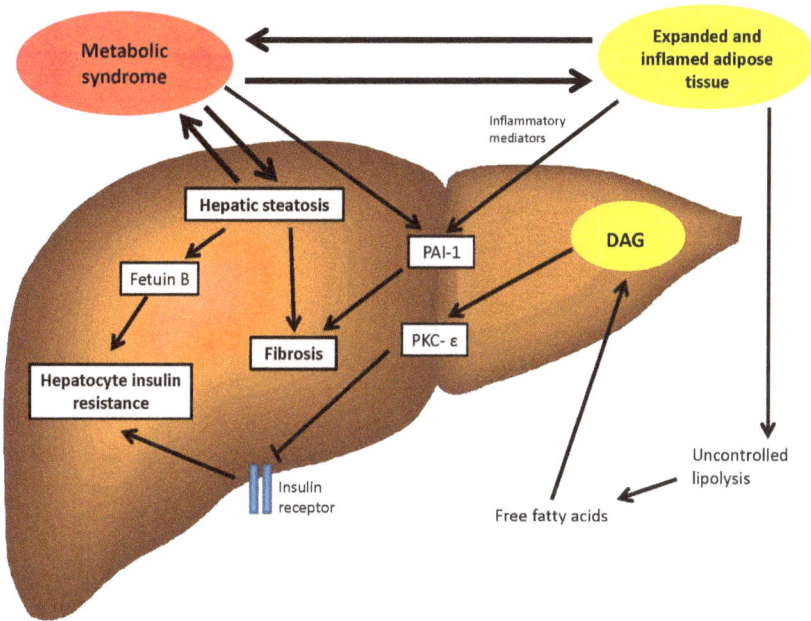

Figure 1. Schematic demonstrating the bidirectional interactions between hepatic steatosis and metabolic syndrome and aspects of how these are mediated. DAG: diacylglycerols; PKC-ε: protein kinase C-ε; PAI-1: plasminogen activator inhibitor-1.

5. Evidence for a Disconnection between Hepatic Steatosis and Metabolic Syndrome

Despite the clear bidirectional causal links between NAFLD and the metabolic syndrome, there are certain situations where this appears to not be the case. In such scenarios there is a clinical disconnect between NAFLD and insulin resistance. Several groups have demonstrated that it is possible experimentally to induce either insulin resistance or hepatic steatosis individually without the presence of the other. The first evidence that hepatic steatosis could occur independently of insulin resistance was published in 2007 [74]. Here mice were raised which over-expressed acyl-CoA:diacylglycerol acyltransferase 2 (DGAT 2), an enzyme which acts to catalyze the final step of hepatic triglyceride biosynthesis. These mice were observed to develop marked hepatic steatosis in the absence of any abnormalities in plasma glucose and insulin levels, glucose and insulin tolerance, or infusion rates during hyperinsulinaemic euglycaemic clamp experiments. A subsequent study investigated variability in the DGAT2 gene to see if this relationship could also be found in humans. The authors investigated 187 individuals from south Germany, and observed 2 single nucleotide polymorphisms (SNPs) in DGAT2 that were associated with smaller decreases in liver fat following an exercise programme than wild type genotype [75]. There were no observed changes in insulin sensitivity among the different genotypes and thus the authors concluded that DGAT2 may play a role in mediating a disconnection between insulin resistance and hepatic steatosis. Additionally, it has been observed that inhibiting secretion of very low density lipoprotein (VLDL) from the liver by a genetic modification or diet-induced choline deficiency in a mouse model results in accumulation of hepatic triglyceride without causing insulin resistance [76,77].

More recently, there has been much interest focused on the patatin-like phospholipase domain-containing protein-3 (PNPLA3) gene, which encodes for a protein called adiponutrin. The exact role of this adiponutrin is currently unclear, however it is recognised as being a membrane-associated protein expressed in hepatic and adipose tissue that possesses lipogenic and lipolytic activities. There is evidence to suggest that it is located in lipid droplets and may play a role in triglyceride hydrolysis [78]. PNPLA3 gene expression is upregulated following the post-prandial insulin spike, and downregulated following fasting. It was reported in 2008 that a particular allele in PNPLA3 (I148M or rs738409) was strongly associated with increased hepatic steatosis and hepatic inflammation, with individuals homozygous for I148M exhibiting twice the level of hepatic fat content than non-carriers [79]. Interestingly, it was also observed that I148M carrier frequency was highest in Hispanic populations who are thought to have highest susceptibility to NAFLD, and regression analysis demonstrated that the presence or absence of this PNPLA3 variant along with another (453I) accounted for 72% of the observed ethnic differences in levels of hepatic steatosis from the Dallas Heart Study. It was subsequently reported that the I148M variant has a marked effect on enzyme activity and results in a disruption to normal hydrolysis of triglycerides leading to impaired secretion of very low density lipoproteins (VLDL) [80,81]. Interestingly, it has subsequently been demonstrated that the association between the I148M variant and NAFLD in independent of insulin sensitivity as measured by hyperinsulinaemic euglycaemic clamp, as well as central obesity [82,83]. Therefore the PNPLA3 I148M variant provides an example of how hepatic steatosis can occur in humans independently of insulin resistance and the metabolic syndrome.

A similar scenario has been identified more recently with the transmembrane 6 superfamily member 2 (TM6SF2) gene. TM6SF2 is expressed largely in the liver and intestine and is thought to play a key role in the regulation of hepatic fat metabolism and the secretion of triglyceride-rich lipoproteins. As with PNPLA3, it is thought to be located in lipid droplets and siRNA inhibition is associated with increased hepatocellular triglyceride concentration and lipid droplet lipid content [84]. Variation in this gene has been shown to be associated with susceptibility to NAFLD independently of variation in PNPLA3, with the variant being identified as E167K or rs58542926 [85]. The allele frequency of this variant was shown to be 7.2% in European populations. A subsequent study of 361 individuals, including 226 patients with biopsy-proven NAFLD, has shown that this variant has a modest effect on NAFLD susceptibility and is associated with a slightly higher risk of developing NASH [86]. A further study of 1074 individuals demonstrated an association between this variant and advanced fibrosis and cirrhosis that occurred independently of potential confounding factors such as age, BMI, presence of type 2 diabetes and PNPLA3 genotype status [87]. However, it should be noted that 2 studies looking at this variant in Japanese [88] and Chinese [89] populations of individuals with biopsy-proven NAFLD failed to show an association between it and fibrosis stage or general histological severity. The Japanese study had relatively small numbers with 211 individuals and just 2 who were homozygous for E167K, and it should be noted that both of these studies focused on a single ethnic group that may not be directly applicable to other populations. A meta-analysis of 10 published studies looked at the relationship between the E167K variant and the presence of NAFLD in a total of 5537 study participants [90]. This revealed a carrier frequency of up to 7%, and demonstrated a moderate effect on the risk of developing NAFLD with an odds ratio of 2.13 (95% confidence interval 1.36–3.30). Crucially, it has been shown in a recent Finnish study that this variant is associated with preserved insulin sensitivity and a lack of hypertriglyceridaemia suggesting that this represents a distinct subtype of NAFLD similar to that associated with the PNPLA3 I148M variant [91]. Figure 2 demonstrates the relationship between the 2 described genetic variants and the lipid droplet within the hepatocyte.

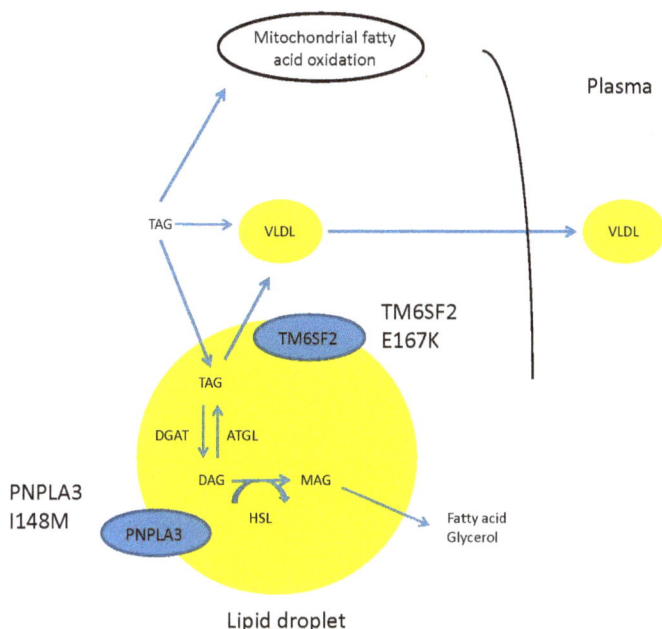

Figure 2. Interaction between PNPLA3 and TM6SF2 variants and lipid metabolism in the hepatic lipid droplet. TAG; triacylglycerol; DAG; diacylglycerol; MAG; monoacylglycerol; VLDL; very low density lipoprotein; DGAT; diglyceride acyltransferase; ATGL; adipose triglyceride lipase; HSL; hormone sensitive lipase.

Further evidence for a dissociation between hepatic steatosis and insulin resistance may be found in the case of familial hypobetalipoproteinaemia (FHBL). Patients with FHBL have very low or absent levels of apolipoprotein B and this leads to an impairment of very low density lipoprotein export from the liver and consequently intra-hepatic accumulation of triglyceride. Amaro *et al.* [92] investigated a small number of overweight or obese patients with FHBL and observed that these individuals had greater insulin sensitivity than BMI- and hepatic triglyceride content-matched subjects with NAFLD alone. The authors speculate that this would support the assertion that hepatic steatosis is a marker rather than a cause of the metabolic syndrome, however this was a very small study and it is not clear how applicable these findings are to the wider population of people with NAFLD. It has also been observed that lysosomal acid lipase deficiency (LAL-D), a rare autosomal recessive inherited condition, can lead to hepatic steatosis in the absence of metabolic syndrome [93].

There is also evidence that adipose triacylglycerol lipase (ATGL) may play a role in a potential dissociation between insulin resistance and hepatic steatosis [94]. ATGL acts to initiate hydrolysis of stored lipid by selectively cleaving triacylglycerols and not diacylglycerols or monoacylglycerols. Knock-out studies have demonstrated that ATGL-deficient mice experience a marked hepatic steatosis [95] and similarly overexpression of the ATGL gene leads to a reduction in liver fat in mice [96]. One study investigated the effects of ATGL gene manipulation on insulin sensitivity in mice, and here the authors observed that while ATGL knock-out mice do develop marked hepatic steatosis this does not result in any changes to their hepatocyte insulin sensitivity [97]. Hepatic ATGL overproduction in the same mice resulted in reduced hepatic steatosis, and interestingly the authors did observe a mild increase in insulin sensitivity although this was not sufficiently large to result in improvements in fasting glucose concentrations or insulinaemia.

Further insights into a possible disconnection between hepatic steatosis and insulin resistance can be gained by looking at disorders of fatty acid oxidation. In health, fasting stimulates gluconeogenesis in the liver fuelled by oxidation of fatty acids. If fatty acid oxidation is impaired this can lead to fasting hypoglycaemia and accumulation of lipids resulting in hepatic steatosis [98]. In such situations individuals will exhibit enhanced glucose tolerance, therefore exhibiting the disconnection. This occurs in numerous inborn errors of fatty acid oxidation such as medium chain acyl-CoA dehydrogenase deficiency (MCADD) and carnitine palmitoyl transferase II (CPT-2) deficiency [99]. Additionally, peroxisome proliferator-activated receptor alpha (PPARα) stimulates the expression of many genes involved in fatty acid oxidation. Experimental mice who have undergone PPARα knock-out develop marked hepatic steatosis after being exposed to a high fat diet, and after fasting demonstrate hypoglycaemia and increased insulin sensitivity [100].

6. Conclusions

It is clear from the literature that there is a complicated causal relationship between NAFLD and the metabolic syndrome. NAFLD is considered by many to represent the hepatic manifestation of the metabolic syndrome however rigidly sticking to this dogma does not appreciate the complexity of the relationship. Clearly the two clinical entities share many aspects of their pathophysiology, and insulin resistance is at the centre of both. There is sufficient evidence now for not only reciprocal causality between these disease states, but also each acting as a perpetuating or exacerbating factor for the other.

There are, however, many aspects of the interactions between NAFLD and the metabolic syndrome that are yet to be fully elucidated, and this is clearly demonstrated by the situations where there is an apparent disconnect or dissociation between them. Arguably, the hepatic steatosis that occurs in these situations due to genetic variation and inborn errors of metabolic can be considered a separate clinical entity to that which is associated with insulin resistance and the metabolic syndrome. However, focusing on the mechanisms that underlie these observations of dissociation could prove valuable for identifying new therapeutic targets in metabolic disease.

Acknowledgments: Christopher D. Byrne is supported in part by the Southampton National Institute for Health Research Biomedical Research Centre.

Author Contributions: Patrick Wainwright and Christopher D. Byrne conceived and designed the review; Patrick Wainwright completed the first draft; Christopher D. Byrne critically reviewed the draft and revised it with changes to the text and figures; Patrick Wainwright and Christopher D. Byrne completed the final draft and prepared it for submission.

Conflicts of Interest: The authors declare no conflict of interest.

Abbreviations

The following abbreviations are used in this manuscript:

NAFLD	Non-alcoholic fatty liver disease
PNPLA3	Patatin-like phospholipase domain-containing protein-3
TM6SF2	Transmembrane 6 superfamily member 2 protein
HDL-C	High density lipoprotein cholesterol
NASH	Non-alcoholic steatohepatitis
PKC-ε	Protein kinase C-ε
FLI	Fatty liver index
PAI-1	Plasminogen activator inhibitor-1
TNF-α	Tumour necrosis factor-α

IL	Interleukin
DAG	Diacylglycerols
DGAT	Diacylglycerol acyltransferase
SNP	Single nucleotide polymorphism
VLDL	Very low density lipoprotein
TAG	Triacylglycerol
MAG	Monoacylglycerol
ATGL	Adipose triglyceride lipase
HSL	Hormone sensitive lipase
FHBL	Familial hypobetalipoproteinaemia
BMI	Body mass index

References

1. Anstee, Q.M.; McPherson, S.; Day, C.P. How big a problem is nonalcoholic fatty liver disease? *BMJ* **2011**, *343*, d3897. [CrossRef] [PubMed]
2. Targher, G.; Byrne, C.D. Clinical review. Nonalcoholic fatty liver disease: A novel cardiometabolic risk factor for type 2 diabetes and its complications. *J. Clin. Endocrinol. Metab.* **2013**, *98*, 483–495. [CrossRef] [PubMed]
3. Chalasani, N.; Younossi, Z.; Lavine, J.E.; Diehl, A.M.; Brunt, E.M.; Cusi, K.; Charlton, M.; Sanyal, A.J. The diagnosis and management of non-alcoholic fatty liver disease: Practice guideline by the American Association for the Study of Liver Diseases, American College of Gastroenterology, and the American Gastroenterological Association. *Hepatology* **2012**, *55*, 2005–2023. [CrossRef] [PubMed]
4. Browning, J.D.; Szczepaniak, L.S.; Dobbins, R.; Nuremberg, P.; Horton, J.D.; Cohen, J.C.; Grundy, S.M.; Hobbs, H.H. Prevalence of hepatic steatosis in an urban population in the United States: Impact of ethnicity. *Hepatology* **2004**, *40*, 1387–1395. [CrossRef] [PubMed]
5. Aguilar, M.; Bhuket, T.; Torres, S.; Liu, B.; Wong, R.J. Prevalence of the metabolic syndrome in the United States 2003–2012. *JAMA* **2015**, *313*, 1973–1974. [CrossRef] [PubMed]
6. Cortez-Pinto, H.; Camilo, M.E.; Baptista, A.; de Oliveira, A.G.; de Moura, M.C. Non-alcoholic fatty liver: Another feature of the metabolic syndrome? *Clin. Nutr.* **1999**, *18*, 353–358. [CrossRef]
7. Bedogni, G.; Miglioli, L.; Masutti, F.; Tiribelli, C.; Marchesini, G.; Bellentani, S. Prevalence of and risk factors for nonalcoholic fatty liver disease: The Dionysos nutrition and liver study. *Hepatology* **2005**, *42*, 44–52. [CrossRef] [PubMed]
8. Souza, M.R.; Diniz Mde, F.; Medeiros-Filho, J.E.; Araujo, M.S. Metabolic syndrome and risk factors for non-alcoholic fatty liver disease. *Arq. Gastroenterol.* **2012**, *49*, 89–96. [CrossRef] [PubMed]
9. Zhang, Y.; Zhang, T.; Zhang, C.; Tang, F.; Zhong, N.; Li, H.; Song, X.; Lin, H.; Liu, Y.; Xue, F. Identification of reciprocal causality between non-alcoholic fatty liver disease and metabolic syndrome by a simplified Bayesian network in a Chinese population. *BMJ Open* **2015**, *5*, e008204. [CrossRef] [PubMed]
10. Alberti, K.G.; Eckel, R.H.; Grundy, S.M.; Zimmet, P.Z.; Cleeman, J.I.; Donato, K.A.; Fruchart, J.C.; James, W.P.; Loria, C.M.; Smith, S.C.; et al. Harmonizing the metabolic syndrome. *Circulation* **2009**, *120*, 1640–1645. [CrossRef] [PubMed]
11. Kim, H.J.; Kim, H.J.; Lee, K.E.; Kim, S.K.; Ahn, C.W.; Lim, S.K.; Kim, K.R.; Lee, H.C.; Huh, K.B.; et al. Metabolic significance of nonalcoholic fatty liver disease in nonobese, nondiabetic adults. *Arch. Intern. Med.* **2004**, *164*, 2169–2175. [CrossRef] [PubMed]
12. Sinn, D.H.; Gwak, G.Y.; Park, H.N.; Kim, J.E.; Min, Y.W.; Kim, K.M.; Kim, Y.J.; Choi, M.S.; Lee, J.H.; Koh, K.C.; et al. Ultrasonographically detected non-alcoholic fatty liver disease is an independent predictor for identifying patients with insulin resistance in non-obese, non-diabetic middle-aged Asian adults. *Am. J. Gastroenterol.* **2012**, *107*, 561–567. [CrossRef] [PubMed]
13. Targher, G.; Bertolini, L.; Padovani, R.; Rodella, S.; Tessari, R.; Zenari, L.; Day, C.; Arcaro, G. Prevalence of nonalcoholic fatty liver disease and its association with cardiovascular disease among type 2 diabetic patients. *Diabetes Care* **2007**, *30*, 1212–1218. [CrossRef] [PubMed]
14. Leite, N.C.; Salles, G.F.; Araujo Antonio, L.E.; Villela-Noqueira, C.A.; Cardosa, C.R. Prevalence and associated factors of non-alcoholic fatty liver disease in patients with type-2 diabetes mellitus. *Liver Int.* **2009**, *29*, 113e9. [CrossRef] [PubMed]

15. Assy, N.; Kaita, K.; Mymin, D.; Levy, C.; Rosser, B.; Minuk, G. Fatty infiltration of liver in hyperlipidemic patients. *Dig. Dis. Sci.* **2000**, *45*, 1929–1934. [CrossRef] [PubMed]

16. Lopez-Suarez, A.; Guerrero, J.M.; Elvira-Gonzalez, J.; Beltran-Robles, M.; Canas-Hormigo, F.; Bascunana-Quirell, A. Nonalcoholic fatty liver disease is associated with blood pressure in hypertensive and nonhypertensive individuals from the general population with normal levels of alanine aminotransferase. *Eur. J. Gastroenterol. Hepatol.* **2011**, *23*, 1011–1017. [CrossRef] [PubMed]

17. Lau, K.; Lorbeer, R.; Haring, R.; Schmidt, C.O.; Wallaschofski, H.; Nauck, M.; John, U.; Baumeister, S.E.; Volzke, H. The association between fatty liver disease and blood pressure in a population-based prospective longitudinal study. *J. Hypertens.* **2010**, *28*, 1829–1835. [CrossRef] [PubMed]

18. Marchesini, G.; Bugianesi, E.; Forlani, G.; Cerelli, F.; Lenzi, M.; Manini, R.; Natale, S.; Vanni, E.; Villanova, N.; Melchionda, N. Nonalcoholic fatty liver, steatohepatitis, and the metabolic syndrome. *Hepatology* **2003**, *37*. [CrossRef] [PubMed]

19. Ryan, M.C.; Wilson, A.M.; Slavin, J.; Best, J.D.; Jenkins, A.J.; Desmond, P.V. Associations between liver histology and severity of the metabolic syndrome in subjects with nonalcoholic fatty liver disease. *Diabetes Care* **2005**, *28*, 1222–1224. [CrossRef] [PubMed]

20. Day, C.P.; James, O.F. Steatohepatitis: A tale of two "hits"? *Gastroenterology* **1998**, *114*, 842–845. [CrossRef]

21. Tilg, H.; Moschen, A.R. Evolution of inflammation in nonalcoholic fatty liver disease: The multiple parallel hits hypothesis. *Hepatology* **2010**, *52*, 1836–1846. [CrossRef] [PubMed]

22. Samuel, V.T.; Liu, Z.-X.; Wang, A.; Beddow, S.A.; Geisler, J.G.; Kahn, M.; Zhang, X.; Monia, B.P.; Bhanot, S.; Shulman, G.I. Inhibition of protein kinase Cε prevents hepatic insulin resistance in nonalcoholic fatty liver disease. *J. Clin. Investig.* **2007**, *117*, 739–745. [CrossRef] [PubMed]

23. Kumashiro, N.; Erion, D.M.; Zhang, D.; Kahn, M.; Beddow, S.A.; Chu, X.; Still, C.D.; Gerhard, G.S.; Han, X.; Dziura, J.; *et al.* Cellular mechanism of insulin resistance in nonalcoholic fatty liver disease. *PNAS* **2011**, *108*, 16381–16385. [CrossRef] [PubMed]

24. Choi, J.W.; Wang, X.; Joo, J.I.; Kim, D.H.; Oh, T.S.; Choi, D.K.; Yun, J.W. Plasma proteome analysis in diet-induced obesity-prone and obesity resistant rats. *Proteomics* **2010**, *10*, 4386–4400. [CrossRef] [PubMed]

25. Meex, R.C.; Hoy, A.J.; Morris, A.; Brown, R.D.; Lo, J.C.; Burke, M.; Goode, R.J.; Kingwell, B.A.; Kraakman, M.J.; Febbraio, M.A.; *et al.* Fetuin B is a secreted hepatocyte factor linking steatosis to impaired glucose metabolism. *Cell Metab.* **2015**, *22*, 1078–1089. [CrossRef] [PubMed]

26. Hamaguchi, M.; Takeda, N.; Kojima, T.; Ohbora, A.; Kato, T.; Sarhui, H.; Fukui, M.; Nagata, C.; Takeda, J. Identification of individuals with non-alcoholic fatty liver disease by the diagnostic criteria for the metabolic syndrome. *World J. Gastroenterol.* **2012**, *18*, 1508–1516. [CrossRef] [PubMed]

27. Zhang, T.; Zhang, Y.; Zhang, C.; Tang, F.; Li, H.; Zhang, Q.; Lin, H.; Wu, S.; Liu, Y.; Xue, F. Prediction of metabolic syndrome by non-alcoholic fatty liver disease in northern urban Han Chinese population: A prospective cohort study. *PLoS ONE* **2014**, *9*, e96651.

28. Smits, M.M.; Ioannou, G.N.; Boyko, E.J.; Utzschneider, K.M. Non-alcoholic fatty liver disease as an independent manifestation of the metabolic syndrome: Results of a US national survey in three ethnic groups. *J. Gastroenterol. Hepatol.* **2013**, *28*, 664–670. [CrossRef] [PubMed]

29. Adams, L.A.; Waters, O.R.; Knuiman, M.W.; Elliott, R.R.; Olynyk, J.K. NAFLD as a risk factor for the development of diabetes and the metabolic syndrome: An eleven-year follow-up study. *Am. J. Gastroenterol.* **2009**, *104*, 861–867. [CrossRef] [PubMed]

30. Ryoo, J.H.; Choi, J.M.; Moon, S.Y.; Suh, Y.J.; Shin, J.Y.; Shin, H.C.; Park, S.K. The clinical availability of non alcoholic fatty liver disease as an early predictor of the metabolic syndrome in Korean men: 5-year's prospective cohort study. *Atherosclerosis* **2013**, *227*, 398–403. [CrossRef] [PubMed]

31. Hamaguchi, M.; Kojima, T.; Itoh, Y.; Harano, Y.; Fujii, K.; Nakajima, T.; Kato, T.; Takeda, N.; Okuda, J.; Ida, K.; *et al.* The severity of ultrasonographic findings in nonalcoholic fatty liver disease reflects the metabolic syndrome and visceral fat accumulation. *Am. J. Gastroenterol.* **2007**, *102*, 2708–2715. [CrossRef] [PubMed]

32. Mohan, V.; Farooq, S.; Deepa, M.; Ravikumar, R.; Pitchumoni, C.S. Prevalence of non-alcoholic fatty liver disease in urban south Indians in relation to different grades of glucose intolerance and metabolic syndrome. *Diabetes Res. Clin. Pract.* **2009**, *84*, 84–91. [CrossRef] [PubMed]

33. Rhoo, J.H.; Suh, Y.J.; Shin, H.C.; Cho, Y.K.; Choi, J.M.; Park, S.K. Clinical association between non-alcoholic fatty liver disease and the development of hypertension. *J. Gastroenterol. Hepatol.* **2014**, *29*, 1926–1931.

34. Rhoo, J.H.; Ham, W.T.; Choi, J.M.; Kang, M.A.; An, S.H.; Lee, J.K.; Shin, H.C.; Park, S.K. Clinical significance of non-alcoholic fatty liver disease as a risk factor for prehypertension. *J. Korean Med. Sci.* **2014**, *29*, 973–979.

35. Huh, J.H.; Ahn, S.V.; Koh, S.B.; Choi, E.; Kim, J.Y.; Sung, K.C.; Kim, E.J.; Park, J.B. A prospective study of fatty liver index and incident hypertension: The KoGES-ARIRANG study. *PLoS ONE* **2015**, *10*, e0143560.

36. Sung, K.C.; Wild, S.H.; Byrne, C.D. Development of new fatty liver, or resolution of existing fatty liver, over five years of follow-up, and risk of incident hypertension. *J. Hepatol.* **2014**, *60*, 1040–1045. [CrossRef] [PubMed]

37. Sung, K.C.; Wild, S.H.; Byrne, C.D. Resolution of fatty liver and risk of incident diabetes. *J. Clin. Endocrinol. Metab.* **2013**, *93*, 3637–3643. [CrossRef] [PubMed]

38. Vozarova, B.; Stefan, N.; Lindsay, R.S.; Saremi, A.; Pratley, R.E.; Bogardus, C.; Tataranni, P.A. High alanine Aminotransferase is associated with decreased hepatic insulin sensitivity and predicts the development of type 2 diabetes. *Diabetes* **2002**, *51*, 1889–1895. [CrossRef] [PubMed]

39. Lee, D.H.; Ha, M.H.; Kim, J.H.; Christiani, D.C.; Gross, M.D.; Steffes, M.; Blomhoff, R.; Jacobs, D.R. Gamma glutamyltransferase and diabetes—A 4 years follow-up study. *Diabetologia* **2003**, *46*, 359–364. [PubMed]

40. Hanley, A.J.; Williams, K.; Festa, A.; Wagenknecht, L.E.; D'Agostino, R.B.; Haffner, S.M. Liver markers and development of the metabolic syndrome: The insulin resistance atherosclerosis study. *Diabetes* **2005**, *54*, 3140–3147. [CrossRef] [PubMed]

41. Ekstedt, M.; Franzén, L.E.; Mathiesen, U.L.; Thorelius, L.; Holmqvist, M.; Bodemar, G.; Kechagias, S. Long-term follow-up of patients with NAFLD and elevated liver enzymes. *Hepatology* **2006**, *44*, 865–873. [CrossRef] [PubMed]

42. Monami, M.; Bardini, G.; Lamanna, C.; Pala, L.; Cresci, B.; Francesconi, P.; Buiatti, E.; Rotella, C.M.; Mannucci, E. Liver enzymes and risk of diabetes and cardiovascular disease: Results of the Firenze Bagno a Ripoli (FIBAR) study. *Metabolism* **2008**, *57*, 387–392. [CrossRef] [PubMed]

43. Goessling, W.; Massaro, J.M.; Vasan, R.S.; D'Agostino, R.B.; Ellison, R.C.; Fox, C.S. Aminotransferase levels and 20-year risk of metabolic syndrome, diabetes, and cardiovascular disease. *Gastroenterology* **2008**, *135*, 1935–1944. [CrossRef] [PubMed]

44. Ryu, S.; Chang, Y.; Woo, H.Y.; Yoo, S.H.; Choi, N.K.; Lee, W.Y.; Kim, I.; Song, J. Longitudinal increase in gamma-glutamyltransferase within the reference interval predicts metabolic syndrome in middle-aged Korean men. *Metabolism* **2010**, *59*, 683–689. [PubMed]

45. Balkau, B.; Lange, C.; Vol, S.; Fumeron, F.; Bonnet, F. Group Study D.E.S.I.R. Nine-year incident diabetes is predicted by fatty liver indices: The French D.E.S.I.R. study. *BMC Gastroenterol.* **2010**, *10*, 56–66. [CrossRef] [PubMed]

46. Sung, K.C.; Kim, S.H. Interrelationship between fatty liver and insulin resistance in the development of type 2 diabetes. *J. Clin. Endocrinol. Metab.* **2011**, *96*, 1093–1097. [CrossRef] [PubMed]

47. Sung, K.C.; Jeong, W.S.; Wild, S.H.; Byrne, C.D. Combined influence of insulin resistance, overweight/obesity, and fatty liver as risk factors for type 2 diabetes. *Diabetes Care* **2012**, *35*, 717–722. [CrossRef] [PubMed]

48. Musso, G.; Gambino, R.; Cassader, M.; Pagano, G. Meta analysis: Natural history of non-alcoholic fatty liver disease (NAFLD) and diagnostic accuracy of non-invasive tests for liver disease severity. *Ann. Med.* **2011**, *43*, 617–649. [CrossRef] [PubMed]

49. Ghosh, A.K.; Vaughan, D.E. PAI-1 in tissue fibrosis. *J. Cell. Physiol.* **2012**, *227*, 493–507. [CrossRef] [PubMed]

50. Cesari, M.; Pahor, M.; Incalzi, R.A. Plasminogen activator inhibitor-1 (PAI-1): A key factor linking fibrinolysis and age-related subclinical and clinical conditions. *Cardiovasc. Ther.* **2010**, *28*, e72–e91. [CrossRef] [PubMed]

51. Oishi, K. Plasminogen activator inhibitor-1 and the circadian clock in metabolic disorders. *Clin. Exp. Hypertens.* **2009**, *31*, 208–219. [CrossRef] [PubMed]

52. Bremer, A.A.; Jialal, I. Adipose tissue dysfunction in nascent metabolic syndrome. *J. Obes.* **2013**, *2013*, 393192. [CrossRef] [PubMed]

53. Takeshita, Y.; Takamura, T.; Hamaguchi, E.; Shimizu, A.; Ota, T.; Sakurai, M.; Kaneko, S. Tumor necrosis factor-alpha-induced production of plasminogen activator inhibitor 1 and its regulation by pioglitazone and cerivastatin in a nonmalignant human hepatocyte cell line. *Metabolism* **2006**, *55*, 1464–1472. [CrossRef] [PubMed]

54. Baranova, A.; Gowder, S.J.; Schlauch, K.; Elariny, H.; Collantes, R.; Afendy, A.; Ong, J.P.; Goodman, Z.; Chandhoke, V.; Younossi, Z.M. Gene expression of leptin, resistin, and adiponectin in the white adipose tissue of obese patients with non-alcoholic fatty liver disease and insulin resistance. *Obes. Surg.* **2006**, *16*, 1118–1125. [CrossRef] [PubMed]

55. Baranova, A.; Schlauch, K.; Elariny, H.; Jarrar, M.; Bennett, C.; Nugent, C.; Gowder, S.J.; Younoszai, Z.; Collantes, R.; Chandhoke, V.; *et al.* Gene expression patterns in the hepatic tissue and in the visceral adipose tissue of patients with non-alcoholic fatty liver disease. *Obes. Surg.* **2007**, *17*, 1111–1118. [CrossRef] [PubMed]

56. Hubscher, S.G. Histological assessment of non-alcoholic fatty liver disease. *J. Clin. Gastroenterol.* **2006**, *40*, S5–S10. [CrossRef] [PubMed]

57. Weltman, M.D.; Farrell, G.C.; Liddle, C. Increased hepatocyte CYP2E1 expression in a rat nutritional model of hepatic steatosis with inflammation. *Gastroenterology* **1996**, *111*, 1645–1653. [CrossRef]

58. Geerts, A. History, heterogeneity, developmental biology, and functions of quiescent hepatic stellate cells. *Semin. Liver Dis.* **2001**, *21*, 3113–3135. [CrossRef] [PubMed]

59. Fain, J.N. Release of interleukins and other inflammatory cytokines by human adipose tissue is enhanced in obesity and primarily due to the nonfat cells. *Vitam. Horm.* **2006**, *74*, 443–477. [PubMed]

60. You, T.; Nicklas, B.J. Chronic inflammation: Role of adipose tissue and modulation by weight loss. *Curr. Diabetes Rev.* **2006**, *2*, 29–37. [CrossRef] [PubMed]

61. Henao-Mejia, J.; Elinav, E.; Cheng-Cheng, J.; Hao, L.; Mehal, W.Z.; Strowig, T.; Thaiss, C.A.; Kau, A.L.; Eisenbarth, S.C.; Jurczak, M.J.; *et al.* Inflammasome-mediated dysbiosis regulates progression of NAFLD and obesity. *Nature* **2012**, *482*, 179–185. [CrossRef] [PubMed]

62. Feldstein, A.E.; Canbay, A.; Angulo, P.; Taniai, M.; Burgart, L.J.; Lindor, K.D.; Gores, G.J. Hepatocyte apoptosis and fas expression are prominent features of human non alcoholic steatohepatitis. *Gastroenterology* **2003**, *125*, 437–443. [CrossRef]

63. Bantel, H.; Ruck, P.; Gregor, M.; Shulze-Oshtoff, K. Detection of elevated caspase activation and early apoptosis in lever disease. *Eur. J. Cell Biol.* **2001**, *80*, 230–239. [CrossRef] [PubMed]

64. Civera, M.; Urios, A.; Garcia-Torres, M.L.; Ortega, J.; Martinez-Valls, J.; Cassinello, N.; Del Olmo, J.A.; Ferrandez, A.; Rodrigo, J.M.; Montoliu, C. Relationship between insulin resistance, inflammation and liver cell apoptosis in patients with severe obesity. *Diabetes Metab. Res. Rev.* **2010**, *26*, 187–192. [CrossRef] [PubMed]

65. Adams, L.A.; Sanderson, S.; Lindor, K.D.; Angulo, P. The histological course of non-alcoholic fatty liver disease: A longitudinal study of 103 patients with sequential liver biopsies. *J. Hepatol.* **2005**, *42*, 132–138. [CrossRef] [PubMed]

66. El-Serag, H.B.; Tran, T.; Everhart, J.E. Diabetes increases the risk of chronic liver disease and hepatocellular carcinoma. *Gastroenterology* **2004**, *126*, 460–468. [CrossRef] [PubMed]

67. Hamaguchi, M.; Kojima, T.; Takeda, N.; Nakagawa, T.; Taniguchi, H.; Fujii, K.; Omatsu, T.; Nakajima, T.; Sarui, H.; Shimazaki, M.; *et al.* The metabolic syndrome as a predictor of nonalcoholic fatty liver disease. *Ann. Intern. Med.* **2005**, *143*, 722–728. [CrossRef] [PubMed]

68. Porepa, L.; Ray, J.G.; Sanchez-Romeu, P.; Booth, G.L. Newly diagnosed diabetes mellitus as a risk factor for serious liver disease. *CMAJ* **2010**, *182*, E526–E531. [CrossRef] [PubMed]

69. Emerging Risk Factors, Collaboration; Seshasai, S.R.; Kaptoge, S.; Thompson, A.; Di Angelantonio, E.; Gao, P.; Sarwar, N.; Whincup, P.H.; Mukamal, K.J.; Gillum, R.F.; *et al.* Diabetes mellitus, fasting glucose, and risk of cause-specific death. *N. Engl. J. Med.* **2011**, *364*, 829–841.

70. Graham, R.C.; Burke, A.; Stettler, N. Ethnic and sex differences in the association between metabolic syndrome and suspected nonalcoholic fatty liver disease in a nationally representative sample of US adolescents. *J. Pediatr. Gastroenterol. Nutr.* **2009**, *49*, 442–449. [CrossRef] [PubMed]

71. Castro-Martinez, M.G.; Banderas-Lares, D.Z.; Ramirez-Martinez, J.C.; Escobedode, I.P.J. Prevalence of nonalcoholic fatty liver disease in subjects with metabolic syndrome. *Cir. Cir.* **2012**, *80*, 128–133. [PubMed]

72. Tsai, C.H.; Li, T.C.; Lin, C.C. Metabolic syndrome as a risk factor for non-alcoholic fatty liver disease. *South Med. J.* **2008**, *101*, 900–905. [CrossRef] [PubMed]

73. Zhang, T.; Zhang, C.; Zhang, Y.; Tang, F.; Li, H.; Zhang, Q.; Lin, H.; Wu, S.; Liu, Y.; Xue, F. Metabolic syndrome and its components as predictors of non-alcoholic fatty liver disease in a northern urban Han Chinese population: A prospective cohort study. *Atherosclerosis* **2015**, *240*, 144–148. [CrossRef] [PubMed]

74. Monetti, M.; Levin, M.C.; Watt, M.J.; Sajan, M.P.; Marmor, S.; Hubbard, B.K.; Stevens, R.D.; Bain, J.R.; Newgard, C.B.; Farese, R.V.; *et al.* Dissociation of hepatic steatosis and insulin resistance in mice overexpressing DGAT in the liver. *Cell Metab.* **2007**, *6*, 69–78. [CrossRef] [PubMed]
75. Kantartzis, K.; Machicao, F.; Machann, J.; Schick, F.; Fritsche, A.; Haring, H.U.; Stefan, N. The *DGAT2* gene is a candidate for the dissociation between fatty liver and insulin resistance in humans. *Clin. Sci.* **2009**, *116*, 531–537. [CrossRef] [PubMed]
76. Niebergall, L.J.; Jacobs, R.L.; Chaba, T.; Vance, D.E. Phosphatidylcholine protects against steatosis in mice but not non-alcoholic steatohepatitis. *Biochim. Biophys. Acta* **2011**, *1811*, 1177–1185. [CrossRef] [PubMed]
77. Jacobs, R.L.; Zhao, Y.; Koonen, D.P.; Sletten, T.; Su, B.; Lingrell, S.; Cao, G.; Peake, D.A.; Kuo, M.S.; Proctor, S.D.; *et al.* Impaired *de novo* choline synthesis explains why phosphatidylethanolamine N-methyltransferase-deficient mice are protected from diet-induced obesity. *J. Biol. Chem.* **2010**, *285*, 22403–22413. [CrossRef] [PubMed]
78. Chamoun, Z.; Vacca, F.; Parton, R.G.; Gruenberg, J. PNPLA3/adiponutrin functions in lipid droplet formation. *Biol. Cell* **2013**, *105*, 219–233. [CrossRef] [PubMed]
79. Romeo, S.; Kozlitina, J.; Xing, C.; Pertsemlidis, A.; Cox, D.; Pennacchio, L.A.; Boerwinkle, E.; Cohen, J.C.; Hobbs, H.H. Genetic variation in *PNPLA3* confers susceptibility to nonalcoholic fatty liver disease. *Nat. Genet.* **2008**, *40*, 1461–1465. [CrossRef] [PubMed]
80. Romeo, S.; Sentinelli, F.; Dash, S.; Yeo, G.S.; Savage, D.B.; Leonetti, F.; Capoccia, D.; Incani, M.; Maglio, C.; Iacovino, M.; *et al.* Morbid obesity exposes the association between PNPLA3 I148M (rs738409) and indices of hepatic injury in individuals of European descent. *Int. J. Obes.* **2010**, *34*, 190–194. [CrossRef] [PubMed]
81. Romeo, S.; Sentinelli, F.; Cambuli, V.M.; Incani, M.; Congiu, T.; Matta, V.; Pilia, S.; Huang-Doran, I.; Cossu, E.; Loche, S.; *et al.* The 148M allele of the PNPLA3 gene is associated with indices of liver damage early in life. *J. Hepatol.* **2010**, *53*, 335–338. [CrossRef] [PubMed]
82. Shen, J.; Wong, G.L.; Chan, H.L.; Chan, H.Y.; Yeung, D.K.; Chan, R.S.; Chim, A.M.; Chan, A.W.; Choi, P.C.; Woo, J.; *et al.* PNPLA3 gene polymorphism accounts for fatty liver in community subjects without metabolic syndrome. *Aliment. Pharmacol. Ther.* **2014**, *39*, 532–539. [CrossRef] [PubMed]
83. Kantartzis, K.; Peter, A.; Machicao, F.; Machann, J.; Wagner, S.; Konigsrainer, I.; Konigsrainer, A.; Schick, F.; Fritsche, A.; Haring, H.U.; *et al.* Dissociation between fatty liver and insulin resistance in humans carrying a variant of the patatin-like phospholipase 3 gene. *Diabetes* **2009**, *58*, 2616–2623. [CrossRef] [PubMed]
84. Mahdessian, H.; Taxiarchis, A.; Popov, S.; Silveira, A.; Franco-Cereceda, A.; Hamsten, A.; Eriksson, P.; van't Hooft, F. TM6SF2 is a regulator of liver fat metabolism influencing triglyceride secretion and hepatic lipid droplet content. *PNAS* **2014**, *111*, 8913–8918. [CrossRef] [PubMed]
85. Kozlitina, J.; Smagris, E.; Stender, S.; Nordestgaard, B.G.; Zhou, H.H.; Tybjærg-Hansen, A.; Vogt, T.F.; Hobbs, H.H.; Choen, J.C. Exome-wide association study identifies a TM6SF2 variant that confers susceptibility to nonalcoholic fatty liver disease. *Nat. Genet.* **2014**, *46*, 352–356. [CrossRef] [PubMed]
86. Sookoian, S.; Castano, G.O.; Scian, R.; Mallardi, P.; Fernandez Gianotti, T.; Burqueno, A.L.; San Martino, J.; Pirola, C.J. Genetic variation in transmembrane 6 superfamily member 2 and the risk of nonalcoholic fatty liver disease and histological disease severity. *Hepatology* **2015**, *61*, 515–525. [CrossRef] [PubMed]
87. Liu, Y.L.; Reeves, H.L.; Burt, A.D.; Tiniakos, D.; McPherson, S.; Leathart, L.B.; Allison, M.E.; Alexander, G.J.; Piquet, A.C.; Anty, R. TM6SF2 rs58542926 influences hepatic fibrosis progression in patients with non-alcoholic fatty liver disease. *Nat. Commun.* **2014**, *5*, 4309. [CrossRef] [PubMed]
88. Akuta, N.; Kawamura, Y.; Arase, Y.; Suzuki, F.; Sezaki, S.; Hosaka, T.; Kobayashi, M.; Kobayashi, M.; Saitoh, S.; Suzuki, Y. Relationships between genetic variations of PNPLA3, TM6SF2 and histological features of nonalcoholic fatty liver disease in Japan. *Gut Liver* **2015**. [CrossRef] [PubMed]
89. Wong, V.W.; Wong, G.L.; Tse, C.H.; Chan, H.L. Prevalence of the TM6SF2 variant and non-alcoholic fatty liver disease in Chinese. *J. Hepatol.* **2014**, *61*, 708–709. [CrossRef] [PubMed]
90. Pirola, C.J.; Sookoian, S. The dual and opposite role of the TM6SF2-rs58542926 variant in protecting against cardiovascular disease and conferring risk for nonalcoholic fatty liver: A meta-analysis. *Hepatology* **2015**, *62*, 1742–1756. [CrossRef] [PubMed]
91. Zhou, Y.; Llaurado, G.; Oresic, M.; Hyotylainen, T.; Orho-Melander, M.; Yki-Jarvinen, H. Circulating triacylglycerol signatures and insulin sensitivity in NAFLD associated with the E167K variant in TM6SF2. *J. Hepatol.* **2015**, *62*, 657–663. [CrossRef] [PubMed]

92. Amaro, A.; Fabbrini, E.; Kars, M.; Yue, P.; Schechtman, K.; Schonfeld, G.; Klein, S. Dissociation between intrahepatic triglyceride content and insulin resistance in familial hypobetalipoproteinemia. *Gastroenterology* **2010**, *139*, 149–153. [CrossRef] [PubMed]
93. Reiner, Z.; Guardamagna, O.; Nair, D.; Soran, H.; Hovingh, K.; Bertolini, S.; Jones, S.; Coric, M.; Calandra, S.; Hamilton, J. Lysosomal acid lipase deficiency–an under-recognized cause of dyslipidaemias and liver dysfunction. *Atherosclerosis* **2014**, *235*, 21–30. [CrossRef] [PubMed]
94. Stefan, N.; Staiger, H.; Haring, H.U. Dissociation between fatty liver and insulin resistance: The role of adipose triacylglycerol lipase. *Diabetologia* **2011**, *54*, 7–9. [CrossRef] [PubMed]
95. Haemmerle, G.; Lass, A.; Zimmermann, R.; Gorkiewicz, G.; Meyer, C.; Rozman, J.; Heldmaier, G.; Maier, R.; Theussl, C.; Eder, S. Defective lipolysis and altered energy metabolism in mice lacking adipose triglyceride lipase. *Science* **2006**, *312*, 734–737. [CrossRef] [PubMed]
96. Reid, B.N.; Ables, G.P.; Otlivanchik, O.A.; Schoiswohl, G.; Zechner, R.; Blaner, W.S.; Goldberg, I.J.; Schwabe, R.F.; Chua, S.C.; Huang, L.S. Hepatic overexpression of hormone-sensitive lipase and adipose triglyceride lipase promotes fatty acid oxidation, stimulates direct release of free fatty acids, and ameliorates steatosis. *J. Biol. Chem.* **2008**, *283*, 13087–13099. [CrossRef] [PubMed]
97. Turpin, S.N.; Hoy, A.J.; Brown, A.D.; Rudaz, C.G.; Honeyman, J.; Matzaris, M.; Watt, M.J. Adipose triacylglycerol lipase is a major regulator of hepatic lipid metabolism but not insulin sensitivity in mice. *Diabetologia* **2011**, *54*, 146–156. [CrossRef] [PubMed]
98. Bennett, M.J. Pathophysiology of fatty acid oxidation disorders. *J. Inherit. Metab. Dis.* **2010**, *33*, 533–537. [CrossRef] [PubMed]
99. Sun, Z.; Lazar, M.A. Dissociating fatty liver and diabetes. *Trends Endocrinol. Metab.* **2013**, *24*, 4–12. [CrossRef] [PubMed]
100. Kersten, S.; Seydoux, J.; Peters, J.M.; Gonzalez, F.J.; Desvergne, B.; Wahli, W. Peroxisome proliferator-activated receptor alpha mediates the adaptive response to fasting. *J. Clin. Invest.* **1999**, *103*, 1489–1498. [CrossRef] [PubMed]

International Journal of
Molecular Sciences

MDPI

Review

Type 2 Diabetes in Non-Alcoholic Fatty Liver Disease and Hepatitis C Virus Infection—Liver: The *"Musketeer"* in the Spotlight

Stefano Ballestri [1], Fabio Nascimbeni [2,3], Dante Romagnoli [2], Enrica Baldelli [3], Giovanni Targher [4] and Amedeo Lonardo [2,*]

[1] Operating Unit Internal Medicine, Pavullo General Hospital, Azienda USL Modena, ViaSuore di San Giuseppe Benedetto Cottolengo, 5, Pavullo, 41026 Modena, Italy; stefanoballestri@tiscali.it
[2] Outpatient Liver Clinic and Operating Unit Internal Medicine, NOCSAE, Azienda USL Modena, Via P. Giardini, 1355, 41126 Modena, Italy; fabio.nascimbeni@libero.it (F.N.); danter1@alice.it (D.R.)
[3] Department of Biomedical, Metabolic and Neural Sciences, University of Modena and Reggio Emilia, Via P. Giardini, 1355, 41126 Modena, Italy; enrica.baldelli@unimore.it
[4] Section of Endocrinology, Diabetes and Metabolism, Department of Medicine, University and Azienda Ospedaliera Universitaria Integrata of Verona, Piazzale Stefani, 1, 37126 Verona, Italy; giovanni.targher@univr.it
*   Correspondence: a.lonardo@libero.it; Tel.: +39-059-396-1807; Fax: +39-059-396-1322

Academic Editor: Giovanni Tarantino
Received: 16 February 2016; Accepted: 2 March 2016; Published: 9 March 2016

Abstract: The pathogenesis of type 2 diabetes (T2D) involves chronic hyperinsulinemia due to systemic and hepatic insulin resistance (IR), which if uncorrected, will lead to progressive pancreatic beta cell failure in predisposed individuals. Non-alcoholic fatty liver disease (NAFLD) encompasses a spectrum of fatty (simple steatosis and steatohepatitis) and non-fatty liver changes (NASH-cirrhosis with or without hepatocellular carcinoma (HCC)) that are commonly observed among individuals with multiple metabolic derangements, notably including visceral obesity, IR and T2D. Hepatitis C virus (HCV) infection is also often associated with both hepatic steatosis and features of a specific HCV-associated dysmetabolic syndrome. In recent years, the key role of the steatotic liver in the development of IR and T2D has been increasingly recognized. Thus, in this comprehensive review we summarize the rapidly expanding body of evidence that links T2D with NAFLD and HCV infection. For each of these two liver diseases with systemic manifestations, we discuss the epidemiological burden, the pathophysiologic mechanisms and the clinical implications. To date, substantial evidence suggests that NAFLD and HCV play a key role in T2D development and that the interaction of T2D with liver disease may result in a "vicious circle", eventually leading to an increased risk of all-cause mortality and liver-related and cardiovascular complications. Preliminary evidence also suggests that improvement of NAFLD is associated with a decreased incidence of T2D. Similarly, the prevention of T2D following HCV eradication in the era of direct-acting antiviral agents is a biologically plausible result. However, additional studies are required for further clarification of mechanisms involved.

Keywords: epidemiology; cirrhosis; clinical implications; direct acting antivirals; fibrosis; insulin resistance; hepatocellular carcinoma; NASH; pathophysiology

---

1. Introduction

1.1. Definitions

Type 2 diabetes (T2D) identifies the more prevalent category of diabetes mellitus and is due to a progressive insulin secretory defect in the background of insulin resistance (IR) [1]. T2D is typically found in obese and overweight middle-aged individuals though the age of its initial manifestation has now been observed shifting towards adolescents and even children [2].

Non-alcoholic fatty liver disease (NAFLD) describes a cluster of hepatic disorders predominantly (though not exclusively) characterized by fatty changes with or without ballooning degeneration and fibrosis (*i.e.*, simple steatosis, steatohepatitis (NASH) and advanced fibrosis), which may evolve into cirrhosis (NASH-cirrhosis will typically lose fatty changes) and hepatocellular carcinoma (HCC); NAFLD is commonly observed in insulin-resistant, dysmetabolic individuals without excessive alcohol consumption and other competing etiologies of liver disease [3,4]. There is now compelling evidence that NAFLD is a multisystem disease associated with a wide range of extra-hepatic manifestations, notably including, among others, IR, dysglycemia and premature atherosclerosis [5,6].

Hepatitis C virus (HCV) is a small enveloped RNA virus belonging to the genus Flaviviridae, of which six different genotypes are recognized and which is transmitted via the parenteral route [7]. In several countries there have been two major HCV epidemics. The first one (mostly sustained by genotype 1 HCV) took place in the 1960s as a result of HCV being transmitted via medical procedures. The second one (predominantly due to genotype 3 HCV) occurred in the 1980s owing to needle-sharing practices among intravenous illicit drug users [7].

The natural course of HCV infection is variable and modulated by the interaction of host and viral factors. Of concern, the chronicity rate following acute infection approximates 85%, giving way to dreadful *sequelae*, such as chronic hepatitis, cirrhosis, end-stage liver failure and HCC [7]. Similarly to NAFLD, HCV infection is increasingly identified as a systemic disease which may be conducive to metabolic disorders (including IR and T2D) and premature atherosclerosis [8].

1.2. Epidemiology and Burden of Type 2 Diabetes

The world prevalence of T2D was estimated to be 6.4% in 2010 and is projected to rise to 7.7% in 2030 [9]. Recent estimates of T2D prevalence in the main five European countries (France, Germany, Italy, Spain and UK) ranged from 4.8% in Italy to 8.9% in Germany, with rates increasing steadily over the past two decades in all these countries. Of concern, in these European countries the total direct medical costs of T2D in 2010 were estimated to range from 5.45 billion euros in Spain to 43.2 billion euros in Germany, with hospitalizations due to T2D-related complications accounting for the greatest proportion of these costs [10]. In the USA, T2D now affects up to 8%–10% of adults in the general population in whom it increases up to four-fold the risk of major cardiovascular events and is the leading cause of blindness, chronic kidney failure and non-traumatic lower extremity amputations [11]. In 2007, T2D posed on society a cost as high as 174 billion dollars in the USA [12]. Of concern, this already alarming prevalence of T2D is predicted to be increasing in all age groups, making it urgent for clinicians, researchers and health authorities to gain a better understanding of the pathophysiology of T2D aimed at preventing the further spread of its disastrous pandemic [13].

1.3. Liver and Type 2 Diabetes: Historical Overview

In the past, clinicians and pathologists viewed the hepatic fatty changes as a histological correlate of the coexistence of T2D and obesity (the so-called *"diabesity"*) [14], a conclusion which has been fully supported by contemporary studies [15]. Stated otherwise, the liver was essentially regarded as a target organ affected by either concurrent or pre-existent *"diabesity"*.

More recently, however, this perspective has been fully overturned. Several studies have now exhaustively proven that hepatic steatosis precedes the development of T2D and Metabolic Syndrome (MetS) in a large proportion of cases [16–18]. *In tandem*, epidemiological evidence has also suggested that HCV infection almost doubles the risk of incident T2D compared to both HBV infection and virus-free individuals [19]. This is of outstanding interest given that HCV infection is a systemic disease [20] that often exhibits hepatic histological changes of variable severity, including hepatic steatosis, which makes it conceptually similar to NAFLD [7,21]. Excitingly, a cure for HCV has recently become available with direct acting antivirals [22–24].

Collectively, all the above findings support the notion that there is a causal, bi-directional link between NAFLD and T2D [25]; that HCV infection is a diabetogenic condition [19]; and that T2D is potentially preventable by curing NAFLD [26] and HCV infection [27].

1.4. Aim of the Review and Evidence Acquisition

The liver, the skeletal muscle and the pancreas are the anatomic basis of IR and they have collectively been alluded as the *"three musketeers"* [28]. Along with these three organs, the adipose tissue is the *"fourth musketeer"* which is implicated in the pathogenesis of IR (Figure 1) [29]. Over the last decade, the liver has been put in the spotlight of research and our group has been gaining particular interest in the association between the steatotic liver and risk of incident T2D. Accordingly, the main purpose of this article was to review data linking T2D with either NAFLD or HCV infection. For each of these two liver diseases, we will discuss systematically the epidemiological burden, the pathophysiologic mechanisms and the clinical implications.

Figure 1. The *"four musketeers"* fighting for maintaining glucose homeostasis. Under normal conditions, muscle and pancreas improve glycemic control. However, an expanded adipose tissue will usually lead to dysglycemia. Similarly, fatty changes occurring in the liver will result in the development of insulin resistance. Hence, this review article puts the liver in the spotlight.

In order to retrieve pertinent articles, the PubMed database was extensively searched for reports published through 31 January 2016. To this end, we used the following keywords "nonalcoholic fatty liver disease" or "NAFLD" combined with "insulin resistance", "type 2 diabetes" or "diabetes". The same keywords were used to identify those articles in which "insulin resistance", "type 2 diabetes" or "diabetes" were combined with either "HCV" or "hepatitis C virus".

The selection of articles was performed based on agreement among the authors. Cross-references were taken in consideration based on the authors' judgment.

2. NAFLD and Type 2 Diabetes

2.1. Epidemiology

The wide spectrum of the extra-hepatic manifestations and correlates of NAFLD includes cardiovascular diseases (CVD), chronic kidney disease, colorectal cancer, obstructive sleep apnea syndrome, psoriasis, endocrine disorders, notably including IR/T2D, thyroid dysfunction, polycystic ovarian syndrome and osteoporosis (Figure 2) [5,6,30–36]. Epidemiological data fully support a bi-directional relationship between NAFLD and T2D [25]. Stated otherwise, NAFLD is associated with established T2D in cross-sectional studies and precedes the development of T2D in follow-up studies [3,16,18].

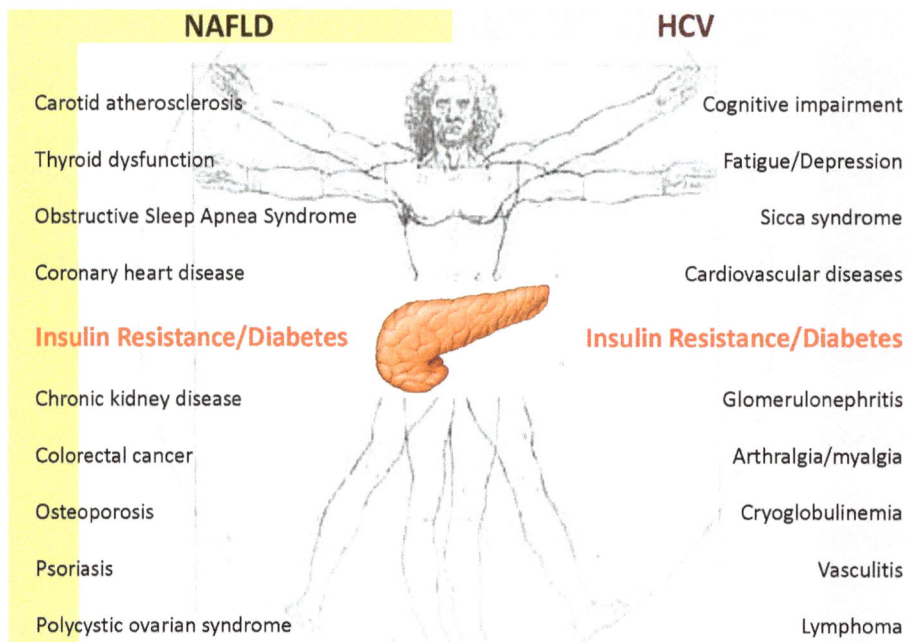

Figure 2. The spectrum of extra-hepatic manifestations and correlates of both non-alcoholic fatty liver disease (NAFLD) and hepatitis C virus (HCV) infection: type 2 diabetes is a shared feature. This figure illustrates the concept that NAFLD and HCV infection are two systemic diseases whose spectrum of clinical manifestations tends to overlap significantly. Type 2 diabetes is a feature shared among the various pathologic conditions included in the NAFLD clinical spectrum [5,6,30–36] as well as in the clinical spectrum of chronic HCV infection [8,37,38].

2.1.1. NAFLD as a "Manifestation" of Type 2 Diabetes

A consistent body of epidemiological evidence supports the conclusion that NAFLD is strongly associated with T2D and that T2D is a major modifier of the epidemiological features of NAFLD [3,39]. For example, the prevalence of NAFLD (assessed by ultrasonography) is approximately 25%–30% in the general adult population, and men outnumber women by 20% to 40%. In patients with T2D, the prevalence of NAFLD is considerably higher (occurring in up to 75% of these patients), and, remarkably, T2D abrogates sex differences among patients with NAFLD [3,39]. The prevalence of NAFLD in patients with T2D ranges widely from 45% to 75% in large hospital-based studies and from 30% to 70% in population-based studies; this wide inter-study variability is largely due to differences in the ethnicity, population characteristics and criteria adopted for the diagnosis of diabetes [39]. The prevalence of histologically diagnosed NASH, *i.e.*, the more rapidly progressive form of NAFLD [40], is estimated to occur in 2%–3% of the general adult population [6]; conversely, it ranges from 56% to 76% in hospital-based studies [41,42] and from 22% to 83% in outpatient cohort-based studies among individuals with T2D [15,43,44]. Notably, a recent study reported a high prevalence of NAFLD (76%) and NASH (56%) in obese T2D patients with normal serum aminotransferase levels [42]. The finding that many T2D patients with NAFLD have fairly normal serum transaminase concentrations is not reassuring given that NASH, advanced fibrosis and even cirrhosis may occur in such patients with "normal" serum aminotransferases [39,45,46]. Taken together, these studies suggest that the "normal" range of serum liver enzymes needs to be lowered to capture more NAFLD cases.

2.1.2. NAFLD as a Precursor of Type 2 Diabetes

Accumulating data from observational prospective studies indicate that NAFLD (as diagnosed by serum liver enzymes or imaging) is strongly associated with an increased incidence of both T2D and MetS [3,45]. Two large meta-analytic studies have provided further evidence for a strong association between NAFLD and increased risk of incident T2D [17,18]. The first of such meta-analyses, published by Musso *et al.*, [17] found an approximately two-fold increased risk of incident T2D among patients with NAFLD. The second one, recently published by our group, confirmed that NAFLD was associated with an almost two-fold increased risk of developing both T2D and MetS over a median period of five years. Worryingly, our meta-analysis is first in suggesting that the risk of developing MetS was much higher in those in whom NAFLD was identified by ultrasonography compared to those in whom NAFLD was identified based on abnormal liver enzymes [18]. In agreement with these findings, a retrospective cohort study by Sung *et al.* [47] showed that individuals in whom ultrasonography-assessed NAFLD developed or worsened over five years had a marked increase in T2D risk, suggesting that more severe NAFLD is associated with a higher risk of incident T2D [47]. Conversely, individuals in whom NAFLD resolved over five years did not show an increased T2D risk [47]. Similarly, a recent retrospective study reported a strong and independent association between NAFLD improvement and reduced incidence of T2D [48]. Moreover, another recent study has shown that non-overweight individuals with NAFLD had a substantially increased risk of incident T2D compared with both overweight and non-overweight NAFLD-free individuals [49]. Finally, the Multi-Ethnic Study of Atherosclerosis [50] has shown that NAFLD, assessed by computed tomography, was associated with an increased of incident T2D independent of common risk factors of T2D.

To date, there is a paucity of published data regarding the association between biopsy proven-NAFLD and the risk of incident T2D or MetS. In a retrospective cohort of 129 Swedish adults with histologically confirmed NAFLD and elevated liver enzymes, the baseline prevalence of T2D was 8.5% and approximately 80% of cases developed T2D (58%) or pre-diabetes (20%) at the end of a 14-year follow-up period [51].

In conclusion, a large body of epidemiological evidence supports the notion that the prevalence of NAFLD is remarkably increased in patients with T2D and that NAFLD is closely associated with an increased risk of incident T2D and MetS.

2.2. Pathophysiology

The pathogenic mechanisms linking NAFLD and T2D encompass a complex cross-talk among different organ systems, notably including the gut and the nervous system further to the previously alluded *"four musketeers"*: the adipose tissue, the skeletal muscle, the liver and the pancreas.

2.2.1. Remodeling of White Adipose Tissue

Excess visceral adiposity is a key factor in connecting NAFLD and T2D. The expansion of white adipose tissue (WAT) is associated with hypoxia and adipocytes necrosis [52–55]. The former causes the release of hypoxia inducible factor 1α (HIF1α), while adipocytes necrosis induces infiltration and M1-polarization of macrophages, thus producing WAT dysfunction, inflammation and fibrosis [53,55–62]. Such a WAT remodeling causes a dysregulation of multiple endocrine and lipid storage functions [54,62]. Dysfunctional WAT, in its turn, is associated with an imbalanced cytokine release, *i.e.*, over-production of multiple pro-inflammatory adipocytokines, such as tumor necrosis factor (TNF)-α and monocyte chemoattractant protein-1/C-C chemokine receptor-2 (MCP-1/CCR-2), and reduction of adiponectin, which contribute to worsen local and systemic metabolic derangements [62–72]. Increased interstitial fibrosis in WAT limits adipose tissue expandability [52,53,62]. Reduction in lipid storage capacity also contributes to ectopic lipid accumulation in the liver, skeletal muscles and pancreas where lipotoxicity triggers multiple pathways that hinder insulin signaling [53,62,73,74]. All of these mechanisms may contribute to the development of IR in the adipose tissue with its inherent failure to suppress adipose lipolysis that results in an overflow of free fatty acids (FFAs) to the liver [74].

2.2.2. Role of Skeletal Muscle and Brown Adipose Tissue

Muscle IR, due to intra-myocellular lipid accumulation, occurs early in the course of T2D. It has been suggested that intra-myocellular diacylglycerol (DAG) accumulation activates protein kinase C-θ (PKCθ), which impairs insulin signaling, impeding muscle glucose uptake and leading to increased delivery of glucose to the liver, where it becomes substrate for hepatic *de-novo* lipogenesis (DNL) [74–77]. Accordingly, it has recently been shown that skeletal muscle steatosis is associated with NAFLD [78].

The myokines, *i.e.*, cytokines produced by the skeletal muscle, have been recently identified as another piece in the interplay linking NAFLD to T2D. Irisin is produced by the skeletal muscle in response to physical exercise and exerts beneficial metabolic effects by recruiting brown adipose tissue (BAT) and triggering thermogenesis [79,80]. Evidence has recently shown that BAT is recruitable post-natally within either WAT or skeletal muscle [81–85]. BAT, through the expression of uncoupling C protein-1 (UCP-1), generates heat and regulates energy expenditure, lipid and glucose metabolism [81,86,87]. For these reasons, both irisin and BAT could be potential targets for the treatment of obesity-related complications. Interestingly, low levels of irisin have been associated with NAFLD and T2D in humans, thus confirming the important role of this myokine in the regulation of energy homeostasis and preservation of a healthy metabolism [88–90].

2.2.3. Intrahepatic Fat Accumulation, Hepatic Insulin Resistance and Hepatokines

In NAFLD, steatogenesis results mainly from increased hepatic esterification of FFAs originating from dysfunctional/inflamed WAT (60%), DNL (25%) and diet (15%) [91,92]. Increased lipolysis drives hepatic lipid synthesis through esterification of FFAs and stimulates hepatic gluconeogenesis [92–94], thus promoting hepatic IR [74,95]. Muscle IR increases glucose delivery to the liver, thus enhancing DNL. Moreover, dietary monosaccharides, particularly fructose, directly promotes hepatic lipogenesis by increasing sterol regulatory element binding protein 1c (SREBP1c), carbohydrate-responsive element-binding protein (chREBP), peroxisome proliferator-activated receptor (PPAR)-γ coactivator 1-β, and liver X receptor expression [74,96–101].

The resulting intrahepatic ectopic storage of lipids has been specifically associated with hepatic IR [74,102]. However, hepatic triglyceride accumulation *per se* is not always harmful. Experimentally, the inhibition of diacylglycerol acyltransferase 2 (DGAT2), an enzyme devoted to hepatocyte triglyceride biosynthesis, decreases hepatic steatosis, but increases markers of lipid peroxidation/oxidant stress, hepatic lobular necro-inflammation and fibrosis [103]. Several lines of evidence support that intrahepatic diacylglycerol (DAG), via activation of PKCε, and ceramides, by impairing Akt2 action and inducing endoplasmic-reticulum stress and mitochondrial dysfunction, are the two major lipid mediators of hepatic IR [74,102,104–114]. Also intracellular localization of lipids in the liver matters [102]. A common single-nucleotide polymorphism of patatin-like phospholipase domain-containing protein 3 (PNPLA3), a lipid droplet protein with triglyceride lipase activity, has been strongly associated with NAFLD, but not with IR [114–120]. This dissociation between hepatic steatosis and IR is likely due to the accumulation of metabolically inert polyunsaturated triacylglycerols in lipid droplets caused by the PNPLA3 I148M variant [114,121,122]. Other underlying mechanisms clearly implicated in the development of hepatic IR and in the progression of NAFLD are low-grade chronic inflammation, elevated production of reactive oxygen species, activation of unfolded protein response and endoplasmic-reticulum stress, activation of Jun N-terminal kinase (JNK)-1, increased hepatocyte apoptosis and lipo-autophagy [25,92,102,123–127].

Finally, the liver releases several endocrine mediators, the so-called hepatokines, able to impact glucose metabolism, insulin action and secretion. Fetuin-A, which is abundantly secreted by steatotic hepatocytes, mediates IR by inhibiting the insulin receptor, reducing adiponectin expression, and enhancing WAT inflammation and dysfunction, and is independently associated with T2D development [128–132]. More recently, also fetuin-B has emerged as a potentially major player in T2D pathogenesis. Indeed, in their seminal study, Meex *et al.* [133], have shown that 32 hepatokines are differently secreted in steatotic *versus* non-steatotic hepatocytes. By inducing inflammation and IR in macrophages and skeletal muscles, these changes in the secretory products may contribute to the development of metabolic dysfunction in other cell types. These authors have identified higher levels of fetuin-B in the altered hepatokine secretory profile of steatotic livers in obese patients, and have also experimentally demonstrated that fetuin-B impairs insulin sensitivity in myotubes and hepatocytes and causes glucose intolerance in mice [133]. Fibroblast growth factor (FGF)-21 acts as a potent activator of glucose uptake and inhibitor of WAT lipolysis, recruits BAT and is associated with obesity, NAFLD and T2D [134–140]. Finally, serpinB1 increases pancreatic β-cell proliferation and its deficiency leads to maladaptive β-cell proliferation in IR [141,142].

2.2.4. Gut-Liver Axis

Compelling evidence links gut microbiota, intestinal barrier integrity and NAFLD. Dysbiosis and impaired gut permeability favor the occurrence of endotoxemia and toll like receptor (TLR) 4-mediated inflammation, thereby contributing to the development of IR and other metabolic complications in obese individuals [143–145]. Other interactions between the gut and the liver may occur through the production of multiple gut hormones and the entero-hepatic circulation of bile acids that activate farnesoid X receptor in the liver [26].

Although further research is needed, these findings underline the importance of NAFLD as a precursor for the development of hepatic and systemic IR. However, the presence of long-standing IR *per se* is not sufficient to lead to the development of T2D. Gluco-lipotoxicity and genetic factors are additional requirements, which induce T2D through the development of pancreatic β-cell failure [25,74,146].

2.3. Clinical Implications

2.3.1. NASH and Fibrosis

Several studies have shown that T2D patients with NAFLD are at a high risk of NASH and cirrhosis [39,147–149]. Data from cross sectional studies [15,150–153] and longitudinal retrospective studies with sequential liver biopsies [154–156] clearly indicate that T2D strongly predicts fibrosis severity and progression in NAFLD patients. Consistently, two studies have demonstrated that poor glycemic control was associated with an increased risk of fibrosis in NASH [157,158].

Interestingly, one study showed that T2D and IR were strongly associated with NASH and severe fibrosis in patients with normal serum liver enzymes [159]. This finding provides further evidence to the clinical wisdom that "normal" serum liver enzyme levels are not a sufficient reason for excluding from liver biopsy those "high-risk" patients in whom advanced liver disease is strongly suggested by non-invasive evaluation. To this end, transient elastography and semi-quantitative ultrasound or non-invasive clinical scores (such as the US-FLI, the NAFLD fibrosis or the Fib4 scores) may be used in most patients with T2D [39,45,160,161].

2.3.2. Cirrhosis and Hepatocellular Carcinoma

Many studies have reported T2D as an established risk factor for cirrhosis [162,163] and HCC [164–166]. Worryingly, a significant proportion of NAFLD patients with HCC have no evidence of cirrhosis [164], implying that they have escaped the normal surveillance strategies implemented in patients with cirrhosis of viral or alcoholic origin, and thus are diagnosed too late to receive radical treatment [167,168].

The presence of NAFLD among patients with T2D is also an important risk factor of increased all-cause and cause-specific mortality. Patients with T2D have an increased mortality risk from cirrhosis of any aetiology [39]. Accordingly, a recent cohort study showed that, compared to the age- and sex-matched general population, patients with T2D had a two- to three-fold higher risk of dying of non-viral and non-alcoholic chronic liver disease, largely attributable to NAFLD [169]. Consistently, a recent Scottish national retrospective cohort study reported that T2D was associated with an increased risk of hospital admissions or deaths for all common chronic liver diseases and, among them, NAFLD had the strongest association with T2D [170]. In agreement, a retrospective USA cohort study on 132 NAFLD patients found that T2D patients with NAFLD were at risk for the development of poor clinical outcomes, such as increased all-cause and liver-related mortality or morbidity after adjusting for potential confounding factors [162]. Finally, NAFLD was associated with a two-fold increased risk of all-cause mortality (mainly due to malignancy (33%), liver-related complications (19%) or ischemic heart disease (19%)) in a cohort study of 337 T2D patients followed-up for a mean period of 11 years [171].

2.3.3. Atherosclerosis

Accumulating evidence indicates that NAFLD is strongly associated not only with liver-related morbidity or mortality, but also with an excess risk of CVD, which is the most common cause of death in T2D [39]. Several studies have reported a strong association between NAFLD and early subclinical or advanced atherosclerosis among patients with and without T2D [172]. These findings have been further confirmed by multiple prospective studies that showed an increased risk of fatal and non-fatal CVD events in patients with and without T2D, independently of several cardiometabolic risk factors [39,172–174]. The association between NAFLD and risk of CVD mortality has been further supported by a milestone meta-analysis [17], although some recent follow-up studies are conflicting [172,175].

Emerging evidence also indicates that NAFLD is independently associated with the development of microvascular diabetic complications, *i.e.*, chronic kidney disease and advanced diabetic retinopathy [5].

Collectively, the above-mentioned studies convincingly show that T2D is strongly associated with an increased risk of progressive NAFLD and an excess risk of overall and cause-specific mortality, including not only liver-related but also CVD-related mortality. These findings fully support careful monitoring and screening for NAFLD and/or advanced fibrosis among patients with T2D.

3. HCV and Type 2 Diabetes

3.1. Epidemiology

3.1.1. HCV and Diabetes: A Non-chance Association

The notion that cirrhosis is a potentially diabetogenic condition dates back to as early as 1906 [176]. More recently, such a view was confirmed in the pre-HBV and pre-HCV age [177]. It was more than 20 years ago that Allison *et al.*, [178] by comparing the rates of T2D among cirrhotic patients undergoing evaluation for liver transplantation, showed that T2D prevalence was 50% in patients with HCV-related *versus* 9% in those with non-HCV-related cirrhosis. Since that pioneering report, this topic has developed into a major line of research and, at the time of this writing, more than 1340 articles can be retrieved [179].

3.1.2. The Burden

Licensing of oral direct acting antivirals (DAA), which deliver sustained virological response (SVR) rates >90%, has led to the revolutionary expectation that HCV infection will possibly be the first chronic viral infection totally eradicated [22]. However, such an inference is premature and, for the time being, HCV still infects from 150,000,000 to 185,000,000 people worldwide, namely up to 2.8% of the world population [180,181]. Moreover, in developing countries, the case-finding and management have not improved *in tandem*, suggesting that continued refinement of epidemiology, cost-utility models and targeted diagnostic strategies remain an unmet need [182]. Worldwide, chronic HCV infection remains a significant public health burden, given that it can lead to cirrhosis in approximately 15% to 20% of those infected within 20 years, resulting in end-stage liver disease and HCC [182]. In Europe, although the iatrogenic HCV transmission was enormously reduced over the last 20 years, transmission related to intravenous recreational drug use is on the increase, especially in Eastern Europe, and the high HCV prevalence in the migrant populations is a challenge [183]. Moreover, HCV-related morbidity and mortality are projected to increase in Europe until 2030 [183]. In the USA, up to 35% of patients on the liver-transplant waiting list are infected with HCV, and global HCV-associated mortality estimates approximate 500,000 deaths per year [184,185].

3.1.3. Extra-Hepatic Manifestations of HCV Infection: Type 2 Diabetes

The clinical spectrum of chronic HCV infection is not limited to liver disease but also includes major extra-hepatic conditions, affecting eyes, salivary glands, skin, kidneys, genital tract, endocrine, neurologic, cardiovascular and immune systems (Figure 2) [8,37,38].

Among the extra-hepatic manifestations of HCV, a mutual and bi-directional relationship connects T2D with HCV infection. HCV infection is more common in patients with T2D than in those without T2D and, conversely, T2D abounds among patients with chronic HCV infection [177]. That said, however, the usual clinical scenario depicts a vignette in which, in predisposed individuals, HCV infection precedes and accelerates the development of new-onset T2D by approximately 10 years [38,186]. This finding suggests that HCV infection observed in T2D patients does not result from the risk of HCV infection associated with medical procedures in the highly medicalized T2D population but is the primary event which may adversely affect the subsequent development of T2D [187].

3.1.4. Heterogeneity in the Distribution of HCV and Type 2 Diabetes and Differential Features of Hepatitis C-Associated Dysmetabolic Syndrome and MetS

There are 170,000,000 individuals with T2D worldwide, namely the same number of individuals with HCV infection [177]. However, HCV infection has undergone epidemiological diffusion in certain age groups and geographical areas as a result of specific lifestyle risk behaviors or transmission via medical practices, whereas T2D reaches its zenith among 45-to-64 year old individuals, particularly in obese and sedentary individuals [177]. Stated otherwise, the epidemiological distribution of HCV infection and T2D does not identify the same geographical areas and groups of individuals. Accordingly, screening campaigns to identify either HCV infection among T2D patients or T2D among those with HCV infection are not justifiable at this time and more accurate strategies are needed in screening selected cohorts of individuals [188].

Finally, it should be pointed out that while T2D is a prominent feature of the MetS which is bi-directionally associated with NAFLD [3], HCV infection is also associated with a specific hepatitis C-associated dysmetabolic syndrome (HCADS), which was first described by Lonardo *et al.* [189]. Table 1 schematically compares the main features of the MetS with those of the HCADS [3,7,168,190–193].

Table 1. Metabolic Syndrome *versus* Hepatitis C-Associated Dysmetabolic Syndrome (HCADS)—A comparison at a glance.

Criteria	Metabolic Syndrome	HCADS	Reference(s)
T2D	Yes	Yes	[3]
Hypertension	Yes	Yes	[3]
Visceral Obesity	Yes	Preliminary evidence suggests that HCV patients have abdominal fat distribution	[3]
Atherogenic dyslipidemia	Yes	Acquired, reversible hypocholesterolemia	[6]
Hepatic steatosis	Not included among diagnostic criteria but often found as a concurrent or precursor finding	In chronic HCV patients, steatosis is two- to three-fold more prevalent than in chronic hepatitides of other etiologies. HCV genotype 3 is associated with a higher prevalence and more severe steatosis	[3,6]
Hyperuricemia	Not included in diagnostic criteria but often associated on pathophysiological grounds	Strongly associated with severity of steatosis	[3,190]
Accelerated atherogenesis	Whether the full-blown MetS adds to the risk of its individual components, particularly T2D, is controversial	Individuals with HCV infection (particularly those with T2D and hypertension) have an excess of cardiovascular morbidity and mortality	[3,191]
HCC risk	Both the MetS and T2D increase the risk of HCC. This likely results via NAFLD/NASH even in non-cirrhotic livers	Concurrent T2D and chronic HCV infection lead to increased risk of HCC. Steatosis and overweight/obesity possibly play a role	[168,192,193]

3.2. Pathophysiology

3.2.1. HCV Increases T2D Risk via Insulin Resistance

Consistent with the development of new-onset T2D observed in the setting of NAFLD, HCV promotes a state of IR that leads, over time, to pancreatic beta-cell dysfunction, eventually culminating in the irreversible damage of such cells and the development of overt T2D [177].

3.2.2. IR Associated with HCV: Antigens, Sites and Determinants

HCV antigens, such as the core protein, play a key role in determining post-receptor defects causing IR by interfering with the AKT signaling pathway via cytokines (such as TNF-α and interleukin-6) and the suppressors of cytokine signaling [194–197]. Strong evidence suggests that the site of IR is not only hepatic but also extra-hepatic [198], predominantly in the skeletal muscle, correlates with subcutaneous, rather than visceral, adiposity, and is independent of liver fat content [199]. These findings conflict with the notion that HCV predominantly infects hepatocytes and suggest that either HCV-infected hepatocytes release a soluble mediator capable of inducing IR in skeletal muscles [38] or, alternatively, that HCV directly infects myocytes. This latter hypothesis appears to be conceptually sustainable based on the findings of a recent case-control study, which provided evidence for a significant association between inclusion body myositis and HCV infection [200].

3.2.3. T2D in the Setting of the HCADS

T2D is not the only metabolic disease observed in the setting of HCV infection. Over time, several features of what is now alluded to as the HCADS have been increasingly identified. For example, hepatic steatosis, which is one of such features, was first identified as a distinct disease entity [7,21,201]. Data comparing hepatic steatosis due to varying viral (HIV-related) and non-viral (NAFLD) steatogenic disorders suggest that IR is a prominent feature specifically associated with HCV infection [202].

Over time, several features have been added to the initial description of the HCADS [203–205], which, presently, is deemed to characterize hyperuricemia, reversible hypocholesterolemia, IR, hypertension and visceral obesity [189]. Collectively, these dysmetabolic disorders may best be interpreted as a Darwinian survival strategy favoring the survival of HCV at the expenses of the host's metabolism [189]. The finding of expanded visceral adipose tissue in patients with HCV infection is consistent with the hepatic and extra-hepatic origin of IR discussed above and prompts further research as to the potential ability of HCV infection to localize directly within adipocytes [206,207].

3.3. Clinical Implications

3.3.1. Risk of Fibrosis

A consistent body of evidence supports the notion that T2D is closely associated with fibrosis in the setting of chronic HCV infection [188]. More recently, a large study conducted in USA in approximately 10,000 patients with hepatitis C found that age, sex, race, HCV genotype, HIV co-infection, alcohol abuse, antiviral therapy and T2D were independently associated with the risk of cirrhosis [208]. Moreover, a recent meta-analysis of 14 studies, involving 3659 participants with HCV infection, reported a significant association between IR and advanced hepatic fibrosis among patients with HCV genotype 1 infection but not among those with HCV genotype 3 [209]. These findings are consistent with those of previous studies reporting that IR was strongly associated with HCV genotypes 1 and 4 [210,211].

3.3.2. Risk of Hepatocellular Carcinoma

Population-based studies fully support T2D being as an emerging risk factor for HCC [192]. In a recent meta-analysis, Dyal *et al.*, [193] have reported that concurrent T2D is strongly associated with an increased risk of HCC among chronic HCV patients. It may be argued, however, that, in these patients, T2D may either be a proxy of more advanced metabolic derangement which leads to excess fibrosis via NASH or that T2D *per se* exposes these individuals to higher risk of developing HCC via increased oxidative stress and hormonal changes (*e.g.*, IR, increased IGF-1 and activation of the renin-angiotensin-aldosterone system) [193,212,213].

An Italian study conducted in 163 consecutive HCV-positive patients with cirrhosis followed-up for a median period of 10.7 years found that HCV genotype 1b was strongly associated with a higher risk of developing HCC [214].

Further studies are needed to control accurately for all viral and host's confounders, such as genotype, obesity and ethnicity, given that an improved understanding of HCC risk factors may provide specific areas of targeted interventions to reduce HCC risk in chronic HCV patients [193].

3.3.3. Risk of Atherosclerosis

The strong association between HCV infection and T2D development is one of the most important mechanisms that may lead to accelerated atherogenesis in chronic HCV patients [215]. Three studies showed that HCV infection is a strong risk factor for carotid subclinical atherosclerosis [216–218]. Consistent with the notion that HCV infection is a systemic disease, the risk of major CVD events is higher in patients with HCV infection than in HCV-negative controls, independently of traditional CVD risk factors and other potential confounding variables [219,220]. In a recent meta-analysis conducted on 22 studies, Petta *et al.* [191] showed that patients with chronic HCV infection had an increased risk of CVD-related morbidity and mortality, especially those with T2D and hypertension. On these grounds, all chronic HCV patients should be non-invasively screened for atherosclerosis [215].

4. Conclusions

Among the "*four musketeers*" fighting for controlling glucose homeostasis, the liver is now in the spotlight of basic, epidemiological and clinical investigations (Figure 1). Indeed, by reviewing the role of HCV and NAFLD in the development of T2D, we found that there is a substantial body of evidence indicating that the liver plays a pathogenic role in T2D development and that the close inter-connections connecting T2D with liver disease may result in a "*vicious circle*" eventually leading to an excess risk of liver-related and CVD complications (Figure 3).

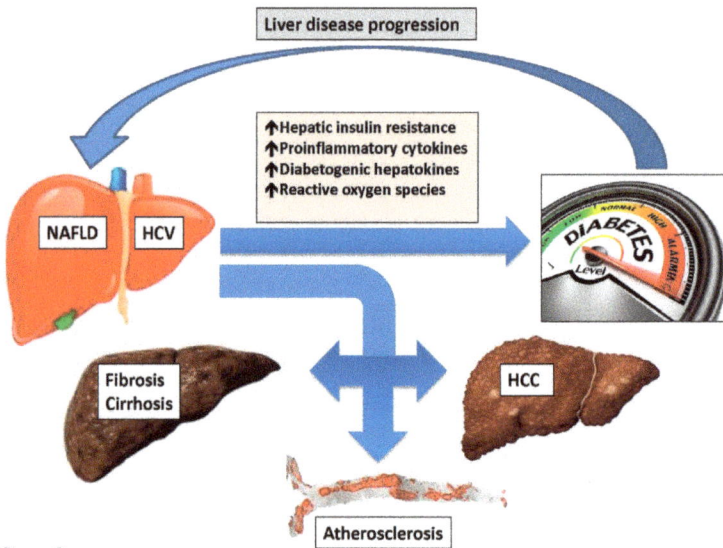

Figure 3. Non-alcoholic fatty liver disease, hepatitis C virus infection and type 2 diabetes: the *"vicious circle"*. The liver plays a pathogenic role in the development of type 2 diabetes both in the context of non-alcoholic fatty liver disease and hepatitis C virus infection through the development of systemic and hepatic insulin resistance, partly mediated by the release of multiple pro-inflammatory cytokines, diabetogenic hepatokines and reactive oxygen species. If left uncorrected, insulin resistance will eventually lead to progressive pancreatic beta cell failure in predisposed individuals. Moreover, the strong interconnection between type 2 diabetes and liver disease may result into a "vicious circle" [25] eventually leading to liver disease progression with an excess risk of liver-related, *i.e.*, cirrhosis and hepatocellular carcinoma (HCC), and cardiovascular complications, *i.e.*, atherosclerosis.

NAFLD and HCV infection are two multisystem diseases whose spectrum of clinical manifestations, seemingly as a result of their sharing hepatic steatosis and IR as prominent features (Figure 2) [205], tends to overlap more and more. Basic research is very active in the arena of NAFLD pathophysiology and extrapolation of notions from the NAFLD to the HCV research field appears to be justified and potentially fruitful [21].

However, several questions remain largely unanswered. For instance: is NAFLD treatment able to reduce the development of T2D and its major complications? Based on preliminary evidence [47,48] one may be tempted to answer affirmatively, though this remains to be fully proven by studies *ad hoc*. Does T2D impair SVR in the era of new direct-acting antivirals? While T2D was associated with a lower SVR rate following interferon-based therapy [7], regimens based on new direct-acting antiviral agents do not appear to be affected by coexisting T2D [221]. Moreover, whether HCV eradication may also have an impact on the future morbidity and mortality due to T2D is a clinically relevant and biologically plausible outcome. However, further studies with new direct-acting antivirals are needed to ultimately settle this issue [27].

In the meantime, it is important to underline that lifestyle changes are the mainstay of treatment for all patients with NAFLD and T2D [173,222]. It has been reported that a combination of educational, behavioral and motivational strategies may help patients with NAFLD in achieving lifestyle changes [223–225]. Preliminary evidence also suggests that body weight reduction may improve liver histology in those patients in whom HCV infection is associated with hepatic steatosis [226]. However, future studies are required to better define effective weight loss strategies in these patients.

Int. J. Mol. Sci. **2016**, *17*, 355

Acknowledgments: Giovanni Targher is supported in part by grants from the University School of Medicine of Verona. We are indebted to Ms. Elisa Gibertini for her helping us as a graphic artist.

Author Contributions: Amedeo Lonardo conceived the idea of this article, wrote the first draft of Chapters 1 and 4, the Table and, with Dante Romagnoli, Chapter 3; Amedeo Lonardo also drew the figures in collaboration with Giovanni Targher and Fabio Nascimbeni; Stefano Ballestri and Fabio Nascimbeni wrote the first draft of Abstract and Chapter 2; Giovanni Targher and Enrica Baldelli contributed to the discussion and reviewed the manuscript. All the Authors took part in the bibliographic research, discussed, edited and approved the final version of the article.

Conflicts of Interest: Stefano Ballestri, Fabio Nascimbeni, Enrica Baldelli, Giovanni Targher and Amedeo Lonardo have nothing to disclose. Dante Romagnoli serves as a consultant for AbbVie.

Abbreviations

The following abbreviations are used in this manuscript:

CCR-2	C-C chemokine receptor-2
CHD	coronary heart disease
chREBP	carbohydrate-responsive element-binding protein
CVD	cardiovascular disease
DAA	direct acting antivirals
DAG	diacylglycerol
DGAT2	diacylglycerolacyltransferase 2
DNL	de-novo lipogenesis
FA	fatty acids
FGF-21	fibroblast growth factor 21
FXR	farnesoid X receptor
HCC	hepatocellular carcinoma
HIF1α	hypoxia inducible factor 1α
HCV	hepatitis C virus
IR	insulin resistance
MCP-1	monocyte chemoattractant protein-1
MetS	metabolic syndrome
PNPLA3	patatin-like phospholipase domain-containing protein 3
PPAR-γ	peroxisome proliferator–activated receptor γ
ROS	reactive oxygen species
SREBP1c	sterol regulatory element binding protein 1c
T2D	type 2 diabetes
TLR-4	toll-like receptor 4
TNFα	tumor necrosis factor α
UCP-1	uncoupling protein-1
WAT	white adipose tissue

References

1. Inzucchi, S.E. Clinical practice. Diagnosis of diabetes. *N. Engl. J. Med.* **2012**, *367*, 542–550. [CrossRef] [PubMed]
2. Cameron, F.J.; Wherrett, D.K. Care of diabetes in children and adolescents: Controversies, changes, and consensus. *Lancet* **2015**, *385*, 2096–2106. [CrossRef]
3. Lonardo, A.; Ballestri, S.; Marchesini, G.; Angulo, P.; Loria, P. Nonalcoholic fatty liver disease: Aprecursor of the metabolic syndrome. *Dig. Liver Dis.* **2015**, *47*, 181–190. [CrossRef] [PubMed]
4. Nascimbeni, F.; Pais, R.; Bellentani, S.; Day, C.P.; Ratziu, V.; Loria, P.; Lonardo, A. From NAFLD in clinical practice to answers from guidelines. *J. Hepatol.* **2013**, *59*, 859–871. [CrossRef] [PubMed]
5. Byrne, C.D.; Targher, G. NAFLD: A multisystem disease. *J. Hepatol.* **2015**, *62*, S47–S64. [CrossRef] [PubMed]
6. Petta, S.; Valenti, L.; Bugianesi, E.; Targher, G.; Bellentani, S.; Bonino, F.; Special Interest Group on Personalised Hepatology of the Italian Association for the Study of the Liver (AISF). A "systems medicine" approach to the study of non-alcoholic fatty liver disease. *Dig. Liver Dis.* **2016**, *48*, 333–342. [CrossRef] [PubMed]
7. Lonardo, A.; Loria, P.; Adinolfi, L.E.; Carulli, N.; Ruggiero, G. Hepatitis C and steatosis: A reappraisal. *J. Viral Hepat.* **2006**, *13*, 73–80. [CrossRef] [PubMed]

8. Negro, F.; Forton, D.; Craxi, A.; Sulkowski, M.S.; Feld, J.J.; Manns, M.P. Extrahepatic morbidity and mortality of chronic hepatitis C. *Gastroenterology* **2015**, *149*, 1345–1360. [CrossRef] [PubMed]
9. Shaw, J.E.; Sicree, R.A.; Zimmet, P.Z. Global estimates of the prevalence of diabetes for 2010 and 2030. *Diabetes Res. Clin. Pract.* **2010**, *87*, 4–14. [CrossRef] [PubMed]
10. Kanavos, P.; van den Aardweg, S.; Schurer, W. Diabetes Expenditure, Burden of Disease and Management in 5 EU Countries. Available online: http://www.lse.ac.uk/LSEHealthAndSocialCare/research/LSEHealth/MTRG/LSEDiabetesReport26Jan2012.pdf (accessed on 8 February 2016).
11. Centers for Disease Control and Prevention. *National Diabetes Fact Sheet: National Estimates and General Information on Diabetes and Prediabetes in the United States*; U.S. Department of Health and Human Services, Centers for Disease Control and Prevention: Atlanta, GA, USA, 2011.
12. American Diabetes Association. Economic costs of diabetes in the U.S. in 2007. *Diabetes Care* **2008**, *31*, 596–615.
13. Sherwin, R.; Jastreboff, A.M. Year in diabetes 2012: The diabetes tsunami. *J. Clin. Endocrinol. Metab.* **2012**, *97*, 4293–4301. [CrossRef] [PubMed]
14. Zimmerman, H.J.; Mac, M.F.; Rappaport, H.; Alpert, L.K. Studies on the liver in diabetes mellitus. II. The significance of fatty metamorphosis and its correlation with insulin sensitivity. *J. Lab. Clin. Med.* **1950**, *36*, 922–928. [PubMed]
15. Ballestri, S.; Nascimbeni, F.; Romagnoli, D.; Lonardo, A. The independent predictors of NASH and its individual histological features. Insulin resistance, serum uric acid, metabolic syndrome, alt and serum total cholesterol are a clue to pathogenesis and candidate targets for treatment. *Hepatol. Res.* **2016**. [CrossRef] [PubMed]
16. Zhang, Y.; Zhang, T.; Zhang, C.; Tang, F.; Zhong, N.; Li, H.; Song, X.; Lin, H.; Liu, Y.; Xue, F. Identification of reciprocal causality between non-alcoholic fatty liver disease and metabolic syndrome by a simplified bayesian network in a chinese population. *BMJ Open* **2015**, *5*, e008204. [CrossRef] [PubMed]
17. Musso, G.; Gambino, R.; Cassader, M.; Pagano, G. Meta-analysis: Natural history of non-alcoholic fatty liver disease (NAFLD) and diagnostic accuracy of non-invasive tests for liver disease severity. *Ann. Med.* **2011**, *43*, 617–649. [CrossRef] [PubMed]
18. Ballestri, S.; Zona, S.; Targher, G.; Romagnoli, D.; Baldelli, E.; Nascimbeni, F.; Roverato, A.; Guaraldi, G.; Lonardo, A. Nonalcoholic fatty liver disease is associated with an almost two-fold increased risk of incident type 2 diabetes and metabolic syndrome. Evidence from a systematic review and meta-analysis. *J. Gastroenterol. Hepatol.* **2015**. [CrossRef] [PubMed]
19. White, D.L.; Ratziu, V.; El-Serag, H.B. Hepatitis Cinfection and risk of diabetes: A systematic review and meta-analysis. *J. Hepatol.* **2008**, *49*, 831–844. [CrossRef] [PubMed]
20. Cacoub, P.; Gragnani, L.; Comarmond, C.; Zignego, A.L. Extrahepatic manifestations of chronic hepatitis Cvirus infection. *Dig. Liver Dis.* **2014**, *46*, S165–S173. [CrossRef] [PubMed]
21. Lonardo, A.; Adinolfi, L.E.; Loria, P.; Carulli, N.; Ruggiero, G.; Day, C.P. Steatosis and hepatitis Cvirus: Mechanisms and significance for hepatic and extrahepatic disease. *Gastroenterology* **2004**, *126*, 586–597. [CrossRef] [PubMed]
22. Asselah, T.; Boyer, N.; Saadoun, D.; Martinot-Peignoux, M.; Marcellin, P. Direct-acting antivirals for the treatment of hepatitis Cvirus infection: Optimizing current IFN-free treatment and future perspectives. *Liver Int.* **2016**, *36*, 47–57. [CrossRef] [PubMed]
23. Ilyas, J.A.; Vierling, J.M. An overview of emerging therapies for the treatment of chronic hepatitis C. *Med. Clin. N. Am.* **2014**, *98*, 17–38. [CrossRef] [PubMed]
24. Welsch, C.; Jesudian, A.; Zeuzem, S.; Jacobson, I. New direct-acting antiviral agents for the treatment of hepatitis Cvirus infection and perspectives. *Gut* **2012**, *61*, i36–i46. [CrossRef] [PubMed]
25. Loria, P.; Lonardo, A.; Anania, F. Liver and diabetes. A vicious circle. *Hepatol. Res.* **2013**, *43*, 51–64. [CrossRef] [PubMed]
26. Ballestri, S.; Nascimbeni, F.; Romagnoli, D.; Baldelli, E.; Lonardo, A. The role of nuclear receptors in the pathophysiology, natural course, and drug treatment of NAFLDin humans. *Adv. Ther.* **2016**. [CrossRef] [PubMed]
27. Vanni, E.; Bugianesi, E.; Saracco, G. Treatment of type 2 diabetes mellitus by viral eradication in chronic hepatitis C: Myth or reality? *Dig. Liver Dis.* **2016**, *48*, 105–111. [CrossRef] [PubMed]

28. Klip, A.; Vranic, M. Muscle, liver, and pancreas: Three musketeers fighting to control glycemia. *Am. J. Physiol. Endocrinol. Metab.* **2006**, *291*, E1141–E1143. [CrossRef] [PubMed]

29. Reaven, G.M. The fourth musketeer—From Alexandre Dumas to Claude Bernard. *Diabetologia* **1995**, *38*, 3–13. [CrossRef] [PubMed]

30. Armstrong, M.J.; Adams, L.A.; Canbay, A.; Syn, W.K. Extrahepatic complications of nonalcoholic fatty liver disease. *Hepatology* **2014**, *59*, 1174–1197. [CrossRef] [PubMed]

31. Carulli, L.; Ballestri, S.; Lonardo, A.; Lami, F.; Violi, E.; Losi, L.; Bonilauri, L.; Verrone, A.M.; Odoardi, M.R.; Scaglioni, F.; *et al.* Is nonalcoholic steatohepatitis associated with a high-though-normal thyroid stimulating hormone level and lower cholesterol levels? *Intern. Emerg. Med.* **2013**, *8*, 297–305. [CrossRef] [PubMed]

32. Nascimbeni, F.; Ballestri, S.; Di Tommaso, L.; Piccoli, M.; Lonardo, A. Inflammatory hepatocellular adenomatosis, metabolic syndrome, polycystic ovary syndrome and non-alcoholic steatohepatitis: Chance tetrad or association by necessity? *Dig. Liver Dis.* **2014**, *46*, 288–289. [CrossRef] [PubMed]

33. Loria, P.; Carulli, L.; Bertolotti, M.; Lonardo, A. Endocrine and liver interaction: The role of endocrine pathways in NASH. *Nat.Rev. Gastroenterol. Hepatol.* **2009**, *6*, 236–247. [CrossRef] [PubMed]

34. Targher, G.; Rossini, M.; Lonardo, A. Evidence that non-alcoholic fatty liver disease and polycystic ovary syndrome are associated by necessity rather than chance: Anovel hepato-ovarian axis? *Endocrine* **2016**, *51*, 211–221. [CrossRef] [PubMed]

35. Targher, G.; Lonardo, A.; Rossini, M. Nonalcoholic fatty liver disease and decreased bone mineral density: Is there a link? *J. Endocrinol. Investig.* **2015**, *38*, 817–825. [CrossRef] [PubMed]

36. Mantovani, A.; Gisondi, P.; Lonardo, A.; Targher, G. Relationship between non-alcoholic fatty liver disease and psoriasis: A novel hepato-dermal axis? *Int. J. Mol. Sci.* **2016**, *17*, 217. [CrossRef] [PubMed]

37. Vigano, M.; Colombo, M. Extrahepatic manifestations of hepatitis C virus. *Gastroenterol. Clin. N. Am.* **2015**, *44*, 775–791. [CrossRef] [PubMed]

38. Negro, F. Facts and fictions of HCV and comorbidities: Steatosis, diabetes mellitus, and cardiovascular diseases. *J. Hepatol.* **2014**, *61*, S69–S78. [CrossRef] [PubMed]

39. Lonardo, A.; Bellentani, S.; Argo, C.K.; Ballestri, S.; Byrne, C.D.; Caldwell, S.H.; Cortez-Pinto, H.; Grieco, A.; Machado, M.V.; *et al.* Epidemiological modifiers of non-alcoholic fatty liver disease: Focus on high-risk groups. *Dig Liver Dis.* **2015**, *47*, 997–1006.

40. Singh, S.; Allen, A.M.; Wang, Z.; Prokop, L.J.; Murad, M.H.; Loomba, R. Fibrosis progression in nonalcoholic fatty liver vs nonalcoholic steatohepatitis: Asystematic review and meta-analysis of paired-biopsy studies. *Clin. Gastroenterol. Hepatol.* **2015**, *13*, 643–654. [CrossRef] [PubMed]

41. Leite, N.C.; Villela-Nogueira, C.A.; Pannain, V.L.; Bottino, A.C.; Rezende, G.F.; Cardoso, C.R.; Salles, G.F. Histopathological stages of nonalcoholic fatty liver disease in type 2 diabetes: Prevalences and correlated factors. *Liver Int.* **2011**, *31*, 700–706. [CrossRef] [PubMed]

42. Portillo Sanchez, P.; Bril, F.; Maximos, M.; Lomonaco, R.; Biernacki, D.; Orsak, B.; Subbarayan, S.; Webb, A.; Hecht, J.; Cusi, K. High prevalence of nonalcoholic fatty liver disease in patients with type 2 diabetes mellitus and normal plasma aminotransferase levels. *J. Clin. Endocrinol. Metab.* **2015**, *100*, 2231–2238. [CrossRef] [PubMed]

43. Williams, C.D.; Stengel, J.; Asike, M.I.; Torres, D.M.; Shaw, J.; Contreras, M.; Landt, C.L.; Harrison, S.A. Prevalence of nonalcoholic fatty liver disease and nonalcoholic steatohepatitis among a largely middle-aged population utilizing ultrasound and liver biopsy: Aprospective study. *Gastroenterology* **2011**, *140*, 124–131. [CrossRef] [PubMed]

44. Kwok, R.; Choi, K.C.; Wong, G.L.; Zhang, Y.; Chan, H.L.; Luk, A.O.; Shu, S.S.; Chan, A.W.; Yeung, M.W.; Chan, J.C.; *et al.* Screening diabetic patients for non-alcoholic fatty liver disease with controlled attenuation parameter and liver stiffness measurements: Aprospective cohort study. *Gut* **2015**. [CrossRef] [PubMed]

45. Anstee, Q.M.; Targher, G.; Day, C.P. Progression of NAFLD to diabetes mellitus, cardiovascular disease or cirrhosis. *Nat.Rev. Gastroenterol. Hepatol.* **2013**, *10*, 330–344. [CrossRef] [PubMed]

46. Maximos, M.; Bril, F.; Portillo Sanchez, P.; Lomonaco, R.; Orsak, B.; Biernacki, D.; Suman, A.; Weber, M.; Cusi, K. The role of liver fat and insulin resistance as determinants of plasma aminotransferase elevation in nonalcoholic fatty liver disease. *Hepatology* **2015**, *61*, 153–160. [CrossRef] [PubMed]

47. Sung, K.C.; Wild, S.H.; Byrne, C.D. Resolution of fatty liver and risk of incident diabetes. *J. Clin. Endocrinol. Metab.* **2013**, *98*, 3637–3643. [CrossRef] [PubMed]

48. Yamazaki, H.; Tsuboya, T.; Tsuji, K.; Dohke, M.; Maguchi, H. Independent association between improvement of nonalcoholic fatty liver disease and reduced incidence of type 2 diabetes. *Diabetes Care* **2015**, *38*, 1673–1679. [CrossRef] [PubMed]

49. Fukuda, T.; Hamaguchi, M.; Kojima, T.; Hashimoto, Y.; Ohbora, A.; Kato, T.; Nakamura, N.; Fukui, M. The impact of non-alcoholic fatty liver disease on incident type 2 diabetes mellitus in non-overweight individuals. *Liver Int.* **2016**, *36*, 275–283. [CrossRef] [PubMed]

50. Shah, R.V.; Allison, M.A.; Lima, J.A.; Bluemke, D.A.; Abbasi, S.A.; Ouyang, P.; Jerosch-Herold, M.; Ding, J.; Budoff, M.J.; Murthy, V.L. Liver fat, statin use, and incident diabetes: The multi-ethnic study of atherosclerosis. *Atherosclerosis* **2015**, *242*, 211–217. [CrossRef] [PubMed]

51. Ekstedt, M.; Franzen, L.E.; Mathiesen, U.L.; Thorelius, L.; Holmqvist, M.; Bodemar, G.; Kechagias, S. Long-term follow-up of patients with NAFLD and elevated liver enzymes. *Hepatology* **2006**, *44*, 865–873. [CrossRef] [PubMed]

52. Buechler, C.; Krautbauer, S.; Eisinger, K. Adipose tissue fibrosis. *World J. Diabetes* **2015**, *6*, 548–553. [PubMed]

53. Sun, K.; Tordjman, J.; Clement, K.; Scherer, P.E. Fibrosis and adipose tissue dysfunction. *Cell Metab.* **2013**, *18*, 470–477. [CrossRef] [PubMed]

54. Sun, K.; Kusminski, C.M.; Scherer, P.E. Adipose tissue remodeling and obesity. *J. Clin. Investig.* **2011**, *121*, 2094–2101. [CrossRef] [PubMed]

55. Cinti, S.; Mitchell, G.; Barbatelli, G.; Murano, I.; Ceresi, E.; Faloia, E.; Wang, S.; Fortier, M.; Greenberg, A.S.; Obin, M.S. Adipocyte death defines macrophage localization and function in adipose tissue of obese mice and humans. *J. Lipid Res.* **2005**, *46*, 2347–2355. [CrossRef] [PubMed]

56. Cancello, R.; Henegar, C.; Viguerie, N.; Taleb, S.; Poitou, C.; Rouault, C.; Coupaye, M.; Pelloux, V.; Hugol, D.; Bouillot, J.L.; et al. Reduction of macrophage infiltration and chemoattractant gene expression changes in white adipose tissue of morbidly obese subjects after surgery-induced weight loss. *Diabetes* **2005**, *54*, 2277–2286. [CrossRef] [PubMed]

57. Halberg, N.; Khan, T.; Trujillo, M.E.; Wernstedt-Asterholm, I.; Attie, A.D.; Sherwani, S.; Wang, Z.V.; Landskroner-Eiger, S.; Dineen, S.; Magalang, U.J.; et al. Hypoxia-inducible factor 1alpha induces fibrosis and insulin resistance in white adipose tissue. *Mol. Cell. Biol.* **2009**, *29*, 4467–4483. [CrossRef] [PubMed]

58. Jiang, C.; Qu, A.; Matsubara, T.; Chanturiya, T.; Jou, W.; Gavrilova, O.; Shah, Y.M.; Gonzalez, F.J. Disruption of hypoxia-inducible factor 1 in adipocytes improves insulin sensitivity and decreases adiposity in high-fat diet-fed mice. *Diabetes* **2011**, *60*, 2484–2495. [CrossRef] [PubMed]

59. Sun, K.; Halberg, N.; Khan, M.; Magalang, U.J.; Scherer, P.E. Selective inhibition of hypoxia-inducible factor 1alpha ameliorates adipose tissue dysfunction. *Mol. Cell. Biol.* **2013**, *33*, 904–917. [CrossRef] [PubMed]

60. Lumeng, C.N.; Bodzin, J.L.; Saltiel, A.R. Obesity induces a phenotypic switch in adipose tissue macrophage polarization. *J. Clin. Investig.* **2007**, *117*, 175–184. [CrossRef] [PubMed]

61. Lumeng, C.N.; DelProposto, J.B.; Westcott, D.J.; Saltiel, A.R. Phenotypic switching of adipose tissue macrophages with obesity is generated by spatiotemporal differences in macrophage subtypes. *Diabetes* **2008**, *57*, 3239–3246. [CrossRef] [PubMed]

62. Suganami, T.; Tanaka, M.; Ogawa, Y. Adipose tissue inflammation and ectopic lipid accumulation. *Endocr. J.* **2012**, *59*, 849–857. [CrossRef] [PubMed]

63. Berg, A.H.; Scherer, P.E. Adipose tissue, inflammation, and cardiovascular disease. *Circ. Res.* **2005**, *96*, 939–949. [CrossRef] [PubMed]

64. Rocha, V.Z.; Libby, P. Obesity, inflammation, and atherosclerosis. *Nat. Rev. Cardiol.* **2009**, *6*, 399–409. [CrossRef] [PubMed]

65. Hotamisligil, G.S.; Shargill, N.S.; Spiegelman, B.M. Adipose expression of tumor necrosis factor-α: Direct role in obesity-linked insulin resistance. *Science* **1993**, *259*, 87–91. [CrossRef] [PubMed]

66. Uysal, K.T.; Wiesbrock, S.M.; Marino, M.W.; Hotamisligil, G.S. Protection from obesity-induced insulin resistance in mice lacking TNF-alpha function. *Nature* **1997**, *389*, 610–614. [PubMed]

67. Kanda, H.; Tateya, S.; Tamori, Y.; Kotani, K.; Hiasa, K.; Kitazawa, R.; Kitazawa, S.; Miyachi, H.; Maeda, S.; Egashira, K.; et al. Mcp-1 contributes to macrophage infiltration into adipose tissue, insulin resistance, and hepatic steatosis in obesity. *J. Clin. Investig.* **2006**, *116*, 1494–1505. [CrossRef] [PubMed]

68. Kamei, N.; Tobe, K.; Suzuki, R.; Ohsugi, M.; Watanabe, T.; Kubota, N.; Ohtsuka-Kowatari, N.; Kumagai, K.; Sakamoto, K.; Kobayashi, M.; et al. Overexpression of monocyte chemoattractant protein-1 in adipose tissues

causes macrophage recruitment and insulin resistance. *J. Biol. Chem.* **2006**, *281*, 26602–26614. [CrossRef] [PubMed]

69. Weisberg, S.P.; Hunter, D.; Huber, R.; Lemieux, J.; Slaymaker, S.; Vaddi, K.; Charo, I.; Leibel, R.L.; Ferrante, A.W., Jr. CCR2 modulates inflammatory and metabolic effects of high-fat feeding. *J. Clin. Investig.* **2006**, *116*, 115–124. [CrossRef] [PubMed]

70. Yamauchi, T.; Kamon, J.; Waki, H.; Terauchi, Y.; Kubota, N.; Hara, K.; Mori, Y.; Ide, T.; Murakami, K.; Tsuboyama-Kasaoka, N.; *et al.* The fat-derived hormone adiponectin reverses insulin resistance associated with both lipoatrophy and obesity. *Nat. Med.* **2001**, *7*, 941–946. [CrossRef] [PubMed]

71. Maeda, N.; Shimomura, I.; Kishida, K.; Nishizawa, H.; Matsuda, M.; Nagaretani, H.; Furuyama, N.; Kondo, H.; Takahashi, M.; Arita, Y.; *et al.* Diet-induced insulin resistance in mice lacking adiponectin/ACRP 30. *Nat. Med.* **2002**, *8*, 731–737. [CrossRef] [PubMed]

72. Wernstedt Asterholm, I.; Tao, C.; Morley, T.S.; Wang, Q.A.; Delgado-Lopez, F.; Wang, Z.V.; Scherer, P.E. Adipocyte inflammation is essential for healthy adipose tissue expansion and remodeling. *Cell Metab.* **2014**, *20*, 103–118. [CrossRef] [PubMed]

73. Divoux, A.; Tordjman, J.; Lacasa, D.; Veyrie, N.; Hugol, D.; Aissat, A.; Basdevant, A.; Guerre-Millo, M.; Poitou, C.; Zucker, J.D.; *et al.* Fibrosis in human adipose tissue: Composition, distribution, and link with lipid metabolism and fat mass loss. *Diabetes* **2010**, *59*, 2817–2825. [CrossRef] [PubMed]

74. Samuel, V.T.; Shulman, G.I. The pathogenesis of insulin resistance: Integrating signaling pathways and substrate flux. *J. Clin. Investig.* **2016**, *126*, 12–22. [CrossRef] [PubMed]

75. Yu, C.; Chen, Y.; Cline, G.W.; Zhang, D.; Zong, H.; Wang, Y.; Bergeron, R.; Kim, J.K.; Cushman, S.W.; Cooney, G.J.; *et al.* Mechanism by which fatty acids inhibit insulin activation of insulin receptor substrate-1 (IRS-1)-associated phosphatidylinositol 3-kinase activity in muscle. *J. Biol. Chem.* **2002**, *277*, 50230–50236. [CrossRef] [PubMed]

76. Griffin, M.E.; Marcucci, M.J.; Cline, G.W.; Bell, K.; Barucci, N.; Lee, D.; Goodyear, L.J.; Kraegen, E.W.; White, M.F.; Shulman, G.I. Free fatty acid-induced insulin resistance is associated with activation of protein kinase Ctheta and alterations in the insulin signaling cascade. *Diabetes* **1999**, *48*, 1270–1274. [CrossRef] [PubMed]

77. Szendroedi, J.; Yoshimura, T.; Phielix, E.; Koliaki, C.; Marcucci, M.; Zhang, D.; Jelenik, T.; Muller, J.; Herder, C.; Nowotny, P.; *et al.* Role of diacylglycerol activation of PKCθ in lipid-induced muscle insulin resistance in humans. *Proc. Natl. Acad. Sci. USA* **2014**, *111*, 9597–9602. [CrossRef] [PubMed]

78. Kitajima, Y.; Hyogo, H.; Sumida, Y.; Eguchi, Y.; Ono, N.; Kuwashiro, T.; Tanaka, K.; Takahashi, H.; Mizuta, T.; Ozaki, I.; *et al.* Severity of non-alcoholic steatohepatitis is associated with substitution of adipose tissue in skeletal muscle. *J. Gastroenterol. Hepatol.* **2013**, *28*, 1507–1514. [CrossRef] [PubMed]

79. Arias-Loste, M.T.; Ranchal, I.; Romero-Gomez, M.; Crespo, J. Irisin, a link among fatty liver disease, physical inactivity and insulin resistance. *Int. J. Mol. Sci.* **2014**, *15*, 23163–23178. [CrossRef] [PubMed]

80. Bostrom, P.; Wu, J.; Jedrychowski, M.P.; Korde, A.; Ye, L.; Lo, J.C.; Rasbach, K.A.; Bostrom, E.A.; Choi, J.H.; Long, J.Z.; *et al.* A PGC 1-α-dependent myokine that drives brown-fat-like development of white fat and thermogenesis. *Nature* **2012**, *481*, 463–468. [CrossRef] [PubMed]

81. Schulz, T.J.; Tseng, Y.H. Brown adipose tissue: Development, metabolism and beyond. *Biochem. J.* **2013**, *453*, 167–178. [CrossRef] [PubMed]

82. Seale, P.; Bjork, B.; Yang, W.; Kajimura, S.; Chin, S.; Kuang, S.; Scime, A.; Devarakonda, S.; Conroe, H.M.; Erdjument-Bromage, H.; *et al.* PRDM16 controls a brown fat/skeletal muscle switch. *Nature* **2008**, *454*, 961–967. [CrossRef] [PubMed]

83. Ishibashi, J.; Seale, P. Medicine. Beige can be slimming. *Science* **2010**, *328*, 1113–1114. [CrossRef] [PubMed]

84. Enerback, S. The origins of brown adipose tissue. *N. Engl. J. Med.* **2009**, *360*, 2021–2023. [CrossRef] [PubMed]

85. Scheja, L.; Heeren, J. Metabolic interplay between white, beige, brown adipocytes and the liver. *J. Hepatol.* **2016**. [CrossRef] [PubMed]

86. Guerra, C.; Navarro, P.; Valverde, A.M.; Arribas, M.; Bruning, J.; Kozak, L.P.; Kahn, C.R.; Benito, M. Brown adipose tissue-specific insulin receptor knockout shows diabetic phenotype without insulin resistance. *J. Clin. Investig.* **2001**, *108*, 1205–1213. [CrossRef] [PubMed]

87. Bartelt, A.; Bruns, O.T.; Reimer, R.; Hohenberg, H.; Ittrich, H.; Peldschus, K.; Kaul, M.G.; Tromsdorf, U.I.; Weller, H.; Waurisch, C.; *et al.* Brown adipose tissue activity controls triglyceride clearance. *Nat. Med.* **2011**, *17*, 200–205. [CrossRef] [PubMed]

88. Assyov, Y.; Gateva, A.; Tsakova, A.; Kamenov, Z. Irisin in the glucose continuum. *Exp. Clin. Endocrinol. Diabetes* **2016**, *124*, 22–27. [CrossRef] [PubMed]

89. Liu, J.J.; Wong, M.D.; Toy, W.C.; Tan, C.S.; Liu, S.; Ng, X.W.; Tavintharan, S.; Sum, C.F.; Lim, S.C. Lower circulating irisin is associated with type 2 diabetes mellitus. *J. Diabetes Complicat.* **2013**, *27*, 365–369. [CrossRef] [PubMed]

90. Zhang, H.J.; Zhang, X.F.; Ma, Z.M.; Pan, L.L.; Chen, Z.; Han, H.W.; Han, C.K.; Zhuang, X.J.; Lu, Y.; Li, X.J.; et al. Irisin is inversely associated with intrahepatic triglyceride contents in obese adults. *J. Hepatol.* **2013**, *59*, 557–562. [CrossRef] [PubMed]

91. Donnelly, K.L.; Smith, C.I.; Schwarzenberg, S.J.; Jessurun, J.; Boldt, M.D.; Parks, E.J. Sources of fatty acids stored in liver and secreted via lipoproteins in patients with nonalcoholic fatty liver disease. *J. Clin. Investig.* **2005**, *115*, 1343–1351. [CrossRef] [PubMed]

92. Haas, J.T.; Francque, S.; Staels, B. Pathophysiology and mechanisms of nonalcoholic fatty liver disease. *Ann. Rev. Physiol.* **2016**, *78*, 181–205. [CrossRef] [PubMed]

93. Seppala-Lindroos, A.; Vehkavaara, S.; Hakkinen, A.M.; Goto, T.; Westerbacka, J.; Sovijarvi, A.; Halavaara, J.; Yki-Jarvinen, H. Fat accumulation in the liver is associated with defects in insulin suppression of glucose production and serum free fatty acids independent of obesity in normal men. *J. Clin. Endocrinol. Metab.* **2002**, *87*, 3023–3028. [CrossRef] [PubMed]

94. Bugianesi, E.; Gastaldelli, A.; Vanni, E.; Gambino, R.; Cassader, M.; Baldi, S.; Ponti, V.; Pagano, G.; Ferrannini, E.; Rizzetto, M. Insulin resistance in non-diabetic patients with non-alcoholic fatty liver disease: Sites and mechanisms. *Diabetologia* **2005**, *48*, 634–642. [CrossRef] [PubMed]

95. Vatner, D.F.; Majumdar, S.K.; Kumashiro, N.; Petersen, M.C.; Rahimi, Y.; Gattu, A.K.; Bears, M.; Camporez, J.P.; Cline, G.W.; Jurczak, M.J.; et al. Insulin-independent regulation of hepatic triglyceride synthesis by fatty acids. *Proc. Natl. Acad. Sci. USA* **2015**, *112*, 1143–1148. [CrossRef] [PubMed]

96. Matsuzaka, T.; Shimano, H.; Yahagi, N.; Amemiya-Kudo, M.; Okazaki, H.; Tamura, Y.; Iizuka, Y.; Ohashi, K.; Tomita, S.; Sekiya, M.; et al. Insulin-independent induction of sterol regulatory element-binding protein-1c expression in the livers of streptozotocin-treated mice. *Diabetes* **2004**, *53*, 560–569. [CrossRef] [PubMed]

97. Stanhope, K.L.; Schwarz, J.M.; Keim, N.L.; Griffen, S.C.; Bremer, A.A.; Graham, J.L.; Hatcher, B.; Cox, C.L.; Dyachenko, A.; Zhang, W.; et al. Consuming fructose-sweetened, not glucose-sweetened, beverages increases visceral adiposity and lipids and decreases insulin sensitivity in overweight/obese humans. *J. Clin. Investig.* **2009**, *119*, 1322–1334. [CrossRef] [PubMed]

98. Uyeda, K.; Repa, J.J. Carbohydrate response element binding protein, chrebp, a transcription factor coupling hepatic glucose utilization and lipid synthesis. *Cell Metab.* **2006**, *4*, 107–110. [CrossRef] [PubMed]

99. Erion, D.M.; Popov, V.; Hsiao, J.J.; Vatner, D.; Mitchell, K.; Yonemitsu, S.; Nagai, Y.; Kahn, M.; Gillum, M.P.; Dong, J.; et al. The role of the carbohydrate response element-binding protein in male fructose-fed rats. *Endocrinology* **2013**, *154*, 36–44. [CrossRef] [PubMed]

100. Nagai, Y.; Yonemitsu, S.; Erion, D.M.; Iwasaki, T.; Stark, R.; Weismann, D.; Dong, J.; Zhang, D.; Jurczak, M.J.; Loffler, M.G.; et al. The role of peroxisome proliferator-activated receptor gamma coactivator-1 β in the pathogenesis of fructose-induced insulin resistance. *Cell Metab.* **2009**, *9*, 252–264. [CrossRef] [PubMed]

101. Bindesboll, C.; Fan, Q.; Norgaard, R.C.; MacPherson, L.; Ruan, H.B.; Wu, J.; Pedersen, T.A.; Steffensen, K.R.; Yang, X.; Matthews, J.; et al. Liver Xreceptor regulates hepatic nuclear O-GlcNAc signaling and carbohydrate responsive element-binding protein activity. *J. Lipid Res.* **2015**, *56*, 771–785. [CrossRef] [PubMed]

102. Samuel, V.T.; Shulman, G.I. Mechanisms for insulin resistance: Common threads and missing links. *Cell* **2012**, *148*, 852–871. [CrossRef] [PubMed]

103. Yamaguchi, K.; Yang, L.; McCall, S.; Huang, J.; Yu, X.X.; Pandey, S.K.; Bhanot, S.; Monia, B.P.; Li, Y.X.; Diehl, A.M. Inhibiting triglyceride synthesis improves hepatic steatosis but exacerbates liver damage and fibrosis in obese mice with nonalcoholic steatohepatitis. *Hepatology* **2007**, *45*, 1366–1374. [CrossRef] [PubMed]

104. Samuel, V.T.; Liu, Z.X.; Wang, A.; Beddow, S.A.; Geisler, J.G.; Kahn, M.; Zhang, X.M.; Monia, B.P.; Bhanot, S.; Shulman, G.I. Inhibition of protein kinase cepsilon prevents hepatic insulin resistance in nonalcoholic fatty liver disease. *J. Clin. Investig.* **2007**, *117*, 739–745. [CrossRef] [PubMed]

105. Qu, X.; Seale, J.P.; Donnelly, R. Tissue and isoform-selective activation of protein kinase Cin insulin-resistant obese zucker rats—Effects of feeding. *J. Endocrinol.* **1999**, *162*, 207–214. [CrossRef] [PubMed]

106. Kumashiro, N.; Erion, D.M.; Zhang, D.; Kahn, M.; Beddow, S.A.; Chu, X.; Still, C.D.; Gerhard, G.S.; Han, X.; Dziura, J.; *et al.* Cellular mechanism of insulin resistance in nonalcoholic fatty liver disease. *Proc. Natl. Acad. Sci. USA* **2011**, *108*, 16381–16385. [CrossRef] [PubMed]

107. Magkos, F.; Su, X.; Bradley, D.; Fabbrini, E.; Conte, C.; Eagon, J.C.; Varela, J.E.; Brunt, E.M.; Patterson, B.W.; Klein, S. Intrahepatic diacylglycerol content is associated with hepatic insulin resistance in obese subjects. *Gastroenterology* **2012**, *142*, 1444–1446. [CrossRef] [PubMed]

108. Schmitz-Peiffer, C.; Craig, D.L.; Biden, T.J. Ceramide generation is sufficient to account for the inhibition of the insulin-stimulated PKBpathway in C2C12 skeletal muscle cells pretreated with palmitate. *J. Biol. Chem.* **1999**, *274*, 24202–24210. [CrossRef] [PubMed]

109. Stratford, S.; Hoehn, K.L.; Liu, F.; Summers, S.A. Regulation of insulin action by ceramide: Dual mechanisms linking ceramide accumulation to the inhibition of AKT/protein kinase B. *J. Biol. Chem.* **2004**, *279*, 36608–36615. [CrossRef] [PubMed]

110. Turinsky, J.; O'Sullivan, D.M.; Bayly, B.P. 1,2-Diacylglycerol and ceramide levels in insulin-resistant tissues of the rat *in vivo*. *J. Biol. Chem.* **1990**, *265*, 16880–16885. [PubMed]

111. Chavez, J.A.; Summers, S.A. A ceramide-centric view of insulin resistance. *Cell Metab.* **2012**, *15*, 585–594. [CrossRef] [PubMed]

112. Hla, T.; Kolesnick, R. C16:0-ceramide signals insulin resistance. *Cell Metab.* **2014**, *20*, 703–705. [CrossRef] [PubMed]

113. Turpin, S.M.; Nicholls, H.T.; Willmes, D.M.; Mourier, A.; Brodesser, S.; Wunderlich, C.M.; Mauer, J.; Xu, E.; Hammerschmidt, P.; Bronneke, H.S.; *et al.* Obesity-induced CERS6-dependent C16:0 ceramide production promotes weight gain and glucose intolerance. *Cell Metab.* **2014**, *20*, 678–686. [CrossRef] [PubMed]

114. Luukkonen, P.K.; Zhou, Y.; Sadevirta, S.; Leivonen, M.; Arola, J.; Oresic, M.; Hyotylainen, T.; Yki-Jarvinen, H. Ceramides dissociate steatosis and insulin resistance in the human liver in non-alcoholic fatty liver disease. *J. Hepatol.* **2016**. [CrossRef] [PubMed]

115. Jenkins, C.M.; Mancuso, D.J.; Yan, W.; Sims, H.F.; Gibson, B.; Gross, R.W. Identification, cloning, expression, and purification of three novel human calcium-independent phospholipase A2 family members possessing triacylglycerol lipase and acylglycerol transacylase activities. *J. Biol. Chem.* **2004**, *279*, 48968–48975. [CrossRef] [PubMed]

116. Romeo, S.; Kozlitina, J.; Xing, C.; Pertsemlidis, A.; Cox, D.; Pennacchio, L.A.; Boerwinkle, E.; Cohen, J.C.; Hobbs, H.H. Genetic variation in PNPLA3 confers susceptibility to nonalcoholic fatty liver disease. *Nat. Genet.* **2008**, *40*, 1461–1465. [CrossRef] [PubMed]

117. Kantartzis, K.; Peter, A.; Machicao, F.; Machann, J.; Wagner, S.; Konigsrainer, I.; Konigsrainer, A.; Schick, F.; Fritsche, A.; Haring, H.U.; *et al.* Dissociation between fatty liver and insulin resistance in humans carrying a variant of the patatin-like phospholipase 3 gene. *Diabetes* **2009**, *58*, 2616–2623. [CrossRef] [PubMed]

118. Kotronen, A.; Johansson, L.E.; Johansson, L.M.; Roos, C.; Westerbacka, J.; Hamsten, A.; Bergholm, R.; Arkkila, P.; Arola, J.; Kiviluoto, T.; *et al.* A common variant in PNPLA3, which encodes adiponutrin, is associated with liver fat content in humans. *Diabetologia* **2009**, *52*, 1056–1060. [CrossRef] [PubMed]

119. Speliotes, E.K.; Butler, J.L.; Palmer, C.D.; Voight, B.F.; Consortium, G.; Consortium, M.I.; Nash, C.R.N.; Hirschhorn, J.N. PNPLA3 variants specifically confer increased risk for histologic nonalcoholic fatty liver disease but not metabolic disease. *Hepatology* **2010**, *52*, 904–912. [CrossRef] [PubMed]

120. Kumari, M.; Schoiswohl, G.; Chitraju, C.; Paar, M.; Cornaciu, I.; Rangrez, A.Y.; Wongsiriroj, N.; Nagy, H.M.; Ivanova, P.T.; Scott, S.A.; *et al.* Adiponutrin functions as a nutritionally regulated lysophosphatidic acid acyltransferase. *Cell Metab.* **2012**, *15*, 691–702. [CrossRef] [PubMed]

121. Smagris, E.; BasuRay, S.; Li, J.; Huang, Y.; Lai, K.M.; Gromada, J.; Cohen, J.C.; Hobbs, H.H. PNPLA3I148Mknockin mice accumulate PNPLA3 on lipid droplets and develop hepatic steatosis. *Hepatology* **2015**, *61*, 108–118. [CrossRef] [PubMed]

122. Wu, J.W.; Yang, H.; Mitchell, G.A. Potential mechanism underlying the PNPLA3^{I148M}-hepatic steatosis connection. *Hepatology* **2016**, *63*, 676–677. [CrossRef] [PubMed]

123. Puri, P.; Mirshahi, F.; Cheung, O.; Natarajan, R.; Maher, J.W.; Kellum, J.M.; Sanyal, A.J. Activation and dysregulation of the unfolded protein response in nonalcoholic fatty liver disease. *Gastroenterology* **2008**, *134*, 568–576. [CrossRef] [PubMed]

124. Malhi, H.; Gores, G.J. Molecular mechanisms of lipotoxity in nonalcoholic fatty liver disease. *Semin. Liver Dis.* **2008**, *28*, 360–369. [CrossRef] [PubMed]

125. Singh, R.; Kaushik, S.; Wang, Y.; Xiang, Y.; Novak, I.; Komatsu, M.; Tanaka, K.; Cuervo, A.M.; Czaja, M.J. Autophagy regulates lipid metabolism. *Nature* **2009**, *458*, 1131–1135. [CrossRef] [PubMed]

126. Wang, Y.; Singh, R.; Xiang, Y.; Czaja, M.J. Macroautophagy and chaperone-mediated autophagy are required for hepatocyte resistance to oxidant stress. *Hepatology* **2010**, *52*, 266–277. [CrossRef] [PubMed]

127. Czaja, M.J. Autophagy in health and disease. 2. Regulation of lipid metabolism and storage by autophagy: Pathophysiological implications. *Am. J. Physiol. Cell Physiol.* **2010**, *298*, C973–C978. [CrossRef] [PubMed]

128. Pal, D.; Dasgupta, S.; Kundu, R.; Maitra, S.; Das, G.; Mukhopadhyay, S.; Ray, S.; Majumdar, S.S.; Bhattacharya, S. Fetuin-A acts as an endogenous ligand of TLR4 to promote lipid-induced insulin resistance. *Nat. Med.* **2012**, *18*, 1279–1285. [CrossRef] [PubMed]

129. Chatterjee, P.; Seal, S.; Mukherjee, S.; Kundu, R.; Mukherjee, S.; Ray, S.; Mukhopadhyay, S.; Majumdar, S.S.; Bhattacharya, S. Adipocyte fetuin-A contributes to macrophage migration into adipose tissue and polarization of macrophages. *J. Biol. Chem.* **2013**, *288*, 28324–28330. [CrossRef] [PubMed]

130. Ix, J.H.; Shlipak, M.G.; Brandenburg, V.M.; Ali, S.; Ketteler, M.; Whooley, M.A. Association between human fetuin-A and the metabolic syndrome: Data from the heart and soul study. *Circulation* **2006**, *113*, 1760–1767. [CrossRef] [PubMed]

131. Ix, J.H.; Wassel, C.L.; Kanaya, A.M.; Vittinghoff, E.; Johnson, K.C.; Koster, A.; Cauley, J.A.; Harris, T.B.; Cummings, S.R.; Shlipak, M.G.; *et al.* Fetuin-A and incident diabetes mellitus in older persons. *JAMA* **2008**, *300*, 182–188. [CrossRef] [PubMed]

132. Stefan, N.; Hennige, A.M.; Staiger, H.; Machann, J.; Schick, F.; Krober, S.M.; Machicao, F.; Fritsche, A.; Haring, H.U. Alpha2-heremans-schmid glycoprotein/fetuin-A is associated with insulin resistance and fat accumulation in the liver in humans. *Diabetes Care* **2006**, *29*, 853–857. [CrossRef] [PubMed]

133. Meex, R.C.; Hoy, A.J.; Morris, A.; Brown, R.D.; Lo, J.C.; Burke, M.; Goode, R.J.; Kingwell, B.A.; Kraakman, M.J.; Febbraio, M.A.; *et al.* Fetuin B is a secreted hepatocyte factor linking steatosis to impaired glucose metabolism. *Cell Metab.* **2015**, *22*, 1078–1089. [CrossRef] [PubMed]

134. Kharitonenkov, A.; Shiyanova, T.L.; Koester, A.; Ford, A.M.; Micanovic, R.; Galbreath, E.J.; Sandusky, G.E.; Hammond, L.J.; Moyers, J.S.; Owens, R.A.; *et al.* FGF-21 as a novel metabolic regulator. *J. Clin. Investig.* **2005**, *115*, 1627–1635. [CrossRef] [PubMed]

135. Zhang, X.; Yeung, D.C.; Karpisek, M.; Stejskal, D.; Zhou, Z.G.; Liu, F.; Wong, R.L.; Chow, W.S.; Tso, A.W.; Lam, K.S.; *et al.* Serum FGF21 levels are increased in obesity and are independently associated with the metabolic syndrome in humans. *Diabetes* **2008**, *57*, 1246–1253. [CrossRef] [PubMed]

136. Itoh, N. FGF21 as a hepatokine, adipokine, and myokine in metabolism and diseases. *Front. Endocrinol. (Lausanne)* **2014**, *5*, 107. [CrossRef] [PubMed]

137. Chavez, A.O.; Molina-Carrion, M.; Abdul-Ghani, M.A.; Folli, F.; Defronzo, R.A.; Tripathy, D. Circulating fibroblast growth factor-21 is elevated in impaired glucose tolerance and type 2 diabetes and correlates with muscle and hepatic insulin resistance. *Diabetes Care* **2009**, *32*, 1542–1546. [CrossRef] [PubMed]

138. Dushay, J.; Chui, P.C.; Gopalakrishnan, G.S.; Varela-Rey, M.; Crawley, M.; Fisher, F.M.; Badman, M.K.; Martinez-Chantar, M.L.; Maratos-Flier, E. Increased fibroblast growth factor 21 in obesity and nonalcoholic fatty liver disease. *Gastroenterology* **2010**, *139*, 456–463. [CrossRef] [PubMed]

139. Li, H.; Dong, K.; Fang, Q.; Hou, X.; Zhou, M.; Bao, Y.; Xiang, K.; Xu, A.; Jia, W. High serum level of fibroblast growth factor 21 is an independent predictor of non-alcoholic fatty liver disease: A 3-year prospective study in china. *J. Hepatol.* **2013**, *58*, 557–563. [CrossRef] [PubMed]

140. Li, H.; Fang, Q.; Gao, F.; Fan, J.; Zhou, J.; Wang, X.; Zhang, H.; Pan, X.; Bao, Y.; Xiang, K.; *et al.* Fibroblast growth factor 21 levels are increased in nonalcoholic fatty liver disease patients and are correlated with hepatic triglyceride. *J. Hepatol.* **2010**, *53*, 934–940. [CrossRef] [PubMed]

141. El Ouaamari, A.; Dirice, E.; Gedeon, N.; Hu, J.; Zhou, J.Y.; Shirakawa, J.; Hou, L.; Goodman, J.; Karampelias, C.; Qiang, G.; *et al.* SerpinB1 promotes pancreatic beta cell proliferation. *Cell Metab.* **2016**, *23*, 194–205. [CrossRef] [PubMed]

142. Tarasov, A.I.; Rorsman, P. Dramatis personae in beta-cell mass regulation: Enter serpinB1. *Cell Metab.* **2016**, *23*, 8–10. [CrossRef] [PubMed]

143. Boursier, J.; Mueller, O.; Barret, M.; Machado, M.; Fizanne, L.; Araujo-Perez, F.; Guy, C.D.; Seed, P.C.; Rawls, J.F.; David, L.A.; *et al.* The severity of NAFLD is associated with gut dysbiosis and shift in the metabolic function of the gut microbiota. *Hepatology* **2016**, *63*, 764–775. [CrossRef] [PubMed]

144. Le Roy, T.; Llopis, M.; Lepage, P.; Bruneau, A.; Rabot, S.; Bevilacqua, C.; Martin, P.; Philippe, C.; Walker, F.; Bado, A.; *et al.* Intestinal microbiota determines development of non-alcoholic fatty liver disease in mice. *Gut* **2013**, *62*, 1787–1794. [CrossRef] [PubMed]

145. Musso, G.; Gambino, R.; Cassader, M. Gut microbiota as a regulator of energy homeostasis and ectopic fat deposition: Mechanisms and implications for metabolic disorders. *Curr. Opin. Lipidol.* **2010**, *21*, 76–83. [CrossRef] [PubMed]

146. Nolan, C.J.; Damm, P.; Prentki, M. Type 2 diabetes across generations: From pathophysiology to prevention and management. *Lancet* **2011**, *378*, 169–181. [CrossRef]

147. Shima, T.; Uto, H.; Ueki, K.; Takamura, T.; Kohgo, Y.; Kawata, S.; Yasui, K.; Park, H.; Nakamura, N.; Nakatou, T.; *et al.* Clinicopathological features of liver injury in patients with type 2 diabetes mellitus and comparative study of histologically proven nonalcoholic fatty liver diseases with or without type 2 diabetes mellitus. *J.Gastroenterol.* **2013**, *48*, 515–525. [CrossRef] [PubMed]

148. Goh, G.B.; Pagadala, M.R.; Dasarathy, J.; Unalp-Arida, A.; Sargent, R.; Hawkins, C.; Sourianarayanane, A.; Khiyami, A.; Yerian, L.; Pai, R.K.; *et al.* Clinical spectrum of non-alcoholic fatty liver disease in diabetic and non-diabetic patients. *BBA Clin.* **2015**, *3*, 141–145. [CrossRef] [PubMed]

149. Nascimbeni, F.; Aron-Wisniewsky, J.; Pais, R.; Tordjman, J.; Poitou, C.; Charlotte, F.; Bedossa, P.; Poynard, T.; Clement, K.; Ratziu, V. Statins, antidiabetic medications and liver histology in diabetic patients with non-alcoholic fatty liver disease. *BMJ Open Gastroenterol.* **2016**. in press.

150. Angulo, P.; Keach, J.C.; Batts, K.P.; Lindor, K.D. Independent predictors of liver fibrosis in patients with nonalcoholic steatohepatitis. *Hepatology* **1999**, *30*, 1356–1362. [CrossRef] [PubMed]

151. De Ledinghen, V.; Ratziu, V.; Causse, X.; Le Bail, B.; Capron, D.; Renou, C.; Pilette, C.; Oules, V.; Gelsi, E.; Oberti, F.; *et al.* Diagnostic and predictive factors of significant liver fibrosis and minimal lesions in patients with persistent unexplained elevated transaminases. A prospective multicenter study. *J. Hepatol.* **2006**, *45*, 592–599. [CrossRef] [PubMed]

152. Hossain, N.; Afendy, A.; Stepanova, M.; Nader, F.; Srishord, M.; Rafiq, N.; Goodman, Z.; Younossi, Z. Independent predictors of fibrosis in patients with nonalcoholic fatty liver disease. *Clin. Gastroenterol. Hepatol.* **2009**, *7*, 1224–1229. [CrossRef] [PubMed]

153. Nakahara, T.; Hyogo, H.; Yoneda, M.; Sumida, Y.; Eguchi, Y.; Fujii, H.; Ono, M.; Kawaguchi, T.; Imajo, K.; Aikata, H.; *et al.* Type 2 diabetes mellitus is associated with the fibrosis severity in patients with nonalcoholic fatty liver disease in a large retrospective cohort of Japanese patients. *J. Gastroenterol.* **2014**, *49*, 1477–1484. [CrossRef] [PubMed]

154. McPherson, S.; Hardy, T.; Henderson, E.; Burt, A.D.; Day, C.P.; Anstee, Q.M. Evidence of NAFLDprogression from steatosis to fibrosing-steatohepatitis using paired biopsies: Implications for prognosis and clinical management. *J. Hepatol.* **2015**, *62*, 1148–1155. [CrossRef] [PubMed]

155. Pais, R.; Charlotte, F.; Fedchuk, L.; Bedossa, P.; Lebray, P.; Poynard, T.; Ratziu, V.; Group, L.S. A systematic review of follow-up biopsies reveals disease progression in patients with non-alcoholic fatty liver. *J. Hepatol.* **2013**, *59*, 550–556. [CrossRef] [PubMed]

156. Adams, L.A.; Sanderson, S.; Lindor, K.D.; Angulo, P. The histological course of nonalcoholic fatty liver disease: A longitudinal study of 103 patients with sequential liver biopsies. *J. Hepatol.* **2005**, *42*, 132–138. [CrossRef] [PubMed]

157. Hamaguchi, E.; Takamura, T.; Sakurai, M.; Mizukoshi, E.; Zen, Y.; Takeshita, Y.; Kurita, S.; Arai, K.; Yamashita, T.; Sasaki, M.; *et al.* Histological course of nonalcoholic fatty liver disease in Japanese patients: Tight glycemic control, rather than weight reduction, ameliorates liver fibrosis. *Diabetes Care* **2010**, *33*, 284–286. [CrossRef] [PubMed]

158. Hashiba, M.; Ono, M.; Hyogo, H.; Ikeda, Y.; Masuda, K.; Yoshioka, R.; Ishikawa, Y.; Nagata, Y.; Munekage, K.; Ochi, T.; *et al.* Glycemic variability is an independent predictive factor for development of hepatic fibrosis in nonalcoholic fatty liver disease. *PLoS ONE* **2013**, *8*, e76161. [CrossRef] [PubMed]

159. Fracanzani, A.L.; Valenti, L.; Bugianesi, E.; Andreoletti, M.; Colli, A.; Vanni, E.; Bertelli, C.; Fatta, E.; Bignamini, D.; Marchesini, G.; *et al.* Risk of severe liver disease in nonalcoholic fatty liver disease with normal aminotransferase levels: Arole for insulin resistance and diabetes. *Hepatology* **2008**, *48*, 792–798. [CrossRef] [PubMed]

160. Ballestri, S.; Romagnoli, D.; Nascimbeni, F.; Francica, G.; Lonardo, A. Role of ultrasound in the diagnosis and treatment of nonalcoholic fatty liver disease and its complications. *Expert Rev. Gastroenterol. Hepatol.* **2015**, *9*, 603–627. [CrossRef] [PubMed]

161. Nascimbeni, F.; Loria, P.; Ratziu, V. Non-alcoholic fatty liver disease: Diagnosis and investigation. *Dig. Dis.* **2014**, *32*, 586–596. [CrossRef] [PubMed]

162. Younossi, Z.M.; Gramlich, T.; Matteoni, C.A.; Boparai, N.; McCullough, A.J. Nonalcoholic fatty liver disease in patients with type 2 diabetes. *Clin. Gastroenterol. Hepatol.* **2004**, *2*, 262–265. [CrossRef]

163. Hessheimer, A.J.; Forner, A.; Varela, M.; Bruix, J. Metabolic risk factors are a major comorbidity in patients with cirrhosis independent of the presence of hepatocellular carcinoma. *Eur. J. Gastroenterol. Hepatol.* **2010**, *22*, 1239–1244. [CrossRef] [PubMed]

164. Ertle, J.; Dechene, A.; Sowa, J.P.; Penndorf, V.; Herzer, K.; Kaiser, G.; Schlaak, J.F.; Gerken, G.; Syn, W.K.; Canbay, A. Non-alcoholic fatty liver disease progresses to hepatocellular carcinoma in the absence of apparent cirrhosis. *Int. J.Cancer* **2011**, *128*, 2436–2443. [CrossRef] [PubMed]

165. Yasui, K.; Hashimoto, E.; Komorizono, Y.; Koike, K.; Arii, S.; Imai, Y.; Shima, T.; Kanbara, Y.; Saibara, T.; Mori, T.; *et al.* Characteristics of patients with nonalcoholic steatohepatitis who develop hepatocellular carcinoma. *Clin. Gastroenterol. Hepatol.* **2011**, *9*, 428–433. [CrossRef] [PubMed]

166. Raff, E.J.; Kakati, D.; Bloomer, J.R.; Shoreibah, M.; Rasheed, K.; Singal, A.K. Diabetes mellitus predicts occurrence of cirrhosis and hepatocellular cancer in alcoholic liver and non-alcoholic fatty liver diseases. *J. Clin. Transl. Hepatol.* **2015**, *3*, 9–16. [CrossRef] [PubMed]

167. Giannini, E.G.; Marabotto, E.; Savarino, V.; Trevisani, F.; di Nolfo, M.A.; Del Poggio, P.; Benvegnu, L.; Farinati, F.; Zoli, M.; Borzio, F.; *et al.* Hepatocellular carcinoma in patients with cryptogenic cirrhosis. *Clin. Gastroenterol. Hepatol.* **2009**, *7*, 580–585. [CrossRef] [PubMed]

168. Piscaglia, F.; Svegliati-Baroni, G.; Barchetti, A.; Pecorelli, A.; Marinelli, S.; Tiribelli, C.; Bellentani, S. HCC-NAFLD Italian Study Group. Clinical patterns of hepatocellular carcinoma (HCC) in nonalcoholic fatty liver disease (NAFLD): Amulticenter prospective study. *Hepatology* **2016**, *63*, 827–838. [CrossRef] [PubMed]

169. Zoppini, G.; Fedeli, U.; Gennaro, N.; Saugo, M.; Targher, G.; Bonora, E. Mortality from chronic liver diseases in diabetes. *Am. J. Gastroenterol.* **2014**, *109*, 1020–1025. [CrossRef] [PubMed]

170. Wild, S.H.; Morling, J.R.; McAllister, D.A.; Kerssens, J.; Fischbacher, C.; Parkes, J.; Roderick, P.J.; Sattar, N.; Byrne, C.D. Scottish and Southampton Diabetes and Liver Disease Group and the Scottish Diabetes Research Network Epidemiology Group. Type 2 diabetes, chronic liver disease and hepatocellular cancer: A national retrospective cohort study using linked routine data. *J. Hepatol.* **2016**. [CrossRef] [PubMed]

171. Adams, L.A.; Harmsen, S.; St Sauver, J.L.; Charatcharoenwitthaya, P.; Enders, F.B.; Therneau, T.; Angulo, P. Nonalcoholic fatty liver disease increases risk of death among patients with diabetes: A community-based cohort study. *Am. J. Gastroenterol.* **2010**, *105*, 1567–1573. [CrossRef] [PubMed]

172. Ballestri, S.; Lonardo, A.; Bonapace, S.; Byrne, C.D.; Loria, P.; Targher, G. Risk of cardiovascular, cardiac and arrhythmic complications in patients with non-alcoholic fatty liver disease. *World J. Gastroenterol.* **2014**, *20*, 1724–1745. [CrossRef] [PubMed]

173. Lonardo, A.; Ballestri, S.; Targher, G.; Loria, P. Diagnosis and management of cardiovascular risk in nonalcoholic fatty liver disease. *Expert Rev. Gastroenterol. Hepatol.* **2015**, *9*, 629–650. [CrossRef] [PubMed]

174. Targher, G.; Bertolini, L.; Rodella, S.; Tessari, R.; Zenari, L.; Lippi, G.; Arcaro, G. Nonalcoholic fatty liver disease is independently associated with an increased incidence of cardiovascular events in type 2 diabetic patients. *Diabetes Care* **2007**, *30*, 2119–2121. [CrossRef] [PubMed]

175. Mantovani, A.; Ballestri, S.; Lonardo, A.; Targher, G. Cardiovascular disease and myocardial abnormalities in nonalcoholic fatty liver disease. *Dig. Dis. Sci.* **2016**. [CrossRef] [PubMed]

176. Naunyn, B. *Der Diabetes Melitis*; A Holder: Wienna, Austria, 1898.

177. Lonardo, A.; Adinolfi, L.E.; Petta, S.; Craxi, A.; Loria, P. Hepatitis C and diabetes: The inevitable coincidence? *Expert Rev. Anti. Infect. Ther.* **2009**, *7*, 293–308. [CrossRef] [PubMed]

178. Allison, M.E.; Wreghitt, T.; Palmer, C.R.; Alexander, G.J. Evidence for a link between hepatitis Cvirus infection and diabetes mellitus in a cirrhotic population. *J. Hepatol.* **1994**, *21*, 1135–1139. [CrossRef]

179. Searched on PubMed, Keywords: "HCV and diabetes". Available online: http://www.ncbi.nlm.nih.gov/pubmed/?term=HCV+and+diabetes (accessed on 24 January 2016).

180. Kohli, A.; Shaffer, A.; Sherman, A.; Kottilil, S. Treatment of hepatitis C: Asystematic review. *JAMA* **2014**, *312*, 631–640. [CrossRef] [PubMed]

181. Hajarizadeh, B.; Grebely, J.; Dore, G.J. Epidemiology and natural history of HCVinfection. *Nat. Rev. Gastroenterol. Hepatol.* **2013**, *10*, 553–562. [CrossRef] [PubMed]
182. Shire, N.J.; Sherman, K.E. Epidemiology of hepatitis Cvirus: Abattle on new frontiers. *Gastroenterol. Clin. N. Am.* **2015**, *44*, 699–716. [CrossRef] [PubMed]
183. Dultz, G.; Zeuzem, S. Hepatitis Cvirus: An European perspective. *Gastroenterol. Clin. N. Am.* **2015**, *44*, 807–824. [CrossRef] [PubMed]
184. Lozano, R.; Naghavi, M.; Foreman, K.; Lim, S.; Shibuya, K.; Aboyans, V.; Abraham, J.; Adair, T.; Aggarwal, R.; Ahn, S.Y.; *et al.* Global and regional mortality from 235 causes of death for 20 age groups in 1990 and 2010: Asystematic analysis for the global burden of disease study 2010. *Lancet* **2012**, *380*, 2095–2128. [CrossRef]
185. Wong, R.J.; Aguilar, M.; Cheung, R.; Perumpail, R.B.; Harrison, S.A.; Younossi, Z.M.; Ahmed, A. Nonalcoholic steatohepatitis is the second leading etiology of liver disease among adults awaiting liver transplantation in the united states. *Gastroenterology* **2015**, *148*, 547–555. [CrossRef] [PubMed]
186. Mehta, S.H.; Brancati, F.L.; Strathdee, S.A.; Pankow, J.S.; Netski, D.; Coresh, J.; Szklo, M.; Thomas, D.L. Hepatitis Cvirus infection and incident type 2 diabetes. *Hepatology* **2003**, *38*, 50–56. [CrossRef] [PubMed]
187. Rudoni, S.; Petit, J.M.; Bour, J.B.; Aho, L.S.; Castaneda, A.; Vaillant, G.; Verges, B.; Brun, J.M. HCV infection and diabetes mellitus: Influence of the use of finger stick devices on nosocomial transmission. *Diabetes Metab.* **1999**, *25*, 502–505. [PubMed]
188. Lonardo, A.; Carulli, N.; Loria, P. HCV and diabetes. A two-question-based reappraisal. *Dig. Liver Dis.* **2007**, *39*, 753–761. [CrossRef] [PubMed]
189. Lonardo, A.; Adinolfi, L.E.; Restivo, L.; Ballestri, S.; Romagnoli, D.; Baldelli, E.; Nascimbeni, F.; Loria, P. Pathogenesis and significance of hepatitis C virus steatosis: An update on survival strategy of a successful pathogen. *World J. Gastroenterol.* **2014**, *20*, 7089–7103. [CrossRef] [PubMed]
190. Petta, S.; Macaluso, F.S.; Camma, C.; Marco, V.D.; Cabibi, D.; Craxi, A. Hyperuricaemia: Another metabolic feature affecting the severity of chronic hepatitis because of HCV infection. *Liver Int.* **2012**, *32*, 1443–1450. [CrossRef] [PubMed]
191. Petta, S.; Maida, M.; Macaluso, F.S.; Barbara, M.; Licata, A.; Craxi, A.; Camma, C. Hepatitis C virus infection is associated with increased cardiovascular mortality: Ameta-analysis of observational studies. *Gastroenterology* **2016**, *150*, 145–155. [CrossRef] [PubMed]
192. Singal, A.G.; El-Serag, H.B. Hepatocellular carcinoma from epidemiology to prevention: Translating knowledge into practice. *Clin. Gastroenterol. Hepatol.* **2015**, *13*, 2140–2151. [CrossRef] [PubMed]
193. Dyal, H.K.; Aguilar, M.; Bartos, G.; Holt, E.W.; Bhuket, T.; Liu, B.; Cheung, R.; Wong, R.J. Diabetes mellitus increases risk of hepatocellular carcinoma in chronic hepatitis C virus patients: Asystematic review. *Dig. Dis. Sci.* **2016**, *61*, 636–645. [CrossRef] [PubMed]
194. Lecube, A.; Hernandez, C.; Genesca, J.; Simo, R. Proinflammatory cytokines, insulin resistance, and insulin secretion in chronic hepatitis C patients: A case-control study. *Diabetes Care* **2006**, *29*, 1096–1101. [CrossRef] [PubMed]
195. Knobler, H.; Zhornicky, T.; Sandler, A.; Haran, N.; Ashur, Y.; Schattner, A. Tumor necrosis factor-alpha-induced insulin resistance may mediate the hepatitis C virus-diabetes association. *Am. J. Gastroenterol.* **2003**, *98*, 2751–2756. [CrossRef] [PubMed]
196. Zheng, Y.Y.; Wang, L.F.; Fan, X.H.; Wu, C.H.; Huo, N.; Lu, H.Y.; Xu, X.Y.; Wei, L. Association of suppressor of cytokine signalling 3 polymorphisms with insulin resistance in patients with chronic hepatitis C. *J. Viral Hepat.* **2013**, *20*, 273–280. [CrossRef] [PubMed]
197. Pazienza, V.; Vinciguerra, M.; Andriulli, A.; Mangia, A. Hepatitis C virus core protein genotype 3a increases SOCS-7 expression through PPAR-{gamma} in Huh-7 cells. *J. Gen. Virol.* **2010**, *91*, 1678–1686. [CrossRef] [PubMed]
198. Vanni, E.; Abate, M.L.; Gentilcore, E.; Hickman, I.; Gambino, R.; Cassader, M.; Smedile, A.; Ferrannini, E.; Rizzetto, M.; Marchesini, G.; *et al.* Sites and mechanisms of insulin resistance in nonobese, nondiabetic patients with chronic hepatitis C. *Hepatology* **2009**, *50*, 697–706. [CrossRef] [PubMed]
199. Milner, K.L.; van der Poorten, D.; Trenell, M.; Jenkins, A.B.; Xu, A.; Smythe, G.; Dore, G.J.; Zekry, A.; Weltman, M.; Fragomeli, V.; *et al.* Chronic hepatitis C is associated with peripheral rather than hepatic insulin resistance. *Gastroenterology* **2010**, *138*, 932–941. [CrossRef] [PubMed]

200. Uruha, A.; Noguchi, S.; Hayashi, Y.K.; Tsuburaya, R.S.; Yonekawa, T.; Nonaka, I.; Nishino, I. Hepatitis C virus infection in inclusion body myositis: A case-control study. *Neurology* **2016**, *86*, 211–217. [CrossRef] [PubMed]

201. Adinolfi, L.E.; Gambardella, M.; Andreana, A.; Tripodi, M.F.; Utili, R.; Ruggiero, G. Steatosis accelerates the progression of liver damage of chronic hepatitis C patients and correlates with specific HCV genotype and visceral obesity. *Hepatology* **2001**, *33*, 1358–1364. [CrossRef] [PubMed]

202. Guaraldi, G.; Lonardo, A.; Ballestri, S.; Zona, S.; Stentarelli, C.; Orlando, G.; Carli, F.; Carulli, L.; Roverato, A.; Loria, P. Human immunodeficiency virus is the major determinant of steatosis and hepatitis C virus of insulin resistance in virus-associated fatty liver disease. *Arch. Med. Res.* **2011**, *42*, 690–697. [CrossRef] [PubMed]

203. Lonardo, A.; Loria, P.; Carulli, N. Dysmetabolic changes associated with HCV: A distinct syndrome? *Intern. Emerg. Med.* **2008**, *3*, 99–108. [CrossRef] [PubMed]

204. Adinolfi, L.E.; Restivo, L.; Zampino, R.; Lonardo, A.; Loria, P. Metabolic alterations and chronic hepatitis C: Treatment strategies. *Expert Opin. Pharmacother.* **2011**, *12*, 2215–2234. [CrossRef] [PubMed]

205. Loria, P.; Marchesini, G.; Nascimbeni, F.; Ballestri, S.; Maurantonio, M.; Carubbi, F.; Ratziu, V.; Lonardo, A. Cardiovascular risk, lipidemic phenotype and steatosis. A comparative analysis of cirrhotic and non-cirrhotic liver disease due to varying etiology. *Atherosclerosis* **2014**, *232*, 99–109. [CrossRef] [PubMed]

206. Mostafa, A.; Mohamed, M.K.; Saeed, M.; Hasan, A.; Fontanet, A.; Godsland, I.; Coady, E.; Esmat, G.; El-Hoseiny, M.; Abdul-Hamid, M.; *et al.* Hepatitis C infection and clearance: Impact on atherosclerosis and cardiometabolic risk factors. *Gut* **2010**, *59*, 1135–1140. [CrossRef] [PubMed]

207. Zampino, R.; Coppola, N.; Cirillo, G.; Boemio, A.; Pisaturo, M.; Marrone, A.; Macera, M.; Sagnelli, E.; Perrone, L.; Adinolfi, L.E.; *et al.* Abdominal fat interacts with PNPLA3 I148M, but not with the APOC3 variant in the pathogenesis of liver steatosis in chronic hepatitis C. *J. Viral Hepat.* **2013**, *20*, 517–523. [CrossRef] [PubMed]

208. Gordon, S.C.; Lamerato, L.E.; Rupp, L.B.; Holmberg, S.D.; Moorman, A.C.; Spradling, P.R.; Teshale, E.; Xu, F.; Boscarino, J.A.; Vijayadeva, V.; *et al.* Prevalence of cirrhosis in hepatitis C patients in the chronic hepatitis cohort study (CHeCS): A retrospective and prospective observational study. *Am. J. Gastroenterol.* **2015**, *110*, 1169–1177. [CrossRef] [PubMed]

209. Patel, S.; Jinjuvadia, R.; Patel, R.; Liangpunsakul, S. Insulin resistance is associated with significant liver fibrosis in chronic hepatitis C patients: A systemic review and meta-analysis. *J. Clin. Gastroenterol.* **2016**, *50*, 80–84. [CrossRef] [PubMed]

210. Moucari, R.; Asselah, T.; Cazals-Hatem, D.; Voitot, H.; Boyer, N.; Ripault, M.P.; Sobesky, R.; Martinot-Peignoux, M.; Maylin, S.; Nicolas-Chanoine, M.H.; *et al.* Insulin resistance in chronic hepatitis C: Association with genotypes 1 and 4, serum HCV RNA level, and liver fibrosis. *Gastroenterology* **2008**, *134*, 416–423. [CrossRef] [PubMed]

211. Serste, T.; Nkuize, M.; Moucari, R.; Van Gossum, M.; Reynders, M.; Scheen, R.; Vertongen, F.; Buset, M.; Mulkay, J.P.; Marcellin, P. Metabolic disorders associated with chronic hepatitis C: Impact of genotype and ethnicity. *Liver Int.* **2010**, *30*, 1131–1136. [CrossRef] [PubMed]

212. Wang, C.S.; Yao, W.J.; Chang, T.T.; Wang, S.T.; Chou, P. The impact of type 2 diabetes on the development of hepatocellular carcinoma in different viral hepatitis statuses. *Cancer Epidemiol. Biomarkers Prev.* **2009**, *18*, 2054–2060. [CrossRef] [PubMed]

213. Arase, Y.; Kobayashi, M.; Suzuki, F.; Suzuki, Y.; Kawamura, Y.; Akuta, N.; Kobayashi, M.; Sezaki, H.; Saito, S.; Hosaka, T.; *et al.* Effect of type 2 diabetes on risk for malignancies includes hepatocellular carcinoma in chronic hepatitis C. *Hepatology* **2013**, *57*, 964–973. [CrossRef] [PubMed]

214. Bruno, S.; Crosignani, A.; Maisonneuve, P.; Rossi, S.; Silini, E.; Mondelli, M.U. Hepatitis C virus genotype 1b as a major risk factor associated with hepatocellular carcinoma in patients with cirrhosis: A seventeen-year prospective cohort study. *Hepatology* **2007**, *46*, 1350–1356. [CrossRef] [PubMed]

215. Adinolfi, L.E.; Zampino, R.; Restivo, L.; Lonardo, A.; Guerrera, B.; Marrone, A.; Nascimbeni, F.; Florio, A.; Loria, P. Chronic hepatitis C virus infection and atherosclerosis: Clinical impact and mechanisms. *World J. Gastroenterol.* **2014**, *20*, 3410–3417. [CrossRef] [PubMed]

216. Adinolfi, L.E.; Restivo, L.; Zampino, R.; Guerrera, B.; Lonardo, A.; Ruggiero, L.; Riello, F.; Loria, P.; Florio, A. Chronic HCV infection is a risk of atherosclerosis. Role of HCV and HCV-related steatosis. *Atherosclerosis* **2012**, *221*, 496–502. [CrossRef] [PubMed]

217. Petta, S.; Torres, D.; Fazio, G.; Camma, C.; Cabibi, D.; Di Marco, V.; Licata, A.; Marchesini, G.; Mazzola, A.; Parrinello, G.; *et al.* Carotid atherosclerosis and chronic hepatitis C: A prospective study of risk associations. *Hepatology* **2012**, *55*, 1317–1323. [CrossRef] [PubMed]

218. Targher, G.; Bertolini, L.; Padovani, R.; Rodella, S.; Arcaro, G.; Day, C. Differences and similarities in early atherosclerosis between patients with non-alcoholic steatohepatitis and chronic hepatitis B and C. *J. Hepatol.* **2007**, *46*, 1126–1132. [CrossRef] [PubMed]

219. Gill, K.; Ghazinian, H.; Manch, R.; Gish, R. Hepatitis C virus as a systemic disease: Reaching beyond the liver. *Hepatol. Int.* **2015**. in press. [CrossRef] [PubMed]

220. Domont, F.; Cacoub, P. Chronic hepatitis C virus infection, a new cardiovascular risk factor? *Liver Int.* **2016**. [CrossRef] [PubMed]

221. Backus, L.I.; Belperio, P.S.; Shahoumian, T.A.; Loomis, T.P.; Mole, L.A. Effectiveness of sofosbuvir-based regimens in genotype 1 and 2 hepatitis C virus infection in 4026 U.S. Veterans. *Aliment. Pharmacol. Ther.* **2015**, *42*, 559–573. [CrossRef] [PubMed]

222. Rinella, M.E. Nonalcoholic fatty liver disease: A systematic review. *JAMA* **2015**, *313*, 2263–2273. [CrossRef] [PubMed]

223. Montesi, L.; Caselli, C.; Centis, E.; Nuccitelli, C.; Moscatiello, S.; Suppini, A.; Marchesini, G. Physical activity support or weight loss counseling for nonalcoholic fatty liver disease? *World J. Gastroenterol.* **2014**, *20*, 10128–10136. [CrossRef] [PubMed]

224. Oliveira, C.P.; de Lima Sanches, P.; de Abreu-Silva, E.O.; Marcadenti, A. Nutrition and physical activity in nonalcoholic fatty liver disease. *J. Diabetes Res.* **2016**, *2016*, 4597246. [CrossRef] [PubMed]

225. Hallsworth, K.; Avery, L.; Trenell, M.I. Targeting lifestyle behavior change in adults with NAFLD during a 20-min consultation: Summary of the dietary and exercise literature. *Curr. Gastroenterol. Rep.* **2016**, *18*, 11. [CrossRef] [PubMed]

226. Hickman, I.J.; Clouston, A.D.; Macdonald, G.A.; Purdie, D.M.; Prins, J.B.; Ash, S.; Jonsson, J.R.; Powell, E.E. Effect of weight reduction on liver histology and biochemistry in patients with chronic hepatitis C. *Gut* **2002**, *51*, 89–94. [CrossRef] [PubMed]

International Journal of
Molecular Sciences

MDPI

Article

Additive Effect of Non-Alcoholic Fatty Liver Disease on Metabolic Syndrome-Related Endothelial Dysfunction in Hypertensive Patients

Maria Perticone [1], Antonio Cimellaro [2], Raffaele Maio [3], Benedetto Caroleo [3], Angela Sciacqua [2], Giorgio Sesti [2] and Francesco Perticone [2,*]

[1] Department of Experimental and Clinical Medicine, University Magna Græcia, Catanzaro 88100, Italy; mariaperticone@hotmail.com

[2] Department of Medical and Surgical Sciences, University Magna Græcia, Catanzaro 88100, Italy; antocime@hotmail.it (A.C.); sciacqua@unicz.it (A.S.); sesti@unicz.it (G.S.)

[3] Unit of Cardiovascular Diseases, Azienda Ospedaliera Mater Domini, Catanzaro 88100, Italy; raf_maio@yahoo.it (R.M.); benedettocaroleo@libero.it (B.C.)

* Correspondence: perticone@unicz.it; Tel.: +39-0961-364-7149

Academic Editors: Amedeo Lonardo and Giovanni Targher
Received: 28 February 2016; Accepted: 22 March 2016; Published: 26 March 2016

Abstract: Metabolic syndrome (MS) is characterized by an increased risk of incident diabetes and cardiovascular (CV) events, identifying insulin resistance (IR) and endothelial dysfunction as key elements. Moreover, non-alcoholic fatty liver disease (NAFLD) is bidirectionally linked with MS as a consequence of metabolic and inflammatory abnormalities. We addressed the question if the evolution in NAFLD might worsen endothelium-dependent vasodilating response in MS hypertensives. We recruited 272 Caucasian newly-diagnosed never-treated hypertensive outpatients divided into three groups according to the presence/absence of MS alone or in combination with NAFLD. MS and NAFLD were defined according to the National Cholesterol Education Program-Adult Treatment Panel III (NCEP-ATPIII) and non-invasive fatty liver index, respectively. We determined IR by using the homeostasis model assessment (HOMA) index. Vascular function, as forearm blood flow (FBF), was determined through strain-gauge plethysmography after intra-arterial infusion of acetylcholine (ACh) and sodium nitroprusside. MS+NAFLD+ group showed worse metabolic, inflammatory and vascular profiles compared with MS−NAFLD− and MS+NAFLD−. HOMA resulted in being the strongest predictor of FBF both in the MS+NAFLD− and in the MS+NAFLD+ groups, accounting for 20.5% and 33.2% of its variation, respectively. In conclusion, we demonstrated that MS+NAFLD+ hypertensives show a worse endothelium-dependent vasodilation compared with MS+NAFLD−, allowing for consideration of NAFLD as an early marker of endothelial dysfunction in hypertensives.

Keywords: endothelial dysfunction; non-alcoholic fatty liver disease; metabolic syndrome; cardiovascular disease and risk; arterial hypertension

1. Introduction

Metabolic syndrome (MS) is a clinical condition characterized by a clustering of hemodynamic and metabolic risk factors including raised blood pressure (BP), atherogenic dyslipidemia, raised fasting glucose and central obesity [1]. All of these factors are interrelated and associated with an increased risk for incident diabetes and cardiovascular (CV) diseases [2,3]. Although the pathogenesis of MS remains not completely clarified, insulin resistance (IR) is believed to play a pivotal pathophysiological role in its development [4].

It is well recognized that endothelial dysfunction, primarily characterized by a reduced nitric oxide (NO) bioavailability, is an early step in the continuum of the atherosclerotic process. In addition, there are several lines of evidence demonstrating that it is a strong and independent predictor of CV events in different settings of patients [5,6], and that it is able to predict the appearance and progression of subclinical organ damage [6–9]. On the other hand, some experimental and clinical data have demonstrated that NO-mediated vasodilation is impaired in patients with IR [10–12], representing a possible pathogenetic mechanism linking MS to increased CV risk.

Non-alcoholic fatty liver disease (NAFLD) is bidirectionally linked with MS (13) as a consequence of the inflammatory and metabolic processes characterizing this condition. In keeping with this, previously published data demonstrated a strong relationship between IR and NAFLD [13–16]. It is plausible that, in visceral obesity, present in the MS, the excess of portal or intra-peritoneal fat promotes the appearance and progression of NAFLD by directly increasing the flux of free fatty acids to the liver [16]. Moreover, we recently reported that hypertensive patients with NAFLD show a significantly reduced endothelium-dependent vasodilation compared with hypertensives without NAFLD [17], confirming that the presence of more risk factors in the same setting of patients differentiates the risk profile of each subject.

However, at this moment, there are no data demonstrating if NAFLD has an additive effect in worsening endothelial function in subjects with MS. Thus, we designed the present study with the aim to demonstrate the additive effect of both MS and NAFLD on endothelium-dependent vasodilating response in hypertensive subjects.

2. Results

2.1. Study Population

Characteristics of the whole study population, stratified according to the presence/absence of MS alone or in combination with NAFLD, are reported in Table 1. In comparison with MS+NAFLD− patients, subjects in the MS+NAFLD+ group had significantly higher body mass index (BMI) and waist circumference. With regards to hemodynamic parameters, MS+NAFLD+ group showed higher systolic BP and pulse pressure (PP) values. As expected, MS+NAFLD+ patients exhibited higher gamma-glutamyltransferase (GGT), aspartate aminotransferase (AST) and alanine aminotransferase (ALT) values, and a worse metabolic and inflammatory profile, compared to the MS+LS− group.

Table 1. Clinical, biochemical and hemodynamic characteristics of subjects in whole study population and in different groups.

Variables	All (n = 272)	MS−NAFLD− (n = 101)	MS+NAFLD− (n = 78)	MS+NAFLD+ (n = 93)	p
Gender, M/F	148/124	63/38	37/41	48/45	0.110 *
Age, years	48.8 ± 9.3	47.2 ± 8.6	49.9 ± 10.3	49.9 ± 9.1	0.082
Smoking, n (%)	17 (17.3)	17 (16.8)	14 (17.9)	16 (17.2)	0.960 *
BMI, kg/m^2	30.1 ± 5.4	26.2 ± 2.5	31.2 ± 4.8	33.3 ± 5.6 ‡	<0.0001
Waist circumference, cm	100.5 ± 14.2	90.2 ± 10.8	104.1 ± 13.2	108.5 ± 11.6 ‡	<0.0001
Systolic BP, mm Hg	141 ± 17	129 ± 13	145 ± 17	150 ± 14 ‡	<0.0001
Diastolic BP, mm Hg	89 ± 11	83 ± 10	92 ± 12	92 ± 10	<0.0001
PP, mm/Hg	52 ± 14	46 ± 15	52 ± 13	59 ± 14 ‡	<0.0001
Total cholesterol, mg/dL	197 ± 33	186 ± 26	204 ± 32	205 ± 37	<0.0001
HDL-cholesterol, mg/dL	47 ± 14	53 ± 16	43 ± 10	43 ± 11	<0.0001
Triglyceride, mg/dL	132 ± 63	107 ± 42	134 ± 65	156 ± 81	<0.0001
GGT, U/L	31 ± 15	21 ± 7	26 ± 8	47 ± 11 ‡	<0.0001
AST, U/L	37.7 ± 24.1	19.4 ± 4.6	30.8 ± 18.3	63.9 ± 20.9 ‡	<0.0001
ALT, U/L	39.4 ± 27.4	18.8 ± 6.2	31.2 ± 16.5	69.2 ± 22.7 ‡	<0.0001
Serum Creatinine, mg/dL	0.9 ± 0.2	0.9 ± 0.3	0.9 ± 0.2	0.9 ± 0.2	0.162
e-GFR, mL/min/1.73 m^2	94.7 ± 20.6	97.1 ± 21.3	93.1 ± 18.7	92.9 ± 25.6	0.287
FP glucose, mg/dL	99.5 ± 19.6	90.1 ± 8.3	102.2 ± 21.9	107.9 ± 21.9	<0.0001

Table 1. *Cont.*

Variables	All (*n* = 272)	MS−NAFLD− (*n* = 101)	MS+NAFLD− (*n* = 78)	MS+NAFLD+ (*n* = 93)	*p*
FP insulin, mU/mL	13.7 ± 6.3	10.3 ± 4.7	14.5 ± 6.0	16.8 ± 6.4 ‡	<0.0001
HOMA	3.4 ± 1.9	2.3 ± 1.0	3.6 ± 1.5	4.5 ± 2.2 ‡	<0.0001
hs-CRP, mg/dL	4.3 ± 2.7	3.2 ± 1.5	4.2 ± 3.0	5.7 ± 2.9 ‡	<0.0001
FBF, mL· 100· mL^{-1} of tissue· min^{-1}					
Basal	3.1 ± 0.7	3.2 ± 0.9	3.0 ± 0.6	3.0 ± 0.7	0.238
ACh, % of increase	328 ± 141	413 ± 136	327 ± 127	236 ± 91 ‡	<0.0001
SNP, % of increase	500 ± 120	507 ± 128	498 ± 121	496 ± 114	0.799

* : X^2 test. ‡ : = $p < 0.05$ by Bonferroni MS+NAFLD− Vs MS+NAFLD+. ACh: acetylcholine; ALT alanine aminotransferase; AST: aspartate aminotransferase; BMI: body mass index; BP: blood pressure; PP: pulse pressure; hs-CRP: high sensitivity C-reactive protein; e-GFR: estimated glomerular filtration rate; FBF: forearm blood flow; FP: fasting plasma; GGT: gamma glutamyl transferase; HDL: high density lipoprotein; HOMA: homeostasis model assessment of insulin resistance; SNP: sodium nitroprusside.

2.2. Endothelium–Dependent and –Independent Vasodilation

The baseline forearm blood flow (FBF) did not differ among the three groups (Table 1). Intra-arterial infusion of achetylcholine (ACh) significantly increased FBF in a dose-dependent manner in all groups. The FBF values at the three incremental doses of ACh were 6.9 ± 3.0, 10.5 ± 4.6 and 16.3 ± 6.5 mL· 100 mL^{-1} of tissue· min^{-1}, 5.2 ± 2.2, 8.1 ± 3.9 and 12.7 ± 4.3 mL· 100 mL^{-1} of tissue· min^{-1} and 4.8 ± 1.8, 6.9 ± 2.4 and 10.2 ± 3.7 mL· 100 mL^{-1} of tissue· min^{-1} for MS−NAFLD−, MS+NAFLD− and MS+NAFLD+ groups, respectively.

As expected, the endothelium-dependent maximal vasodilating response to ACh was significantly ($p < 0.0001$) reduced in both MS+NAFLD− and MS+NAFLD+ groups in comparison with MS−NAFLD− group (Figure 1). In addition, MS+NAFLD+ patients showed a worse ACh peak percent increase when compared to the MS+NAFLD− group (Table 1). On the contrary, all patients showed a normal endothelium-independent vasodilation to sodium nitroprusside (SNP) infusions, without any significant difference among groups.

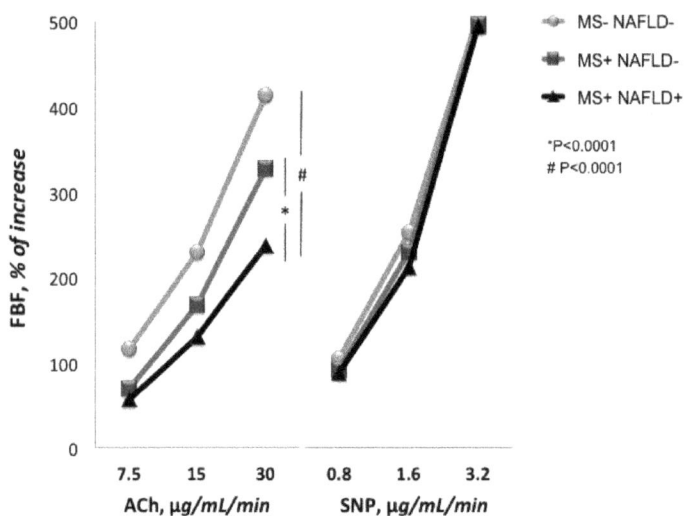

Figure 1. Responses of forearm blood flow (FBF) to intra-arterial infusions of acetylcholine (ACh) and sodium nitroprusside (SNP) in different groups.

Finally, in the logistic regression model (Figure 2), patients with both MS and NAFLD had the highest risk for decreased FBF (OR = 14.81; 95% CI = 6.99–31.38; $p < 0.0001$), whereas the group with MS alone had an almost doubled risk (OR = 2.53; 95% CI = 1.32–4.86; $p = 0.005$).

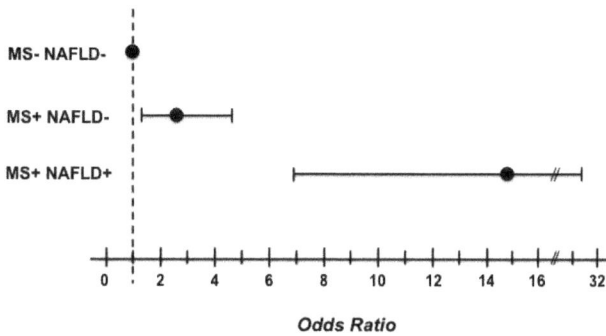

Figure 2. Graphic report of the logistic regression analysis for decreased forearm blood flow.

2.3. Correlational Analysis

A linear regression analysis was performed to test the correlation between FBF and different covariates in the whole study population and in different groups (Table 2). FBF was inversely correlated with homeostasis model assessment (HOMA) ($r = -0.584$, $p < 0.0001$), high sensitivity C-reactive protein (hs-CRP) ($r = -0.528$, $p < 0.0001$), waist circumference ($r = -0.521$, $p < 0.0001$), BMI ($r = -0.505$, $p < 0.0001$), PP ($r = -0.477$, $p < 0.0001$), systolic BP ($r = -0.466$, $p = <0.0001$) and age ($r = -0.319$; $p < 0.0001$).

In the MS-NAFLD- group, FBF was significantly correlated with PP ($r = -0.371$, $p < 0.0001$), systolic BP ($r = -0.361$, $p \leqslant 0.0001$), HOMA ($r = -0.362$, $p < 0.0001$), hs-CRP ($r = -0.329$, $p < 0.0001$), age ($r = -0.282$; $p = 0.002$), BMI ($r = -0.279$, $p = 0.002$) and waist circumference ($r = -0.186$, $p = 0.031$).

In patients with MS alone, the main covariates related with endothelial-dependent vasodilation were HOMA ($r = -0.464$, $p < 0.0001$), hs-CRP ($r = -0.446$, $p < 0.0001$), waist circumference ($r = -0.436$, $p < 0.0001$), BMI ($r = -0.406$, $p < 0.0001$), PP ($r = -0.344$, $p = 0.001$), age ($r = -0.305$; $p = 0.003$) and systolic BP ($r = -0.193$, $p = 0.045$). Finally, when considering MS and NAFLD together, FBF was inversely correlated with HOMA ($r = -0.616$, $p < 0.0001$), hs-CRP ($r = -0.522$, $p < 0.0001$), waist circumference ($r = -0.454$, $p < 0.0001$), BMI ($r = -0.414$, $p < 0.0001$), PP ($r = -0.344$, $p = 0.002$), systolic BP ($r = -0.273$, $p = 0.013$) age ($r = -0.249$; $p = 0.022$).

Variables reaching statistical significance, with the addition of smoking and gender as dichotomic values, were inserted in a stepwise multivariate linear regression model to determine the independent predictors of FBF (Table 3). In the whole population, HOMA was the strongest predictor of FBF, accounting for 33.7% ($p < 0.0001$) of its variation. In addition, the other independent predictors were: PP, waist circumference, hs-CRP, BMI and age accounting for 8.8%, 5.5%, 3.5%, 1.8%, 1.0% of its variation, respectively.

In subjects without MS and NAFLD, pulse pressure was the most important predictor of FBF, justifying about 12.9% ($p < 0.0001$) of its variation, followed by HOMA (9.9%), hs-CRP (6.8%) and age (4.2%).

Of interest, HOMA was the strongest predictor of FBF in patients with MS alone and MS in combination with NAFLD, accounting for 20.5% ($p < 0.0001$) and 33.2% ($p < 0.0001$) of its variation, respectively. Other independent predictors of the endothelial-dependent vasodilation in MS+NAFLD− group were waist circumference and hs-CRP accounting for a further 8.2% and 6.1% of its variation, respectively. Finally, in the MS+NAFLD+ group, hs-CRP, waist circumference and age add another 11.7%, 7.7% and 3.1% of FBF variation, respectively.

Int. J. Mol. Sci. **2016**, *17*, 456

Table 2. Linear regression analysis on forearm blood flow (FBF) as a dependent variable in the whole study population and in different groups.

Variables	All $n = 272$		MS−NAFLD− $n = 101$		MS+NAFLD− $n = 98$		MS+NAFLD+ $n = 73$	
	r	p	r	p	r	p	r	p
Diastolic BP, mmHg	−0.138	ns	0.053	ns	0.122	ns	0.050	ns
HDL cholesterol, mg/dL	0.171	ns	0.125	ns	−0.171	ns	0.001	ns
Total cholesterol, mg/dL	−0.171	ns	−0.094	ns	0.016	ns	0.007	ns
Triglyceride, mg/dL	−0.202	ns	−0.114	ns	−0.005	ns	0.068	ns
Age, years	−0.319	<0.0001	−0.282	0.002	−0.305	0.003	−0.249	0.022
Systolic BP, mmHg	−0.466	<0.0001	−0.361	<0.0001	−0.193	0.045	−0.273	0.013
PP, mmHg	−0.477	<0.0001	−0.371	<0.0001	−0.344	0.001	−0.344	0.002
BMI, kg/m²	−0.505	<0.0001	−0.279	0.002	−0.406	<0.0001	−0.414	<0.0001
Waist circumference, cm	−0.521	<0.0001	−0.186	0.031	−0.436	<0.0001	−0.454	<0.0001
hs-CRP, mg/dL	−0.528	<0.0001	−0.329	<0.0001	−0.446	<0.0001	−0.522	<0.0001
HOMA	−0.584	<0.0001	−0.362	<0.0001	−0.464	<0.0001	−0.616	<0.0001

BP: blood pressure; PP: pulse pressure; HDL: high-density lipoprotein; BMI: body mass index; hs-CRP: high-sensitivity C-reactive protein; HOMA: homeostasis model assessment of insulin resistance.

Table 3. Stepwise multiple regression analysis FBF as a dependent variable in the whole study population and in different groups.

Variables	All ($n = 272$)		MS−NAFLD− ($n = 101$)		MS+NAFLD− ($n = 98$)		MS+NAFLD+ ($n = 73$)	
	Partial R^2 (%)	p	Partial R^2 (%)	p	Partial R^2 (%)	p	Partial R^2 (%)	p
Age, years	1.0	0.012	4.2	0.008	-	-	3.1	0.021
BMI, kg/m²	1.8	0.001	-	-	-	-	-	-
hs-CRP, mg/dL	3.5	<0.0001	6.8	0.002	6.1	0.006	11.7	<0.0001
Waist circumference, cm	5.5	<0.0001	-	-	8.2	0.003	7.7	0.001
PP, mmHg	8.8	<0.0001	12.9	<0.0001	-	-	-	-
HOMA	33.7	<0.0001	9.9	<0.0001	20.5	<0.0001	33.2	<0.0001
Total R^2 (%)	54.3	-	33.8	-	34.8	-	55.7	-

BMI: body mass index; hs-CRP: high-sensitivity C-reactive protein; PP: pulse pressure; HOMA: homeostasis model assessment of insulin resistance.

3. Discussion

The results of our study, obtained in a well characterized cohort of newly-diagnosed never-treated hypertensive patients, demonstrate that the endothelium-dependent vasodilation, evaluated by strain-gauge plethysmography, was significantly reduced in MS+NAFLD+ patients in comparison with patients with only MS. Furthermore, MS+NAFLD+ patients showed a worse metabolic, inflammatory and hemodynamic profile. In particular, patients with NAFLD exhibited greater values of both BMI and waist circumference compared with those without; this is not surprising, since it is well known that obese subjects have a high risk for NAFLD [18] attributable, at least in part, to visceral fat accumulation and consequent increased flux of free fatty acids to the liver [16]. Moreover, the excessive intrahepatic triglyceride content further impairs insulin sensitivity of these subjects, thus creating a vicious circle explaining the observed metabolic and hemodynamic alterations. This is supported by the finding that, in the linear regression analysis, the main covariate related to FBF was PP in MS−NAFLD− group, while, in the other groups, FBF resulted primarily related to HOMA, regardless of the highest BP values. Moreover, HOMA resulted in being the strongest predictor of FBF both in the MS+NAFLD− and in the MS+NAFLD+ groups, accounting for 20.5% and 33.2% of its variation, respectively. These findings are in agreement with previously published data, confirming the presence of a relationship between impaired endothelium-dependent vasodilation and hypertension [5], as well as a negative effect of MS on vascular function. This is not surprising, since both the hemodynamic and metabolic risk factors configuring the MS are all associated with endothelial dysfunction and, consequently, with the risk of CV events. IR, a condition that can be considered the *leitmotiv* underlying the MS, plays a key role also in the appearance and progression of vascular damage, from the endothelial dysfunction to the atherosclerotic plaque. Moreover, IR is also strongly associated with NAFLD, a condition that can be considered as an epiphenomenon of the interaction between the inflammatory and metabolic factors featuring the MS. Since both endothelial dysfunction and IR are characterized by a reduced endothelial-NO synthase (eNOS)-derived NO bioavailability, it is plausible that the link between NAFLD and endothelial dysfunction could be represented by an altered NO balance. In fact, recent published data [19] demonstrated that NO produced by eNOS, plays a key role in liver physiology and pathophysiology, contributing to the maintenance of liver homeostasis; on the contrary, NO derived from inducible-NO synthase (iNOS) is particularly produced under many pathological conditions, and is able to modify many structural liver proteins. In several pathological conditions, such as IR, NO production is shifted from eNOS- to iNOS-derived, with consequent increase in reactive nitrogen species and free radicals. In particular, Pasarin *et al.* [20] demonstrated that the IR exhibited by a rat model of steatotic liver is particularly expressed at the liver endothelium, thus relating IR to iNOS induction; this IR precedes inflammation, fibrosis or other features of advanced liver disease. In keeping with this, it can be supposed that the impairment of both insulin-induced and ACh-dependent vasodilation seen in peripheral vessels of insulin resistant patients can be also observed in the liver vasculature, thus giving a plausible explanation of many events occurring in the disease progression from NAFLD to cirrhosis [21]. In fact, while insulin acts as a vasodilator agent in physiological conditions, throughout the mediation of NO bioavailability, this property resulted in impaired IR status, due to a combined defect in both insulin-mediated glucose transport and in insulin-stimulated endothelial vasodilation, derived from a fault in the phosphatidylinositol 3 kinase/Akt pathway. [22]. Moreover, the findings of the present study strengthen previously published data by our group [17], demonstrating a significant reduction in endothelium-dependent vasodilation evaluated by strain-gauge plethysmography in hypertensives with associated NAFLD, compared with hypertensives without NAFLD. All these data, taken together, endorse the close link between IR and NAFLD observed in other pathological conditions such as type-2 diabetes mellitus, obesity, and other metabolic alterations [14,23,24]. Finally, our data, obtained in a well-characterized population of hypertensive patients, are in agreement with those obtained by Targher and co-workers in diabetic patients, demonstrating that non-alcoholic fatty liver disease significantly increases CV risk in this setting of patients [25].

This study has several potential limitations. First of all, the small sample size and the cross-sectional design impose the data obtained to be confirmed in wider trials. Another limitation is that the diagnosis of NAFLD was performed by using the non-invasive fatty liver index (FLI) instead of liver biopsy that represents the gold standard. In fact, FLI is poorly correlated with liver histology [26], is no better than waist circumference in predicting NAFLD [27], and the pathophysiological information from the NAFLD arena cannot be directly extrapolated and applied to "liver steatosis" of undefined etiology (probably a mixture of alcoholic and nonalcoholic fatty liver disease), although some authors believe that steatosis *per se* may enhance CV risk [28]. Finally, in this study, we determined IR by using the HOMA index that does not allow for discrimination between peripheral or central IR.

In conclusion, we demonstrated that hypertensive patients with both MS and NAFLD show a worst endothelium-dependent vasodilation compared with hypertensives with MS alone, thus enhancing the crucial role of IR in the multifactorial pathway, in which cooperate both metabolic and hemodynamic factors, leading from endothelial dysfunction to the atherosclerotic plaque formation.

Thus, our results have an important clinical implication since allow to consider NAFLD not only as an organ damage consequent to IR, but also a simple and early marker of endothelial dysfunction in essential hypertension, contributing to better stratify CV risk in this setting of patients.

4. Materials and Methods

4.1. Study Population

The study population consisted of outpatients evaluated at the University Hospital of Catanzaro. We recruited 272 Caucasian newly-diagnosed never-treated hypertensive outpatients (148 males and 124 females) divided into three groups according with the presence or absence of MS alone or in combination with NAFLD (MS−NAFLD−, MS+NAFLD−, MS+NAFLD+). All patients participated in the CATAnzaro MEtabolic RIsk Factors Study (CATAMERIS) [29] and underwent physical examination and review of their medical history. None of the patients had history or clinical evidence of chronic hepatitis, alcoholism, coronary artery disease, valvular heart disease, peripheral vascular disease, coagulopathy, or any disease predisposing to vasculitis or Raynaud's phenomenon. A complete anthropometric assessment was performed by measurements of height, weight, and waist circumference according to a standardized protocol. BMI was calculated as kilograms per square meter, and the waist was measured at its smallest point with the abdomen relaxed.

The MS was defined according to NCEP-ATPIII [1]. The presence of NAFLD was detected calculating the non-invasive FLI, as suggested by Bedogni *et al.* [30], according to the formula:

$$FLI = (e^{0.953*\log e \text{ (triglyceride)} + 0.139*BMI + 0.718*\log e \text{ (GGT)} + 0.053*\text{waist circumference} - 15.745})/(1 + e^{0.953*\log e \text{ (triglyceride)} + 0.139*BMI + 0.718*\log e \text{ (GGT)} + 0.053*\text{waist circumference} - 15.745}) * 100.$$

FLI values ⩾60 are significant to rule in fatty liver as detected by ultrasonography. The protocol was approved by the Local Ethical Committee, and all participants gave their informed written consent before the study procedures. All the investigations of this research protocol were performed in accordance with the principles of the Declaration of Helsinki.

4.2. Biochemical Assays

All laboratory determinations were obtained after 12 fasting h. Enzymatic methods were used to measure fasting blood glucose, total and HDL-cholesterol, and triglyceride (Roche Diagnostics, Mannheim, Germany). ALT and AST levels were measured using the α-ketoglutarate reaction; GGT levels with the L-γ-glutamyl-3-carboxy-4-nitroaniliderate method. Serum insulin was measured through a highly specific radioimmunoassay using two monoclonal antibodies; intra-assay coefficient of variation (CofV) 2.1%, inter-assay CofV 2.9%. hs-CRP was measured by a high-sensitivity turbidimetric immunoassay (Behring, Marburg, Germany). Creatinine measurements were performed by use of the Jaffe methodology and the uricase/peroxidase (uricase/POD; Boehringer Mannheim,

Mannheim, Germany) method implemented in an auto-analyzer. Renal function was evaluated by estimated glomerular filtration rate (e-GFR) by using the Chronic Kidney Disease – Epidemiology (CKD-EPI) equation [31]. Insulin sensitivity was estimated by using the HOMA index, calculated according to the formula: HOMA = [insulin (μU/mL) $\times$ glucose (mmol/L)]/22.5. The HOMA index has a strict correlation with the measurement of insulin sensitivity obtained directly from the euglycemic clamp [32,33].

4.3. Blood Pressure Measurements

Clinical BP readings were obtained with a mercury sphygmomanometer in the left arm of patients lying supine, after 5 minutes of quiet rest. Each patient underwent a minimum of three BP measurements on three separate occasions at least two weeks apart. The average of the last two of three consecutive measurements obtained at intervals of three minutes was considered as baseline BP. Systolic and diastolic BP corresponded with the first appearance (phase I) and the disappearance (phase V) of Korotkfoff sounds, respectively. According to current guidelines, patients with a clinical BP $\geqslant$ 140 mmHg systolic and/or 90 mmHg diastolic were defined as hypertensive [34].

4.4. Forearm Blood Flow Measurements

All studies were performed at 09:00 A.M. after overnight fasting, with the subjects lying supine in a quiet air-conditioned room (22–24 °C). Subjects continued their regular diet, but were advised to stop caffeine, alcohol and smoking at least 24 h before the study. Forearm volume was determined by water displacement. A 20-gauge polyethylene catheter (Vasculon 2) was inserted, under local anesthesia and sterile conditions, into the brachial artery of the non-dominant arm for both BP evaluation (Baxter Healthcare Corp., Deerfield, IL, USA) and drug infusion. This arm was elevated above the level of the right atrium, and a mercury-filled elastic strain-gauge, connected to a plethysmograph (model EC-4, D.E. Hokanson, Issaquah, WA, USA) calibrated to measure the percent change in volume which was, in turn, connected to a chart recorder to obtain FBF measurements, was placed on the widest part of the forearm. To exclude venous outflow, a cuff placed on the upper arm was inflated to 40 mmHg with a rapid cuff inflator (model E-10, Hokanson, Issaquah, WA, USA). The hand blood flow was excluded by inflating a wrist cuff to BP values 1 min before each measurement. The antecubital vein in the opposite arm was cannulated. The FBF was measured as the slope of the change in the forearm volume [35]. The mean of at least three measurements was obtained at each time point.

4.5. Vascular Function

For the present study, we used the protocol previously described by Panza *et al.* [36], and subsequently used by our group [5–9,11,12,37]. For each patient, we obtained measurements of FBF and BP during intra-arterial infusion of saline, ACh and SNP at increasing doses. ACh (Sigma, Milan, Italy) was diluted with saline immediately before infusion. SNP (Malesci, Florence, Italy) was diluted in 5% glucose solution immediately before each infusion and protected from light with aluminium foil. To reach a stable baseline before data collection, all participants rested for 30 min after artery cannulation; measurements of FBF were repeated every 5 min until stable. We assessed endothelium-dependent and endothelium-independent vasodilation by a dose–response curve to intra-arterial ACh infusions (7.5, 15, and 30 μg/mL per min, each for 5 min) and SNP infusions (0.8, 1.6, and 3.2 μg/mL per min, each for 5 min), respectively. To avoid any bias related to drug infusion, the sequence of administration of ACh and SNP was randomized. The drug infusion rate, adjusted for the forearm volume of each subject, was 1 mL/min.

4.6. Statistical Analysis

Differences for clinical and biological data were compared by using analysis of variance (ANOVA), Bonferroni *post hoc* *t*-test and chi-square test, as appropriate. The vasodilating responses to ACh and SNP were compared by one-way ANOVA and, when analysis was significant, the Bonferroni *post hoc t*-test was applied. A logistic regression analysis was performed to test the risk for decreased FBF (defined by values <300 mL· 100 mL^{-1} of tissue· min^{-1}) in presence of NAFLD and MS.

Linear regression analysis was performed to correlate FBF with the following covariates: age, waist circumference, BMI, systolic BP, diastolic BP, PP, total and LDL- and HDL-cholesterol, triglyceride, hs-CRP, HOMA. To define the independent predictors of FBF, variables reaching statistical significance were inserted in a stepwise multivariate linear regression model. Moreover, to avoid a possible colinearity, we considered only HOMA and not fasting glucose and insulin.

Parametric data are reported as mean ± SD. Significant differences were assumed to be at $p < 0.05$. All comparisons were performed using the statistical package SPSS 21.0 for Mac (Manufacturer, City, Country).

Author Contributions: Maria Perticone, Raffaele Maio and Francesco Perticone conceived and designed the experiments; Maria Perticone and Antonio Cimellaro performed the experiments; Antonio Cimellaro, Raffaele Maio and Angela Sciacqua analyzed the data; Maria Perticone, Benedetto Caroleo and Giorgio Sesti contributed reagents/materials/analysis tools; Maria Perticone and Francesco Perticone wrote the paper.

Conflicts of Interest: The authors declare no conflict of interest.

Abbreviations

MS	metabolic syndrome
CV	cardiovascular
IR	insulin resistance
NO	nitric oxide
NAFLD	non-alcoholic fatty liver disease
BMI	body mass index
PP	pulse pressure
BP	blood pressure
GGT	gamma-glutamyltransferase
AST	gamma-glutamyltransferase
ALT	alanine aminotransferase
FBF	forearm blood flow
ACh	achetylcholine
SNP	sodium nitroprusside
HOMA	homeostasis model assessment
hs-CRP	high sensitivity C-reactive protein
eNOS	endothelial-nitric oxide synthase
iNOS	inducible-nitric oxide synthase
FLI	fatty liver index
eGFR	estimated glomerular filtration rate

References

1. Alberti, K.G.; Eckel, R.H.; Grundy, S.M.; Zimmet, P.Z.; Cleeman, J.I.; Donato, K.A.; Fruchart, J.C.; James, W.P.; Loria, C.M.; Smith, S.C., Jr.; *et al.* Harmonizing the metabolic syndrome: A joint interim statement of the International Diabetes Federation Task Force on Epidemiology and Prevention; National Heart, Lung, and Blood Institute; American Heart Association; World Heart Federation; International Atherosclerosis Society; and International Association for the study of obesity. *Circulation* **2009**, *120*, 1640–1645. [PubMed]
2. Isomaa, B.; Almgren, P.; Tuomi, T.; Forsén, B.; Lahti, K.; Nissén, M.; Taskinen, M.R.; Groop, L. Cardiovascular morbidity and mortality associated with the metabolic syndrome. *Diabetes Care* **2001**, *24*, 683–689. [CrossRef] [PubMed]
3. Lakka, H.M.; Laaksonen, D.E.; Lakka, T.A.; Niskanen, L.K.; Kumpusalo, E.; Tuomilehto, J.; Salonen, J.T. The metabolic syndrome and total and cardiovascular disease mortality in middle-aged men. *JAMA* **2002**, *288*, 2709–2716. [CrossRef] [PubMed]

4. Hanley, A.J.; Karter, A.J.; Festa, A.; D'Agostino, R., Jr.; Wagenknecht, L.E.; Savage, P.; Tracy, R.P.; Saad, M.F.; Haffner, S. Factor analysis of metabolic syndrome using directly measured insulin sensitivity: The insulin resistance atherosclerosis study. *Diabetes* **2002**, *51*, 2642–2647. [CrossRef] [PubMed]
5. Perticone, F.; Ceravolo, R.; Pujia, A.; Ventura, G.; Iacopino, S.; Scozzafava, A.; Ferraro, A.; Chello, M.; Mastroroberto, P.; Verdecchia, P.; *et al.* Prognostic significance of endothelial dysfunction in hypertensive patients. *Circulation* **2001**, *104*, 191–196. [CrossRef] [PubMed]
6. Sciacqua, A.; Scozzafava, A.; Pujia, A.; Maio, R.; Borrello, F.; Andreozzi, F.; Vatrano, M.; Cassano, S.; Perticone, M.; Sesti, G.; *et al.* Interaction between vascular dysfunction and cardiac mass increases the risk of cardiovascular outcomes in essential hypertension. *Eur. Heart J.* **2005**, *26*, 921–927. [CrossRef] [PubMed]
7. Perticone, F.; Maio, R.; Ceravolo, R.; Cosco, C.; Cloro, C.; Mattioli, P.L. Relationship between left ventricular mass and endothelium-dependent vasodilation in never-treated hypertensive patients. *Circulation* **1999**, *99*, 1991–1996. [CrossRef] [PubMed]
8. Perticone, F.; Maio, R.; Perticone, M.; Miceli, S.; Sciacqua, A.; Tassone, E.J.; Shehaj, E.; Tripepi, G.; Sesti, G. Endothelial dysfunction predicts regression of hypertensive cardiac mass. *Int. J. Cardiol.* **2013**, *167*, 1188–1192. [CrossRef] [PubMed]
9. Perticone, F.; Maio, R.; Perticone, M.; Sciacqua, A.; Shehaj, E.; Naccarato, P.; Sesti, G. Endothelial dysfunction and subsequent decline in glomerular filtration rate in hypertensive patients. *Circulation* **2010**, *122*, 379–384. [CrossRef] [PubMed]
10. Reaven, G.M.; Lithell, H.; Landsberg, L. Hypertension and associated metabolic abnormalities-the role of insulin resistance and the sympathoadrenal system. *N. Engl. J. Med.* **1996**, *334*, 374–381. [PubMed]
11. Perticone, F.; Sciacqua, A.; Scozzafava, A.; Ventura, G.; Laratta, E.; Pujia, A.; Federici, M.; Lauro, R.; Sesti, G. Impaired endothelial function in never-treated hypertensive subjects carrying the Arg972 polymorphism in the insulin receptor substrate-1 gene. *J. Clin. Endocrinol. Metab.* **2004**, *89*, 3606–3609. [CrossRef] [PubMed]
12. Perticone, F.; Ceravolo, R.; Candigliota, M.; Ventura, G.; Iacopino, S.; Sinopoli, F.; Mattioli, P.L. Obesity and body fat distribution induce endothelial dysfunction by oxidative stress: protective effect of vitamin C. *Diabetes* **2001**, *50*, 159–165. [CrossRef] [PubMed]
13. Yki-Järvinen, H. Non-alcoholic fatty liver disease as a cause and a consequence of metabolic syndrome. *Lancet Diabetes Endocrinol.* **2014**, *2*, 901–910. [CrossRef]
14. Marchesini, G.; Brizi, M.; Bianchi, G.; Tomassetti, S.; Bugianesi, E.; Lenzi, M.; McCullough, A.J.; Natale, S.; Forlani, G.; Melchionda, N. Nonalcoholic fatty liver disease: A feature of the metabolic syndrome. *Diabetes* **2001**, *50*, 1844–1850. [CrossRef] [PubMed]
15. Pagano, G.; Pacini, G.; Musso, G.; Gambino, R.; Mecca, F.; Depetris, N.; Cassader, M.; David, E.; Cavallo-Perin, P.; Rizzetto, M. Nonalcoholic steatohepatitis, insulin resistance, and metabolic syndrome: Further evidence for an etiologic association. *Hepatology* **2002**, *35*, 367–372. [CrossRef] [PubMed]
16. Utzschneider, K.M.; Kahn, S.E. Review: The role of insulin resistance in nonalcoholic fatty liver disease. *J. Clin. Endocrinol. Metab.* **2006**, *91*, 4753–4761. [CrossRef] [PubMed]
17. Sciacqua, A.; Perticone, M.; Miceli, S.; Laino, I.; Tassone, E.J.; Grembiale, R.D.; Andreozzi, F.; Sesti, G.; Perticone, F. Endothelial dysfunction and non-alcoholic liver steatosis in hypertensive patients. *Nutr. Metab. Cardiovasc Dis.* **2011**, *21*, 485–491. [CrossRef] [PubMed]
18. Festi, D.; Colecchia, A.; Sacco, T.; Bondi, M.; Roda, E.; Marchesini, G. Hepatic steatosis in obese patients: Clinical aspects and prognostic significance. *Obes. Rev.* **2004**, *5*, 27–42. [CrossRef] [PubMed]
19. Iwakiri, Y.; Kim, M.Y. Nitric oxide in liver diseases. *Trends Pharmacol. Sci.* **2015**, *36*, 524–536. [CrossRef] [PubMed]
20. Pasarín, M.; Abraldes, J.G.; Rodríguez-Vilarrupla, A.; La Mura, V.; García-Pagán, J.C.; Bosch, J. Insulin resistance and liver microcirculation in a rat model of early NAFLD. *J. Hepatol.* **2011**, *55*, 1095–1102. [CrossRef] [PubMed]
21. Duncan, E.R.; Crossey, P.A.; Walker, S.; Anilkumar, N.; Poston, L.; Douglas, G.; Ezzat, V.A.; Wheatcroft, S.B.; Shah, A.M.; Kearney, M.T. Effect of endothelium-specific insulin resistance on endothelial function *in vivo*. *Diabetes* **2008**, *57*, 3307–3314. [CrossRef] [PubMed]
22. Muniyappa, R.; Sowers, J.R. Role of insulin resistance in endothelial dysfunction. *Rev. Endocr. Metab. Disord.* **2013**, *14*, 5–12. [CrossRef] [PubMed]

23. Marchesini, G.; Brizi, M.; Morselli-Labate, A.M.; Bianchi, G.; Bugianesi, E.; McCullough, A.J.; Forlani, G.; Melchionda, N. Association of non-alcoholic fatty liver disease to insulin resistance. *Am. J. Med.* **1999**, *107*, 450–455. [CrossRef]

24. Angelico, F.; Del Ben, M.; Conti, R.; Francioso, S.; Feole, K.; Fiorello, S.; Cavallo, M.G.; Zalunardo, B.; Lirussi, F.; Alessandri, C.; *et al.* Insulin resistance, the metabolic syndrome and non-alcoholic fatty liver disease. *J. Clin. Endocrinol. Metab.* **2005**, *90*, 1578–1582. [CrossRef] [PubMed]

25. Targher, G.; Bertolini, L.; Poli, F.; Rodella, S.; Scala, L.; Tessari, R.; Zenari, L.; Falezza, G. Nonalcoholic fatty liver disease and risk of future cardiovascular events among type 2 diabetic patients. *Diabetes* **2005**, *54*, 3541–3546. [PubMed]

26. Fedchuk, L.; Nascimbeni, F.; Pais, R.; Charlotte, F.; Housset, C.; Ratziu, V. LIDO Study Group. Performance and limitations of steatosis biomarkers in patients with nonalcoholic fatty liver disease. *Aliment. Pharmacol. Ther.* **2014**, *40*, 1209–1222. [CrossRef] [PubMed]

27. Motamed, N.; Sohrabi, M.; Ajdarkosh, H.; Hemmasi, G.; Maadi, M.; Sayeedian, F.S.; Pirzad, R.; Abedi, K.; Aghapour, S.; Fallahnezhad, M.; *et al.* Fatty liver index *vs.* waist circumference for predicting non-alcoholic fatty liver disease. *World J. Gastroenterol.* **2016**, *22*, 3023–3030. [CrossRef] [PubMed]

28. Loria, P.; Marchesini, G.; Nascimbeni, F.; Ballestri, S.; Maurantonio, M.; Carubbi, F.; Ratziu, V.; Lonardo, A. Cardiovascular risk, lipidemic phenotype and steatosis. A comparative analysis of cirrhotic and non-cirrhotic liver disease due to varying etiology. *Atherosclerosis* **2014**, *232*, 99–109. [CrossRef] [PubMed]

29. Succurro, E.; Marini, M.A.; Arturi, F.; Grembiale, A.; Lugarà, M.; Andreozzi, F.; Sciacqua, A.; Lauro, R.; Hribal, M.L.; Perticone, F.; *et al.* Elevated one-hour post-load plasma glucose levels identifies subjects with normal glucose tolerance but early carotid atherosclerosis. *Atherosclerosis* **2009**, *207*, 245–249. [CrossRef] [PubMed]

30. Bedogni, G.; Bellentani, S.; Miglioli, L.; Masutti, F.; Passalacqua, M.; Castiglione, A.; Tiribelli, C. The Fatty Liver Index: A simple and accurate predictor of hepatic steatosis in the general population. *BMC Gastroenterol.* **2006**, *6*. [CrossRef] [PubMed]

31. Levey, A.S.; Stevens, L.A.; Schmid, C.H.; Zhang, Y.L.; Castro, A.F., 3rd; Feldman, H.I.; Kusek, J.W.; Eggers, P.; van Lente, F.; Greene, T.; *et al.* A new equation to estimate glomerular filtration rate. *Ann. Intern. Med.* **2009**, *150*, 604–612. [CrossRef] [PubMed]

32. Bonora, E.; Targher, G.; Alberiche, M.; Bonadonna, R.C.; Saggiani, F.; Zenere, M.B.; Monauni, T.; Muggeo, M. Homeostasis model assessment closely mirrors the glucose clamp technique in the assessment of insulin sensitivity: Studies in subjects with various degrees of glucose tolerance and insulin sensitivity. *Diabetes Care* **2000**, *23*, 57–63. [CrossRef] [PubMed]

33. Matthews, D.R.; Hosker, J.P.; Rudenski, A.S.; Naylor, B.A.; Treacher, D.F.; Turner, R.C. Homeostasis model assessment: insulin resistance and beta-cell function from fasting plasma glucose and insulin concentrations in man. *Diabetologia* **1985**, *28*, 412–419. [CrossRef] [PubMed]

34. Mancia, G.; Fagard, R.; Narkiewicz, K.; Redón, J.; Zanchetti, A.; Böhm, M.; Christiaens, T.; Cifkova, R.; de Backer, G.; Dominiczak, A.; *et al.* 2007 Guidelines for the management of arterial hypertension: the task force for the management of arterial hypertension of the european society of hypertension (ESH) and of the european society of cardiology (ESC). *Eur. Heart J.* **2007**, *28*, 1462–1536. [CrossRef] [PubMed]

35. Whitney, R.J. Measurement of changes in human limb volume by means of a mercury-in-rubber strain gauge. *J. Physiol.* **1949**, *109*, 5.

36. Panza, J.A.; Quyyumi, A.A.; Brush, J.E., Jr.; Epstein, S.E. Abnormal endothelium-dependent vascular relaxation in patients with essential hypertension. *N. Engl. J. Med.* **1990**, *323*, 22–27. [CrossRef] [PubMed]

37. Perticone, F.; Sciacqua, A.; Maio, R.; Perticone, M.; Galiano Leone, G.; Bruni, R.; Di Cello, S.; Pascale, A.; Talarico, G.; Greco, L.; *et al.* Endothelial dysfunction, ADMA and insulin resistance in essential hypertension. *Int. J. Cardiol.* **2010**, *142*, 236–241. [CrossRef] [PubMed]

International Journal of
Molecular Sciences

MDPI

Review

NAFLD and Chronic Kidney Disease

Morgan Marcuccilli [1,*] and Michel Chonchol [2,*]

[1] Division of Renal Diseases and Hypertension, University of Colorado Hospital, Aurora, CO 80045, USA
[2] Division of Renal Diseases and Hypertension, University of Colorado Denver,
   13199 East Montview Boulevard, Suite 495, Aurora, CO 80045, USA
* Correspondence: morgan.marcuccilli@ucdenver.edu (M.M.); michel.chonchol@ucdenver.edu (M.C.);
   Tel.: +1-303-724-4852 (M.M. & M.C.)

Academic Editors: Amedeo Lonardo and Giovanni Targher
Received: 1 March 2016; Accepted: 28 March 2016; Published: 14 April 2016

Abstract: Non-alcoholic fatty liver disease (NAFLD) is the most common cause of chronic liver disease in developed countries and it is now considered a risk factor for cardiovascular disease. Evidence linking NAFLD to the development and progression of chronic kidney disease (CKD) is emerging as a popular area of scientific interest. The rise in simultaneous liver-kidney transplantation as well as the significant cost associated with the presence of chronic kidney disease in the NAFLD population make this entity a worthwhile target for screening and therapeutic intervention. While several cross-sectional and case control studies have been published to substantiate these theories, very little data exists on the underlying cause of NAFLD and CKD. In this review, we will discuss the most recent publications on the diagnosis of NAFLD as well new evidence regarding the pathophysiology of NAFLD and CKD as an inflammatory disorder. These mechanisms include the role of obesity, the renin-angiotensin system, and dysregulation of fructose metabolism and lipogenesis in the development of both disorders. Further investigation of these pathways may lead to novel therapies that aim to target the NAFLD and CKD. However, more prospective studies that include information on both renal and liver histology will be necessary in order to understand the relationship between these diseases.

Keywords: non-alcoholic fatty liver disease; chronic kidney disease; non-alcoholic steatohepatitis; inflammation; review

1. Introduction

Non-alcoholic fatty liver disease (NAFLD) is the most common cause of chronic liver disease worldwide [1]. It is defined as the accumulation of fat (>5%) in liver cells in the absence of excessive alcohol intake or other causes of liver disease including autoimmune, drug-induced, or viral hepatitis [2]. The histologic spectrum of NAFLD ranges from simple steatosis to non-alcoholic steatohepatitis (NASH), liver fibrosis, and cirrhosis [2]. This disease reportedly affects up to 30% of the general population in Western countries, especially in patients with metabolic syndrome, obesity, and type II diabetes [3]. Given the high prevalence of this disease, it has recently been associated with hepatocellular carcinoma (HCC) [3]. In addition, NASH as the primary indication for liver transplantation has increased from 1.2% to 9.7% in the last decade [3]. NAFLD is considered to be an independent risk factor for cardiovascular disease and there is accumulating evidence to support a causative role in the development of chronic kidney disease (CKD) [3].

In addition to NAFLD, CKD represents a significant health burden in the Western adult population, and it affects over 25% of individuals older than 65 years [4]. CKD is defined as decreased estimated glomerular filtration (eGFR) and/or the presence of significant proteinuria (>500 mg) [5]. In the United States, over 400,000 people currently receive some form of renal replacement therapy, and this number is expected to reach 2.2 million by 2030 [6]. However, less than half of CKD patients develop end stage renal disease due to the high risk of mortality associated with cardiovascular events [7]. Furthermore, the incidence of simultaneous liver-kidney transplantation continues to increase exponentially over the last five years [3]. An analysis of the United Network Organ Sharing (UNOS) database during the years 2002–2011, revealed that 35% of patients transplanted for NAFLD-related cirrhosis progressed to stage 3b-4 CKD within two years after liver transplantation in comparison to 10% of patients transplanted for other etiologies [8]. Despite these findings, CKD often goes unrecognized and in the Third National Health and Nutrition Survey (NHANES III), among all individuals with moderately decreased GFR (<60 mL/min; Stage 3), the awareness is approximately 8% [9].

The similarity in traditional risk factors for CKD including hypertension, obesity, dyslipidemia, and insulin resistance make it difficult to determine a causational relationship with NAFLD adjusting for "hepatorenal" and "cardiorenal" features [5]. While a multitude of cross-sectional and longitudinal studies exist, there is still very little prospective data linking NAFLD to CKD. In addition, underlying mechanisms related to inflammation, oxidative stress, and fibrogenesis are currently being investigated in the development of kidney injury in the presence of fatty liver disease [5]. In this review, we will examine new data on the diagnosis of NAFLD, current evidence linking NAFLD to CKD, and new studies revealing the underlying pathophysiology and potential treatments of these globally burdensome diseases.

2. Diagnosis and Screening

2.1. Imaging

Liver biopsy remains the gold standard of diagnosis for NAFLD or NASH. Histologic classifications range from simple steatosis to advanced periportal or perisinusoidal fibrosis [10]. However, a considerable proportion of patients are not diagnosed with NAFLD by biopsy, and this method is unreliable secondary to subjectivity of histologic interpretation as well as sample bias related to patchiness of its distribution in the liver [10]. Ultrasonography remains the recommended first-line imaging modality for diagnosing hepatic lipid accumulation in clinical practice. This method of screening is limited if >30% of hepatocytes are steatoic given its reliance of echogenicity or contrast [5]. A recent meta-analysis has shown that the overall sensitivity and specificity of ultrasonography for the detection of moderate to severe fatty liver compared to histology were 84.8% and 93.6% [11].

Other methods of diagnosis include magnetic resonance imaging (MRI), which can assess decreased liver signal intensity, and proton magnetic resonance spectroscopy, which is used for measuring the area under the lipid spectrum relative to water spectrum [12]. These diagnostic techniques are excellent for assessing the quantitative severity of liver fat accumulation, however, they cannot discriminate simple steatosis from lipid accumulation associated with inflammation and fibrosis (*i.e.*, NASH) [12]. According to systematic review, simple steatosis and NASH are considered different disease states each with its own pathogenesis and cardiovascular risk. In addition, it may be possible that NASH can occur in the absence of simple steatosis and the pathogenesis leading to the progression to fibrosis/cirrhosis is still not entirely clear [13]. Nevertheless, NASH is often progressive, with development of advanced fibrosis in 30%–40% of patients, cirrhosis in 15%–20%, and liver failure in 2%–4% [5].

Another modality for the assessment of NAFLD that has recently gained popularity is the use of transient elastography (TE; Fibroscan®, Echosens, Paris, France), which measures liver stiffness using an ultrasound probe [14]. A new physical parameter based on the properties of ultrasonic signals acquired by this machine has been recently developed to assess liver steatosis known as the controlled attenuation parameter (CAP) score. [14]. A recent study measured the CAP score on 62 patients with CKD stage III and IV in order to quantify liver steatosis and concluded that 53 patients had NAFLD with a positive correlation between severity of liver steatosis and serum creatinine ($p < 0.01$). Limitations included the cross-sectional format of this investigation, which does not allow conclusions to be causal, as well as the absence of a control group of non-steatotic patients, or confirmation of findings by liver biopsy in comparison to CAP score [14]. This study determined that that the severity of liver steatosis is negatively correlated with kidney function, and it documents the value of ultra-sonographic elastography as an effective non-invasive screening method for the diagnosis of NAFLD [14].

2.2. Liver Enzymes and Biomarkers

In addition to imaging, many investigators have explored the use of serum tests in NAFLD ideally for diagnosis, monitoring progression, response to therapeutic intervention, and determining the prognosis of the disease. Mildly elevated serum aminotransferase levels are the primary abnormality seen in patients with NAFLD, however, liver enzymes (LFTs) may be normal in up to 78% of patients with NAFLD [15]. A recent study published by Mikolasevic and associates examined the use of liver enzymes *versus* CAP score in the detection of NAFLD in patients with CKD and coronary artery disease (CAD). This was a cross-sectional study of 202 patients with CKD, end-stage renal disease (ESRD), renal transplant recipients (RTRs) and patients with proven CAD matched against individuals without elevated LFTs and normal kidney function [15]. According to the CAP findings, 76.9% of CKD patients, 82% ESRD patients, 74% RTRs, and 69.1% CAD patients had CAP > 238 decibels to milliwatt (dB.m) and thus by definition NAFLD. However, the results demonstrated that LFTs correlated with liver stiffness acquired with TE only in CAD patients, and therefore is not a reliable marker of the detection of NAFLD in patients with renal disease [15].

While several other biomarkers have been implicated in the diagnosis and screening of NAFLD, there is still a lack of reproducibility in their clinical application. Tumor necrosis factor (TNF-α), which plays an important role in insulin resistance through inhibition of the tyrosine kinase activity of the insulin receptor, has recently gained attention for its potential value [16]. One study reported that patients with NASH had significantly higher serum TNF-α than those with simple steatosis, while another recent study further stated that patients with NASH had higher levels of TNF-α messenger ribonucleic acid (mRNA) than healthy controls with a sensitivity 66.7% and a specificity 74.1% [16]. Still, there are no known studies reporting the relationship of TNF-α as a marker of both NAFLD and CKD. Other potential biomarkers include interleukin-6 (IL-6), adiponectin, and pentraxin-3 (PTX3) are also under investigation [16].

The development of panels has also shown promise in non-invasive testing for NAFLD. There are scoring systems available for the prediction of the presence NASH as well as for prognosis of advanced fibrosis (see Table 1) [17–25]. Diagnostic panels are thought to be more applicable for patients with a BMI > 35 and the presence of hypertension as well as age >50 years [26]. FIB-4 score is a prognostic panel composed of age, alanine aminotransferase (ALT), aspart aminotransferase (AST), and platelet count [27]. A recent study published in *Hepatology Intl.* compared these scoring systems in an effort to identify the presence of CKD in patients with NAFLD. A total of 755 patients diagnosed with NAFLD by ultrasound were assessed for glomerular filtration rate, AST to ALT ratio, AST to platelet ratio, FIB-4 score, NAFLD fibrosis score, and BARD score [27]. The results revealed that a cut-off value of 1.100 for FIB-4 score gave a sensitivity of 68.85% and a specificity of 71.07% for predicting CKD, and only the FIB-4 score, older age, higher uric acid level, and elevated diastolic blood pressure were independent predictors of CKD in comparison to the other scoring panels [27]. While this study was cross-sectional and limited by ultrasound diagnosis of NAFLD, the investigators concluded that a high noninvasive fibrosis score is associated with an increased risk of prevalent CKD, and that FIB-4 is the better predictor than other fibrosis scores in excluding the presence of CKD in patients with NAFLD [27]. Ideally, a combination of non-invasive imaging and serum biomarkers will be verified for practical application in the clinical detection of both NAFLD and CKD.

Table 1. Non-alcoholic fatty liver disease (NAFLD) prognostic panels for fibrosis.

Reference	Test	Components	PPV%	NPV%
Rosenberg [17]	Original European Liver Fibrosis Panel	age, HA, TIMP1, PIIINP for score ⩽1	80	98
Ratziu [18]	BAAT score	BMI ⩾ 28 kg/m^2 age ⩾ 50 years, ALT ⩾ 2 × ULN triglycerides ⩾ 1.7 mmol/L	33	100
Ratziu [19]	Fibrotest	α2 macroglobulin, haptoglobin, GGT, Total bilirubin, apolipoprotein A1	54	90
Angulo [20]	NAFLD Fibrosis Score	age, hyperglycemia, BMI, platelet count, albumin, AAR	56	93
Harrison [21]	BARD	BMI ⩾ 28 kg/m^2, AAR ⩾ 0.8, diabetes	43	96
Cales [22]	Fibrometer NAFLD	glucose, AST, ferritin, ALT, body weight, age	87.9	92.1
Shah [23]	FIB4 index	age, ALT, AST, platelet count	43	90
Sumida [24]	NAFIC score	serum ferritin (⩾200 ng/mL for female, ⩾300 ng/mL for male), fasting insulin ⩾ 10	32	96
Younossi [25]	NAFLD Diagnostic Panel	diabetes, gender, BMI, triglycerides, apoptotic and necrotic CK18 fragments	57.7	85

This table demonstrates various prognostic panels for predicting the severity of fibrosis in NAFLD with respect to their positive predictive value (PPV) and negative predictive value (NPV) as determined by each study and its components. Abbreviations: BAAT=body mass index, aspart aminotransferase, age, triglycerides, HA = hyaluronic acid, TIMP1 = tissue inhibitor of matrix metalloproteinase, PIIINP = N-terminal propeptide of type III procollagen, BMI = body mass index, ALT = alanine aminotransferase, ULN = upper limit of normal , BARD = body mass index, aspart aminotransferase, alanine aminotransferase, diabetes, GGT = gamma-glutamyl transpeptidase, AAR = aspart aminotransferase alanine aminotransferase ratio, AST = aspart transaminase, CK18 = creatinine kinase 18.

3. Epidemiologic Evidence Linking Chronic Kidney Disease (CKD) to Non-Alcoholic Fatty Liver Disease (NAFLD)

As stated above, the similarity in risk factors for NAFLD and CKD including obesity, diabetes, and hypertension make it difficult to delineate a direct association between the diagnosis of fatty liver disease and the development and progression of renal disease. A recent meta-analysis of thirty-three studies for a total of over two-thousand participants found that NAFLD was associated with an increased prevalence odd ratio (OR) 2.12, 95% confidence interval (CI), 1.69–2.66 as well as incidence hazard ratio (HR) 1.79, 95% CI 1.65–1.95 of CKD [28]. In Table 2, there several large cross-sectional as well as case control studies of patients with NAFLD showing the prevalence of CKD between 4%–40% (see Table 2) [29–50]. In addition, there appears to be a correlation between the severity of NAFLD and the progression of CKD [51]. However, nearly half of these studies use ultrasound for the diagnosis of NAFLD or NASH as opposed to biopsy [29–50]. Other limitations include the use of Modification of Diet in Renal Disease (MDRD) and the Chronic Kidney Disease Epidemiology Collaboration (CKD-EPI) algorithms to calculate eGFR, neither of which are reliable in the presence of obesity or cirrhosis [5]. There is also substantial variability in the patient groups studied in regards ethnicity, age, risk factors, and selection bias using hospital based cohorts that often represent a population with advanced disease [29–50]. Fortunately, the majority of the studies found a correlation between NAFLD and CKD with adjustment for these factors, as well as co-morbidities such as insulin resistance and metabolic syndrome [29–50].

While the prevalence of CKD in NAFLD appears to be substantial, studies that examine the incidence of CKD in NAFLD are not as robust [5]. The Valpolicella Heart Diabetes Study of 1760 patients with type 2 diabetes with preserved kidney function followed over a six-year period found an increased incidence of CKD in patients with NAFLD (HR 1.49; CI 95%, 1.1–2.2) independent of sex, age, blood pressure, duration of diabetes and smoking [31]. Additionally, a retrospective study on a cohort of 8329 non-diabetic, non-hypertensive men with normal kidney function revealed that NAFLD was associated with an increased incidence of CKD (HR 1.60; CI 95%, 1.3–2.0) over a three year period after adjustment for age, cholesterol, and other factors [31]. However, both of these studies also used ultrasound for the diagnosis of NAFLD [31,32]. Finally, none of these studies have used renal biopsy to examine the pathology of their CKD. In the future, randomized studies with larger cohorts of patients and longer follow-up and histologically confirmed fatty liver disease are needed to verify a causal relationship between NAFLD and CKD.

Table 2. Principal retrospective studies of the association between nonalcoholic fatty liver disease and the prevalence of chronic kidney disease (CKD).

Study	Characteristics	CKD Diagnosis and Prevalence	Liver Disease Diagnosis and Prevalence	Risk Factors Adjusted in Analysis
Targher, 2008 [29]	Outpatient; n = 103; HTN 63%	eGFR < 60 mL/min/1.73 m² (CKD-EPI) and/or overt proteinuria; 15%	Ultrasound; 48%	Age, sex, BMI, waist circumference, HTN, alcohol consumption, diabetes duration, HbA1c, LDL cholesterol, Tg
Campos, 2008 [30]	Hospital; n = 197; HTN 56%, DM 26%	eGFR < 60 mL/min/1.73 m² (CKD-EPI); 10%	Liver biopsy: NAFLD 63%, NASH 32%	Age, gender, BMI, waist circumference, HTN
Chang, 2008 [31]	Population; n = 8329; DM 0%, HTN 0%, metabolic syndrome 6%	eGFR < 60 mL/min/1.73 m² (MDRD) or morning proteinuria >1+; 4%	Ultrasound; 73%	Age, eGFR, dyslipidemia, BMI, CRP, sys BP
Targher, 2008 [32]	Population; n = 1760; DM 100%, HTN 65%, metabolic syndrome 55%	eGFR < 60 mL/min/1.73 m² (MDRD) or ACR = 300 mg/g; 31%	Ultrasound; 30%	Age, gender, BMI, waist circumference, BP, LDL-C, Tg, smoking, DM duration, medications
Targher, 2010 [33]	Outpatient; n = 202 adults; HTN 35%, DM 0%	eGFR < 60 mL/min/1.73 m² and/or ACR ≥ 30 mg/g; 37.8%	Ultrasound	Age, sex, BMI, systolic BP, alcohol consumption, diabetes duration, HbA1c, Tg, medication use
Targher, 2010 [34]	Hospital; n = 160; DM 6%, HTN 60%, metabolic syndrome 29%	eGFR < 60 mL/min/1.73 m² (CKD-EPI) or ACR = 30 mg/g; 14%	Biopsy: NASH 100%	Age, sex, BMI, waist circumference, smoking, systolic BP, insulin resistance
Yilmaz, 2010 [35]	Hospital; n = 87; DM 0%, HTN 30%, metabolic syndrome 27%	eGFR < 60 mL/min/1.73 m² (CKD-EPI) or ACE 30–300 mg/d; 16%	Biopsy: NAFLD 100%, NASH 67%	Age, gender, BMI, waist circumference, BP, lipids, smoking, insulin resistance, metabolic syndrome
Soderberg, 2010 [36]	Hospital; n = 125; DM 24%, HTN 37%, metabolic syndrome 31%	eGFR < 60 mL/min/1.73 m² (CKD-EPI); 27%	Biopsy: NAFLD 67%, NASH 33%	Age, BMI, HTN, smoking, DM, metabolic syndrome
Wong 2010 [37]	Hospital; n = 51; DM 50%, HTN 37%, metabolic syndrome 65%	eGFR < 60 mL/min/1.73 m² (CKD-EPI) or ACR > 30mg/g; 8%	Biopsy: NAFLD 100%, NASH 33%	Age, BMI, DM, HTN, waist circumference, metabolic syndrome, smoking
Lau 2010 [38]	Population; n = 2888; DM 8.9%, HTN 47%, metabolic syndrome 24%	eGFR < 60 mL/min/1.73 m² (CKD-EPI) or ACR > 30 mg/g; 8%	Ultrasound; 30%	Age, BMI, metabolic syndrome, HTN, dyslipidemia, smoking
Yasui 2011 [39]	Hospital; n = 169; DM 31%, HTN 34%, metabolic syndrome 30%	eGFR < 60 mL/min/1.73 m² (CKD-EPI) or am proteinuria 1+; 14%	Biopsy: NAFLD 100%, NASH 53%	BMI, HTN, waist circumference, dyslipidemia, smoking, DM
Machado 2012 [40]	Hospital; n = 148; HTN 67%	eGFR < 60 mL/min/1.73 m²; 8%	Biopsy: NAFLD 100%	Age, sex, HTN, DM, dyslipidemia
Targher 2012 [41]	Hospital; n = 343; DM 100%, HTN 43%, metabolic syndrome 46%	eGFR < 60 mL/min/1.73 m² (MDRD) or ACR > 30 mg/g; 40%	Ultrasound 53%	Age, gender, BMI, family history, systolic BP, dyslipidemia, smoking, DM, medications, microalbuminuria
Sirota 2012 [42]	Population; n = 11469; HTN 24%	eGFR < 60 mL/min/1.73 m² and/or ACR > 30 mg/g; 42%	Ultrasound	Age, sex, race, HTN, diabetes, waist circumference, dyslipidemia, insulin resistance
Armstrong 2012 [43]	Population; n = 146; DM 0%, HTN 36%	eGFR < 60 mL/min/1.73 m² (CKD-EPI); 25%	Ultrasound; 50%	BMI, HTN

Table 2. Cont.

Study	Characteristics	CKD Diagnosis and Prevalence	Liver Disease Diagnosis and Prevalence	Risk Factors Adjusted in Analysis
Musso 2012 [44]	Hospital; n = 80; DM 0%, HTN 52%, metabolic syndrome 31%	eGFR < 60 mL/min/1.73 m² (CKD-EPI) or ACR > 30 mg/d; 20%	Biopsy; NAFLD 50%, NASH 20%	Age, gender, BMI, waist circumference, HTN, smoking, metabolic syndrome
Francque 2012 [45]	Hospital; n = 230; DM 0%, HTN 50%, metabolic syndrome 47%	eGFR < 60 mL/min/1.73 m² (CKD-EPI) or proteinuria > 300 mg/d; 9%	Biopsy; NAFLD 100%, NASH 52%	Age, BMI, HTN, waist circumference, smoking, metabolic syndrome
Casoinic 2012 [46]	Hospital; n = 145; DM 100%; HTN 55%; metabolic syndrome 80%	eGFR < 60 mL/min/1.73 m² (CKD-EPI) or ACE 30–300 mg/g; 10%	Ultrasound; 51%	Age; gender, CRP
Xia 2012 [47]	Population; n = 1144; DM 0%, HTN 38%, metabolic syndrome 32%	eGFR < 60 mL/min/1.73 m² (mDRD) or ACR > 30 mg/g; 12%	Ultrasound; 41%	Age, BMI, smoking, HTN, metabolic syndrome, uric acid
Kim 2013 [48]	Hospital; n = 96; DM 100%, HTN 66%, metabolic syndrome 56%	eGFR < 60 mL/min/1.73 m² (MDRD) or proteinuria > 1+ am; 25%	Biopsy; NAFLD 100%, NASH 56%	Age, BMI, HTN, waist circumference, smoking, metabolic syndrome, dyslipidemia
Angulo 2013 [49]	Hospital; n = 191; DM 17%, HTN 32%, metabolic syndrome 25%	eGFR < 60 mL/min/1.73 m² (CKD-EPI) or am proteinuria >1+; 18%	Biopsy	Age, BMI, DM, HTN, smoking, dyslipidemia, metabolic syndrome
El Azeem 2013 [50]	Population; n = 747; DM 57%, HTN 32%, metabolic syndrome 67%	eGFR < 60 mL/min/1.73 m² (MDRD) or ACE > 30 mg/g; 29%	Ultrasound 35%	Age, BMI, HTN, dyslipidemia, smoking, metabolic syndrome

This table represents the major retrospective studies linking the prevalence of CKD in NAFLD. The data is organized chronologically and include the cohort, definition of CKD and NAFLD with prevalence as well as adjustment variables. Studies using liver enzymes for the diagnosis of NAFLD or survey data were not included in this review. Abbreviations: HTN = hypertension, DM = diabetes mellitus, eGFR = estimated glomerular filtration rate, CKD-EPI = chronic kidney disease epidemiology collaboration, MDRD = modification of diet in renal disease, BMI=body mass index, HbA1C = hemoglobin A1C %, LDL = low density lipoprotein, Tg = triglyceride, BP = blood pressure, CRP = c-reactive protein.

4. Mechanisms Linking NAFLD to CKD

According to the Center for Disease Control (CDC), more than one-third of U.S. adults are obese [52]. This epidemic affects over 78 million people with co-morbidities of insulin resistance, diabetes, and atherosclerosis leading to an estimated annual medical cost of 147 billion dollars [52]. The liver is the key regulator of glucose and lipid metabolism as well as the main source of inflammatory elements thought to be involved in the development of cardiovascular and kidney disease [5]. It is known that obesity is an independent risk factor for CKD and it is associated with the development of proteinuria and pathologic findings of podocyte hypertrophy and focal segmental glomerular sclerosis even in the absence of diabetes and hypertension [53]. In addition, studies have shown that obesity as well as metabolic syndrome is a strong predictor of the development of NAFLD [54]. While the complex "crosstalk" among adipose tissue, the liver, and kidneys make it difficult to delineate the specific processes underlying NAFLD as a cause of CKD, it is not surprising that these diseases may be linked. Mounting evidence on liver-kidney interactions including; altered renin-angiotensin system (RAS) activation, impaired antioxidant defense, and damaged lipogenesis is currently emerging as a major area of research (Figure 1) [51]. Understanding these mechanisms may lead to modifiable risk factors and therapeutic targets for the prevention and treatment of NAFLD and CKD.

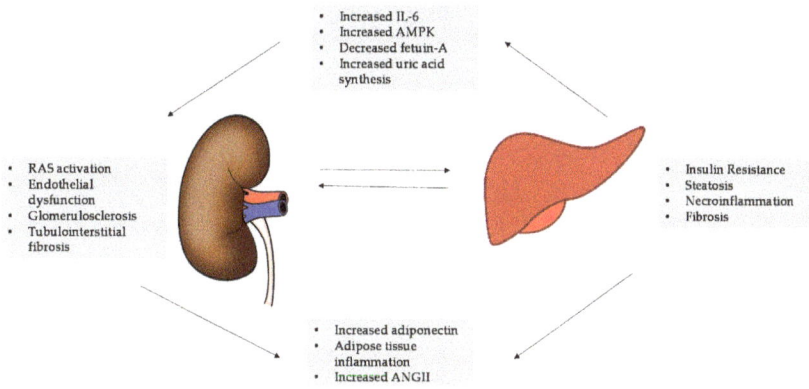

Figure 1. This figure demonstrates the various mechanisms associated with non-alcoholic fatty liver disease (NAFLD) and chronic kidney disease (CKD). The liver-kidney crosstalk in NAFLD includes altered renin-angiotensin system (RAS) and activated protein kinase (AMPK) activation, impaired antioxidant defense, and excessive dietary fructose intake, which affects renal injury through altered lipogenesis and inflammatory response. In turn, 8 the kidney reacts promoting further RAS activation, increased angiotensin II (ANGII) and uric acid production in a vicious cycle leading to fibrosis [20].

4.1. AMPK, Fetuin-A, and Adiponectin

The role of the energy sensor 5′-AMP activated protein kinase (AMPK) and its regulation of fetuin-A and adiponectin in liver and kidney fat cells is currently an area of investigation in animal models as well as human subjects [53]. Fetuin-A is a serum protein mediated through AMPK as an important promoter of insulin resistance found in both podocytes and hepatocytes [53]. Observations in fetuin-A null mice include resistance to weight gain when challenged with a high fat diet and increased insulin levels [55]. Similarly in humans, higher fetuin-A levels are associated with obesity and found in patients with NAFLD and CKD [55]. Adversely, adiponectin, which is regulated by fetuin A, is present in low levels with similar characteristics of elevated body mass index and hypertriglyceridemia [56]. Interestingly, therapeutic maneuvers including caloric restriction, exercise, and insulin sensitizing medications are associated with declines in levels of serum fetuin-A, increases in adiponectin levels, and stimulation of AMPK [53]. Although direct causation cannot be implied, it appears that increased caloric intake and adiposity initiates an inflammatory cascade through AMPK, fetuin-A, and adiponectin between fat cells in the liver and kidney leading to end-organ damage [53].

4.2. Renin-Angiotensin System (RAS) in NAFLD and CKD

The renin-angiotensin system (RAS) is also believed to play a key role in the pathogenesis of NAFLD and CKD. Adipocytes express all components of RAS and contribute up to 30% of circulating renin, angiotensin converting enzyme (ACE), and angiotensin II (AngII) [51]. The kidney and liver also express RAS constituents, and experimental studies support a role for both systemic and local activation of AngII in NAFLD and CKD. In the liver, AngII promotes insulin resistance, *de novo* lipogenesis, and pro-inflammatory cytokine production such as interleukin-6 (IL-6) and tumor growth factor-β (TGF-β) [51]. These processes are thought to trigger fibrogenesis contributing to the entire spectrum of histological changes seen with NASH [51]. In the kidney, RAS activation plays a key role in determining renal ectopic lipid deposition which is known to cause oxidative stress and inflammation through hemodynamic effects of glomerular efferent arteriole vasoconstriction leading to glomerulosclerosis [57]. In addition, a process known as the ACE2-Ang (1–7)-Mas receptor axes whose activity is known to oppose that of AngII has been shown in animal models to inhibit liver fibrosis [58]. The role of the RAS system in the liver and kidneys makes it a prime target for blockade in an attempt to attenuate fibrosis in NAFLD and CKD.

4.3. Fructose Metabolism in NAFLD and CKD

Based on the NHANESIII study, over 10% of Americans' daily calories are from fructose and consumption in high fructose corn syrup (HFCS) has increased 8% over the last decade especially amongst adolescents [59]. Several observational studies have implicated HFCS in the incidence and severity of NAFLD and CKD [51]. Fructose acts independently of calorie excess by initiating fructose phosphorylation to fructose-1-phosphate by fructokinase in the liver, ultimately leading to the accumulation of uric acid [51]. Research investigations support that uric acid promotes the development and progression of NAFLD and CKD via hepatocyte ATP depletion, which causes enhanced hepatic and renal lipogenesis, mitochondrial ROS generation, endothelial dysfunction and pro-inflammatory cytokine secretion similar to overexpression of RAS [51]. Mouse models unable to metabolize fructose are protected from obesity, metabolic syndrome, and a reduction in fructose intake or uric acid production improved experimental NAFLD and CKD [60]. Also in a recent study of 341 adult NAFLD patients, investigators evaluated whether increased fructose consumption correlates with the development of NAFLD and found that after controlling for age, gender, BMI, and total calorie intake, increased daily fructose consumption was associated with lower steatosis grade and higher fibrosis stage in comparison to groups ($p < 0.05$) [61]. Finally, a meta-analysis examined four studies that assess the association between consumption of artificially sweetened soda verses regular soda and CKD and concluded the pooled risk reduction of CKD in patients consuming artificially sweetened soda was 1.33 (95% CI 0.82–2.15) [62]. Limitations in this study include its retrospective nature, which cannot imply causation as well as variability in types of soda consumed [62]. Future prospective studies on human subjects and limitations of fructose as well as reductions in uric acid levels in patients with NAFLD and CKD are necessary to confirm these hypotheses.

4.4. Impaired Oxidative Stress

As stated above increased oxidative stress is believed to play a key role in the pathogenesis of NAFLD and CKD. Nuclear erythroid related factor-2 (Nrf2), which is expressed ubiquitously in human tissues with its highest expression in the liver and kidney, upregulates the transcription of numerous antioxidant and detoxification enzymes by binding to their antioxidant response elements [63]. Experimental data support a key protective role for Nrf2 against NAFLD and CKD using wild-type and Nrf2-null mice fed a high fat diet. Their specimens were analyzed for pathology as well as for fatty acid content and revealed the wild-type mice had increased hepatic fat deposition without fibrosis while the Nrf2-null mice had significantly more hepatic steatosis and substantial inflammation [63]. Based on these results, several natural and artificial Nrf2 activators are being evaluated in the treatment of diabetic CKD patients in the "Bardoxolone ethyl and kidney function in CKD with type 2 diabetes (BEAM)" study and previously in the "Bardoxolone methyl evaluation in patients with chronic kidney disease and type 2 diabetes: the occurrence of renal events (BEACON)" trial [64,65]. Mechanisms linked to fibroblastic growth factor 21, gut microflora, and other proteins such as sirtuin-1 are also showing promise in the development of CKD in NAFLD [51].

5. Therapeutic Interventions in NAFLD and CKD

Based on the newer mechanisms discussed as well as aims at reducing insulin resistance, several therapeutic interventions for the treatment of NAFLD are currently under investigation. The mainstay of management of for NASH is lifestyle intervention, which includes diet and exercise with a 5%–10% weight reduction associated with improvement in hepatic steatosis [5]. While there are very few studies examining the use of medications and behavioral modification in both NAFLD and CKD, the shared cardiometabolic risk factors and underlying pathophysiology may make these therapies applicable to both diseases.

RAS blockade using angiotensin converting enzyme inhibitors (ACE-) and angiotensin receptor blockers (ARBs) has been studied in NAFLD and CKD. Limited data from 223 patients in three randomized controlled trials in NAFLD suggests that ARBs attenuate steatosis, insulin resistance, and inflammatory markers independent of reduction in blood pressure [51]. In addition, telmisartan which is an ARB with peroxisome proliferator activated receptor [PPAR]-γ-regulating activity was compared to the use of valsartan in the Fatty Liver Protection by Telmisartan (FANTASY Trial) and found to cause reduction in necroinflammation, NAFLD activity score, fibrosis stage in NASH, as well as microalbuminuria [66]. Not surprisingly, the use of these medications in CKD has been extensively evaluated and based on the Collaborative Study Group Trial and several others, the use of ACE- and ARBs in patients with CKD with proteinuria is now a level one recommendation by Kidney Disease Outcomes Quality Initiative (KDOQI) [67]. A recent cross-sectional study of 191 patients with CKD III, IV, ESRD, and renal transplant recipients (n = 68) treated with ACE- or ARBs for >1 year and examined liver stiffness with the use of TE and a CAP score to evaluate whether CKD patients receiving these medications have a lower frequency of NAFLD [68]. Investigators determined that CKD-NAFLD patients taking ACE-I or ARBs had lower degree of liver stiffness in comparison to the patients not on medications (p = 0.0005) [68]. However, there was no statistical significance in degree of fibrosis or grade of steatosis in the two groups based on CAP score [68].

Evidence from recent clinical trials suggests that insulin-sensitizing agents including thiazolidinediones (TZDs) such as pioglitazone are beneficial in the treatment of NAFLD. As stated above, pioglitazone is associated with a decline in levels of serum fetuin-A and concomitant increase in adiponectin levels resulting in decreased insulin resistance [53]. A recent meta-analysis using only liver biopsy studies, found that TZDs as well as pentoxifylline, which has shown *in vitro* to inhibit proinflammatory cytokines as well as reduce fibrogenesis, are superior to placebo for improving steatosis and lobular inflammation [69]. This review also examined studies on obeticholic acid (OCA), a semi-synthetic bile acid analogue and vitamin E, both which have been used in the treatment of NAFLD and revealed improvement in ballooning degeneration and fibrosis in comparison to placebo [69]. While many of these studies have a small cohort of patients and the histological endpoints were not standardized, the American Association for the Study of Liver Disease (AASLD) published guidelines recommending the use of vitamin E and pioglitazone in non-diabetic adults with biopsy-proven NASH [69].

Pharmacologic treatments related to disordered cholesterol metabolism and insulin resistance including statins, fibrates, metformin, and glucagon-like peptide (GLP-1) analogues have shown potential benefit in adult patients with NAFLD and NASH [5]. However, the effects of these treatments are improvement in liver enzymes, decreased plasma glucose and weight loss without changes in histologic staging of the disease. There are three major post-hoc analysis reviewing the use of statins including the "Greek Atorvastatin and Coronary-Heart-Disease Evaluation" (GREACE), and "Incremental Decrease in End Points Through Aggressive Lipid Lowering" (IDEAL) trials that showed a significant reduction in cardiovascular disease events in patients with NAFLD/NASH [70,71]. Also, the GREACE study, revealed normal liver enzymes with the use of atorvastatin *versus* usual care in a three year follow-up period [51]. Therefore, it appears that the use of statins may also be safe in this patient population. Finally, lifestyle interventions including exercise, weight loss, and gastric bypass surgery will decrease hepatic fat content and inflammation, however, require significant effort and often financial burden on individual patients [5]. However, these may be worthwhile efforts in patients with early steatosis in order to prevent progression of to NAFLD with CKD. Novel therapies including translational approaches based on the mechanisms discussed, as well as more traditional methods need to be evaluated in large randomized controlled trials for their potential value in the treatment of both NAFLD and CKD.

6. Conclusions

Based on the data presented as well as several other ongoing trials, there is substantial evidence linking NAFLD to the development of CKD. It is clear that the mechanisms underlying these diseases are complexly inter-woven requiring additional investigation with animal and human models. Furthermore, prospective studies on NAFLD and CKD must include information on hepatic and renal histology. Preventative measures including lifestyle modification aiming toward weight loss and physical activity may be of benefit in both diseases. Furthermore, physician awareness for screening of CKD in NAFLD may lead to earlier detection and treatment of this disease leading to better outcomes in patients with liver steatosis as well as more advanced fibrosis requiring organ transplantation.

Conflicts of Interest: The founding sponsors had no role in the design of the study; in the collection, analyses, or interpretation of data; in the writing of the manuscript, and in the decision to publish this review.

Abbreviations

DM	diabetes mellitus
HTN	hypertension
Tg	triglycerides
A1C%	hemoglobin A1C
eGFR	estimated glomerular filtration rate
MDRD	Modification of Diet in Renal Disease
CKD-EPI	Chronic Kidney Disease Epidemiology Collaboration
CRP	C-reactive protein
LFTs	liver function tests
HR	hazard ration
CI	confidence interval

References

1. Vernon, G.; Baranova, A.; Younossi, Z.M. Systematic review: The epidemiology and natural history of non-alcoholic fatty liver disease and non-alcoholic steatohepatitis in adults. *Aliment. Pharmacol. Ther.* **2011**, *34*, 274–285. [CrossRef] [PubMed]
2. Chalasani, N.; Younossi, Z.; Lavine, J.E.; Diehl, A.M.; Brunt, E.M.; Cusi, K.; Charlton, M.; Sanyal, A.J. The diagnosis and management of non-alcoholic fatty liver disease: Practice guideline by the American Association for the Study of Liver Diseases, American College of Gastroenterology, and the American Gastroenterological Association. *Hepatology* **2012**, *55*, 2005–2023.
3. Loomba, R.; Sanyal, A.J. The global NAFLD epidemic. *Nat. Rev. Gastroenterol. Hepatol.* **2013**, *10*, 686–690. [CrossRef] [PubMed]

4. McCullough, K.; Sharma, P.; Ali, T.; Khan, I.; Smith, W.C.; MacLeod, A.; Black, C. Measuring the population burden of chronic kidney disease: A systematic literature review of the estimated prevalence of impaired kidney function. *Nephrol. Dial. Transplant.* **2012**, *27*, 1812–1821. [CrossRef] [PubMed]

5. Targher, G.; Chonchol, M.B.; Byrne, C.D. CKD and non-alcoholic fatty liver disease. *AJKD* **2014**, *64*, 638–652. [CrossRef] [PubMed]

6. Black, C.; Sharma, P.; Scotland, G.; McCullough, K.; McGurn, D.; Robertson, L.; Fluck, N.; MacLeod, A.; McNamee, P.; Prescott, G.; *et al.* Early referral strategies for management of people with markers of renal disease: A systematic review of the evidence of clinical effectiveness, cost-effectiveness and economic analysis. *Health Technol. Assess.* **2010**, *14*, 1–184. [CrossRef] [PubMed]

7. Athyros, V.; Tziomalos, K.; Katsiki, N.; Doumas, M.; Karagiannis, A.; Mikhailidis, D.P. Cardiovascular risk across the histological spectrum and the clinical manifestations of non-alcoholic fatty liver disease; an update. *World J. Gastroenterol.* **2015**, *21*, 6820–6834. [PubMed]

8. Singal, A.K.; Salameh, H.; Kuo, Y.F.; Wiesner, R.H. Evolving frequency and outcomes of simultaneous liver kidney transplants based on liver disease etiology. *Transplantation* **2014**, *98*, 216–221. [CrossRef] [PubMed]

9. Coresh, J.; Byrd-Holt, D.; Astor, B.C.; Briggs, J.P.; Eggers, P.W.; Lacher, D.A.; Hostetter, T.H. Chronic kidney disease awareness, prevalence, and trends among US adults, 1999 to 2000. *J. Am. Soc. Nephrol.* **2005**, *16*, 180–188. [CrossRef] [PubMed]

10. Kim, D.; Kim, W.R.; Kim, H.J.; Therneau, T.M. Association between noninvasive fibrosis markers and mortality among adults with nonalcoholic fatty liver disease in the United States. *Hepatology* **2013**, *57*, 1357–1365. [CrossRef] [PubMed]

11. Hernaez, R.; Lazo, M.; Bonekamp, S.; Kamel, I.; Brancati, F.L.; Guallar, E.; Clark, J.M. Diagnostic accuracy and reliability of ultrasonography for the detection of fatty liver: A meta-analysis. *Hepatology* **2011**, *54*, 1082–1090. [CrossRef] [PubMed]

12. Anstee, Q.M.; Targher, G.; Day, C.P. Progression of NAFLD to diabetes mellitus, cardiovascular disease or cirrhosis. *Nat. Rev. Gastroenterol. Hepatol.* **2013**, *10*, 330–344. [CrossRef] [PubMed]

13. Dowman, J.K.; Tomlinson, J.W.; Newsome, P.N. Systematic review; the diagnosis and staging of non-alcoholic fatty liver disease and non-alcoholic steatohepatitis. *Aliment. Pharmacol. Ther.* **2011**, *33*, 525–540. [CrossRef] [PubMed]

14. Mikolasevic, I.; Racki, S.; Bubic, I.; Jelic, I.; Stimac, D.; Orlic, L. Chronic kidney disease and nonalcoholic fatty liver disease proven by transient elastography. *Kidney Blood Press Res.* **2013**, *37*, 305–310. [CrossRef] [PubMed]

15. Mikolasevic, I.; Orlic, L.; Zaputovic, L.; Racki, S.; Cubranic, Z.; Anic, K.; Devcic, B.; Stimac, D. Usefulness of liver test and controlled attenuation parameter in detection of nonalcoholic fatty liver disease in patients with chronic renal failure and coronary heart disease. *Wien. Klin. Wochenschr.* **2015**, *127*, 451–458. [CrossRef] [PubMed]

16. Satapathy, S.K.; Garg, S.; Chauhan, R.; Sakhuja, P.; Malhotra, V.; Sharma, B.C.; Sarin, S.K. Beneficial effects of tumor necrosis factor-α inhibition by pentoxyfilline on clinical, biochemical, and metabolic parameters of patients with nonalcoholic steatohepatitis. *Am. J. Gastroenterol.* **2004**, *99*, 1946–1952. [CrossRef] [PubMed]

17. Rosenberg, W.M.; Voelker, M.; Thiel, R.; Becka, M.; Burt, A.; Schuppan, D.; Hubscher, S.; Roskams, T.; Pinzani, M.; Arthur, M.J. European Liver Fibrosis Group: Serum markers detect the presence of liver fibrosis: A cohort study. *Gastroenterology* **2004**, *127*, 1704–1713. [CrossRef] [PubMed]

18. Ratziu, V.; Gira, P.; Charlotte, F.; Bruckert, E.; Thibault, V.; Theodorou, I.; Khalil, L.; Turpin, G.; Opolon, P.; Poynard, T. Liver fibrosis in overweight patient. *Gastroenterology* **2000**, *118*, 1117–1123. [CrossRef]

19. Ratziu, V.; Massard, J.; Charlotte, F.; Messous, D.; Imbert-Bismut, F.; Bonyhay, L.; Tahiri, M.; Munteanu, M.; Thabut, D.; Cadranel, J.F.; *et al.* Diagnostic value of biochemical markers (FibroTest-FibroSURE) for the prediction of liver fibrosis in patients with non-alcoholic fatty liver disease. *BMC Gastroenterol.* **2006**, *6*, 6. [CrossRef] [PubMed]

20. Angulo, P.; Keach, J.C.; Batts, K.P.; Lindor, K.D. Independent predictor of liver fibrosis in patients with nonalcoholic steatohepatitis. *Hepatology* **1999**, *30*, 1356–1362. [CrossRef] [PubMed]

21. Harrison, S.A.; Oliver, D.; Arnod, H.L.; Gogia, S.; Neuschwander-Tetri, B.A. Development and validation of a simple NAFLD clinical scoring system for identifying patients without advanced disease. *Gut* **2008**, *57*, 1441–1447. [CrossRef] [PubMed]

22. Cales, P.; Laine, F.; Boursier, J.; Deugnier, Y.; Moal, V.; Oberti, F.; Hunault, G.; Rousselet, M.C.; Hubert, I.; Laafi, J.; *et al.* Comparison of blood tests for liver fibrosis specific or not to NAFLD. *J. Hepatol.* **2009**, *50*, 165–173. [CrossRef] [PubMed]

23. Shah, A.; Lydecker, A.; Murray, K.; Tetri, B.N.; Contos, M.J.; Sanyal, A.J. Nash Clinical Research Network. Comparison of noninvasive markers of fibrosis in patients with nonalcoholic fatty liver disease. *Clin. Gastroenterol. Hepatol.* **2009**, *7*, 1104–1112. [CrossRef] [PubMed]

24. Sumida, Y.; Yoneda, M.; Hyogo, H.; Yamaguchi, K.; Ono, M.; Fujii, H.; Eguchi, Y.; Suzuki, Y.; Imai, S.; Kanemasa, K.; *et al.* Japan Study Group of Nonalcoholic Fatty Liver Disease (JSG-NAFLD): A simple clinical scoring system using ferritin, fasting insulin, and type IV collagen 7S for predicting steatohepatitis in nonalcoholic fatty liver disease. *J. Gastroenterol.* **2011**, *46*, 257–268. [CrossRef] [PubMed]

25. Younossi, Z.; Page, S.; Rafiq, N.; Birerdinc, A.; Stepanova, M.; Hossain, N.; Afendy, A.; Younoszai, Z.; Goodman, Z.; Baranova, A. A biomarker panel for non-alcoholic steatohepatitis (NASH) and NASH-related fibrosis. *Obes. Surg.* **2011**, *21*, 431–439. [CrossRef] [PubMed]

26. Pearce, S.G.; Thosani, N.C.; Pan, J. Noninvasive biomarkers for the diagnosis of steatohepatitis and advanced fibrosis in NAFLD. *Biomark. Res.* **2013**, *1*, 7. [CrossRef] [PubMed]

27. Xu, H.W.; Hsu, Y.C.; Chang, C.H.; Wei, K.L.; Lin, C.L. High FIB-4 index as an independent risk factor of prevalent chronic kidney disease in patients with nonalcoholic fatty liver disease. *Hepatol. Int.* **2016**, *10*, 340–346. [CrossRef] [PubMed]

28. Musso, G.; Gambino, R.; Tabibian, J.H.; Ekstedt, M.; Kechagias, S.; Hamaguchi, M.; Hultcrantz, R.; Hagström, H.; Yoon, S.K.; Charatcharoenwitthaya, P.; *et al.* Association of non-alcoholic fatty liver disease with chronic kidney disease: A systematic review and meta-analysis. *PLoS Med.* **2014**, *11*, e1001680. [CrossRef] [PubMed]

29. Targher, G.; Bertolini, L.; Rodella, S.; Zoppini, G.; Lippi, G.; Day, C.; Muggeo, M. Non-alcoholic fatty liver disease is independently associated with an increased prevalence of chronic kidney disease and proliferative/laser-treated retinopathy in type 2 diabetic patients. *Diabetologia* **2008**, *51*, 444–450. [CrossRef] [PubMed]

30. Campos, G.M.; Bambha, K.; Vittinghoff, E.; Rabl, C.; Posselt, A.M.; Ciovica, R.; Tiwari, U.; Ferrel, L.; Pabst, M.; Bass, N.M.; *et al.* A clinical scoring system for predicting nonalcoholic steatohepatitis in morbidly obese patients. *Hepatology* **2008**, *47*, 1916–1923. [CrossRef] [PubMed]

31. Chang, Y.; Ryu, S.; Sung, E.; Woo, H.Y.; Oh, E.; Cha, K.; Jung, E.; Kim, W.S. Nonalcoholic fatty liver disease predicts chronic kidney disease in nonhypertensive and nondiabetic Korean men. *Metabolism* **2008**, *57*, 569–576. [CrossRef] [PubMed]

32. Targher, G.; Chonchol, M.; Bertolini, L.; Rodella, S.; Zenari, L.; Ciovica, R.; Tiwari, U.; Ferrel, L.; Pabst, M.; Bass, N.M.; *et al.* Increased risk of CKD among type 2 diabetics with nonalcoholic fatty liver disease. *J. Am. Soc. Nephrol.* **2008**, *19*, 1564–1570. [CrossRef] [PubMed]

33. Targher, G.; Bertolini, L.; Chonchol, M.; Rodella, S.; Zoppini, G.; Lippi, G. Nonalcoholic fatty liver disease is independently associated with an increased prevalence of chronic kidney disease and retinopathy in type 1 diabetic patients. *Diabetologia* **2010**, *53*, 1341–1348. [CrossRef] [PubMed]

34. Targher, G.; Bertolini, L.; Rodella, S.; Lippi, G.; Zoppini, G.; Chonchol, M. Relationship between kidney function and liver histology in subjects with nonalcoholic steatohepatitis. *Clin. J. Am. Soc. Nephrol.* **2010**, *5*, 2166–2171. [CrossRef] [PubMed]

35. Yilmaz, Y.; Alahdab, Y.O.; Yonal, O.; Kurt, R.; Kedrah, A.E.; Celikel, C.A.; Ozdogan, O.; Duman, D.; Imeryuz, N.; Avsar, E.; *et al.* Microalbuminuria in nondiabetic patients with nonalcoholic fatty liver disease: Association with liver fibrosis. *Metabolism* **2010**, *59*, 1327–1330. [CrossRef] [PubMed]

36. Söderberg, C.; Stål, P.; Askling, J.; Glaumann, H.; Lindberg, G.; Marmur, J.; Hultcrantz, R. Decreased survival of subjects with elevated liver function tests during a 28-year follow-up. *Hepatology* **2010**, *51*, 595–602. [CrossRef] [PubMed]

37. Wong, V.W.; Wong, G.L.; Choi, P.C.; Chan, A.W.; Li, M.K.; Chan, H.Y.; Chim, A.M.; Yu, J.; Sung, J.J.; Chan, H.L. Disease progression of non-alcoholic fatty liver disease: A prospective study with paired liver biopsies at 3 years. *Gut* **2010**, *59*, 969–974. [CrossRef] [PubMed]

38. Lau, K.; Lorbeer, R.; Haring, R.; Schmidt, C.O.; Wallaschofski, H.; Nauck, M.; John, U.; Baumeister, S.E.; Völzke, H. The association between fatty liver disease and blood pressure in a population-based prospective longitudinal study. *J. Hypertens.* **2010**, *28*, 1829–1835. [CrossRef] [PubMed]

39. Yasui, K.; Sumida, Y.; Mori, Y.; Mitsuyoshi, H.; Minami, M.; Itoh, Y.; Kanemasa, K.; Matsubara, H.; Okanoue, T.; Yoshikawa, T. Nonalcoholic steatohepatitis and increased risk of chronic kidney disease. *Metabolism* **2011**, *60*, 735–739. [CrossRef] [PubMed]

40. Machado, M.V.; Gonçalves, S.; Carepa, F.; Coutinho, J.; Costa, A.; Cortez-Pinto, H. Impaired renal function in morbid obese patients with nonalcoholic fatty liver disease. *Liver Int.* **2012**, *32*, 241–248. [CrossRef] [PubMed]

41. Targher, G.; Pichiri, I.; Zoppini, G.; Trombetta, M.; Bonora, E. Increased prevalence of chronic kidney disease in patients with Type 1 diabetes and non-alcoholic fatty liver. *Diabet. Med.* **2012**, *29*, 220–226. [CrossRef] [PubMed]

42. Sirota, J.C.; McFann, K.; Targher, G.; Chonchol, M.; Jalal, D.I. Association between nonalcoholic liver disease and chronic kidney disease: An ultrasound analysis from NHANES 1988–1994. *Am. J. Nephrol.* **2012**, *36*, 466–471. [CrossRef] [PubMed]

43. Armstrong, M.J.; Houlihan, D.D.; Bentham, L.; Shaw, J.C.; Cramb, R.; Olliff, S.; Gill, P.S.; Neuberger, J.M.; Lilford, R.J.; Newsome, P.N. Presence and severity of non-alcoholic fatty liver disease in a large prospective primary care cohort. *J. Hepatol.* **2012**, *56*, 234–240. [CrossRef] [PubMed]

44. Musso, G.; Cassader, M.; de Michieli, F.; Rosina, F.; Orlandi, F.; Gambino, R. Nonalcoholic steatohepatitis *versus* steatosis: Adipose tissue insulin resistance and dysfunctional response to fat ingestion predict liver injury and altered glucose and lipoprotein. *Metab. Hepatol.* **2012**, *56*, 933–942. [CrossRef] [PubMed]

45. Francque, S.M.; Verrijken, A.; Mertens, I.; Hubens, G.; van Marck, E.; Pelckmans, P.; Michielsen, P.; van Gaal, L. Noninvasive assessment of nonalcoholic fatty liver disease in obese or overweight patients. *Clin. Gastroenterol. Hepatol.* **2012**, *10*, 1162–1168. [CrossRef] [PubMed]

46. Casoinic, F.; Sâmpelean, D.; Bădău, C.; Prună, L. Nonalcoholic fatty liver disease–A risk factor for microalbuminuria in type 2 diabetic patients. *Rom. J. Int. Med.* **2009**, *47*, 55–59.

47. Xia, M.F.; Lin, H.D.; Li, X.M.; Yan, H.M.; Bian, H.; Chang, X.X.; He, W.Y.; Jeekel, J.; Hofman, A.; Gao, X. Renal function-dependent association of serum uric acid with metabolic syndrome and hepatic fat content in a middle-aged and elderly Chinese population. *Clin. Exp. Pharmacol. Physiol.* **2012**, *39*, 930–937. [CrossRef] [PubMed]

48. Kim, Y.S.; Jung, E.S.; Hur, W.; Bae, S.H.; Choi, J.Y.; Chang, X.X.; He, W.Y.; Jeekel, J.; Hofman, A.; Gao, X. Noninvasive predictors of nonalcoholic steatohepatitis in Korean patients with histologically proven nonalcoholic fatty liver disease. *Clin. Mol. Hepatol.* **2013**, *19*, 120–130. [CrossRef] [PubMed]

49. Angulo, P.; Bugianesi, E.; Bjornsson, E.S.; Charatcharoenwitthaya, P.; Mills, P.R.; Barrera, F.; Haflidadottir, S.; Day, C.P.; George, J. Simple noninvasive systems predict long-term outcomes of patients with nonalcoholic fatty liver disease. *Gastroenterology* **2013**, *145*, 782–789. [CrossRef] [PubMed]

50. El Azeem, H.A.; Khalek, E.A.; El-Akabawy, H.; Naeim, H.; Khalik, H.A.; Alfifi, A.A. Association between nonalcoholic fatty liver disease and the incidence of cardiovascular and renal events. *J. Saudi. Heart Assoc.* **2013**, *25*, 239–246. [CrossRef] [PubMed]

51. Musso, G.; Cassader, M.; Cohney, S.; Pinach, S.; Saba, F.; Gambino, R. Emerging liver–kidney interactions in nonalcoholic fatty liver disease. *Trends Mol. Med.* **2015**, *21*, 645–662. [CrossRef] [PubMed]

52. Ogden, C.L.; Carroll, M.D.; Kit, B.K.; Flegal, K.M. Prevalence of childhood and adult obesity in the United States, 2011–2012. *JAMA* **2014**, *311*, 806–814. [CrossRef] [PubMed]

53. Ix, J.H.; Sharma, K. Mechanisms linking obesity, chronic kidney disease, and fatty liver disease: The roles of fetuin-A, adiponectin, and AMPK. *J. Am. Soc. Nephrol.* **2010**, *21*, 406–412. [CrossRef] [PubMed]

54. Hamaguchi, M.; Kojima, T.; Takeda, N.; Nakagawa, T.; Taniguchi, H.; Fujii, K.; Omatsu, T.; Nakajima, T.; Sarui, H.; Shimazaki, M.; *et al.* The metabolic syndrome as a predictor of nonalcoholic fatty liver disease. *Ann. Intern. Med.* **2005**, *143*, 722–728. [CrossRef] [PubMed]

55. Mathews, S.T.; Rakhade, S.; Zhou, X.; Parker, G.C.; Coscina, D.V.; Grunberger, G. Fetuin-null mice are protected against obesity and insulin resistance associated with aging. *Biochem. Biophys. Res. Commun.* **2006**, *350*, 437–443. [CrossRef] [PubMed]

56. Ix, J.H.; Chertow, G.M.; Shlipak, M.G.; Brandenburg, V.M.; Ketteler, M.; Whooley, M.A. Fetuin-A and kidney function in persons with coronary artery disease—Data from the Heart and Soul Study. *Nephrol. Dial. Transplant.* **2006**, *21*, 2144–2151. [CrossRef] [PubMed]

57. De Vries, A.P.; Ruggenenti, P.; Ruan, X.Z.; Praga, M.; Cruzado, J.M.; Bajema, I.M.; D'Agati, V.D.; Lamb, H.J.; Pongrac Barlovic, D.; Hojs, R.; *et al.* Fatty kidney: Emerging role of ectopic lipid in obesity-related renal disease. *Lancet Diabetes Endocrinol.* **2014**, *2*, 417–426. [CrossRef]

58. Osterreicher, C.H.; Taura, K.; de Minicis, S.; Seki, E.; Penz-Osterreicher, M.; Kodama, Y.; Kluwe, J.; Schuster, M.; Oudit, G.Y.; Penninger, J.M.; *et al.* Angiotensin-converting-enzyme 2 inhibits liver fibrosis in mice. *Hepatology* **2009**, *50*, 929–938. [CrossRef] [PubMed]

59. Vos, M.; Kimmons, J.; Gillespie, C.; Welsh, J.; Blanck, H. Dietary fructose consumption among US children and adults: The Third National Health and Nutrition Examination Survey. *Medscape J. Med.* **2008**, *10*, 160. [PubMed]

60. Osterreicher, C.H.; Taura, K.; de Minicis, S.; Seki, E.; Penz-Osterreicher, M.; Kodama, Y.; Kluwe, J.; Schuster, M.; Oudit, G.Y.; Penninger, J.M.; *et al.* Betaine supplementation protects against high-fructose-induced renal injury in rats. *J. Nutr. Biochem.* **2014**, *25*, 353–362.

61. Abdelmalek, M.F.; Suzuki, A.; Guy, C.; Unalp-Arida, A.; Colvin, R.; Johnson, R.J.; Diehl, A.M. Nonalcoholic Steatohepatitis Clinical Research Network. Increased fructose consumption is associated with fibrosis severity in patients with nonalcoholic fatty liver disease. *Hepatology* **2010**, *51*, 1961–1971. [CrossRef] [PubMed]

62. Cheungpasitporn, W.; Thongprayoon, C.; O'Corragain, O.A.; Edmonds, P.J.; Kittanamongkolchai, W.; Erickson, S.B. Associations of sugar and artificially sweetened soda and chronic kidney disease: A systematic review and meta-analysis. *Nephrology* **2014**, *19*, 791–797. [CrossRef] [PubMed]

63. Wang, C.; Cui, Y.; Li, C.; Zhang, Y.; Xu, S.; Li, X.; Li, H.; Zhang, X. Nrf2 deletion causes "benign" simple steatosis to develop into nonalcoholic steatohepatitis in mice fed a high-fat diet. *Lipids Health Dis.* **2013**, *12*, 165–171. [CrossRef] [PubMed]

64. Pergola, P.E.; Raskin, P.; Toto, R.D.; Meyer, C.J.; Huff, W.; Grossman, E.B.; Krauth, M.A.B.; Ruiz, S.; Audhya, P.; Christ-Schmidt, H.; *et al.* Bardoxolone methyl and kidney function in CKD with type 2 diabetes. *N. Engl. J. Med.* **2011**, *365*, 327–336. [CrossRef] [PubMed]

65. De Zeeuw, D.; Akizawa, T.; Agarwal, R.; Audhya, P.; Bakris, G.L.; Chin, M.; Krauth, M.; Lambers Heerspink, H.J.; Meyer, C.J.; McMurray, J.J.; *et al.* Rationale and trial design of bardoxolone methyl evaluation in patients with chronic kidney disease and type 2 diabetes: The occurrence of renal events (BEACON). *Am. J. Nephrol.* **2013**, *37*, 212–222. [CrossRef] [PubMed]

66. Hirata, T.; Tomita, K.; Kawai, T.; Yokoyama, H.; Shimada, A.; Kikuchi, M.; Hirose, H.; Ebinuma, H.; Irie, J.; Ojiro, K.; *et al.* Effect of telmisartan or losartan for treatment of nonalcoholic fatty liver disease: Fatty Liver Protection Trial by Telmisartan or Losartan Study (FANTASY). *Int. J. Endocrinol.* **2013**, *2013*, 587140. [CrossRef] [PubMed]

67. Bain, R.; Rohde, R.; Hunsicker, L.G.; McGill, J.; Kobrin, S.; Lewis, E.J. A controlled clinical trial of angiotensin-converting enzyme inhibition in type I diabetic nephropathy: Study design and patient characteristics. The Collaborative Study Group. *J. Am. Soc. Nephrol.* **1992**, *3*, S97–S103. [PubMed]

68. Orlic, L.; Mikolasevic, I.; Lukenda, V.; Anic, K.; Jelic, I.; Racki, S. Nonalcoholic fatty liver disease and the renin-angiotensin system blockers in the patients with chronic kidney disease. *Wien. Klin. Wochenschr.* **2015**, *127*, 355–362. [CrossRef] [PubMed]

69. Singh, S.; Khera, R.; Allen, A.M.; Murad, H.; Loomba, R. Comparative effectiveness of pharmacologic interventions for non-alcoholic steatohepatitis: A systemic review and network meta-analysis. *Hepatology* **2015**, *62*, 1417–1432. [CrossRef] [PubMed]

70. Athyros, V.G.; Tziomalos, K.; Gossios, T.D.; Griva, T.; Anagnostis, P.; Kargiotis, K.; Pagourelias, E.D.; Theocharidou, E.; Karagiannis, A.; Mikhailidis, D.P. Safety and efficacy of long-term statin treatment for cardiovascular events in patients with coronary heart disease and abnormal liver tests in the Greek Atorvastatin and Coronary Heart Disease Evaluation (GREACE) Study: A post-hoc analysis. *Lancet* **2010**, *376*, 1916–1922. [CrossRef]

71. Tikkanen, M.J.; Fayyad, R.; Faergeman, O.; Olsson, A.G.; Wun, C.C.; Laskey, R.; Kastelein, J.J.; Holme, I.; Pedersen, T.R. Effect of intensive lipid lowering with atorvastatin on cardiovascular outcomes in coronary heart disease patients with mild-to-moderate baseline elevations in alanine aminotransferase levels. *Int. J. Cardiol.* **2013**, *168*, 3846–3852. [CrossRef] [PubMed]

International Journal of
Molecular Sciences

MDPI

Review

NAFLD and Increased Aortic Stiffness: Parallel or Common Physiopathological Mechanisms?

Cristiane A. Villela-Nogueira, Nathalie C. Leite, Claudia R. L. Cardoso and Gil F. Salles *

Department of Internal Medicine, Medical School and University Hospital Clementino Fraga Filho, Universidade Federal do Rio de Janeiro, Rua Croton 72, Rio de Janeiro 22750-240, Brasil; crisvillelanog@gmail.com (C.A.V.-N.); nathaliecleite@gmail.com (N.C.L.); claudiacardoso@hucff.ufrj.br (C.R.L.C.)
* Correspondence: gilsalles@hucff.ufrj.br; Tel.: +55-21-2447-3577; Fax: +55-21-3938-2514

Academic Editor: Giovanni Targher
Received: 18 February 2016; Accepted: 21 March 2016; Published: 20 April 2016

Abstract: Non-alcoholic fatty liver disease (NAFLD) has become the leading cause of chronic liver diseases worldwide. Liver inflammation and fibrosis related to NAFLD contribute to disease progression and increasing liver-related mortality and morbidity. Increasing data suggest that NAFLD may be linked to atherosclerotic vascular disease independent of other established cardiovascular risk factors. Central arterial stiffness has been recognized as a measure of cumulative cardiovascular risk marker load, and the measure of carotid-femoral pulse wave velocity (cf-PWV) is regarded as the gold standard assessment of aortic stiffness. It has been shown that increased aortic stiffness predicts cardiovascular morbidity and mortality in several clinical settings, including type 2 diabetes mellitus, a well-known condition associated with advanced stages of NAFLD. Furthermore, recently-published studies reported a strong association between NAFLD and increased arterial stiffness, suggesting a possible link in the pathogenesis of atherosclerosis and NAFLD. We sought to review the published data on the associations between NAFLD and aortic stiffness, in order to better understand the interplay between these two conditions and identify possible common physiopathological mechanisms.

Keywords: non-alcoholic fatty liver disease; steatohepatitis; liver fibrosis; arterial stiffness; pulse wave velocity

1. Introduction

Non-alcoholic fatty liver disease (NAFLD) is currently the most prevalent chronic liver disease worldwide and the most frequent cause of abnormal liver enzymes in daily practice [1]. It is clearly related to metabolic syndrome, and its association with progressive liver fibrosis leading to cirrhosis and hepatocellular carcinoma has also been well established [2–5]. In addition to liver disease, NAFLD is also associated with extrahepatic diseases. Type 2 diabetes mellitus, an increasingly prevalent disease worldwide, is currently regarded as one of NAFLD's main risk factors, and it correlates with the severest histological aspects of NAFLD, with a growing prevalence of hepatocellular carcinoma [6–9]. Furthermore, NAFLD has also been linked to increased cardiovascular risk. A recent meta-analysis showed a 57% increase in overall mortality in patients with NAFLD, not only related to liver disease, but also due to cardiovascular disease (CVD) [10].

Regarding epidemiological aspects, NAFLD affects nearly 20% of the population worldwide, with its highest prevalence being described in South America (35%) and in Middle East (32%) [11]. In patients with associated risk factors, such as morbidly obese patients, NAFLD prevalence can achieve rates as high as 80% [12].

The spectrum of NAFLD encompasses a group of distinct liver diseases. Excluding alcohol ingestion greater than 20 g/day in women and 30 g/day in men and additional specific causes of steatosis, such as drug-induced and malnutrition among others, NAFLD ranges from simple steatosis, defined when at least 5% of hepatocytes are affected by fat; steatohepatitis (NASH), which comprises inflammation with ballooning; and ultimately, fibrosis, evolving to cirrhosis and its complications, such as hepatocellular carcinoma [13,14].

Increased arterial stiffness is an established cardiovascular risk marker in several clinical settings and had been proposed to reflect the cumulative burden of cardiovascular risk factors on the vascular wall [15,16]. Moreover, some recent studies have reported strong associations between increased aortic stiffness and NAFLD, particularly at its more advanced stages [17]. Hence, the aim of this review is to provide a comprehensive overview of previous studies assessing relationships between NAFLD and increased arterial stiffness in order to better understand the interplay between these two conditions and identify possible common physiopathological mechanisms.

2. Cardiovascular Risk and Non-Alcoholic Fatty Liver Disease (NAFLD)

Growing evidence has shown that NAFLD may be closely related to atherosclerotic vascular disease over and beyond other well-known cardiovascular risk factors [18,19]. Cardiovascular disease is the most common cause of mortality among patients with NAFLD [20,21]. Kim *et al.*, in 4023 individuals without any suspicion of liver disease or coronary artery disease, described that increased coronary artery calcification scores were associated with the presence of NAFLD, independent of traditional risk factors and of visceral adiposity, suggesting that NAFLD might be a risk factor for coronary artery disease [22]. A recent meta-analysis showed that NAFLD was associated with increased carotid-artery intima media thickness, impaired flow-mediated vasodilatation, increased arterial stiffness and increased coronary artery calcification. These associations were all independent of known risk factors and metabolic syndrome traits in a wide range of patient populations [23]. Further, the Framingham Heart study observed, among 3014 participants who performed a multidetector computed tomography (CT)-scan, that there was a significant association between NAFLD and coronary artery calcium and a trend towards a significant association between hepatic steatosis and previous clinical cardiovascular disease [24]. In a cohort of 755 healthy males who performed 18F-fluorodeoxyglucose (FDG) positron emission tomography with computed tomography, patients with NAFLD showed elevated carotid FDG uptake, besides an augmented carotid intima media thickness. These findings hinted that they might be at an increased risk of having inflammatory atherosclerotic plaques in the carotid arteries [25]. Targher *et al.* also demonstrated that patients with steatohepatitis when compared to those with simple steatosis and to controls had a greater carotid artery intima media thickness. Moreover, the same study showed that the histologic severity of nonalcoholic steatohepatitis was also related to carotid artery intima media thickness, regardless of traditional cardiovascular risk factors, insulin resistance and metabolic syndrome elements [26]. In resume, there is well-established evidence of associations between NAFLD and clinical and pre-clinical cardiovascular diseases.

Nevertheless, the physiopathological mechanisms underlying the associations between NAFLD and cardiovascular disease development are much debated, but still largely unsettled. Yoneda *et al.* showed, for the first time, elevated levels of high-sensitivity C-reactive protein (hs-CRP) in patients with biopsy-proven NASH, implying there may be a shared pathway between the severity of liver disease and the levels of hs-CRP, a well-known marker of cardiovascular risk [27]. Some studies observed that intrahepatic messenger RNA expression of C-reactive protein, interleukin-6 or plasminogen activator inhibitor 1 (PAI-1) was associated with the severest forms of NAFLD, mostly steatohepatitis [27–29]. Wieckoswska *et al.* correlated interleukin-6 liver expression with plasma levels and liver histology in patients with NASH and diabetes, hinting at a possible link between NAFLD and insulin resistance [28]. Similarly, Thuy *et al.* demonstrated an association between PAI-1, ingestion of a fructose-enriched diet and NAFLD [29]. Cigolini *et al.* also showed that increased PAI-1 was correlated with liver steatosis, implying that it might be mediated by concomitant alterations in plasma triglycerides and insulin concentrations [30]. In the same direction, Targher *et al.* reported that levels of fibrinogen and PAI-1 activity were higher in men with NASH, as well as plasma hs-CRP levels. They also had lower adiponectin levels compared to overweight men without steatosis with comparable visceral adiposity, suggesting that nonalcoholic steatohepatitis may be a factor for a more atherogenic risk profile besides its contribution to visceral adiposity [31]. In this setting, adiponectin concentrations may play a role [32–34]. Higher adiponectin levels were associated with a minor risk of myocardial infarction on a nested case control study among 18,225 male participants [33]. Low adiponectin levels are frequently observed in patients with NAFLD. We evaluated cytokine levels in 84 diabetic patients with biopsy-proven NAFLD: patients with NASH or with advanced fibrosis had equal cytokine levels to those without NASH or with absent/light fibrosis, except for lower serum adiponectin levels [34].

3. Prognostic Markers: The Role of Fibrosis

The conundrum of NAFLD is to identify patients whose disease will progress and impact survival. The natural history of NAFLD is a dynamic process that has been frequently revised. NAFLD has been considered a stable disease that seldom leads to advanced fibrosis. In a long-term follow-up study, only 1% of patients with simple steatosis presented cirrhosis, whereas among those with NASH, 11% developed cirrhosis and 7.3% died from a liver-related cause after 15.6 years of follow-up [35]. Overall liver-related survival was reduced in Swedish subjects with NAFLD and NASH, particularly in those with significant liver fibrosis, whereas bland steatosis was not associated with any increase in mortality risk, compared to the Swedish general population, followed for a median of 21 years [36]. Thus, current studies support the concept that the presence and severity of liver fibrosis on liver biopsy is the main surrogate marker of long-term prognosis. Hence, it would be important to implement accurate non-invasive markers to identify fibrosis to help to manage high risk patients.

Besides identifying early fibrosis, the recognition of patients who might be at risk for fibrosis progression is of utmost importance in order to define the best management for this specific population. Studies with paired biopsies identified clinical and biochemical aspects that helped in risk stratification regarding fibrosis progression. A recent meta-analysis [37], which included 11 cohort studies with biopsy-proven NAFLD (150 with simple steatosis and 261 with NASH), described that arterial hypertension and a low AST/ALT ratio at baseline predicted liver fibrosis progression. In this meta-analysis, two subgroups of patients were identified according to the rate of fibrosis progression: rapid and slow progressors. The first group comprised 21.1% of patients who had Stage 0 fibrosis at baseline, but in an average of 5.9 years developed fibrosis Stages 3 or 4. The majority of patients were categorized in the second group, which consisted of patients who had low fibrosis progression rate, changing their subsequent biopsies by one or two stages. Two of four studies in the systematic review observed that patients with a higher steatosis grade were more likely to develop progressive fibrosis. Remarkably, in this meta-analysis, no association was found between baseline severity of necroinflammation and risk of progressive fibrosis. This led to the concept that both patients with simple steatosis and with NASH may develop progressive liver fibrosis [37]. However, comparing patients with simple steatosis and NASH at baseline who had no fibrosis at baseline (F0), the rate of fibrosis progression was twice faster in patients with NASH (0.14 *vs.* 0.07 stages). Hence, although fibrosis progression was observed in both groups, it was slower in the simple steatosis group. Nevertheless, these findings differ from those reported in a previous meta-analysis of patients with NASH [38]. It estimated an overall fibrosis progression of 0.03 stages per year, and only age and inflammation on initial biopsy were predictors of progression to advanced fibrosis. Otherwise, in a review of 70 patients with untreated NAFLD who performed two liver biopsies with an interval of more than one year, a significant proportion of patients with NAFLD progressed towards well-defined NASH with bridging fibrosis, especially if metabolic risk factors deteriorated [39]. In this study, even mild inflammation or fibrosis could be considered as prognostic markers, increasing the risk of progression when compared to steatosis alone [39]. It is thus important to define two distinct situations in NAFLD that is simple steatosis, which seems to have a benign course with slower liver fibrosis progression, and steatosis with inflammation that could point to a progressive disease [40].

4. Aortic Stiffness and NAFLD

Arterial stiffness is the consequence of a complex interaction between stable and dynamic effects in structural and cellular components of the vascular wall. These vascular changes result from hemodynamic forces and extrinsic factors, like hormones, salt and glucose regulation. Arterial stiffness depends on the structural and geometric properties of the arterial wall and on the distending pressure. Its main determinants are aging and blood pressure [41,42]. Increased arterial stiffness occurs in a heterogeneous pattern predominantly on central segments, sparing peripheral arteries [43]. The stability, resiliency and compliancy properties of the vascular wall rely on two important scaffolding proteins: collagen and elastin. The quantity of such molecules is generally kept stable by a slow, but dynamic interplay of production and degradation. Deregulation of this balance, which may be stimulated by an inflammatory milieu, may lead to overproduction of altered collagen and reduced quantities of normal elastin, leading to increased arterial stiffness [44]. Prevalent diseases, such as arterial hypertension and diabetes mellitus in conjunction with ageing, augment these vascular alterations that worsen artery stiffening in different and synergistic ways. The evaluation of carotid-femoral pulse wave velocity (cf-PWV) can be easily obtained and is regarded as the gold standard method of assessing central aortic stiffness [40]. Further, increased aortic stiffness has been shown to predict cardiovascular morbidity and mortality in individuals with end-stage renal disease [45], hypertension [46], diabetes [47] and in general population-based samples [48,49].

Several previous studies [50–65], resumed in Table 1, have evaluated the relationships between NAFLD and arterial stiffness. All studies, except two of them [64,65], had cross-sectional designs, and all confirmed an association between increased arterial stiffness and NAFLD (mainly detected by ultrasonography), independent of other traditional cardiometabolic risk factors. Of note, one of these studies [56] demonstrated that the association between NAFLD and increased arterial stiffness was already present at adolescence. In this study, on a 17-year old population cohort from Australia, two groups were categorized according to their metabolic profile as a "high risk" and a "low risk" metabolic cluster. Central PWV was evaluated in both group, and NAFLD was diagnosed by abdominal ultrasound. Males and females with NAFLD in the presence of the metabolic cluster had greater PWV. They concluded that NAFLD was associated with increased arterial stiffness only in the presence of the "high risk" metabolic cluster, suggesting that arterial stiffness associated with NAFLD was linked to the presence of an adverse metabolic profile in adolescents [56]. However, because of their cross-sectional designs, no causal deductions could be drawn, only mere correlations. Of note, only three studies were performed in patients with NAFLD confirmed by histologic evaluation [52,57,62]. Sunbul *et al.* [57] evaluated in 100 biopsy-proven NAFLD patients the relation among arterial stiffness measures and the histological severity of NAFLD and epicardial fat thickness. Among the included patients matched to 50 control individuals, 33% were diabetic, and 55% fulfilled the criteria for metabolic syndrome. Measurements of arterial stiffness using cf-PWV and the augmentation index (AIx) were performed, and epicardial fat thickness was assessed by echocardiography. Patients with NAFLD showed significantly higher aortic PWV (7.0 ± 1.1 *vs.* 6.2 ± 0.8 m/s, $p < 0.001$) and AIx values (22.2% ± 13.1% *vs.* 17.4% ± 12.3%, $p = 0.02$) compared to controls, after adjusting for all potential confounders. Their results corroborated that NAFLD patients had an increased arterial stiffness, which was independently related to the severity of the liver fibrosis and increased epicardial fat thickness [57]. Otherwise, Ozturk *et al.* [62], evaluating 61 biopsy-proven NAFLD patients and 40 matched controls, found significant associations between NAFLD and aortic stiffness, independent of the presence of metabolic syndrome; but no correlation with histological liver fibrosis or inflammatory activity. Chen *et al.* [60] also described the association of advanced fibrosis with subclinical atherosclerosis in 2550 participants with ultrasound-diagnosed NAFLD. In this study, the NAFLD fibrosis score was calculated to assess the severity of the fibrosis of NAFLD patients. An NAFLD score >0.676

indicated the presence of advanced fibrosis in their study. The indicators of early atherosclerosis in the study were the carotid intima media thickness, carotid plaques and brachial-ankle pulse wave velocity (ba-PWV). They found that advanced fibrosis indicated by the NAFLD score was associated with carotid intima media thickness, with the presence of carotid plaques and with increased arterial stiffness, independent of usual cardiometabolic risk factors and insulin resistance [60]. There are only two longitudinal studies [64,65] evaluating the progression of arterial stiffness and the presence of NAFLD. The first one [64], with two arterial stiffness evaluations, employed brachial-ankle PWV, hence measuring principally peripheral arterial stiffness. It was accomplished in 1225 individuals on a five-year follow-up. This study concluded that individuals with NAFLD at first evaluation (diagnosed by ultrasonography) had a faster arterial stiffening than individuals without NAFLD, regardless of the concomitance of metabolic syndrome. We [65] performed serial cf-PWV measurements and evaluated liver fibrosis by transient elastography in 291 diabetic patients with NAFLD over a median follow-up of seven years. We observed that both a high aortic stiffness at the second cf-PWV examination (odds ratio (OR): 3.0; 95% confidence interval (CI): 1.3–7.2; $p = 0.011$) and a further augment in aortic stiffness (OR: 2.1; 95% CI: 1.0–4.3; $p = 0.046$) pointed to the increased likelihood of presenting advanced liver fibrosis on transient elastography examination [65]. Thus, it is possible that the chronological longitudinal associations between NAFLD and arterial stiffness may be bidirectional: NAFLD may hasten arterial stiffness progression, whilst increasing aortic stiffness may lead prior NAFLD in the direction of advanced liver fibrosis [65].

Table 1. Studies evaluating associations between non-alcoholic fatty liver disease (NAFLD) and arterial stiffness.

Author, Year	Number of Participants and Methods of Liver Investigation	Study Design	Aims	Conclusions
Shiotani et al., 2005 [50]	353 young university Japanese adults, submitted to abdominal ultrasound.	Transversal	To evaluate the validity of noninvasive ba-PWV measurements in overweight young adults.	ba-PWV was increased in males with NAFLD and might conceivably be useful to predict NAFLD.
Salvi et al., 2010 [51]	220 participants (123 women), aged between 30 and 70 years, from the Cardio-gambettola observatory liver steatosis estimation (GOOSE) study, submitted to abdominal ultrasound.	Transversal	To evaluate the relationship between metabolic syndrome, NAFLD and subclinical vascular disease, evaluated by carotid IMT and cf-PWV.	A possible independent role of NAFLD in determining arterial stiffness.
Vlachopoulos et al., 2010 [52]	23 biopsy-proven NAFLD patients and 28 matched controls.	Transversal	To investigate associations between NAFLD and functional arterial changes and early atherosclerosis.	NAFLD was associated with endothelial dysfunction and aortic stiffness (cf-PWV).
Kim et al., 2012 [53]	467 patients submitted to abdominal ultrasound.	Transversal	To evaluate the association of NAFLD and ba-PWV in patients with and without metabolic syndrome.	NAFLD was independently associated with increased ba-PWV, irrespective of multiple covariates, only in patients without metabolic syndrome.
Huang et al., 2012 [54]	8632 Chinese from a population-based sample; NAFLD detected by ultrasound.	Transversal	To evaluate associations between NAFLD and early atherosclerosis (carotid IMT and ba-PWV).	NAFLD was associated with increased carotid IMT and ba-PWV, independent of traditional CV risk factors and metabolic syndrome.
Lee et al., 2012 [55]	1442 healthy adults; NAFLD detected by ultrasound.	Transversal	To evaluate association between NAFLD and arterial stiffness (ba-PWV).	Arterial stiffness was associated with NAFLD, independent of classical CV risk factors.
Huang et al., 2013 [56]	964 adolescents (17-year-olds) from an Australian birth cohort, submitted to abdominal ultrasound.	Transversal	To examine if NAFLD was associated with aortic PWV, independent of cardiometabolic factors.	Aortic PWV was related to the presence of NAFLD that was predicated by the presence of an adverse metabolic profile in adolescents.
Sunbul et al., 2014 [57]	100 patients with biopsy-proven NAFLD and 50 age- and sex-matched controls.	Transversal	To examine the relationship between aortic PWV and AIx, the histological severity of NAFLD and epicardial fat thickness (EFT).	Patients with NAFLD have an increased arterial stiffness, which reflects both the severity of liver fibrosis and increased EFT values.
Omelchenko et al., 2014 [58]	52 NAFLD patients detected by ultrasound.	Transversal	To evaluate associations between adiponectin levels and arterial stiffness parameters (cf-PWV and AIx).	Adiponectin remained a significant predictor of PWV, even after controlling for age and gender, suggesting an active role of adiponectin in the pathophysiology of vascular disease in NAFLD patients.

Table 1. *Cont.*

Author, Year	Number of Participants and Methods of Liver Investigation	Study Design	Aims	Conclusions
Yu *et al.*, 2014 [59]	1296 non-obese, non-hypertensive, non-diabetic adults, NAFLD by ultrasound.	Transversal	To evaluate then association between NAFLD and arterial stiffness (ba-PWV).	NAFLD was associated with ba-PWV in Chinese individuals without obesity, hypertension and diabetes.
Chen *et al.*, 2015 [60]	2550 participants with ultrasound-confirmed NAFLD from a community-based sample.	Transversal	To evaluate whether advanced fibrosis assessed by NAFLD fibrosis score was associated with subclinical atherosclerosis in NAFLD patients.	Advanced fibrosis was associated with carotid intima media thickness, the presence of carotid plaques and arterial stiffness, independent of cardiometabolic risk factors and insulin resistance.
Chou *et al.*, 2015 [61]	4860 non-diabetic, pre-diabetic and newly-diagnosed T2DM individuals, evaluated by abdominal ultrasound.	Transversal	To evaluate PWV in patients with NAFLD.	The effect of NAFLD on arterial stiffness was apparent only in subjects with normal glucose tolerance.
Ozturk *et al.*, 2015 [62]	61 biopsy-proven NAFLD patients and 41 controls without NAFLD; adult male patients between 20 and 40 years of age.	Transversal	To evaluate the relationship between NAFLD and subclinical atherosclerosis and to investigate the associations according to the presence or absence of metabolic syndrome.	The presence of NAFLD was associated with endothelial dysfunction and atherosclerosis, independent of metabolic syndrome.
Chung *et al.*, 2015 [63]	2954 healthy individuals; NAFLD detected by ultrasound.	Transversal	To evaluate the association between NAFLD and arterial stiffness (cardio-ankle vascular index).	NAFLD was associated with increased arterial stiffness, independent of cardio-metabolic risk factors.
Li *et al.*, 2015 [64]	728 men and 497 women without hypertension and diabetes; NAFLD detected by ultrasound.	Longitudinal	To evaluate the relationship between the presence of NAFLD at baseline and progression of arterial stiffness (ba-PWV) during follow-up (5 years).	Patients with NAFLD had a faster progression of arterial stiffness, independent of other CV risk factors.
Leite *et al.*, 2015 [65]	291 T2DM patients; NAFLD by abdominal ultrasound or liver biopsy.	Longitudinal	To evaluate the association between progressions of aortic PWV (7 years of follow-up) with advanced liver fibrosis identified by transient elastography.	High or increasing aortic stiffness predicted the development of advanced liver fibrosis on transient elastography.

Abbreviations: T2DM, type-2 diabetes mellitus; NAFLD, non-alcoholic fatty liver disease; cf-PWV, carotid-femoral pulse-wave velocity; ba-PWV, brachial-ankle pulse wave velocity; AIx, arterial augmentation index; IMT, intima media thickness.

5. NAFLD and Arterial Stiffness: Is There an Interplay?

Many studies evaluated if NAFLD contributed to other outcomes, such as cardiovascular mortality; and most of them demonstrated an association, but no causality could be shown [20]. Liver disease and atherogenesis might be mediated by inflamed visceral adipose tissue. In this scenario, the liver might play a role of both the target of the resulting systemic abnormalities and as the source of many proatherogenic variables. In this setting, nonalcoholic steatohepatitis might contribute to the pathogenesis of cardiovascular disease in two ways: first, through the systemic release of several inflammatory, prothrombotic and oxidative-stress substances and, second, through the contribution of nonalcoholic fatty liver disease to insulin resistance and atherogenic dyslipidemia.

Insulin resistance is the utmost important factor that triggers the development of NAFLD. This notwithstanding, insulin resistance is probably one of the mechanisms that is also linked to increased arterial stiffness. Both chronic hyperglycemia, as well as hyperinsulinemia have been demonstrated to increase the local activity of the renin-angiotensin-aldosterone system and also the expression of the angiotensin type I receptor in the vascular milieu, leading to hypertrophy of vascular wall and fibrosis [66–68]. Due to insulin resistance, the proliferative effects of hyperinsulinemia prevails and promotes an impairment of phosphatidylinositol 3 (PI3)-kinase-dependent signaling responsible for the acute metabolic effects of insulin; still preserving the activity of growth promoting mitogen-activated kinase pathways [69]. Triglyceride in the liver has been considered as an epiphenomenon being a marker of a dysmetabolic state, not adding directly to the genesis of the extrahepatic manifestations of this complication.

Omelchenko *et al.* evaluated the relation between the levels of adiponectin and arterial stiffness parameters using pulse wave velocity (PWV) and the arterial augmentation index (Aix) in NAFLD patients [58]. In their study, adiponectin was positively correlated with Aix ($r = 0.467$; $p < 0.0001$) and with PWV ($r = 0.348$; $p = 0.011$), in spite of a weak correlation coefficient. In a multiple linear regression analysis, adiponectin persisted as a significant predictor of abnormal PWV after controlling for age and gender, suggesting an active role of adiponectin in the pathophysiology of vascular disease in NAFLD patients [58]. Remarkably, it was observed by Kim *et al.* [53] that NAFLD and arterial stiffness have been related even in the absence of arterial hypertension, diabetes and metabolic syndrome. Abdominal ultrasound and brachial-ankle pulse wave velocity (ba-PWV) were investigated in 4467 individuals. NAFLD individuals were classified in non-NAFLD, mild and moderate-to-severe NAFLD groups, respectively. The NAFLD group had higher levels of ba-PWV. NAFLD was independently associated with increased ba-PWV ($\geqslant$1366 cm/s), independent of multiple covariates (OR: 1.24 and 95% CI: 1.05–1.46). Subgroup analyses revealed that there was a significant association between NAFLD and increased ba-PWV only in individuals without metabolic syndrome (OR: 1.27 and 95% CI: 1.07–1.51). The multivariate linear regression models for the overall study population and for individuals without metabolic syndrome also showed a significant association between NAFLD and the absolute values of ba-PWV; however, the result for individuals with metabolic syndrome did not demonstrate an association [53]. This might point to the possibility that NAFLD pathogenetic mechanism per se could be linked to abnormal arterial stiffness not requiring the coexistence of metabolic syndrome for its occurrence. Recently, Chou *et al.* [61] investigated 4860 subjects who were categorized into normal glucose tolerance, pre-diabetes and newly-diagnosed diabetes groups and, after excluding known diabetes, the independent relationship between non-alcoholic fatty liver disease and arterial stiffness. The severity of non-alcoholic fatty liver disease was divided into mild and moderate-to-severe. Increased arterial stiffness was defined as brachial-ankle pulse wave velocity (ba-PWV) >1400 cm/s. They concluded that the effect of NAFLD on arterial stiffness was apparent in subjects with normal glucose tolerance, but not in diabetes and pre-diabetes [61].

In resume, the possible biological mechanisms linking NAFLD and increased arterial stiffness remain largely unknown, but possibly involve common pathways of chronic low-grade inflammation and adipokines imbalance [70,71]. More prospective studies, including diabetic and non-diabetic patients, are necessary to investigate whether there are causal relationships between them. On the

Int. J. Mol. Sci. **2016**, *17*, 460

other hand, aortic stiffness, ideally measured by carotid-femoral PWV, may be a useful tool to identify high-risk patients concerning both cardiovascular and liver disease. Its use as a prognostic marker may help define better strategies to slow the progression of both liver and cardiovascular disease. In the future, prospective studies with serial PWV and liver disease severity evaluation may confirm its utility in assessing improvement in both scenarios' outcomes.

Acknowledgments: This study was supported by grants from Conselho Brasileiro de Desenvolvimento Científico e Tecnológico (CNPq-Brazil) and Fundação Carlos Chagas Filho de Amparo à Pesquisa do Estado do Rio de Janeiro (FAPERJ-Brazil).

Author Contributions: Cristiane A. Villela-Nogueira reviewed the literature and drafted the manuscript; Nathalie C. Leite, Claudia R. L. Cardoso and Gil F. Salles revised the manuscript and contributed with important intellectual content.

Conflicts of Interest: The authors declare no conflict of interest.

References

1. Angulo, P. Nonalcoholic fatty liver disease. *N. Engl. J. Med.* **2002**, *346*, 1221–1231. [PubMed]
2. Marchesini, G.; Bugianesi, E.; Forlani, G.; Cerrelli, F.; Lenzi, M.; Manini, R.; Natale, S.; Vanni, E.; Villanova, N.; Melchionda, N.; *et al.* Nonalcoholic fatty liver, steatohepatitis, and the metabolic syndrome. *Hepatology* **2003**, *37*, 917–923. [CrossRef] [PubMed]
3. Bedogni, G.; Miglioli, L.; Masutti, F.; Tiribelli, C.; Marchesini, G.; Bellentani, S. Prevalence of and risk factors for nonalcoholic fatty liver disease: The Dionysos nutrition and liver study. *Hepatology* **2005**, *42*, 44–52. [CrossRef] [PubMed]
4. Bhala, N.; Angulo, P.; van der Poorten, D.; Lee, E.; Hui, J.M.; Saracco, G.; Adams, L.A.; Charatcharoenwitthaya, P.; Topping, J.H.; Bugianesi, E.; *et al.* The natural history of nonalcoholic fatty liver disease with advanced fibrosis or cirrhosis: An international collaborative study. *Hepatology* **2011**, *54*, 1208–1216. [CrossRef] [PubMed]
5. White, D.L.; Kanwal, F.; El-Serag, H.B. Association between nonalcoholic fatty liver disease and risk for hepatocellular cancer, based on systematic review. *Clin. Gastroenterol. Hepatol.* **2012**, *10*, 1342–1359. [CrossRef] [PubMed]
6. Hossain, N.; Afendy, A.; Stepanova, M.; Nader, F.; Srishord, M.; Rafiq, N.; Goodman, Z.; Younossi, Z. Independent predictors of fibrosis in patients with nonalcoholic fatty liver disease. *Clin. Gastroenterol. Hepatol.* **2009**, *7*, 1224–1229. [CrossRef] [PubMed]
7. Prashanth, M.; Ganesh, H.K.; Vima, M.V.; John, M.; Bandgar, T.; Joshi, S.R.; Shah, S.R.; Rathi, P.M.; Joshi, A.S.; Thakkar, H.; *et al.* Prevalence of nonalcoholic fatty liver disease in patients with type 2 diabetes mellitus. *J. Assoc. Physicians India* **2009**, *57*, 205–210. [PubMed]
8. Leite, N.; Villela-Nogueira, C.; Pannain, V.; Bottino, A.; Rezende, G.; Cardoso, C.; Salles, G. Histopathological stages of nonalcoholic fatty liver disease in type 2 diabetes: Prevalences and correlated factors. *Liver Int.* **2011**, *31*, 700–706. [CrossRef] [PubMed]
9. Mittal, S.; El-Serag, H.B.; Sada, Y.H.; Kanwal, F.; Duan, Z.; Temple, S.; May, S.B.; Kramer, J.R.; Richardson, P.A.; Davila, J.A. Hepatocellular carcinoma in the absence of cirrhosis in United States veterans is associated with nonalcoholic fatty liver disease. *Clin. Gastroenterol. Hepatol.* **2016**, *14*, 124–131. [CrossRef] [PubMed]
10. Musso, G.; Gambino, R.; Cassader, M.; Pagano, G. Meta-analysis: Natural history of non-alcoholic fatty liver disease (NAFLD) and diagnostic accuracy of non-invasive tests for liver disease severity. *Ann. Med.* **2011**, *43*, 617–649. [CrossRef] [PubMed]
11. Younossi, Z.M.; Koenig, A.B.; Abdelatif, D.; Fazel, Y.; Henry, L.; Wymer, M. Global Epidemiology of Non-Alcoholic Fatty Liver Disease-Meta-Analytic Assessment of Prevalence, Incidence and Outcomes. *Hepatology* **2015**, in press. [CrossRef] [PubMed]
12. Morita, S.; Neto, D.D.S.; Morita, F.H.; Morita, N.K.; Lobo, S.M. Prevalence of Non-alcoholic Fatty Liver Disease and Steatohepatitis Risk Factors in Patients Undergoing Bariatric Surgery. *Obes. Surg.* **2015**, *25*, 2335–2343. [CrossRef] [PubMed]
13. Matteoni, C.; Younossi, Z.; Gramlich, T.; Boparai, N.; Liu, Y.; McCullough, A. Nonalcoholic fatty liver disease: A spectrum of clinical and pathological severity. *Gastroenterology* **1999**, *116*, 1413–1419. [CrossRef]

14. Brunt, E.M.; Janney, C.G.; Di Bisceglie, A.M.; Neuschwander-Tetri, B.A.; Bacon, B.R. Nonalcoholic steatohepatitis: A proposal for grading and staging the histological lesions. *Am. J. Gastroenterol.* **1999**, *94*, 2467–2474. [CrossRef] [PubMed]

15. Ben-Shlomo, Y.; Spears, M.; Boustred, C.; May, M.; Anderson, S.G.; Benjamin, E.J.; Boutouyrie, P.; Cameron, J.; Chen, C.H.; Cruickshank, J.K.; *et al.* Aortic pulse wave velocity improves cardiovascular event prediction: An individual participant meta-analysis of prospective observational data from 17,635 subjects. *J. Am. Coll. Cardiol.* **2014**, *63*, 636–646. [CrossRef] [PubMed]

16. Cavalcante, J.L.; Lima, J.A.; Redheuil, A.; Al-Mallah, M.H. Aortic stiffness: Current understanding and future directions. *J. Am. Coll. Cardiol.* **2011**, *57*, 1511–1522. [CrossRef] [PubMed]

17. Athyros, V.G.; Tziomalos, K.; Katsiki, N.; Doumas, M.; Karagiannis, A.; Mikhailidis, D.P. Cardiovascular risk across the histological spectrum and the clinical manifestations of non-alcoholic fatty liver disease: An update. *World J. Gastroenterol.* **2015**, *21*, 6820–6834. [PubMed]

18. Targher, G.; Bertolini, L.; Rodella, S.; Tessari, R.; Zenari, L.; Lippi, G.; Arcaro, G. Nonalcoholic fatty liver disease is independently associated with an increased incidence of cardiovascular events in type 2 diabetic patients. *Diabetes Care* **2007**, *30*, 2119–2121. [CrossRef] [PubMed]

19. Targher, G.; Bertolini, L.; Padovani, R.; Rodella, S.; Tessari, R.; Zenari, L.; Day, C.; Arcaro, G. Prevalence of nonalcoholic fatty liver disease and its association with cardiovascular disease among type 2 diabetic patients. *Diabetes Care* **2007**, *30*, 1212–1218. [CrossRef] [PubMed]

20. Targher, G.; Day, C.P.; Bonora, E. Risk of cardiovascular disease in patients with nonalcoholic fatty liver disease. *N. Engl. J. Med.* **2010**, *363*, 1341–1350. [CrossRef] [PubMed]

21. Anstee, Q.M.; Targher, G.; Day, C.P. Progression of NAFLD to diabetes mellitus, cardiovascular disease or cirrhosis. *Nat. Rev. Gastroenterol. Hepatol.* **2013**, *10*, 330–344. [CrossRef] [PubMed]

22. Kim, D.; Choi, S.Y.; Park, E.H.; Lee, W.; Kang, J.H.; Kim, W.; Kim, Y.J.; Yoon, J.H.; Jeong, S.H.; Lee, D.H.; *et al.* Nonalcoholic fatty liver disease is associated with coronary artery calcification. *Hepatology* **2012**, *56*, 605–613. [CrossRef] [PubMed]

23. Oni, E.T.; Agatston, A.S.; Blaha, M.J.; Fialkow, J.; Cury, R.; Sposito, A.; Erbel, R.; Blankstein, R.; Feldman, T.; Al-Mallah, M.; *et al.* A systematic review: Burden and severity of subclinical cardiovascular disease among those with nonalcoholic fatty liver; should we care? *Atherosclerosis* **2013**, *230*, 258–267. [CrossRef] [PubMed]

24. Mellinger, J.L.; Pencina, K.M.; Massaro, J.M.; Hoffmann, U.; Seshadri, S.; Fox, C.S.; O'Donnell, C.J.; Speliotes, E.K. Hepatic steatosis and cardiovascular disease outcomes: An analysis of the Framingham Heart Study. *J. Hepatol.* **2015**, *63*, 470–476. [CrossRef] [PubMed]

25. Moon, S.H.; Noh, T.S.; Cho, Y.S.; Hong, S.P.; Hyun, S.H.; Choi, J.Y.; Kim, B.T.; Lee, K.H. Association between nonalcoholic fatty liver disease and carotid artery inflammation evaluated by 18F-fluorodeoxyglucose positron emission tomography. *Angiology* **2015**, *66*, 472–480. [CrossRef] [PubMed]

26. Targher, G.; Zenari, L.; Bertolini, L.; Cigolini, M.; Padovani, R.; Falezza, G.; Rodella, S.; Arcaro, G.; Zoppini, G. Relations between carotid artery wall thickness and liver histology in subjects with nonalcoholic fatty liver disease. *Diabetes Care* **2006**, *29*, 1325–1330. [CrossRef] [PubMed]

27. Yoneda, M.; Mawatari, H.; Fujita, K.; Iida, H.; Yonemitsu, K.; Kato, S.; Takahashi, H.; Kirikoshi, H.; Inamori, M.; Nozaki, Y.; *et al.* High-sensitivity C-reactive protein is an independent clinical feature of nonalcoholic steatohepatitis (NASH) and also of the severity of fibrosis in NASH. *J. Gastroenterol.* **2007**, *42*, 573–582. [CrossRef] [PubMed]

28. Wieckowska, A.; Papouchado, B.G.; Li, Z.; Lopez, R.; Zein, N.N.; Feldstein, A.E. Increased hepatic and circulating interleukin-6 levels in human nonalcoholic steatohepatitis. *Am. J. Gastroenterol.* **2008**, *103*, 1372–1379. [CrossRef] [PubMed]

29. Thuy, S.; Ladurner, R.; Volynets, V.; Wagner, S.; Strahl, S.; Konigsrainer, A.; Maier, K.P.; Bischoff, S.C.; Bergheim, I. Nonalcoholic fatty liver disease in humans is associated with increased plasma endotoxin and plasminogen activator inhibitor 1 concentrations and with fructose intake. *J. Nutr.* **2008**, *138*, 1452–1455. [PubMed]

30. Cigolini, M.; Targher, G.; Agostino, G.; Tonoli, M.; Muggeo, M.; DeSandre, G. Liver steatosis and its relation to plasma haemostatic factors in apparently healthy men—Role of the metabolic syndrome. *Thromb. Haemost.* **1996**, *76*, 69–73. [PubMed]

31. Targher, G.; Bertolini, L.; Rodella, S.; Lippi, G.; Franchini, M.; Zoppini, G.; Muggeo, M.; Day, C. NASH predicts plasma inflammatory biomarkers independently of visceral fat in men. *Obesity* **2008**, *16*, 1394–1399. [CrossRef] [PubMed]

32. Leung, C.; Herath, C.B.; Jia, Z.; Goodwin, M.; Mak, K.Y.; Watt, M.J.; Forbes, J.M.; Angus, P.W. Dietary glycotoxins exacerbate progression of experimental fatty liver disease. *J. Hepatol.* **2014**, *60*, 832–838. [CrossRef] [PubMed]

33. Pischon, T.; Girman, C.J.; Hotamisligil, G.S.; Rifai, N.; Hu, F.B.; Rimm, E.B. Plasma adiponectin levels and risk of myocardial infarction in men. *J. Am. Med. Assoc.* **2004**, *291*, 1730–1737. [CrossRef] [PubMed]

34. Leite, N.; Salles, G.; Cardoso, C.; Villela-Nogueira, C. Serum biomarkers in type 2 diabetic patients with non-alcoholic steatohepatitis and advanced fibrosis. *Hepatol. Res.* **2013**, *43*, 508–515. [CrossRef] [PubMed]

35. Ekstedt, M.; Franzen, L.; Mathiesen, U.; Thorelius, L.; Holmqvist, M.; Bodemar, G.; Kechagias, S. Long-term follow-up of patients with NAFLD and elevated liver enzymes. *Hepatology* **2006**, *44*, 865–873. [CrossRef] [PubMed]

36. Soderberg, C.; Stal, P.; Askling, J.; Glaumann, H.; Lindberg, G.; Marmur, J.; Hultcrantz, R. Decreased Survival of Subjects with Elevated Liver Function Tests During a 28-Year Follow-Up. *Hepatology* **2010**, *51*, 595–602. [CrossRef] [PubMed]

37. Singh, S.; Allen, A.M.; Wang, Z.; Prokop, L.J.; Murad, M.H.; Loomba, R. Fibrosis progression in nonalcoholic fatty liver *vs.* nonalcoholic steatohepatitis: A systematic review and meta-analysis of paired-biopsy studies. *Clin. Gastroenterol. Hepatol.* **2015**, *13*, 643–654. [CrossRef] [PubMed]

38. Argo, C.K.; Northup, P.G.; Al-Osaimi, A.M.; Caldwell, S.H. Systematic review of risk factors for fibrosis progression in non-alcoholic steatohepatitis. *J. Hepatol.* **2009**, *51*, 371–379. [CrossRef] [PubMed]

39. Pais, R.; Charlotte, F.; Fedchuk, L.; Bedossa, P.; Lebray, P.; Poynard, T.; Ratziu, V.; Group, L.S. A systematic review of follow-up biopsies reveals disease progression in patients with non-alcoholic fatty liver. *J. Hepatol.* **2013**, *59*, 550–556. [CrossRef] [PubMed]

40. Harrison, S.A. Nonalcoholic fatty liver disease and fibrosis progression: The good, the bad, and the unknown. *Clin. Gastroenterol. Hepatol.* **2015**, *13*, 655–657. [CrossRef] [PubMed]

41. Laurent, S.; Cockcroft, J.; van Bortel, L.; Boutouyrie, P.; Giannattasio, C.; Hayoz, D.; Pannier, B.; Vlachopoulos, C.; Wilkinson, I.; Struijker-Boudier, H. European Network for Non-invasive Investigation of Large, A., Expert consensus document on arterial stiffness: Methodological issues and clinical applications. *Eur. Heart J.* **2006**, *27*, 2588–2605. [CrossRef] [PubMed]

42. Laurent, S.; Boutouyrie, P. Recent advances in arterial stiffness and wave reflection in human hypertension. *Hypertension* **2007**, *49*, 1202–1206. [CrossRef] [PubMed]

43. Zieman, S.J.; Melenovsky, V.; Kass, D.A. Mechanisms, pathophysiology, and therapy of arterial stiffness. *Arterioscler. Thromb. Vasc. Biol.* **2005**, *25*, 932–943. [CrossRef] [PubMed]

44. Johnson, C.P.; Baugh, R.; Wilson, C.A.; Burns, J. Age related changes in the tunica media of the vertebral artery: Implications for the assessment of vessels injured by trauma. *J. Clin. Pathol.* **2001**, *54*, 139–145. [CrossRef] [PubMed]

45. Blacher, J.; Guerin, A.P.; Pannier, B.; Marchais, S.J.; Safar, M.E.; London, G.M. Impact of aortic stiffness on survival in end-stage renal disease. *Circulation* **1999**, *99*, 2434–2439. [CrossRef] [PubMed]

46. Laurent, S.; Boutouyrie, P.; Asmar, R.; Gautier, I.; Laloux, B.; Guize, L.; Ducimetiere, P.; Benetos, A. Aortic stiffness is an independent predictor of all-cause and cardiovascular mortality in hypertensive patients. *Hypertension* **2001**, *37*, 1236–1241. [CrossRef] [PubMed]

47. Cardoso, C.R.; Ferreira, M.T.; Leite, N.C.; Salles, G.F. Prognostic impact of aortic stiffness in high-risk type 2 diabetic patients: The Rio deJaneiro Type 2 Diabetes Cohort Study. *Diabetes Care* **2013**, *36*, 3772–3778. [CrossRef] [PubMed]

48. Willum-Hansen, T.; Staessen, J.A.; Torp-Pedersen, C.; Rasmussen, S.; Thijs, L.; Ibsen, H.; Jeppesen, J. Prognostic value of aortic pulse wave velocity as index of arterial stiffness in the general population. *Circulation* **2006**, *113*, 664–670. [CrossRef] [PubMed]

49. Mitchell, G.F.; Hwang, S.J.; Vasan, R.S.; Larson, M.G.; Pencina, M.J.; Hamburg, N.M.; Vita, J.A.; Levy, D.; Benjamin, E.J. Arterial stiffness and cardiovascular events: The Framingham Heart Study. *Circulation* **2010**, *121*, 505–511. [CrossRef] [PubMed]

50. Shiotani, A.; Motoyama, M.; Matsuda, T.; Miyanishi, T. Brachial-ankle pulse wave velocity in Japanese university students. *Intern. Med.* **2005**, *44*, 696–701. [CrossRef] [PubMed]

51. Salvi, P.; Ruffini, R.; Agnoletti, D.; Magnani, E.; Pagliarani, G.; Comandini, G.; Pratico, A.; Borghi, C.; Benetos, A.; Pazzi, P. Increased arterial stiffness in nonalcoholic fatty liver disease: The Cardio-GOOSE study. *J. Hypertens.* **2010**, *28*, 1699–1707. [CrossRef] [PubMed]

52. Vlachopoulos, C.; Manesis, E.; Baou, K.; Papatheodoridis, G.; Koskinas, J.; Tiniakos, D.; Aznaouridis, K.; Archimandritis, A.; Stefanadis, C. Increased arterial stiffness and impaired endothelial function in nonalcoholic Fatty liver disease: A pilot study. *Am. J. Hypertens.* **2010**, *23*, 1183–1189. [CrossRef] [PubMed]

53. Kim, B.J.; Kim, N.H.; Kim, B.S.; Kang, J.H. The association between nonalcoholic fatty liver disease, metabolic syndrome and arterial stiffness in nondiabetic, nonhypertensive individuals. *Cardiology* **2012**, *123*, 54–61. [CrossRef] [PubMed]

54. Huang, Y.; Bi, Y.; Xu, M.; Ma, Z.; Xu, Y.; Wang, T.; Li, M.; Liu, Y.; Lu, J.; Chen, Y.; *et al.* Nonalcoholic fatty liver disease is associated with atherosclerosis in middle-aged and elderly Chinese. *Arterioscler. Thromb. Vasc. Biol.* **2012**, *32*, 2321–2326. [CrossRef] [PubMed]

55. Lee, Y.J.; Shim, J.Y.; Moon, B.S.; Shin, Y.H.; Jung, D.H.; Lee, J.H.; Lee, H.R. The relationship between arterial stiffness and nonalcoholic fatty liver disease. *Dig. Dis. Sci.* **2012**, *57*, 196–203. [CrossRef] [PubMed]

56. Huang, R.C.; Beilin, L.J.; Ayonrinde, O.; Mori, T.A.; Olynyk, J.K.; Burrows, S.; Hands, B.; Adams, L.A. Importance of cardiometabolic risk factors in the association between nonalcoholic fatty liver disease and arterial stiffness in adolescents. *Hepatology* **2013**, *58*, 1306–1314. [CrossRef] [PubMed]

57. Sunbul, M.; Agirbasli, M.; Durmus, E.; Kivrak, T.; Akin, H.; Aydin, Y.; Ergelen, R.; Yilmaz, Y. Arterial stiffness in patients with non-alcoholic fatty liver disease is related to fibrosis stage and epicardial adipose tissue thickness. *Atherosclerosis* **2014**, *237*, 490–493. [CrossRef] [PubMed]

58. Omelchenko, E.; Gavish, D.; Shargorodsky, M. Adiponectin is better predictor of subclinical atherosclerosis than liver function tests in patients with nonalcoholic fatty liver disease. *J. Am. Soc. Hypertens* **2014**, *8*, 376–380. [CrossRef] [PubMed]

59. Yu, X.Y.; Zhao, Y.; Song, X.X.; Song, Z.Y. Association between non-alcoholic fatty liver disease and arterial stiffness in the non-obese, non-hypertensive, and non-diabetic young and middle-aged Chinese population. *J. Zhejiang Univ. Sci. B* **2014**, *15*, 879–887. [CrossRef] [PubMed]

60. Chen, Y.; Xu, M.; Wang, T.; Sun, J.; Sun, W.; Xu, B.; Huang, X.; Xu, Y.; Lu, J.; Li, X.; *et al.* Advanced fibrosis associates with atherosclerosis in subjects with nonalcoholic fatty liver disease. *Atherosclerosis* **2015**, *241*, 145–150. [CrossRef] [PubMed]

61. Chou, C.Y.; Yang, Y.C.; Wu, J.S.; Sun, Z.J.; Lu, F.H.; Chang, C.J. Non-alcoholic fatty liver disease associated with increased arterial stiffness in subjects with normal glucose tolerance, but not pre-diabetes and diabetes. *Diabetes Vasc. Dis. Res.* **2015**, *12*, 359–365. [CrossRef] [PubMed]

62. Ozturk, K.; Uygun, A.; Guler, A.K.; Demirci, H.; Ozdemir, C.; Cakir, M.; Sakin, Y.S.; Turker, T.; Sari, S.; Demirbas, S.; *et al.* Nonalcoholic fatty liver disease is an independent risk factor for atherosclerosis in young adult men. *Atherosclerosis* **2015**, *240*, 380–386. [CrossRef] [PubMed]

63. Chung, G.E.; Choi, S.Y.; Kim, D.; Kwak, M.S.; Park, H.E.; Kim, M.K.; Yim, J.Y. Nonalcoholic fatty liver disease as a risk factor of arterial stiffness measured by the cardioankle vascular index. *Medicine* **2015**, *94*, e654. [CrossRef] [PubMed]

64. Li, N.; Zhang, G.W.; Zhang, J.R.; Jin, D.; Li, Y.; Liu, T.; Wang, R.T. Non-alcoholic fatty liver disease is associated with progression of arterial stiffness. *Nutr. Metab. Cardiovasc. Dis.* **2015**, *25*, 218–223. [CrossRef] [PubMed]

65. Leite, N.C.; Villela-Nogueira, C.A.; Fereira, M.T.; Cardoso, C.R.; Salles, G.F. Increasing aortic stiffness is predictive of advanced liver fibrosis in patients with type 2 diabetes: The Rio-T2DM cohort study. *Liver. Int.* **2015**. [CrossRef] [PubMed]

66. Nickenig, G.; Roling, J.; Strehlow, K.; Schnabel, P.; Bohm, M. Insulin induces upregulation of vascular AT1 receptor gene expression by posttranscriptional mechanisms. *Circulation* **1998**, *98*, 2453–2460. [CrossRef] [PubMed]

67. Jesmin, S.; Sakuma, I.; Salah-Eldin, A.; Nonomura, K.; Hattori, Y.; Kitabatake, A. Diminished penile expression of vascular endothelial growth factor and its receptors at the insulin-resistant stage of a type II diabetic rat model: A possible cause for erectile dysfunction in diabetes. *J. Mol. Endocrinol.* **2003**, *31*, 401–418. [CrossRef] [PubMed]

68. Rizzoni, D.; Porteri, E.; Guelfi, D.; Muiesan, M.L.; Valentini, U.; Cimino, A.; Girelli, A.; Rodella, L.; Bianchi, R.; Sleiman, I.; *et al.* Structural alterations in subcutaneous small arteries of normotensive and hypertensive patients with non-insulin-dependent diabetes mellitus. *Circulation* **2001**, *103*, 1238–1244. [CrossRef] [PubMed]

69. Cusi, K.; Maezono, K.; Osman, A.; Pendergrass, M.; Patti, M.E.; Pratipanawatr, T.; DeFronzo, R.A.; Kahn, C.R.; Mandarino, L.J. Insulin resistance differentially affects the PI 3-kinase- and MAP kinase-mediated signaling in human muscle. *J. Clin. Investig.* **2000**, *105*, 311–320. [CrossRef] [PubMed]

70. Jain, S.; Khera, R.; Corrales-Medina, V.F.; Townsend, R.R.; Chirinos, J.A. Inflammation and arterial stiffness in humans. *Atherosclerosis* **2014**, *237*, 381–390. [CrossRef] [PubMed]

71. Fargion, S.; Porzio, M.; Fracanzani, A.L. Nonalcoholic fatty liver disease and vascular disease: State-of-the-art. *World J. Gastroenterol.* **2014**, *20*, 13306–13324. [CrossRef] [PubMed]

International Journal of
Molecular Sciences

MDPI

Review

Non-Alcoholic Fatty Liver Disease and Extra-Hepatic Cancers

Claudia Sanna, Chiara Rosso, Milena Marietti and Elisabetta Bugianesi *

Division of Gastroenterology, Department of Medical Sciences, A.O. Città della Salute e della Scienza di Torino, University of Turin, 10126 Turin, Italy; sanna.cla@gmail.com (C.S.); chiara.rosso84@tiscali.it (C.R.); milena.marietti@gmail.com (M.M.)
* Correspondence: elisabetta.bugianesi@unito.it; Tel.: +39-011-633-3532; Fax: +39-011-633-5927

Academic Editors: Amedeo Lonardo and Giovanni Targher
Received: 5 March 2016; Accepted: 9 May 2016; Published: 12 May 2016

Abstract: Non-alcoholic fatty liver disease (NAFLD) is a leading cause of chronic liver disease but the second cause of death among NAFLD patients are attributed to malignancies at both gastrointestinal (liver, colon, esophagus, stomach, and pancreas) and extra-intestinal sites (kidney in men, and breast in women). Obesity and related metabolic abnormalities are associated with increased incidence or mortality for a number of cancers. NAFLD has an intertwined relationship with metabolic syndrome and significantly contributes to the risk of hepatocellular carcinoma (HCC), but recent evidence have fuelled concerns that NAFLD may be a new, and added, risk factor for extra-hepatic cancers, particularly in the gastrointestinal tract. In this review we critically appraise key studies on NAFLD-associated extra-hepatic cancers and speculate on how NAFLD may influence carcinogenesis at these sites.

Keywords: fatty liver; colorectal cancer; adipokines; gut microbiota

1. Introduction

Nonalcoholic fatty liver disease (NAFLD) is one of the most common causes of chronic liver disease worldwide, with an estimated global prevalence of 25% in adults and around 10% in children [1–3]. The term NAFLD includes two distinct conditions with different histologic features and prognoses: non-alcoholic fatty liver (NAFL) and non-alcoholic steatohepatitis (NASH) [4]; the presence of steatohepatitis and significant fibrosis are considered harbingers of adverse outcomes in individuals with NAFLD and are associated with an increased risk for morbidity and mortality through hepatic and non-hepatic complications [5–7]. In descending order, the majority of deaths in patients with NAFLD are, first, attributed to cardiovascular events, and, second, to malignancies at both gastrointestinal (liver, colon, esophagus, stomach, and pancreas) and extra-intestinal site (kidney in men, and breast in women), while end-stage liver disease is the third cause of death [8,9]. NAFLD is traditionally considered the hepatic manifestation of metabolic syndrome (MetS) and an impressive body of evidence indicates an increased general risk of cancer in subjects with MetS, particularly in the gastrointestinal tract. In this setting, NAFLD can either share common risk factors (*i.e.*, obesity and type 2 diabetes) or actively mediate some pathogenic mechanism, as in the case of liver cancer (hepatocellular carcinoma, HCC). Excluding the latter one, colorectal cancer (CRC) has been consistently associated with NAFLD thus far [10,11]. The mechanisms underlying the link between NAFLD and risk of neoplasms are not fully elucidated but they probably stem from the bidirectional relationship between NAFLD and MetS [12–14]. In this review we critically appraise the key studies on the association between NAFLD and extra-hepatic cancers and speculate on how NAFLD may influence carcinogenesis at these sites.

2. Nonalcoholic Fatty Liver Disease (NAFLD) and Colorectal Cancer

The association between NAFLD and CRC is the best investigated in literature (details are summarized in Table 1). Almost all of the studies showed a higher prevalence of colorectal lesions in patients with NAFLD compared to patients without. Hwang and colleagues presented the first evidence for an association of NAFLD with an increased rate of colorectal adenomatous polyps [15]. In their study, a population of 2917 participants was investigated via colonoscopy, abdominal ultrasonography, and liver tests. The prevalence of NAFLD was 41.5% in the adenomatous polyp group *versus* 30.2% in the control group; with multivariate analysis, NAFLD was associated with a three-fold increased risk of colorectal adenomas. This preliminary finding was confirmed in a large retrospective cohort study of 5.517 Korean women, where a two-fold increase in the occurrence of adenomatous polyps and a three-fold increase in the risk of colorectal cancer was found in patients with NAFLD compared to controls. However, the presence of NAFLD had no influence on the prognosis of colorectal cancer and, in particular, on the disease recurrence during follow-up [16]. Among NAFLD patients, those with histological diagnosis of NASH harbinger the most increased risk for CRC. In a cross-sectional study patients with NAFLD, diagnosed by both proton magnetic resonance spectroscopy and liver biopsy, had a significantly higher rate of colorectal adenomas (34.7% *vs.* 21.5%) and advanced neoplasms (18.6% *vs.* 5.5%) than healthy controls [17]. Almost half of NAFLD patients with advanced neoplasm had right-sided colorectal carcinoma. Importantly, CRC was more often found in patients with NASH compared to those with simple steatosis (51.0% *vs.* 25.6% and 34.7% *vs.* 14.0%). NASH remained associated with a higher risk of both adenomas (Odds Ratio (OR) 4.89) and advanced neoplasms (OR 5.34) even after adjusting for demographic and metabolic risk factor, thus, the authors concluded that screening colonoscopy should be strongly recommended in these patients [17]. In the largest study performed so far in Europe, male patients with NAFLD had significantly more colorectal adenomas and early colorectal cancers compared to those without NAFLD [18]. Multivariate regression analysis confirmed an independent association of colorectal adenomas with NAFLD (OR 1.47) [17]. Data stemming from cross-sectional studies have also been replicated longitudinally. In a prospective study where 1522 subjects underwent paired colonoscopies, while the index colonoscopy was negative in all of them, the incidence of *de novo* adenoma development was increased by 45% in those with NAFLD [19]. Lastly, a Danish cohort study evaluating the global risk of cancer in hospitalized patient showed an increased risk of CRC in those with fatty liver compared to the general population, but no difference was noticed between alcoholic and non-alcoholic fatty liver [20].

In contrast, only two studies failed to demonstrate an increased incidence of colorectal adenomas in patients with NAFLD compared to healthy controls [21,22]. The first one found a higher burden of adenomas in patients with NAFLD, but data did not reach a statistical significance, probably for the smaller sample size and the younger median age. The second one remarkably showed a lower prevalence of CRC in NAFLD patients but a higher risk for CRC in the presence of insulin resistance; however it is well known that both raised alanine aminotransferase (ALT) levels and ultrasound can underestimate the diagnosis of NAFLD.

Overall, it appears that NAFLD patients are more likely to have multiple polyps [23], more often localized more in the right and transverse segments of colon [17,23]; importantly, patients with histologic diagnosis of NASH are at higher risk for adenomatous polyps with high grade dysplasia (HGD) compared to those with simple fatty liver [17]. The relationship between NAFLD and CRC once again emphasizes the importance of a healthy lifestyle to prevent and treat the MetS and its systemic manifestations. Certainly these data suggest that NAFLD patients should undergo a closer surveillance for CRC risk according to screening guidelines [24]. If the evidence of this association will be further confirmed in larger population studies, probably these patients should be screened in advance and total colonoscopy considered as the preferred screening method, as neoplasms are more commonly found in the proximal colon [19,24].

Table 1. Principal studies on the association between nonalcoholic fatty liver disease (NAFLD) and colorectal neoplasms *.

Study	Country	Type of Study	Population Enrolled	Exclusion Criteria	NAFLD Diagnosis	Prevalence of Colorectal Lesions in Patients with NAFLD vs. Patients without NAFLD
Bhatt BD et al. [33] (2015)	USA	Retrospective	591 pts who completed LT evaluation (68 NAFLD vs. 523 non-NAFLD)	<50 years old at LT; IBD; history of multiple/recurrent adenomas; family history of CRC; known cancer-predisposing gene alteration; history of solid organ transplant; HIV pts; personal history of cancer	Biopsy + clinical criteria	Polyps prevalence: 59% vs. 40%; $p < 0.003$. OR (Odds Ratio) 2.16; $p = 0.003$. Adenomatous polyps prevalence: 32% vs. 21%; $p = 0.04$. OR 1.95, $p = 0.02$
Basyigit S et al. [32] (2015)	Turkey	Prospective observational	127 consecutive pts who underwent colonoscopy	Other causes of hepatic disease; incomplete colonoscopy; IBD; active gastrointestinal bleeding; history of colorectal surgery; history of CRC; hereditary cancer syndrome	US	Adenomas prevalence: 20% vs. 25.8%; OR 1. CRC prevalence: 4.6% vs. 24.2%; OR 1
Lin XF et al. [34] (2014)	China	Retrospective and consecutive cohort study	2315 community subjects who underwent a routine colonoscopy (263 NAFLD vs. 2052 non-NAFLD)	History of CRC, adenoma and polyp; history of other extraintestinal malignancies; contraindications to colonoscopy	US	Total colorectal lesions prevalence: 90.0% vs. 93.3%. Adenomatous polyps prevalence: 44.5% vs. 55.7%. CRC prevalence: 29.3% vs. 18%; $p = 0.001$. OR 1.868; 95% CI 1.360–2.567; $p < 0.05$
Wong VW-S et al. [17] (2012)	China	Cross-sectional	380 community pts + consecutive pts with biopsy proven NAFLD (in total 199 NAFLD vs. 181-non-NAFLD)	Other causes of hepatic disease; history of CRC or polyps; IBD; bowel symptoms including per rectal bleeding and altered bowel habit; prior CRC screening; contraindications to colonoscopy	Proton-magnetic resonance spectroscopy or liver biopsy	Total polyps prevalence: 52.8% vs. 38.7%; $p = 0.057$. Adenomatous polyps prevalence: 34.7% vs. 21.5%; $p = 0.043$. OR 1.61; 95% CI 0.9–2.9, $p = 0.11$. Villous polyps prevalence: 6% vs. 0.6%; $p = 0.042$. High grade dysplasia polyps prevalence: 18.1% vs. 3%; $p = 0.002$. Advance neoplasm prevalence: 18.6% vs. 5.5%; $p = 0.005$. OR 3.04; 95% CI 1.29–7.2; $p = 0.011$. CRC 1% vs. 0.6%; $p = 0.65$
Stadlmayr A et al. [18] (2011)	Austria	Cross-sectional	1211 consecutive pts who underwent screening colonoscopy (632 NAFLD vs. 597 non-NAFLD)	Incomplete colonoscopy; recent colorectal polypectomy, asymptomatic IBD; extraintestinal malignancies	US + exclusion of other causes of hepatic disease	Total colorectal lesions prevalence: 34% vs. 21.7%; $p < 0.001$. Tubular adenoma prevalence in men: 34.6% vs. 23.7%; $p = 0.006$. Rectum adenoma prevalence in men: 11% vs. 3%; $p = 0.004$. CRC prevalence in men: 1.6% vs. 0.4%; $p < 0.001$
Lee YI et al. [16] (2011)	South Korea	Retrospective cohort study	5517 women who underwent life insurance company health examinations (831 NAFLD vs. 4686 non-NAFLD)	Other causes of hepatic disease; history of receiving previous medical insurance benefits	US + exclusion of other causes of hepatic disease	Adenomatous polyps incidence: 628 vs. 185.2/10^5 person year. RR 1.94; 95% CI 1.11–3.40. CRC incidence: 233.6 vs. 27/10^5 person year. RR 3.08; 95% CI 1.02–9.34
Touzin NT et al. [21] (2011)	USA	Retrospective cohort study	233 patients who underwent screening colonoscopies (94 NAFLD vs. 139 non-NAFLD)	Not available	US + liver biopsy	Adenoma prevalence: 24.4% vs. 25.1%; $p = 1$
Huang KW et al. [19] (2012)	Taiwan	Retrospective cohort study	1522 pts with two consecutive colonoscopies (216 with colorectal adenoma vs. 1306 without colorectal adenoma after negative baseline colonoscopy)	History of colorectal adenoma or CRC; adenomas during baseline colonoscopy; incomplete medical record data; alcohol consumption >20 g/day	US + exclusion of other causes of hepatic disease	NAFLD prevalence: 55.6% vs. 38.8%; $p < 0.05$. OR = 1.45; 95% CI 1.07–1.98; $p = 0.016$
Hwang ST et al. [15] (2009)	South Korea	Cross-sectional	2917 pts who underwent routine colonoscopy (556 with polyps vs. 2361 without polyps)	Incomplete colonoscopies; history of polypectomy; IBD; history of cancer; cancer detected during the study; pts with anticoagulant therapy; other causes of hepatic disease	US	NAFLD prevalence: 41.5% vs. 30.2%; $p < 0.001$. OR, 1.30; 95% CI 1.02–1.66; $p = 0.034$

* CI, confidence interval; CRC, colorectal cancer; IBD, intestinal bowel disease; LT, liver transplant; NAFLD, non-alcoholic fatty liver disease; OR, odds ratio; pts, patients; RR, relative risk; US, ultrasound.

3. NAFLD and Cancers in Other Sites

The association of NAFLD with other extra-hepatic cancers is less proven. In the previously-mentioned Danish study all-cancers risk was increased by 70% in subjects with fatty liver, either alcoholic or non-alcoholic [20]; however, those with NAFLD had a higher risk of pancreatic and kidney cancer (standardized incidence ratio (SIR) 3; 95% confidence interval (CI) 1.3–5.8 and SIR 2.7; 95% CI 1.1–5.6, respectively), malignant melanoma (SIR 2.4; 95% CI 0.8–5.6) and cancer metastases from primary unspecified sites (SIR 6.3; 95% CI 1.3–18.4), while those with alcoholic fatty liver had a higher risk for lung and breast cancer (SIR 2.2; 95% CI 1.7–2.8 and SIR 1.5; 95% CI 0.9–2.2, respectively). The latter observation contrasts with another study where a higher prevalence of breast cancers was observed in patients with ultrasound diagnosed NAFLD compared with healthy controls (63% *vs.* 48%, respectively) [26]. The burden of data available is currently too limited to draw definite conclusions about a specific role of NAFLD, as the link can be mediated by visceral obesity, which in turn is strongly associated to fatty liver in the so-called "central-axis" of obesity. A recent review summarized the well-recognized role of visceral obesity in the onset and development of various cancers [27], including CRC [28–31], esophageal [32–38] and pancreatic cancer [39], breast [40], thyroid [41], and probably prostate cancer [42]. What is currently unknown is whether both NAFLD and visceral obesity are just markers of an increased risk of cancers or also active players in this process. With this caveat in mind, we will briefly examine the association between NAFLD, visceral obesity, and cancers other than CRC.

3.1. Esophageal and Gastric Cancer

Esophageal cancer is the eighth most common form of cancer worldwide, and the World Cancer Research Fund has identified obesity as a major risk factor, able to increase the risk up to four-fold compared with lean populations [43]. Several more recent studies suggest a stronger impact of visceral fat distribution rather than body mass index (BMI) *per se* [37,44,45], but no study specifically examined hepatic fat. Strikingly, the association between visceral obesity and esophageal adenocarcinoma is independent of gastro-oesophageal reflux disease (GORD), and possibly mediated by adipose tissue insulin resistance and chronic inflammation [32,46,47]. A possible direct link between NAFLD and gastric cancer has been suggested in a recent study, performed on 1840 patients undergoing upper endoscopies over a six-month time frame; despite the limited number of gastric cancer diagnosed, the prevalence of NAFLD in subjects with gastric cancers was higher compared to the average in the Turkish population [48].

3.2. Pancreatic Cancer

In 2007 the World Cancer Research Fund/American Institute for Cancer Research (WCRF) definitively established the association between pancreatic cancer and overweight/obesity. A meta-analysis published in 2012 showed a linear increase between pancreatic cancer risk and waist circumference, with a relative risk (RR) of 1.11 (95% CI 1.05–1.18) for every 10 cm increase, and waist-to-hip ratio, with a RR of 1.19 (95% CI 1.09–1.31) for every 0.1 unit increment [39]. In a meta-analysis performed in 2012, MetS has been identified itself as a neoplastic risk factor, with a RR of 1.58 ($p < 0.0001$) for pancreatic cancer in female gender, possibly mediated by decreased physical activity, consumption of high-calorie dense foods, high dietary fat intake, low fiber intake, and oxidative stress [49]. As for esophageal cancer, NAFLD can be implicated in this association, although no direct evidence is yet available.

3.3. Renal Cancer

In addition to smoking and dietary habits, whose association with renal cancer is well established, some of the components of MetS, such as obesity and hypertension, have been recognized etiological factors and listed in specialist guidelines [50,51]. In a large study of seven European cohorts, high level of a metabolic risk score, based on the combination of BMI, blood pressure, and plasma levels of glucose, total cholesterol and triglycerides, was linearly and positively associated to higher incidence of renal cell cancer (risk increase per standard deviation of metabolic risk score increment: 43% in men and 40% in women) [52]. In patients with cT1a renal cell carcinoma visceral fat, assessed by computed tomography (CT) scan, is strongly associated with Fuhrman grade, the most frequently used neoplastic nuclear grading system for kidney, and is an independent predictor of high-grade renal cell carcinoma (RCC) [53]. In a study performed on 118 consecutive patients undergoing surgical treatment for RCC, adiponectin levels are inversely proportional to the severity of disease, with the lower levels in patients with metastatic cancer [54].

3.4. Breast Cancer

The association between breast cancer risk in postmenopausal women and components of MetS has been provided by several large studies [49,55–57]. In combined analyses of two case-control study on 3869 postmenopausal women with breast cancer and 4082 postmenopausal control cases, authors registered a higher neoplastic risk in women with MetS than those without (OR 1.75; 95% CI 1.37–2.22). In the analysis of distribution of cases and controls according to individual components of the syndrome, the resulting corresponding odds ratios were 1.33 (95% CI 1.09–1.62) for diabetes, 1.19 (95% CI 1.07–1.33) for hypertension, 1.08 (95% CI 0.95–1.22) for hyperlipidemia, 1.26 (95% CI 1.11–1.44) for BMI $\geqslant$ 30 kg/m^2, and 1.22 (95% CI 1.09–1.36) for waist circumference $\geqslant$88 cm [56]. In a study on 2092 patients, surgically treated for stage I–III invasive breast cancer in the previous five years and followed-up over 2.8 years on average, MetS appeared a major determinant of the occurrence of additional related events, such as specific mortality, presence of distant metastasis, or local recurrences and incidence of contralateral breast cancer [58]. Although each component was associated with an increased risk of cancer recurrence, the risk associated with the full syndrome was the highest, likely to be the expression of a general dysmetabolic condition rather than of a specific trait.

3.5. Prostate Cancer

The link between dysmetabolic factors, NAFLD and prostate cancer is controversial. In a systematic review and meta-regression analysis, including 31 cohort and 25 case-control, for every five kg/m^2 increment in BMI, authors described a 1.05 relative risk (95% CI 1.01–1.08), higher in patients with progressed diseases than localized diseases [59]. Two studies specifically investigated the role of NALFD. In the first one, NAFLD was found to be protective against neoplastic recurrence after radical prostatectomy for prostate cancer in 293 consecutive patients [60]. The NAFLD group showed significantly longer time-to-recurrence compared with patients without NAFLD both in the training and validation set (hazard ratio: 0.33 and 0.22; 95% CI 0.16–0.69, and 95% CI 0.11–0.43, respectively). The second one analyzed the development of malignancies and the specific site of disease in 1600 US-defined NAFLD subjects and in 1600 matched hepatitis C virus (HCV)-infected patients: prostate cancer developed in 12.6% of NAFLD compared to 3.5% in HCV patients [61], and the incidence of prostate cancer in NAFLD was higher than in the general population.

4. Putative Role of Insulin Resistance and Gut Microbiota in the Development of Extra-Hepatic Cancers in NAFLD

Although the most extensive evidence of a possible mechanistic link between NAFLD and extra-hepatic carcinogenesis currently comes from data on the pro-inflammatory and pro-carcinogenic effects of insulin resistance (IR), gut microbiota has been recently identified as a novel and intriguing player in the development of obesity, NAFLD and several types of cancer (details are summarized in Table 2). Patients with NAFLD are characterized by dysbiosis [62] and the liver stays at the cross-road of the complex interaction between changes in microbiota composition, IR, inflammation, and carcinogenesis [63,64]. Dysbiosis has been found in patients with colon cancer [65] and the possible correlation has been widely studied. Quantitative and qualitative alterations of gut microbiota lead to increased intestinal permeability through several mechanisms, including the regulation of tight junctions, such as zonulin-1, and occluding by toll like receptor 2 (TLR2) in the ileum. These alterations favor the translocation of bacterial metabolites and activation of TLRs via the recognition of microorganism-associated molecular patterns (MAMPs) and can promote tumorigenesis through the reduced release of the inflammasome-derived interleukin 18 (IL-18) and the increased IL-6 signaling which, in turn, protects normal and premalignant cells from apoptosis [11,66,67].

Table 2. Putative mechanisms linking NAFLD and extra-hepatic cancers.

Mechanism	Effects	Extra-Hepatic Site
Insulin resistance		
↑ IGF-1 axis	Proliferative and anti-apoptotic effects	Prostate/colorectal/lung/Breast cancers, Barrett's esophagus, esophageal adenocarcinoma
Dysfunctional adipose tissue		
↓ adiponectin/caspase activation ↓ adiponectin/TNF-α ↑ leptin/MAPK ↑ resistin/NF-κB	Anti-apoptotic effects Proliferation and angiogenesis Invasiveness, motility, lamellipodia formation	Gastrointestinal and extra-intestinal cancer Gastrointestinal and extra-intestinal cancer Colon/breast cancer, Barrett's esophagus, esophageal adenocarcinoma Breast/gastrointestinal and non-small cell lung cancers
Inflammation		
IL-6/JAK/STAT3 and IL-6/MAPK TNF-α/Wnt/β-catenin	Proliferation Angiogenesis, differentiation and metastasis development	Renal/gastric/colorectal cancers Colorectal cancer
Gut microbiota		
MAMPs/TLRs Inflammasome-derived IL-18	Inflammation Anti-apoptotic effects	Colon cancer Colon cancer

IGF-1, insulin growth factor-1; IL, interleukin; MAMPs, microorganism-associated molecular patterns; MAPK, mitogen-activated protein kinase; NF-κB, nuclear factor-κ B; STAT3, signal transducer and activator of transcription 3; TLRs, toll-like receptors; TNF-α, tumor necrosis factor-α.

It is well known that host diet significantly impacts on gut microbial composition. Diet-induced NAFLD may be mediated by the myeloid differentiation factor 88 (MyD88)-dependent pathway [68]. This factor is an adaptor molecule, essential for the signaling through TLRs. It is recruited after the interaction among the microorganism-associated molecular patterns (MAMPs) and TLRs (particularly TLR4) and promotes the transcription of several pro-inflammatory cytokines through the activation of NF-κB or c-Jun NH$_2$-terminal kinase (JNK) leading to the induction of IR. Loss-of-function mutation or knockout mice in TLR4 prevents IR induced by obesity underlying the important role of this receptor in the modulation of the innate immune system.

NAFLD and visceral adipose tissue are the main components of the axis of central obesity. In this setting, low-grade chronic inflammation and insulin resistance (IR) create a microenvironment suitable for cancer development through the stimulation of the insulin growth factor-1 (IGF-1) axis by hyperinsulinemia [9,69–71]. Through its proliferative and anti-apoptotic effects, this pathway can boost mutations favoring carcinogenesis [72,73]. Elevated serum levels of IGF-1 have been associated with prostate [74,75], colorectal [76], lung [77], and breast cancer [78]. Importantly, the insulin/IGF system is able to influence the risk of Barrett's esophagus and of esophageal adenocarcinoma [37,79,80], although there is no full agreement about this [81].

Several adipokines, involved in the modulation of metabolism, inflammation and fibrogenesis, can also be involved in carcinogenic processes. Adiponectin has anti-carcinogenic effects mediated by its ability to stop colon cancer cell growth through the AMPc-activated protein kinase (AMPK) and to induce a caspase-dependent pathway resulting in endothelial cell apoptosis. Adiponectin can also directly inhibit tumor necrosis factor α (TNF-α), involved in tumor cell proliferation and angiogenesis. Since NAFLD patients have reduced serum levels of adiponectin, the above described mechanisms represent an interesting link between NAFLD and cancer development at both gastrointestinal and extra-intestinal site.

The pro-carcinogenic effects of leptin, especially in the presence of low adiponectin levels, have been widely investigated. In obese animal models, leptin acts as a growth factor for CRC at early stages through the activation of signal transducer and activator of transcription 3 (STAT 3) pathway [82]. In human colon cancer cells leptin is able to promote motility and invasiveness by activation of mitogen-activated protein kinase (MAPK) pathway [83]. A case-cohort study in post-menopausal women with CRC demonstrated that high plasma concentrations of leptin were associated with an increased risk for CRC [84]. In obese subjects the combination of high leptin and low adiponectin levels may also increase the risk of Barrett's esophagus [85–90] and esophageal adenocarcinoma by enhanced cell proliferation and reduced apoptosis via extracellular signal-regulated kinase (ERK), p38 MAPK, phosphatidylinositol 3′-kinase/Akt, and Janus kinase-2 (JAK2)-dependent activation of cyclooxygenase-2 (COX-2) and prostaglandin E2 (PGE2). The association between leptin serum levels and the size of breast tumors has been summarized in a recent review [91]; higher leptin levels are related to a more aggressive disease, presence of metastasis and a lower survival rate [92] mostly in obese patients [93].

Finally, resistin can also be linked to obesity-related malignancies via activation of nuclear factor-κ B (NF-κB) pathway and amplification of the procarcinogenic effects of interleukin (IL)-1, IL-6 and TNF-α [94]. To date, a putative role of resistin has been suggested in breast cancer [94], non-small cell lung cancer [95] and in gastrointestinal tumors [96].

The low-grade chronic inflammation associated with IR also favors macrophages recruitment and massive release of several proinflammatory cytokines, such as IL-6 and TNF-α, into the systemic circulation. IL-6 induces the Janus kinase/signal transducer and activator of transcription (JAK/STAT) and MAPK pathways, stimulating cell proliferation and tumor progression, while TNF-α influences cancer angiogenesis, metastasis development and cell survival, growth, and differentiation [97–99]. Animal models have shown a relationship between TNF-α and several malignancies [100–102] including colorectal cancer [103]. Obese mice have higher TNF-α levels in the colonic mucosa, leading to β-catenin stabilization and increased transcription of the downstream Wnt pathway gene c-Myc [104]. IL-6 has been linked to renal cell carcinoma [105], gastric cancer [106], and colorectal cancer [107,108], through its modulation of several genes involved in proliferation, survival, and angiogenesis [109].

In consideration of the above described mechanisms, the increased risk of gastrointestinal cancers associated to NAFLD does not appear causal, although more extensive studies are required to demonstrate a direct link between NAFLD and cancers at various sites.

5. Conclusions

NAFLD is a complex multifactorial disease closely interrelated with obesity and type 2 diabetes, and shares with them a significant increased risk of several types of cancer. Beyond the risk of HCC, clearly mediated by NASH, substantial evidence is accumulating for a role of NAFLD as independent risk factor for cancers, particularly in the gastrointestinal tract. Once again, these preliminary, but intriguing, data convey that NAFLD patients require a multidisciplinary evaluation with a particular attention to the development of extra-hepatic complications. Further studies are necessary to better define high-risk NAFLD patients and effective screening strategies, but we encourage health care providers taking care of NAFLD patients to be vigilant for any signs and symptoms of cancer, particularly colorectal, and refer the patients for further assessment and management.

Conflicts of Interest: The authors declare no conflict of interest.

Abbreviations

AMPK	AMPc-activated protein kinase
CI	confidence interval
COX-2	cyclooxygenase 2
CRC	colorectal cancer
ERK	extracellular signal-regulated kinase
HCC	hepatocellular carcinoma
HGD	high grade dysplasia
IBD	inflammatory bowel disease
IGF	insulin growth factors
IL	interleukin
IR	insulin resistance
LT	liver transplant
MAMPs	microorganism-associated molecular patterns
MAPK	mitogen-activated protein kinase
MetS	metabolic syndrome
mTOR	mammalian target of rapamycin
NAFL	non-alcoholic fatty liver
NAFLD	non-alcoholic fatty liver disease
NASH	non-alcoholic steatohepatitis
NF-kB	nuclear factor-κ B
OR	odds ratio
PGE2	Prostaglandin E2
RR	relative risk
SIR	standardized incidence ratio
STAT3	signal transducer and activator of transcription
TNF-α	tumor necrosis factor α
US	ultrasound
JAK2	Janus kinase-2

References

1. Armstrong, M.J.; Houlihan, D.D.; Bentham, L.; Shaw, J.C.; Cramb, R.; Olliff, S.; Gill, P.S.; Neuberger, J.M.; Lilford, R.J.; Newsome, P.N. Presence and severity of non-alcoholic fatty liver disease in a large prospective primary care cohort. *J. Hepatol.* **2012**, *56*, 234–240. [CrossRef] [PubMed]
2. Younossi, Z.M.; Koenig, A.B.; Abdelatif, D.; Fazel, Y.; Henry, L.; Wymer, M. Global epidemiology of non-alcoholic fatty liver disease-meta-analytic assessment of prevalence, incidence and outcomes. *Hepatology* **2015**. [CrossRef] [PubMed]
3. Abd El-Kader, S.M.; El-Den Ashmawy, E.M.S. Non-alcoholic fatty liver disease: The diagnosis and management. *World J. Hepatol.* **2015**, *7*, 846–858. [CrossRef] [PubMed]
4. Musso, G.; Gambino, R.; Cassader, M.; Pagano, G. Meta-analysis: Natural history of non-alcoholic fatty liver disease (NAFLD) and diagnostic accuracy of non-invasive tests for liver disease severity. *Ann. Med.* **2011**, *43*, 617–649. [CrossRef] [PubMed]
5. Adams, L.A.; Lymp, J.F.; St Sauver, J.; Sanderson, S.O.; Lindor, K.D.; Feldstein, A.; Angulo, P. The natural history of nonalcoholic fatty liver disease: A population-based cohort study. *Gastroenterology* **2005**, *129*, 113–121. [CrossRef] [PubMed]
6. Ekstedt, M.; Franzén, L.E.; Mathiesen, U.L.; Thorelius, L.; Holmqvist, M.; Bodemar, G.; Kechagias, S. Long-term follow-up of patients with NAFLD and elevated liver enzymes. *Hepatology* **2006**, *44*, 865–873. [CrossRef] [PubMed]
7. Rafiq, N.; Bai, C.; Fang, Y.; Srishord, M.; McCullough, A.; Gramlich, T.; Younossi, Z.M. Long-term follow-up of patients with nonalcoholic fatty liver. *Clin. Gastroenterol. Hepatol.* **2009**, *7*, 234–238. [CrossRef] [PubMed]
8. Angulo, P. Long-term mortality in nonalcoholic fatty liver disease: Is liver histology of any prognostic significance? *Hepatology* **2010**, *51*, 373–375. [CrossRef] [PubMed]

9. Tilg, H.; Moschen, A.R. Mechanisms behind the link between obesity and gastrointestinal cancers. *Best Pract. Res. Clin. Gastroenterol.* **2014**, *28*, 599–610. [CrossRef] [PubMed]

10. Tilg, H.; Diehl, A.M. NAFLD and extrahepatic cancers: Have a look at the colon. *Gut* **2011**, *60*, 745–746. [CrossRef] [PubMed]

11. Vanni, E.; Marengo, A.; Mezzabotta, L.; Bugianesi, E. Systemic complications of nonalcoholic fatty liver disease: When the liver is not an innocent bystander. *Semin. Liver Dis.* **2015**, *35*, 236–249. [CrossRef] [PubMed]

12. Bugianesi, E.; McCullough, A.J.; Marchesini, G. Insulin resistance: A metabolic pathway to chronic liver disease. *Hepatology* **2005**, *42*, 987–1000. [CrossRef] [PubMed]

13. Perseghin, G. Viewpoints on the way to a consensus session: Where does insulin resistance start? The liver. *Diabetes Care* **2009**, *32*, S164–S167. [CrossRef] [PubMed]

14. Scalera, A.; Tarantino, G. Could metabolic syndrome lead to hepatocarcinoma via non-alcoholic fatty liver disease? *World J. Gastroenterol.* **2014**, *20*, 9217–9228. [PubMed]

15. Hwang, S.T.; Cho, Y.K.; Park, J.H.; Kim, H.J.; Park, D.I.; Sohn, C.I.; Jeon, W.K.; Kim, B.I.; Won, K.H.; Jin, W. Relationship of non-alcoholic fatty liver disease to colorectal adenomatous polyps. *J. Gastroenterol. Hepatol.* **2010**, *25*, 562–567. [CrossRef] [PubMed]

16. Lee, Y.I.; Lim, Y.-S.; Park, H.S. Colorectal neoplasms in relation to non-alcoholic fatty liver disease in Korean women: A retrospective cohort study. *J. Gastroenterol. Hepatol.* **2012**, *27*, 91–95. [CrossRef] [PubMed]

17. Wong, V.W.-S.; Wong, G.L.-H.; Tsang, S.W.-C.; Fan, T.; Chu, W.C.; Woo, J.; Chan, A.W.; Choi, P.C.; Chim, A.M.; Lau, J.Y.; et al. High prevalence of colorectal neoplasm in patients with non-alcoholic steatohepatitis. *Gut* **2011**, *60*, 829–836. [CrossRef] [PubMed]

18. Stadlmayr, A.; Aigner, E.; Steger, B.; Scharinger, L.; Lederer, D.; Mayr, A.; Strasser, M.; Brunner, E.; Heuberger, A.; Hohla, F.; et al. Nonalcoholic fatty liver disease: An independent risk factor for colorectal neoplasia. *J. Intern. Med.* **2011**, *270*, 41–49.

19. Huang, K.-W.; Leu, H.-B.; Wang, Y.-J.; Luo, J.C.; Lin, H.C.; Lee, F.Y.; Chan, W.L.; Lin, J.K.; Chang, F.Y. Patients with nonalcoholic fatty liver disease have higher risk of colorectal adenoma after negative baseline colonoscopy. *Colorectal. Dis.* **2013**, *15*, 830–835. [CrossRef] [PubMed]

20. Sørensen, H.T.; Mellemkjaer, L.; Jepsen, P.; Thulstrup, A.M.; Baron, J.; Olsen, J.H.; Vilstrup, H. Risk of cancer in patients hospitalized with fatty liver: A Danish cohort study. *J. Clin. Gastroenterol.* **2003**, *36*, 356–359.

21. Touzin, N.T.; Bush, K.N.V.; Williams, C.D.; Harrison, S.A. Prevalence of colonic adenomas in patients with nonalcoholic fatty liver disease. *Ther. Adv. Gastroenterol.* **2011**, *4*, 169–176. [CrossRef]

22. Basyigit, S.; Uzman, M.; Kefeli, A.; Sapmaz, F.P.; Yeniova, A.O.; Nazligul, Y.; Asiltürk, Z. Absence of non-alcoholic fatty liver disease in the presence of insulin resistance is a strong predictor for colorectal carcinoma. *Int. J. Clin. Exp. Med.* **2015**, *8*, 18601–18610. [PubMed]

23. Bhatt, B.D.; Lukose, T.; Siegel, A.B.; Brown, R.S.; Verna, E.C. Increased risk of colorectal polyps in patients with non-alcoholic fatty liver disease undergoing liver transplant evaluation. *J. Gastrointest. Oncol.* **2015**, *6*, 459–468. [PubMed]

24. Wong, M.C.S.; Ching, J.Y.L.; Chan, V.C.W.; Lam, T.Y.; Luk, A.K.; Wong, S.H.; Ng, S.C.; Wong, V.W.; Ng, S.S.; Wu, J.C.; et al. Screening strategies for colorectal cancer among patients with nonalcoholic fatty liver disease and family history. *Int. J. Cancer* **2015**. [CrossRef]

25. Lin, X.F.; Shi, K.Q.; You, J.; Liu, W.Y.; Luo, Y.W.; Wu, F.L.; Chen, Y.P.; Wong, D.K.; Yuen, M.F.; Zheng, M.H. Increased risk of colorectal malignant neoplasm in patients with nonalcoholic fatty liver disease: A large study. *Mol. Biol. Rep.* **2014**, *41*, 2989–2997. [PubMed]

26. Bilici, A.; Ozguroglu, M.; Mihmanlı, İ.; Turna, H.; Adaletli, İ. A case—Control study of non-alcoholic fatty liver disease in breast cancer. *Med. Oncol.* **2007**, *24*, 367–371. [CrossRef]

27. Vongsuvanh, R.; George, J.; Qiao, L.; van der Poorten, D. Visceral adiposity in gastrointestinal and hepatic carcinogenesis. *Cancer Lett.* **2013**, *330*, 1–10.

28. Moore, L.L.; Bradlee, M.L.; Singer, M.R.; Splansky, G.L.; Proctor, M.H.; Ellison, R.C.; Kreger, B.E. BMI and waist circumference as predictors of lifetime colon cancer risk in Framingham Study adults. *Int. J. Obes. Relat. Metab. Disord.* **2004**, *28*, 559–567.

29. Giovannucci, E.; Ascherio, A.; Rimm, E.B.; Colditz, G.A.; Stampfer, M.J.; Willett, W.C. Physical activity, obesity, and risk for colon cancer and adenoma in men. *Ann. Intern. Med.* **1995**, *122*, 327–334. [CrossRef] [PubMed]

30. Schoen, R.E.; Tangen, C.M.; Kuller, L.H.; Burke, G.L.; Cushman, M.; Tracy, R.P.; Dobs, A.; Savage, P.J. Increased blood glucose and insulin, body size, and incident colorectal cancer. *J. Natl. Cancer Inst.* **1999**, *91*, 1147–1154. [CrossRef] [PubMed]

31. Pischon, T.; Lahmann, P.H.; Boeing, H.; Friedenreich, C.; Norat, T.; Tjønneland, A.; Halkjaer, J.; Overvad, K.; Clavel-Chapelon, F.; Boutron-Ruault, M.C.; *et al.* Body size and risk of colon and rectal cancer in the European Prospective Investigation Into Cancer and Nutrition (EPIC). *J. Natl. Cancer Inst.* **2006**, *98*, 920–931. [CrossRef] [PubMed]

32. Beddy, P.; Howard, J.; McMahon, C.; Knox, M.; de Blacam, C.; Ravi, N.; Reynolds, J.V.; Keogan, M.T. Association of visceral adiposity with oesophageal and junctional adenocarcinomas. *Br. J. Surg.* **2010**, *97*, 1028–1034. [CrossRef] [PubMed]

33. Corley, D.A.; Kubo, A.; Levin, T.R.; Block, G.; Habel, L.; Zhao, W.; Leighton, P.; Quesenberry, C.; Rumore, G.J.; Buffler, P.A. Abdominal obesity and body mass index as risk factors for Barrett's esophagus. *Gastroenterology* **2007**, *133*, 34–41. [CrossRef] [PubMed]

34. Edelstein, Z.R.; Farrow, D.C.; Bronner, M.P.; Rosen, S.N.; Vaughan, T.L. Central adiposity and risk of Barrett's esophagus. *Gastroenterology* **2007**, *133*, 403–411. [CrossRef] [PubMed]

35. El-Serag, H.B.; Kvapil, P.; Hacken-Bitar, J.; Kramer, J.R. Abdominal obesity and the risk of Barrett's esophagus. *Am. J. Gastroenterol.* **2005**, *100*, 2151–2156. [CrossRef] [PubMed]

36. Renehan, A.G.; Tyson, M.; Egger, M.; Heller, R.F.; Zwahlen, M. Body-mass index and incidence of cancer: A systematic review and meta-analysis of prospective observational studies. *Lancet* **2008**, *371*, 569–578. [CrossRef]

37. Singh, S.; Sharma, A.N.; Murad, M.H.; Buttar, N.S.; El-Serag, H.B.; Katzka, D.A.; Iyer, P.G. Central adiposity is associated with increased risk of esophageal inflammation, metaplasia, and adenocarcinoma: A systematic review and meta-analysis. *Clin. Gastroenterol. Hepatol.* **2013**, *11*, 1399–1412. [CrossRef] [PubMed]

38. Steffen, A.; Schulze, M.B.; Pischon, T.; Dietrich, T.; Molina, E.; Chirlaque, M.D.; Barricarte, A.; Amiano, P.; Quirós, J.R.; Tumino, R.; *et al.* Anthropometry and esophageal cancer risk in the European prospective investigation into cancer and nutrition. *Cancer Epidemiol. Biomark. Prev.* **2009**, *18*, 2079–2089. [CrossRef] [PubMed]

39. Aune, D.; Greenwood, D.C.; Chan, D.S.; Vieira, R.; Vieira, A.R.; Navarro Rosenblatt, D.A.; Cade, J.E.; Burley, V.J.; Norat, T. Body mass index, abdominal fatness and pancreatic cancer risk: A systematic review and non-linear dose-response meta-analysis of prospective studies. *Ann. Oncol.* **2012**, *23*, 843–852. [CrossRef] [PubMed]

40. Rose, D.P.; Vona-Davis, L. Biochemical and molecular mechanisms for the association between obesity, chronic inflammation, and breast cancer. *Biofactors* **2013**, *40*, 1–12. [CrossRef] [PubMed]

41. Schmid, D.; Ricci, C.; Behrens, G.; Leitzmann, M.F. Adiposity and risk of thyroid cancer: A systematic review and meta-analysis. *Obes. Rev.* **2015**, *16*, 1042–1054. [CrossRef] [PubMed]

42. McGrowder, D.A.; Jackson, L.A.; Crawford, T.V. Prostate cancer and metabolic syndrome: Is there a link? *Asian Pac. J. Cancer Prev.* **2012**, *13*, 1–13. [CrossRef] [PubMed]

43. Merry, A.; Schouten, L.; Goldbohm, R.; van Den Brandt, P. Body mass index, height and risk of adenocarcinoma of the oesophagus and gastric cardias: A prospective cohort study. *Gut* **2007**, *56*, 1503–1511. [CrossRef] [PubMed]

44. El-Serag, H.; Ergun, G.; Pandolfino, J.; Fitzgerald, S.; Tran, T.; Kramer, J. Obesity increases oesophageal acid exposure. *Gut* **2007**, *56*, 749–755. [CrossRef] [PubMed]

45. Kubo, A.; Cook, M.; Shaheen, N.; Vaughan, T.; Whiteman, D.; Murray, L.; Corley, D.A. Sexspecific associations between body mass index, waist circumference and the risk of Barrett's oesophagus: A pooled analysis from the international BEACON consortium. *Gut* **2013**, *62*, 1684–1691. [CrossRef] [PubMed]

46. El-Serag, H.; Hashmi, A.; Garcia, J.; Richardson, P.; Alsarraj, A.; Fitzgerald, S.; Vela, M.; Shaib, Y.; Abraham, N.S.; Velez, M.; *et al.* Visceral abdominal obesity measured by CT scan is associated with an increased risk of Barrett's oesophagus: A case-control study. *Gut* **2014**, *63*, 220–229. [CrossRef] [PubMed]

47. Garcia, J.; Splenser, A.; Kramer, J.; Alsarraj, A.; Fitzgerald, S.; Ramsey, D.; El-Serag, H.B. Circulating inflammatory cytokines and adipokines are associated with increased risk of Barrett's esophagus: A case-control study. *Clin. Gastroenterol. Hepatol.* **2014**, *12*, 229–238. [CrossRef] [PubMed]

48. Uzel, M.; Sahiner, Z.; Filik, L. Non-alcoholic fatty liver disease, metabolic syndrome and gastric cancer: Single center experience. *J. BUON* **2015**, *20*, 662. [PubMed]

49. Esposito, K.; Chiodini, P.; Colao, A.; Lenzi, A.; Giugliano, D. Metabolic syndrome and risk of cancer. *Diabetes Care* **2012**, *35*, 2402–2411. [CrossRef] [PubMed]

50. Ljungberg, B.; Bensalah, K.; Canfield, S.; Dabestani, S.; Hofmann, F.; Hora, M.; Kuczyk, M.A.; Lam, T.; Marconi, L.; Merseburger, A.S.; *et al.* EAU guidelines on renal cell carcinoma: 2014 update. *Eur. Urol.* **2015**, *67*, 913–924. [CrossRef] [PubMed]

51. Escudier, B.; Porta, C.; Schmidinger, M.; Algaba, F.; Patard, J.J.; Khoo, V.; Eisen, T.; Horwich, A. Renal cell carcinoma: ESMO clinical practice guidelines. *Ann. Oncol.* **2014**, *25*, iii49–iii56. [CrossRef] [PubMed]

52. Stocks, T.; Bjørge, T.; Ulmer, H.; Manjer, J.; Häggström, C.; Nagel, G.; Engeland, A.; Johansen, D.; Hallmans, G.; Selmer, R.; *et al.* Metabolic risk score and cancer risk: Pooled analysis of seven cohorts. *Int. J. Epidemiol.* **2015**, *44*, 1353–1363. [CrossRef] [PubMed]

53. Zhu, Y.; Wang, H.K.; Zhang, H.L.; Yao, X.D.; Zhang, S.L.; Dai, B.; Shen, Y.J.; Liu, X.H.; Zhou, L.P.; Ye, D.W. Visceral obesity and risk of high grade disease in clinical T1A renal cell carcinoma. *J. Urol.* **2013**, *189*, 447–453. [CrossRef] [PubMed]

54. Horiguchi, A.; Ito, K.; Sumitomo, M.; Kimura, F.; Asano, T.; Hayakawa, M. Decreased serum adiponectin levels in patients with metastatic renal cell carcinoma. *Jpn. J. Clin. Oncol.* **2008**, *38*, 106–111. [CrossRef] [PubMed]

55. Lawlor, D.A.; Smith, G.D.; Ebrahim, S. Hyperinsulinaemia and increased risk of breast cancer: Findings from the British Women's Heart and Health Study. *Cancer Causes Control* **2004**, *15*, 267–275. [CrossRef] [PubMed]

56. Rosato, V.; Bosetti, C.; Talamini, R.; Levi, F.; Montella, M.; Giacosa, A.; Negri, E.; La Vecchia, C. Metabolic syndrome and the risk of breast cancer in postmenopausal women. *Ann. Oncol.* **2011**, *22*, 2687–2692. [CrossRef] [PubMed]

57. Agnoli, C.; Berrino, F.; Abagnato, C.A.; Muti, P.; Panico, S.; Crosignani, P.; Krogh, V. Metabolic syndrome and postmenopausal breast cancer in the ORDET cohort: A nested case-control study. *Nutr. Metab. Cardiovasc. Dis.* **2010**, *20*, 41–48. [CrossRef] [PubMed]

58. Berrino, F.; Villarini, A.; Traina, A.; Bonanni, B.; Panico, S.; Mano, M.P.; Mercandino, A.; Galasso, R.; Barbero, M.; Simeoni, M.; *et al.* Metabolic syndrome and breast cancer prognosis. *Breast Cancer Res. Treat.* **2014**, *147*, 159–165. [CrossRef] [PubMed]

59. MacInnis, R.J.; English, D.R. Body size and composition and prostate cancer risk: Systematic review and meta-regression analysis. *Cancer Causes Control* **2006**, *17*, 989–1003. [CrossRef] [PubMed]

60. Choi, W.M.; Lee, J.H.; Yoon, J.H.; Kwak, C.; Lee, Y.J.; Cho, Y.Y.; Lee, Y.B.; Yu, S.J.; Kim, Y.J.; Kim, H.H.; *et al.* Nonalcoholic fatty liver disease is a negative risk factor for prostate cancer recurrence. *Endocr. Relat. Cancer* **2014**, *21*, 343–353. [CrossRef] [PubMed]

61. Arase, Y.; Kobayashi, M.; Suzuki, F.; Suzuki, Y.; Kawamura, Y.; Akuta, N.; Imai, N.; Kobayashi, M.; Sezaki, H.; Matsumoto, N.; *et al.* Difference in malignancies of chronic liver disease due to non-alcoholic fatty liver disease or hepatitis C in Japanese elderly patients. *Hepatol. Res.* **2012**, *42*, 264–272. [CrossRef] [PubMed]

62. Wigg, A.J.; Roberts-Thomson, I.C.; Dymock, R.B.; McCarthy, P.J.; Grose, R.H.; Cummins, A.G. The role of small intestinal bacterial overgrowth, intestinal permeability, endotoxaemia, and tumour necrosis factor α in the pathogenesis of non-alcoholic steatohepatitis. *Gut* **2001**, *48*, 206–211. [CrossRef] [PubMed]

63. Ohtani, N.; Yoshimoto, S.; Hara, E. Obesity and cancer: A gut microbial connection. *Cancer Res.* **2014**, *74*, 1885–1889. [CrossRef] [PubMed]

64. Lee, Y.Y. What is obesity doing to your gut? *Malays. J. Med. Sci.* **2015**, *22*, 1–3. [PubMed]

65. Moran, C.P.; Shanahan, F. Gut microbiota and obesity: Role in aetiology and potential therapeutic target. *Best Pract. Res. Clin. Gastroenterol.* **2014**, *28*, 585–597. [CrossRef] [PubMed]

66. Mehal, W.Z. The Gordian Knot of dysbiosis, obesity and NAFLD. *Nat. Rev. Gastroenterol. Hepatol.* **2013**, *10*, 637–644. [CrossRef] [PubMed]

67. Louis, P.; Hold, G.L.; Flint, H.J. The gut microbiota, bacterial metabolites and colorectal cancer. *Nat. Rev. Microbiol.* **2014**, *12*, 661–672. [CrossRef] [PubMed]

68. Spruss, A.; Kanuri, G.; Wagnerberger, S.; Haub, S.; Bischoff, S.C.; Bergheim, I. Toll-like receptor 4 is involved in the development of fructose-induced hepatic steatosis in mice. *Hepatology* **2009**, *50*, 1094–1104. [CrossRef] [PubMed]

69. Gilbert, C.A.; Slingerland, J.M. Cytokines, obesity, and cancer: New insights on mechanisms linking obesity to cancer risk and progression. *Annu. Rev. Med.* **2013**, *64*, 45–57. [CrossRef] [PubMed]

70. Hui, J.M.; Hodge, A.; Farrell, G.C.; Kench, J.G.; Kriketos, A.; George, J. Beyond insulin resistance in NASH: TNF-α or adiponectin? *Hepatology* **2004**, *40*, 46–54. [CrossRef] [PubMed]

71. Giovannucci, E. Nutrition, insulin, insulin-like growth factors and cancer. *Horm. Metab. Res.* **2003**, *35*, 694–704. [PubMed]

72. Pérez-Hernández, A.I.; Catalán, V.; Gómez-Ambrosi, J.; Rodríguez, A.; Frühbeck, G. Mechanisms linking excess adiposity and carcinogenesis promotion. *Front. Endocrinol.* **2014**, *5*, 65. [CrossRef]

73. Van Kruijsdijk, R.C.M.; van der Wall, E.; Visseren, F.L.J. Obesity and cancer: The role of dysfunctional adipose tissue. *Cancer Epidemiol. Biomark. Prev.* **2009**, *18*, 2569–2578. [CrossRef] [PubMed]

74. Grimberg, A.; Cohen, P. Role of insulin-like growth factors and their binding proteins in growth control and carcinogenesis. *J. Cell. Physiol.* **2000**, *183*, 1–9. [CrossRef]

75. Chan, J.M.; Stampfer, M.J.; Giovannucci, E.; Gann, P.H.; Ma, J.; Wilkinson, P.; Hennekens, C.H.; Pollak, M. Plasma insulin-like growth factor-I and prostate cancer risk: A prospective study. *Science* **1998**, *279*, 563–566. [CrossRef] [PubMed]

76. Giovannucci, E.; Pollak, M.N.; Platz, E.A.; Willett, W.C.; Stampfer, M.J.; Majeed, N.; Colditz, G.A.; Speizer, F.E.; Hankinson, S.E. A prospective study of plasma insulin-like growth factor-1 and binding protein-3 and risk of colorectal neoplasia in women. *Cancer Epidemiol. Biomark. Prev.* **2000**, *9*, 345–349.

77. Yu, H.; Spitz, M.R.; Mistry, J.; Gu, J.; Hong, W.K.; Wu, X. Plasma levels of insulin-like growth factor-I and lung cancer risk: A case-control analysis. *J. Natl. Cancer Inst.* **1999**, *91*, 151–156. [CrossRef] [PubMed]

78. Hankinson, S.E.; Willett, W.C.; Colditz, G.A.; Hunter, D.J.; Michaud, D.S.; Deroo, B.; Rosner, B.; Speizer, F.E.; Pollak, M. Circulating concentrations of insulin-like growth factor-I and risk of breast cancer. *Lancet* **1998**, *351*, 1393–1396. [CrossRef]

79. Donohoe, C.L.; O'Farrell, N.J.; Doyle, S.L.; Reynolds, J.V. The role of obesity in gastrointestinal cancer: Evidence and opinion. *Ther. Adv. Gastroenterol.* **2014**, *7*, 38–50. [CrossRef] [PubMed]

80. Doyle, S.L.; Donohoe, C.L.; Finn, S.P.; Howard, J.M.; Lithander, F.E.; Reynolds, J.V.; Pidgeon, G.P.; Lysaght, J. IGF-1 and its receptor in esophageal cancer: Association with adenocarcinoma and visceral obesity. *Am. J. Gastroenterol.* **2012**, *107*, 196–204. [CrossRef] [PubMed]

81. Siahpush, S.H.; Vaughan, T.L.; Lampe, J.N.; Freeman, R.; Lewis, S.; Odze, R.D.; Blount, P.L.; Ayub, K.; Rabinovitch, P.S.; Reid, B.J.; *et al.* Longitudinal study of insulin-like growth factor, insulin-like growth factor binding protein-3, and their polymorphisms: Risk of neoplastic progression in Barrett's esophagus. *Cancer Epidemiol. Biomark. Prev.* **2007**, *16*, 2387–2395. [CrossRef] [PubMed]

82. Endo, H.; Hosono, K.; Uchiyama, T.; Sakai, E.; Sugiyama, M.; Takahashi, H.; Nakajima, N.; Wada, K.; Takeda, K.; Nakagama, H.; *et al.* Leptin acts as a growth factor for colorectal tumours at stages subsequent to tumour initiation in murine colon carcinogenesis. *Gut* **2011**, *60*, 1363–1371. [CrossRef] [PubMed]

83. Jaffe, T.; Schwartz, B. Leptin promotes motility and invasiveness in human colon cancer cells by activating multiple signal-transduction pathways. *Int. J. Cancer* **2008**, *123*, 2543–2556. [CrossRef] [PubMed]

84. Ho, G.Y.F.; Wang, T.; Gunter, M.J.; Strickler, H.D.; Cushman, M.; Kaplan, R.C.; Wassertheil-Smoller, S.; Xue, X.; Rajpathak, S.N.; Chlebowski, R.T.; *et al.* Adipokines linking obesity with colorectal cancer risk in postmenopausal women. *Cancer Res.* **2012**, *72*, 3029–3037. [CrossRef] [PubMed]

85. Rubenstein, J.H.; Dahlkemper, A.; Kao, J.Y.; Zhang, M.; Morgenstern, H.; McMahon, L.; Inadomi, J.M. A pilot study of the association of low plasma adiponectin and Barrett's esophagus. *Am. J. Gastroenterol.* **2008**, *103*, 1358–1364. [CrossRef] [PubMed]

86. Rubenstein, J.H.; Morgenstern, H.; McConell, D.; Scheiman, J.M.; Schoenfeld, P.; Appelman, H.; McMahon, L.F., Jr.; Kao, J.Y.; Metko, V.; Zhang, M.; *et al.* Associations of diabetes mellitus, insulin, leptin, and ghrelin with gastroesophageal reflux and Barrett's esophagus. *Gastroenterology* **2013**, *145*, 1237–1244. [CrossRef] [PubMed]

87. Ryan, A.M.; Healy, L.A.; Power, D.G.; Byrne, M.; Murphy, S.; Byrne, P.J.; Kelleher, D.; Reynolds, J.V. Barrett esophagus: Prevalence of central adiposity, metabolic syndrome, and a proinflammatory state. *Ann. Surg.* **2008**, *247*, 909–915. [CrossRef] [PubMed]

88. Chandar, A.K.; Devanna, S.; Lu, C.; Singh, S.; Greer, K.; Chak, A.; Iyer, P.G. Association of serum levels of adipokines and insulin with risk of barrett's esophagus: A systematic review and meta-analysis. *Clin. Gastroenterol. Hepatol.* **2015**, *13*, 2241–2255. [CrossRef] [PubMed]

89. Francois, F.; Roper, J.; Goodman, A.J.; Pei, Z.; Ghumman, M.; Mourad, M.; de Perez, A.Z.; Perez-Perez, G.I.; Tseng, C.; Blaser, M.J. The association of gastric leptin with oesophageal inflammation and metaplasia. *Gut* **2008**, *57*, 16–24. [CrossRef] [PubMed]

90. Kendall, B.J.; Macdonald, G.A.; Hayward, N.K.; Prins, J.B.; Brown, I.; Walker, N.; Pandeya, N.; Green, A.C.; Webb, P.M.; Whiteman, D.C.; *et al.* Leptin and the risk of Barrett's oesophagus. *Gut* **2008**, *57*, 448–454. [CrossRef] [PubMed]

91. Delort, L.; Rossary, A.; Farges, M.-C.; Vasson, M.-P.; Caldefie-Chézet, F. Leptin, adipocytes and breast cancer: Focus on inflammation and anti-tumor immunity. *Life Sci.* **2015**, *140*, 37–48. [CrossRef] [PubMed]

92. Macciò, A.; Madeddu, C.; Mantovani, G. Adipose tissue as target organ in the treatment of hormone-dependent breast cancer: New therapeutic perspectives. *Obes. Rev.* **2009**, *10*, 660–670. [CrossRef] [PubMed]

93. Caldefie-Chézet, F.; Dubois, V.; Delort, L.; Rossary, A.; Vasson, M.-P. Leptin: Involvement in the pathophysiology of breast cancer. *Ann. Endocrinol.* **2013**, *74*, 90–101. [CrossRef] [PubMed]

94. Filková, M.; Haluzík, M.; Gay, S.; Senolt, L. The role of resistin as a regulator of inflammation: Implications for various human pathologies. *Clin. Immunol.* **2009**, *133*, 157–170. [CrossRef] [PubMed]

95. Karapanagiotou, E.M.; Tsochatzis, E.A.; Dilana, K.D.; Tourkantonis, I.; Gratsias, I.; Syrigos, K.N. The significance of leptin, adiponectin, and resistin serum levels in non-small cell lung cancer (NSCLC). *Lung Cancer* **2008**, *61*, 391–397. [CrossRef] [PubMed]

96. Tiaka, E.K.; Manolakis, A.C.; Kapsoritakis, A.N.; Potamianos, S.P. The implication of adiponectin and resistin in gastrointestinal diseases. *Cytokine Growth Factor Rev.* **2011**, *22*, 109–119. [CrossRef] [PubMed]

97. Codoñer-Franch, P.; Alonso-Iglesias, E. Resistin: Insulin resistance to malignancy. *Clin. Chim. Acta* **2015**, *438*, 46–54. [CrossRef] [PubMed]

98. Hursting, S.D.; Dunlap, S.M. Obesity, metabolic dysregulation, and cancer: A growing concern and an inflammatory (and microenvironmental) issue. *Ann. N. Y. Acad. Sci.* **2012**, *1271*, 82–87. [CrossRef] [PubMed]

99. Yadav, A.; Kumar, B.; Datta, J.; Teknos, T.N.; Kumar, P. IL-6 promotes head and neck tumor metastasis by inducing epithelial-mesenchymal transition via the JAK-STAT3-SNAIL signaling pathway. *Mol. Cancer Res.* **2011**, *9*, 1658–1667. [CrossRef] [PubMed]

100. Naylor, M.S.; Stamp, G.W.; Foulkes, W.D.; Eccles, D.; Balkwill, F.R. Tumor necrosis factor and its receptors in human ovarian cancer. Potential role in disease progression. *J. Clin. Investig.* **1993**, *91*, 2194–2206. [CrossRef] [PubMed]

101. Ferrajoli, A.; Keating, M.J.; Manshouri, T.; Giles, F.J.; Dey, A.; Estrov, Z.; Koller, C.A.; Kurzrock, R.; Thomas, D.A.; Faderl, S.; *et al.* The clinical significance of tumor necrosis factor-α plasma level in patients having chronic lymphocytic leukemia. *Blood* **2002**, *100*, 1215–1219. [PubMed]

102. Pikarsky, E.; Porat, R.M.; Stein, I.; Abramovitch, R.; Amit, S.; Kasem, S.; Gutkovich-Pyest, E.; Urieli-Shoval, S.; Galun, E.; Ben-Neriah, Y. NF-κB functions as a tumour promoter in inflammation-associated cancer. *Nature* **2004**, *431*, 461–466. [CrossRef] [PubMed]

103. Balkwill, F. Tumour necrosis factor and cancer. *Nat. Rev. Cancer* **2009**, *9*, 361–371. [CrossRef] [PubMed]

104. Liu, Z.; Brooks, R.S.; Ciappio, E.D.; Kim, S.J.; Crott, J.W.; Bennett, G.; Greenberg, A.S.; Mason, J.B. Diet-induced obesity elevates colonic TNF-α in mice and is accompanied by an activation of Wnt signaling: A mechanism for obesity-associated colorectal cancer. *J. Nutr. Biochem.* **2012**, *23*, 1207–1213. [CrossRef] [PubMed]

105. Angelo, L.S.; Talpaz, M.; Kurzrock, R. Autocrine interleukin-6 production in renal cell carcinoma: Evidence for the involvement of p53. *Cancer Res.* **2002**, *62*, 932–940. [PubMed]

106. Kai, H.; Kitadai, Y.; Kodama, M.; Cho, S.; Kuroda, T.; Ito, M.; Tanaka, S.; Ohmoto, Y.; Chayama, K. Involvement of proinflammatory cytokines IL-1β and IL-6 in progression of human gastric carcinoma. *Anticancer Res.* **2005**, *25*, 709–713. [PubMed]

107. Sethi, G.; Shanmugam, M.K.; Ramachandran, L.; Kumar, A.P.; Tergaonkar, V. Multifaceted link between cancer and inflammation. *Biosci. Rep.* **2012**, *32*, 1–15. [CrossRef] [PubMed]

108. Chung, Y.-C.; Chang, Y.-F. Serum interleukin-6 levels reflect the disease status of colorectal cancer. *J. Surg. Oncol.* **2003**, *83*, 222–226. [CrossRef] [PubMed]
109. Lin, W.-W.; Karin, M. A cytokine-mediated link between innate immunity, inflammation, and cancer. *J. Clin. Investig.* **2007**, *117*, 1175–1183. [CrossRef] [PubMed]

International Journal of
Molecular Sciences

MDPI

Review

The Natural Course of Non-Alcoholic Fatty Liver Disease

Luis Calzadilla Bertot [1] and Leon Anton Adams [1,2,]*

[1] School of Medicine and Pharmacology, the University of Western Australia, Nedlands, WA 6009, Australia; lcbertot@gmail.com
[2] Department of Hepatology, Sir Charles Gairdner Hospital, Nedlands, WA 6009, Australia
*   Correspondence: leon.adams@uwa.edu.au; Tel.: +61-8-6151-1052; Fax: +61-8-6151-1028

Academic Editors: Amedeo Lonardo and Giovanni Targher
Received: 29 April 2016; Accepted: 12 May 2016; Published: 20 May 2016

Abstract: Non-alcoholic fatty liver disease (NAFLD) is the most prevalent form of chronic liver disease in the world, paralleling the epidemic of obesity and Type 2 diabetes mellitus (T2DM). NAFLD exhibits a histological spectrum, ranging from "bland steatosis" to the more aggressive necro-inflammatory form, non-alcoholic steatohepatitis (NASH) which may accumulate fibrosis to result in cirrhosis. Emerging data suggests fibrosis, rather than NASH *per se*, to be the most important histological predictor of liver and non-liver related death. Nevertheless, only a small proportion of individuals develop cirrhosis, however the large proportion of the population affected by NAFLD has led to predictions that NAFLD will become a leading cause of end stage liver disease, hepatocellular carcinoma (HCC), and indication for liver transplantation. HCC may arise in non-cirrhotic liver in the setting of NAFLD and is associated with the presence of the metabolic syndrome (MetS) and male gender. The MetS and its components also play a key role in the histological progression of NAFLD, however other genetic and environmental factors may also influence the natural history. The importance of NAFLD in terms of overall survival extends beyond the liver where cardiovascular disease and malignancy represents additional important causes of death.

Keywords: nonalcoholic fatty liver; non-alcoholic steatohepatitis; fibrosis; hepatocellular carcinoma; cirrhosis; non-cirrhotic

1. Introduction

The prevalence of non-alcoholic fatty liver disease (NAFLD) parallels that of obesity, which has steadily risen throughout the world over the past thirty years [1]. The natural history of NAFLD in some individuals, is to progress to end-stage liver disease. Thus, NAFLD is projected to become the leading cause of liver related morbidity and mortality within 20 years and a leading indication for liver transplantation in the next few years [2]. Although the potential for NAFLD to progress to both cirrhosis and hepatocellular carcinoma (HCC) has been recognized for decades, more recent insights have helped define the magnitude of risk of progression and led to the understanding that NAFLD is a leading cause of cryptogenic cirrhosis [3–6]. More recently, accumulating evidence has also led to the hypotheses that even steatosis and mild inflammation can progress to fibrosis and HCC [7–9]. Nevertheless, the natural history of NAFLD remains incompletely defined, with key knowledge gaps including the lack of understanding behind the substantial inter-individual variation in disease progression and outcomes and understanding of the links between NAFLD and HCC. In this review we provide an up to date assessment of the natural history of NAFLD and emerging evidence that may impact the management of this disease in the future.

2. Histological Course of Non-Alcoholic Fatty Liver Disease (NAFLD)

Non-alcoholic fatty liver disease (NAFLD) encompasses a histological spectrum from non-alcoholic fatty liver (NAFL), which is characterized by steatosis with no or minor inflammation, to non-alcoholic steatohepatitis (NASH) where inflammation and ballooning is present, with or without fibrosis. The natural history of NASH tends to parallels the more aggressive histological picture, with prospective cohort studies demonstrating a higher rate of morbidity and mortality compared to NAFL, particularly when fibrosis is present [10,11]. Nevertheless, a limited amount of high-quality prospective data on the progression of NAFLD exists, particularly in the primary-care setting, where routine biochemical indices do not accurately reflect disease activity or progression. Paired liver biopsy studies from tertiary care cohorts provide valuable information however are limited in their generalizability due to selection bias.

At least 12 studies have analysed the progression of steatosis, steatohepatitis, and fibrosis in NAFLD cohorts by utilizing paired liver biopsies [7,9,11–20]. These studies suggest that one third of patients with NAFL and NASH have progressive fibrosis and 20% will have some regression over an average follow-up between 2.2 and 13.8 years [7,9,11–23]. The rate of fibrosis progression is characteristically slow with a recent meta-analysis determining an average progression of one stage to take 7.7 years [24]. Nevertheless, the rate of progression is twice as high in NASH subjects and a sub-group of both NASH and NAFL patients may progress rapidly from no fibrosis to advanced fibrosis over an average six year period [8,9]. In contrast to fibrosis progression over time, features of steatosis, inflammation and ballooning tend to reduce which is paralleled by reduction in amino-transaminase levels [12]. Factors that may influence the histological progression of NASH are illustrated in Table 1, Figure 1 and outlined below.

Table 1. Risk factors for fibrosis progression in non-alcoholic fatty liver disease (NAFLD): Results from paired liver biopsy studies.

Study Author, Year	*n*	Mean/Median (Standard Deviation or Range) Follow up in Years	Predictors of Fibrosis Progression	Odds Ratio (95% CI)
Adams (2005)	103	3.2 (±3.0)	Diabetes	1.48
			Fibrosis stage	0.80
			BMI (per kg/m^2)	1.04
Fassio (2004)	22	4.3 (3.0–14.3)	Obesity	NR
Argo (2009) *	221	5.3 (1.0–21.3)	Age	0.98 (0.96–0.99)
			Any inflammation at initial biopsy	2.5 (1.4–4.3)
Wong (2010)	52	3, NR	High LDL	2.7 (1.2 to 6.1)
			High waist circumference	1.3 (1.1 to 1.5)
Sorrentino (2010)	149	6.4	Fibronectin immunohistochemistry	14.1 (6.9–32.3)
			Hypertension	4.8 (2.7–18.2)
			HOMA-IR > 10	1.9 (1.6–12.1)
Pais (2013)	70	3.7 (±2.1)	^ steatosis grade	NR
Chan (2014)	35	6.4 (±0.8)	nil	-
McPherson (2014)	108	6.6 (1.3–22.6)	At baseline biopsy FIB 4 score	2.1 (1.1–3.9)
			At follow up biopsy FIB 4 score	3.1 (1.4–6.8)
			Diabetes	6.25 (1.88–20)
Singh (2015) **	411	NR	Hypertension	1.94 (1.00–3.74)
			Low AST:ALT ratio at baseline biopsy	−0.08 (−0.16–0.00)

* A systematic review comprising 10 studies; ** A meta-analysis including 11 cohort studies; ^ Progression defined by progression from non-alcoholic fatty liver (NAFL) to non-alcoholic steatohepatitis (NASH), occurrence of bridging fibrosis or at least one point increase in the NAFLD activity score (NAS) score from <5 to 5, or greater; NR = Not reported; HOMA–IR = homeostasis model of assessment-insulin resistance.

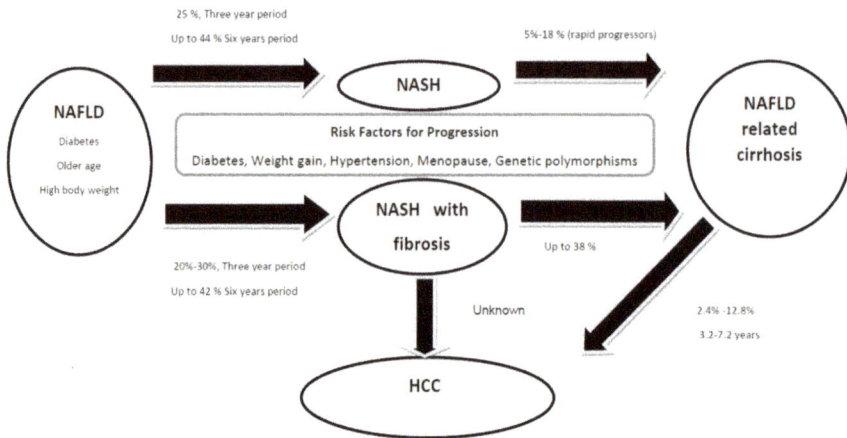

Figure 1. Progression of non-alcoholic fatty liver disease (NAFLD) to non-alcoholic steatohepatitis (NASH) with or without fibrosis, cirrhosis, and hepatocellular carcinoma. Data adapted form [7–9] and [24].

3. Predictors of Progressive Fibrosis in Non-Alcoholic Steatohepatitis (NASH)

3.1. Sex

No consistent relationship between sex and fibrosis has been found in NASH, with cross-sectional studies reporting conflicting findings [25,26]. The relationship between sex and fibrosis may be influenced by menopausal status; cross-sectional studies have found men and post-menopausal women to have a higher risk of fibrosis compared with pre-menopausal women, and early menopause and duration of menopause to be associated with a higher risk of fibrosis [27,28].

3.2. Race and Ethnicity

Hispanic patients have an increased prevalence of NAFLD compared to Caucasians; however, there appears to be no difference in degree of liver injury between these ethnic groups [29,30]. In contrast, Asian patients may be prone to more severe histological changes including ballooning, whereas African-Americans may have less severe histology, although factors such as diet may be confounding this relationship [31–33].

3.3. Genetic Polymorphisms

Polymorphisms in the *PNPLA3* and *TM6SF2* genes are common in the general population with minor allele frequencies of 20%–50% and 10%, respectively [34]. The rs738409 and rs58542926 single nucleotide polymorphisms (SNP's) of these respective genes have been identified by genome-wide association studies to be associated with an increased risk of NAFLD, as well the presence of more severe liver histology (*i.e.*, NASH and fibrosis) [34–38]. One study of over 1000 individuals with biopsy proven NAFLD, demonstrated these SNPs were associated with a 40% to 88% increased risk for advanced (F2-4) fibrosis after adjustment for age, sex, and metabolic variables [34]. Similarly, a SNP in the *IFNL4* gene, which is associated with response to interferon based treatment in chronic hepatitis C, has also been associated with fibrosis in NAFLD and has been amalgamated into a predictive score in conjunction with other clinical factors [39].

3.4. Age

Cross-sectional studies have demonstrated increasing age to be consistently associated with more severe fibrosis in NASH patients; however, this may reflect the cumulative sum of metabolic exposures and longer duration of NAFL/NASH in these populations [26,40,41]. In contrast, longitudinal studies have not consistently demonstrated age to impact the rate of fibrosis progression [24].

3.5. Metabolic Features

Diabetes and obesity have demonstrated to be predictive of a higher rate of fibrosis progression in some but not all longitudinal studies [7–9,12,22]. An increase or decrease in body mass index over time, has been associated with progression or resolution of liver fibrosis respectively in NAFLD patients and the emergence of diabetes also appears to parallel fibrosis progression, whereas improved glycemic control parallels fibrosis improvement [7–9,22]. One meta-analysis examining the full spectrum of NAFLD found hypertension to be a risk factor for fibrosis progression, however an earlier meta-analysis limited to NASH patients did not [24,42].

3.6. Histological Factors

The degree of hepatic steatosis does not appear to predict disease progression in NASH. The degree of inflammation however, has been associated with progression to advanced fibrosis in a meta-analysis, but not in any single cohort study [24].

4. Clinical Course of NAFLD

4.1. Liver Cirrhosis, Decompensation, and Liver Related Mortality

Overall, the risk of progression to cirrhosis and decompensation in NAFLD patients is low with a population based study demonstrating an incidence of 3.1% for both end-points over a mean 7.6 year follow-up [43]. Nevertheless, the risk of cirrhosis may be underestimated given the lack of systematic evaluation for its development in the community.

The risk of progression to end-stage liver disease is influenced by the severity of underlying liver histology; the majority of patients with NAFLD have simple steatosis, however, up to 30% of patients may have NASH [44] and are at greater risk. Several studies with up to 20 years follow-up, have demonstrated that the risk of progression to cirrhosis in patients with simple steatosis is between 0% and 4% [6,45,46]. In contrast, estimates of progression to cirrhosis in NASH patients varies with 10% developing decompensated liver disease over 13 years [11] and 25% developing cirrhosis over nine years [11]. The rate of progression is clearly heavily influenced by the underlying fibrosis stage, with NASH patients without fibrosis at significantly lower risk compared to those with advanced fibrosis. Progression to advanced fibrosis and cirrhosis is not uniform in all patients and metabolic factors such as presence of glucose intolerance and Type 2 diabetes mellitus (T2DM) may play a key role in this progression [47,48].

Once cirrhosis has developed, the risk of developing a major complication of portal hypertension is 17%, 23%, and 52% at one, three, and 10 years, respectively [49]. The survival of patients with NASH cirrhosis falls markedly once decompensation occurs, with a median survival of approximately two years [50]. Today, NAFLD is the second commonest etiology for listing for liver transplantation, and on the trajectory of becoming the most common cause [51–54]. Notably, the burden of NAFLD related cirrhosis may be under-estimated, as the histological signs of steatohepatitis may no longer be present at the cirrhotic stage of disease [55]. Caldwell *et al.* noted that a large proportion of patients with cryptogenic cirrhosis had been exposed to metabolic risk factors [4] and almost half of the cases of "cryptogenic" cirrhosis could ultimately be traced to the end-stage evolution of NASH [39].

Compared with individuals of the general population of the same age and gender, those with NAFLD have a lower than expected survival, at a standardized mortality ratio from 1.34 to 1.69 according to American and Swedish studies [11,12]. The increase in mortality hazard is likely in part, to be related to increased liver related mortality, with liver death the third commonest cause of death in two large cohort studies [11,12].

4.2. Non-Liver Related Death

NAFLD is associated with a significantly higher overall mortality compared to the age and sex-matched general population, which in part is likely related to excess vascular as well as liver-related death. Cross-sectional population-based studies and meta-analysis have demonstrated NAFLD to be independently associated with predictors of cardiovascular disease including endothelial dysfunction, arterial stiffness and myocardial dysfunction [56–59]. Notably, NAFLD results in hepatic insulin resistance, increased fasting glucose levels and an atherogenic lipid profile [60], and NASH is associated with increased levels of inflammatory pro-atherogenic cytokines, hyper-coagulable factors, and adhesion molecules [61].

Supporting these observations, analysis of over 11,000 participants in the NAHNES study conducted between 1989 and 2004 with median follow up of 14.5 years, demonstrated increased (69%) overall mortality in NAFLD patients with advanced fibrosis assessed by means of NAFLD fibrosis score, APRI and FIB 4. The increase in mortality in this subgroup was largely driven by cardiovascular disease (CVD) (adjusted hazard ratio 2.7 to 3.5) [62]. Other cohort studies have suggested that other sub-groups of NAFLD patients, such as those with type 2 diabetes [63] or men with an elevated gamma-glutamyl transpeptidase [57], may have an increased risk of CVD events compared to subjects without NAFLD. Thus, there may be other genetic or environmental factors that modify the association between NAFLD and CVD. Lastly, severity of liver histology may stratify risk of cardiovascular mortality with Ekstedt and colleagues demonstrating that subjects with simple steatosis did not have an increased risk of all-cause death or death related to CVD, but those with NASH were twice as likely to die from CVD compared to the reference general population (15.5% *vs.* 7.5%) over a mean follow-up period of 13.7 years [64].

5. Evolving Concepts

5.1. NAFL vs. NASH

A pioneer research published in 2006 compared the levels of serum concentrations of transforming growth factor-beta1 (TGF-β1) a marker of fibrosis, and ferritin between NAFL, and NASH patients [40]. No differences in the serum levels of TGF-β1 and ferritin were found between NAFL and NASH groups. Authors suggested that both NAFLD spectrums share common aspects regarding their progression and NAFL perhaps not so benign. Recent reports suggest NAFL may not be as benign as previously thought, with evidence of progression to advanced fibrosis, challenging the paradigm that risk of fibrosis progression is dichotomized according to the presence or absence of NASH (Table 2). Wong *et al.* [7] reported in a prospective study of paired liver biopsies taken a median three years apart, that 58% of patients with histological NAFLD activity score (NAS) <3 (*i.e.*, non-NASH) increased their activity score and 28% had fibrosis progression at three years. Fibrosis progression was seen in 20% to 30% of patients with both low and high NAS scores. Twenty-three per cent of patients with simple steatosis developed NASH in 3 years.

A retrospective study analysing a database of 70 NAFLD patients with paired biopsies showed that patients with NAFL can evolve towards well-defined steatohepatitis, and in some of them, bridging fibrosis after a follow-up of less than 5 years. The presence of mild lobular inflammation or any amount of fibrosis substantially increased the risk of histological progression in the mid-term while those with steatosis alone are at lowest risk [8]. More recently McPherson *et al.* [9] in the DELTA study included 108 patients with paired liver biopsies over a median of 6.6 years; they found overall that NAFLD had a variable natural history with 42% of patients having progression of fibrosis and 18% having regression of fibrosis. Of those with NAFL at the index liver biopsy, 44% progressed to NASH and 37% had progression of fibrosis, including 6 patients who developed stage three fibrosis.

Lastly, Singh *et al.* conducted a systematic review and meta-analysis of 11 studies involving 411 patients with paired liver biopsies [24]. Patients with both NAFL and NASH were found to develop progressive liver fibrosis, although the rate of fibrosis progression was higher in those with NASH than NAFL (one-stage progression over 7.1 years *vs.* 14.3 years, respectively). Collectively, these studies suggest that overall NAFL has a more indolent rate of progression than NASH; however, there is considerable heterogeneity, with one quarter of NAFL patients developing bridging fibrosis over a relatively short time period. Currently, reliable histological and clinical predictors of disease progression are lacking, however it appears that worsening metabolic disease (weight gain, diabetes) frequently parallels the histological progression [8,9].

Table 2. Fibrosis stage as predictor of liver related complications, death, and overall mortality.

Study Author, Year	NAFLD Patients (n)	Mean Follow up (Years)	Histological Subgroup (N)	Cirrhosis and Liver Related Complications HR	Liver Related Mortality HR	Overall Mortality HR
Ekstedt *et al.*, 2015	229	26.4	NAS 0–8 Fibrosis stage 3–4 n = 16	10.8	3.3	3.28
Younossi *et al.*, 2011	257	12.1	Fibrosis stage 3–4 n = NR	-	5.68	-
Angulo *et al.*, 2015	619	12.6	Fibrosis stage			
			F1 n = 141	* 2.38	-	1.88
			F2 n = 85	* 7.51	11.2	2.89
			F3 n = 53	* 13.78	85.79	3.76
			F4 n = 18	* 47.46	-	10.9

* Results derived from a multivariate model including age, sex, race, BMI, diabetes, hypertension, statin use, site, and smoking. HR (hazard ratio).

5.2. Prognostic Significance of NASH vs. Fibrosis

The prognosis of an individual patient with NAFLD is highly variable. A greater likelihood of progressive disease was initially described in those patients with NASH, which is often defined according to the NAFLD activity score (NAS score). The NAS is the unbalanced sum of steatosis, ballooning, and lobular inflammation [10], and was originally developed as a tool for assessing efficacy in clinical trials, however has been applied more widely to define NASH and assess histological activity.

Recent evidence coming from prospective cohort studies suggest that fibrosis predicts liver and non-liver related mortality more reliably than NAS or its individual components [64–66]. A study by Younossi *et al.* of 209 NAFLD patients with a median follow up of 12 years found that advanced fibrosis was the only histological lesion independently associated with liver-related mortality (hazard ratio = 5.68, 95% confidence interval (1.5–21.4) [66] More recently Ekstedt and colleagues analysed a cohort of 229 biopsy proven NAFLD patients followed for a mean of 26.4 years [62]. Overall, NAFLD patients had an increased mortality compared with a matched reference population with NAFLD subjects with fibrosis stage three or four at baseline having the worst prognosis (HR 3.3, CI 2.27–4.76, $p < 0.001$). In contrast patients with a high NAS (5–8) without severe fibrosis did not have increase mortality compared with reference population. Finally, Angulo *et al.* conducted an international multicentre cohort study to determine the long term prognostic significance of histologic features of NAFLD [65]. This study confirmed that fibrosis stage rather than NASH, was the most important histological feature associated with overall survival and liver-related complications. Notably, even patients with mild fibrosis (stage 1) had a greater hazard for overall mortality compared to those with no fibrosis, although only those with moderate fibrosis (stage F2 and above) had a greater risk of liver related complications such as ascites, encephalopathy or varices. These studies emphasize the need to assess fibrosis routinely in all patients with NAFLD to assess their prognosis and, thus, need for monitoring and liver targeted treatment.

6. Hepatocellular Carcinoma (HCC)

6.1. HCC in NAFLD

HCC is the six most common cancer worldwide, the third most common cause of cancer related death and has a globally rising incidence [67,68]. Several studies have demonstrated an association between MetS, T2DM as well as obesity, with HCC, suggesting that NAFLD is playing a significant role in the rising incidence of HCC [67,69,70]. The potential mechanisms relating MetS, obesity, diabetes, NAFLD, and HCC, particularly in the absence of cirrhosis, are probably related to the pathogenesis of the underlying disease rather than to fibrosis alone. A fertile soil for liver carcinogenesis include insulin resistance and hepatic steatosis promoting adipose tissue-derived inflammation, hormonal changes (adipokines), oxidative stress, lipopoxicity, and stimulation of insulin-like growth factor [21,69,70]. Gut microbiome, diet, and genetics are increasingly important factors. Intestinal dysbiosis associated with obesity modify the gut microbiome and promotes the release of endotoxins [22]. High-fat diets and high fructose intake can worsen the cytokine pattern and promote lipoperoxidation [70]. Genetics contributes to increase the risk of HCC, mainly through the *PNPLA3* rs738409 variant [23].

NASH was found to be the third most common risk factor for HCC in a U.S. veterans population of 1500 with HCC diagnosed over a six year period [71]. Nevertheless, HCC remains an uncommon complication of NAFLD and heavily influenced by the presence or absence of underlying cirrhosis. For example, one Japanese study of 6508 individuals with ultrasound diagnosed NAFLD, found the HCC incidence to be only 0.2% after eight years, however subjects with advanced fibrosis determined by the AST-Platelet Ratio Index, had a 25-fold increase in risk [72]. Of concern however, are emerging reports of the development of HCC in non-cirrhotic patients; however, the magnitude of this risk remains to be defined [73–75].

6.2. HCC in NAFLD Cirrhosis

The cumulative incidence of HCC in NASH cirrhosis ranges between 2.4% and 12.8% over a 3.2–7.2 year period, and the cumulative HCC mortality in NAFLD/NASH cohorts is 0%–3% over 5.6–21 years [76]. A large series of 195 NAFLD cirrhosis patients from the Cleveland Clinic found the annual incidence of HCC to be marginally lower than a comparative population of hepatitis C cirrhosis patients (2.6% *vs.* 4.0%, $p = 0.09$) [77]. These findings have been replicated in other American and Japanese cohorts [50,78]. All these studies performs a defined protocol excluding other etiologies of HCC including Hepatitis C and Hepatitis B virus infection. Risk factors for HCC development in the NASH population included diabetes, age, any previous alcohol consumption and the presence of intra-hepatic iron [77,79]. Interestingly, the use of metformin in patients with type 2 diabetes has been associated with a reduced risk of HCC, suggesting that this risk factor may be modifiable [80].

Once HCC develops in NAFLD cirrhotic patients, survival appears to be shorter survival than patients with HCV-HCC [81]. This may be related to patients with HCC resulting from NAFLD being older, having larger tumours, and being less likely to be diagnosed by surveillance compared with HCC caused by viral hepatitis [82–84]. Nevertheless, among patients that have liver function and tumours eligible for curative HCC treatment, overall survival is similar or better that comparable patients with hepatitis C or alcohol induced cirrhosis [81,84].

6.3. HCC in NAFLD without Cirrhosis

The development of HCC in non-cirrhotic patients with NAFLD is increasingly reported with cross-sectional studies demonstrating between 15% and 50% of cases being diagnosed without cirrhosis [73,81,85,86]. Moreover, HCCs have been reported to arise in subjects without evidence of NASH or fibrosis but just simple steatosis [83]. A minority of these cases may be related to transformation of hepatic adenomas, whereas the majority appear to be related to risk factors for NAFLD, namely the MetS, obesity, and diabetes [87]. Several studies have also suggested that HCC originating in non-cirrhotic patients with NASH and/or the metabolic syndrome, are more likely to be male [85–87].

Not surprisingly, HCC associated with non-cirrhotic NAFLD is less likely to be detected during surveillance and thus is more likely to be more advanced when compared to HCC in cirrhosis patients [68,81,84]. Nevertheless, survival is equivalent or better in non-cirrhotic NAFLD patients when compared to subjects with cirrhotic-HCC, likely due to preserved liver function.

7. Conclusions

NAFLD is common in the general population, however the natural history and impact on patient morbidity and mortality is widely divergent. Metabolic factors, such as diabetes, obesity, and hypertension, as well as common genetic polymorphisms in the *PNPLA3* and *TM6SF2* genes, influence the severity of underlying liver histology and, thus, are likely to impact on risk of developing cirrhosis and HCC. Recent studies have demonstrated NAFL in addition to NASH, may lead to progressive fibrosis and have emphasized the importance of fibrosis level in determining future mortality risk. A greater understanding of the factors that alter the natural history of NAFLD will lead to better prognostication and targeting of NAFLD populations at greatest risk for specific therapies.

Acknowledgments: Luis Calzadilla Bertot has been awarded a scholarship from the Liver Foundation of Western Australia.

Author Contributions: Luis Calzadilla Bertot and Leon Anton Adams reviewed the literature and wrote the article.

Conflicts of Interest: The authors declare no conflict of interest.

Abbreviations

NAFLD	Nonalcoholic fatty liver disease
T2DM	Type 2 Diabetes mellitus
NASH	Nonalcoholic steatohepatitis
HCC	Hepatocellular carcinoma
MetS	Metabolic syndrome
NAFL	Nonalcoholic fatty liver
SNP's	Single nucleotide polymorphisms
CVD	Cardiovascular disease
NAS	NAFLD activity score
TGF-β1	Transforming growth factor-beta1

References

1. NCD-RisC. Trends in adult body mass index in 200 countries from 1975 to 2014. *Lancet* **2016**, *387*, 1377–1396.
2. Ray, K. NAFLD–The next global epidemic. *Nat. Rev. Gastroenterol. Hepatol.* **2013**, *10*, 621. [CrossRef] [PubMed]
3. Powell, E.E.; Cooksley, W.G.E.; Hanson, R.; Searle, J.; Halliday, J.W.; Powell, W. The natural history of nonalcoholic steatohepatitis: A follow-up study of forty-two patients for up to 21 years. *Hepatology* **1990**, *11*, 74–80. [CrossRef] [PubMed]
4. Caldwell, S.H.; Oelsner, D.H.; Iezzoni, J.C.; Hespenheide, E.E.; Battle, E.H.; Driscoll, C.J. Cryptogenic cirrhosis: Clinical characterization and risk factors for underlying disease. *Hepatology* **1999**, *29*, 664–669. [CrossRef] [PubMed]
5. Poonawala, A.; Nair, S.P.; Thuluvath, P.J. Prevalence of obesity and diabetes in patients with cryptogenic cirrhosis: A case-control study. *Hepatology* **2000**, *32*, 689–692. [CrossRef] [PubMed]
6. Teli, M.R.; James, O.F.; Burt, A.D.; Bennett, M.K.; Day, C.P. The natural history of nonalcoholic fatty liver: A follow-up study. *Hepatology* **1995**, *22*, 1714–1719. [CrossRef] [PubMed]
7. Wong, V.W.-S.; Wong, G.L.-H.; Choi, P.C.-L.; Chan, A.W.-H.; Li, M.K.-P.; Chan, H.-Y.; Chim, A.M.; Yu, J.; Sung, J.J.; Chan, H.L. Disease progression of non-alcoholic fatty liver disease: A prospective study with paired liver biopsies at 3 years. *Gut* **2010**, *59*, 969–974. [CrossRef] [PubMed]
8. Pais, R.; Charlotte, F.; Fedchuk, L.; Bedossa, P.; Lebray, P.; Poynard, T.; Ratziu, V.; LIDO Study Group. A systematic review of follow-up biopsies reveals disease progression in patients with non-alcoholic fatty liver. *J. Hepatol.* **2013**, *59*, 550–556. [CrossRef] [PubMed]
9. McPherson, S.; Hardy, T.; Henderson, E.; Burt, A.D.; Day, C.P.; Anstee, Q.M. Evidence of NAFLD progression from steatosis to fibrosing-steatohepatitis using paired biopsies: Implications for prognosis and clinical management. *J. Hepatol.* **2015**, *62*, 1148–1155. [CrossRef] [PubMed]

10. Angulo, P.; Hui, J.M.; Marchesini, G.; Bugianesi, E.; George, J.; Farrell, G.C.; Enders, F.; Saksena, S.; Burt, A.D.; Bida, J.P.; *et al.* The NAFLD fibrosis score: A noninvasive system that identifies liver fibrosis in patients with NAFLD. *Hepatology* **2007**, *45*, 846–854. [CrossRef] [PubMed]

11. Ekstedt, M.; Franzén, L.E.; Mathiesen, U.L.; Thorelius, L.; Holmqvist, M.; Bodemar, G.; Kechagias, S. Long-term follow-up of patients with NAFLD and elevated liver enzymes. *Hepatology* **2006**, *44*, 865–873. [CrossRef] [PubMed]

12. Adams, L.A.; Sanderson, S.; Lindor, K.D.; Angulo, P. The histological course of nonalcoholic fatty liver disease: A longitudinal study of 103 patients with sequential liver biopsies. *J. Hepatol.* **2005**, *42*, 132–138. [CrossRef] [PubMed]

13. Angulo, P.; Keach, J.C.; Batts, K.P.; Lindor, K.D. Independent predictors of liver fibrosis in patients with nonalcoholic steatohepatitis. *Hepatology* **1999**, *30*, 1356–1362. [CrossRef] [PubMed]

14. Bacon, B.R.; Farahvash, M.J.; Janney, C.G.; Neuschwander-Tetri, B.A. Nonalcoholic steatohepatitis: An expanded clinical entity. *Gastroenterol.-Orlando* **1994**, *107*, 1103–1109.

15. Evans, C.; Oien, K.; MacSween, R.; Mills, P. Non-alcoholic steatohepatitis: A common cause of progressive chronic liver injury? *J. Clin. Pathol.* **2002**, *55*, 689–692. [CrossRef] [PubMed]

16. Fassio, E.; Álvarez, E.; Domínguez, N.; Landeira, G.; Longo, C. Natural history of nonalcoholic steathepatitis: A longitudinal study of repeat liver biopsies. *Hepatology* **2004**, *40*, 820–826. [CrossRef] [PubMed]

17. Harrison, S.A.; Torgerson, S.; Hayashi, P.H. The natural history of nonalcoholic fatty liver disease: A clinical histopathological study. *Am. J. Gastroenterol.* **2003**, *98*, 2042–2047. [CrossRef] [PubMed]

18. Hui, A.; Wong, V.S.; Chan, H.Y.; Liew, C.T.; Chan, J.Y.; Chan, F.L.; Sung, J.Y. Histological progression of non-alcoholic fatty liver disease in Chinese patients. *Aliment. Pharmacol. Ther.* **2005**, *21*, 407–413. [CrossRef] [PubMed]

19. Lee, R.G. Nonalcoholic steatohepatitis: A study of 49 patients. *Hum. Pathol.* **1989**, *20*, 594–598. [CrossRef]

20. Ratziu, V.; Giral, P.; Charlotte, F.; Bruckert, E.; Thibault, V.; Theodorou, I.; Khalil, L.; Turpin, G.; Opolon, P.; Poynard, T. Liver fibrosis in overweight patients. *Gastroenterology* **2000**, *118*, 1117–1123. [CrossRef]

21. Duan, X.F.; Tang, P.; Li, Q.; Yu, Z.T. Obesity, adipokines and hepatocellular carcinoma. *Int. J. Cancer* **2013**, *133*, 1776–1783. [CrossRef] [PubMed]

22. Henao-Mejia, J.; Elinav, E.; Jin, C.; Hao, L.; Mehal, W.Z.; Strowig, T.; Thaiss, C.A.; Kau, A.L.; Eisenbarth, S.C.; Jurczak, M.J.; *et al.* Inflammasome-mediated dysbiosis regulates progression of NAFLD and obesity. *Nature* **2012**, *482*, 179–185. [CrossRef] [PubMed]

23. Oliveira, C.P.; Stefano, J.T. Genetic polymorphisms and oxidative stress in non-alcoholic steatohepatitis (NASH): A mini review. *Clin. Res. Hepatol. Gastroenterol.* **2015**, *39*, S35–S40. [CrossRef] [PubMed]

24. Singh, S.; Allen, A.M.; Wang, Z.; Prokop, L.J.; Murad, M.H.; Loomba, R. Fibrosis progression in nonalcoholic fatty liver *vs.* nonalcoholic steatohepatitis: A systematic review and meta-analysis of paired-biopsy studies. *Clin. Gastroenterol. Hepatol.* **2015**, *13*, 643–654. [CrossRef] [PubMed]

25. McPherson, S.; Stewart, S.F.; Henderson, E.; Burt, A.D.; Day, C.P. Simple non-invasive fibrosis scoring systems can reliably exclude advanced fibrosis in patients with non-alcoholic fatty liver disease. *Gut* **2010**, *59*, 1265–1269. [CrossRef] [PubMed]

26. Hossain, N.; Afendy, A.; Stepanova, M.; Nader, F.; Srishord, M.; Rafiq, N.; Goodman, Z.; Younossi, Z. Independent predictors of fibrosis in patients with nonalcoholic fatty liver disease. *Clin. Gastroenterol. Hepatol.* **2009**, *7*, 1224–1229. [CrossRef] [PubMed]

27. Yang, J.D.; Abdelmalek, M.F.; Pang, H.; Guy, C.D.; Smith, A.D.; Diehl, A.M.; Suzuki, A. Gender and menopause impact severity of fibrosis among patients with nonalcoholic steatohepatitis. *Hepatology* **2014**, *59*, 1406–1414. [CrossRef] [PubMed]

28. Klair, J.S.; Yang, J.D.; Abdelmalek, M.F.; Guy, C.D.; Gill, R.M.; Yates, K.; Unalp-Adrida, A.; Lavine, J.; Clark, J.; Diehl, A.M.; *et al.* A longer duration of estrogen deficiency increases fibrosis risk among postmenopausal women with nonalcoholic fatty liver disease. *Hepatology* **2016**. [CrossRef] [PubMed]

29. Lomonaco, R.; Ortiz-Lopez, C.; Orsak, B.; Finch, J.; Webb, A.; Bril, F.; Louden, C.; Tio, F.; Cusi, K. Role of ethnicity in overweight and obese patients with nonalcoholic steatohepatitis. *Hepatology* **2011**, *54*, 837–845. [CrossRef] [PubMed]

30. Bambha, K.; Belt, P.; Abraham, M.; Wilson, L.A.; Pabst, M.; Ferrell, L.; Unalp-Arida, A.; Bass, N. Ethnicity and nonalcoholic fatty liver disease. *Hepatology* **2012**, *55*, 769–780. [CrossRef] [PubMed]

31. Mohanty, S.R.; Troy, T.N.; Huo, D.; O'Brien, B.L.; Jensen, D.M.; Hart, J. Influence of ethnicity on histological differences in non-alcoholic fatty liver disease. *J. Hepatol.* **2009**, *50*, 797–804. [CrossRef] [PubMed]

32. Solga, S.F.; Clark, J.M.; Alkhuraishi, A.R.; Torbenson, M.; Tabesh, A.; Schweitzer, M.; Diehl, A.M.; Magnuson, T.H. Race and comorbid factors predict nonalcoholic fatty liver disease histopathology in severely obese patients. *Surg. Obes. Relat. Dis.* **2005**, *1*, 6–11. [CrossRef] [PubMed]

33. Kallwitz, E.R.; Guzman, G.; TenCate, V.; Vitello, J.; Layden-Almer, J.; Berkes, J.; Patel, R.; Layden, T.J.; Cotler, S.J. The histologic spectrum of liver disease in African-American, non-Hispanic white, and Hispanic obesity surgery patients. *Am. J. Gastroenterol.* **2009**, *104*, 64–69. [CrossRef] [PubMed]

34. Liu, Y.L.; Reeves, H.L.; Burt, A.D.; Tiniakos, D.; McPherson, S.; Leathart, J.B.; Allison, M.E.; Alexander, G.J.; Piguet, A.C.; Anty, R.; *et al.* *TM6SF2* rs58542926 influences hepatic fibrosis progression in patients with non-alcoholic fatty liver disease. *Nat. Commun.* **2014**, *5*, 4309. [CrossRef] [PubMed]

35. Romeo, S.; Kozlitina, J.; Xing, C.; Pertsemlidis, A.; Cox, D.; Pennacchio, L.A.; Boerwinkle, E.; Cohen, J.C.; Hobbs, H.H. Genetic variation in *PNPLA3* confers susceptibility to nonalcoholic fatty liver disease. *Nat. Genet.* **2008**, *40*, 1461–1465. [CrossRef] [PubMed]

36. Valenti, L.; Al-Serri, A.; Daly, A.K.; Galmozzi, E.; Rametta, R.; Dongiovanni, P.; Nobili, V.; Mozzi, E.; Roviaro, G.; Vanni, E.; *et al.* Homozygosity for the patatin-like phospholipase-3/adiponutrin I148M polymorphism influences liver fibrosis in patients with nonalcoholic fatty liver disease. *Hepatology* **2010**, *51*, 1209–1217. [CrossRef] [PubMed]

37. Eslam, M.; Hashem, A.M.; Romero-Gomez, M.; Berg, T.; Dore, G.J.; Mangia, A.; Chan, H.L.; Irving, W.L.; Sheridan, D.; Abate, M.L.; *et al.* FibroGENE: A gene-based model for staging liver fibrosis. *J. Hepatol.* **2016**, *64*, 390–398. [CrossRef] [PubMed]

38. Yki-Järvinen, H. Non-alcoholic fatty liver disease as a cause and a consequence of metabolic syndrome. *Lancet Diabetes Endocrinol.* **2014**, *2*, 901–910. [CrossRef]

39. Neuschwander-Tetri, B.A.; Clark, J.M.; Bass, N.M.; van Natta, M.L.; Unalp-Arida, A.; Tonascia, J.; Zein, C.O.; Brunt, E.M.; Kleiner, D.E.; McCullough, A.J.; *et al.* Clinical, laboratory and histological associations in adults with nonalcoholic fatty liver disease. *Hepatology* **2010**, *52*, 913–924. [CrossRef] [PubMed]

40. Tarantino, G.; Conca, P.; Riccio, A.; Tarantino, M.; di Minno, M.N.; Chianese, D.; Pasanisi, F.; Contaldo, F.; Scopacasa, F.; Capone, D. Enhanced serum concentrations of transforming growth factor-β1 in simple fatty liver: Is it really benign? *J. Transl. Med.* **2008**, *6*, 72. [CrossRef] [PubMed]

41. Adams, L.A.; Lymp, J.F.; Sauver, J.S.; Sanderson, S.O.; Lindor, K.D.; Feldstein, A.; Angulo, P. The natural history of nonalcoholic fatty liver disease: A population-based cohort study. *Gastroenterology* **2005**, *129*, 113–121. [CrossRef] [PubMed]

42. Williams, C.D.; Stengel, J.; Asike, M.I.; Torres, D.M.; Shaw, J.; Contreras, M.; Landt, C.L.; Harrison, S.A. Prevalence of nonalcoholic fatty liver disease and nonalcoholic steatohepatitis among a largely middle-aged population utilizing ultrasound and liver biopsy: A prospective study. *Gastroenterology* **2011**, *140*, 124–131. [CrossRef] [PubMed]

43. Dam-Larsen, S.; Becker, U.; Franzmann, M.B.; Larsen, K.; Christoffersen, P.; Bendtsen, F. Final results of a long-term, clinical follow-up in fatty liver patients. *Scand. J. Gastroenterol.* **2009**, *44*, 1236–1243. [CrossRef] [PubMed]

44. Matteoni, C.A.; Younossi, Z.M.; Gramlich, T.; Boparai, N.; Liu, Y.C.; McCullough, A.J. Nonalcoholic fatty liver disease: A spectrum of clinical and pathological severity. *Gastroenterology* **1999**, *116*, 1413–1419. [CrossRef]

45. El-serag, H.B.; Tran, T.; Everhart, J.E. Diabetes increases the risk of chronic liver disease and hepatocellular carcinoma. *Gastroenterology* **2004**, *126*, 460–468. [CrossRef] [PubMed]

46. Loomba, R.; Abraham, M.; Unalp, A.; Wilson, L.; Lavine, J.; Doo, E.; Bass, N.M. Association between diabetes, family history of diabetes, and risk of nonalcoholic steatohepatitis and fibrosis. *Hepatology* **2012**, *56*, 943–951. [CrossRef] [PubMed]

47. Hui, J.M.; Kench, J.G.; Chitturi, S.; Sud, A.; Farrell, G.C.; Byth, K.; Hall, P.; Khan, M.; George, J. Long-term outcomes of cirrhosis in nonalcoholic steatohepatitis compared with hepatitis C. *Hepatology* **2003**, *38*, 420–427. [CrossRef] [PubMed]

48. Sanyal, A.J.; Banas, C.; Sargeant, C.; Luketic, V.A.; Sterling, R.K.; Stravitz, R.T.; Shiffman, M.L.; Heuman, D.; Coterrell, A.; Fisher, R.A.; *et al.* Similarities and differences in outcomes of cirrhosis due to nonalcoholic steatohepatitis and hepatitis C. *Hepatology* **2006**, *43*, 682–689. [CrossRef] [PubMed]

49. Singal, A.K.; Guturu, P.; Hmoud, B.; Kuo, Y.-F.; Salameh, H.; Wiesner, R.H. Evolving frequency and outcomes of liver transplantation based on etiology of liver disease. *Transplantation* **2013**, *95*, 755–760. [CrossRef] [PubMed]

50. Agopian, V.G.; Kaldas, F.M.; Hong, J.C.; Whittaker, M.; Holt, C.; Rana, A.; Zarrinpar, A.; Petrowsky, H.; Farmer, D.; Yersiz, H.; *et al.* Liver transplantation for nonalcoholic steatohepatitis: The new epidemic. *Ann. Surg.* **2012**, *256*, 624–633. [CrossRef] [PubMed]
51. Charlton, M.R.; Burns, J.M.; Pedersen, R.A.; Watt, K.D.; Heimbach, J.K.; Dierkhising, R.A. Frequency and outcomes of liver transplantation for nonalcoholic steatohepatitis in the United States. *Gastroenterology* **2011**, *141*, 1249–1253. [CrossRef] [PubMed]
52. Wong, R.J.; Aguilar, M.; Cheung, R.; Perumpail, R.B.; Harrison, S.A.; Younossi, Z.M.; Ahmed, A. Nonalcoholic steatohepatitis is the second leading etiology of liver disease among adults awaiting liver transplantation in the United States. *Gastroenterology* **2015**, *148*, 547–555. [CrossRef] [PubMed]
53. Caldwell, S.H.; Crespo, D.M. The spectrum expanded: Cryptogenic cirrhosis and the natural history of non-alcoholic fatty liver disease. *J. Hepatol.* **2004**, *40*, 578–584. [CrossRef] [PubMed]
54. Long, M.T.; Wang, N.; Larson, M.G.; Mitchell, G.F.; Palmisano, J.; Vasan, R.S.; Hoffmann, U.; Speliotes, E.K.; Vita, J.A.; Benjamin, E.J.; *et al.* Nonalcoholic fatty liver disease and vascular function: Cross-sectional analysis in the Framingham heart study. *Arterioscler. Thromb. Vasc. Biol.* **2015**, *35*, 1284–1291. [CrossRef] [PubMed]
55. Huang, R.C.; Beilin, L.J.; Ayonrinde, O.; Mori, T.A.; Olynyk, J.K.; Burrows, S.; Hands, B.; Adams, L.A. Importance of cardiometabolic risk factors in the association between nonalcoholic fatty liver disease and arterial stiffness in adolescents. *Hepatology* **2013**, *58*, 1306–1314. [CrossRef] [PubMed]
56. VanWagner, L.B.; Wilcox, J.E.; Colangelo, L.A.; Lloyd-Jones, D.M.; Carr, J.J.; Lima, J.A.; Lewis, C.E.; Rinella, M.E.; Shah, S.J. Association of nonalcoholic fatty liver disease with subclinical myocardial remodeling and dysfunction: A population-based study. *Hepatology* **2015**, *62*, 773–783. [CrossRef] [PubMed]
57. Oni, E.T.; Agatston, A.S.; Blaha, M.J.; Fialkow, J.; Cury, R.; Sposito, A.; Erbel, R.; Blankstein, R.; Feldman, T.; Al-Mallah, M.H.; *et al.* A systematic review: Burden and severity of subclinical cardiovascular disease among those with nonalcoholic fatty liver; should we care? *Atherosclerosis* **2013**, *230*, 258–267. [CrossRef] [PubMed]
58. Anstee, Q.M.; Targher, G.; Day, C.P. Progression of NAFLD to diabetes mellitus, cardiovascular disease or cirrhosis. *Nat. Rev. Gastroenterol. Hepatol.* **2013**, *10*, 330–344. [CrossRef] [PubMed]
59. Vanni, E.; Marengo, A.; Mezzabotta, L.; Bugianesi, E. Systemic complications of nonalcoholic fatty liver disease: When the liver is not an innocent bystander. *Semin. Liver Dis.* **2015**, *35*, 236–249. [CrossRef] [PubMed]
60. Kim, D.; Kim, W.R.; Kim, H.J.; Therneau, T.M. Association between noninvasive fibrosis markers and mortality among adults with nonalcoholic fatty liver disease in the United States. *Hepatology* **2013**, *57*, 1357–1365. [CrossRef] [PubMed]
61. Haring, R.; Wallaschofski, H.; Nauck, M.; Dorr, M.; Baumeister, S.E.; Volzke, H. Ultrasonographic hepatic steatosis increases prediction of mortality risk from elevated serum gamma-glutamyl transpeptidase levels. *Hepatology* **2009**, *50*, 1403–1411. [CrossRef] [PubMed]
62. Ekstedt, M.; Hagström, H.; Nasr, P.; Fredrikson, M.; Stål, P.; Kechagias, S.; Hultcrantz, R. Fibrosis stage is the strongest predictor for disease-specific mortality in NAFLD after up to 33 years of follow-up. *Hepatology* **2015**, *61*, 1547–1554. [CrossRef] [PubMed]
63. Adams, L.A.; Ratziu, V. Non-alcoholic fatty liver—Perhaps not so benign. *J. Hepatol.* **2015**, *62*, 1002–1004. [CrossRef] [PubMed]
64. Younossi, Z.M.; Stepanova, M.; Rafiq, N.; Makhlouf, H.; Younoszai, Z.; Agrawal, R.; Goodman, Z. Pathologic criteria for nonalcoholic steatohepatitis: Interprotocol agreement and ability to predict liver-related mortality. *Hepatology* **2011**, *53*, 1874–1882. [CrossRef] [PubMed]
65. Angulo, P.; Kleiner, D.E.; Dam-Larsen, S.; Adams, L.A.; Bjornsson, E.S.; Charatcharoenwitthaya, P.; Mills, P.R.; Keach, J.C.; Lafferty, H.D.; Stahler, A.; *et al.* Liver fibrosis, but no other histologic features, is associated with long-term outcomes of patients with nonalcoholic fatty liver disease. *Gastroenterology* **2015**, *149*, 389–397. [CrossRef] [PubMed]
66. Bruix, J.; Gores, G.J.; Mazzaferro, V. Hepatocellular carcinoma: Clinical frontiers and perspectives. *Gut* **2014**, *63*, 844–855. [CrossRef] [PubMed]
67. Dyson, J.; Jaques, B.; Chattopadyhay, D.; Lochan, R.; Graham, J.; Das, D.; Aslam, T.; Patanwala, I.; Gaggar, S.; Cole, M.; *et al.* Hepatocellular cancer: The impact of obesity, type 2 diabetes and a multidisciplinary team. *J. Hepatol.* **2014**, *60*, 110–117. [CrossRef] [PubMed]
68. Baffy, G.; Brunt, E.M.; Caldwell, S.H. Hepatocellular carcinoma in non-alcoholic fatty liver disease: An emerging menace. *J. Hepatol.* **2012**, *56*, 1384–1391. [CrossRef] [PubMed]

69. Park, E.J.; Lee, J.H.; Yu, G.-Y.; He, G.; Ali, S.R.; Holzer, R.G.; Österreicher, C.H.; Takahashi, H.; Karin, M. Dietary and genetic obesity promote liver inflammation and tumorigenesis by enhancing IL-6 and TNF expression. *Cell* **2010**, *140*, 197–208. [CrossRef] [PubMed]

70. Zámbó, V.; Simon-Szabó, L.; Szelényi, P.; Kereszturi, E.; Bánhegyi, G.; Csala, M. Lipotoxicity in the liver. *World J. Hepatol.* **2013**, *5*, 550–557. [PubMed]

71. Mittal, S.; Sada, Y.H.; El-Serag, H.B.; Kanwal, F.; Duan, Z.; Temple, S.; May, S.B.; Kramer, J.R.; Richardson, P.A.; Davila, J.A. Temporal trends of nonalcoholic fatty liver disease-related hepatocellular carcinoma in the veteran affairs population. *Clin. Gastroenterol. Hepatol.* **2015**, *13*, 594–601. [CrossRef] [PubMed]

72. Kawamura, Y.; Arase, Y.; Ikeda, K.; Seko, Y.; Imai, N.; Hosaka, T.; Kobayashi, M.; Saitoh, S.; Sezaki, H.; Akuta, N.; *et al.* Large-scale long-term follow-up study of Japanese patients with non-alcoholic fatty liver disease for the onset of hepatocellular carcinoma. *Am. J. Gastroenterol.* **2012**, *107*, 253–261. [CrossRef] [PubMed]

73. Ertle, J.; Dechene, A.; Sowa, J.P.; Penndorf, V.; Herzer, K.; Kaiser, G.; Schlaak, J.F.; Gerken, G.; Syn, W.K.; Canbay, A. Non-alcoholic fatty liver disease progresses to hepatocellular carcinoma in the absence of apparent cirrhosis. *Int. J. Cancer* **2011**, *128*, 2436–2443. [CrossRef] [PubMed]

74. White, D.L.; Kanwal, F.; El-Serag, H.B. Association between nonalcoholic fatty liver disease and risk for hepatocellular cancer, based on systematic review. *Clin. Gastroenterol. Hepatol.* **2012**, *10*, 1342–1359. [CrossRef] [PubMed]

75. Ascha, M.S.; Hanouneh, I.A.; Lopez, R.; Tamimi, T.A.; Feldstein, A.F.; Zein, N.N. The incidence and risk factors of hepatocellular carcinoma in patients with nonalcoholic steatohepatitis. *Hepatology* **2010**, *51*, 1972–1978. [CrossRef] [PubMed]

76. Yatsuji, S.; Hashimoto, E.; Tobari, M.; Taniai, M.; Tokushige, K.; Shiratori, K. Clinical features and outcomes of cirrhosis due to non-alcoholic steatohepatitis compared with cirrhosis caused by chronic hepatitis C. *J. Gastroenterol. Hepatol.* **2009**, *24*, 248–254. [CrossRef] [PubMed]

77. Sorrentino, P.; D'Angelo, S.; Ferbo, U.; Micheli, P.; Bracigliano, A.; Vecchione, R. Liver iron excess in patients with hepatocellular carcinoma developed on non-alcoholic steato-hepatitis. *J. Hepatol.* **2009**, *50*, 351–357. [CrossRef] [PubMed]

78. Singh, S.; Singh, P.P.; Singh, A.G.; Murad, M.H.; Sanchez, W. Anti-diabetic medications and the risk of hepatocellular cancer: A systematic review and meta-analysis. *Am. J. Gastroenterol.* **2013**, *108*, 881–891. [CrossRef] [PubMed]

79. Piscaglia, F.; Svegliati-Baroni, G.; Barchetti, A.; Pecorelli, A.; Marinelli, S.; Tiribelli, C.; Bellentani, S.; Bolondi, L.; Zoli, M.; Malagotti, D.; *et al.* Clinical patterns of hepatocellular carcinoma (HCC) in non alcoholic fatty liver disease (NAFLD): A multicenter prospective study. *Hepatology* **2015**, *47*, e36–e37.

80. Marrero, J.A.; Fontana, R.J.; Su, G.L.; Conjeevaram, H.S.; Emick, D.M.; Lok, A.S. NAFLD may be a common underlying liver disease in patients with hepatocellular carcinoma in the United States. *Hepatology* **2002**, *36*, 1349–1354. [CrossRef] [PubMed]

81. Guzman, G.; Brunt, E.M.; Petrovic, L.M.; Chejfec, G.; Layden, T.J.; Cotler, S.J. Does nonalcoholic fatty liver disease predispose patients to hepatocellular carcinoma in the absence of cirrhosis? *Arch. Pathol. Lab. Med.* **2008**, *132*, 1761–1766. [PubMed]

82. Reddy, S.K.; Steel, J.L.; Chen, H.W.; DeMateo, D.J.; Cardinal, J.; Behari, J.; Humar, A.; Marsh, J.W.; Geller, D.A.; Tsung, A. Outcomes of curative treatment for hepatocellular cancer in nonalcoholic steatohepatitis *versus* hepatitis C and alcoholic liver disease. *Hepatology* **2012**, *55*, 1809–1819. [CrossRef] [PubMed]

83. Leung, C.; Yeoh, S.W.; Patrick, D.; Ket, S.; Marion, K.; Gow, P.; Angus, P.W. Characteristics of hepatocellular carcinoma in cirrhotic and non-cirrhotic non-alcoholic fatty liver disease. *World J. Gastroenterol.* **2015**, *21*, 1189–1196. [CrossRef] [PubMed]

84. Calle, E.E.; Rodriguez, C.; Walker-Thurmond, K.; Thun, M.J. Overweight, obesity, and mortality from cancer in a prospectively studied cohort of U.S. adults. *N. Engl. J. Med.* **2003**, *348*, 1625–1638. [CrossRef] [PubMed]

85. Paradis, V.; Zalinski, S.; Chelbi, E.; Guedj, N.; Degos, F.; Vilgrain, V.; Bedossa, P.; Belghiti, J. Hepatocellular carcinomas in patients with metabolic syndrome often develop without significant liver fibrosis: A pathological analysis. *Hepatology* **2009**, *49*, 851–859. [CrossRef] [PubMed]

86. Liu, T.C.; Vachharajani, N.; Chapman, W.C.; Brunt, E.M. Noncirrhotic hepatocellular carcinoma: Derivation from hepatocellular adenoma? Clinicopathologic analysis. *Mod. Pathol.* **2014**, *27*, 420–432. [CrossRef] [PubMed]

87. Yasui, K.; Hashimoto, E.; Komorizono, Y.; Koike, K.; Arii, S.; Imai, Y.; Shima, T.; Kanbara, Y.; Saibara, T.; Mori, T.; *et al.* Characteristics of patients with nonalcoholic steatohepatitis who develop hepatocellular carcinoma. *Clin. Gastroenterol. Hepatol.* **2011**, *9*, 428–433. [CrossRef] [PubMed]

International Journal of
Molecular Sciences

MDPI

Review

Non-Alcoholic Fatty Liver Disease and Metabolic Syndrome after Liver Transplant

Stefano Gitto and Erica Villa *

Department of Gastroenterology, Azienda Ospedaliero-Universitaria and University of Modena and Reggio Emilia, Via del Pozzo 1, 41124 Modena, Italy; stefano.gitto@studio.unibo.it
* Correspondence: erica.villa@unimore.it; Tel.: +39-059-422-5308

Academic Editors: Amedeo Lonardo and Giovanni Targher
Received: 16 March 2016; Accepted: 28 March 2016; Published: 2 April 2016

Abstract: Liver transplant is the unique curative therapy for patients with acute liver failure or end-stage liver disease, with or without hepatocellular carcinoma. Increase of body weight, onset of insulin resistance and drug-induced alterations of metabolism are reported in liver transplant recipients. In this context, post-transplant diabetes mellitus, hyperlipidemia, and arterial hypertension can be often diagnosed. Multifactorial illnesses occurring in the post-transplant period represent significant causes of morbidity and mortality. This is especially true for metabolic syndrome. Non-alcoholic steatosis and steatohepatitis are hepatic manifestations of metabolic syndrome and after liver transplant both recurrent and *de novo* steatosis can be found. Usually, post-transplant steatosis shows an indolent outcome with few cases of fibrosis progression. However, in the post-transplant setting, both metabolic syndrome and steatosis might play a key role in the stratification of morbidity and mortality risk, being commonly associated with cardiovascular disease. The single components of metabolic syndrome can be treated with targeted drugs while lifestyle intervention is the only reasonable therapeutic approach for transplant patients with non-alcoholic steatosis or steatohepatitis.

Keywords: liver transplant; multifactorial disease; metabolic syndrome; non-alcoholic fatty liver disease; non-alcoholic steatohepatitis

1. Introduction

Liver transplant (LT) represents the curative treatment for patients with acute liver failure, end-stage liver disease and/or non-resectable hepatocellular carcinoma worldwide. After surgery, transplanted patients often develop an increase of body weight, insulin resistance (IR) and metabolic alterations [1]. Multifactorial disease such as diabetes mellitus (DM), hyperlipidemia and arterial hypertension are common complications after LT, all negatively affecting quality of life, morbidity and mortality [1]. Consolidated immunosuppressant drugs such as corticosteroids, calcineurin inhibitors (CNIs) (cyclosporine (CSA) and tacrolimus (TAC)) and mammalian target of rapamycin inhibitors (mTORs) (such as sirolimus (SIR)) play a key role in the metabolic balance, favoring hyperglycemia, arterial hypertension and hyperlipidemia [2]. In this context, a significant amount of transplanted patients fulfill the criteria of metabolic syndrome (MS) which is strongly associated with an increased cardiovascular risk [1]. Since non-alcoholic fatty liver disease (NAFLD) and non-alcoholic steatohepatitis (NASH) are considered the liver expression of MS, it is not surprising that both recurrent and *de novo* NAFLD/NASH can be found after LT [3]. Although post-LT steatosis shows an indolent outcome in terms of fibrosis progression, NAFLD/NASH should be considered for the stratification of morbidity and mortality risk of transplant patients. Notably, cardiovascular disease represents the major cause of death unrelated to liver disease and the third most common cause of mortality among transplant patients, accounting for 12%–16% of deaths. Today, targeted drugs for MS and NAFLD/NASH do not exist. Clinicians can use specific drugs against the single components of MS while a strong improvement of behavior in terms of diet and aerobic exercise is the only reasonable approach for recurrent or *de novo* NAFLD/NASH [1].

This review article focuses on the current literature regarding the main metabolic diseases affecting transplanted patients, the clinical impact of post-LT MS and NAFLD/NASH and, finally, the feasible therapeutic strategies.

2. Multifactorial Disease after Liver Transplant

The majority of transplant patients develop a rise in body weight after surgery. The highest weight increase occurs after the first six months and at one and three years from LT, and the median weight gain is 5.1 and 9.5 kg, respectively. Notably, at one and three years, 24% and 31% of transplant patients become obese [4]. However, the above-cited authors [4] reported that the vast part of enrolled patients were also obese before LT. Considering only patients who were not obese at the time of surgery, 15.5% at one year and 26.3% at three years had a body mass index (BMI) >30 [4]. In a further study, 23 patients were followed for nine months after LT. At the end of the study, 87 of the subjects were overweight or obese with a significant increase in fat mass and a minor improvement in lean mass [5]. Another study [6] showed progressive weight gain in the first year after LT, with one-third of patients becoming obese at the end of observation. Considering a follow-up of four years, overweight and obesity were found in 58% and 21% of cases and high BMI before LT was the main risk factor of post-LT obesity [7].

In this context, DM, hyperlipidemia and arterial hypertension can be often diagnosed after LT [1] (see Table 1).

Table 1. Multifactorial conditions affecting transplant patients.

Disease	Incidence	Risk Factors	References
Diabetes mellitus	10%–64%	Male gender, high pre-LT BMI, family history, hepatitis C, older age, immunosuppressants, rapamycin gene polymorphisms, *TCF7L2* gene polymorphisms (donor)	[8–11]
Hyperlipidemia	45%–69%	Diet, older age, high BMI, DM, renal impairment, immunosuppressants, low-density lipoprotein receptor gene polymorphism (donor)	[12–15]
Arterial hypertension	50%–100%	Obesity, older age, impaired glycemia, immunosuppressants	[9,16,17]

LT: liver transplant; BMI, body mass index; TCF7L2, Transcription factor 7-like 2; DM, diabetes mellitus.

Post-LT DM is associated with more significant morbidity with respect to pre-LT disease, determining an increased risk of post-operative infection and cardiovascular events [8,18]. The incidence of post-LT DM ranges from 10% to 64% [9]. Ahn *et al.* [19] showed that among 74 patients transplanted with post-LT DM, post-LT DM was transient in 56.8%, while in the others it was persistent. Although the underlying mechanisms are not yet clear, the main risk factors for the onset of post-LT DM are the following: male gender, high pre-LT BMI, positive family history, hepatitis C virus infection, older age, high dosage of immunosuppressant drugs and rapamycin gene polymorphisms [8]. A meta-analysis confirmed that male gender, high pre-LT BMI and positive family history are predictive of post-LT DM development [10]. Transcription factor 7-like 2 (TCF7L2) protein regulates cell proliferation and differentiation modifying the insulin secretion [20]. Notably, it was reported that polymorphisms of the *TCF7L2* gene in LT donors are another independent risk factor of post-LT DM [11].

Among transplanted patients, a percentage ranging from 45% to 69% develops hyperlipidemia, which is a significant risk factor for cardiovascular morbidity and mortality [12]. Increased nutrient intake, older age, body weight, presence of DM, renal impairment, immunosuppressive drugs, such as steroids, CSA, TAC, and SIR, are risk factors for post-LT hyperlipidemia [13,14].

Interestingly, the polymorphism of the low-density lipoprotein receptor gene in the donor may facilitate the development of hyperlipidemia in the recipient [15].

Arterial hypertension, an uncommon feature in subjects with chronic liver disease, arises in 50%–100% of patients after LT [9,16]. Post-LT hypertension usually develops in the first six months after LT as a consequence of systemic vasoconstriction, elevation in plasma endothelin-1 concentrations, and increased arterial stiffness [21]. Occurrence of post-LT hypertension is favored by obesity and older age and is often associated with impaired glycemia. Moreover, it is well known that both CNIs and corticosteroids have negative effects on pressure control [17].

3. Metabolic Impact of Immunosuppressant Drugs

It is well known that immunosuppressive agents might exert negative metabolic effects [22] (see Table 2).

Table 2. Most used immunosuppressant drugs and main metabolic side effects.

Drug	Side Effects	References
Corticosteroids	Increased fat depositions, decreased fat oxidation, increased proteolysis, reduced protein synthesis, IR, hyperlipidemia, sodium retention, NAFLD	[23–25]
CSA	Decreased energy metabolism and muscle mass, weight gain, hyperlipidemia, arterial hypertension	[26–30]
TAC	DM, hyperlipidemia, arterial hypertension	[10,27–30]
SIR	Decreased muscle mass, hyperlipidemia, glycemic alteration	[31–33]

CSA: cyclosporine; TAC: tacrolimus; SIR: sirolimus; IR, insulin resistance; NAFLD, non-alcoholic fatty liver disease; DM, diabetes mellitus.

Corticosteroids represent a key component of the immunosuppressant protocol in the first months after LT but are also necessary in the long-term management of patients transplanted for autoimmune or cholestatic liver disease. Corticosteroids show dose-related metabolic side effects. They increase appetite and fat depositions, drop fat oxidation, and lead to increased proteolysis and reduced protein synthesis [23,24]. Moreover, high doses of corticosteroids determine the rise of both IR and gluconeogenesis [25]. Corticosteroids also negatively alter lipid metabolism and steroid-free protocols might lead to a significant decrease in hypertriglyceridemia [34]. Corticosteroids also influence mineralocorticoid metabolism, causing sodium retention. Interestingly, steroids directly correlate with NAFLD/NASH occurrence in liver allografts [35].

CNIs may negatively affect energy metabolism and muscle mass [26] and CSA represents an independent predictor of post-LT weight gain [36]. Through a meta-analysis including 10 studies, Li *et al.* [10] demonstrated that TAC is an independent risk factor for post-LT DM. Regarding lipid metabolism, CSA has a more negative effect in comparison with TAC. The incidence of hyperlipidemia is higher in patients treated with CSA than with TAC (14% *versus* 5% and 49% *versus* 17%) [27,28]. CNIs also favor the onset of arterial hypertension determining arterial vasoconstriction. Among CNIs, TAC seems to have a lesser impact on arterial pressure in comparison to CSA, but data are not conclusive [29,30]. As expected, minimizing the use of CNIs improves their metabolic profile and, consequently, the long-term outcome of patients [37,38].

SIR increases triglyceride production, being the most dangerous immunosuppressant in terms of lipid alteration. Among patients treated with SIR, 55% develop hyperlipidemia [31]. In addition, SIR alters the insulin signaling pathway [31] and negatively affects muscle mass status [32]. Recently, Zimmermann *et al.* [33] conducted a study involving 92 transplant patients, reporting that patients treated with mTORs were at higher risk of hyperlipidemia and glycemic alteration with respect to patients under CNIs.

4. Metabolic Syndrome after Transplant

The definition of MS includes a combination of at least three of the following factors: arterial hypertension, IR, hypertriglyceridemia, low high-density lipoprotein and obesity [39]. In the post-LT period, MS can be found in 50%–60% of patients. MS represents a relevant risk factor for atherosclerosis and cardiovascular disease, which are the main causes of post-LT morbidity and mortality [39]. Interestingly, the prevalence of post-LT MS is about twice that of the general North American population [40]. Older age, obesity, pre-LT DM, genetic polymorphisms in the living donor and the use of high-dosage immunosuppressive drugs are risk factors for post-LT MS [9]. Sprinzl *et al.* [41] analyzed a cohort of 170 transplant patients with a follow-up of two years. The authors showed that *de novo* MS was present in one-third of patients and glycosylated hemoglobin ≥5% and arterial hypertension were independent risk factors for it. Moreover, the authors demonstrated a negative dose-dependent role for steroids. It was also confirmed that in the post-LT period, MS could be considered as a link toward NAFLD/NASH. Interestingly, it was reported that changes in intestinal microbiota might also play a relevant role in the development of MS after LT [42]. Fussner *et al.* [43] retrospectively analyzed 455 consecutive LT recipients with a long follow-up (8–12 years), suggesting that increased BMI was a strong predictor of MS at one year from the LT. Consequently, the authors suggested that preventing weight gain in the early months after LT might decrease the probability of MS. However, the authors suggested that older age, post-LT DM, prior family history of cardiovascular disease, altered serum troponin, but not MS, were independent predictors of cardiovascular events. It has to be underlined that specific treatments for MS are not yet available, while the only feasible way to manage it is to treat its single components [44].

5. Post-Transplant Non-Alcoholic Fatty Liver Disease

In the pre-LT period, NAFLD and NASH represent the liver expression of altered metabolic status being associated in a large number of cases to IR, dyslipidemia and obesity. Considering the significant prevalence of metabolic diseases after LT, it is clear why both recurrent and *de novo* NAFLD/NASH can be found in transplant patients [41].

Burra *et al.* [45] reported that NASH recurrence ranges from 20% to 40%, this wide variability depending on the methodology used for the diagnosis. Notably, in the majority of cases the outcome of recurrent NAFLD/NASH is harmless, without an evolution toward cirrhosis [46]. Nevertheless, patients with recurrent NAFLD/NASH more frequently show cardiovascular disease and worse infection-related morbidity and mortality. This is evident considering that the recurrence of NASH is associated with DM, weight gain, and dyslipidemia [47]. Interestingly, genetic predisposition might play a role in the recurrence of NAFLD and NASH. The presence of the rs738409-G allele of the Patatin-like phospholipase in the LT recipients represents an independent risk factor for post-LT obesity, DM and steatosis [48,49].

The leading risk factors for the development of *de novo* NAFLD/NASH are the following: obesity, hyperlipidemia, DM, arterial hypertension, TAC-based immunosuppression, pre-LT alcoholic cirrhosis and liver graft steatosis [50]. Sprinzl *et al.* [41] analyzed the association between MS and post-LT NAFLD/NASH. Mixed vesicular steatosis was observed in 34.1% of patients. Hepatic steatosis was mild, moderate, and severe in 16.5%, 7.1%, and 2.9% of cases. Among patients with MS and steatosis, NASH was diagnosed only in 5.4% of patients, confirming that post-LT metabolic liver disease might be relevant not as a primary liver disease but as an indicator of cardiovascular risk. Remarkably, NAFLD/NASH patients showed higher triglyceride levels, elevated uric acid and higher BMI with respect to patients with MS but without liver disease. The authors demonstrated that obesity and dyslipidemia but not arterial hypertension and DM favored the onset of NAFLD/NASH among transplanted patients with MS. Another interesting assumption was that a BMI greater than 28.9 was the only specific risk factor for histological NASH. Mikolasevic *et al.* [51] identified the association between NAFLD/NASH and the development of post-LT cardiovascular and chronic kidney disease.

Consequently, according to these authors, diagnosing NAFLD/NASH in the post-LT period might improve the stratification of cardiovascular and kidney damage risk.

6. Therapeutic Approach against Post-Transplant Dysmetabolism

The knowledge of pathogenesis is central for understanding the rationale of the therapeutic approach against MS and NAFLD/NASH. The onset of IR represents a true turning point. In fact, IR determines a status of chronic inflammation that favors the other metabolic alterations [52]. The molecular basis of IR depends on both genetic and non-genetic mechanisms. IR determines a chain of events involving inflammation, hypercoagulability, and atherogenesis. Notably, IR occurs firstly in the vascular structures, and this is one of the main reasons for its association with cardiovascular disease [53]. Regarding the NAFLD/NASH, the latest proposed model is the "multiparallel hits" [54]. According to this hypothesis, many events happen in parallel, and all are potential therapeutic targets. The main pathological characters are IR, oxidative stress, adipose and pancreatic tissues, altered lipid metabolism, bile acids, gut microbiota, and bacterial endotoxins.

As we reported, transplant patients often develop IR and an increase in body weight [1]. Interestingly, Kouz *et al.* [55] demonstrated that in patients transplanted for NASH-cirrhosis, most of the weight gain occurs in the first year after LT, while the increase of the weight is more progressive in subjects with a different etiology. However, regardless of the kind of pre-LT liver disease, after LT a relevant increase in dietary intake can be found, especially in patients with pre-LT severe dietary restrictions, gastrointestinal symptoms or anorexia. In detail, from the pre-LT period to one year after LT, calories rise from 27 to 32 kCal/kg and proteins from 0.8 to 1.3 g/kg per day [56]. Richardson *et al.* [5] showed that in overweight or obese transplant patients, more significant energy intake, higher consumption of both proteins and carbohydrates and doubled intake of fat can be found with respect to the pre-LT period.

The feasible pharmacological tools for treating the single metabolic disease, associated or not with NAFLD/NASH, should be used with caution for the possible drug-drug interactions [57]. Notably, a single drug for post-LT MS is not available. Based on these considerations, the main intervention after surgery should be a strong lifestyle control for both prevention and treatment of MS. However, the only randomized trial of exercise and dietary counseling after LT published in 2006 did not show a real advantage with this approach [58]. In this study, 151 liver transplant patients, randomized into exercise and dietary counseling or usual care, showed a similar increase in body weight, fat mass and lean mass. It should be underlined that full adherence to exercise and nutrition was obtained only in 37% of subjects.

Many drugs have been proposed for the treatment of NAFLD/NASH, but lifestyle intervention should be the first-line therapy. In particular, lifestyle modification is the standard of care according to the Italian, European, Asian-Pacific and North American guidelines [59–62]. The main targets for the usefulness evaluation should be a weight loss of 7% and 150 min/week of physical activity [63,64]. In particular, a weight loss of 7% has been seen to significantly decrease fat accumulation and reduce necroinflammation in non-transplanted patients with NAFLD/NASH [63]. Markedly, aerobic and resistance physical activity have an independent positive effect in decreasing fat in the liver, regardless of the weight loss [65,66]. Furthermore, clinicians should take into account that the physical activity *per se* improves cardio-respiratory fitness [67,68]. Vitamin E and pioglitazone represent the first-line pharmacological options. Both vitamin E and pioglitazone improve fat accumulation and liver inflammation. However, the use of vitamin E is limited to patients without DM and it has no clear effects on fibrosis. On the other hand, pioglitazone shows a negative impact on patients' weight. In addition, the long-term safety of these drugs is uncertain. Many other drugs such as metformin, ursodeoxycholic acid, statins, pentoxifylline, and orlistat have been tested in pilot studies or randomized clinical trials with few results in terms of efficacy. Telmisartan, a safe antihypertensive drug, is an emerging drug with an interesting preliminary effect on NAFLD/NASH. It seems to have a positive impact on IR, liver steatosis, inflammation, and fibrosis [52]. As recently reported in a review article by Lassailly *et al.* [69], many other drugs are in progress for the treatment of NAFLD/NASH, including obeticholic acid, liraglutide and elafibranor. Authors also suggest that bariatric surgery may be successful in well-selected obese patients with NAFLD/NASH.

Concerning the transplanted patient, none of the cited therapeutic options have been validated.

7. Conclusions

Starting in the first months after surgery, transplant patients tend to develop overweight or obesity, IR and, consequently, multifactorial diseases. Consequently, a high prevalence of multifactorial disease such as DM, hyperlipidemia and arterial hypertension can be found. All these metabolic features negatively influence the outcome of transplant patients in terms of quality of life, morbidity and mortality.

All the main immunosuppressant drugs, such as corticosteroids, CSA, TAC and SIR, favor the onset of metabolic alterations. Corticosteroids are surely very important in the first months after LT but also in the long-term in selected cases. They lead to weight gain and fat accumulation negatively affecting lipid, glycemic and pressure profiles. Moreover, they directly increase the risk of steatosis development. CNIs have a negative metabolic impact since they increase weight gain and reduce muscle mass. TAC seems to be superior compared to CSA concerning the metabolic risk in terms of the alteration of lipid and arterial pressure. It should be the first choice among CNIs. SIR is the immunosuppressant with the worst lipid profile. Moreover, SIR shows a worse glycemic profile with respect to CNIs and has a negative effect on the muscle mass status. The choice of immunosuppressant is central and related to many aspects and evaluations such as the cardiovascular and renal risks. In general, one of the main aims of clinicians should be to minimize the dosage of immunosuppressants. This last assumption is true especially in the long-term period and in patients with pre-LT etiology different from autoimmune or cholestatic disease and without a history of graft rejection.

The presence of criteria for MS is frequent in the post-LT period and represents the main indicator of cardiovascular-related morbidity and mortality. NAFLD and its progressive form, represented by NASH, can be considered the liver expression of MS. Indeed, both recurrent and *de novo* NAFLD can be diagnosed in transplanted patients. The hepatic outcome of steatosis after surgery is generally not very aggressive, with few percentages of advanced fibrosis, in comparison with the pre-LT phase. However, together with MS, steatosis is a relevant indicator of increased cardiovascular risk. This assumption is important if we consider that cardiovascular disease is found in 10.6%, 20.7%, and 30.3% of recipients at one, five, and eight years from the LT [43]. Interestingly, post-LT NAFLD/NASH is also associated with an increased risk of infections and renal injury.

Clinicians might definitely use the diagnosis of NAFLD in the post-LT period as an indicator of increased cardiovascular and renal risk. Transplant patients with a first diagnosis of NAFLD should be closely monitored regarding peripheral atherosclerotic signs and kidney function. In this direction, the development of diagnostic algorithms with the use non-invasive tools is warranted. Karlas *et al.* [70] demonstrated that modern non-invasive liver graft assessments such as hepatic ultrasound and transient elastography might be able to properly detect both steatosis and graft fibrosis.

Specific therapeutic options against post-LT MS or NAFLD are not available. Targeted pharmacological tools can be used for each component of MS. So far, a strong behavioral change in terms of diet and aerobic exercise is the only reasonable approach for transplant patients for both primary and secondary care. Transplant patients should be educated starting from the first weeks after surgery for preventing the development of multifactorial diseases, MS and metabolic liver illness. A well-done stratification of the cardiovascular risk should be developed as soon as possible after LT. In the next years, the genetic study of recipients and donors might improve the quality of organ allocation, decreasing the metabolic complications after LT.

Int. J. Mol. Sci. **2016**, *17*, 490

Author Contributions: Stefano Gitto and Erica Villa conceived and designed the article; Stefano Gitto wrote the paper; Erica Villa reviewed the manuscript and performed a critical revision.

Conflicts of Interest: The authors declare no conflict of interest.

Abbreviations

LT	Liver Transplant
IR	insulin resistance
DM	Diabetes mellitus
CNIs	calcineurin inhibitors
CSA	cyclosporine
TAC	tacrolimus
mTORs	mammalian target of rapamycin inhibitors
SIR	sirolimus
MS	Metabolic Syndrome
NAFLD	Non-alcoholic fatty liver disease
NASH	Non-alcoholic steatohepatitis
BMI	body mass index
TCF7L2	Transcription factor 7-like 2

References

1. Watt, K.D.; Pedersen, R.A.; Kremers, W.K.; Heimbach, J.K.; Charlton, M.R. Evolution of causes and risk factors for mortality post-liver transplant: Results of the NIDDK long-term follow-up study. *Am. J. Transplant.* **2010**, *10*, 1420–1427. [CrossRef] [PubMed]
2. Charco, R.; Cantarell, C.; Vargas, V.; Capdevila, L.; Lázaro, J.L.; Hidalgo, E.; Murio, E.; Margarit, C. Serum cholesterol changes in long-term survivors of liver transplantation: A comparison between cyclosporine and tacrolimus therapy. *Liver Transpl. Surg.* **1999**, *5*, 204–208. [CrossRef] [PubMed]
3. Bhagat, V.; Mindikoglu, A.L.; Nudo, C.G.; Schiff, E.R.; Tzakis, A.; Regev, A. Outcomes of liver transplantation in patients with cirrhosis due to nonalcoholic steatohepatitis *versus* patients with cirrhosis due to alcoholic liver disease. *Liver Transplant.* **2009**, *15*, 1814–1820. [CrossRef] [PubMed]
4. Richards, J.; Gunson, B.; Johnson, J.; Neuberger, J. Weight gain and obesity after liver transplantation. *Transpl. Int.* **2005**, *18*, 461–466. [CrossRef] [PubMed]
5. Richardson, R.A.; Garden, O.J.; Davidson, H.I. Reduction in energy expenditure after liver transplantation. *Nutrition* **2001**, *17*, 585–589. [CrossRef]
6. Ferreira, L.G.; Santos, L.F.; Anastácio, L.R.; Lima, A.S.; Correia, M.I. Resting energy expenditure, body composition, and dietary intake: A longitudinal study before and after liver transplantation. *Transplantation* **2013**, *96*, 579–585. [CrossRef] [PubMed]
7. Anastácio, L.R.; Ferreira, L.G.; de Sena Ribeiro, H.; Lima, A.S.; Vilela, E.G.; Toulson Davisson Correia, M.I. Body composition and over-weight of liver transplant recipients. *Transplantation* **2011**, *92*, 947–951. [CrossRef] [PubMed]
8. Lane, J.T.; Dagogo-Jack, S. Approach to the patient with new-onset diabetes after transplant (NODAT). *J. Clin. Endocrinol. Metab.* **2011**, *96*, 3289–3297. [CrossRef] [PubMed]
9. Parekh, J.; Corley, D.A.; Feng, S. Diabetes, hypertension and hyperlipidemia: Prevalence over time and impact on long-term survival after liver transplantation. *Am. J. Transplant.* **2012**, *12*, 2181–2187. [CrossRef] [PubMed]
10. Li, D.W.; Lu, T.F.; Hua, X.W.; Dai, H.J.; Cui, X.L.; Zhang, J.J.; Xia, Q. Risk factors for new onset diabetes mellitus after liver transplantation: A meta-analysis. *World J. Gastroenterol.* **2015**, *21*, 6329–6340. [CrossRef] [PubMed]
11. Ling, Q.; Xie, H.; Lu, D.; Wei, X.; Gao, F.; Zhou, L.; Xu, X.; Zheng, S. Association between donor and recipient *TCF7L2* gene polymorphisms and the risk of new-onset diabetes mellitus after liver transplantation in a Han Chinese population. *J. Hepatol.* **2013**, *58*, 271–277. [CrossRef] [PubMed]

12. Bianchi, G.; Marchesini, G.; Marzocchi, R.; Pinna, A.D.; Zoli, M. Metabolic syndrome in liver transplantation: Relation to etiology and immunosuppression. *Liver Transplant.* **2008**, *14*, 1648–1654. [CrossRef] [PubMed]

13. Singh, S.; Watt, K.D. Long-term medical management of the liver transplant recipient: What the primary care physician needs to know. *Mayo Clin. Proc.* **2012**, *87*, 779–790. [CrossRef] [PubMed]

14. Morrisett, J.D.; Abdel-Fattah, G.; Hoogeveen, R.; Mitchell, E.; Ballantyne, C.M.; Pownall, H.J.; Opekun, A.R.; Jaffe, J.S.; Oppermann, S.; Kahan, B.D. Effects of sirolimus on plasma lipids, lipoprotein levels, and fatty acid metabolism in renal transplant patients. *J. Lipid Res.* **2002**, *43*, 1170–1180. [PubMed]

15. Nikkilä, K.; Åberg, F.; Isoniemi, H. Transmission of LDLR mutation from donor through liver transplantation resulting in hypercholesterolemia in the recipient. *Am. J. Transplant.* **2014**, *14*, 2898–2902. [CrossRef] [PubMed]

16. Hryniewiecka, E.; Zegarska, J.; Paczek, L. Arterial hypertension in liver transplant recipients. *Transplant. Proc.* **2011**, *43*, 3029–3034. [CrossRef] [PubMed]

17. Zheng, J.; Wang, W.L. Risk factors of metabolic syndrome after liver transplantation. *Hepatobiliary Pancreat. Dis. Int.* **2015**, *14*, 582–587. [CrossRef]

18. Wilkinson, A.; Davidson, J.; Dotta, F.; Home, P.D.; Keown, P.; Kiberd, B.; Jardine, A.; Levitt, N.; Marchetti, P.; Markell, M.; *et al.* Guidelines for the treatment and management of new-onset diabetes after transplantation. *Clin. Transplant.* **2005**, *19*, 291–298. [CrossRef] [PubMed]

19. Ahn, H.Y.; Cho, Y.M.; Yi, N.J.; Suh, K.S.; Lee, K.U.; Park, K.S.; Kim, S.Y.; Lee, H.K. Predictive factors associated with the reversibility of post-transplantation diabetes mellitus following liver transplantation. *J. Korean Med. Sci.* **2009**, *24*, 567–570. [CrossRef] [PubMed]

20. Musavi, Z.; Azarpira, N.; Sangtarash, M.H.; Kordi, M.; Kazemi, K.; Geramizadeh, B.; Malek-Hosseini, S.A. Polymorphism of transcription factor-7-Like 2 (*TCF7L2*) gene and new-onset diabetes after liver transplantation. *Int. J. Organ Transplant. Med.* **2015**, *6*, 14–22. [PubMed]

21. Neal, D.A.; Brown, M.J.; Wilkinson, I.B.; Alexander, G.J. Mechanisms of hypertension after liver transplantation. *Transplantation* **2005**, *79*, 935–940. [CrossRef] [PubMed]

22. Giusto, M.; Lattanzi, B.; Di Gregorio, V.; Giannelli, V.; Lucidi, C.; Merli, M. Changes in nutritional status after liver transplantation. *World J. Gastroenterol.* **2014**, *20*, 10682–10690. [CrossRef] [PubMed]

23. Van den Ham, E.C.; Kooman, J.P.; Christiaans, M.H.; Leunissen, K.M.; van Hooff, J.P. Posttransplantation weight gain is predominantly due to an increase in body fat mass. *Transplantation* **2000**, *70*, 241–242. [PubMed]

24. Mercier, J.G.; Hokanson, J.F.; Brooks, G.A. Effects of cyclosporine A on skeletal muscle mitochondrial respiration and endurance time in rats. *Am. J. Respir. Crit. Care Med.* **1995**, *151*, 1532–1536. [CrossRef] [PubMed]

25. Rodríguez-Perálvarez, M.; Germani, G.; Darius, T.; Lerut, J.; Tsochatzis, E.; Burroughs, A.K. Tacrolimus trough levels, rejection and renal impairment in liver transplantation: A systematic review and meta-analysis. *Am. J. Transplant.* **2012**, *12*, 2797–2814. [CrossRef] [PubMed]

26. Sakuma, K.; Yamaguchi, A. The functional role of calcineurin in hypertrophy, regeneration, and disorders of skeletal muscle. *J. Biomed. Biotechnol.* **2010**, *2010*. [CrossRef] [PubMed]

27. Rabkin, J.M.; Corless, C.L.; Rosen, H.R.; Olyaei, A.J. Immunosuppression impact on long-term cardiovascular complications after liver transplantation. *Am. J. Surg.* **2002**, *183*, 595–599. [CrossRef]

28. Manzarbeitia, C.; Reich, D.J.; Rothstein, K.D.; Braitman, L.E.; Levin, S.; Munoz, S.J. Tacrolimus conversion improves hyperlipidemic states in stable liver transplant recipients. *Liver Transplant.* **2001**, *7*, 93–99. [CrossRef] [PubMed]

29. Ojo, A.O.; Held, P.J.; Port, F.K.; Wolfe, R.A.; Leichtman, A.B.; Young, E.W.; Arndorfer, J.; Christensen, L.; Merion, R.M. Chronic renal failure after transplantation of a nonrenal organ. *N. Engl. J. Med.* **2003**, *349*, 931–940. [CrossRef] [PubMed]

30. Rossetto, A.; Bitetto, D.; Bresadola, V.; Lorenzin, D.; Baccarani, U.; de Anna, D.; Bresadola, F.; Adani, G.L. Cardiovascular risk factors and immunosuppressive regimen after liver transplantation. *Transplant. Proc.* **2010**, *42*, 2576–2578. [CrossRef] [PubMed]

31. Neff, G.W.; Montalbano, M.; Tzakis, A.G. Ten years of sirolimus therapy in orthotopic liver transplant recipients. *Transplant. Proc.* **2003**, *35*, 209S–216S. [CrossRef]

32. Miyabara, E.H.; Conte, T.C.; Silva, M.T.; Baptista, I.L.; Bueno, C.; Fiamoncini, J.; Lambertucci, R.H.; Serra, C.S.; Brum, P.C.; Curi, T.; *et al.* Mammalian target of rapamycin complex 1 is involved in differentiation of regenerating myofibers *in vivo. Muscle Nerve* **2010**, *42*, 778–787. [CrossRef] [PubMed]

33. Zimmermann, A.; Zobeley, C.; Weber, M.M.; Lang, H.; Galle, P.R.; Zimmermann, T. Changes in lipid and carbohydrate metabolism under mTOR- and calcineurin-based immunosuppressive regimen in adult patients after liver transplantation. *Eur. J. Intern. Med.* **2016**, *29*, 104–109. [CrossRef] [PubMed]

34. Klintmalm, G.B.; Washburn, W.K.; Rudich, S.M.; Heffron, T.G.; Teperman, L.W.; Fasola, C.; Eckhoff, D.E.; Netto, G.J.; Katz, E. Corticosteroid-free immunosuppression with daclizumab in HCV⁺ liver transplant recipients: 1-Year interim results of the HCV-3 study. *Liver Transplant.* **2007**, *13*, 1521–1531. [CrossRef] [PubMed]

35. Contos, M.J.; Cales, W.; Sterling, R.K.; Luketic, V.A.; Shiffman, M.L.; Mills, A.S.; Fisher, R.A.; Ham, J.; Sanyal, A.J. Development of nonalcoholic fatty liver disease after orthotopic liver transplantation for cryptogenic cirrhosis. *Liver Transplant.* **2001**, *7*, 363–373. [CrossRef] [PubMed]

36. Iadevaia, M.; Giusto, M.; Giannelli, V.; Lai, Q.; Rossi, M.; Berloco, P.; Corradini, S.G.; Merli, M. Metabolic syndrome and cardiovascular risk after liver transplantation: A single-center experience. *Transplant. Proc.* **2012**, *44*, 2005–2006. [CrossRef] [PubMed]

37. Rodríguez-Perálvarez, M.; Germani, G.; Papastergiou, V.; Tsochatzis, E.; Thalassinos, E.; Luong, T.V.; Rolando, N.; Dhillon, A.P.; Patch, D.; O'Beirne, J.; *et al.* Early tacrolimus exposure after liver transplantation: Relationship with moderate/severe acute rejection and long-term outcome. *J. Hepatol.* **2013**, *58*, 262–270. [CrossRef] [PubMed]

38. Heisel, O.; Heisel, R.; Balshaw, R.; Keown, P. New onset diabetes mellitus in patients receiving calcineurin inhibitors: A system-atic review and meta-analysis. *Am. J. Transplant.* **2004**, *4*, 583–595. [CrossRef] [PubMed]

39. Watt, K.D.; Charlton, M.R. Metabolic syndrome and liver transplantation: A review and guide to management. *J. Hepatol.* **2010**, *53*, 199–206. [CrossRef] [PubMed]

40. Ford, E.S.; Giles, W.H.; Dietz, W.H. Prevalence of the metabolic syndrome among US adults: Findings from the third National Health and Nutrition Examination Survey. *JAMA* **2002**, *287*, 356–359. [CrossRef] [PubMed]

41. Sprinzl, M.F.; Weinmann, A.; Lohse, N.; Tönissen, H.; Koch, S.; Schattenberg, J.; Hoppe-Lotichius, M.; Zimmermann, T.; Galle, P.R.; Hansen, T.; *et al.* Metabolic syndrome and its association with fatty liver disease after orthotopic liver transplantation. *Transpl. Int.* **2013**, *26*, 67–74. [CrossRef] [PubMed]

42. Qin, N.; Yang, F.; Li, A.; Prifti, E.; Chen, Y.; Shao, L.; Guo, J.; Le Chatelier, E.; Yao, J.; Wu, L.; *et al.* Alterations of the human gut microbiome in liver cirrhosis. *Nature* **2014**, *513*, 59–64. [CrossRef] [PubMed]

43. Fussner, L.A.; Heimbach, J.K.; Fan, C.; Dierkhising, R.; Coss, E.; Leise, M.D.; Watt, K.D. Cardiovascular disease after liver transplantation: When, what, and who is at risk. *Liver Transplant.* **2015**, *21*, 889–896. [CrossRef] [PubMed]

44. Pagadala, M.; Dasarathy, S.; Eghtesad, B.; McCullough, A.J. Posttransplant metabolic syndrome: An epidemic waiting to happen. *Liver Transplant.* **2009**, *15*, 1662–1670. [CrossRef] [PubMed]

45. Burra, P.; Germani, G. Orthotopic liver transplantation in non-alcoholic fatty liver disease patients. *Rev. Recent Clin. Trials* **2014**, *9*, 210–216. [CrossRef] [PubMed]

46. Dureja, P.; Mellinger, J.; Agni, R.; Chang, F.; Avey, G.; Lucey, M.; Said, A. NAFLD recurrence in liver transplant recipients. *Transplantation* **2011**, *91*, 684–689. [CrossRef] [PubMed]

47. Malik, S.M.; de Vera, M.E.; Fontes, P.; Shaikh, O.; Sasatomi, E.; Ahmad, J. Recurrent disease following liver transplantation for nonalcoholic steatohepatitis cirrhosis. *Liver Transplant.* **2009**, *15*, 1843–1851. [CrossRef] [PubMed]

48. Finkenstedt, A.; Auer, C.; Glodny, B.; Posch, U.; Steitzer, H.; Lanzer, G.; Pratschke, J.; Biebl, M.; Steurer, M.; Graziadei, I.; *et al.* Patatin-like phospholipase domain-containing protein 3 rs738409-G in recipients of liver transplants is a risk factor for graft steatosis. *Clin. Gastroenterol. Hepatol.* **2013**, *11*, 1667–1672. [CrossRef] [PubMed]

49. Watt, K.D.; Dierkhising, R.; Fan, C.; Heimbach, J.K.; Tillman, H.; Goldstein, D.; Thompson, A.; Krishnan, A.; Charlton, M.R. Investigation of PNPLA3 and IL28B genotypes on diabetes and obesity after liver transplantation: Insight into mechanisms of disease. *Am. J. Transplant.* **2013**, *13*, 2450–2457. [CrossRef] [PubMed]

50. Dumortier, J.; Giostra, E.; Belbouab, S.; Morard, I.; Guillaud, O.; Spahr, L.; Boillot, O.; Rubbia-Brandt, L.; Scoazec, J.Y.; Hadengue, A. Non-alcoholic fatty liver disease in liver transplant recipients: Another story of "seed and soil". *Am. J. Gastroenterol.* **2010**, *105*, 613–620. [CrossRef] [PubMed]

51. Mikolasevic, I.; Orlic, L.; Hrstic, I.; Milic, S. Metabolic syndrome and non-alcoholic fatty liver disease after liver or kidney transplantation. *Hepatol. Res.* **2015**. [CrossRef] [PubMed]

52. Gitto, S.; Vitale, G.; Villa, E.; Andreone, P. Treatment of nonalcoholic steatohepatitis in adults: Present and future. *Gastroenterol. Res. Pract.* **2015**, *2015*. [CrossRef] [PubMed]

53. Kim, F.; Pham, M.; Maloney, E.; Rizzo, N.O.; Morton, G.J.; Wisse, B.E.; Kirk, E.A.; Chait, A.; Schwartz, M.W. Vascular inflammation, insulin resistance, and reduced nitric oxide production precede the onset of peripheral insulin resistance. *Arterioscler. Thromb. Vasc. Biol.* **2008**, *28*, 1982–1988. [CrossRef] [PubMed]

54. Tilg, H.; Moschen, A.R. Evolution of inflammation in nonalcoholic fatty liver disease: The multiple parallel hits hypothesis. *Hepatology* **2010**, *52*, 1836–1846. [CrossRef] [PubMed]

55. Kouz, J.; Vincent, C.; Leong, A.; Dorais, M.; Räkel, A. Weight gain after orthotopic liver transplantation: Is nonalcoholic fatty liver disease cirrhosis a risk factor for greater weight gain? *Liver Transplant.* **2014**, *20*, 1266–1274. [CrossRef] [PubMed]

56. Merli, M.; Giusto, M.; Riggio, O.; Gentili, F.; Molinaro, A.; Attili, A.F.; Ginanni Corradini, S.; Rossi, M. Improvement of nutritional status in malnourished cirrhotic patients one year after liver transplantation. *e-SPEN* **2011**, *6*, e142–e147. [CrossRef]

57. Charlton, M. Evolving aspects of liver transplantation for nonalcoholic steatohepatitis. *Curr. Opin. Organ Transplant.* **2013**, *18*, 251–258. [CrossRef] [PubMed]

58. Krasnoff, J.B.; Vintro, A.Q.; Ascher, N.L.; Bass, N.M.; Paul, S.M.; Dodd, M.J.; Painter, P.L. A randomized trial of exercise and dietary counseling after liver transplantation. *Am. J. Transplant.* **2006**, *6*, 1896–1905. [CrossRef] [PubMed]

59. Loria, P.; Adinolfi, L.E.; Bellentani, S.; Bugianesi, E.; Grieco, A.; Fargion, S.; Gasbarrini, A.; Loguercio, C.; Lonardo, A.; Marchesini, G.; *et al.* Practice guidelines for the diagnosis and management of nonalcoholic fatty liver disease: A decalogue from the Italian Association for the Study of the Liver (AISF) Expert Committee. *Dig. Liver Dis.* **2010**, *42*, 272–282. [CrossRef] [PubMed]

60. Ratziu, V.; Bellentani, S.; Cortez-Pinto, H.; Day, C.; Marchesini, G. A position statement on NAFLD/NASH based on the EASL 2009 special conference. *J. Hepatol.* **2010**, *53*, 372–384. [CrossRef] [PubMed]

61. Farrell, G.C.; Chitturi, S.; Lau, G.K.; Sollano, J.D.; Asia-Pacific Working Party on NAFLD. Guidelines for the assessment and management of non-alcoholic fatty liver disease in the Asia-Pacific region: Executive summary. *J. Gastroenterol. Hepatol.* **2007**, *22*, 775–777. [CrossRef] [PubMed]

62. Chalasani, N.; Younossi, Z.; Lavine, J.E.; Diehl, A.M.; Brunt, E.M.; Cusi, K.; Charlton, M.; Sanyal, A.J.; American Gastroenterological Association; American Association for the Study of Liver Diseases; *et al.* The diagnosis and management of non-alcoholic fatty liver disease: Practice guideline by the American Gastroenterological Association, American Association for the Study of Liver Diseases, and American College of Gastroenterology. *Gastroenterology* **2012**, *142*, 1592–1609. [PubMed]

63. Promrat, K.; Kleiner, D.E.; Niemeier, H.M.; Jackvony, E.; Kearns, M.; Wands, J.R.; Fava, J.L.; Wing, R.R. Randomized controlled trial testing the effects of weight loss on nonalcoholic steatohepatitis. *Hepatology* **2010**, *51*, 121–129. [CrossRef] [PubMed]

64. Diabetes Prevention Program (DPP) Research Group. The Diabetes Prevention Program (DPP): Description of lifestyle intervention. *Diabetes Care* **2002**, *25*, 2165–2171.

65. George, A.; Bauman, A.; Johnston, A.; Farrell, G.; Chey, T.; George, J. Independent effects of physical activity in patients with nonalcoholic fatty liver disease. *Hepatology* **2009**, *50*, 68–76. [CrossRef] [PubMed]

66. Hallsworth, K.; Fattakhova, G.; Hollingsworth, K.G.; Thoma, C.; Moore, S.; Taylor, R.; Day, C.P.; Trenell, M.I. Resistance exercise reduces liver fat and its mediators in non-alcoholic fatty liver disease independent of weight loss. *Gut* **2011**, *60*, 1278–1283. [CrossRef] [PubMed]

67. Kantartzis, K.; Thamer, C.; Peter, A.; Machann, J.; Schick, F.; Schraml, C.; Königsrainer, A.; Königsrainer, I.; Kröber, S.; Niess, A.; *et al.* High cardiorespiratory fitness is an independent predictor of the reduction in liver fat during a lifestyle intervention in non-alcoholic fatty liver disease. *Gut* **2009**, *58*, 1281–1288. [CrossRef] [PubMed]

68. Targher, G.; Marra, F.; Marchesini, G. Increased risk of cardiovascular disease in non-alcoholic fatty liver disease: Causal effect or epiphenomenon? *Diabetologia* **2008**, *51*, 1947–1953. [CrossRef] [PubMed]

69. Lassailly, G.; Caiazzo, R.; Pattou, F.; Mathurin, P. Perspectives on treatment for nonalcoholic steatohepatitis. *Gastroenterology* **2016**. [CrossRef] [PubMed]

70. Karlas, T.; Kollmeier, J.; Böhm, S.; Müller, J.; Kovacs, P.; Tröltzsch, M.; Weimann, A.; Bartels, M.; Rosendahl, J.; Mössner, J.; *et al.* Noninvasive characterization of graft steatosis after liver transplantation. *Scand. J. Gastroenterol.* **2015**, *50*, 224–232. [CrossRef] [PubMed]

International Journal of
Molecular Sciences

MDPI

Review

A Guide to Non-Alcoholic Fatty Liver Disease in Childhood and Adolescence

Jonathan L. Temple [1], Paul Cordero [2,*], Jiawei Li [2], Vi Nguyen [2] and Jude A. Oben [2,3,*]

[1] Faculty of Life Sciences and Medicine, King's College London, Strand, London WC2R 2LS, UK;
    jonathan.temple@kcl.ac.uk
[2] Institute for Liver and Digestive Health, University College London, Rowland Hill Street,
    London NW3 2PF, UK; jiawei.li.10@ucl.ac.uk (J.L.); v.nguyen@ucl.ac.uk (V.N.)
[3] Department of Gastroenterology and Hepatology, Guy's and St Thomas' Hospital, NHS Foundation Trust,
    Westminster Bridge Rd., London SE1 7EH, UK
*   Correspondence: paul.sanchez@ucl.ac.uk (P.C.); j.oben@ucl.ac.uk (J.A.O.);
    Tel.: +44-207-433-2875 (P.C. & J.A.O.)

Academic Editors: Amedeo Lonardo and Giovanni Targher
Received: 17 May 2016; Accepted: 7 June 2016; Published: 15 June 2016

Abstract: Non-Alcoholic Fatty Liver Disease (NAFLD) is now the most prevalent form of chronic liver disease, affecting 10%–20% of the general paediatric population. Within the next 10 years it is expected to become the leading cause of liver pathology, liver failure and indication for liver transplantation in childhood and adolescence in the Western world. While our understanding of the pathophysiological mechanisms underlying this disease remains limited, it is thought to be the hepatic manifestation of more widespread metabolic dysfunction and is strongly associated with a number of metabolic risk factors, including insulin resistance, dyslipidaemia, cardiovascular disease and, most significantly, obesity. Despite this, "paediatric" NAFLD remains under-studied, under-recognised and, potentially, undermanaged. This article will explore and evaluate our current understanding of NAFLD in childhood and adolescence and how it differs from adult NAFLD, in terms of its epidemiology, pathophysiology, natural history, diagnosis and clinical management. Given the current absence of definitive radiological and histopathological diagnostic tests, maintenance of a high clinical suspicion by all members of the multidisciplinary team in primary and specialist care settings remains the most potent of diagnostic tools, enabling early diagnosis and appropriate therapeutic intervention.

Keywords: NAFLD; steatosis; obesity; children; adolescent

1. Introduction

Non-Alcoholic Fatty Liver Disease (NAFLD) encompasses a spectrum of chronic liver disease, characterised by excessive hepatic fat accumulation (steatosis) in the absence of significant alcohol consumption, occurring with or without hepatic inflammation and fibrosis [1]. Simple or bland hepatic steatosis describes the abnormal accumulation of fat in >5% of hepatocytes, without evidence of hepatocellular injury or fibrosis. A significant proportion of patients with hepatic steatosis, however, progress to a more advanced form of the disease, Non-Alcoholic Steatohepatitis (NASH), where steatosis coexists with hepatocellular injury and inflammation, which can precipitate hepatic necrosis, fibrosis and cirrhosis, as well as a significantly increased risk of hepatocellular carcinoma [1–3].

NAFLD is thought to be a hepatic manifestation of more widespread and underlying metabolic dysfunction and is strongly associated with a number of metabolic risk factors, including insulin resistance, dyslipidaemia, cardiovascular disease and, most significantly, obesity [2,4,5]. Our understanding of the pathophysiological mechanisms underpinning these relationships, however, remains incomplete.

While detailed clinico-pathological descriptions of NAFLD in adults can be found in the literature as far back as the 1850s, the first case of paediatric NAFLD was reported in 1983 by Moran *et al.* [6,7]. It is now the most prevalent form of chronic liver disease in childhood and adolescence, affecting approximately 10%–20% of the general paediatric population. Within the next 10 years, paediatric NAFLD is expected to become the most prevalent cause of liver pathology, liver failure and indication for liver transplantation in childhood and adolescence in the Western world [8–13].

Despite this, "paediatric" NAFLD remains under-studied, under-recognised and, potentially, undermanaged [14]. Important gaps remain in our overall approach to screening, diagnosis, management and follow-up, particularly during the transition between paediatric and adult clinical services [15]. More accurate epidemiological and pathophysiological data derived from larger longitudinal cohort studies are needed in order to better determine the true prevalence and natural history of paediatric NAFLD among different ethnic groups, aiding the selection and widespread implementation of more effective therapeutic interventions [13,16]. Recognition, first, of the occurrence of NAFLD in the paediatric population and, second, the differences in its clinical presentation, pathophysiology, histology and prognosis when compared to adult disease, is of critical importance.

2. Clinical Presentation of Paediatric Non-Alcoholic Fatty Liver Disease (NAFLD)

Although cases of paediatric NAFLD and NASH-related cirrhosis have been reported in patients as young as 2 and 8 years old, respectively, most usually present clinically above the age of 10 years. The mean age of diagnosis is 11–13 years old [11,12,17]. However, NAFLD often remains asymptomatic until significant damage to the liver and/or other systems has occurred or coincident acute liver injury manifests worse clinical outcomes than would otherwise be expected or NAFLD-associated comorbidities, including insulin resistance and Type II Diabetes Mellitus, develop. Diagnosis, therefore, is often incidental on physical examination or routine blood testing, accounting for approximately 7%–11% of abnormal liver function tests (LFTs) and 74% of liver biopsies in obese patients with metabolic risk factors [8,9].

Children may also report non-specific symptoms, including abdominal pain due to stretching of the liver capsule, fatigue, irritability, headaches and difficulty concentrating [12,14]. Hepatomegaly may be appreciated on manual palpation in up to 50% of cases but can be difficult to discern in obese patients. Acanthosis nigricans, a clinical marker of hyperinsulinemia that can manifest on the back of the neck, intertriginous areas or joints, has been reported in 33%–50% of children with biopsy-proven NAFLD [8,9,11,17,18].

A landmark study of 742 autopsy specimens from children in San Diego County (CA, USA) between 1993 and 2003 found evidence of NAFLD in 17.3% of children aged 15–19 years old [9]. This is consistent with other more recent studies [11,19,20], including one involving 995 adolescents aged 17 years old, which reported a prevalence of NAFLD of greater than 15% [21]. The true prevalence of paediatric NAFLD, however, is difficult to determine and may be even higher, given the marked variations in the populations studied, in terms of age, ethnicity, the diagnostic parameters applied and clinical bias with regards to the "appropriateness" of diagnosing NAFLD in children, as well as the general paucity of research.

Certainly, the prevalence of NAFLD in childhood and adolescence has greatly increased in recent decades, in the wake of rising levels of childhood obesity [22]. Paediatric NAFLD is strongly associated with a number of metabolic risk factors, including increased insulin resistance, dyslipidaemia, cardiovascular disease and, most significantly, visceral adiposity [12,22–24]. A number of studies now suggest the prevalence of NAFLD in overweight and obese youth to be up to 70%, compared to 7% in those of normal weight [25,26]. Severe obesity (>95th centile for age and gender-adjusted body mass index) is also associated with more adverse clinical outcomes and greater risk of progression to NASH and cirrhosis in childhood [14].

Below 3 years of age, obesity does not usually produce hepatic steatosis and, as such, its incidence may well indicate more severe underlying metabolic dysfunction with worse prognosis [17]. Therefore, 'brightness' of the liver on ultrasound or increased aminotransferases in this age group requires a detailed clinical workup, to exclude many rare metabolic or systemic diseases that may also present with hepatic steatosis, collectively referred to by some authors as the "NASH trash bin" [17].

While simple steatosis carries a minimal risk of cirrhosis and liver failure in adults, it appears to follow a more aggressive course in paediatric cases, with many children progressing to NASH and hepatic fibrosis either in childhood or early adulthood [27,28]. Paediatric patients with more advanced fibrosis on liver biopsy tend to have more hepatic complications and a worse prognosis, particularly regarding the risk of cirrhosis [29]. A high clinical suspicion should therefore be maintained, particularly in children more than 10 years old who are overweight or obese and have a waist circumference above the 95th centile, in the context of other metabolic risk factors, abnormal LFTs and a family history of severe NAFLD [17].

Some studies have suggested, however, that normal-weight individuals with NAFLD appear to present at a younger age than those who are overweight or obese and demonstrate a decreased association with components of the metabolic syndrome, such as hypertension and insulin resistance [30,31]. This has given rise to the controversial hypothesis that paediatric NAFLD might, in fact, represent a group of related but pathophysiologically distinct clinical phenomenologies.

2.1. NAFLD and Obesity

The single greatest risk factor for paediatric NAFLD is obesity, with an estimated prevalence in overweight and obese youth of 50%–80% compared to 2%–7% in children of normal weight [25,26]. A recent cross-sectional study of 182 obese sedentary children and adolescents demonstrated a positive correlation between increased abdominal fat and the incidence of NAFLD, independently of insulin resistance and dyslipidaemia [32]. Central obesity has also been shown to reliably predict evidence of NAFLD on ultrasound and aminotransferase elevation in a cohort of more than 11,000 obese patients aged 6–18 years old [33]. A further study by Manco *et al.* [34] reported that 92% of paediatric NAFLD patients had a Body Mass Index (BMI) higher than the 85th centile and 84% had a waist circumference greater than the 90th centile. Moreover, significant correlation between waist circumference, total fat mass and intra-abdominal adipose tissue and the incidence of NAFLD was also reported in a cross-sectional study of 145 patients aged 11–17 years [10]. Waist circumference may, therefore, represent an interesting and reliable screening tool in paediatric NAFLD.

While obesity is thought to cause an overabundance of circulating free fatty acids, increasing hepatic steatosis, as well as contributing to the development of insulin resistance, the exact pathophysiological mechanisms by which obesity increases the risk of paediatric NAFLD remain poorly understood [14,35]. Indeed, not all children who are obese develop NAFLD, suggesting that other factors may inform risk such as the preferential deposition of visceral, as opposed to subcutaneous, adipose tissue [6,36].

Visceral adipose tissue is the primary source of hepatic fat in adults, contributing 59% of the triglyceride found in the liver; the main component of fat accumulation in NAFLD [9]. Increasing evidence also suggests that adipose tissue fulfils important and distinct endocrine functions, producing multiple pro-inflammatory adipocytokines, including TNF-α, IL-6, leptin and adiponectin, which are implicated in the clinical manifestation of NAFLD and its progression to NASH and cirrhosis [37,38]. Pentoxifylline, a phosphodiesterase inhibitor and non-specific TNF-α pathway antagonist, has been shown to promote a reduction in serum Alanine Aminotransferase (ALT) levels and improvement of the histological features of NASH in adult patients [12,39]. Other TNF-α inhibitors, such as infliximab, a selective chimeric monoclonal antibody against TNF-α, and resveratrol, a polyphenol with anti-inflammatory activity, have shown interesting results in adult clinical trials [12,39].

Furthermore, abdominal visceral adipose tissue has peculiarities of its own, including higher lipolysis and greater release of adipokines [32]. There is also evidence to suggest that, as the adipose bed expands, adipocytes suffer from a micro-hypoxic environment, due to insufficiency of its vascular network, resulting in cell injury and death and consequent upregulation of the pro-inflammatory cascade [9]. Circulating adipokines also appear to promote specific patterns of lipid storage and metabolic stress, which in turn activate signalling cascades that induce oxidative stress and trigger a local and/or systemic inflammatory response [35]. However, visceral adipose mass is much less developed in children, compared with adults, though it accumulates rapidly with weight gain, particularly in males. It has, therefore, been suggested that subcutaneous adipose tissue, although less metabolically active than visceral adipose tissue, may play a greater role in paediatric NAFLD [6,36]. Indeed, recent reports describe specific differences in the distribution of subcutaneous adipose tissue between adolescents with NAFLD and those without. These differences are apparent from three years old but not at birth, suggesting that the first three years of life might represent a critical window in which various interactions between genetic, environmental, epigenetic and metabolic factors contribute to the future risk of NAFLD [6] (Figure 1).

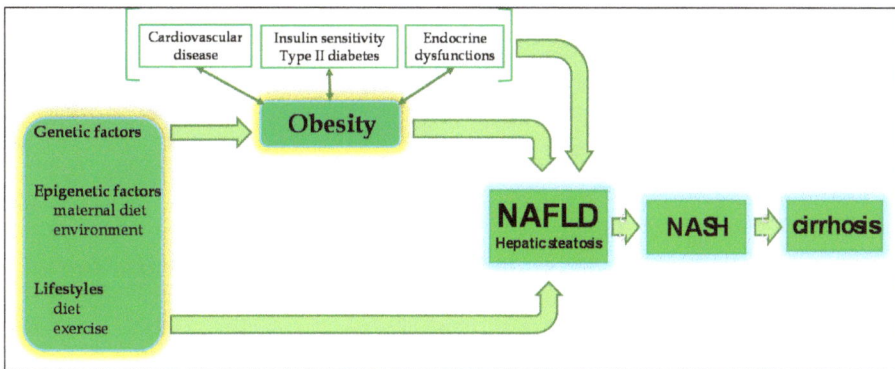

Figure 1. Obesity and Non-Alcoholic Fatty Liver Disease (NAFLD). Abbreviations: NAFLD: non-alcoholic fatty liver disease; NASH: non-alcoholic steatohepatitis.

2.2. Hepatic Complications of NAFLD

Non-Alcoholic Steatohepatitis (NASH) is commonly considered a more advanced form of NAFLD, where steatosis coexists with hepatocellular injury and inflammation, precipitating hepatic necrosis, fibrosis and cirrhosis and a significantly increased risk of hepatocellular carcinoma [1,19]. NASH significantly increases both overall and liver-related mortality, with the most common causes of death being cirrhosis and liver failure, neoplasia, sepsis, variceal haemorrhage and cardiovascular disease [11]. Long-term follow-up studies have shown that, in adults, NASH increases overall mortality by 35%–58% compared with age and sex-matched controls, while liver-related mortality is increased 9–10 fold [40–42]. NAFLD is, by far, the most common cause of hepatic fibrosis and cirrhosis in adults and children with unexplained or cryptogenic increases in serum alanine aminotransferase. However, advanced fibrosis can readily coexist with normal serum aminotransferase levels and has been reported in up to a third of patients with isolated simple steatosis [11].

2.2.1. Fibrosis

Approximately 25% of paediatric patients will progress to NASH, though the risk increases significantly in the context of obesity [43]. For example, a recent study of 24 severely obese bariatric adolescent patients found 63% had definitive NASH and a further 25% had "borderline" NASH [44]. Hepatic fibrosis has been documented retrospectively in more than one third of adult patients with NASH [11]. In a national multi-centre study, advanced fibrosis was reported at the time of diagnostic liver biopsy in nearly one in seven children with NAFLD [43]. Another study reported similar findings, with 17% of children with NAFLD having advanced fibrosis. After adjusting for fibrotic confounders, NASH appears to have a fibrotic potential similar to that of chronic Hepatitis C [11,45]. The main predictors of the severity of fibrosis are increasing age, BMI > 28–30 kg/m^2, hypertension, the degree of insulin resistance and diabetes [11]. Hepatic fibrosis also appears more prevalent in adolescents with severe obesity (83% *vs.* 29% in adults), further suggesting that paediatric patients, especially those who are obese, tend to follow a more aggressive clinical course than adults with NAFLD [14].

2.2.2. Cirrhosis

After 10 years, the risk of cirrhosis in adult patients with NASH is 15%–25%. Once cirrhosis is established, 30%–40% of these die within another 10 years [23]. Current evidence suggests that children have similar risks of progressing from NASH to decompensated end-stage liver disease, requiring transplantation [44].

End-stage NASH is a frequent and important cause of cryptogenic cirrhosis, mainly because hepatic fat accumulation and evidence of hepatocellular injury can disappear at this advanced stage; a phenomenon sometimes referred to as "burned out" NASH [11]. It has been shown that if a diagnosis of NASH were made on the basis of past or present exposure to metabolic risk factors, such as obesity, diabetes and hypertension, when histological signs are lacking, approximately 30%–75% of cryptogenic cirrhosis could be attributed to "burned-out" NASH. Liver failure is often the first presentation of patients with cirrhotic NASH and usually occurs after 7–10 years in adults but due to its quicker development, it may occur even more rapidly in paediatric cases [11].

2.2.3. Hepatocellular Carcinoma

Hepatocellular carcinoma can occur in both cirrhotic and, it appears, non-cirrhotic NASH. Its prevalence is greater still in obese or diabetic NAFLD patients [46,47]. In a study cohort of 285,884 boys and girls in Copenhagen who were followed for over three decades, higher body mass index (BMI) in childhood was associated with an increased risk of primary liver cancer in adulthood [48]. The hazard ratio (95% CI) of adult liver cancer was 1.20 (1.07–1.33) and 1.30 (1.16–1.46) per unit BMI z-score at 7 and 13 years, respectively. Similar associations were found for boys and girls for hepatocellular carcinoma only, across years of birth, and after accounting for diagnoses of viral hepatitis, alcohol-related disorders and biliary cirrhosis [48]. There is also, likely, a chronic underestimation of the proportion of NASH progressing towards end-stage liver disease, as many patients are no longer listed because of the co-occurrence of associated diseases, including obesity, cardiovascular disease and diabetes [11].

2.3. Extra-Hepatic Complications of NAFLD

While NAFLD is not a formal component of the diagnostic criteria for the metabolic syndrome, they do share common major risk factors, including central obesity, high serum triglycerides and high-density lipoprotein cholesterol (HDL-C), hypertension and insulin resistance, as well as altered glucose and lipid metabolism. Nearly 90% of NAFLD patients have at least one feature of the metabolic syndrome and up to 33% meet the complete diagnosis [4,18,49].

What is clear is that patient outcomes worsen when both conditions co-occur in an apparently synergistic manner [4,24,35,44] The presence of the metabolic syndrome, also, is a strong clinical predictor of NASH, particularly in overweight and obese paediatric patients [19,32]. This has led some to describe paediatric NAFLD in terms of either the hepatic manifestation or precursor of the metabolic syndrome [12,44,49]. Others, however, have suggested that both conditions may feed into one another, creating a vicious cycle of worsening metabolic disease, likely indicative of more widespread underlying metabolic dysfunction [35]. However, while we might infer that there exists significant overlap between the pathophysiological mechanisms that underlie these two conditions, their nature and extent remain poorly understood [4,18,49].

2.3.1. Cardiovascular Disease

NAFLD is an independent risk factor for coronary artery disease, as well as being strongly associated with a number of other cardiovascular risk factors, including multi-organ insulin resistance, dyslipidaemia and impaired flow-mediated vasodilatation [50]. Significant carotid atherosclerosis has been shown to occur 5–10 years earlier in patients with NAFLD than in those without and, in cases of biopsy proven NAFLD, hepatic steatosis is associated with increased carotid artery intima-media thickness and the presence of carotid plaques [11]. Biochemical surrogates of NAFLD, γ-glutamyl transferase (GGT) and ALT, predict the incidence of coronary artery disease and other cardiovascular disease, which is further elevated in NAFLD patients who suffer co-morbidly with diabetes mellitus [11]. Furthermore, in adults, NAFLD has been associated with myocardial insulin resistance, altered cardiac energy metabolism, abnormal left ventricular structure and impaired diastolic function; the duration and severity of these abnormalities in cardiac function likely contributing to the increased risk of heart failure and cardiovascular mortality in obese patients and, particularly, those with NAFLD [50]. Indeed, adult patients with NAFLD are at a significantly higher risk of cardiovascular mortality than the general population, with cardiovascular disease being the most common cause of death in NAFLD patients [11,44].

Cardiac functional abnormalities have also been reported in obese adolescents that were independent of traditional cardiac risk factors (*i.e.*, high systolic and diastolic pressures, total and low-density lipoprotein cholesterol and BMI) and correlated with insulin resistance [50]. One study assessing 50 children with biopsy-proven NAFLD using 24 h blood pressure monitoring and Doppler echocardiography parameters reported instances of cardiac dysfunction that were detectable in early NAFLD and were linked to no other cardiovascular or metabolic alteration other than liver damage. Left ventricular hypertrophy was present in 35% of patients, concentric remodelling in 14% and left atrial dilatation in 16%. Furthermore, children with simple steatosis showed lesser cardiac alterations than NASH patients [51]. Pacifico *et al.* [52] went on to demonstrate that even asymptomatic obese children with NAFLD exhibit early left ventricular diastolic and systolic dysfunctions, becoming more severe in patients with NASH. Hence, as NAFLD advances, the extent of cardiovascular dysfunction increases, with several other studies demonstrating greater endothelial dysfunction, an early proatherogenic lesion, and carotid intima thickness in NASH than in simple steatosis.

Elsewhere, Nobili *et al.* [53] have demonstrated that the severity of liver injury is strongly associated with the presence of a more atherogenic lipid profile, in terms of triglyceride/high density lipoprotein cholesterol (HDL), total cholesterol/HDL and low density lipoprotein (LDL)/HDL ratios. A further study of 548 children with a high triglycerides/HDL ratio reported an increased risk of insulin resistance that correlated independently, with more advanced NAFLD [54].

2.3.2. Insulin Resistance and Type II Diabetes Mellitus

Insulin Resistance (IR) is the most common metabolic abnormality associated with NAFLD and, perhaps, the most useful indicator of disease severity and progression in adults and children [19,49]. The severity of IR is strongly associated with the amount of hepatic fat accumulation, independently of global and intra-abdominal adiposity and the prevalence of NAFLD is greater in patients with hyperglycaemia and type II diabetes, with evidence of NAFLD present on ultrasound in up to 70% of clinical cases [14,32].

The key question remains, however, as to whether this relationship is causal or whether hepatic fat accumulation is, itself, a consequence of insulin resistance. On the one hand, hepatic steatosis and impairment reduces insulin clearance and, over time, greater insulin resistance [11]. Indeed, in NAFLD, steatosis and hepatic IR have been shown to occur in advance of peripheral IR, suggesting that the former is the primary defect in the development of the latter. Hepatic steatosis has, in turn, been shown to exacerbate insulin resistance by interfering with the phosphorylation of insulin receptor substrates, with the amount of hepatic steatosis correlating with the severity of IR [11,12].

On the other hand, insulin is an anabolic hormone that promotes glucose uptake in the liver, skeletal muscle and adipose tissue [9,10,12]. Increasing insulin resistance precipitates a reduction in glucose uptake by the liver and a compensatory increase in circulating levels of insulin. This drives increased hepatic and peripheral glycogenesis and lipogenesis, via sterol regulatory binding element (SREBP-1c) mediated upregulation of several prolipogenic genes, as well as impairing hepatocytic fatty acid metabolism [9,10,12]. As a result, circulating free fatty acids become increasingly abundant, most being taken up by the liver, where they are invariably processed into triglycerides and deposited within the cytoplasm of hepatocytes in large triglyceride-filled vacuoles, manifesting hepatic steatosis. As insulin resistance develops, high serum glucose levels also activate the carbohydrate responsive element binding protein, which further promotes lipogenesis and hepatic fat deposition [9].

It has also been suggested, therefore, that insulin resistance and hyperglycaemia may induce fibrosis directly or via upregulation of connective tissue growth factor, the generation of advanced glycation end products or through upregulation of pro-inflammatory cytokine production [11,55].

Controversially, others have sought to describe hepatic steatosis in terms of an adaptive, albeit imperfect, hepatic response to hepatic stress that forestalls the onset of NASH, albeit one that, in children, appears less effective and more prone to its own complications [9,11,56]. Indeed, Choi and Diehl suggested that the formation of lipid droplets may actually be protective by sequestering toxic free fatty acids in the form of triglycerides but, that when this buffer exceeds its capacity, certain free fatty acids begin to exert their toxic effect [57]. Work done in mice demonstrated that when triglyceride synthesis was inhibited, hepatic fat accumulation decreased but liver damage worsened, as measured by necroinflammation and fibrosis [58]. Conversely, up-regulation of diacylglycerol O-acyltransferase 2 (DGAT2) resulted in increased hepatic steatosis and was associated with a significant increase in liver inflammatory markers. Free fatty acids and their lipotoxic intermediates have been implicated in the promotion of inflammation, endoplasmic reticular stress, mitochondrial dysfunction and oxidant stress. These processes are injurious to hepatocytes, which, in turn, release pro-inflammatory cytokines and reactive oxygen species as they die, driving further hepatic inflammation [9]. Therefore, we are forced to consider whether steatosis, while a useful biomarker of ongoing injurious and fibrotic mechanisms resulting in disease progression, should be considered at all a therapeutic target and whether such interventions are in actual fact more damaging [11]. Instead, Wanless and Shiota [59] postulated that extracellular fat accumulation after hepatocyte necrosis might also impair hepatic blood flow through hepatic veins but this remains unproven.

2.3.3. Other Endocrine Disorders

There is evidence to suggest that other endocrine disorders, such as hypothyroidism, hypogonadism, hypopituitarism and polycystic ovary syndrome, independently of obesity, are important risk factors for NAFLD [11,60,61]. Several studies have addressed the association between thyroid dysfunction and NAFLD. Pacifico *et al.* [62] were the first to provide evidence of such a link between NAFLD, thyroid function and the metabolic syndrome in childhood, demonstrating a positive correlation between thyroid function tests, thyroid stimulating hormone (TSH) in particular, and the incidence of NAFLD in overweight and obese children, independently of visceral adiposity. Subsequently, Torun *et al.* [61] showed that TSH levels significantly increase in accordance with the extent of steatosis on ultrasound and ALT and BMI.

3. The Pathogenesis of NAFLD

Traditionally, the pathogenesis of NAFLD has been described in terms of a two-hit hypothesis, where hepatic steatosis sensitises the liver to the effects of oxidative stress and the action of various pro-inflammatory cytokines, which would, over time, drive the development of necroinflammation, fibrosis and, ultimately, cirrhosis [11,12]. However, increasing evidence of the complexity and inter-relatedness of numerous pathophysiological mechanisms, both hepatic and extra-hepatic, implicated in the development and progression of NAFLD, has precipitated a change in thinking.

Int. J. Mol. Sci. **2016**, *17*, 947

The now widely accepted "multiple-hit model" instead approaches NAFLD in terms of a hepatic manifestation of more widespread metabolic dysfunction, brought about through the interaction of numerous genetic and environmental factors, as well as changes in cross-talk between different organs, including adipose tissue, the pancreas, gut and liver [4,6,12,44]. Obesity and insulin resistance have repeatedly been suggested as the first "true" hits.

The development of NAFLD in children, in particular, it seems is characterised by an intricate network of interactions between resident hepatic and recruited cells, such as Kupffer cells, T cells and hepatic stellate cells, which drive disease progression alongside other infiltrating inflammatory cell-derived factors released either as a direct result of hepatic steatosis, hepatocyte injury and apoptosis or as an indirect response to hepatic damage and/or gut-derived bacterial products acting on Toll-like pattern recognition (TLR) receptors [63,64]. Indeed, dysregulation of pro-inflammatory cytokines and adipokines are almost universally detected in NAFLD patients, while endoplasmic reticular, mitochondrial and cytokine-mediated oxidative stress and hepatocytic apoptosis appear to contribute to the development of NASH [65–67]. TLR antagonists may also, in time, prove effective therapeutic agents for NASH; a potential that mandates further study [12].

Hepatic Stellate cells are considered the main extracellular matrix-producing cells during NASH development and are activated following hepatocyte injury and apoptosis, mediating the development of hepatic fibrosis and, if activation is chronic, cirrhosis. Hepatic Progenitor Cells (HPC), the resident stem cell population within the liver, have recently been shown to be expanded in paediatric NAFLD [66]. They appear to play a role in the liver's response to oxidative stress, their levels correlating with fibrosis and NASH progression [66]. Furthermore, HPCs can undergo an epithelial-mesenchymal transition, resulting in a profibrogenic myofibroblast-like cell population, a process involving the Hedgehog signalling pathway [68].

Kupffer Cells are important regulators of the biological exchanges between hepatocytes and other liver cells, engaging and sustaining the action of neutrophils, natural killer T lymphocytes (NKT) and blood monocyte-derived macrophages, as well as phagocytosing and removing microorganisms, apoptotic cells and cell debris themselves, processing and presenting antigens to attract cytotoxic and regulatory T cells, contributing to adaptive immunity. Increasing evidence suggests that they fulfil many diverse roles in the pathogenesis and progression of NAFLD, including the regulation of immune tolerance and lipid homeostasis [63,69]. Indeed, Stienstra *et al.* [70] further demonstrated the integral role of Kupffer cells in regulating hepatic triglyceride storage and the promotion of hepatic steatosis via IL-1β-mediated suppression of perioxisome proliferator-activated receptor-α (PPAR-α) activity, while others have reported that Kupffer cell depletion, in a murine experimental model of NASH, prevented hepatic fat accumulation and liver damage [63].

Several studies have described subsequent changes in the frequency and/or functionality of peripheral T cell subpopulations, manifesting an altered phenotype of infiltrating and circulating immune cells that appears to be distinct between adult and paediatric NASH [64]. Several studies have reported a predominance of CD8+ T cells over CD4+ and CD20+ subpopulations undergoing activation in paediatric NASH, in association with increased levels of IFN-γ within the hepatic microenvironment, a high number of infiltrating neutrophils in correlation with Reactive Oxygen Species (ROS) generation in peripheral neutrophils and further alterations in the phenotype and functionality of circulating lymphocytes and neutrophils compared with age-matched controls. By contrast, CD8+ cells were a minor component of Natural Killer (NK) and NKT cells in adult NASH [19,64]. The molecular and immunological phenomenology of these systems both locally and systematically, in both paediatric and adult NASH, are complex and are only just beginning to be recognised, let alone understood.

Increasing evidence suggests that dysregulation of the autonomic nervous system innervation of the liver fulfils a critical role in the progression of simple steatosis to NASH and cirrhosis. Indeed, Hepatic Stellate Cell (HSC) autonomic receptors are reportedly upregulated in the livers of adult NAFLD patients and may represent another potential target for future anti-fibrotic therapies [71,72].

3.1. Genetics of Paediatric NAFLD

Over the last decade, with the advent of next-generation sequencing technologies, polymorphisms associated with the incidence and severity of paediatric NAFLD have been identified in numerous genes involved in lipid metabolism, insulin sensitivity, oxidative stress, regulation of the immune system and the development of fibrosis [4,73]. Furthermore, evidence of the strong genetic contribution to the pathogenesis of paediatric NAFLD comes from reports familial clustering of metabolic risk factors, including obesity, insulin resistance and type II diabetes. One study of children with biopsy-proven NAFLD, for example, reported that 59% of their siblings and 78% of their parents were found to have evidence of hepatic steatosis on MRI, significantly more than in relatives of age and BMI-matched children without NAFLD [74].

The prevalence and genetic variants associated with NAFLD also vary between different ethnic groups, likely affecting the heritability of metabolic risk factors that contribute to individual susceptibility to the disease [75]. Hispanic children demonstrate the highest prevalence of NAFLD (36%), greater than that of Afro-Caribbeans (14%), Asians (10.2%) and non-Hispanic whites (8.6%) despite these populations exhibiting similar obesity rates [13]. Hispanic patients have also been shown to be at higher risk of type II diabetes and tend to display more features of the metabolic syndrome than non-Hispanic whites, which may further contribute to their greater risk. It has also been suggested that differences in body fat distribution among Afro-Caribbean children, who notably have more subcutaneous fat and less visceral fat and consequently a lesser predisposition towards hepatic fat accumulation, may explain their lower prevalence of NAFLD. Indeed, visceral adiposity is less associated with NAFLD among Afro-Caribbean adolescents than among non-Hispanic whites. Furthermore, insulin resistance appears less tightly linked to visceral adiposity in Afro-Caribbean children with NAFLD and tends to be more associated with the extent and severity of liver damage. Conversely, the extent to which the relationship between insulin resistance and NAFLD severity varies between Hispanics and non-Hispanic whites appears negligible [13,75].

A recent genome-wide association study (GWAS) conducted by the Genetics of Obesity-Related Liver Disease Consortium identified robust associations between polymorphisms of the genes neurocan (NCAN), lysophospholipase-like 1 (LYPLAL1), glucokinase regulatory protein (GCKR) and protein phosphatase 1 regulatory subunit 3b (PPP1R3B) and NAFLD in adults of European ancestry [76]. However, Palmer *et al.* [16] reported that the allele frequency and effect size of PNPLA3 rs738409, NCAN rs2228603, LYPLAL1 rs12137855, GCKR rs780094 and PPP1R3B rs4240624 varied between adult patients of African and Hispanic ethnicity. Hernaez *et al.* [77] also reported a lack of consistency of these variants in the NHANES III study population of multiple ethnicities. Another GWAS conducted by Romeo *et al.* [78] also found that the PNPLA3 rs738409 variant was seen more commonly in Hispanics than in other ethnic groups and was associated with increased liver fat and hepatic inflammation, whereas PNPLA3 rs6006460 was seen more commonly in Afro-Caribbeans and correlated with lesser hepatic fat accumulation. This has been confirmed by another study of 83 obese children using MRI to quantify hepatic lipid content [79]. Further studies have also shown PNPLA3 rs738409 to be associated with greater hepatic steatosis and disease severity, as well as earlier clinical presentation [55,80].

The fat mass and obesity associated (FTO) gene variant rs9939609 has also been associated with increased risk of NAFLD and the Melanocortin 4 Receptor (MC4R) rs12970134 variant with increased ALT levels, independently of BMI, in children aged 7–18 years old with NAFLD [81]. Other genetic variants associated with NASH, hepatic fibrosis and the severity of liver damage in both adults and children have been described in genes involved in lipid metabolism, such as adiponutrin/patatin-like phospholipase domain-containing 3 (PNPLA3), Lipin 1 (LPIN1), adipoprotein C3 (APOC3), endocannabinoid receptor CB2, as well as the hereditary hemochromatosis (HFE) gene [55,82]. For example, PNPLA3 rs738409 has been associated with the presence and severity of hepatic steatosis in numerous studies, independently of insulin resistance or inflammatory changes, lobular inflammation and perivenular fibrosis in both adult and paediatric NAFLD [55,77,80,83]. Other genes associated with progression to NASH relate to oxidative stress and include the rs4880 variant of manganese-dependent superoxide dismutase (SOD2) gene, the rs1801278 variant of insulin receptor substrate-1 (IRS-1) and the rs3750861 variant of tumour suppressor gene Kruppel-like factor 6 (KLF-6) [55].

Our understanding of the mechanisms by which variation in these genes affects the incidence and progression of NAFLD, however, remains limited. PNPLA3, for example, is most robustly expressed in the liver. Its expression appears to be directly related to nutritional intake, being down-regulated in the fasting state and upregulated during feeding. *In vitro* and mouse models have shown that SREBP-1, which is activated by insulin, induces PNPLA3, which then promotes lipogenesis and modulates glucose homeostasis [84]. Additionally, cytochrome P450 oxidative enzyme family 2 subfamily E member 1 (CYP2E1) is a risk factor for oxidative stress and may be implicated in NAFLD [85,86]. Polymorphism of the cytokine Interleukin 6 (IL-6) have been associated with serum of liver damage markers [87]. Variants in the UGT1A1 gene (Gilbert syndrome) have also been shown to contribute to increased bilirubin levels, thus reducing the risk for NAFLD onset and development [88].

Accumulating evidence also suggests the involvement of the endocannabinoid system in NAFLD, which has many diverse roles in humans. For example, in studies of obese children with steatosis and biopsy-proven NAFLD, a functional variant of the otherwise hepatoprotective cannabinoid receptor 2 (CB2), Q63R, was associated with elevated serum aminotransferase levels [89]. Others have suggested that the CB2 Q63R variant fulfils a critical role in modulating hepatic inflammation in obese children, manifesting an increased susceptibility to liver damage in these patients [82].

Given that the effect of genetic variants tends to be more pronounced in children than in adults, due to a lack of confounding long-term environmental exposures, the investigation of relevant genetic variants associated with paediatric NAFLD, whilst not, at present, consequent to our clinical approach, may prove instructive for both paediatric and adult disease as our understanding of their pathophysiological role increases.

3.2. Maternal Diet, Intrauterine Growth and Neonatal Diet

In recent years, the critical role of maternal physiology and metabolism during the perinatal, foetal and even pre-conceptual phases of development in predisposing the unborn towards developing NAFLD within their own lifetimes and making it more likely that they will progress to NASH, has become ever more apparent [69,90–92].

This phenomenon, referred to as developmental programming, appears to be driven by the complex interaction of diverse communities of epigenetic modifications at key genes, which change the phenotypic characteristics of different cell types, hence the offspring's metabolic profile [93]. Recent evidence even suggests that, in addition to the effects of epigenetic programming upon first generation offspring, subsequent generations may also be affected [94].

A greater understanding of the molecular phenomenology underlying maternal epigenetic programming in obesity may well lead to the development of effective therapeutic interventions that may be targeted during key developmental windows to ameliorate the risk of maternal obesity and maternal diet to the unborn. Several studies have now demonstrated that controlled maternal weight loss prior to pregnancy is effective in reducing their offspring's lifetime risk of developing NAFLD, which is of particular relevance in the context of the rising global prevalence of obesity among women of childbearing age [94]. However, specific and coherent guidelines regarding when and how to effectively intervene in clinical practice have yet to be defined.

Several studies have also found an association between intrauterine growth restriction (IUGR) and obesity, dyslipidaemia, hepatic steatosis and steatohepatitis [4,95]. Although the pathogenic mechanisms underlying these relationships remain unclear, they are also thought to have their origins in adverse foetal epigenetic programming [93,94]. Similarly, while some studies have suggested that breastfeeding may be protective against the development of NASH in childhood, this likely depends greatly upon the physiological profile of the maternal source [4,96]. Others have also suggested that rapid weight gain, particularly in the first 3 months of post-natal life, rather than small birth size in and of itself, might increase the risk of NAFLD in childhood and later life, although further study is required to determine safe trends of neonatal weight gain [96].

3.3. Gender Differences and Puberty

In adults, numerous studies report that the prevalence of NAFLD, specifically simple steatosis, is twice as great in men as in women. While the exact reasons for these gender differences remain unclear, some have suggested that they might be explained by differences in fat distribution, serum lipid profile or a protective action of oestrogens and other hormonal differences between the sexes [14,97]. There are, however, no apparent gender differences in the risk of progression to NASH in adult or paediatric patients, although some studies have suggested that boys are more likely to develop a periportal paediatric pattern of NASH than girls [68].

However, in childhood and adolescence, gender differences appear to be more complex, with some studies supporting a higher risk in boys, similar to that in adults, while others do not. Instead, gender disparity with regards to NAFLD prevalence appears to increase with age and has been attributed to the physiological alterations that occur at the onset of puberty impacting the pathogenesis of this disease. Indeed, there is increasing evidence that associates rising levels of sex hormones during puberty with modification of diverse biological processes, including adipocyte development and function [4,24]. For example, animal studies have indicated that oestrogens reduce the severity of oxidative stress, impair hepatocellular mitochondrial function and inhibit hepatic stellate cell activation and fibrogenesis, which might significantly affect the development and progression of NAFLD by modifying the hepatic and systemic responses to hepatocellular injury [98–100]. Furthermore, the diminishing disparity in NAFLD prevalence between the genders, especially after middle age, has been widely noted, with some attributing it to hormonal changes that occur around menopause [101].

It has also been suggested that the rise in serum oestrogen levels in both boys and girls during puberty might also contribute to the reduced severity of NAFLD, particularly the more benign clinical course of simple steatosis, in adults. For example, in one study of 186 children with biopsy-proven NAFLD, after adjusting for confounders, patients at or beyond puberty were less likely to have high-grade steatosis, severe portal inflammation, borderline steatohepatitis (zone 1) or a high stage of fibrosis than patients who had not entered puberty [102]. There is also evidence to suggest that steatosis, inflammation and fibrosis are less severe during and after puberty among NAFLD patients [102].

3.4. Dysregulation of Hedgehog Signalling Pathway in NAFLD

Deregulation of the Hedgehog (Hh) Signalling Pathway, which morphologically orchestrates organogenesis during development, also appears to have a role in the pathogenesis and progression of NAFLD in adults and children [68]. While in the healthy adult this pathway is usually silent, it is reactivated when hepatic injury stimulates the production of Hh ligands, triggering the growth of various cell types involved in wound-healing, including resident hepatic immune cells, hepatic stellate cells and hepatic progenitor cells. While effective Hh signalling is necessary for injured mature livers to regenerate, prolongation or upregulation of this pathway's activity has been linked to chronic inflammation, fibrosis and liver cancer [68].

Others have demonstrated that damaged or ballooned hepatocytes produce Hh ligands in adults with NASH, whose previous levels correlated with numbers of Hh-responsive cells within the liver and the severity of inflammation and fibrosis [103]. Whether or not similar mechanisms exist in children remains unclear but highly plausible, given that children generally harbour greater numbers of Hh-producing cells and Hh-responsive cells than adults and that these populations have been shown to expand even in response to relatively minor parenchymal injury, which may make them especially vulnerable to insults that stimulate liver damage and may even go some way towards explaining why simple steatosis has a much less benign course in children than in adults and why advanced fibrosis/cirrhosis can occur relatively rapidly [68].

Moreover, as hepatic development is not completed until adolescence, changes in the clinical presentation and course of NAFLD prior to and during adolescence, the latter being more in line with the adult pattern of disease, may reflect changes in the liver's vulnerability to derangement of Hh pathway signalling [68]. It has even been suggested that age, gender and/or pubertal status may reciprocally influence Hh pathway activity in children, modulating the liver's response to steatosis and hepatocyte injury and hence the histological features of paediatric NAFLD [12,68]. For example, in contrast to the adult liver, the periportal compartment of prepubescent male livers, where fibrosis characteristic of paediatric NAFLD is observed on histological analysis, exhibits high Hh pathway activity. Hh-mediated repair responses also appear to be more robust and readily engaged in prepubescent boys with NAFLD, which may explain why they display a much greater disease prevalence than girls [68].

Hh pathway activation also stimulates hepatic stellate cells to become myofibroblastic and function as the major collagen matrix-producing cells in response to liver injury. There is further evidence to suggest that, even once liver injury has dissipated and these cells revert to a quiescent state, they remain "primed" to more readily reacquire their myofibroblastic and fibrogenic characteristics upon subsequent hepatic injury, which may further contribute to the aggressive pattern of paediatric NASH [104].

4. Making the Diagnosis

Paediatric NAFLD remains underdiagnosed due to a lack of recognition, under-appreciation of its associated complications or questions regarding the appropriateness of such a diagnosis in children by healthcare professionals. Far from being a process of exclusion, as it has often been described both clinically and in the literature, the diagnosis of NAFLD should be actively considered in all overweight or obese children >10 years old, particularly in the context of hypertension, evidence of hepatomegaly, acanthosis nigricans, insulin resistance and Type II diabetes mellitus [8,12,17,19,60].

Differential diagnosis should first be based on the clinical features, then on blood tests, imaging techniques, and, finally, liver biopsy (Figure 2), which is currently considered the gold standard for the diagnosis of NAFLD [17], facilitating differentiation between simple steatosis and NASH, determining the presence and severity of hepatic fibrosis and providing prognostic information regarding the potential for disease progression [11,19,49]. Any evidence of hepatic steatosis in children <10 years old, with or without elevated liver function tests (LFTs), hepatomegaly or splenomegaly, is of particular concern and should be assessed comprehensively and expediently in order to exclude other aetiologies, including infectious hepatitis, autoimmune hepatitis, Wilson's disease, haemochromatosis, α-1 antitrypsin deficiency and other monogenic causes of impaired fatty acid metabolism or lysosomal or peroxisomal storage. Despite being much less common in the paediatric population, Alcohol-induced Fatty Liver Disease must also be excluded and should not be discounted out of hand, even in young children [9,11,19,43,49].

Positive serum autoantibodies (anti-mitochondrial and anti-nuclear) are often present in paediatric NAFLD patients (~20%), even in the absence of autoimmune hepatitis, although their clinical significance remains unclear [12]. NAFLD is also often associated with abnormalities in iron metabolism, raising intra-hepatic free iron alongside mildly elevated serum ferritin and transferrin, in the absence of genetic haemochromatosis, seemingly mediated by pro-inflammatory adipokines. As such, liver biopsy is required in order to assess hepatic iron concentration and exclude significant hepatic injury and fibrosis, in patients with suspected NAFLD who demonstrate persistently elevated serum ferritin and increased transferrin saturation, especially in the context of homozygote or heterozygote C282Y mutations in the HFE gene [4,19,105]. Furthermore, due to its high prevalence, NAFLD can readily co-occur with other chronic liver diseases, worsening clinical outcomes that, otherwise, can be improved by concurrently treating the metabolic risk factors underlying NAFLD, such as obesity and insulin resistance [11,19].

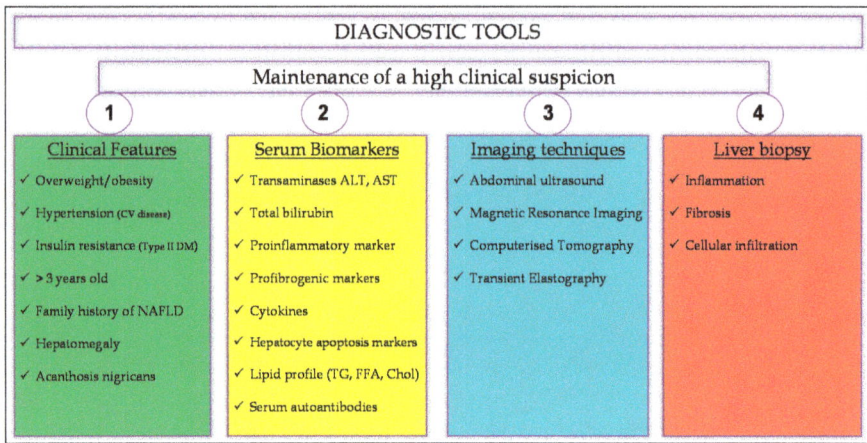

Figure 2. Diagnostic tools for children and adolescent NAFLD. Abbreviations: NAFLD: non-alcoholic fatty liver disease; DM: diabetes mellitus; ALT: alanine aminotransferase; AST: aspartate aminotransferase; TG: triglycerides; FFA: free fatty acids; Chol: cholesterol.

Although possessing limited sensitivity, abdominal ultrasound and liver function tests remain the first choice in diagnosing NAFLD in children [11,19]. As such, while not recommended in the general paediatric population, biannual screening for elevated serum alanine aminotransferase (ALT) and aspartate aminotransferase (AST) should be undertaken in all obese patients above 10 years old, as well as those whose BMI falls between the 85th and 94th centiles and have associated metabolic risk factors. However, as a result of the pathophysiological and clinical differences between paediatric and adult NAFLD, diagnostic algorithms and risk prediction scores, such as the NAFLD activity score, which were developed for use in adults, are of limited utility in children and should not be relied upon [9,29]. Furthermore, radiological and histopathological findings should be interpreted with caution, as serum aminotransferase levels remain normal in the majority of paediatric cases, irrespective of disease severity and the often negligible levels of hepatic steatosis in advanced paediatric NASH rendering hepatic ultrasound insensitive. Even liver biopsy is not always reliable in paediatric NAFLD due to steatotic lesioning within the liver being less diffuse and characterised by much more subtle histopathological changes [17,19,106].

In the absence of definitive radiological and histopathological diagnostic tests, maintenance of a high clinical suspicion in both primary and specialist care settings and by all members of the multidisciplinary team remains the most potent of diagnostic tools, enabling early diagnosis and appropriate therapeutic intervention designed to stymie disease progression.

4.1. Alternative Classification System

The term 'Non-alcoholic', although originally intended to clearly differentiate the aetiology of this disease from Alcohol-Induced Fatty Liver Disease, is often extremely unhelpful and perpetuates the false assumption among healthcare professionals that paediatric NAFLD represents a diagnosis of exclusion. Furthermore, what constitutes the threshold of "significant" alcohol consumption, particularly in paediatric cases, remains moot. Others have, therefore, suggested the adoption of "Obesity-induced Liver Disease" as a replacement term but this could also prove misleading, given that, while obesity is the single greatest risk factor for this disease, NAFLD can develop in normo-weight children [27,35,107]. Such terminology is also likely to be the focus of significant social stigma, which is of particular concern in younger and more emotionally and psychologically vulnerable patients, potentially affecting their engagement with clinical services.

In light of the significant pathophysiological overlap between NAFLD and Alcohol-induced Fatty Liver Disease, it may be more helpful to think of "Fatty" Liver Disease or, less pejoratively, "Steatotic" Liver Disease (SLD) in terms of "primary", "secondary", "mixed" and "complex" aetiological subtypes. As such, "Primary" or "Type 1" SLD would encompass what is currently referred to as "Non-alcoholic Fatty Liver Disease", which represents the phenotypic manifestation of underlying metabolic dysfunction in the absence of other causes of liver injury. "Secondary" or "Type 2" SLD would describe pathology resulting from a number of medical or surgical conditions or drug intake, including alcohol. In such cases where metabolic dysfunction and significant alcohol consumption coincide, the term "Mixed" or "Type 3" SLD could be used and, where Steatotic Liver Disease coincides with another form of chronic liver disease, such as autoimmune hepatitis, "Complex" or "Type 4" SLD. Thus, by appropriately reviewing the clinical nomenclature, we might better emphasise the importance of the diagnostic, pathophysiological, therapeutic and prognostic relationships between NAFLD and other chronic liver diseases in childhood and adolescence, as well as clearly directing intervention to improve clinical outcomes.

4.2. Serum Biomarkers for Liver Damage

Elevated levels of various circulating biomarkers have been described in patients with NAFLD, including AST and ALT, cytokeratin 18 (CK-18) fragments, apolipoprotein A1, total bilirubin, hyaluronic acid, C-reactive protein, fibroblast growth factor-21, interleukin 1 receptor antagonist, adiponectin, and TNF-α [83]. However, at present, there remains no readily available biomarker that reliably differentiates between simple steatosis and NASH.

Aminotransferases, AST and ALT, are the most commonly referenced serum biomarkers for liver damage in a wide variety of liver diseases, including NAFLD. They are easily obtained, low in cost and elevated levels have been associated across numerous studies with the presence and severity of NAFLD in adults [9,11,22,101]. Furthermore, in one multicentre study of 176 children, AST and GGT were predictive of both NAFLD and NASH but lacked the discriminatory power to accurately and reliably delineate cases of NASH from simple steatosis [108]. However, consensus as to what constitutes "normal" aminotransferase levels in children has yet to be established. Indeed, another study of 502 18–64 year olds with NAFLD demonstrated progressive decline of ALT levels with advancing age, while AST remained stable, suggesting that ALT elevation in childhood may be less diagnostically useful than in adult disease [101]. Most importantly, several studies have reported that up to two thirds of children with NASH did not display elevated serum ALT and AST levels, even in more advanced disease [109–112]. While normal AST and ALT levels do not exclude severe liver damage or fibrosis in paediatric NAFLD, when elevated they should inspire a high level of clinical suspicion, particularly in overweight or obese patients with a family history of NAFLD and, thus, may still be of significant use as a screening tool [9,74].

Elevated serum CK-18 fragments, markers of hepatocyte apoptosis, have demonstrated robust association with the incidence and severity of NASH in both adults and children [113]. Wieckowska *et al.* [114], for example, reported a strong positive correlation between CK-18 in plasma obtained from patients with suspected NAFLD at the time of liver biopsy and hepatic damage. Plasma CK-18 levels were also markedly increased in patients with NASH compared to those with simple steatosis, and were capable of accurately predicting NASH. These observations have been reproduced in subsequent studies, collectively suggesting CK18 levels to have a sensitivity of 78% and specificity of 87% for steatohepatitis in patients with NAFLD [115]. However, CK-18 would likely only be of use once the diagnosis of NAFLD had been made, as hepatocyte apoptosis is not unique to NAFLD. Furthermore, despite its significant clinical potential, CK-18 is not, at the present time, readily available and a standardised cut-off has yet to be established.

Total Bilirubin was also found by Puri *et al.* [116] to inversely correlate with the prevalence of NASH in children, which it is thought may reflect some anti-oxidative protective effect of bilirubin within the liver.

Finally, serum lipid profile, including total cholesterol, while potentially reflective of abnormal lipid metabolism that may contribute to NASH, has yet to be adequately investigated in paediatric liver disease. As such, its sensitivity, specificity and clinical utility remain unclear [53,117]. However, analysis of molecular lipid concentrations in blood samples taken from 679 adults found that those with NAFLD displayed increased triglycerols with low carbon number and double-bond content, while lysophosphotidylcholines and either phospholipids were diminished [118]. A serum lipid signature comprising these three molecular lipids had a sensitivity of 69.1% and a specificity of 73.8% in the subsequent validation series. Further investigation is required to validate these results in children, however.

4.3. Abdominal Ultrasound

Abdominal ultrasound is the most commonly used imaging modality for NAFLD, both clinically and in research [10,12]. It has been shown to be an effective means of identifying pure hepatic steatosis and mild NASH in children and has led to a great increase in findings of NAFLD in recent years. Its relatively low cost, wide availability and safety also make it an ideal screening tool [10,17]. In NAFLD, the liver is usually enlarged and appears echogenic, or "bright", which indicates fatty accumulation within the parenchyma. However, it is unable to quantify the true extent of steatosis and its sensitivity diminishes significantly in cases where hepatic fat accumulation remains below 30%, in individuals who are severely obese (BMI > 40) and in severe NASH [9,44,119]. Ultrasound is unable to reliably differentiate between simple steatosis and steatohepatitis or exclude fibrosis. Accurately differentiating between focal steatosis or steatohepatitis and hepatic tumours or inflammatory vascular conditions is also challenging, given their close resemblance to one another on ultrasound and the potential for steatosis to obscure the imaging of other hepatic lesions [106,119]. However, while the focal manifestations of NAFLD may be characterised by poorly delineated margins and similar contrast enhancement with normal liver parenchyma, they do not exert a mass effect on the surrounding tissue and, at least in adults, favour certain topographical configurations, mainly occurring adjacent to the falciform ligament or ligamentum venosum, in the porta hepatis and gallbladder. Whether such distributions of focal fatty lesions hold true in paediatric NAFLD, however, remains to be established [11,119]. Furthermore, atypical focal fatty liver sparing can also mimic hepatic neoplasia, manifesting round or oval-shaped phenomena with clear margins. The diagnostic efficacy of abdominal ultrasound is also greatly dependent upon operator proficiency and lacks standard methods of interpretation for paediatric NAFLD, underscoring the importance of considering the wider clinical picture throughout the diagnostic process and selection of appropriate therapeutic intervention.

4.4. Magnetic Resonance Imaging

Unlike abdominal ultrasound, MRI exhibits high sensitivity and specificity for paediatric NAFLD and is able to differentiate, even in severely obese patients, between simple steatosis and NASH [17,20]. It is also able to quantify the distribution and severity of even mild steatosis and fibrosis throughout the entire liver and with moderate to strong correlation with histological grading in children and adults [28,120,121]. However, the relatively high cost of MRI, as well as the need for sedation in young children prohibits widespread use in clinical practice and, as such, it remains primarily a research tool. It is also, at present, unable to assess the extent of inflammation or cirrhosis in the liver parenchyma but rather identifies the consequences of chronic liver disease, such as hepatosplenomegaly and portal hypertension.

4.5. Other Imaging Techniques

While Computerised Tomography (CT) offers greater sensitivity than abdominal ultrasound in detecting the presence and extent of hepatic fat accumulation in NAFLD, the high radiation exposure it encumbers prohibits routine use in young children [20,121]. Furthermore, it also lacks the sensitivity required to detect mild steatosis and small changes in fat content over time.

Transient Elastography is able to detect hepatic fibrosis in paediatric NAFLD, using a technique similar to abdominal ultrasound to measure hepatic "stiffness" non-invasively. However, at present, it cannot reliably determine the extent or severity of hepatic fibrosis, particularly in its early stages, as both steatosis and inflammatory activity also marginally increase liver stiffness. This technique also suffers from diminished sensitivity and specificity in severely obese patients [122,123].

4.6. Liver Biopsy and Histopathology

Liver biopsy remains the gold standard for diagnosing NAFLD, differentiating between simple steatosis and NASH and determining the severity of liver damage, inflammation and fibrosis [19,29]. It also allows the clinician to rule out other causes of liver pathology, especially in cases of significant liver damage where abdominal ultrasound demonstrates reduced sensitivity and specificity. However, it is invasive and, as such, carries significant risks that render it unsuitable for use as a screening tool, particularly in children. It is also expensive and subject to sampling error, where subsequent histopathological analysis is unrepresentative of the liver as a whole. As such, even a normal liver biopsy cannot fully exclude NAFLD and should always be considered in context of the wider clinical picture.

The key decision pertains as to when biopsy is indicated and when it is not. In each case, the clinician must weigh the potential risks associated with biopsy against the likelihood that it will impact clinical management. Ideally, this would mean that we should only biopsy children who are at significant risk of NASH. However, our incomplete understanding of the natural history of this disease, at present, confounds any attempt to reliably stratify patients according to such risk, as the alteration of clinical outcomes based on the severity of histology at baseline remains unknown [124]. Nevertheless, current guidelines published by the American Association for the Study of Liver Diseases (AASLD) recommend that liver biopsy should only be undertaken in patients younger than 10 years old with a family history of severe NAFLD, the presence of hepatosplenomegaly at physical examination and abnormal laboratory results, encompassing transaminasaemia, insulin resistance, absence of autoantibodies and inconclusive results from biochemical tests for severe/progressive liver disease [19].

While children with NAFLD may exhibit the same morphological lesions as adults, these are often more subtle and can be absent altogether [44]. Hepatocyte ballooning, for example, which describes the enlargement of hepatocyte diameter by a factor of 1.5–2 and the main morphological feature of hepatocellular damage in adult NASH, is often not observed in paediatric cases. Similarly, the distinctive clarification and rarefication of hepatocyte cytoplasm and the inclusion therein of eosinophilic cytoskeletal peptide aggregates, referred to as Mallory Denk bodies, so characteristic of adult NASH, is relatively uncommon [11,12,19].

The distribution of fatty accumulation and fibrotic lesioning within the liver also differs between paediatric and adult disease. Adult NAFLD is characterised by microvacuolar periportal or panacinar hepatocellular steatosis, portal inflammation, portal fibrosis and perisinusoidal fibrosis. In contrast, paediatric NAFLD is characterised by macrovacuolar, azonal hepatocellular steatosis, portal inflammation and portal fibrosis [44,125].

Inflammation is characteristic of NASH across all age groups and comprises mixed inflammatory cells which infiltrate the hepatic parenchyma, including lymphocytes, histiocytes, Kupffer cells (KC) and granulocytes [63,64]. While, in adults, lobular inflammation is nearly universal and portal inflammation associated with more severe/advanced cases of NASH, portal inflammation is more typical of paediatric cases, providing further evidence that childhood disease follows a more severe course [125]. Furthermore, while isolated steatosis or steatosis with lobular inflammation without signs of hepatocellular injury are considered part of the wider spectrum of NAFLD in adults and insufficient evidence to suggest NASH, in children, where signs of hepatocellular injury are less obvious, this distinction is less clear. However, Schwimmer and others go on to describe both patterns of

NAFLD in children, suggesting that factors other than age might determine the histological appearance of the disease [125]. Although the mechanistic underpinnings of this phenomenon remain unclear, Swiderska-Syn *et al.* [68] hypothesised that the Hedgehog pathway, which is involved in the fibro-ductal response, may effect such differences.

4.7. Non-Invasive Diagnostic Scoring Systems

The invasiveness, cost, morbidity and impracticality of liver biopsy in at-risk patients and especially in children has driven the development of non-invasive clinical risk prediction scores. However, many have yet to be validated in the paediatric population. Non-invasive hepatic fibrosis scores, AST/ALT, NFS and Fib-4 or AST/platelet ratio were developed for use in adults but have performed poorly in diagnosing significant fibrosis in children with NAFLD [29,126]. The paediatric NAFLD fibrosis index (PNFI) is calculated from the patient's age, waist circumference and triglyceride levels and aims to predict liver fibrosis in children [126]. However, although it provides a good positive predictive value, its negative predictive value for ruling out fibrosis is sub-optimal. Several studies have suggested that the enhanced liver fibrosis (ELF) score, an algorithmic composite of serum markers of liver fibrosis, including hyaluronic acid, amino terminal propeptide of collagen type III and the tissue inhibitor of metalloproteinase, can be used to accurately predict fibrosis in children with NAFLD [126,127]. While the potential of these scores is great, their clinical utility remains, at present, unclear.

5. Management of Paediatric NAFLD

There is, currently, a lack of consensus as to how NAFLD in childhood and adolescence should be managed in clinical practice [65]. However, it is clear that effective therapeutic strategies should recognise that this is a multifactorial disease in which metabolic dysfunction is widespread, multifaceted, interdependent and is founded upon the interaction between numerous genetic and environmental forces. As such, therapeutic intervention should be adapted to each patient in context of their existing co-morbidities and how they might best be managed, including obesity, hyperlipidaemia, insulin resistance, Type II diabetes mellitus and cardiovascular disease. High clinical suspicion, enabling appropriate referral to paediatric gastroenterology, early diagnosis and intervention, has consistently been shown to be effective in improving overall quality of life for the patient, as well as reducing their long-term cardiovascular and hepatic morbidity and mortality [14,24,128].

First-line interventions should focus on appropriately reducing central obesity and insulin resistance, primarily through dietary modification and increased physical exercise in order to effect therapeutic weight loss [129]. Depending on the extent of hepatic fibrosis, patients with NASH may also benefit from pharmacological therapies designed to slow or reverse disease progression [24]. Unlike in adults, where simple steatosis appears benign and, thus, pharmacological intervention is not recommended, in children the evidence suggests that it tends to follow a more aggressive course and, as such, pharmacological intervention, although not currently recommended, may be prudent before the transition to NASH occurs (Figure 3).

An approach that combines reducing visceral adiposity, insulin resistance and hyperinsulinemia with the prevention or reversal of hepatocellular damage appear to be the most successful rather than employing one or other of these strategies in isolation. The efficacy of any intervention should be assessed after a six-month period and, if ineffective, additional therapeutic options might then be considered, including pharmacological therapy or surgical intervention [24,65,128,130,131]. The development of comprehensive, evidence-based and internationally accepted clinical guidelines specifically for paediatric NAFLD will depend upon rectification of the current paucity of research and lack of robust epidemiological data. Nevertheless, they should emphasise the importance of the multidisciplinary team and the effective management of metabolic risk factors, as well as improving the interconnectedness of diverse health disciplines, especially during the transition from paediatric to adult clinical services and in those patients at the extreme end of the obesity spectrum, in whom non-surgical therapies for weight loss are currently non-existent.

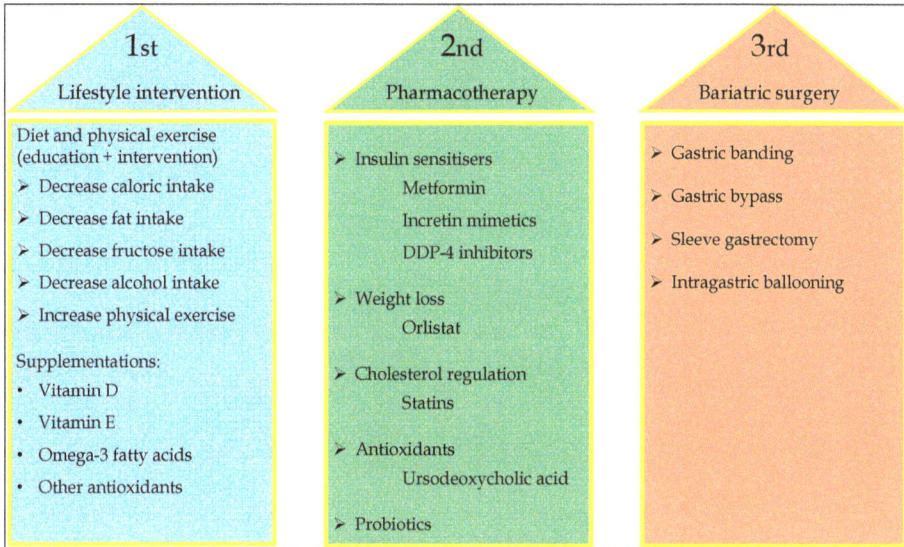

Figure 3. Management of paediatric NAFLD.

Sleep shortage as a result of lifestyle, as well as major sleep disorders, such as sleep apnea and insomnia, have also been associated with NAFLD and may benefit from more active clinical consideration and therapeutic intervention. While the nature of these pathological relationships, remains the subject of much debate, various metabolic or endocrine effects in the context of obesity are thought to play a role [30].

5.1. Diet and Physical Exercise

Western diet, which is characterised by a hyper-caloric intake high in fats and simple sugars, precipitates a rapid increase in post-prandial plasma glucose and insulin levels, increasing hepatic *de novo*-lipogenesis, steatosis, insulin resistance, central obesity and the risk of NAFLD [21,132]. The Western Australian Pregnancy (Raine) Cohort Study (*n* = 995), for example, found that a Western dietary pattern at 14 years old was associated with an increased frequency of NAFLD at 17 years, independent of sex, dietary misreporting, family income, frequency of physical activity and sedentary behaviour [132]. As most paediatric patients with NAFLD are obese, addressing their obesity by means of dietary modifications, including reduction of caloric, fat and fast-release carbohydrate intake, as well as increasing physical exercise in order to effect weight loss should be considered the first-line of any effective interventional strategy. Indeed, current AASLD guidelines recommend limiting overall dietary fat intake to less than 5% of total caloric intake, while limiting trans-fats to <1% and saturated fats to <7% [74].

Numerous studies have shown that even a moderate reduction in weight, 5% in steatosis and 10% in NASH, has the potential to reduce hepatic steatosis, improve insulin sensitivity and significantly improve clinical outcomes in adults [14,19,44]. However, its effectiveness in patients with pre-existing NASH-induced hepatic fibrosis remains uncertain. Although few in number, paediatric studies seem to support these findings. One study in children with biopsy-proven NAFLD demonstrated that a reduction of 20% or more over 12 months precipitated significant improvement in serum ALT and steatosis in 68% of children [133]. Another study of 53 paediatric patients with NAFLD also reported significant reduction of steatosis, inflammation and hepatocyte ballooning on liver biopsy following similar lifestyle interventions [131].

Improvements may even be possible in a much shorter timeframe. Indeed, a recent Danish study of 117 obese children demonstrated marked improvement in their insulin sensitivity, liver fat accumulation and serum aminotransferase levels in two thirds of the cohort after only ten weeks of dietary intervention and one hour of moderate exercise daily [134]. Moreover, patients with NAFLD undertook less physical exercise than age and sex-matched controls and only 20%–33% of them met current recommendations for physical activity [135–137]. Physical activity correlates inversely with hepatic steatosis, independently of changes in body weight or dietary intake, increases insulin sensitivity and reduces central obesity, even in the absence of dietary alteration [11]. Furthermore, the extent of these changes appears, while apparent even in the short-term, to be proportional to the intensity and duration of lifestyle modification [135,138]. There is also evidence in adults to suggest that vigorous exercise is more beneficial than longer intervals of moderate exercise [139].

The minimum amount of weight loss necessary to improve clinical outcomes for patients with NASH, however, remains unclear. The current lack of specific clinical guidelines regarding which dietary modifications or physical exercise regimes would be most effective in inducing metabolic and histological improvement in children with NAFLD, beyond achieving weight loss in overweight children, perturbs a more systematic and evidence-based approach to the clinical management of this disease [19,24,65]. That said, any diet, whether alone or in conjunction with increased physical activity, that facilitates weight loss can effectively reduce hepatic steatosis, provided that the patient adheres to it. Early dietary intervention in childhood is especially important, given that dietary patterns formed in childhood tend to be retained into adulthood [132].

Lifestyle modification, however, can be difficult for younger patients to engage with and maintain long-term, particularly in the context of negative perceptions of dietary intervention and the prescription of physical exercise in children, among patients and their parents [9]. As such, lifestyle intervention should be tailored towards patients as individuals, taking account of the cultural and socioeconomic determinants of diet and exercise habits, as well as differences in patient perceptions of obesity and body image, particularly in adolescence, before setting clear and achievable goals derived by the patient and clinician in partnership. The adoption of similar lifestyle modifications by family members and, in some cases, behavioural therapy may aid compliance [15]. More effective and straightforward tools for monitoring day-to-day quality and quantity of dietary intake and physical activity in childhood, as well as greater efforts to educate and provide guidance for parents and their children regarding maintaining a healthy diet and the importance of physical activity are needed [140].

5.1.1. Dietary Fructose

Besides the control of total caloric intake, the consumption of certain micronutrients, such as fructose, which is a constituent of sucrose, corn syrup, fruit juice, soft-drinks and various sweeteners, should also be reduced. Unlike glucose, fructose is metabolised exclusively in the liver and is preferentially shunted into the *de novo*-lipogenesis pathway via glyceraldehyde-3-phosphate, contributing to increased triglyceride synthesis and hepatic steatosis [141,142]. It has also been suggested that fructose may interact with nuclear transcription factors, such as sterol response element binding protein-1c, precipitating alterations in the expression of genes involved in liver glycolysis and lipogenesis [143]. It may also promote liver injury in NAFLD by causing bacterial overgrowth and increased intestinal permeability, precipitating endotoxemia and subsequent initiation of inflammation but this has yet to be proven [142,143].

In adults and in rodents, fructose has also been associated, particularly in the context of a high-fat diet, with a higher risk of NAFLD and increased liver fibrosis [21,44,142]. Moreover, the severity of hepatic steatosis and inflammation in rats fed fructose-enriched diets tends to be more severe than in controls [144]. Human studies also report greater fructose consumption in adult NAFLD patients and greater soft drink consumption and fasting serum triglyceride levels in children with NAFLD relative to controls [142]. Indeed, fructose consumption has dramatically increased in recent years and has also been associated with increased central obesity, dyslipidaemia and insulin resistance, all independent risk factors for NAFLD [27,145].

5.1.2. Vitamin D

Vitamin D plasma levels have also been shown to inversely correlate with NASH and fibrosis in children and adolescents [146,147]. Furthermore, Vitamin D deficiency is more common in obese patients than those of normal weight and was shown to be associated with the incidence of NAFLD, liver steatosis, necroinflammation and fibrosis in adults [146,148].

Vitamin D receptors regulate the expression of numerous genes, some of which are involved in glucose and lipid metabolism, and are widely distributed throughout the liver [146,148]. In rats exposed to obesogenic diet, Vitamin D deficiency exacerbates NAFLD through the activation of Toll-like receptors and is associated with insulin resistance, hepatic inflammatory markers and oxidative stress [149].

Growing evidence also suggests that low serum Vitamin D is associated with insulin resistance and Type II diabetes and that appropriate Vitamin D supplementation can improve insulin sensitivity [150]. However, in the Western Australian Pregnancy (Raine) Cohort, others have reported the association of low Vitamin D levels with evidence of NAFLD on ultrasound at 17 years of age was independent of adiposity and insulin resistance [146]. As such, screening for Vitamin D deficiency in adolescents otherwise considered at high risk of NAFLD may be appropriate. Further clinical and experimental investigation of this phenomenon, as well as the benefits of dietary supplementation, is warranted [146].

5.1.3. ω-3 Fatty Acids

Experimental models in animals and adults have shown that long chain ω-3 fatty acids, known important regulators of hepatic gene transcription, can decrease hepatic steatosis, improve insulin sensitivity and cardiovascular disease and decrease markers of inflammation [24,151,152].

Elsewhere, dietary depletion of polyunsaturated fats, such as ω-3, has been associated with the pathogenesis of NAFLD, while its progression has been associated with high circulating and hepatic levels of saturated fatty acids and industrial trans-fats. As such, limiting daily consumption of foods high in saturated fatty acids, while supplementing ω-3 intake may have a role in NAFLD treatment [9,153,154].

It is thought that the beneficial effects of ω-3 supplementation may be secondary to their known anti-inflammatory, antithrombotic, antiarrhythmic, hypolipidaemic and vasodilatory properties. There is evidence to suggest that they might also improve lipid profiles, lowering triglyceride serum levels, decreasing insulin resistance, hepatic steatosis and cytokine synthesis [153]. For example, dietary supplementation with docosahexaenoic acid (DHA), the major dietary long-chain polyunsaturated (ω-3) fatty acid, which exerts a potent anti-inflammatory effect through the G protein-coupled receptor 120 (GPR-120), has been associated with significant improvement in the histological parameters of NAFLD, including NAFLD activity score, hepatocyte ballooning and steatosis in children, after 18 months [154]. Interestingly, hepatic progenitor cell proliferation was also reduced in correlation with these same histological parameters, as were the numbers of inflammatory macrophages on biopsy, while GPR-120 expression in hepatocytes was markedly increased. As such, it was suggested that DHA might also modulate hepatic progenitor cell activation, hepatocyte survival and macrophage polarisation through interaction with GPR-120 and NF-κB repression [154]. Another study also described that, after 6 months of ω-3 supplementation, hepatic echogenicity and insulin sensitivity were significantly improved in children with NAFLD, although no change in serum ALT or BMI was observed [155]. More recently, another RCT reported the use of probiotics and ω-3 fatty acids showed encouraging early results, with improvement of serum liver enzymes but without validating liver histology [156]. AASLD guidelines currently state that it would be premature to recommend ω-3 fatty acids for the specific treatment of NAFLD or NASH but they may be considered first-line therapeutic agents to treat hypertriglyceridaemia in patients with NAFLD [19].

5.2. Alcohol

Heavy alcohol consumption is a risk factor for chronic liver disease and should be avoided in patients with simple steatosis and NASH [19]. There is even evidence to suggest that regular consumption of smaller quantities of alcohol (below 20 g/day) may be harmful [30]. However, there are no studies reporting the effect of ongoing alcohol consumption on disease severity or natural history of NAFLD or the risk of liver cancer in childhood and adolescence in the long-term.

5.3. Bariatric Surgery

Bariatric surgery has been shown to significantly improve weight and comorbid disease in patients with NAFLD. It encompasses a range of restrictive procedures, which promote satiety and delayed gastric emptying, including adjustable gastric banding and sleeve gastrectomy, malabsorptive procedures, including biliopancreatic diversion, and combinatorial procedures, such as Roux-en-Y gastric bypass [11,14,19,157].

At present, bariatric surgery is only recommended for severely obese adolescents with significant steatohepatitis in whom therapeutic lifestyle intervention has been unsuccessful [14,157]. In such patients, it has been shown to significantly reduce the extent and severity of hepatic injury, steatosis and systemic inflammation, as well as having broader metabolic benefits, improving insulin sensitivity, positively modifying levels of circulating adipokines and the intestinal microbiome, particularly in the case of malabsorptive procedures [14]. Furthermore, it has been suggested that malabsorptive procedures might also have additional effects on gut hormone profiles, reducing ghrelin, enhancing Glucagon-like peptide-1 (GLP1) secretion and facilitating early ileal exposure to nutrients, alongside reduced expression of peptide YY (PYY) and oxyntomodulin obesity-related genes and altered bile metabolism [14,158].

However, despite a large body of evidence suggesting histological improvement secondary to weight loss in adults, bariatric surgery in NASH patients of any age group remains controversial [11,12,14,19,159]. Indeed, a lack of randomised controlled studies, small sample sizes variable inclusion criteria, incomplete longitudinal follow-up and lack of clear identification of confounding factors, such as insulin resistance led the Cochrane meta-analysis to conclude that the impact of bariatric surgery on NASH in childhood and adolescence is unconvincing [160]. As such, current AASLD guidelines state that while bariatric surgery is not contraindicated in otherwise eligible obese patients, it is "not an established option for NASH treatment" [19].

Reports of *de novo* progression of NASH and even hepatic fibrosis and cirrhosis following bariatric surgery are also highly controversial [14]. Although some have sought to attribute this phenomenon to a state of "heightened metabolic stress", in other surgical series, massive weight loss was shown to improve steatohepatitis and fibrosis. In this case, overall improvement was found to be dependent on the degree of insulin resistance, although long-term histological outcomes were not assessed [14,161].

Given the more aggressive nature of simple steatosis in paediatric disease, some have suggested that more earnest clinical intervention to reduce weight loss, including consideration of bariatric surgery, may be beneficial, even before the transition to steatohepatitis, in patients who are severely obese [12,28,159,160]. Further standardisation of eligibility criteria for surgery in the paediatric population, as well as studies on the safety and long-term efficacy of this approach, are warranted.

5.4. Pharmacological Intervention

Our understanding of the molecular pathogenesis of NAFLD remains limited and so current pharmacological intervention consists of strategies aimed at decreasing the incidence and severity of metabolic risk factors, such as obesity, insulin resistance, dyslipidaemia, as well as some drugs that target the major molecular pathways involved in the pathogenesis and progression of this disease of which we are aware, such as decreasing hepatic damage mediated by oxidative stress [67].

The aim of therapy is to forestall and, in some cases, reverse the progression of NAFLD to end-stage liver disease [11,162]. In particular, there remains a need for effective pharmacological therapies for children who do not adhere to or are unresponsive to lifestyle modification, in order to avoid severe organ damage [9,12].

Given the more aggressive clinical course of paediatric as opposed to adult NAFLD, targeted pharmacological intervention, although not presently recommended, may be prudent even before evidence of the transition to NASH is observed [11,14,19,28,68].

Collaboration between hepatologists and other relevant specialties, including endocrinology, paediatrics, dietetics, cardiology and primary care should be encouraged in order to optimise treatment, particularly in the current absence of clear clinical guidelines for pharmacological intervention in paediatric NAFLD.

5.4.1. Insulin Sensitizers

Insulin resistance and Type II diabetes mellitus are strongly associated with the incidence, severity and progression of NAFLD in the paediatric population. As such, drugs that can improve insulin sensitivity have a key role in the prognostication and therapeutic management of this disease, potentially reversing even advanced liver damage and hepatic fibrosis, improving long-term clinical outcomes [24].

Metformin, an oral insulin-sensitising agent, lowers hepatic glucose production and promotes glucose uptake in the periphery and, when given in 500 mg doses twice daily for 24 weeks, has been shown to reduce hepatic steatosis on magnetic resonance spectroscopy and ALT levels in non-diabetic children with biopsy-proven NASH [163]. That said, while the Treatment of NAFLD in Children (TONIC) trial, in which a large non-diabetic paediatric cohort was used to compare metformin with Vitamin E therapy, found metformin to be no more effective than a placebo in achieving a sustained decrease in ALT levels, it did show significant improvement in hepatocyte ballooning [164]. Current AASLD guidelines do not recommend the prescription of metformin for NAFLD in non-diabetic paediatric patients [19]. Its effectiveness at doses higher than 500 mg twice daily, however, remains unknown. Moreover, specific guidelines for prescribing metformin in children and adolescents with NAFLD and Type II Diabetes are needed.

Pioglitazone, a Peroxisome-Proliferator Activated Receptor-γ (PPARg) agonist, increases insulin sensitivity and reduces hepatic fat content by promoting the redistribution of triacylglycerols from the liver and muscle to adipose tissue [19,24]. Therefore, while they have shown great promise in studies of adult NAFLD, their use often results in weight gain. Their safety and therapeutic efficacy in children, however, has yet to be determined and, indeed, there is a general reluctance to prescribe thiazolidinediones in paediatric patients, due to the potential side effects of long-term therapy, which include cardiotoxicity, fluid retention, osteoporosis and, as in adults, obesity [24].

Only glitazones have consistently shown some benefit in the treatment of patients with NASH in randomised-controlled trials [19,128]. Recent research suggests that pioglitazone can improve hepatic steatosis and inflammation, as well as reducing aminotransferase levels and histological evidence of hepatocyte injury in patients with biopsy-proven NASH [24,165,166]. However, the majority of patients in these trials were non-diabetic and, furthermore, the treatment had no apparent effect on the extent or severity of hepatic fibrosis.

Incretin mimetics and dipeptidyl peptidase-4 (DPP-4) inhibitors, which increase insulin secretion, decrease fatty acid oxidation and lipogenesis and improve hepatic glucose metabolism, may also have a role in NAFLD therapeutics [12,165–167]. DPP-4 is an enzyme implicated in the degradation of circulating GLP1, an incretin secreted in response to food intake that stimulates insulin secretion and inhibits glucagon release. Studies conducted in animals and adult humans have demonstrated the efficacy of GLP-1 receptor agonists, which were resistant to DPP-4 degradation, and DPP-4 inhibitors [12,167–169].

Suppressors of the renin-angiotensin system, such as losartan, reportedly improve insulin sensitivity and adipokine production/release and prevent hepatic stellate cell activation by exerting preventative effects on hepatic inflammation and fibrogenesis [12,168,170]. However, because of their contraindications, there is no available data on their therapeutic effects in children.

5.4.2. Weight Loss Drugs

Orlistat, an enteric lipase inhibitor, is the only FDA approved therapy for weight loss in adolescents. It is moderately effective in achieving short-term weight loss but is limited in young patients due to adverse gastrointestinal side effects. However, despite several studies reporting improved ALT levels and hepatic steatosis in patients with NAFLD, others have failed to demonstrate histological improvement on biopsy. As such, their use in NAFLD remains controversial [171,172].

5.4.3. Statins

Patients with simple steatosis and NASH are at increased risk of cardiovascular disease, with several studies having demonstrated this to be the most common cause of death in NAFLD. Effective therapeutic intervention in NAFLD, therefore, should encompass stratification of patients in terms of cardiovascular risk factors, including dyslipidaemia, and the appropriate clinical management thereof [11,19,27].

Despite general reluctance to prescribe statins to treat dyslipidaemia in patients with suspected or established chronic liver disease and the not uncommon occurrence of elevated aminotransferases in patients receiving statins, serious liver injury as a direct consequence of their use is rarely seen in clinical practice. Indeed, the risk of serious hepatic injury in patients with chronic liver disease, including NAFLD, does not appear to exceed that of patients without [173,174]. The evidence in children, however, remains less certain.

Several studies have thus far reported that statins can significantly improve liver biochemistries and cardiovascular outcomes in patients with elevated liver enzymes likely due to NAFLD. However, there remain no randomised-controlled trials with histological endpoints to support this either in simple steatosis or in NASH [11,174]. While current AASLD guidelines state that statins can be used to treat dyslipidaemia in adult patients with simple steatosis and NASH [19], their prescription in paediatric patients remains controversial.

5.5. Antioxidant Therapies

Oxidative stress is considered a key mechanism of hepatocellular injury and the progression of simple steatosis to NASH in children [88,175]. Given that, within hepatocytes, reactive oxygen species (ROS) are mostly generated in the mitochondria, some have suggested that, in hepatic steatosis, increased intracellular fatty acid levels may act as an overabundant substrate for mitochondrial malfunctioning, increasing ROS and, downstream, inflammatory cytokine and adipokine production, as well as, via their oxidation by peroxisomal acyl-CoA oxidases, the production of hydrogen peroxide, another reactive oxygen species [176,177].

Ordinarily, various enzymatic antioxidant mechanisms protect the liver from such oxidative injury, which in NAFLD, it seems, are simply overwhelmed. Therefore, the employ of antioxidant therapies would be expected to break this chain of lipid peroxidation and restore the endogenous antioxidant/oxidant equilibrium, halting the progression of NASH [148,178].

5.6. Vitamin E

Vitamin E therapy has been shown to reduce histological evidence of hepatic steatosis, inflammation and hepatocyte ballooning, as well as a reduction in aminotransferase levels in patients with NASH [148]. It has even been associated with the clinical resolution of steatohepatitis in adult NAFLD patients, although it does not appear to affect the extent or severity of hepatic fibrosis once it is established [179]. Studies in children have also reported improvement of liver function and glucose metabolism following a 12-month regime of Vitamin E (600 IU/day) and ascorbic acid (500 mg/day) in combination with dietary modification and physical exercise [133].

More recently, the NASH Clinical Research Network's Treatment of NAFLD children (TONIC) trial, reported a modest benefit on hepatocyte ballooning following Vitamin E therapy in combination with similar lifestyle modifications in 8–17 year olds with biopsy proven NASH [164]. While aminotransferase levels were unaffected, statistically significant improvement of the NAS score and resolution of NASH with Vitamin E therapy was also observed over the following two years [164]. However, whether similar improvements can still be achieved in the absence of concurrent lifestyle modification remains controversial, as does the appropriate dosing of antioxidant therapies, including Vitamin E, in children. Indeed, there is some concern as to whether or not Vitamin E therapy increases all-cause mortality, as well as the risk of certain cancers, when administered in high doses [180].

While the most recent EASL guidelines advocate Vitamin E as a first-line pharmacotherapy in non-diabetic adults with biopsy proven NASH, the AASLD 2005 guidelines suggest that although Vitamin E also appears to be beneficial in non-diabetic children with NASH, confirmatory studies are needed before its use can be recommended in clinical practice. Furthermore, due to a similar lack of evidence, its use is not supported in diabetic patients with NASH, NAFLD without liver biopsy, NASH cirrhosis or cryptogenic cirrhosis at any age [11,19,148,162].

5.7. Ursodeoxycholic Acid

Ursodeoxycholic acid is one of the most widely used cytoprotective and antioxidant agents, able to protect hepatocytes from bile salt-mediated mitochondrial injury, as well as activating anti-apoptotic signalling pathways, fulfilling diverse immunomodulatory functions, in theory, stabilising cellular and organelle membranes in patients with NASH [24,181,182].

In children, a randomised controlled trial of ursodeoxycholic acid in combination with vitamin E therapy induced long-term improvements in liver function tests [183]. However, in another study of obese children with NAFLD, it was ineffective both alone and when combined with dietary intervention in decreasing serum ALT or the appearance of steatosis on ultrasound [184]. In another study in children, high doses of this acid induced a significant reduction in aminotransferase levels, although this was not the case with lower doses [185]. That said, its histological impact and therapeutic dose-threshold, as well as its effect on disease progression remains unclear. For example, in another study, two years of low-dose ursodeoxycholic acid in combination with vitamin E therapy was reported to improve biochemical and histological biomarkers [186]. Thus, the potential of ursodeoxycholic acid for reversing liver damage in paediatric NAFLD requires further attention.

5.8. Probiotic Therapy

Persistent cross-talk among the gut, the immune system and the liver appears to play an increasingly pivotal role in the pathogenesis and progression of NAFLD [63,64,154]. Emerging evidence suggests that specific nutrients are capable of increasing intestinal permeability to bacterial endotoxins, which, in turn, stimulate an immune-mediated inflammatory response from liver-resident cells, precipitating a profibrogenic phenotype. Several studies have also shown that the composition of the gut microbiome differs in NASH patients differs from that of obese patients without NASH and normoweight controls, specifically displaying a greater abundance of gram-negative bacteria [56,149].

Loguercio *et al.* [187] reported reduced hepatic injury and improved liver function tests following probiotic treatment in patients with various forms of chronic liver disease, including NAFLD. More recently, probiotic therapy in obese children with lactobacillus has been associated with significant improvement in serum aminotransferases and anti-peptidoglycan polysaccharide antibody levels, irrespective of BMI and visceral fat [188]. Further studies, have suggested that probiotics may reduce liver inflammation and improve gut epithelial barrier function. Probiotic therapy, therefore, represents a promising tool for the treatment of NAFLD in children by restoring the normal balance of gut microbiota [12,189].

Farnesoid X receptors (FXR), which are expressed in the bowel and liver, have also been implicated in the pathogenesis of NAFLD by mediating control of lipid and glucose homeostasis and bacterial flora growth and may, therefore, represent a novel therapeutic target [12,190].

6. Conclusions

Non-Alcoholic Fatty Liver Disease (NAFLD) is now the most common form of chronic liver disease, affecting 10%–20% of the general paediatric population and 50%–80% of those who are obese [27,35]. Within the next 10 years, it is expected to become the leading cause of liver pathology, liver failure and indication for liver transplantation in childhood and adolescence in the Western world [19,29,49,117]. Despite this, "paediatric" NAFLD remains under-studied, under-recognised and, potentially, undermanaged. Important gaps remain in our overall approach to screening, diagnosis, management and follow-up, particularly during the transition between paediatric and adult clinical services and in those patients at the extreme end of the obesity spectrum, in whom non-surgical therapies for weight loss are currently non-existent [9,11,44].

The importance of raising clinical and public awareness of NAFLD in childhood and adolescence, as well as addressing widespread misconceptions regarding its prevalence, natural history and prognosis among healthcare professionals at all stages of their training and in light of emerging evidence, cannot be overstated. The strong association between paediatric NAFLD and metabolic risk factors, including insulin resistance, dyslipidaemia, cardiovascular disease and, most significantly, obesity, highlights the need for greater interconnectedness and collaboration between diverse clinical specialties and the potential for significantly improving patient outcomes through targeted dietary modification, reduction of caloric intake, increased physical exercise and, where appropriate, pharmacological therapy [9,21,67,131].

The current paucity of research in paediatric NAFLD has perpetuated a limited understanding of its pathophysiology and hampered the selection and development of more effective therapeutic interventions since this disease was first described in children in the mid-1970s. More accurate epidemiological data derived from longitudinal and larger cohort studies will be needed in order to determine the true prevalence of NAFLD in childhood and adolescence and allow the development of more accurate risk prediction scores to augment clinical screening and surveillance, as well as comprehensive clinical guidelines specifically for the diagnosis and management of paediatric disease, which are currently lacking.

By appropriately reviewing the nomenclature, we might better emphasise the importance of the clinicopathological relationships between NAFLD and other chronic liver diseases in childhood and adolescence.

In the absence of definitive radiological and histopathological diagnostic tests, maintenance of a high clinical suspicion in both primary and specialist care settings and by all members of the multidisciplinary team remains the most potent of diagnostic tools, enabling early diagnosis and appropriate therapeutic intervention.

Acknowledgments: This work has been funded by the Welcome Trust and the Obesity Action Campaign. We also acknowledge all the researchers that contribute to the understanding of this field.

Conflicts of Interest: The authors declare no conflict of interest.

Abbreviations

LD	Linear dichroism
AASLD	American Association for the Study of Liver Diseases
ALT	Alanine Aminotransferase
AMPK	AMP-activated Protein Kinase
APOC3	Adipoprotein C3
AST	Aspartate Aminotransferase
BMI	Body Mass Index
CB2	Cannabinoid Receptor 2
CK-18	Cytokeratin 18
CT	Computerized Tomography
CYP2E1	Cytochrome P450 family 2 subfamily E member 1
DGAT2	Diacylglycerol O-Acyltransferase 2
DHA	Docosahexaenoic Acid
DPP-4	Incretin Mimetics and Dipeptidyl Peptidase-4
EASL	European Association for the Study of the Liver
ELF	Enhanced Liver Fibrosis
FTO	Fat Mass and Obesity associated
FXR	Farnesoid X Receptor
GCKR	Glucokinase Regulatory Protein
GGT	γ-glutamyl Transferase
GLP1	Glucagon-Like Peptide-1
GRP-120	G Protein-coupled Receptor 120
GWAS	Genome-Wide Association Study
HDL	High-Density Lipoprotein
HPC	Hepatic Progenitor Cells
HSC	Hepatic Stellate Cells
IL-6	Interleukin 6
IR	Insulin Resistance
IRS-1	Insulin Receptor Substrate-1
IUGR	Intrauterine Growth Restriction
KC	Kupffer Cells
KLF-6	Kruppel-Like Factor 6
LDL	Low Density Lipoprotein
LFTs	Liver Function Tests
LPIN1	Lipin 1
LYPLAL1	Lysophospholipase-Like 1
MC4R	Melanocortin 4 Receptor
NAFLD	Non-Alcoholic Fatty Liver Disease
NASH	Non-Alcoholic Steatohepatitis
NCAN	Neurocan
NKT	Natural Killer T lymphocytes
PNFI	Pediatric NAFLD Fibrosis Index
PNPLA3	Adiponutrin/Patatin-like Phospholipase Domain-containing 3
PPARg	Peroxisome-Proliferator Activated Receptor-γ
PPP1R3B	Protein Phosphatase 1 Regulatory Subunit 3b
PYY	Peptide YY
ROS	Reactive Oxygen Species
SLD	Steatotic Liver Disease
SOD2	Manganese-dependent Superoxide Dismutase
SREBP1c	Sterol Regulatory Binding Element
TNF-α	Tumor Necrosis Factor α
TONIC	Treatment of NAFLD in Children

References

1. Angulo, P. Nonalcoholic fatty liver disease. *N. Engl. J. Med.* **2002**, *346*, 1221–1231. [CrossRef] [PubMed]
2. Lawlor, D.A.; Callaway, M.; Macdonald-Wallis, C.; Anderson, E.; Fraser, A.; Howe, L.D.; Day, C.; Sattar, N. Nonalcoholic fatty liver disease, liver fibrosis, and cardiometabolic risk factors in adolescence: A cross-sectional study of 1874 general population adolescents. *J. Clin. Endocrinol. Metab.* **2014**, *99*, E410–E417. [CrossRef] [PubMed]
3. Alexander, J.; Torbenson, M.; Wu, T.T.; Yeh, M.M. Non-alcoholic fatty liver disease contributes to hepatocarcinogenesis in non-cirrhotic liver: A clinical and pathological study. *J. Gastroenterol. Hepatol.* **2013**, *28*, 848–854. [CrossRef] [PubMed]
4. Alisi, A.; Cianfarani, S.; Manco, M.; Agostoni, C.; Nobili, V. Non-alcoholic fatty liver disease and metabolic syndrome in adolescents: Pathogenetic role of genetic background and intrauterine environment. *Ann. Med.* **2012**, *44*, 29–40. [CrossRef] [PubMed]
5. Perticone, M.; Cimellaro, A.; Maio, R.; Caroleo, B.; Sciacqua, A.; Sesti, G.; Perticone, F. Additive effect of non-alcoholic fatty liver disease on metabolic syndrome-related endothelial dysfunction in hypertensive patients. *Int. J. Mol. Sci.* **2016**, *17*. [CrossRef] [PubMed]
6. Ayonrinde, O.T.; Olynyk, J.K.; Marsh, J.A.; Beilin, L.J.; Mori, T.A.; Oddy, W.H.; Adams, L.A. Childhood adiposity trajectories and risk of nonalcoholic fatty liver disease in adolescents. *J. Gastroenterol. Hepatol.* **2015**, *30*, 163–171. [CrossRef] [PubMed]
7. Moran, J.R.; Ghishan, F.K.; Halter, S.A.; Greene, H.L. Steatohepatitis in obese children: A cause of chronic liver dysfunction. *Am. J. Gastroenterol.* **1983**, *78*, 374–377. [PubMed]
8. Marcason, W. What are the current guidelines for pediatric non-alcoholic fatty liver disease? *J. Acad. Nutr. Diet.* **2013**, *113*, 1772. [CrossRef] [PubMed]
9. Mencin, A.A.; Lavine, J.E. Advances in pediatric nonalcoholic fatty liver disease. *Pediatr. Clin. N. Am.* **2011**, *58*, 1375–1392. [CrossRef] [PubMed]
10. Monteiro, P.A.; Antunes Bde, M.; Silveira, L.S.; Christofaro, D.G.; Fernandes, R.A.; Freitas Junior, I.F. Body composition variables as predictors of nafld by ultrasound in obese children and adolescents. *BMC Pediatr.* **2014**, *14*, 25. [CrossRef] [PubMed]
11. Ratziu, V.; Bellentani, S.; Cortez-Pinto, H.; Day, C.; Marchesini, G. A position statement on NAFLD/NASH based on the EASL 2009 special conference. *J. Hepatol.* **2010**, *53*, 372–384. [CrossRef] [PubMed]
12. Berardis, S.; Sokal, E. Pediatric non-alcoholic fatty liver disease: An increasing public health issue. *Eur. J. Pediatr.* **2014**, *173*, 131–139. [CrossRef] [PubMed]
13. Schwimmer, J.B.; Deutsch, R.; Kahen, T.; Lavine, J.E.; Stanley, C.; Behling, C. Prevalence of fatty liver in children and adolescents. *Pediatrics* **2006**, *118*, 1388–1393. [CrossRef] [PubMed]
14. Holterman, A.; Gurria, J.; Tanpure, S.; DiSomma, N. Nonalcoholic fatty liver disease and bariatric surgery in adolescents. *Semin. Pediatr. Surg.* **2014**, *23*, 49–57. [CrossRef] [PubMed]
15. Vajro, P.; Ferrante, L.; Lenta, S.; Mandato, C.; Persico, M. Management of adults with paediatric-onset chronic liver disease: Strategic issues for transition care. *Dig. Liver Dis.* **2014**, *46*, 295–301. [CrossRef] [PubMed]
16. Palmer, N.D.; Musani, S.K.; Yerges-Armstrong, L.M.; Feitosa, M.F.; Bielak, L.F.; Hernaez, R.; Kahali, B.; Carr, J.J.; Harris, T.B.; Jhun, M.A.; et al. Characterization of european ancestry nonalcoholic fatty liver disease-associated variants in individuals of african and hispanic descent. *Hepatology* **2013**, *58*, 966–975. [CrossRef] [PubMed]
17. Vajro, P.; Lenta, S.; Socha, P.; Dhawan, A.; McKiernan, P.; Baumann, U.; Durmaz, O.; Lacaille, F.; McLin, V.; Nobili, V. Diagnosis of nonalcoholic fatty liver disease in children and adolescents: Position paper of the espghan hepatology committee. *J. Pediatr. Gastroenterol. Nutr.* **2012**, *54*, 700–713. [CrossRef] [PubMed]
18. Boyraz, M.; Hatipoglu, N.; Sari, E.; Akcay, A.; Taskin, N.; Ulucan, K.; Akcay, T. Non-alcoholic fatty liver disease in obese children and the relationship between metabolic syndrome criteria. *Obes. Res. Clin. Pract.* **2014**, *8*, e356–e363. [CrossRef] [PubMed]
19. Chalasani, N.; Younossi, Z.; Lavine, J.E.; Diehl, A.M.; Brunt, E.M.; Cusi, K.; Charlton, M.; Sanyal, A.J. The diagnosis and management of non-alcoholic fatty liver disease: Practice guideline by the American association for the study of liver diseases, American college of gastroenterology, and the American gastroenterological association. *Am. J. Gastroenterol.* **2012**, *107*, 811–826. [CrossRef] [PubMed]

20. Deng, J.; Fishbein, M.H.; Rigsby, C.K.; Zhang, G.; Schoeneman, S.E.; Donaldson, J.S. Quantitative MRI for hepatic fat fraction and T2* measurement in pediatric patients with non-alcoholic fatty liver disease. *Pediatr. Radiol.* **2014**, *44*, 1379–1387. [CrossRef] [PubMed]

21. Liccardo, D.; Alisi, A.; Porta, G.; Nobili, V. Is there any link between dietary pattern and development of nonalcoholic fatty liver disease in adolescence? An expert review. *Expert Rev. Gastroenterol. Hepatol.* **2013**, *7*, 601–604. [CrossRef] [PubMed]

22. Lerret, S.M.; Garcia-Rodriguez, L.; Skelton, J.; Biank, V.; Kilway, D.; Telega, G. Predictors of nonalcoholic steatohepatitis in obese children. *Gastroenterol. Nurs.* **2011**, *34*, 434–437. [CrossRef] [PubMed]

23. Navarro-Jarabo, J.M.; Ubina-Aznar, E.; Tapia-Ceballos, L.; Ortiz-Cuevas, C.; Perez-Aisa, M.A.; Rivas-Ruiz, F.; Andrade, R.J.; Perea-Milla, E. Hepatic steatosis and severity-related factors in obese children. *J. Gastroenterol. Hepatol.* **2013**, *28*, 1532–1538. [CrossRef] [PubMed]

24. Alisi, A.; Nobili, V. Non-alcoholic fatty liver disease in children now: Lifestyle changes and pharmacologic treatments. *Nutrition* **2012**, *28*, 722–726. [CrossRef] [PubMed]

25. Ozhan, B.; Ersoy, B.; Kiremitci, S.; Ozkol, M.; Taneli, F. Insulin sensitivity indices: Fasting *versus* glucose-stimulated indices in pediatric non-alcoholic fatty liver disease. *Eur. Rev. Med. Pharmacol. Sci.* **2015**, *19*, 3450–3458. [PubMed]

26. Anderson, E.L.; Howe, L.D.; Jones, H.E.; Higgins, J.P.; Lawlor, D.A.; Fraser, A. The prevalence of non-alcoholic fatty liver disease in children and adolescents: A systematic review and meta-analysis. *PLoS ONE* **2015**, *10*, e0140908. [CrossRef] [PubMed]

27. Kelsey, M.M.; Zaepfel, A.; Bjornstad, P.; Nadeau, K.J. Age-related consequences of childhood obesity. *Gerontology* **2014**, *60*, 222–228. [CrossRef] [PubMed]

28. Regnell, S.E.; Peterson, P.; Trinh, L.; Broberg, P.; Leander, P.; Lernmark, A.; Mansson, S.; Elding Larsson, H. Magnetic resonance imaging reveals altered distribution of hepatic fat in children with type 1 diabetes compared to controls. *Metabolism* **2015**, *64*, 872–878. [CrossRef] [PubMed]

29. Mansoor, S.; Yerian, L.; Kohli, R.; Xanthakos, S.; Angulo, P.; Ling, S.; Lopez, R.; Christine, C.K.; Feldstein, A.E.; Alkhouri, N. The evaluation of hepatic fibrosis scores in children with nonalcoholic fatty liver disease. *Dig. Dis. Sci.* **2015**, *60*, 1440–1447. [CrossRef] [PubMed]

30. Trovato, F.M.; Martines, G.F.; Brischetto, D.; Catalano, D.; Musumeci, G.; Trovato, G.M. Fatty liver disease and lifestyle in youngsters: Diet, food intake frequency, exercise, sleep shortage and fashion. *Liver Int.* **2016**, *36*, 427–433. [CrossRef] [PubMed]

31. Younossi, Z.M.; Stepanova, M.; Negro, F.; Hallaji, S.; Younossi, Y.; Lam, B.; Srishord, M. Nonalcoholic fatty liver disease in lean individuals in the United States. *Medicine* **2012**, *91*, 319–327. [CrossRef] [PubMed]

32. Silveira, L.S.; Monteiro, P.A.; Antunes Bde, M.; Seraphim, P.M.; Fernandes, R.A.; Christofaro, D.G.; Freitas Junior, I.F. Intra-abdominal fat is related to metabolic syndrome and non-alcoholic fat liver disease in obese youth. *BMC Pediatr.* **2013**, *13*, 115. [CrossRef] [PubMed]

33. Kelishadi, R.; Cook, S.R.; Adibi, A.; Faghihimani, Z.; Ghatrehsamani, S.; Beihaghi, A.; Salehi, H.; Khavarian, N.; Poursafa, P. Association of the components of the metabolic syndrome with non-alcoholic fatty liver disease among normal-weight, overweight and obese children and adolescents. *Diabetol. Metab. Syndr.* **2009**, *1*, 29. [CrossRef] [PubMed]

34. Manco, M.; Bedogni, G.; Marcellini, M.; Devito, R.; Ciampalini, P.; Sartorelli, M.R.; Comparcola, D.; Piemonte, F.; Nobili, V. Waist circumference correlates with liver fibrosis in children with non-alcoholic steatohepatitis. *Gut* **2008**, *57*, 1283–1287. [CrossRef] [PubMed]

35. Alterio, A.; Alisi, A.; Liccardo, D.; Nobili, V. Non-alcoholic fatty liver and metabolic syndrome in children: A vicious circle. *Horm. Res. Paediatr.* **2014**, *82*, 283–289. [CrossRef] [PubMed]

36. Mager, D.R.; Yap, J.; Rodriguez-Dimitrescu, C.; Mazurak, V.; Ball, G.; Gilmour, S. Anthropometric measures of visceral and subcutaneous fat are important in the determination of metabolic dysregulation in boys and girls at risk for nonalcoholic fatty liver disease. *Nutr. Clin. Pract.* **2013**, *28*, 101–111. [CrossRef] [PubMed]

37. Boyraz, M.; Cekmez, F.; Karaoglu, A.; Cinaz, P.; Durak, M.; Bideci, A. Relationship of adipokines (adiponectin, resistin and RBP4) with metabolic syndrome components in pubertal obese children. *Biomark. Med.* **2013**, *7*, 423–428. [CrossRef] [PubMed]

38. Sayin, O.; Tokgoz, Y.; Arslan, N. Investigation of adropin and leptin levels in pediatric obesity-related nonalcoholic fatty liver disease. *J. Pediatr. Endocrinol. Metab.* **2014**, *27*, 479–484. [CrossRef] [PubMed]

39. Li, W.; Zheng, L.; Sheng, C.; Cheng, X.; Qing, L.; Qu, S. Systematic review on the treatment of pentoxifylline in patients with non-alcoholic fatty liver disease. *Lipids Health Dis.* **2011**, *10*, 49. [CrossRef] [PubMed]

40. Adams, L.A.; Lymp, J.F.; St Sauver, J.; Sanderson, S.O.; Lindor, K.D.; Feldstein, A.; Angulo, P. The natural history of nonalcoholic fatty liver disease: A population-based cohort study. *Gastroenterology* **2005**, *129*, 113–121. [CrossRef] [PubMed]

41. Ekstedt, M.; Franzen, L.E.; Mathiesen, U.L.; Thorelius, L.; Holmqvist, M.; Bodemar, G.; Kechagias, S. Long-term follow-up of patients with NAFLD and elevated liver enzymes. *Hepatology* **2006**, *44*, 865–873. [CrossRef] [PubMed]

42. Ong, J.P.; Pitts, A.; Younossi, Z.M. Increased overall mortality and liver-related mortality in non-alcoholic fatty liver disease. *J. Hepatol.* **2008**, *49*, 608–612. [CrossRef] [PubMed]

43. Schwimmer, J.B.; Newton, K.P.; Awai, H.I.; Choi, L.J.; Garcia, M.A.; Ellis, L.L.; Vanderwall, K.; Fontanesi, J. Paediatric gastroenterology evaluation of overweight and obese children referred from primary care for suspected non-alcoholic fatty liver disease. *Aliment. Pharmacol. Ther.* **2013**, *38*, 1267–1277. [CrossRef] [PubMed]

44. Holterman, A.X.; Guzman, G.; Fantuzzi, G.; Wang, H.; Aigner, K.; Browne, A.; Holterman, M. Nonalcoholic fatty liver disease in severely obese adolescent and adult patients. *Obesity* **2013**, *21*, 591–597. [CrossRef] [PubMed]

45. Charlotte, F.; Le Naour, G.; Bernhardt, C.; Poynard, T.; Ratziu, V.; Group, L.S. A comparison of the fibrotic potential of nonalcoholic fatty liver disease and chronic hepatitis C. *Hum. Pathol.* **2010**, *41*, 1178–1185. [CrossRef] [PubMed]

46. Caldwell, S.H.; Crespo, D.M.; Kang, H.S.; Al-Osaimi, A.M. Obesity and hepatocellular carcinoma. *Gastroenterology* **2004**, *127*, S97–S103. [CrossRef] [PubMed]

47. El-Serag, H.B.; Hampel, H.; Javadi, F. The association between diabetes and hepatocellular carcinoma: A systematic review of epidemiologic evidence. *Clin. Gastroenterol. Hepatol.* **2006**, *4*, 369–380. [CrossRef] [PubMed]

48. Berentzen, T.L.; Gamborg, M.; Holst, C.; Sorensen, T.I.; Baker, J.L. Body mass index in childhood and adult risk of primary liver cancer. *J. Hepatol.* **2014**, *60*, 325–330. [CrossRef] [PubMed]

49. Atabek, M.E.; Selver Eklioglu, B.; Akyurek, N. Which metabolic syndrome criteria best predict non-alcoholic fatty liver disease in children? *Eat. Weight Disord.* **2014**, *19*, 495–501. [CrossRef] [PubMed]

50. Singh, G.K.; Vitola, B.E.; Holland, M.R.; Sekarski, T.; Patterson, B.W.; Magkos, F.; Klein, S. Alterations in ventricular structure and function in obese adolescents with nonalcoholic fatty liver disease. *J. Pediatr.* **2013**, *162*, 1160–1168. [CrossRef] [PubMed]

51. Fintini, D.; Chinali, M.; Cafiero, G.; Esposito, C.; Giordano, U.; Turchetta, A.; Pescosolido, S.; Pongiglione, G.; Nobili, V. Early left ventricular abnormality/dysfunction in obese children affected by NAFLD. *Nutr. Metab. Cardiovasc. Dis.* **2014**, *24*, 72–74. [CrossRef] [PubMed]

52. Pacifico, L.; Di Martino, M.; de Merulis, A.; Bezzi, M.; Osborn, J.F.; Catalano, C.; Chiesa, C. Left ventricular dysfunction in obese children and adolescents with nonalcoholic fatty liver disease. *Hepatology* **2014**, *59*, 461–470. [CrossRef] [PubMed]

53. Nobili, V.; Alkhouri, N.; Bartuli, A.; Manco, M.; Lopez, R.; Alisi, A.; Feldstein, A.E. Severity of liver injury and atherogenic lipid profile in children with nonalcoholic fatty liver disease. *Pediatr. Res.* **2010**, *67*, 665–670. [CrossRef] [PubMed]

54. Pacifico, L.; Bonci, E.; Andreoli, G.; Romaggioli, S.; Di Miscio, R.; Lombardo, C.V.; Chiesa, C. Association of serum triglyceride-to-HDL cholesterol ratio with carotid artery intima-media thickness, insulin resistance and nonalcoholic fatty liver disease in children and adolescents. *Nutr. Metab. Cardiovasc. Dis.* **2014**, *24*, 737–743. [CrossRef] [PubMed]

55. Nobili, V.; Donati, B.; Panera, N.; Vongsakulyanon, A.; Alisi, A.; Dallapiccola, B.; Valenti, L. A 4-polymorphism risk score predicts steatohepatitis in children with nonalcoholic fatty liver disease. *J. Pediatr. Gastroenterol. Nutr.* **2014**, *58*, 632–636. [CrossRef] [PubMed]

56. Yuan, J.; Baker, S.S.; Liu, W.; Alkhouri, R.; Baker, R.D.; Xie, J.; Ji, G.; Zhu, L. Endotoxemia unrequired in the pathogenesis of pediatric nonalcoholic steatohepatitis. *J. Gastroenterol. Hepatol.* **2014**, *29*, 1292–1298. [CrossRef] [PubMed]

57. Choi, S.S.; Diehl, A.M. Hepatic triglyceride synthesis and nonalcoholic fatty liver disease. *Curr. Opin. Lipidol.* **2008**, *19*, 295–300. [CrossRef] [PubMed]

58. Yamaguchi, K.; Yang, L.; McCall, S.; Huang, J.; Yu, X.X.; Pandey, S.K.; Bhanot, S.; Monia, B.P.; Li, Y.X.; Diehl, A.M. Inhibiting triglyceride synthesis improves hepatic steatosis but exacerbates liver damage and fibrosis in obese mice with nonalcoholic steatohepatitis. *Hepatology* **2007**, *45*, 1366–1374. [CrossRef] [PubMed]

59. Wanless, I.R.; Shiota, K. The pathogenesis of nonalcoholic steatohepatitis and other fatty liver diseases: A four-step model including the role of lipid release and hepatic venular obstruction in the progression to cirrhosis. *Semin. Liver Dis.* **2004**, *24*, 99–106. [PubMed]

60. Morandi, A.; Maffeis, C. Predictors of metabolic risk in childhood obesity. *Horm. Res. Paediatr.* **2014**, *82*, 3–11. [CrossRef] [PubMed]

61. Torun, E.; Ozgen, I.T.; Gokce, S.; Aydin, S.; Cesur, Y. Thyroid hormone levels in obese children and adolescents with non-alcoholic fatty liver disease. *J. Clin. Res. Pediatr. Endocrinol.* **2014**, *6*, 34–39. [CrossRef] [PubMed]

62. Pacifico, L.; Bonci, E.; Ferraro, F.; Andreoli, G.; Bascetta, S.; Chiesa, C. Hepatic steatosis and thyroid function tests in overweight and obese children. *Int. J. Endocrinol.* **2013**, *2013*, 381014. [CrossRef] [PubMed]

63. De Vito, R.; Alisi, A.; Masotti, A.; Ceccarelli, S.; Panera, N.; Citti, A.; Salata, M.; Valenti, L.; Feldstein, A.E.; Nobili, V. Markers of activated inflammatory cells correlate with severity of liver damage in children with nonalcoholic fatty liver disease. *Int. J. Mol. Med.* **2012**, *30*, 49–56. [PubMed]

64. Ferreyra Solari, N.E.; Inzaugarat, M.E.; Baz, P.; de Matteo, E.; Lezama, C.; Galoppo, M.; Galoppo, C.; Chernavsky, A.C. The role of innate cells is coupled to a Th1-polarized immune response in pediatric nonalcoholic steatohepatitis. *J. Clin. Immunol.* **2012**, *32*, 611–621. [CrossRef] [PubMed]

65. Barshop, N.J.; Sirlin, C.B.; Schwimmer, J.B.; Lavine, J.E. Review article: Epidemiology, pathogenesis and potential treatments of paediatric non-alcoholic fatty liver disease. *Aliment. Pharmacol. Ther.* **2008**, *28*, 13–24. [CrossRef] [PubMed]

66. Nobili, V.; Carpino, G.; Alisi, A.; Franchitto, A.; Alpini, G.; de Vito, R.; Onori, P.; Alvaro, D.; Gaudio, E. Hepatic progenitor cells activation, fibrosis, and adipokines production in pediatric nonalcoholic fatty liver disease. *Hepatology* **2012**, *56*, 2142–2153. [CrossRef] [PubMed]

67. Yoon, H.J.; Cha, B.S. Pathogenesis and therapeutic approaches for non-alcoholic fatty liver disease. *World J. Hepatol.* **2014**, *6*, 800–811. [CrossRef] [PubMed]

68. Swiderska-Syn, M.; Suzuki, A.; Guy, C.D.; Schwimmer, J.B.; Abdelmalek, M.F.; Lavine, J.E.; Diehl, A.M. Hedgehog pathway and pediatric nonalcoholic fatty liver disease. *Hepatology* **2013**, *57*, 1814–1825. [CrossRef] [PubMed]

69. Mouralidarane, A.; Soeda, J.; Visconti-Pugmire, C.; Samuelsson, A.M.; Pombo, J.; Maragkoudaki, X.; Butt, A.; Saraswati, R.; Novelli, M.; Fusai, G.; *et al.* Maternal obesity programs offspring nonalcoholic fatty liver disease by innate immune dysfunction in mice. *Hepatology* **2013**, *58*, 128–138. [CrossRef] [PubMed]

70. Stienstra, R.; Saudale, F.; Duval, C.; Keshtkar, S.; Groener, J.E.; van Rooijen, N.; Staels, B.; Kersten, S.; Muller, M. Kupffer cells promote hepatic steatosis via interleukin-1β-dependent suppression of peroxisome proliferator-activated receptor α activity. *Hepatology* **2010**, *51*, 511–522. [CrossRef] [PubMed]

71. Morgan, M.L.; Sigala, B.; Soeda, J.; Cordero, P.; Nguyen, V.; McKee, C.; Mouralidarane, A.; Vinciguerra, M.; Oben, J.A. Acetylcholine induces fibrogenic effects via M2/M3 acetylcholine receptors in non-alcoholic steatohepatitis and in primary human hepatic stellate cells. *J. Gastroenterol. Hepatol.* **2016**, *31*, 475–483. [CrossRef] [PubMed]

72. Sigala, B.; McKee, C.; Soeda, J.; Pazienza, V.; Morgan, M.; Lin, C.I.; Selden, C.; Vander Borght, S.; Mazzoccoli, G.; Roskams, T.; *et al.* Sympathetic nervous system catecholamines and neuropeptide y neurotransmitters are upregulated in human nafld and modulate the fibrogenic function of hepatic stellate cells. *PLoS ONE* **2013**, *8*, e72928. [CrossRef] [PubMed]

73. Shang, X.R.; Song, J.Y.; Liu, F.H.; Ma, J.; Wang, H.J. Gwas-identified common variants with nonalcoholic fatty liver disease in Chinese children. *J. Pediatr. Gastroenterol. Nutr.* **2015**, *60*, 669–674. [CrossRef] [PubMed]

74. Schwimmer, J.B.; Celedon, M.A.; Lavine, J.E.; Salem, R.; Campbell, N.; Schork, N.J.; Shiehmorteza, M.; Yokoo, T.; Chavez, A.; Middleton, M.S.; *et al.* Heritability of nonalcoholic fatty liver disease. *Gastroenterology* **2009**, *136*, 1585–1592. [CrossRef] [PubMed]

75. Deboer, M.D.; Wiener, R.C.; Barnes, B.H.; Gurka, M.J. Ethnic differences in the link between insulin resistance and elevated ALT. *Pediatrics* **2013**, *132*, e718–e726. [CrossRef] [PubMed]

76. Lin, Y.C.; Chang, P.F.; Chang, M.H.; Ni, Y.H. Genetic variants in GCKR and PNPLA3 confer susceptibility to nonalcoholic fatty liver disease in obese individuals. *Am. J. Clin. Nutr.* **2014**, *99*, 869–874. [CrossRef] [PubMed]

77. Hernaez, R.; McLean, J.; Lazo, M.; Brancati, F.L.; Hirschhorn, J.N.; Borecki, I.B.; Harris, T.B.; Genetics of Obesity-Related Liver Disease (GOLD) Consortium; Nguyen, T.; Kamel, I.R.; *et al.* Association between variants in or near PNPLA3, GCKR, and PPP1R3B with ultrasound-defined steatosis based on data from the third national health and nutrition examination survey. *Clin. Gastroenterol. Hepatol.* **2013**, *11*, 1183–1190. [CrossRef] [PubMed]

78. Romeo, S.; Kozlitina, J.; Xing, C.; Pertsemlidis, A.; Cox, D.; Pennacchio, L.A.; Boerwinkle, E.; Cohen, J.C.; Hobbs, H.H. Genetic variation in *PNPLA3* confers susceptibility to nonalcoholic fatty liver disease. *Nat. Genet.* **2008**, *40*, 1461–1465. [CrossRef] [PubMed]

79. Santoro, N.; Kursawe, R.; D'Adamo, E.; Dykas, D.J.; Zhang, C.K.; Bale, A.E.; Cali, A.M.; Narayan, D.; Shaw, M.M.; Pierpont, B.; *et al.* A common variant in the patatin-like phospholipase 3 gene (*PNPLA3*) is associated with fatty liver disease in obese children and adolescents. *Hepatology* **2010**, *52*, 1281–1290. [CrossRef] [PubMed]

80. Mangge, H.; Baumgartner, B.G.; Zelzer, S.; Pruller, F.; Schnedl, W.J.; Reininghaus, E.Z.; Haybaeck, J.; Lackner, C.; Stauber, R.; Aigner, E.; *et al.* Patatin-like phospholipase 3 (*rs738409*) gene polymorphism is associated with increased liver enzymes in obese adolescents and metabolic syndrome in all ages. *Aliment. Pharmacol. Ther.* **2015**, *42*, 99–105. [CrossRef] [PubMed]

81. Guan, L.; Shang, X.R.; Liu, F.H.; Song, J.Y.; Ma, J.; Wang, H.J. Association of INSIG2 rs9308762 with alt level independent of BMI. *J. Pediatr. Gastroenterol. Nutr.* **2014**, *58*, 155–159. [CrossRef] [PubMed]

82. Rossi, F.; Bellini, G.; Alisi, A.; Alterio, A.; Maione, S.; Perrone, L.; Locatelli, F.; Miraglia del Giudice, E.; Nobili, V. Cannabinoid receptor type 2 functional variant influences liver damage in children with non-alcoholic fatty liver disease. *PLoS ONE* **2012**, *7*, e42259. [CrossRef] [PubMed]

83. Hyysalo, J.; Mannisto, V.T.; Zhou, Y.; Arola, J.; Karja, V.; Leivonen, M.; Juuti, A.; Jaser, N.; Lallukka, S.; Kakela, P.; *et al.* A population-based study on the prevalence of NASH using scores validated against liver histology. *J. Hepatol.* **2014**, *60*, 839–846. [CrossRef] [PubMed]

84. Qiao, A.; Liang, J.; Ke, Y.; Li, C.; Cui, Y.; Shen, L.; Zhang, H.; Cui, A.; Liu, X.; Liu, C.; *et al.* Mouse patatin-like phospholipase domain-containing 3 influences systemic lipid and glucose homeostasis. *Hepatology* **2011**, *54*, 509–521. [CrossRef] [PubMed]

85. Weltman, M.D.; Farrell, G.C.; Hall, P.; Ingelman-Sundberg, M.; Liddle, C. Hepatic cytochrome P450 2E1 is increased in patients with nonalcoholic steatohepatitis. *Hepatology* **1998**, *27*, 128–133. [CrossRef] [PubMed]

86. Weltman, M.D.; Farrell, G.C.; Liddle, C. Increased hepatocyte CYP2E1 expression in a rat nutritional model of hepatic steatosis with inflammation. *Gastroenterology* **1996**, *111*, 1645–1653. [CrossRef]

87. Sugimoto, Y.; Wakai, K.; Nakagawa, H.; Suma, S.; Sasakabe, T.; Sakamoto, T.; Takashima, N.; Suzuki, S.; Ogawa, S.; Ohnaka, K.; *et al.* Associations between polymorphisms of interleukin-6 and related cytokine genes and serum liver damage markers: A cross-sectional study in the Japan Multi-Institutional Collaborative Cohort (J-MICC) study. *Gene* **2015**, *557*, 158–162. [CrossRef] [PubMed]

88. Lin, Y.C.; Chang, P.F.; Hu, F.C.; Chang, M.H.; Ni, Y.H. Variants in the *UGT1A1* gene and the risk of pediatric nonalcoholic fatty liver disease. *Pediatrics* **2009**, *124*, e1221–e1227. [CrossRef] [PubMed]

89. Rossi, F.; Bellini, G.; Nobili, B.; Maione, S.; Perrone, L.; del Giudice, E.M. Association of the cannabinoid receptor 2 (Cb2) Gln63Arg polymorphism with indices of liver damage in obese children: An alternative way to highlight the CB2 hepatoprotective properties. *Hepatology* **2011**, *54*, 1102. [CrossRef] [PubMed]

90. Cordero, P.; Milagro, F.I.; Campion, J.; Martinez, J.A. Supplementation with methyl donors during lactation to high-fat-sucrose-fed dams protects offspring against liver fat accumulation when consuming an obesogenic diet. *J. Dev. Orig. Health Dis.* **2014**, *5*, 385–395. [CrossRef] [PubMed]

91. Cordero, P.; Milagro, F.I.; Campion, J.; Martinez, J.A. Maternal methyl donors supplementation during lactation prevents the hyperhomocysteinemia induced by a high-fat-sucrose intake by dams. *Int. J. Mol. Sci.* **2013**, *14*, 24422–24437. [CrossRef] [PubMed]

92. Mouralidarane, A.; Soeda, J.; Sugden, D.; Bocianowska, A.; Carter, R.; Ray, S.; Saraswati, R.; Cordero, P.; Novelli, M.; Fusai, G.; *et al.* Maternal obesity programs offspring non-alcoholic fatty liver disease through disruption of 24-h rhythms in mice. *Int. J. Obes.* **2015**, *39*, 1339–1348. [CrossRef] [PubMed]

93. Cordero, P.; Li, J.; Oben, J.A. Epigenetics of obesity: Beyond the genome sequence. *Curr. Opin. Clin. Nutr. Metab. Care* **2015**, *18*, 361–366. [CrossRef] [PubMed]

94. Cordero, P.; Li, J.; Temple, J.L.; Nguyen, V.; Oben, J.A. Epigenetic mechanisms of maternal obesity effects on the descendants. In *Parental Obesity: Intergenerational Programming and Consequences*; Green, L.R., Hester, R.L., Eds.; Springer-Verlag New York: New York, NY, USA, 2016.

95. Alisi, A.; Panera, N.; Agostoni, C.; Nobili, V. Intrauterine growth retardation and nonalcoholic fatty liver disease in children. *Int. J. Endocrinol.* **2011**, *2011*, 269853. [CrossRef] [PubMed]

96. Breij, L.M.; Kerkhof, G.F.; Hokken-Koelega, A.C. Accelerated infant weight gain and risk for nonalcoholic fatty liver disease in early adulthood. *J. Clin. Endocrinol. Metab.* **2014**, *99*, 1189–1195. [CrossRef] [PubMed]

97. Amarapurkar, D.; Kamani, P.; Patel, N.; Gupte, P.; Kumar, P.; Agal, S.; Baijal, R.; Lala, S.; Chaudhary, D.; Deshpande, A. Prevalence of non-alcoholic fatty liver disease: Population based study. *Ann. Hepatol.* **2007**, *6*, 161–163. [PubMed]

98. Hanada, S.; Snider, N.T.; Brunt, E.M.; Hollenberg, P.F.; Omary, M.B. Gender dimorphic formation of mouse mallory-denk bodies and the role of xenobiotic metabolism and oxidative stress. *Gastroenterology* **2010**, *138*, 1607–1617. [CrossRef] [PubMed]

99. Kozlov, A.V.; Duvigneau, J.C.; Hyatt, T.C.; Raju, R.; Behling, T.; Hartl, R.T.; Staniek, K.; Miller, I.; Gregor, W.; Redl, H.; *et al.* Effect of estrogen on mitochondrial function and intracellular stress markers in rat liver and kidney following trauma-hemorrhagic shock and prolonged hypotension. *Mol. Med.* **2010**, *16*, 254–261. [CrossRef] [PubMed]

100. Yasuda, M.; Shimizu, I.; Shiba, M.; Ito, S. Suppressive effects of estradiol on dimethylnitrosamine-induced fibrosis of the liver in rats. *Hepatology* **1999**, *29*, 719–727. [CrossRef] [PubMed]

101. Goh, G.B.; Pagadala, M.R.; Dasarathy, J.; Unalp-Arida, A.; Pai, R.K.; Yerian, L.; Khiyami, A.; Sourianarayanane, A.; Sargent, R.; Hawkins, C.; *et al.* Age impacts ability of aspartate-alanine aminotransferase ratio to predict advanced fibrosis in nonalcoholic fatty liver disease. *Dig. Dis. Sci.* **2015**, *60*, 1825–1831. [CrossRef] [PubMed]

102. Suzuki, A.; Abdelmalek, M.F.; Schwimmer, J.B.; Lavine, J.E.; Scheimann, A.O.; Unalp-Arida, A.; Yates, K.P.; Sanyal, A.J.; Guy, C.D.; Diehl, A.M.; *et al.* Association between puberty and features of nonalcoholic fatty liver disease. *Clin. Gastroenterol. Hepatol.* **2012**, *10*, 786–794. [CrossRef] [PubMed]

103. Rangwala, F.; Guy, C.D.; Lu, J.; Suzuki, A.; Burchette, J.L.; Abdelmalek, M.F.; Chen, W.; Diehl, A.M. Increased production of sonic hedgehog by ballooned hepatocytes. *J. Pathol.* **2011**, *224*, 401–410. [CrossRef] [PubMed]

104. Li, T.; Leng, X.S.; Zhu, J.Y.; Wang, G. Suppression of hedgehog signaling regulates hepatic stellate cell activation and collagen secretion. *Int. J. Clin. Exp. Pathol.* **2015**, *8*, 14574–14579. [PubMed]

105. Hernaez, R.; Yeung, E.; Clark, J.M.; Kowdley, K.V.; Brancati, F.L.; Kao, W.H. Hemochromatosis gene and nonalcoholic fatty liver disease: A systematic review and meta-analysis. *J. Hepatol.* **2011**, *55*, 1079–1085. [CrossRef] [PubMed]

106. Wu, S.; Tu, R.; Liu, G.; Huang, L.; Guan, Y.; Zheng, E. Focal fatty sparing usually does not arise in preexisting nonalcoholic diffuse homogeneous fatty liver. *J. Ultrasound Med.* **2014**, *33*, 1447–1452. [CrossRef] [PubMed]

107. Bellentani, S.; Saccoccio, G.; Masutti, F.; Croce, L.S.; Brandi, G.; Sasso, F.; Cristanini, G.; Tiribelli, C. Prevalence of and risk factors for hepatic steatosis in Northern Italy. *Ann. Intern. Med.* **2000**, *132*, 112–117. [CrossRef] [PubMed]

108. Patton, H.M.; Lavine, J.E.; van Natta, M.L.; Schwimmer, J.B.; Kleiner, D.; Molleston, J.; Nonalcoholic Steatohepatitis Clinical Research Network. Clinical correlates of histopathology in pediatric nonalcoholic steatohepatitis. *Gastroenterology* **2008**, *135*, 1961–1971. [CrossRef] [PubMed]

109. Fracanzani, A.L.; Valenti, L.; Bugianesi, E.; Andreoletti, M.; Colli, A.; Vanni, E.; Bertelli, C.; Fatta, E.; Bignamini, D.; Marchesini, G.; *et al.* Risk of severe liver disease in nonalcoholic fatty liver disease with normal aminotransferase levels: A role for insulin resistance and diabetes. *Hepatology* **2008**, *48*, 792–798. [CrossRef] [PubMed]

110. Mofrad, P.; Contos, M.J.; Haque, M.; Sargeant, C.; Fisher, R.A.; Luketic, V.A.; Sterling, R.K.; Shiffman, M.L.; Stravitz, R.T.; Sanyal, A.J. Clinical and histologic spectrum of nonalcoholic fatty liver disease associated with normal ALT values. *Hepatology* **2003**, *37*, 1286–1292. [CrossRef] [PubMed]

111. Vernon, G.; Baranova, A.; Younossi, Z.M. Systematic review: The epidemiology and natural history of non-alcoholic fatty liver disease and non-alcoholic steatohepatitis in adults. *Aliment. Pharmacol. Ther.* **2011**, *34*, 274–285. [CrossRef] [PubMed]

112. Wilson, H.K.; Monster, A.C. New technologies in the use of exhaled breath analysis for biological monitoring. *Occup. Environ. Med.* **1999**, *56*, 753–757. [CrossRef] [PubMed]

113. Feldstein, A.E.; Alkhouri, N.; de Vito, R.; Alisi, A.; Lopez, R.; Nobili, V. Serum cytokeratin-18 fragment levels are useful biomarkers for nonalcoholic steatohepatitis in children. *Am. J. Gastroenterol.* **2013**, *108*, 1526–1531. [CrossRef] [PubMed]

114. Wieckowska, A.; Zein, N.N.; Yerian, L.M.; Lopez, A.R.; McCullough, A.J.; Feldstein, A.E. *In vivo* assessment of liver cell apoptosis as a novel biomarker of disease severity in nonalcoholic fatty liver disease. *Hepatology* **2006**, *44*, 27–33. [CrossRef] [PubMed]

115. Musso, G.; Gambino, R.; Cassader, M.; Pagano, G. Meta-analysis: Natural history of non-alcoholic fatty liver disease (NAFLD) and diagnostic accuracy of non-invasive tests for liver disease severity. *Ann. Med.* **2011**, *43*, 617–649. [CrossRef] [PubMed]

116. Puri, K.; Nobili, V.; Melville, K.; Corte, C.D.; Sartorelli, M.R.; Lopez, R.; Feldstein, A.E.; Alkhouri, N. Serum bilirubin level is inversely associated with nonalcoholic steatohepatitis in children. *J. Pediatr. Gastroenterol. Nutr.* **2013**, *57*, 114–118. [CrossRef] [PubMed]

117. Eng, K.; Lopez, R.; Liccardo, D.; Nobili, V.; Alkhouri, N. A non-invasive prediction model for non-alcoholic steatohepatitis in paediatric patients with non-alcoholic fatty liver disease. *Dig. Liver Dis.* **2014**, *46*, 1008–1013. [CrossRef] [PubMed]

118. Oresic, M.; Hyotylainen, T.; Kotronen, A.; Gopalacharyulu, P.; Nygren, H.; Arola, J.; Castillo, S.; Mattila, I.; Hakkarainen, A.; Borra, R.J.; *et al.* Prediction of non-alcoholic fatty-liver disease and liver fat content by serum molecular lipids. *Diabetologia* **2013**, *56*, 2266–2274. [CrossRef] [PubMed]

119. Yilmaz, Y.; Ergelen, R.; Akin, H.; Imeryuz, N. Noninvasive detection of hepatic steatosis in patients without ultrasonographic evidence of fatty liver using the controlled attenuation parameter evaluated with transient elastography. *Eur. J. Gastroenterol. Hepatol.* **2013**, *25*, 1330–1334. [CrossRef] [PubMed]

120. Schwimmer, J.B.; Middleton, M.S.; Behling, C.; Newton, K.P.; Awai, H.I.; Paiz, M.N.; Lam, J.; Hooker, J.C.; Hamilton, G.; Fontanesi, J.; *et al.* Magnetic resonance imaging and liver histology as biomarkers of hepatic steatosis in children with nonalcoholic fatty liver disease. *Hepatology* **2015**, *61*, 1887–1895. [CrossRef] [PubMed]

121. Tovo, C.V.; de Mattos, A.Z.; Coral, G.P.; Branco, F.S.; Suwa, E.; de Mattos, A.A. Noninvasive imaging assessment of non-alcoholic fatty liver disease: Focus on liver scintigraphy. *World J. Gastroenterol.* **2015**, *21*, 4432–4439. [PubMed]

122. Kim, K.M.; Choi, W.B.; Park, S.H.; Yu, E.; Lee, S.G.; Lim, Y.S.; Lee, H.C.; Chung, Y.H.; Lee, Y.S.; Suh, D.J. Diagnosis of hepatic steatosis and fibrosis by transient elastography in asymptomatic healthy individuals: A prospective study of living related potential liver donors. *J. Gastroenterol.* **2007**, *42*, 382–388. [CrossRef] [PubMed]

123. Nobili, V.; Vizzutti, F.; Arena, U.; Abraldes, J.G.; Marra, F.; Pietrobattista, A.; Fruhwirth, R.; Marcellini, M.; Pinzani, M. Accuracy and reproducibility of transient elastography for the diagnosis of fibrosis in pediatric nonalcoholic steatohepatitis. *Hepatology* **2008**, *48*, 442–448. [CrossRef] [PubMed]

124. Ovchinsky, N.; Moreira, R.K.; Lefkowitch, J.H.; Lavine, J.E. Liver biopsy in modern clinical practice: A pediatric point-of-view. *Adv. Anat. Pathol.* **2012**, *19*, 250–262. [CrossRef] [PubMed]

125. Schwimmer, J.B.; Behling, C.; Newbury, R.; Deutsch, R.; Nievergelt, C.; Schork, N.J.; Lavine, J.E. Histopathology of pediatric nonalcoholic fatty liver disease. *Hepatology* **2005**, *42*, 641–649. [CrossRef] [PubMed]

126. Mansoor, S.; Collyer, E.; Alkhouri, N. A comprehensive review of noninvasive liver fibrosis tests in pediatric nonalcoholic fatty liver disease. *Curr. Gastroenterol. Rep.* **2015**, *17*, 23. [CrossRef] [PubMed]

127. Nobili, V.; Parkes, J.; Bottazzo, G.; Marcellini, M.; Cross, R.; Newman, D.; Vizzutti, F.; Pinzani, M.; Rosenberg, W.M. Performance of ELF serum markers in predicting fibrosis stage in pediatric non-alcoholic fatty liver disease. *Gastroenterology* **2009**, *136*, 160–167. [CrossRef] [PubMed]

128. Musso, G.; Gambino, R.; Cassader, M.; Pagano, G. A meta-analysis of randomized trials for the treatment of nonalcoholic fatty liver disease. *Hepatology* **2010**, *52*, 79–104. [CrossRef] [PubMed]

129. Nobili, V.; Marcellini, M.; Devito, R.; Ciampalini, P.; Piemonte, F.; Comparcola, D.; Sartorelli, M.R.; Angulo, P. Nafld in children: A prospective clinical-pathological study and effect of lifestyle advice. *Hepatology* **2006**, *44*, 458–465. [CrossRef] [PubMed]

130. DeVore, S.; Kohli, R.; Lake, K.; Nicholas, L.; Dietrich, K.; Balistreri, W.F.; Xanthakos, S.A. A multidisciplinary clinical program is effective in stabilizing BMI and reducing transaminase levels in pediatric patients with NAFLD. *J. Pediatr. Gastroenterol. Nutr.* **2013**, *57*, 119–123. [CrossRef] [PubMed]

131. Nobili, V.; Manco, M.; Devito, R.; Di Ciommo, V.; Comparcola, D.; Sartorelli, M.R.; Piemonte, F.; Marcellini, M.; Angulo, P. Lifestyle intervention and antioxidant therapy in children with nonalcoholic fatty liver disease: A randomized, controlled trial. *Hepatology* **2008**, *48*, 119–128. [CrossRef] [PubMed]

132. Oddy, W.H.; Herbison, C.E.; Jacoby, P.; Ambrosini, G.L.; O'Sullivan, T.A.; Ayonrinde, O.T.; Olynyk, J.K.; Black, L.J.; Beilin, L.J.; Mori, T.A.; *et al.* The western dietary pattern is prospectively associated with nonalcoholic fatty liver disease in adolescence. *Am. J. Gastroenterol.* **2013**, *108*, 778–785. [CrossRef] [PubMed]

133. Nobili, V.; Manco, M.; Devito, R.; Ciampalini, P.; Piemonte, F.; Marcellini, M. Effect of Vitamin E on aminotransferase levels and insulin resistance in children with non-alcoholic fatty liver disease. *Aliment. Pharmacol. Ther.* **2006**, *24*, 1553–1561. [CrossRef] [PubMed]

134. Gronbaek, H.; Lange, A.; Birkebaek, N.H.; Holland-Fischer, P.; Solvig, J.; Horlyck, A.; Kristensen, K.; Rittig, S.; Vilstrup, H. Effect of a 10-week weight loss camp on fatty liver disease and insulin sensitivity in obese Danish children. *J. Pediatr. Gastroenterol. Nutr.* **2012**, *54*, 223–228. [CrossRef] [PubMed]

135. Zelber-Sagi, S.; Nitzan-Kaluski, D.; Goldsmith, R.; Webb, M.; Zvibel, I.; Goldiner, I.; Blendis, L.; Halpern, Z.; Oren, R. Role of leisure-time physical activity in nonalcoholic fatty liver disease: A population-based study. *Hepatology* **2008**, *48*, 1791–1798. [CrossRef] [PubMed]

136. Barlow, S.E.; Expert, C. Expert committee recommendations regarding the prevention, assessment, and treatment of child and adolescent overweight and obesity: Summary report. *Pediatrics* **2007**, *120*, S164–S192. [CrossRef] [PubMed]

137. Haukeland, J.W.; Konopski, Z.; Eggesbo, H.B.; von Volkmann, H.L.; Raschpichler, G.; Bjoro, K.; Haaland, T.; Loberg, E.M.; Birkeland, K. Metformin in patients with non-alcoholic fatty liver disease: A randomized, controlled trial. *Scand. J. Gastroenterol.* **2009**, *44*, 853–860. [CrossRef] [PubMed]

138. Krasnoff, J.B.; Painter, P.L.; Wallace, J.P.; Bass, N.M.; Merriman, R.B. Health-related fitness and physical activity in patients with nonalcoholic fatty liver disease. *Hepatology* **2008**, *47*, 1158–1166. [CrossRef] [PubMed]

139. Kistler, K.D.; Brunt, E.M.; Clark, J.M.; Diehl, A.M.; Sallis, J.F.; Schwimmer, J.B.; Group, N.C.R. Physical activity recommendations, exercise intensity, and histological severity of nonalcoholic fatty liver disease. *Am. J. Gastroenterol.* **2011**, *106*, 460–468. [CrossRef] [PubMed]

140. Niblett, P. Statistics on Obesity, Physical Activity and Diet—England, 2015. Available online: http://www.hscic.gov.uk/catalogue/PUB16988 (accessed on 14 June 2016).

141. Jin, R.; Le, N.A.; Liu, S.; Farkas Epperson, M.; Ziegler, T.R.; Welsh, J.A.; Jones, D.P.; McClain, C.J.; Vos, M.B. Children with nafld are more sensitive to the adverse metabolic effects of fructose beverages than children without NAFLD. *J. Clin. Endocrinol. Metab.* **2012**, *97*, E1088–E1098. [CrossRef] [PubMed]

142. O'Sullivan, T.A.; Oddy, W.H.; Bremner, A.P.; Sherriff, J.L.; Ayonrinde, O.T.; Olynyk, J.K.; Beilin, L.J.; Mori, T.A.; Adams, L.A. Lower fructose intake may help protect against development of nonalcoholic fatty liver in adolescents with obesity. *J. Pediatr. Gastroenterol. Nutr.* **2014**, *58*, 624–631. [CrossRef] [PubMed]

143. Spruss, A.; Bergheim, I. Dietary fructose and intestinal barrier: Potential risk factor in the pathogenesis of nonalcoholic fatty liver disease. *J. Nutr. Biochem.* **2009**, *20*, 657–662. [CrossRef] [PubMed]

144. Kawasaki, T.; Igarashi, K.; Koeda, T.; Sugimoto, K.; Nakagawa, K.; Hayashi, S.; Yamaji, R.; Inui, H.; Fukusato, T.; Yamanouchi, T. Rats fed fructose-enriched diets have characteristics of nonalcoholic hepatic steatosis. *J. Nutr.* **2009**, *139*, 2067–2071. [CrossRef] [PubMed]

145. Kar, S.; Khandelwal, B. Fast foods and physical inactivity are risk factors for obesity and hypertension among adolescent school children in east district of sikkim, india. *J. Nat. Sci. Biol. Med.* **2015**, *6*, 356–359. [CrossRef] [PubMed]

146. Black, L.J.; Jacoby, P.; Ping-Delfos, S.; Chan, W.; Mori, T.A.; Beilin, L.J.; Olynyk, J.K.; Ayonrinde, O.T.; Huang, R.C.; Holt, P.G.; *et al.* Low serum 25-hydroxyvitamin D concentrations associate with non-alcoholic fatty liver disease in adolescents independent of adiposity. *J. Gastroenterol. Hepatol.* **2014**, *29*, 1215–1222. [CrossRef] [PubMed]

147. Nobili, V.; Giorgio, V.; Liccardo, D.; Bedogni, G.; Morino, G.; Alisi, A.; Cianfarani, S. Vitamin D levels and liver histological alterations in children with nonalcoholic fatty liver disease. *Eur. J. Endocrinol.* **2014**, *170*, 547–553. [CrossRef] [PubMed]

148. Li, J.; Cordero, P.; Nguyen, V.; Oben, J.A. The role of vitamins in the pathogenesis of non-alcoholic fatty liver disease. *Integr. Med. Insights* **2016**, *11*, 19–25. [CrossRef] [PubMed]
149. Roth, C.L.; Elfers, C.T.; Figlewicz, D.P.; Melhorn, S.J.; Morton, G.J.; Hoofnagle, A.; Yeh, M.M.; Nelson, J.E.; Kowdley, K.V. Vitamin D deficiency in obese rats exacerbates nonalcoholic fatty liver disease and increases hepatic resistin and toll-like receptor activation. *Hepatology* **2012**, *55*, 1103–1111. [CrossRef] [PubMed]
150. George, P.S.; Pearson, E.R.; Witham, M.D. Effect of Vitamin D supplementation on glycaemic control and insulin resistance: A systematic review and meta-analysis. *Diabet. Med.* **2012**, *29*, e142–e150. [CrossRef] [PubMed]
151. Flachs, P.; Rossmeisl, M.; Bryhn, M.; Kopecky, J. Cellular and molecular effects of *n*-3 polyunsaturated fatty acids on adipose tissue biology and metabolism. *Clin. Sci.* **2009**, *116*, 1–16. [CrossRef] [PubMed]
152. Masterton, G.S.; Plevris, J.N.; Hayes, P.C. Review article: ω-3 fatty acids—A promising novel therapy for non-alcoholic fatty liver disease. *Aliment. Pharmacol. Ther.* **2010**, *31*, 679–692. [CrossRef] [PubMed]
153. Janczyk, W.; Socha, P.; Lebensztejn, D.; Wierzbicka, A.; Mazur, A.; Neuhoff-Murawska, J.; Matusik, P. ω-3 fatty acids for treatment of non-alcoholic fatty liver disease: Design and rationale of randomized controlled trial. *BMC Pediatr.* **2013**, *13*, 85. [CrossRef] [PubMed]
154. Nobili, V.; Carpino, G.; Alisi, A.; de Vito, R.; Franchitto, A.; Alpini, G.; Onori, P.; Gaudio, E. Role of docosahexaenoic acid treatment in improving liver histology in pediatric nonalcoholic fatty liver disease. *PLoS ONE* **2014**, *9*, e88005. [CrossRef] [PubMed]
155. Nobili, V.; Bedogni, G.; Alisi, A.; Pietrobattista, A.; Rise, P.; Galli, C.; Agostoni, C. Docosahexaenoic acid supplementation decreases liver fat content in children with non-alcoholic fatty liver disease: Double-blind randomised controlled clinical trial. *Arch. Dis. Child.* **2011**, *96*, 350–353. [CrossRef] [PubMed]
156. Nobili, V.; Alkhouri, N.; Alisi, A.; Della Corte, C.; Fitzpatrick, E.; Raponi, M.; Dhawan, A. Nonalcoholic fatty liver disease: A challenge for pediatricians. *JAMA Pediatr.* **2015**, *169*, 170–176. [CrossRef] [PubMed]
157. Loy, J.J.; Youn, H.A.; Schwack, B.; Kurian, M.; Ren Fielding, C.; Fielding, G.A. Improvement in nonalcoholic fatty liver disease and metabolic syndrome in adolescents undergoing bariatric surgery. *Surg. Obes. Relat. Dis.* **2015**, *11*, 442–449. [CrossRef] [PubMed]
158. Peterli, R.; Steinert, R.E.; Woelnerhanssen, B.; Peters, T.; Christoffel-Courtin, C.; Gass, M.; Kern, B.; von Fluee, M.; Beglinger, C. Metabolic and hormonal changes after laparoscopic Roux-en-Y gastric bypass and sleeve gastrectomy: A randomized, prospective trial. *Obes. Surg.* **2012**, *22*, 740–748. [CrossRef] [PubMed]
159. Sasaki, A.; Nitta, H.; Otsuka, K.; Umemura, A.; Baba, S.; Obuchi, T.; Wakabayashi, G. Bariatric surgery and non-alcoholic fatty liver disease: Current and potential future treatments. *Front. Endocrinol.* **2014**, *5*, 164. [CrossRef] [PubMed]
160. Chavez-Tapia, N.C.; Tellez-Avila, F.I.; Barrientos-Gutierrez, T.; Mendez-Sanchez, N.; Lizardi-Cervera, J.; Uribe, M. Bariatric surgery for non-alcoholic steatohepatitis in obese patients. *Cochrane Database Syst. Rev.* **2010**, *1*. [CrossRef]
161. Lassailly, G.; Caiazzo, R.; Buob, D.; Pigeyre, M.; Verkindt, H.; Labreuche, J.; Raverdy, V.; Leteurtre, E.; Dharancy, S.; Louvet, A.; *et al.* Bariatric surgery reduces features of nonalcoholic steatohepatitis in morbidly obese patients. *Gastroenterology* **2015**, *149*, 379–388. [CrossRef] [PubMed]
162. Nanda, K. Non-alcoholic steatohepatitis in children. *Pediatr. Transpl.* **2004**, *8*, 613–618. [CrossRef] [PubMed]
163. Schwimmer, J.B.; Middleton, M.S.; Deutsch, R.; Lavine, J.E. A phase 2 clinical trial of metformin as a treatment for non-diabetic paediatric non-alcoholic steatohepatitis. *Aliment. Pharmacol. Ther.* **2005**, *21*, 871–879. [CrossRef] [PubMed]
164. Lavine, J.E.; Schwimmer, J.B.; van Natta, M.L.; Molleston, J.P.; Murray, K.F.; Rosenthal, P.; Abrams, S.H.; Scheimann, A.O.; Sanyal, A.J.; Chalasani, N.; *et al.* Effect of Vitamin E or metformin for treatment of nonalcoholic fatty liver disease in children and adolescents: The tonic randomized controlled trial. *JAMA* **2011**, *305*, 1659–1668. [CrossRef] [PubMed]
165. Belfort, R.; Harrison, S.A.; Brown, K.; Darland, C.; Finch, J.; Hardies, J.; Balas, B.; Gastaldelli, A.; Tio, F.; Pulcini, J.; *et al.* A placebo-controlled trial of pioglitazone in subjects with nonalcoholic steatohepatitis. *N. Engl. J. Med.* **2006**, *355*, 2297–2307. [CrossRef] [PubMed]
166. Sanyal, A.J.; Chalasani, N.; Kowdley, K.V.; McCullough, A.; Diehl, A.M.; Bass, N.M.; Neuschwander-Tetri, B.A.; Lavine, J.E.; Tonascia, J.; Unalp, A.; *et al.* Pioglitazone, Vitamin E, or placebo for nonalcoholic steatohepatitis. *N. Engl. J. Med.* **2010**, *362*, 1675–1685. [CrossRef] [PubMed]

167. Lee, J.; Hong, S.W.; Rhee, E.J.; Lee, W.Y. GLP-1 receptor agonist and non-alcoholic fatty liver disease. *Diabetes Metab. J.* **2012**, *36*, 262–267. [CrossRef] [PubMed]

168. Duvnjak, M.; Tomasic, V.; Gomercic, M.; Smircic Duvnjak, L.; Barsic, N.; Lerotic, I. Therapy of nonalcoholic fatty liver disease: Current status. *J. Physiol. Pharmacol.* **2009**, *60*, 57–66. [PubMed]

169. Tilg, H.; Moschen, A. Update on nonalcoholic fatty liver disease: Genes involved in nonalcoholic fatty liver disease and associated inflammation. *Curr. Opin. Clin. Nutr. Metab. Care* **2010**, *13*, 391–396. [CrossRef] [PubMed]

170. Georgescu, E.F. Angiotensin receptor blockers in the treatment of NASH/NAFLD: Could they be a first-class option? *Adv. Ther.* **2008**, *25*, 1141–1174. [CrossRef] [PubMed]

171. Carter, R.; Mouralidarane, A.; Ray, S.; Soeda, J.; Oben, J. Recent advancements in drug treatment of obesity. *Clin. Med.* **2012**, *12*, 456–460. [CrossRef]

172. Harrison, S.A.; Fecht, W.; Brunt, E.M.; Neuschwander-Tetri, B.A. Orlistat for overweight subjects with nonalcoholic steatohepatitis: A randomized, prospective trial. *Hepatology* **2009**, *49*, 80–86. [CrossRef] [PubMed]

173. Wierzbicki, A.S.; Oben, J. Nonalcoholic fatty liver disease and lipids. *Curr. Opin. Lipidol.* **2012**, *23*, 345–352. [CrossRef] [PubMed]

174. Tziomalos, K.; Athyros, V.G.; Paschos, P.; Karagiannis, A. Nonalcoholic fatty liver disease and statins. *Metabolism* **2015**, *64*, 1215–1223. [CrossRef] [PubMed]

175. Desai, S.; Baker, S.S.; Liu, W.; Moya, D.A.; Browne, R.W.; Mastrandrea, L.; Baker, R.D.; Zhu, L. Paraoxonase 1 and oxidative stress in paediatric non-alcoholic steatohepatitis. *Liver Int.* **2014**, *34*, 110–117. [CrossRef] [PubMed]

176. Li, Z.; Berk, M.; McIntyre, T.M.; Gores, G.J.; Feldstein, A.E. The lysosomal-mitochondrial axis in free fatty acid-induced hepatic lipotoxicity. *Hepatology* **2008**, *47*, 1495–1503. [CrossRef] [PubMed]

177. Koliaki, C.; Szendroedi, J.; Kaul, K.; Jelenik, T.; Nowotny, P.; Jankowiak, F.; Herder, C.; Carstensen, M.; Krausch, M.; Knoefel, W.T.; *et al.* Adaptation of hepatic mitochondrial function in humans with non-alcoholic fatty liver is lost in steatohepatitis. *Cell Metab.* **2015**, *21*, 739–746. [CrossRef] [PubMed]

178. Guo, H.; Zhong, R.; Liu, Y.; Jiang, X.; Tang, X.; Li, Z.; Xia, M.; Ling, W. Effects of bayberry juice on inflammatory and apoptotic markers in young adults with features of non-alcoholic fatty liver disease. *Nutrition* **2014**, *30*, 198–203. [CrossRef] [PubMed]

179. Ji, H.F.; Sun, Y.; Shen, L. Effect of Vitamin E supplementation on aminotransferase levels in patients with nafld, nash, and chc: Results from a meta-analysis. *Nutrition* **2014**, *30*, 986–991. [CrossRef] [PubMed]

180. Bjelakovic, G.; Nikolova, D.; Gluud, C. Antioxidant supplements and mortality. *Curr. Opin. Clin. Nutr. Metab. Care* **2014**, *17*, 40–44. [CrossRef] [PubMed]

181. Ratziu, V. Treatment of NASH with ursodeoxycholic acid: Pro. *Clin. Res. Hepatol. Gastroenterol.* **2012**, *36*, S41–S45. [CrossRef]

182. Xiang, Z.; Chen, Y.P.; Ma, K.F.; Ye, Y.F.; Zheng, L.; Yang, Y.D.; Li, Y.M.; Jin, X. The role of ursodeoxycholic acid in non-alcoholic steatohepatitis: A systematic review. *BMC Gastroenterol.* **2013**, *13*, 140. [CrossRef] [PubMed]

183. Pietu, F.; Guillaud, O.; Walter, T.; Vallin, M.; Hervieu, V.; Scoazec, J.Y.; Dumortier, J. Ursodeoxycholic acid with Vitamin E in patients with nonalcoholic steatohepatitis: Long-term results. *Clin. Res. Hepatol. Gastroenterol.* **2012**, *36*, 146–155. [CrossRef] [PubMed]

184. Vajro, P.; Franzese, A.; Valerio, G.; Iannucci, M.P.; Aragione, N. Lack of efficacy of ursodeoxycholic acid for the treatment of liver abnormalities in obese children. *J. Pediatr.* **2000**, *136*, 739–743. [CrossRef]

185. Van de Meeberg, P.C.; Houwen, R.H.; Sinaasappel, M.; Heijerman, H.G.; Bijleveld, C.M.; Vanberge-Henegouwen, G.P. Low-dose versus high-dose ursodeoxycholic acid in cystic fibrosis-related cholestatic liver disease. Results of a randomized study with 1-year follow-up. *Scand. J. Gastroenterol.* **1997**, *32*, 369–373. [CrossRef] [PubMed]

186. Dufour, J.F.; Oneta, C.M.; Gonvers, J.J.; Bihl, F.; Cerny, A.; Cereda, J.M.; Zala, J.F.; Helbling, B.; Steuerwald, M.; Zimmermann, A.; *et al.* Randomized placebo-controlled trial of ursodeoxycholic acid with Vitamin E in nonalcoholic steatohepatitis. *Clin. Gastroenterol. Hepatol.* **2006**, *4*, 1537–1543. [CrossRef] [PubMed]

187. Loguercio, C.; Federico, A.; Tuccillo, C.; Terracciano, F.; D'Auria, M.V.; de Simone, C.; del Vecchio Blanco, C. Beneficial effects of a probiotic VSL#3 on parameters of liver dysfunction in chronic liver diseases. *J. Clin. Gastroenterol.* **2005**, *39*, 540–543. [PubMed]

188. Vajro, P.; Mandato, C.; Licenziati, M.R.; Franzese, A.; Vitale, D.F.; Lenta, S.; Caropreso, M.; Vallone, G.; Meli, R. Effects of lactobacillus rhamnosus strain GG in pediatric obesity-related liver disease. *J. Pediatr. Gastroenterol. Nutr.* **2011**, *52*, 740–743. [CrossRef] [PubMed]
189. Machado, M.V.; Cortez-Pinto, H. Diet, microbiota, obesity, and NAFLD: A dangerous quartet. *Int. J. Mol. Sci.* **2016**, *17*. [CrossRef] [PubMed]
190. Fuchs, M. Non-alcoholic fatty liver disease: The bile acid-activated farnesoid x receptor as an emerging treatment target. *J. Lipids* **2012**, *2012*, 934396. [CrossRef] [PubMed]

International Journal of
Molecular Sciences

MDPI

Article

The Impact of Nonalcoholic Fatty Liver Disease on Renal Function in Children with Overweight/Obesity

Lucia Pacifico [1,*], Enea Bonci [2], Gian Marco Andreoli [1], Michele Di Martino [3], Alessia Gallozzi [1], Ester De Luca [1] and Claudio Chiesa [4]

[1]   Policlinico Umberto I Hospital, Sapienza University of Rome, Viale Regina Elena 324, 00161 Rome, Italy; gianmarcoandreoli@gmail.com (G.M.A.); alessia.gallozzi@gmail.com (A.G.); esterdeluca91@libero.it (E.D.L.)
[2]   Department of Experimental Medicine, Sapienza University of Rome, Viale Regina Elena 324, 00161 Rome, Italy; enea.bonci@uniroma1.it
[3]   Department of Radiological Sciences, Sapienza University of Rome, Viale Regina Elena 324, 00161 Rome, Italy; micdimartino@hotmail.it
[4]   Institute of Translational Pharmacology, National Research Council, Via Fosso del Cavaliere 100, 00133 Rome, Italy; claudio.chiesa@ift.cnr.it
*   Correspondence: lucia.pacifico@uniroma1.it; Tel.: +39-06-4997-9215

Academic Editor: Giovanni Tarantino
Received: 25 June 2016; Accepted: 21 July 2016; Published: 27 July 2016

Abstract: The association between nonalcoholic fatty liver disease (NAFLD) and chronic kidney disease has attracted interest and attention over recent years. However, no data are available in children. We determined whether children with NAFLD show signs of renal functional alterations, as determined by estimated glomerular filtration rate (eGFR) and urinary albumin excretion. We studied 596 children with overweight/obesity, 268 with NAFLD (hepatic fat fraction $\geqslant$5% on magnetic resonance imaging) and 328 without NAFLD, and 130 healthy normal-weight controls. Decreased GFR was defined as eGFR < 90 mL/min/1.73 m^2. Abnormal albuminuria was defined as urinary excretion of $\geqslant$30 mg/24 h of albumin. A greater prevalence of eGFR < 90 mL/min/1.73 m^2 was observed in patients with NAFLD compared to those without liver involvement and healthy subjects (17.5% vs. 6.7% vs. 0.77%; p < 0.0001). The proportion of children with abnormal albuminuria was also higher in the NAFLD group compared to those without NAFLD, and controls (9.3% vs. 4.0% vs. 0; p < 0.0001). Multivariate logistic regression analysis revealed that NAFLD was associated with decreased eGFR and/or microalbuminuria (odds ratio, 2.54 (confidence interval, 1.16–5.57); p < 0.05) independently of anthropometric and clinical variables. Children with NAFLD are at risk for early renal dysfunction. Recognition of this abnormality in the young may help to prevent the ongoing development of the disease.

Keywords: nonalcoholic fatty liver disease; renal function; obesity; children

1. Introduction

Concurrent with the epidemic of obesity across the world, nonalcoholic fatty liver disease (NAFLD) is becoming one of the most prevalent chronic liver disorders in both adults and children. It is now known that NAFLD is not only a risk factor for hepatic failure and hepatic carcinoma, but it is also associated with a spectrum of extrahepatic diseases generally linked to metabolic syndrome (MetS) such as type 2 diabetes, and cardiovascular disease [1,2]. Recent studies in the pediatric obese population have demonstrated that the prevalence of prediabetes and MetS is significantly increased in subjects with increased hepatic fat content, and that liver steatosis, independently of visceral and intramyocellular lipid content, is a key determinant of the impairment of liver, muscle, and adipose insulin sensitivity [3,4]. Several studies have reported associations between NAFLD and subclinical atherosclerosis and between NAFLD and cardiac function alterations, independently of established risk factors [5–7]. In addition, emerging evidence suggests that subjects with NAFLD have an increased risk of chronic kidney disease (CKD), defined by a decline in the estimated glomerular filtration rate (eGFR) and/or microalbuminuria and/or overt proteinuria [8–12]. However, no data are available in children regarding a possible association between NAFLD and impaired renal function. Recognition of the influence of NAFLD on renal function in the early age would enable us to better understand the association of NAFLD and CKD, since there is less potential for confusion with adult-onset complications.

Thus, in this study we sought to determine whether children with overweight/obesity and NAFLD show signs of renal functional alterations, as assessed by eGFR and urinary albumin excretion, compared to children with overweight/obesity but without NAFLD as well as to healthy normal-weight controls.

2. Results

2.1. Clinical and Laboratory Data from the Study Population

Clinical and laboratory data from the study population are presented in Table 1. None of the enrollees had type 2 diabetes mellitus. Patients with NAFLD were on average older than those without NAFLD and healthy controls, and had higher waist circumference (WC) as well as higher values for systolic and diastolic blood pressure (BP), higher triglycerides, aspartate aminotransferase (AST), alanine aminotransferase (ALT), uric acid, fasting glucose, insulin levels and homeostasis model assessment of insulin resistance (HOMA-IR) values, and lower high-density lipoprotein-cholesterol (HDL-C) concentrations. Patients with NAFLD had significantly lower whole-body insulin sensitivity index (WBISI) than those without NAFLD. Obese children with NAFLD and obese subjects without NAFLD had significantly higher eGFR compared to healthy controls (median, 115 (interquartile range, 104–134) and 115 (96–132) vs. 108 (100–118) mL/min/1.73 m^2; $p < 0.0001$), whereas no differences were found between patients with and without NAFLD. However, a greater frequency of reduced eGFR (<90 mL/min/1.73 m^2) was observed in obese subjects with NAFLD compared to obese children without liver involvement and healthy controls (17.5% vs. 6.7% vs. 0.77%, respectively; $p < 0.0001$). The proportion of children with microalbuminuria was also higher in the NAFLD group compared to obese children without liver involvement and healthy controls (9.3% vs. 4.0% vs. 0; $p < 0.0001$). None of the participants had eGFR < 60 mL/min/1.73 m^2 or macroalbuminuria. Compared to healthy controls, the prevalence of hyperfiltration was higher in the obese cohort, regardless of liver involvement (Table 1).

To analyze the variables associated with decreased eGFR and/or microalbuminuria, we performed a logistic regression analysis in the cohort of subjects with overweight/obesity. NAFLD (odds ratio (OR), 2.34; 95% confidence interval (CI), 1.31–4.16; $p < 0.01$) was associated with abnormal renal function independently of age, gender, and pubertal status. After further adjustment for body mass index-standard deviation (BMI-SD) score, WC, hypertension, low HDL-C values, elevated triglycerides, and glucose impairment, results did not substantially change (Table 2).

Int. J. Mol. Sci. **2016**, *17*, 1218

Table 1. Clinical and laboratory characteristics of the study population.

	Normal Weight	NO NAFLD	NAFLD	p Value *
No. patients	130	328	268	
Age, years	10.6 (3.5)	10.1 (2.9)	11.2 (2.9) [d]	<0.0001
Male sex, n (%)	61 (46.9)	151 (46.0)	166 (61.9) [a,d]	<0.0001
BMI-SD score	0.17 (0.85)	1.85 (0.45) [a]	2.0 (0.45) [a,d]	<0.0001
Waist circumference, cm	65 (10)	82 (12) [a]	92 (13) [a,d]	<0.0001
Systolic BP, mmHg	102 (11)	107 (12) [b]	114 (12) [a,d]	<0.0001
Diastolic BP, mmHg	63 (7)	65 (9) [c]	69 (8) [a,d]	<0.0001
Total cholesterol, mg/dL	166 (145–186)	161 (139–187)	159 (137–181)	0.077
LDL-C	92 (72–118)	94 (76–115)	94 (74–111)	0.78
HDL-C, mg/dL	56 (50–83)	51 (44–60) [a]	46 (38–53) [a,d]	<0.0001
Triglycerides, mg/dL	62 (50–83)	70 (50–99)	89 (58–127) [a,d]	<0.0001
AST, U/L	22 (20–30)	23 (20–27) [c]	26 (21–35) [a,d]	<0.0001
ALT, U/L	16 (13–20)	18 (14–23) [b]	31 (19–54) [a,d]	<0.0001
Uric acid	0.21 (0.18–0.25)	0.25 (0.22–0.29) [a]	0.28 (0.24–0.34) [a,d]	<0.0001
Glucose, mg/dL	83 (7)	83 (7)	85 (11)	0.002
Insulin, µU/mL	7.5 (4.3–10.5)	11.1 (7.5–15.4) [a]	15.2 (10.1–23.2) [a,d]	<0.0001
HOMA-IR	1.58 (0.90–2.20)	2.30 (1.55–3.22) [a]	3.23 (2.05–5.0) [a,d]	<0.0001
WBISI	-	6.5 (4.5–9.0)	3.5 (2.4–5.6) [d]	-
eGFR, mL/min/1.73 m^2	108 (100–118)	115 (104–134) [a]	115 (96–132) [a]	<0.0001
eGFR < 90 mL/min/1.73 m^2, n (%)	1 (0.77)	22 (6.7) [a]	47 (17.5) [a,d]	<0.0001
eGFR > 139 mL/min/1.73 m^2, n (%)	6 (4.6)	56 (17.0) [a]	46 (17.2) [a]	0.002
Microalbuminuria, n (%)	0	13 (4.0) [a]	25 (9.3) [a,d]	<0.0001

Results are expressed as n (%), mean (standard deviation), or median (interquartile ranges). * Anova or Kruskal-Wallis test; [a] $p < 0.0001$; [b] $p < 0.01$; [c] $p < 0.05$ vs. controls; [d] $p < 0.0001$ vs. obese children without NAFLD: NAFLD, nonalcoholic fatty liver disease; BMI-SD score, Body mass index- standard deviation score; BP, Blood pressure; LDL-C, Low density lipoprotein-cholesterol; HDL-C, High-density lipoprotein-cholesterol; AST, Aspartate aminotransferase; ALT, Alanine aminotransferase; HOMA-IR, Homeostasis model assessment of insulin resistance; WBISI, Whole-body insulin sensitivity index; eGFR, estimated glomerular filtration rate.

Table 2. Associations of NAFLD with eGFR < 90 mL/min/1.73 m^2 and/or microalbuminuria in children with overweight/obesity.

Variables	Odds Ratio (95% CI)	p Value
Adjusted model 1: age, gender, pubertal status	2.34 (1.31–4.16)	0.004
Adjusted model 2: model 1 plus BMI-SD score, WC, High BP, High TG, low HDL-C, and high FG	2.54 (1.16–5.57)	0.02
Adjusted model 3: model 1 plus BMI-SD score, WC, High BP, High TG, low HDL-C, and IR	2.30 (1.02–5.17)	0.04

CI, confidence interval; eGFR, estimated glomerular filtration rate; BMI-SD score, Body mass index- standard deviation score; WC, waist circumference; BP, Blood pressure; TG, triglycerides; HDL-C, High-density lipoprotein-cholesterol; FG, fasting glucose; IR, insulin resistance.

2.2. Findings in Children with Biopsy-Proven Nonalcoholic Fatty Liver Disease (NAFLD)

To investigate the association of renal dysfunction further with advanced stages of NAFLD such as steatohepatitis (NASH), we analysed the data obtained in the small subgroup of 41 patients who underwent liver biopsy. Definite-NASH was diagnosed in 26 (63.4%) children, while not-NASH in 15 (36.5%). Compared to children without NASH, those with NASH had significantly lower eGFR (median, 88 (83–107) vs. 123 (110–130) mL/min/1.73 m^2; $p < 0.01$). In addition, more children with NASH had eGFR of <90 mL/min/1.73 m^2 and/or microalbuminuria than those without NASH (17/26 (65.4%) vs. 6/15 (40.0%); $p < 0.01$).

3. Discussion

Early recognition of impaired renal function, in particular reduced GFR, is crucial to prevent serious complications [13]. Large epidemiologic studies have found a robust relationship between obesity and risk for CKD [14–16]. In a community-based sample of 2585 adult individuals with renal disease at baseline and a mean follow-up of 18.5 years, BMI was reported to determine a significant increase in the odds of developing kidney disease by 23% (OR, 1.23; 95% CI, 1.08–1.41) per standard deviation unit [14]. In 9685 adults participating to the Hypertension Detection and Follow-Up Program, free of CKD at baseline, the incidence of CKD was 28%, 31%, and 34%, respectively, in the ideal body mass index, overweight, and obese groups, after a follow-up of five years [15]. After adjustment for variables, such as age, gender, race, diabetes mellitus, mean baseline diastolic BP, and slope of diastolic BP, at baseline both overweight (OR, 1.21; 95% CI, 1.05 to 1.41) and obesity (OR, 1.40; 95% CI, 1.20 to 1.63) were associated with increased incident CKD odds at year 5 [15]. In addition, a retrospective cohort study of 320,252 adults, who were followed for 15 to 35 years, showed that a high BMI (⩾25.0 kg/m^2) determined who is at high risk of developing end-stage renal disease [16]. Taken together, these studies indicate that higher BMI in adults is a risk factor for the development of new onset kidney disease. Several possible pathophysiologic pathways may underlie this association. One possibility is that particular characteristics of obesity may account for the association between obesity and CKD. Indeed, obesity constitutes a complex syndrome involving metabolic traits and other factors that may interact with other environmental factors, leading to an increased risk for developing kidney disease. Clustering of these traits defines MetS, which has been reported to be consistently associated with CKD in cross-sectional studies [17,18].

NAFLD has been recently found to be an additional feature of MetS, with the main underlying cardiometabolic risk factors of the syndrome being abdominal obesity and insulin resistance [19,20]. Of note, insulin resistance is not only a metabolic determinant for the development of NAFLD but is also a predictor of incident CKD [21,22]. In addition, atherogenic dyslipidemia and type 2 diabetes are established risk factors for CKD [23,24]. As a consequence, many authors have concluded that NAFLD may have a pathogenic role in the development of CKD. The results of a recent meta-analysis have shown that (1) there is a positive relationship between NAFLD and an increased risk of CKD in adults; (2) the severity of liver disease is associated with an increased risk and severity of CKD; and (3) these relationships are maintained even after taking account of the well-known risk factors for CKD, and are independent of whole body/abdominal obesity and insulin resistance [8].

In our study, we investigated the influence of NAFLD on kidney function in a large pediatric population. This is the first study to demonstrate that overweight/obese children with NAFLD have a greater frequency of eGFR of <90 mL/min/1.73 m^2 as well as of microalbuminuria than overweight/obese children without NAFLD. Furthermore, in the small number of children with biopsy-proven NAFLD we were able to show that the decline in renal function was greater in those with NASH. It is important to point out that subjects with obesity represent a particular population in whom early renal lesion consists of hyperfiltration. In fact, in line with previous studies [25–27], one of the main findings of this study was that children with overweight/obesity compared to normal-weight subjects had a higher prevalence of hyperfiltration, regardless of liver involvement. Glomerular hyperfiltration is well-recognized as an early renal injury occurring in a number of clinical conditions, including diabetes, hypertension, and obesity [28]. Hyperfiltration is hypothesized to be a precursor of intraglomerular hypertension responsible for albuminuria. GFR then declines progressively as albuminuria increases which may cause, in the long run, end-stage renal failure [28]. Thus, in obese patients with NAFLD, we should pay attention for minor impairment on renal function, since hyperfiltration may mask a pathological decline in renal function.

The most plausible explanation for our findings is that the renal abnormalities in overweight/obese children with NAFLD may reflect the coexistence of underlying metabolic risk factors including higher BP, more dyslipidemia, and more insulin resistance compared to children without liver involvement. However, because in our study the presence of NAFLD remained significantly associated with decreased eGFR and/or microalbuminuria after taking account of traditional metabolic traits, we cannot rule out the possibility that NAFLD might at least in part contribute to the development of renal dysfunction independently of shared cardiometabolic risk factors.

The strength of our study includes a large sample size and an extensive and complete analysis of metabolic variables. Nonetheless, some limitations require consideration. First, the cross-sectional design of the study precludes the establishment of causal relationship between NAFLD and abnormal kidney function. Second, we used an estimated GFR instead of a directly measured GFR to define renal function. The gold standard technique is clearance of inulin, but practical problems limit the application of this cumbersome methodology in children because of the necessity for steady-state infusion, and a urine sampling with a bladder catheter. Other tests for determining GFR are clearance of alternative exogenous markers such as iothalamate, which are also complex and difficult to do in routine clinical practice. Recent studies in children have reported current eGFR creatinine- and/or cystatin C-based equations to be reliable methods to assess kidney function, with some variations depending on the GFR ranges and the BMI classes [29–31]. The updated Schwartz formula has been shown to be accurate for estimating GFR when compared to inulin clearance as well as to iothalamate clearance in children and adolescents, with a wide range of renal function [29,30]. Moreover, obesity has not been found to affect GFR as estimated by Schwartz formula [31]. Finally, we measured creatinine concentration by kinetic colorimetric compensated technique, whereas in the updated Schwartz formula, it was determined by an enzymatic method. The two methods, however, are highly correlated [29].

In conclusion, our present study suggests that obese children with NAFLD are at risk for early renal dysfunction. Recognition of this abnormality in the young may be important because treatment to reverse the process is most likely to be effective if applied earlier in the disease process.

4. Materials and Methods

4.1. Study Subjects

This observational cross-sectional study included 596 children and adolescents with overweight/obesity who were consecutively recruited at the outpatient Clinics (Hepatology, Lipid and Nutrition) of the Department of Pediatrics, Sapienza University of Rome, Italy, between 2007 and 2015. Two hundred and sixty eight subjects met the criteria for the diagnosis of NAFLD (i.e., hepatic fat fraction (HFF) ⩾5% on magnetic resonance imaging (MRI)) [32]. In all enrollees, hepatic virus infections (hepatitis A–E and G, cytomegalovirus, and Epstein–Barr virus), autoimmune hepatitis, metabolic liver disease, α-1-antitrypsin deficiency, cystic fibrosis, Wilson's disease, hemochromatosis, and celiac disease were excluded using appropriate tests [6,7]. In 41 of the NAFLD patients, due to persistent elevations in ALT concentrations, a liver biopsy was performed. The other 328 participants had HFF < 5% on MRI, normal levels of aminotransferases, and no evidence of chronic liver diseases (see above). Use of hepatotoxic drugs, as well as a history of type 1 or 2 diabetes, smoking and chronic alcohol intake were also exclusion criteria. None of the subjects had a history or known clinical, laboratory, and imaging signs of renal disease.

The study also included a total of 130 apparently healthy normal-weight school students drawn from four randomly selected schools in the Rome area. All students were invited to take part in a pilot study whose objective was the prevention of cardiovascular disease in childhood. Eligibility criteria included age- and gender-specific BMI; no history of renal and liver diseases as well as of alcohol consumption and smoking; normal liver ultrasound, and normal biochemical values.

All study subjects had a complete physical examination, as reported in detail elsewhere [5,6]. The degree of obesity was quantified using Cole's least mean-square method, which normalizes the skewed distribution of BMI and expresses BMI as SD score [33].

The study protocol was reviewed and approved by the Ethics Committee of Policlinico Umberto I Hospital, Rome, Italy. Written informed consent was obtained from the parents, or guardians of the children included in this study, in accordance with principles of Helsinki Declaration.

4.2. Laboratory Mmeasurements

Blood samples were taken from all study subjects, after an overnight fast, for estimation of glucose, insulin, urea nitrogen, creatinine, uric acid, total cholesterol, HDL-C, triglycerides, ALT, AST, and gamma-glutamyl transferase. An oral glucose tolerance test was performed for all overweight/obese children using 1.75 g/kg of glucose up to a maximum of 75 g. Two-hour post-load glucose and insulin were analyzed. Insulin resistance was calculated by the HOMA-IR. Insulin sensitivity was calculated by the WBISI with reduced time points according to the following formula: $10,000/\sqrt{}$ (fasting glucose × fasting insulin × 2 h post-load glucose × 2 h post-load insulin) [34].

All analyses were performed on COBAS 6000 (Roche Diagnostics, Risch-Rotkreuz, Switzerland). Creatinine concentrations were measured by the kinetic colorimetric compensated Jaffé method using the Roche platform and the CREJ2–creatinine Jaffé Gen.2 assay (Roche Diagnostics, Identification number, 0769282), which was isotope-dilution mass spectrometry standardized, traceable to National Institute of Standards and Technology creatinine standard reference material (SRM 914 and SRM 967). Urinary albumin was determined on 24 h urine collections by the turbidimetric immunoassay ALBT2 (Roche Diagnostics, Identification number, 0767433).

eGFR was calculated using the updated Schwartz formula: 0.413 × height (cm)/serum creatinine (mg/dL) [35].

4.3. Liver Ultrasound Eexamination and Magnetic Resonance Imaging

Liver ultrasound was performed by a single operator. Hepatic steatosis was diagnosed on the basis of the following features: a diffuse increase in echogenicity (a bright liver), liver to kidney contrast, deep beam attenuation, vascular blurring, and loss of definition of the diaphragm [36]. The amount of HFF was measured by MRI using the two-point Dixon method as modified by Fishbein [37], as previously described and validated [32,38].

4.4. Liver Biopsy

Liver biopsy was performed in 41 subjects because of persistent elevation in ALT. The clinical indication for biopsy was either to assess the presence of nonalcoholic steatohepatitis (NASH) or to determine the presence of other independent or competing liver diseases. The main histologic features of NAFLD were scored using the NASH Clinical Research Network criteria [39]. Biopsies were categorized into not-NASH and definite-NASH.

4.5. Definitions

Overweight and obesity were defined according to age- and gender-specific cut-off points of BMI defined by the International Obesity Task Force criteria as proposed by Cole et al. [33]. Elevated BP was defined as systolic or diastolic BP $\geqslant$ 90th percentile for age, gender, and height [40]. Impaired fasting glucose was defined as glucose $\geqslant$5.6 mmol/L. High waist circumference (WC), high triglycerides, and low HDL-C were defined using the cut-off proposed by Cook et al. [41]. Insulin resistance was defined by 90th percentile of HOMA-IR for age and gender in our population of healthy normal-weight children. Abnormal albuminuria was defined as a 24-h urinary albumin excretion rate ⩾30 mg (i.e., microalbuminuria was diagnosed if the 24-h albumin excretion rate was 30–299 mg and macroalbuminuria if the 24-h albumin excretion rate was ⩾300 mg) [42]. As recommended by Kidney Disease Improving Global Outcomes (KDIGO) guidelines, eGFR categories were classified as follows: normal or high ⩾90 mL/min/1.73 m^2; mildly decreased, 60–89; mildly to moderately decreased, 45–59; moderately to severely decreased, 30–44; severely decreased, 15–29; and kidney failure <15 [42]. In the absence of an agreement in the literature, we defined glomerular hyperfiltration as eGFR > 95th percentile of that observed in our population of healthy normal-weight subjects (i.e., eGFR > 139 mL/min/1.73 m^2).

4.6. Statistical Analysis

Statistical analyses were performed using the SPSS package (version 22.0, SPSS Inc., Chicago, IL, USA). Data are reported as means and standard deviations for normally distributed variables, or as median and interquartile range for non-normally distributed variables. Differences between study groups in quantitative variables were evaluated by one-way analysis of variance (ANOVA) or Kruskal–Wallis test, as appropriate. Proportions were compared by the chi square test. Logistic regression analysis was used to assess the independent association of NAFLD with abnormal kidney function, after adjustment for age, gender, pubertal status, BMI-SD score, WC, hypertension, low HDL-C values, elevated triglycerides, and glucose impairment.

Acknowledgments: This study was supported by Sapienza University of Rome (Progetti di Ricerca Universitaria 2013/2014).

Author Contributions: Lucia Pacifico, Enea Bonci, Claudio Chiesa conceived and designed the study; Lucia Pacifico, Enea Bonci, Gian Marco Andreoli, Michele Di Martino, Alessia Gallozzi, and Ester De Luca collected and analyzed the data; Lucia Pacifico, Enea Bonci, Gian Marco Andreoli, Michele Di Martino, and Claudio Chiesa interpreted the data; Lucia Pacifico, Enea Bonci, and Claudio Chiesa wrote the manuscript. All authors read and approved the final version of the manuscript.

Conflicts of Interest: The authors declare no conflicts of interest.

References

1. Vanni, E.; Marengo, A.; Mezzabotta, L.; Bugianesi, E. Systemic complications of nonalcoholic fatty liver disease: When the liver is not an innocent bystander. *Semin. Liver Dis.* **2015**, *35*, 236–249. [CrossRef] [PubMed]

2. Chatterjee, R.; Mitra, A. An overview of effective therapies and recent advances in biomarkers for chronic liver diseases and associated liver cancer. *Int. Immunopharmacol.* **2015**, *24*, 335–345. [CrossRef] [PubMed]

3. Schwimmer, J.B.; Pardee, P.E.; Lavine, J.E.; Blumkin, A.K.; Cook, S. Cardiovascular risk factors and the metabolic syndrome in pediatric nonalcoholic fatty liver disease. *Circulation* **2008**, *118*, 277–283. [CrossRef] [PubMed]

4. D'Adamo, E.; Cali, A.M.; Weiss, R.; Santoro, N.; Pierpont, B.; Northrup, V.; Caprio, S. Central role of fatty liver in the pathogenesis of insulin resistance in obese adolescents. *Diabetes Care* **2010**, *33*, 1817–1822. [CrossRef] [PubMed]

5. Targher, G.; Day, C.P.; Bonora, E. Risk of cardiovascular disease in patients with nonalcoholic fatty liver disease. *N. Engl. J. Med.* **2010**, *363*, 1341–1350. [CrossRef] [PubMed]

6. Pacifico, L.; Anania, C.; Martino, F.; Cantisani, V.; Pascone, R.; Marcantonio, A.; Chiesa, C. Functional and morphological vascular changes in pediatric nonalcoholic fatty liver disease. *Hepatology* **2010**, *52*, 1643–1651. [CrossRef] [PubMed]

7. Pacifico, L.; Di Martino, M.; De Merulis, A.; Bezzi, M.; Osborn, J.F.; Catalano, C.; Chiesa, C. Left ventricular dysfunction in obese children and adolescents with nonalcoholic fatty liver disease. *Hepatology* **2014**, *59*, 461–470. [CrossRef] [PubMed]

8. Musso, G.; Gambino, R.; Tabibian, J.H.; Ekstedt, M.; Kechagias, S.; Hamaguchi, M.; Hultcrantz, R.; Hagström, H.; Yoon, S.K.; Charatcharoenwitthaya, P.; et al. Association of non-alcoholic fatty liver disease with chronic kidney disease: A systematic review and meta-analysis. *PLoS Med.* **2014**, *11*. [CrossRef] [PubMed]

9. Sesti, G.; Fiorentino, T.V.; Arturi, F.; Perticone, M.; Sciacqua, A.; Perticone, F. Association between noninvasive fibrosis markers and chronic kidney disease among adults with nonalcoholic fatty liver disease. *PLoS ONE* **2014**, *9*, e88569. [CrossRef] [PubMed]

10. Machado, M.V.; Gonçalves, S.; Carepa, F.; Coutinho, J.; Costa, A.; Cortez-Pinto, H. Impaired renal function in morbid obese patients with nonalcoholic fatty liver disease. *Liver Int.* **2012**, *32*, 241–248. [CrossRef] [PubMed]

11. Targher, G.; Mantovani, A.; Pichiri, I.; Mingolla, L.; Cavalieri, V.; Mantovani, W.; Pancheri, S.; Trombetta, M.; Zoppini, G.; Chonchol, M.; et al. Nonalcoholic fatty liver disease is independently associated with an increased incidence of chronic kidney disease in patients with type 1 diabetes. *Diabetes Care* **2014**, *37*, 1729–1736. [CrossRef] [PubMed]

12. Pan, L.L.; Zhang, H.J.; Huang, Z.F.; Sun, Q.; Chen, Z.; Li, Z.B.; Yang, S.Y.; Li, X.Y.; Li, X.J. Intrahepatic triglyceride content is independently associated with chronic kidney disease in obese adults: A cross-sectional study. *Metabolism* **2015**, *64*, 1077–1085. [CrossRef] [PubMed]

13. Gansevoort, R.T.; Matsushita, K.; van der Velde, M.; Astor, B.C.; Woodward, M.; Levey, A.S.; de Jong, P.E.; Coresh, J.; Chronic Kidney Disease Prognosis Consortium. Lower estimated GFR and higher albuminuria are associated with adverse kidney outcomes. A collaborative meta-analysis of general and high-risk population cohorts. *Kidney Int.* **2011**, *80*, 93–104. [CrossRef] [PubMed]

14. Fox, C.S.; Larson, M.G.; Leip, E.P.; Culleton, B.; Wilson, P.W.F.; Levy, D. Predictors of new-onset kidney disease in a community-based population. *JAMA* **2004**, *291*, 844–850. [CrossRef] [PubMed]

15. Kramer, H.; Luke, A.; Bidani, A.; Cao, G.; Cooper, R.; McGee, D. Obesity and prevalent and incident CKD: The Hypertension Detection and Follow-Up Program. *Am. J. Kidney Dis.* **2005**, *46*, 587–594. [CrossRef] [PubMed]

16. Hsu, C.Y.; McCulloch, C.E.; Iribarren, C.; Darbinian, J.; Go, A.S. Body mass index and risk for end-stage renal disease. *Ann. Intern. Med.* **2006**, *144*, 21–28. [CrossRef] [PubMed]

17. Chen, J.; Muntner, P.; Hamm, L.L.; Jones, D.W.; Batuman, V.; Fonseca, V.; Whelton, P.K.; He, J. The metabolic syndrome and chronic kidney disease in U.S. adults. *Ann. Intern. Med.* **2004**, *140*, 167–174. [CrossRef] [PubMed]

18. Hoehner, C.M.; Greenlund, K.J.; Rith-Najarian, S.; Casper, M.L.; McClellan, W.M. Association of the insulin resistance syndrome and microalbuminuria among nondiabetic native Americans. The Inter-Tribal Heart Project. *J. Am. Soc. Nephrol.* **2002**, *13*, 1626–1634. [CrossRef] [PubMed]

19. Speliotes, E.K.; Massaro, J.M.; Hoffmann, U.; Vasan, R.S.; Meigs, J.B.; Sahani, D.V.; Hirschhorn, J.N.; O'Donnell, C.J.; Fox, C.S. Fatty liver is associated with dyslipidemia and dysglycemia independent of visceral fat: The Framingham Heart Study. *Hepatology* **2010**, *51*, 1979–1987. [CrossRef] [PubMed]

20. Grundy, S.M. Metabolic syndrome pandemic. *Arterioscler. Thromb. Vasc. Biol.* **2008**, *28*, 629–636. [CrossRef] [PubMed]

21. Bugianesi, E.; Moscatiello, S.; Ciaravella, M.F.; Marchesini, G. Insulin resistance in nonalcoholic fatty liver disease. *Curr. Pharm. Des.* **2010**, *16*, 1941–1951. [CrossRef] [PubMed]

22. Cheng, H.T.; Huang, J.W.; Chiang, C.K.; Yen, C.J.; Hung, K.Y.; Wu, K.D. Metabolic syndrome and insulin resistance as risk factors for development of chronic kidney disease and rapid decline in renal function in elderly. *J. Clin. Endocrinol. Metab.* **2012**, *97*, 1268–1276. [CrossRef] [PubMed]

23. Vlagopoulos, P.T.; Sarnak, M.J. Traditional and non-traditional cardiovascular risk factors in chronic kidney disease. *Med. Clin. N. Am.* **2005**, *89*, 587–611. [CrossRef] [PubMed]

24. Athyros, V.G.; Tziomalos, K.; Katsiki, N.; Doumas, M.; Karagiannis, A.; Mikhailidis, D.P. Cardiovascular risk across the histological spectrum and the clinical manifestations of non-alcoholic fatty liver disease: An update. *World J. Gastroenterol.* **2015**, *21*, 6820–6834. [PubMed]

25. Wuerzner, G.; Pruijm, M.; Maillard, M.; Bovet, P.; Renaud, C.; Burnier, M.; Boshud, M. Marked association between obesity and glomerular hyperfiltration: A cross-sectional study in an African population. *Am. J. Kidney Dis.* **2010**, *56*, 303–312. [CrossRef] [PubMed]

26. Xiao, N.; Jenkins, T.M.; Nehus, E.; Inge, T.H.; Michalsky, M.P.; Harmon, C.M.; Helmrath, M.A.; Brandt, M.L.; Courcoulas, A.; Moxey-Mims, M.; et al. Kidney function in severely obese adolescents undergoing bariatric surgery. *Obesity* **2014**, *22*, 2319–2325. [CrossRef] [PubMed]

27. Franchini, S.; Savino, A.; Marcovecchio, M.L.; Tumini, S.; Chiarelli, F.; Mohn, A. The effect of obesity and type 1 diabetes on renal function in children and adolescents. *Pediatr. Diabetes* **2015**, *16*, 427–433. [CrossRef] [PubMed]

28. Palatini, P. Glomerular hyperfiltration: A marker of early renal damage in prediabetes and pre-hypertension. *Nephrol. Dial. Transplant.* **2012**, *27*, 1708–1714. [CrossRef] [PubMed]

29. Bacchetta, J.; Cochat, P.; Rognant, N.; Ranchin, B.; Hadj-Aissa, A.; Dubourg, L. Which creatinine and cystatin C equations can be reliably used in children? *Clin. J. Am. Soc. Nephrol.* **2011**, *6*, 552–560. [CrossRef] [PubMed]

30. Staples, A.; LeBlond, R.; Watkins, S.; Wong, C.; Brandt, J. Validation of the revised Schwartz estimating equation in a predominantly non-CKD population. *Pediatr. Nephrol.* **2010**, *25*, 2321–2326. [CrossRef] [PubMed]

31. Fadrowski, J.J.; Neu, A.M.; Schwartz, G.J.; Furth, S.L. Pediatric GFR estimating equations applied to adolescents in the general population. *Clin. J. Am. Soc. Nephrol.* **2011**, *6*, 1427–1435. [CrossRef] [PubMed]

32. Pacifico, L.; Di Martino, M.; Catalano, C.; Panebianco, V.; Bezzi, M.; Anania, C.; Chiesa, C. T1-weighted dual-echo MRI for fat quantification in pediatric nonalcoholic fatty liver disease. *World J. Gastroenterol.* **2011**, *17*, 3012–3019. [CrossRef] [PubMed]

33. Cole, T.J.; Bellizzi, M.C.; Flegal, K.M.; Dietz, W.H. Establishing a standard definition for child overweight and obesity worldwide: International survey. *BMJ* **2000**, *320*, 1240–1243. [CrossRef] [PubMed]

34. DeFronzo, R.A.; Matsuda, M. Reduced time points to calculate the composite index. *Diabetes Care* **2010**, *33*, e93. [CrossRef] [PubMed]

35. Schwartz, G.J.; Muñoz, A.; Schneider, M.F.; Mak, R.H.; Kaskel, F.; Warady, B.A.; Furth, S.L. New equations to estimate GFR in children with CKD. *J. Am. Soc. Nephrol.* **2009**, *20*, 629–637. [CrossRef] [PubMed]

36. Hamer, O.W.; Aguirre, D.A.; Casola, G.; Lavine, J.E.; Woenckhaus, M.; Sirlin, C.B. Fatty liver: Imaging patterns and pitfalls. *Radiographics* **2006**, *26*, 1637–1653. [CrossRef] [PubMed]

37. Fishbein, M.H.; Gardner, K.G.; Potter, C.J.; Schmalbrock, P.; Smith, M.A. Introduction of fast MR imaging in the assessment of hepatic steatosis. *Magn. Reson. Imaging* **1997**, *15*, 287–293. [CrossRef]

38. Pacifico, L.; Di Martino, M.; Anania, C.; Andreoli, G.M.; Bezzi, M.; Catalano, C.; Chiesa, C. Pancreatic fat and β-cell function in overweight/obese children with nonalcoholic fatty liver disease. *World J. Gastroenterol.* **2015**, *21*, 4688–4695. [PubMed]

39. Kleiner, D.E.; Brunt, E.M.; van Natta, M.; Behling, C.; Contos, M.J.; Cummings, O.W.; Ferrell, L.D.; Liu, Y.C.; Torbenson, M.S.; Unalp-Arida, A.; et al. Design and validation of a histological scoring system for nonalcoholic fatty liver disease. *Hepatology* **2005**, *41*, 1313–1321. [CrossRef] [PubMed]

40. National High Blood Pressure Education Program Working Group on High Blood Pressure in Children and Adolescents. The fourth report on the diagnosis, evaluation, and treatment of high blood pressure in children and adolescents. *Pediatrics* **2004**, *114* (Suppl. 2), 555–576.

41. Cook, S.; Auinger, P.; Huang, T.T. Growth curves for cardio-metabolic risk factors in children and adolescents. *J. Pediatr.* **2009**, *155* (Suppl. 6), e15–e26. [CrossRef] [PubMed]

42. Levey, A.S.; de Jong, P.E.; Coresh, J.; Nahas, M.E.; Astor, B.C.; Matsushita, K.; Gansevoort, R.T.; Kasiske, B.L.; Eckardt, K.U. The definition, classification, and prognosis of chronic kidney disease: A KDIGO controversities conference report. *Kidney Int.* **2011**, *80*, 17–28. [CrossRef] [PubMed]

International Journal of
Molecular Sciences

MDPI

Review

NAFLD and NASH in HCV Infection: Prevalence and Significance in Hepatic and Extrahepatic Manifestations

Luigi Elio Adinolfi *, Luca Rinaldi, Barbara Guerrera, Luciano Restivo, Aldo Marrone, Mauro Giordano and Rosa Zampino

Department of Medical, Surgical, Neurological, Metabolic, and Geriatric Sciences, Second University of Naples, Naples 80100, Italy; lucarinaldi@hotmail.it (L.R.); barbara.guerrera@alice.it (B.G.); luciano.restivo@gmail.it (L.R.); Aldo.marrone@unina2.it (A.M.); mauro.giordano@unina2.it (M.G.); rosa.zampino@unina2.it (R.Z.)
* Correspondence: luigielio.adinolfi@unina2.it; Tel.: +39-0823-690642

Academic Editors: Amedeo Lonardo and Giovanni Targher
Received: 14 March 2016; Accepted: 19 May 2016; Published: 25 May 2016

Abstract: The aim of this paper is to review and up to date the prevalence of hepatitis C virus (HCV)-associated non-alcoholic fatty liver disease (NAFLD) and non-alcoholic steatohepatitis (NASH) and their significance in both accelerating progression of HCV-related liver disease and development of HCV-associated extrahepatic diseases. The reported mean prevalence of HCV-related NAFLD was 55%, whereas NASH was reported in 4%–10% of cases. HCV genotype 3 directly induces fatty liver deposition, namely "viral steatosis" and it is associated with the highest prevalence and degree of severity, whereas, HCV non-3 genotype infection showed lower prevalence of steatosis, which is associated with metabolic factors and insulin resistance. The host's genetic background predisposes him or her to the development of steatosis. HCV's impairment of lipid and glucose metabolism causes fatty liver accumulation; this seems to be a viral strategy to optimize its life cycle. Irrespective of insulin resistance, HCV-associated NAFLD, in a degree-dependent manner, contributes towards accelerating the liver fibrosis progression and development of hepatocellular carcinoma by inducing liver inflammation and oxidative stress. Furthermore, NAFLD is associated with the presence of metabolic syndrome, type 2 diabetes, and atherosclerosis. In addition, HCV-related "metabolic steatosis" impairs the response rate to interferon-based treatment, whereas it seems that "viral steatosis" may harm the response rate to new oral direct antiviral agents. In conclusion, a high prevalence of NAFLD occurs in HCV infections, which is, at least in part, induced by the virus, and that NAFLD significantly impacts progression of the liver disease, therapeutic response, and some extrahepatic diseases.

Keywords: HCV-associated NAFLD; insulin resistance; liver fibrosis; HCC; metabolic syndrome; diabetes; atherosclerosis

---

1. Introduction

Non-alcoholic fatty liver disease (NAFLD) is a condition characterized by fatty liver accumulation with a spectrum of liver damage ranging from simple steatosis to non-alcoholic steatohepatitis (NASH). The latter accounted for one third of cases [1] and it is a common cause of chronic liver diseases, including cirrhosis and hepatocellular carcinoma (HCC) [2]. NAFLD is strictly associated with metabolic syndrome in the general population and can be considered as a multisystem disease associated with inflammation, oxidative stress, and insulin resistance with an increasing risk of type 2 diabetes mellitus, cardiovascular diseases, and chronic kidney diseases [1]. Moreover, irrespective of metabolic syndrome, recently, several host genetic backgrounds have been reported as potential risk factors for development of NAFLD [1].

NAFLD is a prominent feature of chronic hepatitis C virus (HCV) infection [3]. Both viral and host factors contribute to the development of steatosis. NAFLD in HCV genotype 3 infected patients is strictly associated with serum viral load [3–7], thus steatosis in this setting is considered to be of viral origin and it is namely "viral steatosis"; whereas in HCV non-3 genotype infected patients, NAFLD is mainly linked to host factors such as body mass index (BMI), obesity, particular visceral obesity [8], insulin resistance, and type 2 diabetes mellitus, and it is called "metabolic steatosis". Accordingly, liver steatosis localization in HCV non-3 genotypes infected patients is similar to that observed in NAFLD/NASH (*i.e.*, mostly in the centrolobular zone (acinar 3)) [9], whereas in genotype 3 infection steatosis is localized mainly in the periportal zone (acinar 1) [10]. With respect to the sustained virologic response rate to interferon-based treatment, a substantial difference in the behavior of the two types of HCV-associated NAFLD has been reported. Metabolic steatosis significantly reduces response rate to interferons [6,11–14], whereas virologic steatosis does not impact the interferon response rate and it even disappears following HCV clearance with reappearance in relapse cases [5,15]. In addition, HCV-related metabolic steatosis is strictly associated with insulin resistance; although HCV *per sé* induces insulin resistance, which predates the development of steatosis, that, in turn, aggravates insulin resistance [16,17]. Furthermore, it has been demonstrated that HCV-associated steatosis induces hepatic and systemic inflammation and oxidative stress [18,19].

The mechanisms by which HCV induces steatosis are complex and specific for genotype 3 (viral steatosis) and non-3 genotypes (metabolic steatosis). However, the two forms of steatosis share some mechanisms and overlapping conditions may occur. Recently, we reviewed the main molecular mechanisms by which HCV induces steatosis [20] and in Figure 1 the chief genotype-specific mechanisms are reported.

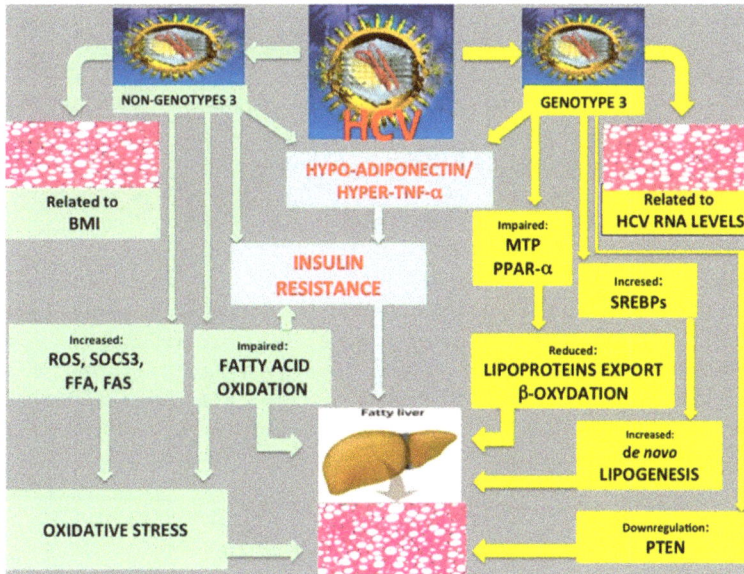

Figure 1. Schematically are illustrated the mains HCV genotype-specific molecular mechanisms of steatogenesis. Abbreviations used: HCV: hepatitis C virus; BMI: body mass index; MTP: microsomal triglyceride transfer protein; PPAR-α: peroxisome proliferator-activated receptor α; SREBPs: sterol regulatory element-binding proteins; ROS: reactive oxygen species; SOCS3: suppressor of cytokine signaling 3; FFA: free fatty acid; FAS: fatty acid synthase; PTEN: phosphatase and tensin homolog.

Chronic HCV infection is considered a systemic disease and there is evidence that steatosis may change the natural history of both HCV-related hepatic and extrahepatic diseases, and that host genetic backgrounds may promote HCV-associated steatosis and progression of liver disease.

In this paper we reviewed the prevalence and associated factors which promote NAFLD/NASH in chronic HCV infections and the evidence that highlights the role of steatosis in both accelerating the progression of HCV-related liver disease and the development of HCV-associated extrahepatic diseases.

2. Prevalence of NAFLD/NASH and Associated Conditions in Chronic HCV Infection

In chronic HCV infection, NAFLD has been reported with a mean prevalence of about 55%, ranging from 40% to 86% [3,5,6,21–30] depending on HCV genotype and local prevalence of metabolic syndrome. HCV genotype 3 infected patients showed the highest prevalence of steatosis (up to 86%), whereas in HCV genotype 1 and 2 the mean reported prevalence was about 40% and 50%, respectively. The above reported prevalence of NAFLD-associated to HCV infection is higher than the rates observed in non-HCV infected subjects in the general population (*i.e.*, 20%–30%) [31], and of the rates reported for other hepatic diseases, such as HBV infection (about 22%) and autoimmune hepatitis (about 16%) [17].

Data on the prevalence of NASH in chronic hepatitis C cases are less consistent than those reported for NAFLD. The published data reported an occurrence of NASH from 4% to 10% [25,32–35]. Risk factors associated with development of HCV-associated NASH include BMI and, for HCV genotype 1, triglyceride and HDL-cholesterol levels, whereas for genotype 3, aspartate transaminase levels are a contributing factor [35,36].

A strict association between HCV-associated NAFLD and insulin resistance has been reported. However, insulin resistance can be both a direct consequence of HCV infection and a result of NAFLD, and *vice versa* [17]. Overall, insulin resistance has been reported with high prevalence in chronic hepatitis C infection cases (up to 80%) and it is commonly observed in HCV non-3 genotypes infected patients, whereas it is not a feature of HCV genotype 3 infection [19].

Overweight and obese BMI levels significantly contribute to the development of HCV-associated NAFLD, in particular, it has been demonstrated that visceral obesity has a preeminent role [2]. Visceral obesity plays an important role in the regulation of glucose and lipid metabolism in chronic HCV infection. In HCV-infected patients with visceral obesity, it has been reported that there are increased levels of pro-inflammatory cytokines (IL-6 and TNF-α) that inhibit insulin signaling and the secretion of adiponectin, which results in corresponding consequences for the development of liver steatosis and insulin resistance [37]. The latter represents the pathophysiological link between steatosis and the metabolic syndrome. Despite chronic HCV patients showing a high prevalence of insulin resistance, an overall low prevalence of full-blown metabolic syndrome was reported [38]. Patients with HCV-associated steatosis presented a higher prevalence of metabolic syndrome than those without steatosis, but a lower prevalence than that observed in NAFLD patients [38]. However, HCV infection is associated with multiple metabolic derangements, which has been termed hepatitis C associated dysmetabolic syndrome (HCADS) [20]. Such metabolic derangements are characterized by insulin resistance, hypocholesterolemia, hyperuricemia, and altered body fat distribution [20].

It has been demonstrated that oxidative stress occurs with high prevalence in chronic HCV infection (e.g., greater that 60% [18]), and that it contributes to the development of NAFLD in HCV non-3 genotypes, but not in "viral steatosis" associated with HCV genotype 3 infections.

The host's genetic background has an important impact on the development of NAFLD in chronic HCV infections. It has been demonstrated that microsomal triglyceride transfer protein (MTP) polymorphism (493GT) was associated with a higher prevalence of NAFLD in HCV genotype 3 [39]; methylene tetrahydrofolate reductase (MTHFR) polymorphism (C677T) [40] was correlated with an increased prevalence of NAFLD in chronic HCV infections as well as an increased risk to develop severe steatosis (*i.e.*, 6-fold higher for hosts with a MTHFR "CT" genotype and 20-fold higher for those with a "TT" genotype) [40]. The patatin-like phospholipase domain-containing 3 (PNPLA3) gene, in particular, its I148M variant, has been linked with an increased prevalence of HCV-related

NAFLD and with visceral obesity [41,42]. Recently, we demonstrated that the TM6SF2, E167K variant, contributes to liver steatosis in chronic hepatitis C [43].

3. HCV-Induces Steatosis: Is It a Finalistic Condition?

A characteristic feature of HCV infections is the strict association between viral factors and host metabolic factors (*i.e.*, lipid and glucose metabolism), which are involved in the development of liver steatosis. Experimental and clinical evidence showed that HCV core proteins, in a genotype-specific manner, cause hepatic fat accumulation by activating SREBP-1 and 2 [44], inhibiting MTP activity [45], impairing peroxisome proliferator-activated receptor (PPAR) expression, and promoting de novo lipid synthesis [46], which harms assembly, excretion, and uptake of very low density lipoprotein (VLDL).

The interaction between HCV and the host's lipid metabolism seems to be crucial for the viral life cycle. It is reported that triglyceride-rich VLDL represents an essential role in the assembly and secretion of HCV. Elements of infective HCV circulate in patient sera as lipo-viro particles (LVPs) in association with ApoB- and ApoE-containing lipoproteins, which suggests the association of viral particles with LDL and VLDL. It was reported that the interaction with the LDL receptor is important for HCV entry into hepatocytes [47]. Similarly, synthesis of farnesyl pyrophosphate and geranylgeranyl pyrophosphate are essential for HCV replication [48]. On the bases of this evidence it has been hypothesized that the abnormalities of hepatic lipid content are essential to perpetuate the HCV life cycle [49].

4. HCV-Associated Steatosis and Progression of Liver Damage

One important question was to define if NAFLD/NASH could impact hepatic fibrosis progression in chronic hepatitis C infections through modifying the natural history of liver damage. Earlier cross-sectional studies demonstrated an association between NAFLD and advanced liver fibrosis [3,8] as well as an association between NAFLD and liver inflammation, which was also strictly associated with progression of fibrosis [50]. Such data were confirmed by prospective studies using paired liver biopsies. A study by Westin *et al.* [25] that featured paired liver biopsies for98 HCV patients showed that steatosis, especially in genotype 3, was an independent factor associated with fibrosis progression. Similarly, Castera *et al.* [28] evaluated the fibrosis progression in 96 chronic hepatitis C patients by means of paired liver biopsy with a mean interval of four years, and found that steatosis was an independent factor associated with fibrosis progression via performing a multivariate analysis (odds ratio (OR) = 4.7%–95% CI = 1.3–10.8; p = 0.0001). In addition, Cross *et al.* [51] also used multivariate analysis tin a study involving 112 chronic hepatitis C patients with serial liver biopsy to show that fibrosis progression was associated with steatosis (OR: 14.3; 95% CI: 2.1–1110; p = 0.006).

Twenty-eight other cross-sectional or prospective studies, carefully reviewed by Lonardo *et al.* [20], evaluated the association between steatosis and fibrosis confirming that steatosis is strictly associated with liver fibrosis in chronic HCV infections. However, there were some studies that reported an association between steatosis and liver fibrosis that was genotype-dependent [7,25,29,51,52].

A meta-analysis, including data from 10 centers in Europe, Australia, and North America for 3068 individuals with chronic hepatitis C, analyzed the independent factors associated with liver fibrosis [53]. The meta-analysis showed that steatosis was independently associated with liver fibrosis (OR: 1.66; 1.27–2.18: p < 0.001) and with liver inflammation. The data of the meta-analysis also reinforce the hypothesis that inflammation is the link between steatosis and liver fibrosis progression.

It is important to underline that there were a marginal number of studies that were not able to demonstrate an association between liver fibrosis and steatosis [22,29,53–56]. The discrepancy of such results may be explained by differences in study design, patient demographic characteristics, differences in histological grading of steatosis/fibrosis, type of statistical analysis performed, and confounding variables, in particular, insulin resistance which has been reported to be independently associated with both steatosis and liver fibrosis progression [53,57–59]. Overall, the majority of the studies evaluated the role of steatosis without considering insulin resistance or *vice versa*, due to the overlapping conditions, thus their independent role in the progression of liver fibrosis has not yet been adequately assessed. However, Moucari *et al.* [60] evaluated 500 patients with chronic hepatitis C and the multivariate analysis showed that both steatosis (adjusted OD 1.95, 1.24–3.06, $p = 0.004$) and insulin resistance (adjusted OD: 1.80, 1.15–2.81, $p = 0.009$) were independently associated with advanced liver fibrosis. Hu *et al.* [61], in a retrospective study including 460 patients with chronic hepatitis C, also showed that grade 2 and 3 levels of steatosis were independently associated with liver fibrosis.

The mechanisms by which steatosis and insulin resistance induce progression of liver fibrosis seem to be different. On the basis of the data within the literature [17,52,62,63], in Figure 2 we schematically reported such mechanisms. Both steatosis and insulin resistance activate connective tissue growth factor (CTGF), but steatosis does so by increasing inflammation [17,53] while insulin resistance does so by increasing glucose and insulin levels [62,63].

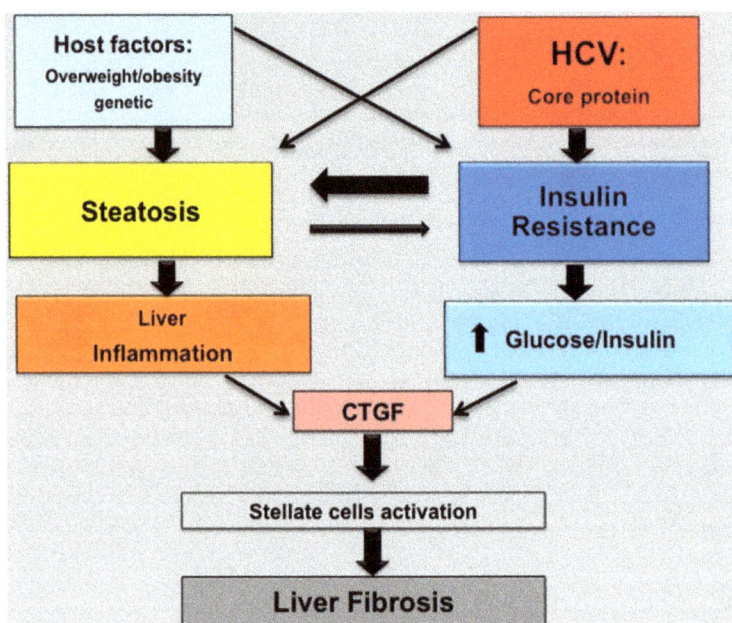

Figure 2. Schematic representation of factors and mechanisms involved in the progression of liver fibrosis in chronic hepatitis C patients. HCV: hepatitis C virus: CTGF: connective tissue growth factor.

Fartoux *et al.* [64] showed that the cumulative probability of progression of fibrosis in mild chronic hepatitis C during a follow up period of more than 90 months was strictly associated with the presence of steatosis. In Fartoux's study, patients with less than 5% steatosis showed a negligible progression of liver fibrosis; patients with steatosis greater than 30% showed the highest (and statistically significant) progression of fibrosis ($p < 0.0001$), and patients with steatosis between 5% and 30% showed an intermediate progression of liver fibrosis.

It has been reported that similar to patients with HCV-associated NAFLD, those with NASH showed advanced fibrosis [32]. The data seem to suggest that the biological significance of NASH-associated with HCV infection is similar to that observed for cases with a high-degree of steatosis.

In conclusion, there is significant evidence that steatosis is strictly associated with faster progression of liver fibrosis in chronic hepatitis C. The fibrogenic effect of HCV-associated steatosis seems to be multi-factorial involving pro-inflammatory cytokines, oxidative stress, insulin resistance, glucose levels, and increased susceptibility to apoptosis.

There is experimental and clinical evidence supporting a role of HCV-related steatosis in the development of HCC. In experimental models, using transgenic mice, HCV core proteins showed a causative role in the development of steatosis and HCC [65–68]. The experimental evidence has been confirmed in the majority of clinical studies performed [67,69–76]. Both retrospective and prospective studies, with only a few exceptions, showed that HCV-related steatosis was strictly associated with the development of HCC and that the amount of fatty liver deposition was an important risk factor for HCC [67,69–76]. Thus, HCV patients with the highest degree of steatosis carry a higher risk of HCC. Accordingly, HCV genotype 3 infection has been reported to convey the highest risk to develop HCC [67]. However, at present, direct evidence supporting a role for viral steatosis in inducing HCC is lacking. It has also been shown that patients with HCV-related steatosis and diabetes have an enhanced risk of HCC [77]. The data underline the necessity to increase surveillance for HCC in patients with HCV-related steatosis and advanced liver disease.

It seems that HCV-related steatosis may influence the development of HCC by several mechanisms. Among these, it has been suggested that oxidative stress may have a role through reactive oxygen species inducing mutagenesis [78] and both insulin resistance and lipid metabolic alterations are considered hepato-carcinogenic factors in HCV-related steatosis [79].

5. HCV-Associated Steatosis, Diabetes, Metabolic Syndrome, and Atherosclerosis

HCV infection is associated with an increased risk of type 2 diabetes [80]; HCV patients showed a 12 times higher risk to develop type 2 diabetes [81]. Similarly, diabetes patients had a 5–10 times increased risk of being HCV positive [82]. It has been demonstrated that, in predisposed individuals, chronic HCV infection accelerates the appearance of type 2 diabetes by at least 10 years [81]. The mechanism involved in HCV-induced diabetes is insulin resistance, which is strictly associated with both viral infection and steatosis. It has been reported that 75% of HCV patients with diabetes have steatosis [83] and that HCV-related steatosis is associated with diabetes [53]. Thus, HCV-related steatosis may influence diabetes by aggravating insulin resistance. Otherwise, it is also possible that both insulin resistance and type 2 diabetes can increase or aggravate steatosis in chronic HCV infection.

The presence of steatosis, insulin resistance, and diabetes are associated with advanced liver fibrosis, HCC, and poor outcome of chronic hepatitis C infections [84–86].

The prevalence of metabolic syndrome in chronic hepatitis C patients was about 5% and was similar to that observed in the general population [37]. However, metabolic syndrome was significantly higher in patients with HCV-related steatosis as compared with HCV patients without steatosis (13.3% *vs.* 1.8%) [50]. The data indicate that in chronic hepatitis C patients the presence of liver steatosis predicts metabolic syndrome.

There is a consistent body of literature demonstrating that chronic HCV infection is a risk factor for atherosclerosis, cardiovascular diseases, and related forms of mortality [18]. It has been demonstrated that HCV may live and replicate within carotid plaque [87]. Moreover, chronic HCV infection is associated with many pro-atherogenic conditions such as inflammation, hypoadiponectinemia, hyperhomocysteinemia, increased oxidative stress, insulin resistance, and diabetes [18]. HCV-related steatosis was associated with the above reported pro-atherogenic conditions [50]. Thus, it was anticipated that hepatic steatosis might predict the presence of atherosclerosis in chronic hepatitis C patients. Accordingly, it has been demonstrated that in HCV patients, steatosis is an independent factor associated with the highest prevalence of atherosclerosis [50]. Steatosis predicted, with a good specificity (81.7%) and sensitivity (74.2%), both early (intima-media thickness) and advanced (plaques) lesions of carotid atherosclerosis. It has been suggested that steatosis may modulate atherogenic factors; such as inflammation and metabolic elements favoring the development of atherosclerosis and that patients with HCV-associated steatosis should be screened for atherosclerosis [50].

6. HCV-Associated Steatosis and Response to Antiviral Treatments

HCV-related "metabolic steatosis" has been reported as a negative predictor of response to interferon-based antiviral therapy in genotypes 1 and 2 infections [6,11–14]. In this setting of treatment, patients with "viral steatosis" associated with HCV genotype 3 infection were considered easy to treat.

In the last few years, the new oral direct antiviral agents (DAAs) are becoming the standard of HCV treatment. The impact of steatosis on DAAs treatment has been scantly evaluated. However, there is an agreement that the HCV genotype 3 showed lower response rate to DAAs and now it has been considered to be difficult to treat. It has been proposed that steatosis could partly explain the lower response rate in HCV genotype 3 infections [88]. Thus, specific studies are needed to evaluate the impact of steatosis and metabolic factors on the response rate of the new DAAs.

7. Conclusions

The data demonstrate that hepatic steatosis is a feature of chronic HCV infections and that liver fatty accumulation seems to be a finalistic condition favoring the persistence and replication of HCV. HCV-associated steatosis, in a degree-dependent fashion, producing hepatic inflammation and oxidative stress, induces a more rapid progression of liver fibrosis and increases the risk of the development of HCC. HCV-associated steatosis also influences the development of some extrahepatic manifestations of chronic HCV infection such as diabetes, metabolic syndrome, and atherosclerosis. In addition, the presence of steatosis impairs the response rate to interferons based anti-HCV treatments and could have a role in the lower response rate observed in HCV genotype 3 treated with new DAAs. Thus, steatosis should be regarded as a marker to individuate patients at higher risk of progression of HCV-associated liver disease, development of extrahepatic diseases, and lower therapeutic response rate, perhaps even in the era of new DAAs.

Author Contributions: All authors equally contributed to this review.

Conflicts of Interest: The authors declare no conflict of interest.

References

1. Christopher, D.; Byrne, C.D.; Targher, G. NAFLD: A multisystem disease. *J. Hepatol.* **2015**, *62*, S47–S64.
2. Baffy, G.; Brunt, E.M.; Caldwell, S.H. Hepatocellular carcinoma in non-alcoholic fatty liver disease: An emerging menace. *J. Hepatol.* **2012**, *56*, 1384–1391. [CrossRef] [PubMed]
3. Adinolfi, L.E.; Gambardella, M.; Andreana, A.; Tripodi, M.F.; Utili, R.; Ruggiero, G. Steatosis accelerates the progression of liver damage of chronic hepatitis C patients and correlates with specific HCV genotype and visceral obesity. *Hepatology* **2001**, *33*, 1358–1364. [CrossRef] [PubMed]
4. Adinolfi, L.E.; Utili, R.; Ruggiero, G. Body composition and hepatic steatosis as precursors of fibrosis in chronic hepatitis C patients. *Hepatology* **1999**, *30*, 1530–1531. [CrossRef] [PubMed]
5. Rubbia-Brandt, L.; Quadri, R.; Abid, K.; Giostra, E.; Malé, P.J.; Mentha, G.; Spahr, L.; Zarski, J.P.; Borisch, B.; Hadengue, A.; *et al.* Hepatocyte steatosis is a cytopathic effect of hepatitis C virus genotype 3. *J. Hepatol.* **2000**, *33*, 106–115. [CrossRef]
6. Poynard, T.; Ratziu, V.; McHutchison, J.; Manns, M.; Goodman, Z.; Zeuzem, S.; Younossi, Z.; Albrecht, J. Effect of treatment with peginterferon or interferon alfa-2b and ribavirin on steatosis in patients infected with hepatitis C. *Hepatology* **2003**, *38*, 75–85. [CrossRef] [PubMed]
7. Patton, H.M.; Patel, K.; Behling, C.; Bylund, D.; Blatt, L.M.; Vallée, M.; Heaton, S.; Conrad, A.; Pockros, P.J.; McHutchison, J.G. The impact of steatosis on dise. *J. Hepatol.* **2004**, *40*, 484–490. [CrossRef] [PubMed]
8. Hickman, I.J.; Powell, E.E.; Prins, J.B.; Clouston, A.D.; Ash, S.; Purdie, D.M.; Jonsson, J.R. In overweight patients with chronic hepatitis C, circulating insulin is associated with hepatic fibrosis: Implications for therapy. *J. Hepatol.* **2003**, *39*, 1042–1048. [CrossRef]
9. Zubair, A.; Jamal, S.; Mubarik, A.; Saudi, J. Morphometric analysis of hepatic steatosis in chronic hepatitis C infection. *Saudi J. Gastroenterol.* **2009**, *15*, 11–14. [PubMed]

10. Pazienza, V.; Clément, S.; Pugnale, P.; Conzelman, S.; Foti, M.; Mangia, A.; Negro, F. The hepatitis C virus core protein of genotypes 3A and 1b downregulates insulin receptor substrate 1 through genotype-specific mechanisms. *Hepatology* **2007**, *45*, 1164–1171. [CrossRef] [PubMed]

11. Hwang, S.J.; Luo, J.C.; Chu, C.W.; Lai, C.R.; Lu, C.L.; Tsay, S.H.; Wu, J.C.; Chang, F.Y.; Lee, S.D. Hepatic steatosis in chronic hepatitis C virus infection: Prevalence and clinical correlation. *J. Gastroenterol. Hepatol.* **2001**, *16*, 190–195. [CrossRef] [PubMed]

12. Zeuzem, S.; Hultcrantz, R.; Bourliere, M.; Goeser, T.; Marcellin, P.; Sanchez-Tapias, J.; Sarrazin, C.; Harvey, J.; Brass, C.; Albrecht, J. Peginterferon alfa-2b plus ribavirin for treatment of chronic hepatitis C in previously untreated patients infected with HCV genotypes 2 or 3. *J. Hepatol.* **2004**, *40*, 993–999. [CrossRef] [PubMed]

13. Harrison, S.A.; Brunt, E.M.; Qazi, R.A.; Oliver, D.A.; Neuschwander-Tetri, B.A.; Di Bisceglie, A.M.; Bacon, B.R. Effect of significant histologic steatosis or steatohepatitis on response to antiviral therapy in patients with chronic hepatitis C. *Clin. Gastroenterol. Hepatol.* **2005**, *3*, 604–609. [CrossRef]

14. Romero-Gómez, M.; del Mar Viloria, M.; Andrade, R.J.; Salmerón, J.; Diago, M.; Fernández-Rodríguez, C.M.; Corpas, R.; Cruz, M.; Grande, L.; Vázquez, L.; *et al.* Insulin resistance impairs sustained response rate to peginterferon plus ribavirin in chronic hepatitis C patients. *J. Gastroenterol.* **2005**, *128*, 636–641. [CrossRef]

15. Kumar, D.; Farrell, G.C.; Fung, C.; George, J. Hepatitis C virus genotype 3 is cytopathic to hepatocytes: Reversal of hepatic steatosis after sustained therapeutic response. *Hepatology* **2002**, *36*, 1266–1272. [CrossRef] [PubMed]

16. Shintani, Y.; Fujie, H.; Miyoshi, H.; Tsutsumi, T.; Tsukamoto, K.; Kimura, S.; Moriya, K.; Koike, K. Hepatitis C virus infection and diabetes: Direct involvement of the virus in the development of insulin resistance. *Gastroenterology* **2004**, *126*, 840–848. [CrossRef] [PubMed]

17. Lonardo, A.; Adinolfi, L.E.; Loria, P.; Carulli, N.; Ruggiero, G.; Day, C.P. Steatosis and hepatitis C virus: Mechanisms and significance for hepatic and extrahepatic disease. *Gastroenterology* **2004**, *126*, 586–597. [CrossRef] [PubMed]

18. Adinolfi, L.E.; Zampino, R.; Restivo, L.; Lonardo, A.; Guerrera, B.; Marrone, A.; Nascimbeni, F.; Florio, A.; Loria, P. Chronic hepatitis C virus infection and atherosclerosis: Clinical impact and mechanisms. *World J. Gastroenterol.* **2014**, *20*, 3410–3417. [CrossRef] [PubMed]

19. Vidali, M.; Tripodi, M.F.; Ivaldi, A.; Zampino, R.; Occhino, G.; Restivo, L.; Sutti, S.; Marrone, A.; Ruggiero, G.; Albano, E.; *et al.* Interplay between oxidative stress and hepatic steatosis in the progression of chronic hepatitis C. *J. Hepatol.* **2008**, *48*, 399–406. [CrossRef] [PubMed]

20. Lonardo, A.; Adinolfi, L.E.; Restivo, L.; Ballestri, S.; Romagnoli, D.; Baldelli, E.; Nascimbeni, F.; Loria, P. Pathogenesis and significance of hepatitis C virus steatosis: An update on survival strategy of a successful pathogen. *World J. Gastroenterol.* **2014**, *23*, 7089–7103. [CrossRef] [PubMed]

21. Mihm, S.; Fayyazi, A.; Hartmann, H.; Ramadori, G. Analysis of histopathological manifestations of chronic hepatitis C virus infection with respect to virus genotype. *Hepatology* **1997**, *25*, 735–739. [CrossRef] [PubMed]

22. Czaja, A.J.; Carpenter, H.A.; Santrach, P.J.; Moore, S.B. Host- and disease-specific factors affecting steatosis in chronic hepatitis C. *J. Hepatol.* **1998**, *29*, 198–206. [CrossRef]

23. Hourigan, L.F.; Macdonald, G.A.; Purdie, D.; Whitehall, V.H.; Shorthouse, C.; Clouston, A.; Powell, E.E. Fibrosis in chronic hepatitis C correlates significantly with body mass index and steatosis. *Hepatology* **1999**, *29*, 1215–1219. [CrossRef] [PubMed]

24. Serfaty, L.; Andreani, T.; Giral, P.; Carbonell, N.; Chazouillères, O.; Poupon, R. Hepatitis C virus induced hypobetalipoproteinemia: A possible mechanism for steatosis in chronic hepatitis C. *J. Hepatol.* **2001**, *34*, 428–434. [CrossRef]

25. Monto, A.; Alonzo, J.; Watson, J.J.; Grunfeld, C.; Wright, T.L. Steatosis in chronic hepatitis C: Relative contributions of obesity, diabetes mellitus, and alcohol. *Hepatology* **2002**, *36*, 729–736. [CrossRef] [PubMed]

26. Westin, J.; Nordlinder, H.; Lagging, M.; Norkrans, G.; Wejstål, R. Steatosis accelerates fibrosis development over time in hepatitis C virus genotype 3 infected patients. *J. Hepatol.* **2002**, *37*, 837–842. [CrossRef]

27. Hui, J.M.; Kench, J.; Farrell, G.C.; Lin, R.; Samarasinghe, D.; Liddle, C.; Byth, K.; George, J. Genotype-specific mechanisms for hepatic steatosis in chronic hepatitis C infection. *J. Gastroenterol. Hepatol.* **2002**, *17*, 873–881. [CrossRef] [PubMed]

28. Castéra, L.; Hézode, C.; Roudot-Thoraval, F.; Bastie, A.; Zafrani, E.S.; Pawlotsky, J.M.; Dhumeaux, D. Worsening of steatosis is an independent factor of fibrosis progression in untreated patients with chronic hepatitis C and paired liver biopsies. *Gut* **2003**, *52*, 288–292. [CrossRef] [PubMed]

29. Asselah, T.; Boyer, N.; Guimont, M.C.; Cazals-Hatem, D.; Tubach, F.; Nahon, K.; Daïkha, H.; Vidaud, D.; Martinot, M.; Vidaud, M.; *et al.* Liver fibrosis is not associated with steatosis but with necroinflammation in French patients with chronic hepatitis C. *Gut* **2003**, *52*, 1638–1643. [CrossRef] [PubMed]

30. Rubbia-Brandt, L.; Fabris, P.; Paganin, S.; Leandro, G.; Male, P.J.; Giostra, E.; Carlotto, A.; Bozzola, L.; Smedile, A.; Negro, F. Steatosis affects chronic hepatitis C progression in a genotype specific way. *Gut* **2004**, *53*, 406–412. [CrossRef] [PubMed]

31. Clark, J.M.; Brancati, F.L.; Diehl, A.M. Nonalcoholic fatty liver disease. *Gastroenterology* **2002**, *122*, 1649–1657. [CrossRef] [PubMed]

32. Ong, J.P.; Younossi, Z.M.; Speer, C.; Olano, A.; Gramlich, T.; Boparai, N. Chronic hepatitis C and superimposed nonalcoholic fatty liver disease. *Liver* **2001**, *21*, 266–271. [CrossRef] [PubMed]

33. Brunt, E.M.; Ramrakhiani, S.; Cordes, B.G.; Neuschwander-Tetri, B.A.; Janney, C.G.; Bacon, B.R.; di Bisceglie, A.M. Concurrence of histologic features of steatohepatitis with other forms of chronic liver disease. *Mod. Pathol.* **2003**, *16*, 49–56. [CrossRef] [PubMed]

34. Liu, C.J.; Jeng, Y.M.; Chen, P.J.; Lai, M.Y.; Yang, H.C.; Huang, W.L.; Kao, J.H.; Chen, D.S. Influence of metabolic syndrome, viral genotype and antiviral therapy on superimposed fatty liver disease in chronic hepatitis C. *Antivir. Ther.* **2005**, *10*, 405–415. [PubMed]

35. Bedossa, P.; Moucari, R.; Chelbi, E.; Asselah, T.; Paradis, V.; Vidaud, M.; Cazals-Hatem, D.; Boyer, N.; Valla, D.; Marcellin, P. Evidence for a role of nonalcoholic steatohepatitis in hepatitis C: A prospective study. *Hepatology* **2007**, *46*, 380–387. [CrossRef] [PubMed]

36. Solis-Herruzo, J.A.; Pérez-Carreras, M.; Rivas, E.; Fernández-Vázquez, I.; Garfia, C.; Bernardos, E.; Castellano, G.; Colina, F. Factors associated with the presence of nonalcoholic steatohepatitis in patients with chronic hepatitis C. *Am. J. Gastroenterol.* **2005**, *100*, 1091–1098. [CrossRef] [PubMed]

37. Jonsson, J.R.; Barrie, H.D.; O'Rourke, P.; Clouston, A.D.; Powell, E.E. Obesity and steatosis influence serum and hepatic inflammatory markers in chronic hepatitis C. *Hepatology* **2008**, *48*, 80–87. [CrossRef] [PubMed]

38. Lonardo, A.; Ballestri, S.; Adinolfi, L.E.; Violi, E.; Carulli, L.; Lombardini, S.; Scaglioni, F.; Ricchi, M.; Ruggiero, G.; Loria, P. Hepatitis C virus-infected patients are "spared" from the metabolic syndrome but not from insulin resistance. A comparative study of nonalcoholic fatty liver disease and hepatitis C virus-related steatosis. *Can. J. Gastroenterol.* **2009**, *23*, 273–278. [CrossRef] [PubMed]

39. Zampino, R.; Ingrosso, D.; Durante-Mangoni, E.; Capasso, R.; Tripodi, M.F.; Restivo, L.; Zappia, V.; Ruggiero, G.; Adinolfi, L.E. Microsomal triglyceride transfer protein (MTP)-493G/T gene polymorphism contributes to fat liver accumulation in HCV genotype 3 infected patients. *J. Viral. Hepat.* **2008**, *10*, 740–746. [CrossRef] [PubMed]

40. Adinolfi, L.E.; Ingrosso, D.; Cesaro, G.; Cimmino, A.; D'Antò, M.; Capasso, R.; Zappia, V.; Ruggiero, G. Hyperhomocysteinemia and the MTHFR C677T polymorphism promote steatosis and fibrosis in chronic hepatitis C patients. *Hepatology* **2005**, *41*, 995–1003. [CrossRef] [PubMed]

41. Valenti, L.; Fargion, S. Patatin-like phospholipase domain containing-3 Ile148Met and fibrosis progression after liver transplantation. *Hepatology* **2011**, *54*, 1484. [CrossRef] [PubMed]

42. Zampino, R.; Coppola, N.; Cirillo, G.; Boemio, A.; Grandone, A.; Stanzione, M.; Capoluongo, N.; Marrone, A.; Macera, M.; Sagnelli, E.; *et al.* Patatin-like phospholipase domain-containing 3 I148M variant is associated with liver steatosis and fat distribution in chronic hepatitis B. *Dig. Dis. Sci.* **2015**, *60*, 3005–3010. [CrossRef] [PubMed]

43. Coppola, N.; Rosa, Z.; Cirillo, G.; Stanzione, M.; Macera, M.; Boemio, A.; Grandone, A.; Pisaturo, M.; Marrone, A.; Adinolfi, L.E.; *et al.* TM6SF2 E167K variant is associated with severe steatosis in chronic hepatitis C, regardless of PNPLA3 polymorphism. *Liver Int.* **2015**, *35*, 1959–1963. [CrossRef] [PubMed]

44. Oem, J.K.; Jackel-Cram, C.; Li, Y.P.; Zhou, Y.; Zhong, J.; Shimano, H.; Babiuk, L.A.; Liu, Q. Activation of sterol regulatory element-binding protein 1C and fatty acid synthase transcription by hepatitis C virus non-structural protein 2. *J. Gen. Virol.* **2008**, *89*, 1225–1230. [CrossRef] [PubMed]

45. Perlemuter, G.; Sabile, A.; Letteron, P.; Vona, G.; Topilco, A.; Chrétien, Y.; Koike, K.; Pessayre, D.; Chapman, J.; Barba, G.; *et al.* Hepatitis C virus core protein inhibits microsomal triglyceride transfer protein activity and very low density lipoprotein secretion: A model of viral-related steatosis. *FASEB J.* **2002**, *16*, 185–194. [CrossRef] [PubMed]

46. De Gottardi, A.; Pazienza, V.; Pugnale, P.; Bruttin, F.; Rubbia-Brandt, L.; Juge-Aubry, C.E.; Meier, C.A.; Hadengue, A.; Negro, F. Peroxisome proliferator-activated receptor-α and -γ mRNA levels are reduced in chronic hepatitis C with steatosis and genotype 3 infection. *Aliment. Pharmacol. Ther.* **2006**, *23*, 107–114. [CrossRef] [PubMed]

47. Burlone, M.E.; Budkowska, A. Hepatitis C virus cell entry: Role of lipoproteins and cellular receptors. *J. Gen. Virol.* **2009**, *90*, 1055–1070. [CrossRef] [PubMed]

48. Kapadia, S.B.; Chisari, F.V. Hepatitis C virus RNA replication is regulated by host geranylgeranylation and fatty acids. *Proc. Natl. Acad. Sci. USA* **2005**, *102*, 2561–2566. [CrossRef] [PubMed]

49. Westin, J.; Lagging, M.; Dhillon, A.P.; Norkrans, G.; Romero, A.I.; Pawlotsky, J.M.; Zeuzem, S.; Schalm, S.W.; Verheij-Hart, E.; Negro, F.; *et al.* Impact of hepatic steatosis on viral kinetics and treatment outcome during antiviral treatment of chronic HCV infection. *J. Viral Hepat.* **2007**, *14*, 29–35. [CrossRef] [PubMed]

50. Adinolfi, L.E.; Restivo, L.; Guerrera, B.; Sellitto, A.; Ciervo, A.; Iuliano, N.; Rinaldi, L.; Santoro, A.; li Vigni, G.; Marrone, A. Chronic HCV infection is a risk factor of ischemic stroke. *Atherosclerosis* **2013**, *23*, 22–26. [CrossRef] [PubMed]

51. Cross, T.J.; Quaglia, A.; Hughes, S.; Joshi, D.; Harrison, P.M. The impact of hepatic steatosis on the natural history of chronic hepatitis C infection. *J. Viral Hepat.* **2009**, *16*, 492–499. [CrossRef] [PubMed]

52. Nieminen, U.; Arkkila, P.E.; Kärkkäinen, P.; Färkkilä, M.A. Effect of steatosis and inflammation on liver fibrosis in chronic hepatitis C. *Liver Int.* **2009**, *29*, 153–158. [CrossRef] [PubMed]

53. Leandro, G.; Mangia, A.; Hui, J.; Fabris, P.; Rubbia-Brandt, L.; Colloredo, G.; Adinolfi, L.E.; Asselah, T.; Jonsson, J.R.; Smedile, A.; *et al.* Relationship between steatosis, inflammation, and fibrosis in chronic hepatitis C: A meta-analysis of individual patient data. *Gastroenterology* **2006**, *130*, 1636–1642. [CrossRef] [PubMed]

54. Sterling, R.K.; Wegelin, J.A.; Smith, P.G.; Stravitz, R.T.; Luketic, V.A.; Fuchs, M.; Puri, P.; Shiffman, M.L.; Contos, M.A.; Mills, A.S.; *et al.* Similar progression of fibrosis between HIV/HCV-infected and HCV-infected patients: Analysis of paired liver biopsy samples. *Clin. Gastroenterol. Hepatol.* **2010**, *8*, 1070–1076. [CrossRef] [PubMed]

55. Matos, C.A.; Perez, R.M.; Pacheco, M.S.; Figueiredo-Mendes, C.G.; Lopes-Neto, E.; Oliveira, E.B.; Lanzoni, V.P.; Silva, A.E.; Ferraz, M.L. Steatosis in chronic hepatitis C: Relationship to the virus and host risk factors. *J. Gastroenterol. Hepatol.* **2006**, *21*, 1236–1239. [CrossRef] [PubMed]

56. Macías, J.; Berenguer, J.; Japón, M.A.; Girón, J.A.; Rivero, A.; López-Cortés, L.F.; Moreno, A.; González-Serrano, M.; Iribarren, J.A.; Ortega, E.; *et al.* Fast fibrosis progression between repeated liver biopsies in patients coinfected with human immunodeficiency virus/hepatitis C virus. *Hepatology* **2009**, *50*, 1056–1063. [CrossRef] [PubMed]

57. Taura, N.; Ichikawa, T.; Hamasaki, K.; Nakao, K.; Nishimura, D.; Goto, T.; Fukuta, M.; Kawashimo, H.; Fujimoto, M.; Kusumoto, K.; *et al.* Association between liver fibrosis and insulin sensitivity in chronic hepatitis C patients. *Am. J. Gastroenterol.* **2006**, *101*, 2752–2759. [CrossRef] [PubMed]

58. Fartoux, L.; Poujol-Robert, A.; Guéchot, J.; Wendum, D.; Poupon, R.; Serfaty, L. Insulin resistance is a cause of steatosis and fibrosis progression in chronic hepatitis C. *Gut* **2005**, *54*, 1003–1008. [CrossRef] [PubMed]

59. Perumalswami, P.; Kleiner, D.E.; Lutchman, G.; Heller, T.; Borg, B.; Park, Y.; Liang, T.J.; Hoofnagle, J.H.; Ghany, M.G. Steatosis and progression of fibrosis in untreated patients with chronic hepatitis C infection. *Hepatology* **2006**, *43*, 780–787. [CrossRef] [PubMed]

60. Moucari, R.; Asselah, T.; Cazals-Hatem, D.; Voitot, H.; Boyer, N.; Ripault, M.P.; Sobesky, R.; Martinot-Peignoux, M.; Maylin, S.; Nicolas-Chanoine, M.H.; *et al.* Insulin resistance in chronic hepatitis C: Association with genotypes 1 and 4, serum HCV RNA level, and liver fibrosis. *Gastroenterology* **2008**, *134*, 416–423. [CrossRef] [PubMed]

61. Hu, S.X.; Kyulo, N.L.; Xia, V.W.; Hillebrand, D.J.; Hu, K.Q. Factors associated with hepatic fibrosis in patients with chronic hepatitis C: A retrospective study of a large cohort of U.S. patients. *J. Clin. Gastroenterol.* **2009**, *43*, 758–764. [CrossRef] [PubMed]

62. Paradis, V.; Perlemuter, G.; Bonvoust, F.; Dargere, D.; Parfait, B.; Vidaud, M.; Conti, M.; Huet, S.; Ba, N.; Buffet, C.; *et al.* High glucose and hyperinsulinemia stimulate connective tissue growth factor expression:

A potential mechanism involved in progression to fibrosis in nonalcoholic steatohepatitis. *Hepatology* **2001**, *34*, 738–744. [CrossRef] [PubMed]

63. Ratziu, V.; Munteanu, M.; Charlotte, F.; Bonyhay, L.; Poynard, T. LIDO Study Group. Fibrogenic impact of high serum glucose in chronic hepatitis C. *J. Hepatol.* **2003**, *39*, 1049–1055. [CrossRef]

64. Fartoux, L.; Chazouillères, O.; Wendum, D.; Poupon, R.; Serfaty, L. Impact of steatosis on progression of fibrosis in patients with mild hepatitis C. *Hepatology* **2005**, *41*, 82–87. [CrossRef] [PubMed]

65. Moriya, K.; Fujie, H.; Shintani, Y.; Yotsuyanagi, H.; Tsutsumi, T.; Ishibashi, K.; Matsuura, Y.; Kimura, S.; Miyamura, T.; Koike, K. The core protein of hepatitis C virus induces hepatocellular carcinoma in transgenic mice. *Nat. Med.* **1998**, *4*, 1065–1067. [CrossRef] [PubMed]

66. Kanwal, F.; Kramer, J.R.; Ilyas, J.; Duan, Z.; El-Serag, H.B. HCV genotype 3 is associated with an increased risk of cirrhosis and hepatocellular cancer in a national sample of U.S. Veterans with HCV. *Hepatology* **2014**, *60*, 98–105. [CrossRef] [PubMed]

67. Nkontchou, G.; Ziol, M.; Aout, M.; Lhabadie, M.; Baazia, Y.; Mahmoudi, A.; Roulot, D.; Ganne-Carrie, N.; Grando-Lemaire, V.; Trinchet, J.C.; *et al.* HCV genotype 3 is associated with a higher hepatocellular carcinoma incidence in patients with ongoing viral C cirrhosis. *J. Viral Hepat.* **2011**, *18*, e516–e522. [CrossRef] [PubMed]

68. van der Meer, A.J.; Veldt, B.J.; Feld, J.J.; Wedemeyer, H.; Dufour, J.F.; Lammert, F.; Duarte-Rojo, A.; Heathcote, E.J.; Manns, M.P.; Kuske, L.; *et al.* Association between sustained virological response and all-cause mortality among patients with chronic hepatitis C and advanced hepatic fibrosis. *JAMA* **2012**, *308*, 2584–2593. [CrossRef] [PubMed]

69. Asahina, Y.; Tsuchiya, K.; Nishimura, T.; Muraoka, M.; Suzuki, Y.; Tamaki, N.; Yasui, Y.; Hosokawa, T.; Ueda, K.; Nakanishi, H.; *et al.* α-fetoprotein levels after interferon therapy and risk of hepatocarcinogenesis in chronic hepatitis C. *Hepatology* **2013**, *58*, 1253–1262. [CrossRef] [PubMed]

70. Salomao, M.; Yu, W.M.; Brown, R.S.; Emond, J.C.; Lefkowitch, J.H. Steatohepatitic hepatocellular carcinoma (SH-HCC): A distinctive histological variant of HCC in hepatitis C virus-related cirrhosis with associated NAFLD/NASH. *Am. J. Surg. Pathol.* **2010**, *34*, 1630–1636. [CrossRef] [PubMed]

71. Nojiri, K.; Sugimoto, K.; Shiraki, K.; Kusagawa, S.; Tanaka, J.; Beppu, T.; Yamamoto, N.; Takei, Y.; Hashimoto, A.; Shimizu, A.; *et al.* Development of hepatocellular carcinoma in patients with chronic hepatitis C more than 10 years after sustained virological response to interferon therapy. *Oncol. Lett.* **2010**, *1*, 427–430. [PubMed]

72. Tanaka, A.; Uegaki, S.; Kurihara, H.; Aida, K.; Mikami, M.; Nagashima, I.; Shiga, J.; Takikawa, H. Hepatic steatosis as a possible risk factor for the development of hepatocellular carcinoma after eradication of hepatitis C virus with antiviral therapy in patients with chronic hepatitis C. *World J. Gastroenterol.* **2007**, *13*, 5180–5187. [CrossRef] [PubMed]

73. Takuma, Y.; Nouso, K.; Makino, Y.; Saito, S.; Takayama, H.; Takahara, M.; Takahashi, H.; Murakami, I.; Takeuchi, H. Hepatic steatosis correlates with the postoperative recurrence of hepatitis C virus-associated hepatocellular carcinoma. *Liver Int.* **2007**, *27*, 620–626. [CrossRef] [PubMed]

74. Pekow, J.R.; Bhan, A.K.; Zheng, H.; Chung, R.T. Hepatic steatosis is associated with increased frequency of hepatocellular carcinoma in patients with hepatitis C-related cirrhosis. *Cancer* **2007**, *109*, 2490–2496. [CrossRef] [PubMed]

75. Kumar, D.; Farrell, G.C.; Kench, J.; George, J. Hepatic steatosis and the risk of hepatocellular carcinoma in chronic hepatitis C. *J. Gastroenterol. Hepatol.* **2005**, *20*, 1395–1400. [CrossRef] [PubMed]

76. Ohata, K.; Hamasaki, K.; Toriyama, K.; Matsumoto, K.; Saeki, A.; Yanagi, K.; Abiru, S.; Nakagawa, Y.; Shigeno, M.; Miyazoe, S.; *et al.* Hepatic steatosis is a risk factor for hepatocellular carcinoma in patients with chronic hepatitis C virus infection. *Cancer* **2003**, *97*, 3036–3043. [CrossRef] [PubMed]

77. Tazawa, J.; Maeda, M.; Nakagawa, M.; Ohbayashi, H.; Kusano, F.; Yamane, M.; Sakai, Y.; Suzuki, K. Diabetes mellitus may be associated with hepatocarcinogenesis in patients with chronic hepatitis C. *Dig. Dis. Sci.* **2002**, *47*, 710–715. [CrossRef] [PubMed]

78. Jahan, S.; Ashfaq, U.A.; Qasim, M.; Khaliq, S.; Saleem, M.J.; Afzal, N. Hepatitis C virus to hepatocellular carcinoma. *Infect. Agents Cancer* **2012**, *7*. [CrossRef] [PubMed]

79. Koike, K. Hepatitis C virus contributes to hepatocarcinogenesis by modulating metabolic and intracellular signaling pathways. *J. Gastroenterol. Hepatol.* **2007**, *22*, S108–S111. [CrossRef] [PubMed]

80. Adinolfi, L.E.; Restivo, L.; Zampino, R.; Lonardo, A.; Loria, P. Metabolic alterations and chronic hepatitis C: Treatment strategies. *Expert Opin. Pharmacother.* **2011**, *12*, 2215–2234. [CrossRef] [PubMed]

81. Mehta, S.H.; Brancati, F.L.; Sulkowski, M.S.; Strathdee, S.A.; Szklo, M.; Thomas, D.L. Prevalence of type 2 diabetes mellitus among persons with hepatitis C virus infection in the United States. *Ann. Intern. Med.* **2000**, *133*, 592–599. [CrossRef] [PubMed]

82. Simó, R.; Hernández, C.; Genescà, J.; Jardí, R.; Mesa, J. High prevalence of hepatitis C virus infection in diabetic patients. *Diabetes Care* **1996**, *19*, 998–1000. [CrossRef] [PubMed]

83. Hadziyannis, S.J. The spectrum of extrahepatic manifestations in hepatitis C virus infection. *J. Viral Hepat.* **1997**, *4*, 9–28. [CrossRef] [PubMed]

84. Petta, S.; Cammà, C.; di Marco, V.; Alessi, N.; Cabibi, D.; Caldarella, R.; Licata, A.; Massenti, F.; Tarantino, G.; Marchesini, G.; *et al.* Insulin resistance and diabetes increase fibrosis in the liver of patients with genotype 1 HCV infection. *Am. J. Gastroenterol.* **2008**, *103*, 1136–1144. [CrossRef] [PubMed]

85. Kwon, S.Y.; Kim, S.S.; Kwon, O.S.; Kwon, K.A.; Chung, M.G.; Park, D.K.; Kim, Y.S.; Koo, Y.S.; Kim, Y.K.; Choi, D.J.; *et al.* Prognostic significance of glycaemic control in patients with HBV and HCV-related cirrhosis and diabetes mellitus. *Diabet. Med.* **2005**, *22*, 1530–1535. [CrossRef] [PubMed]

86. Chen, C.L.; Yang, H.I.; Yang, W.S.; Liu, C.J.; Chen, P.J.; You, S.L.; Wang, L.Y.; Sun, C.A.; Lu, S.N.; Chen, D.S.; *et al.* Metabolic factors and risk of hepatocellular carcinoma by chronic hepatitis B/C infection: A follow-up study in Taiwan. *Gastroenterology* **2008**, *135*, 111–121. [CrossRef] [PubMed]

87. Boddi, M.; Abbate, R.; Chellini, B.; Giusti, B.; Giannini, C.; Pratesi, G.; Rossi, L.; Pratesi, C.; Gensini, G.F.; Paperetti, L.; *et al.* Hepatitis C virus RNA localization in human carotid plaques. *J. Clin. Virol.* **2010**, *47*, 72–75. [CrossRef] [PubMed]

88. Ampuero, J.; Romero-Gómez, M.; Reddy, K.R. HCV genotype 3. The new treatment challenge. *Aliment. Pharmacol. Ther.* **2014**, *39*, 686–698. [CrossRef] [PubMed]

International Journal of
Molecular Sciences

MDPI

Article

Correlations of Hepatic Hemodynamics, Liver Function, and Fibrosis Markers in Nonalcoholic Fatty Liver Disease: Comparison with Chronic Hepatitis Related to Hepatitis C Virus

Ryuta Shigefuku [1,*,†], Hideaki Takahashi [1,2,†], Hiroyasu Nakano [1], Tsunamasa Watanabe [1],
Kotaro Matsunaga [1], Nobuyuki Matsumoto [1], Masaki Kato [1], Ryo Morita [1], Yousuke Michikawa [1],
Tomohiro Tamura [1,2], Tetsuya Hiraishi [1,3], Nobuhiro Hattori [1], Yohei Noguchi [1,2],
Kazunari Nakahara [1], Hiroki Ikeda [1], Toshiya Ishii [1,3], Chiaki Okuse [1,3], Shigeru Sase [4],
Fumio Itoh [1] and Michihiro Suzuki [1,3]

[1] Division of Gastroenterology and Hepatology, St. Marianna University School of Medicine,
    Kanagawa, Kawasaki 216-8511, Japan; hide-bo@marianna-u.ac.jp (H.T.); h-nakano@marianna-u.ac.jp (H.N.);
    twatanab@marianna-u.ac.jp (T.W.); kotarom@marianna-u.ac.jp (K.M.); nobu1020@marianna-u.ac.jp (N.M.);
    masaki0801_3@marianna-u.ac.jp (M.K.); r2morita@marianna-u.ac.jp (R.M.);
    y2michikawa@marianna-u.ac.jp (Y.M.); t2tamura@marianna-u.ac.jp (T.T.);
    t2hiraishi@marianna-u.ac.jp (T.H.); hattyorina.224@gmail.com (N.H.); y2noguchi@marianna-u.ac.jp (Y.N.);
    nakahara@marianna-u.ac.jp (K.N.); ikedahi@marianna-u.ac.jp (H.I.); t2ishii@marianna-u.ac.jp (T.I.);
    c2okuse@marianna-u.ac.jp (C.O.); fitoh@marianna-u.ac.jp (F.I.); michstmu@marianna-u.ac.jp (M.S.)
[2] Division of Gastroenterology, St. Marianna University School of Medicine, Yokohama City Seibu Hospital,
    Kanagawa, Yokohama 241-0811, Japan
[3] Division of Gastroenterology and Hepatology, Department of Internal Medicine, Kawasaki Municipal Tama
    Hospital, Kanagawa, Kawasaki 214-8525, Japan
[4] Anzai Medical Company, Ltd., Tokyo 141-0033, Japan; sase@anzai-med.co.jp
*   Correspondence: r2shigefuku@marianna-u.ac.jp; Tel.: +81-44-977-8111; Fax: +81-44-976-5805
†   These authors contributed equally to this work.

Academic Editors: Amedeo Lonardo and Giovanni Targher
Received: 30 June 2016; Accepted: 8 September 2016; Published: 14 September 2016

Abstract: The progression of chronic liver disease differs by etiology. The aim of this study was to elucidate the difference in disease progression between chronic hepatitis C (CHC) and nonalcoholic fatty liver disease (NAFLD) by means of fibrosis markers, liver function, and hepatic tissue blood flow (TBF). Xenon computed tomography (Xe-CT) was performed in 139 patients with NAFLD and 152 patients with CHC (including liver cirrhosis (LC)). The cutoff values for fibrosis markers were compared between NAFLD and CHC, and correlations between hepatic TBF and liver function tests were examined at each fibrosis stage. The cutoff values for detection of the advanced fibrosis stage were lower in NAFLD than in CHC. Although portal venous TBF (PVTBF) correlated with liver function tests, PVTBF in initial LC caused by nonalcoholic steatohepatitis (NASH-LC) was significantly lower than that in hepatitis C virus (C-LC) ($p = 0.014$). Conversely, the liver function tests in NASH-LC were higher than those in C-LC ($p < 0.05$). It is important to recognize the difference between NAFLD and CHC. We concluded that changes in hepatic blood flow occurred during the earliest stage of hepatic fibrosis in patients with NAFLD; therefore, patients with NAFLD need to be followed carefully.

Keywords: nonalcoholic steatohepatitis; chronic hepatitis C; liver function; hepatic hemodynamics; WFA$^+$-M2BP

1. Introduction

Nonalcoholic fatty liver disease (NAFLD) and nonalcoholic steatohepatitis (NASH) are increasingly recognized as common clinicopathological entities that occur in individuals without significant alcohol use [1]. The former is believed to have a benign clinical course, whereas the latter represents a form of liver injury that carries a risk for progressive fibrosis, liver cirrhosis (LC), and hepatocellular carcinoma (HCC) [2,3]. Due to the obesity epidemic and the increasing prevalence of metabolic syndrome, NAFLD and its progressive form, NASH, are seen more commonly in different parts of the world [4,5]. NAFLD has become a serious public health issue not only in Western countries, but also in many Asian countries, including Japan [6–8]. NASH is characterized by parenchymal injuries, including macrovesicular steatosis, ballooning degeneration, Mallory-Denk bodies, and inflammation in hepatic lobes [9]. On the other hand, chronic hepatitis C (CHC) is characterized by portal tract infiltration of dense aggregates of lymphocytes with follicle formation, and mild macrovesicular steatosis can be seen in lobules, particular in periportal hepatocytes [10,11]. Thus, the manner of fibrosis progression in NASH is different from that in CHC. Although there is currently no validated test involving serum biomarkers available to diagnose NASH, and histologic evaluation with a liver biopsy remains the gold standard, and screening for fibrosis is recommended in patients with suspected NASH. However, liver biopsy has some clinical problems related to its invasiveness and complications. On the other hand, there are validated tests with serum biomarkers available to diagnose the stage of hepatic fibrosis (e.g., Wisteria floribunda agglutinin positive Mac-2-binding protein (WFA$^+$-M2BP), hyaluronic acid (HA), 7S domain of type IV collagen, tissue inhibitor of metalloproteinase-1 (TIMP-1), type III procollagen N peptide (PIIIP), FIB4-index, etc.). Recently, WFA$^+$-M2BP has been reported to be a useful marker for staging in patients with NAFLD [12] and CHC [13,14]. Especially in CHC patients, WFA$^+$-M2BP can be a useful surrogate marker not only as a fibrotic marker, but also for the risk of HCC development [13,14]. However, there are few reports about WFA$^+$-M2BP on the basis of the etiology of chronic liver disease (CLD).

Since the liver receives blood flow from both the portal vein and hepatic artery, which account for 70% and 30%, respectively, this double blood supply mechanism is a specific characteristic of the liver. The portal vein receives the blood supply from the intestine, which engages in metabolism as a functional vessel. Xenon-CT has been established as a non-invasive technique to visualize tissue blood flow (TBF) in the neurosurgical field [15,16]. Xe-CT can also be applied to obtain separate measurements of hepatic arterial and venous blood flow to detect changes in hepatic blood flow (HBF). We previously reported that PVTBF and total hepatic TBF (THTBF) decrease with the progression of liver fibrosis in patients with CHC [17,18] and NAFLD [19,20]. However, few reports have addressed the association between HBF and liver function; no report has examined the progression of liver function according to the etiology of CLD. Moreover we previously reported that hepatic TBF in patients with liver cirrhosis varied according to the etiology of the disease and there is a close correlation between liver function and hepatic blood flow in patients with alcoholic liver cirrhosis [21,22]. In the present study, we investigated the difference in the fibrosis markers between patients with initial chronic hepatitis and those with advanced chronic hepatitis in NASH and CH-C. Furthermore, we attempted to clarify the relationship between hepatic TBF and liver function. It is extremely important to understand the characteristics of CLD progression for the management and treatment of CLD. The aim of this study was to elucidate the difference in disease progression between CHC and NAFLD in CLD by comparing the cutoff values for fibrosis markers and the associations of liver function and HBF.

2. Results

2.1. The Cutoff Value and Diagnostic Ability of Each Fibrosis Marker in NAFLD Patients

The receiver operating characteristic (ROC) curve and the area under the ROC (AUC) for each fibrosis marker predict definitive advanced fibrosis. The AUC values of WFA$^+$-M2BP, TIMP-1, HA,

PIIIP, platelet count (Plt), FIB4-index, aspartate aminotransferase-platelet index (APRI), AST/ALT ratio, and ICG-R$_{15}$ were 0.70, 0.50, 0.87, 0.58, 0.74, 0.77, 0.62, 0.75, and 0.74, respectively (Table 1).

Table 1. The cutoff value and diagnostic ability of each fibrosis marker in NAFLD patients.

		NAFLD (*n* = 58)			
Fibrosis Markers		Cutoff	AUROC	Sensitivity	Specificity
WFA$^+$-M2BP	C.O.I	1.06	0.70	75	67
TIMP-1	ng/mL	242.0	0.50	50	68
HA	ng/mL	58.9	0.87	80	86
PIIIP	ng/mL	11.4	0.58	50	74
Platelet count	×10^4/μL	17.7	0.74	67	80
FIB-4 Index	–	1.95	0.77	67	78
APRI	–	3.25	0.62	50	70
AST/ALT ratio	–	0.82	0.75	75	78
ICG-R$_{15}$	%	10.5	0.74	67	64

Stage 0–2 (*n* = 46) vs. Stage 3–4 (*n* = 12). AUROC, area under the receiver operating characteristic curve; NAFLD: nonalcoholic fatty liver disease.

2.2. The Cutoff Value and Diagnostic Ability of Each Fibrosis Marker in CHC Patients

The ROC curve and the area under the ROC (AUC) for each fibrosis marker predict definitive advanced fibrosis. The AUC values of WFA$^+$-M2BP, TIMP-1, HA, PIIIP, Plt, FIB4-index, APRI, AST/ALT ratio, and ICG-R$_{15}$ were 0.89, 0.84, 0.87, 0.71, 0.82, 0.87, 0.82, 0.62, and 0.86, respectively (Table 2).

Table 2. The cutoff value and diagnostic ability of each fibrosis marker in CHC patients.

		CHC (*n* = 72)			
Fibrosis Markers		Cutoff	AUROC	Sensitivity	Specificity
WFA$^+$-M2BP	C.O.I	3.28	0.89	84	85
TIMP-1	ng/mL	297.6	0.84	88	72
HA	ng/mL	116.5	0.87	79	79
PIIIP	ng/mL	10.6	0.71	74	64
Platelet count	×10^4/μL	13.9	0.82	74	75
FIB-4 Index	–	3.19	0.87	89	79
APRI	–	5.41	0.82	79	79
AST/ALT ratio	–	0.76	0.62	63	53
ICG-R$_{15}$	%	11.5	0.86	84	76

Stage 0–2 (*n* = 53) vs. Stage 3–4 (*n* = 19). AUROC, area under the receiver operating characteristic curve; CHC: chronic hepatitis related to hepatitis C virus.

2.3. Liver Function and Hepatic TBF in Each Stage of NAFLD Patients

Liver function and hepatic TBF in each stage of NAFLD patients are shown in Table 3. With fibrosis progression, Alb, ChE, TC, PT, Plt, PVTBF, and THTBF decreased significantly ($p < 0.001$, $r = -0.47$; $p < 0.001$, $r = -0.52$; $p < 0.01$, $r = -0.26$; $p < 0.001$, $r = -0.69$; $p < 0.001$, $r = -0.66$; $p < 0.001$, $r = -0.32$; $p < 0.01$, $r = -0.22$, respectively). On the other hand, with fibrosis progression, ICG-R$_{15}$, HA, and WFA$^+$-M2BP increased significantly ($p < 0.001$, $r = 0.58$; $p < 0.001$, $r = 0.78$; $p < 0.001$, $r = 0.50$, respectively).

Table 3. Liver function and hepatic tissue blood flow in each fibrosis stage in NAFLD.

Fibrosis Stage	NAFL	Stage 1	Stage 2	Stage 3	Initial LC	Advanced LC	p-Value *	r
	n = 15	n = 47	n = 30	n = 15	n = 25	n = 7		
Alb (g/dL)	4.5 ± 0.3	4.5 ± 0.3	4.4 ± 0.3	4.4 ± 0.3	4.0 ± 0.3	3.1 ± 0.4	<0.001	−0.47
ChE (IU/L)	390.1 ± 107.2	372.8 ± 104.3	346.3 ± 96.0	260.5 ± 149.3	254.8 ± 63.2	155.4 ± 95.7	<0.001	−0.52
TC (mg/dL)	200.8 ± 40.9	200.4 ± 33.5	180.3 ± 62.0	170.3 ± 73.9	179.5 ± 36.3	119.7 ± 39.0	<0.01	−0.26
PT (%)	100.8 ± 5.4	98.9 ± 9.0	96.4 ± 6.5	87.0 ± 10.1	76.4 ± 16.2	57.0 ± 7.7	<0.001	−0.69
ICG-R_{15} (%)	5.9 ± 2.9	9.8 ± 13.0	11.6 ± 6.6	17.7 ± 18.1	21.9 ± 12.5	26.0 ± 8.4	<0.001	0.58
HA (ng/mL)	20.4 ± 16.5	53.4 ± 98.0	63.4 ± 51.3	151.4 ± 98.7	268.9 ± 193.9	347.3 ± 181.9	<0.001	0.78
WFA^+-M2BP (C.O.I)	0.7 ± 0.3	0.8 ± 0.4	1.2 ± 0.7	1.3 ± 0.6	1.8 ± 1.5	4.4 ± 0.2	<0.001	0.50
Plt (×10^4/μL)	24.2 ± 4.5	23.7 ± 6.5	20.1 ± 5.2	18.3 ± 7.3	11.5 ± 3.5	5.3 ± 3.0	<0.001	−0.66
PVTBF (mL/100 mL/min)	41.0 ± 6.3	34.3 ± 7.2	33.8 ± 7.0	29.9 ± 6.7	29.3 ± 7.9	29.9 ± 2.4	<0.001	−0.32
HATBF (mL/100 mL/min)	23.8 ± 9.0	21.30 ± 10.2	19.6 ± 10.1	20.5 ± 8.3	18.8 ± 8.6	24.2 ± 6.2	NS	−0.09
THTBF (mL/100 mL/min)	64.9 ± 13.4	55.6 ± 14.0	53.4 ± 14.2	48.1 ± 10.1	46.5 ± 10.9	54.9 ± 9.4	<0.01	−0.22
P/A ratio Fibro	1.9 ± 0.7	1.9 ± 0.7	2.0 ± 0.6	1.6 ± 0.5	1.6 ± 0.5	1.4 ± 0.4	NS	−0.15

* Spearman's rank correlation coefficient was used to examine correlations of TBF with the progression of fibrosis; NS: not significant; P/A ratio: portal flow/hepatic arterial flow ratio.

Table 4. Liver function and hepatic tissue blood flow in each fibrosis stage in CHC.

Fibrosis Stage	Stage 1 n = 45	Stage 2 n = 29	Stage 3 n = 21	Initial LC n = 30	Advanced LC n = 27	p-Value *	r
Alb (g/dL)	4.3 ± 0.3	4.3 ± 0.3	4.1 ± 0.3	3.8 ± 0.8	3.1 ± 0.3	<0.001	−0.67
ChE (IU/L)	329.0 ± 81.4	268.2 ± 74.7	226.0 ± 54.8	202.9 ± 75.4	113.0 ± 40.7	<0.001	−0.65
TC (mg/dL)	182.8 ± 31.0	167.4 ± 34.7	150.7 ± 28.4	149.3 ± 33.9	120.8 ± 36.0	<0.001	−0.64
PT (%)	96.2 ± 8.7	88.0 ± 8.8	81.5 ± 10.9	86.4 ± 10.9	64.0 ± 9.7	<0.001	−0.69
ICG-R15 (%)	7.4 ± 3.7	13.5 ± 9.6	14.1 ± 5.1	21.7 ± 10.0	34.2 ± 11.2	<0.001	0.39
HA (ng/mL)	54.8 ± 60.3	156.1 ± 203.4	275.8 ± 202.2	425.1 ± 362.7	565.2 ± 370.7	<0.001	0.76
WFA$^+$-M2BP (C.O.I)	1.5 ± 1.5	1.9 ± 1.9	4.5 ± 4.5	4.0 ± 4.2	5.6 ± 5.8	<0.001	0.62
Plt ($\times 10^4$/µL)	18.4 ± 4.8	15.1 ± 5.0	12.1 ± 3.6	9.3 ± 3.6	7.3 ± 2.7	<0.001	−0.74
PVTBF (mL/100 mL/min)	48.8 ± 13.9	40.4 ± 13.5	36.3 ± 7.9	36.3 ± 11.2	26.6 ± 7.5	<0.001	−0.56
HATBF (mL/100 mL/min)	26.1 ± 14.2	21.9 ± 8.6	20.5 ± 11.7	21.6 ± 15.0	21.5 ± 13.1	NS	−0.18
THTBF (mL/100 mL/min)	74.9 ± 21.8	62.4 ± 16.9	56.8 ± 12.7	54.6 ± 15.1	48.3 ± 14.2	<0.001	−0.48
P/A ratio	2.1 ± 1.0	1.9 ± 0.9	1.9 ± 1.0	1.9 ± 0.8	1.6 ± 0.9	NS	−0.17

* Spearman's rank correlation coefficient was used to examine correlations of TBF with the progression of fibrosis; NS: not significant; P/A ratio: portal flow/hepatic arterial flow ratio.

2.4. Liver Function and Hepatic TBF in Each Stage of CHC Patients

Liver function and hepatic TBF in each stage of CHC patients are shown in Table 4. With fibrosis progression, Alb, Ch-E, TC, PT, Plt, PVTBF, and THTBF decreased significantly ($p < 0.001$, $r = -0.67$; $p < 0.001$, $r = -0.65$; $p < 0.001$, $r = -0.64$; $p < 0.001$, $r = -0.69$; $p < 0.001$, $r = -0.74$; $p < 0.001$, $r = -0.56$; $p < 0.001$, $r = -0.48$, respectively). On the other hand, with fibrosis progression, ICG-R_{15}, HA, and WFA^{+}-M2BP increased significantly ($p < 0.001$, $r = 0.39$; $p < 0.001$, $r = 0.76$; $p < 0.001$, $r = 0.62$, respectively).

2.5. Correlation between Hepatic TBF and Liver Function in NAFLD Patients

Correlations between hepatic TBF, as measured by Xe-CT and liver function in NAFLD patients, are shown in Table 5. There were significant correlations between PVTBF and Alb, ChE, TC, PT, ICG-R_{15}, HA, and Plt ($p < 0.001$, $r = 0.53$; $p < 0.001$, $r = 0.46$; $p < 0.001$, $r = 0.29$; $p < 0.001$, $r = 0.40$; $p < 0.001$, $r = -0.25$; $p < 0.05$, $r = -0.17$; $p < 0.01$, $r = 0.25$, respectively). There were also significant correlations between HATBF and ChE and HA ($p < 0.05$, $r = 0.21$; $p < 0.05$, $r = 0.21$, respectively). There were significant correlations between THTBF and ChE, TC, and ICG-R_{15} ($p < 0.001$, $r = 0.39$; $p < 0.001$, $r = 0.34$; $p < 0.05$, $r = 0.21$, respectively). There were significant correlations between the P/A ratio and ChE, TC, and PT ($p < 0.001$, $r = 0.37$; $p < 0.001$, $r = 0.42$; $p < 0.05$, $r = 0.17$, respectively) (Table 5).

Table 5. Correlations of liver function and hepatic tissue blood flow in NAFLD.

TBF	PVTBF		HATBF		THTBF		P/A Ratio	
	p-Value *	*r*	*p*-Value *	*r*	*p*-Value *	*r*	*p*-Value *	*r*
Alb (g/dL)	<0.001	0.53	NS	−0.04	NS	0.02	NS	0.14
ChE (IU/L)	<0.001	0.46	<0.05	0.21	<0.001	0.39	<0.001	0.37
TC (mg/dL)	<0.001	0.29	NS	0.16	<0.001	0.34	<0.001	0.42
PT (%)	<0.001	0.40	NS	−0.06	NS	0.02	<0.05	0.17
ICG-R_{15} (%)	<0.01	−0.25	NS	0.09	<0.05	0.21	NS	−0.01
HA (ng/mL)	<0.05	−0.17	<0.05	0.21	NS	0.03	NS	0.06
Plt ($\times 10^4$/μL)	<0.01	0.25	NS	−0.02	NS	0.07	NS	0.05

* The Pearson product-moment correlation coefficient was used to examine correlations between TBF parameters and liver function tests. TBF: tissue blood flow; NS: not significant; P/A ratio: portal flow/hepatic arterial flow ratio.

2.6. Correlation between Hepatic Blood Flow and Liver Function in CHC Patients

Correlations between hepatic blood flow and liver function in CHC patients are shown in Table 6. There were significant correlations between PVTBF and Alb, ChE, TC, PT, ICG-R_{15}, HA, and Plt ($p < 0.001$, $r = 0.50$; $p < 0.001$, $r = 0.66$; $p < 0.001$, $r = 0.66$; $p < 0.001$, $r = 0.70$; $p < 0.001$, $r = -0.36$; $p < 0.001$, $r = 0.37$; $p < 0.001$, $r = 0.37$, respectively). There was also a significant correlation between HATBF and PT ($p < 0.05$, $r = 0.18$). There were significant correlations between THTBF and Alb, ChE, TC, PT, and Plt ($p < 0.001$, $r = 0.42$; $p < 0.001$, $r = 0.55$; $p < 0.001$, $r = 0.67$; $p < 0.001$, $r = 0.37$; $p < 0.001$, $r = 0.35$, respectively). There were significant correlations between the P/A ratio and Alb and ChE ($p < 0.01$, $r = 0.21$; $p < 0.001$, $r = 0.34$; $p < 0.01$, $r = 0.27$, respectively) (Table 6).

Table 6. Correlations of liver function and hepatic tissue blood flow in CHC.

TBF	PVTBF		HATBF		THTBF		P/A Ratio	
	p-Value *	*r*	*p*-Value *	*r*	*p*-Value *	*r*	*p*-Value *	*r*
Alb (g/dL)	<0.001	0.50	NS	−0.05	<0.001	0.42	<0.01	0.21
ChE (IU/L)	<0.001	0.66	NS	0.12	<0.001	0.55	<0.001	0.34
TC (mg/dL)	<0.001	0.66	NS	0.10	<0.001	0.67	<0.01	0.27
PT (%)	<0.001	0.70	<0.05	0.18	<0.001	0.37	NS	0.09
ICG-R_{15} (%)	<0.001	−0.36	NS	0.07	NS	0.10	NS	0.05
HA (ng/mL)	<0.001	0.37	NS	−0.13	NS	−0.10	NS	0.06
Plt ($\times 10^4$/μL)	<0.001	0.37	NS	0.07	<0.001	0.35	NS	0.07

* The Pearson product-moment correlation coefficient was used to examine correlations between TBF parameters and liver function tests; TBF: tissue blood flow; NS: not significant; P/A ratio: portal flow/hepatic arterial flow ratio.

2.7. Comparison of Each TBF at Initial LC (Child-Pugh A) in NASH-LC and C-LC

PVTBF and THTBF were significantly lower in NASH-LC than in C-LC ($p = 0.014$, $p = 0.048$, respectively). Hepatic arterial TBF (HATBF) did not differ significantly between the groups (Figure 1).

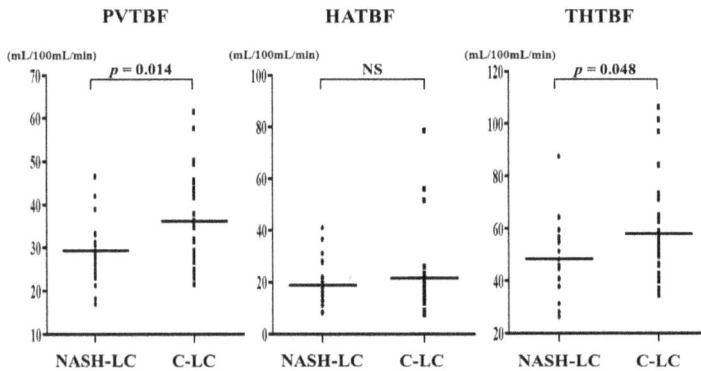

Figure 1. Comparison of each TBF at initial LC (Child-Pugh A) in NASH-LC and C-LC. PVTBF and THTBF are significantly lower in NASH-LC than in C-LC ($p = 0.014$, $p = 0.048$, respectively). HATBF is not significantly different between the LC groups. NS: not significant; PVTBF: portal venous tissue blood flow; HATBF: hepatic arterial tissue blood flow; THTBF: total hepatic tissue blood flow; NASH-LC: liver cirrhosis related to nonalcoholic steatohepatitis; C-LC: liver cirrhosis related to hepatitis C virus.

2.8. Comparison of Each Liver Function Test at Initial LC (Child-Pugh A) in NASH-LC and C-LC

Alb, Ch-E, TC, and Plt were significantly higher in NASH-LC than in C-LC ($p = 0.016$, $p = 0.016$, $p = 0.004$, $p = 0.021$, respectively). PT and ICG-R_{15} were not significantly different between the groups (Figure 2).

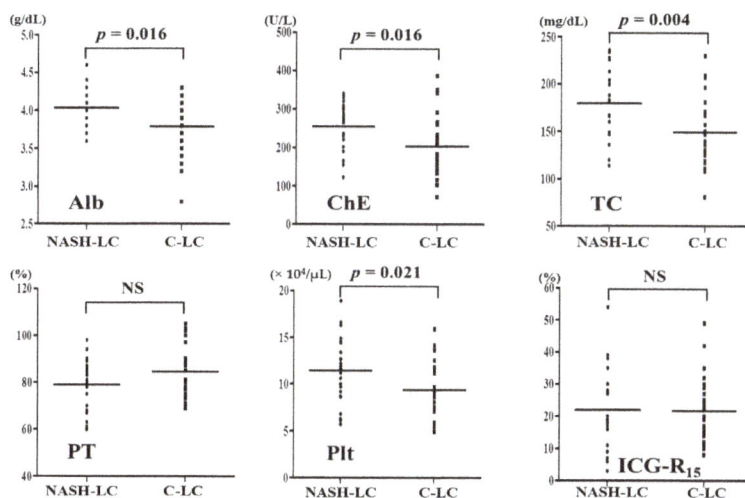

Figure 2. Comparison of each liver function test at initial LC (Child-Pugh A) in NASH-LC and C-LC. Albumin, cholinesterase, total cholesterol, and platelet count are significantly higher in NASH-LC than in C-LC ($p = 0.016$, $p = 0.016$, $p = 0.004$, $p = 0.021$, respectively). NS: not significant; NASH-LC: liver cirrhosis related to nonalcoholic steatohepatitis; C-LC: liver cirrhosis related to hepatitis C virus; Alb: albumin; ChE: cholinesterase; TC: total cholesterol; PT: prothrombin time; Plt: platelet count; ICG-R_{15}: retention rate of indocyanine green 15 min after administration.

2.9. Comparison of Typical Cases at Initial LC (Child-Pugh A) in NASH-LC and C-LC

Figure 3 shows cases of the advanced fibrosis stage in NASH and CHC. An 85-year-old Japanese man (case 1) was pathologically diagnosed with Stage 4 NASH (Brunt's classification [23]). His clinical features were also obviously LC-like (e.g., thrombocytopenia, HCC, and esophagogastric varices). His fibrosis markers were increased, reflecting advanced liver fibrosis. A 75-year-old Japanese man (case 2) was pathologically diagnosed with stage 3 CHC (Desmet's classification [24]). The WFA$^+$-M2BP was significantly lower in NASH-LC than in CHC (Figure 3). In this way, the cutoff values of fibrosis markers, including WFA$^+$-M2BP, might differ by the etiology of liver disease. The present results showed that the cutoff values (WFA$^+$-M2BP, TIMP-1, HA, and FIB-4 index) to detect the advanced fibrosis stage were lower in NAFLD than in CHC (Tables 1 and 2). Furthermore, the diagnostic reliability to detect the advanced fibrosis stage was lower in NAFLD than in CHC (Tables 1 and 2). The reason for this is that the manner of fibrosis progression differs between NASH and CHC. With fibrosis progression, PVTBF gradually decreases in both CHC and NASH. However, PVTBF decreases at an earlier stage in NAFLD than in CHC. This might be attributed to the different manner of fibrosis between NASH and CHC.

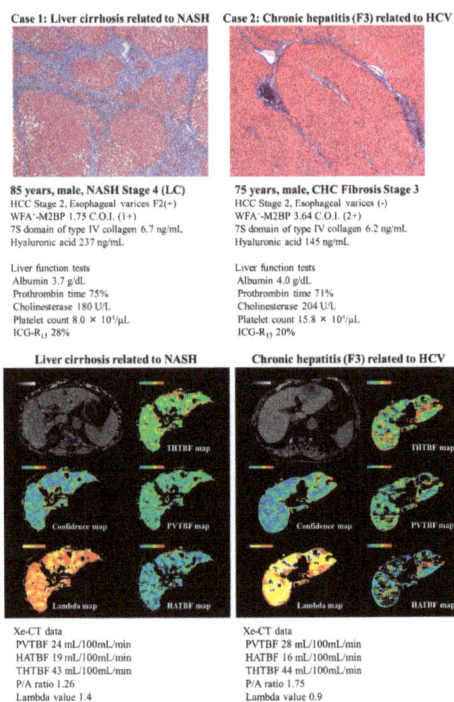

Figure 3. Cases of advanced fibrosis stage in NASH and CHC. Figure 3 shows cases of the advanced fibrosis stage in NASH and CHC. An 85-year-old Japanese man (case 1) was pathologically diagnosed with Stage 4 NASH (Brunt's classification [23]). His clinical features were also obviously LC-like (e.g., thrombocytopenia, hepatocellular carcinoma, and esophagogastric varices). His fibrosis markers were increased to reflect advanced liver fibrosis. A 75-year-old Japanese man (case 2) was pathologically diagnosed with stage 3 CHC (Desmet's classification [24]). In case 2, TBF was evaluated in the whole liver excluding the region of hepatocellular carcinoma. The WFA$^+$-M2BP of the NASH-LC case was significantly lower than that of the CHC case. TBF was evaluated in both cases. PVTBF and the P/A ratio are lower in NASH-LC (case 1) than in CHC (case 2).

3. Discussion

A definite diagnosis of NASH requires liver biopsy, though various non-invasive measures are under development [6]. NASH is characterized by parenchymal injury, including macrovesicular steatosis, ballooning degeneration, Mallory-Denk bodies, and inflammation in hepatic lobes [9]. Fibrosis begins in zone 3 or the centrilobular area of the hepatic lobule. Periportal and bridging fibrosis develop with progression of the disease, and once cirrhosis is established, features of steatohepatitis and perisinusoidal fibrosis may be obscured. It is well known that exercise, itself, is an important factor to treat NASH and, therefore, the role of exercise should be emphasized. Exercise, in fact, improves NASH-related fibrosis markers (collagen 1α1 mRNA, $p < 0.05$ and fibrosis score, $p < 0.01$) and the inflammation score; exercise increases the hepatic stellate cell senescence marker CCN1 [25,26].

On the other hand, fibrosis begins in zone 1 or the periportal area of the hepatic lobule in patients with CHC. CHC is characterized by a portal tract that is infiltrated by dense aggregates of lymphocytes with follicle formation, and mild macrovesicular steatosis can be seen in lobules, particularly in periportal hepatocytes [10,11]. Moreover, it has been reported that daily use of recreational drugs, in particular cannabis, has a deleterious effect on the speed of progression of fibrosis and steatosis in patients suffering from chronic hepatitis C [27]. There are other differences between NAFLD and CHC. Previous reports indicated that at the early stages of CLD the numbers of liver monocytes/macrophages were elevated without the evidence of local proliferation, supporting a role for infiltrating monocyte-derived macrophages in disease progression in patients with both CHC and NAFLD. However, CHC and NAFLD differentially affected the circulating monocyte phenotype, suggesting that unique injury-induced signals may contribute to the intrahepatic monocyte recruitment and the systemic activation state. Moreover, it was also shown that monocyte function was similarly impaired in patients with both CHC and NAFLD, particularly in advanced disease [28]. Thus, the manner of fibrosis progression resulting from inflammation could be different between NASH and CHC.

The results of present study showed the relationship between liver function and PVTBF (Tables 5 and 6). PVTBF was well correlated with hepatic synthesis capacity, which included Alb, ChE, TC, and PT. The reason why liver function tests in NASH was better than that in CHC is suggested the excess energy intake and lipid hypermetabolism [29]. ICG-R_{15} is the indicator which reflects liver function [30] and the presence of portal hypertension. Furthermore ICG-R_{15} is well correlated to the hepatic tissue blood flow [31]. Lisotti et al. reported that the ICG-R_{15} test is an effective tool for assessment of portal hypertension in patients with compensated cirrhosis [30]. We confirmed that the hemodynamic changes occurred earlier in NAFLD relative to CHC. For example, 15% of ICG-R_{15} correspond to the stage 3 in NASH and LC in CHC (Tables 3 and 4). Yamazaki reported that the average of ICG-R_{15} was 15.4% in which the presence of esophageal varices cases [32], and their data, supported our results.

Alteration in hepatic microcirculation in human donor livers with steatosis was first reported during organ retrieval before mobilization by Seifalian et al. [33] using laser Doppler flowmetry. A significant decrease in hepatic microcirculation in liver donors with steatosis was observed in comparison with that in normal liver donors [34]. Experimental studies in animal models with fatty liver showed that steatosis led to reduce hepatic blood flow and microcirculation, and that there was an inverse correlation between the degree of steatosis and both total hepatic blood flow and flow in the microcirculation [30]. The severity of fatty infiltration has a greater effect on the microcirculation than on total hepatic blood flow [35,36]. In spite of steatosis alone, hepatic blood flow reduced. Moreover, hepatic blood flow reduced with fibrosis development, in addition to steatosis [37]. Fat-laden hepatocytes are swollen, and in steatohepatitis, further swelling occurs due to the ballooning of hepatocytes, causing sinusoidal distortion, as visualized by in vivo microscopy, reducing intrasinusoidal volume and microcirculation [38].

In addition to steatosis, a mechanism of decreasing portal blood flow other than steatosis has been reported in NAFLD. In livers with perfusion from cafeteria diet-fed rats, there was increased portal pressure and decreased endothelium-dependent vasodilation. This was associated with decreased Akt-dependent endothelial nitric-oxide synthase (eNOS) phosphorylation and NOS activity. They demonstrated in a rat model of the metabolic syndrome that hepatic endothelial dysfunction occurs before the development of fibrosis and inflammation [39]. Ying-Ying Yang et al. reported that hyperleptinemia increases hepatic endocannabinoid production, promotes hepatic fibrogenesis, enhances the hepatic vasoconstrictive response to endothelin-1, and aggravates hepatic microcirculatory dysfunction. These events subsequently increase intrahepatic resistance and portal hypertension in NASH cirrhotic rats [40].

The present data show that the liver function was better in initial NASH-LC than in C-LC. However, because PVTBF was lower in NASH than in C-LC, portal hypertension might occur at an earlier stage in NASH than in CHC. In fact, portal hypertension occurs without LC in NASH [41–43]. Mendes et al. investigated the prevalence of portal hypertension in NAFLD patients, and found that clinical signs of portal hypertension, including esophageal varices, splenomegaly, portosystemic encephalopathy, and ascites, were present in 25% of patients at the time of diagnosis. Furthermore, portal hypertension can occur in a small proportion of patients with mild or no fibrosis and is associated with the extent of steatosis [44]. Brunt et al. reported that hepatic fibrosis in

NAFLD patients was found in the pericellular space around the central vein and in the presinusoidal region in zone 3 in the early stage [23]. The pericellular fibrosis in the early stage of NAFLD patients may lead to an elevated portal vascular resistance and result in a change of hepatic blood flow [45]. Therefore, we considered that the hemodynamic changes occurred earlier in NAFLD relative to CHC.

In this study, there are two limitations, such as sampling error during liver biopsy and by permeation of Xe gas. Xe-CT cannot monitor the exact result in the patients with chronic lung disease (e.g., chronic obstructive pulmonary disease, lung cancer) and heart failure, because Xe gas is taken up by the lung via the respiratory tract. On the contrary, we believe that there are also many strong points of Xe-CT which objectively and repeatedly measure hepatic blood flow with reproducibility. Moreover, we have safely performed a Xe-CT for patients with acute or chronic renal failure because there are no complications associated with the contrast agent, such as allergic reactions and radiocontrast nephropathy.

Thus, in the present study, the difference between NAFLD and CHC was investigated based on TBF, fibrosis markers, and liver function. In conclusion, compared to C-LC, PVTBF decreased significantly in the Child-Pugh A stage of NASH-LC, indicating that portal hemodynamic changes could occur earlier in NASH-LC without impaired liver function. Therefore, patients with NASH should be monitored carefully for portal hypertensive complications in the early fibrosis stage.

4. Materials and Methods

4.1. Patients

Between October 2001 and March 2016, 730 patients underwent Xe-CT at the St. Marianna University School of Medicine Hospital. Of the 730 patients, 291 with NAFLD and CHC were enrolled in this study. Liver biopsy was performed for 118 of the 139 NAFLD patients and 106 of the 152 CHC patients. During hospitalization for three days, Xe-CT was performed before or after each liver biopsy. The NAFLD patients included 80 men and 59 women, with a mean age of 53.2 ± 11.2 years and a mean body mass index (BMI) of 28.5 ± 4.9 kg/m^2. The CHC patients included 75 men and 77 women, with a mean age of 59.9 ± 11.2 years and a mean BMI of 23.2 ± 3.7 kg/m^2 (Table 7).

Table 7. Characteristics of patients.

Group	NAFLD	CHC
Number of cases	139	152
Sex (Male/Female)	80/59	75/77
Age (years)	53.2 ± 11.2	59.9 ± 11.2 *
BMI (kg/m^2)	28.5 ± 4.9	23.2 ± 3.7 *
Staging for fibrosis	NAFL/NASH Stage 1/2/3/4 + Child A/Child B,C	Stage 0,1/2/3/4 + Child A/Child B,C
	(Brunt's classification) 15/47/30/15/25/7	(Desmet's classification) 45/29/21/30/27
Number of cases **	58	72
Mild fibrosis group (Stage 0–2)	46	53
Advanced fibrosis group (Stage 3–4)	12	19

* $p < 0.05$ (unpaired t-test); ** In this study, 58 samples of NAFLD and 72 samples of CH-C were enrolled. The blood sample was taken on the day of the liver biopsy.

The diagnosis of NAFLD was based on: (1) substantial alcohol consumption (>20 g/day for women or >30 g/day for men); (2) pathological findings showing characteristics of NAFLD (large-droplet fat deposits, hepatocyte ballooning, inflammatory cell infiltration, and fibrosis around the central vein); and (3) the exclusion of other liver diseases, such as viral hepatitis, autoimmune liver disease, and drug-induced liver injury. The diagnosis of CHC was based on anti-HCV antibodies and HCV-RNA. Patients were excluded for the presence of other causes of liver disease, acute illness, acute or chronic inflammatory or infective diseases, an end-stage malignant disease, or other confounding conditions. Liver biopsy was performed through the right intercostal space under ultrasonography-guided liver biopsy using a 16-gauge needle biopsy kit (Quick-Core® biopsy needle set; Cook Medical, Bloomington, IN, USA). The aims of liver biopsy were to assess fibrosis and steatosis and to exclude other liver disease. Histological diagnosis was confirmed by two experienced pathologists who were blinded to the clinical data. There were 15 patients with nonalcoholic fatty liver (NAFL) who had no fibrosis and inflammatory cell infiltration. The patients with NASH were evaluated on the basis of Brunt's classification [21,46,47], while those with CHC were evaluated on the basis of Desmet's classification [22]. Staging fibrosis in NASH based on Brunt's classification: Stage 1: zone 3 perivenular perisinusoidal/pericellular fibrosis, focal or extensive; Stage 2: as above with focal or extensive periportal fibrosis; Stage 3: bridging fibrosis, focal or extensive; and Stage 4: cirrhosis. Staging fibrosis in CHC based on Desmet's classification: Stage 0: lack of fibrosis; Stage 1: fibrosis confined to portal tract; Stage 2: bridging fibrosis; Stage 3: bridging fibrosis with structural distortion; and Stage 4: cirrhosis. Clinical liver cirrhosis was defined by the presence of a portosystemic shunt or ascites.

4.2. Xe-CT Theory and Imaging Protocol

As described in previous publications, 25% stable Xe gas was used in conjunction with an AZ-726 Xe gas inhalation system (Anzai Medical, Tokyo, Japan) [48,49]. The wash-in and wash-out periods were both 4 min. The entire liver was CT-scanned at 1-min intervals at four levels, including the porta hepatis (nine scans in total, including the baseline scan). Using an AZ-7000W image processing system (Anzai Medical), PVTBF and HATBF were calculated, and PVTBF and HATBF maps were created. THTBF was calculated as the sum of PVTBF and HATBF, and THTBF maps were also created. The time course change rate for the arterial Xe concentration, which was needed to calculate PVTBF and HATBF, was derived using the time course of the Xe concentration in splenic tissue. An Aquilion CT scanner (Toshiba Medical Systems, Tokyo, Japan) was used, with exposure factors of 120 kV, 150 mA, and 13.8 mGy. All examinations were performed with the patients in the fasting state. Informed consent was obtained from each patient. All study protocols were reviewed and approved by the ethics committee at our institution (approval No. 480, 18 September 2001), and conformed to the ethics guidelines of the 1975 Declaration of Helsinki (Allen, 1991).

4.3. Liver Function Tests and Fibrosis Markers

Liver function tests were measured on admission. Liver function tests included the following parameters: albumin (Alb) (g/dL), cholinesterase (ChE) (IU/L), total cholesterol (TC) (mg/dL), prothrombin time (PT) (%), Plt ($\times 10^4$ μL^{-1}), hyaluronic acid (HA) (ng/mL), Wisteria floribunda agglutinin positive Mac-2-binding protein (WFA⁺-M2BP) (C.O.I.), and the retention rate of indocyanine green 15 min after administration (ICG-R$_{15}$) (%). ICG (Diagnogreen®, Daiichisankyo Pharmaceutical Co., Tokyo, Japan; 0.5 mg/kg body weight) was administered via a peripheral vein, and venous blood was sampled before and 15 min after injection. Specimens were analyzed for ICG concentrations on a spectrophotometer (HITACHI, Tokyo, Japan) at 805 nm.

4.4. Measurements of TIMP-1, HA, PIIIP, and WFA⁺-M2BP

For all patients in the cohort, the blood sample was taken on the day of the liver biopsy at the St. Marianna University School of Medicine Hospital. All samples were processed to separate serum and stored at −80 °C. At the time of blood withdrawal, all patients underwent liver biopsy. In this study, 58 samples of NAFLD and 72 samples of CHC were enrolled (Table 7). TIMP-1, HA, and PIIIP were measured using a fully automatic immunoanalyzer (Sysmex Co., Hyogo, Japan). WFA⁺-M2BP quantification was measured based on a lectin-Ab sandwich immunoassay using a fully automatic immunoanalyzer, HISCL-2000i (Sysmex Co., Hyogo, Japan) [50].

4.5. Statistical Analysis

Each parameter is expressed as the mean ± standard deviation (SD). Spearman's rank correlation coefficient was used to examine correlations of TBF with progression of fibrosis. The Pearson product-moment correlation coefficient was used to examine correlations between TBF parameters and liver function tests. To assess the utility of each fibrosis marker to distinguish the advanced fibrosis stage, the sensitivity and specificity were calculated for each value, and then ROC curves were constructed by plotting the sensitivity against the reverse specificity (1-the specificity) for each value. We used Student's *t*-test, which was two-tailed and performed by the statistical software GraphPad Prism (GraphPad Software, San Diego, CA, USA). *p*-Values of <0.05 were considered significant.

5. Conclusions

It is important to recognize the difference between NAFLD and CHC. We concluded that changes in hepatic blood flow occurred during the earliest stage of hepatic fibrosis in patients with NAFLD and, therefore, patients with NAFLD need to be followed carefully.

Acknowledgments: The authors wish to thank the technical assistants at the Imaging Center of St. Marianna University School of Medicine Hospital for their assistance. This study was supported in part by JSPS KAKENHI Grant Number 16K19371.

Author Contributions: Ryuta Shigefuku, Hideaki Takahashi and Tunamasa Watanabe conceived and designed the experiments; Ryuta Shigefuku and Kotaro Matsunaga performed the experiments; Ryuta Shigefuku, Hideaki Takahashi, Hiroki Ikeda and Shigeru Sase analyzed the data; Ryuta Shigefuku, Hiroyasu Nakano, Masaki Kato, Ryo Morita, Yousuke Michikawa, Tomohiro Tamura, Tetsuya Hiraishi, Nobuhiro Hattori, Yohei Noguchi, Kazunari Nakahara, Toshiya Ishii, Nobuyuki Matsumoto, Chiaki Okuse, Fumio Itoh and Michihiro Suzuki contributed reagents/materials/analysis tools; Ryuta Shigefuku wrote the paper.

Conflicts of Interest: The authors declare no conflict of interest.

Abbreviations

Alb	albumin
APRI	aspartate aminotransferase-platelet index
CHC	chronic hepatitis related to hepatitis C virus
ChE	cholinesterase
CLD	chronic liver disease
CT	computed tomography
HA	hyaluronic acid
HATBF	hepatic arterial tissue blood flow
HBF	hepatic blood flow
HCV	hepatitis C virus
ICG-R_{15}	retention rate of indocyanine green 15 min after administration
LC	liver cirrhosis
MRI	magnetic resonance imaging
NAFLD	nonalcoholic fatty liver disease
NASH	nonalcoholic steatohepatitis
Plt	platelet count
PT	prothrombin time
P/A	portal flow / hepatic arterial flow ratio
PVTBF	portal venous tissue blood flow
PIIIP	type III procollagen N peptide
ROI	region of interest
TC	total cholesterol
TBF	tissue blood flow
THTBF	total hepatic tissue blood flow
TIMP-1	tissue inhibitor of metalloproteinase-1
US	ultrasonography
WFA$^+$-M2BP	Wisteria floribunda agglutinin positive Mac-2-binding protein
Xe-CT	Xenon computed tomography

References

1. Ludwig, J.; Viggiano, T.R.; McGill, D.B.; Oh, B.J. Nonalcoholic steatohepatitis: Mayo clinic experiences with a hitherto unnamed disease. *Mayo Clin. Proc.* **1980**, *55*, 434–438. [PubMed]
2. Matteoni, C.A.; Younossi, Z.M.; Gramlich, T.; Boparai, N.; Liu, Y.C.; Mc Cullough, A.J. Nonalcoholic fatty liver disease: A spectrum of clinical and pathological severity. *Gastroenterology* **1999**, *116*, 1413–1419. [CrossRef]
3. Farrell, G.C.; Larter, C.Z. Nonalcoholic fatty liver disease: From steatosis to cirrhosis. *Hepatology* **2006**, *43*, S99–S112. [CrossRef] [PubMed]
4. Sayiner, M.; Koenig, A.; Henry, L.; Younossi, Z.M. Epidemiology of nonalcoholic fatty liver disease and nonalcoholic steatohepatitis in the United States and the rest of the world. *Clin. Liver Dis.* **2016**, *20*, 205–214. [CrossRef] [PubMed]
5. Sherif, Z.A.; Saeed, A.; Ghavimi, A.; Nouraie, S.-M.; Laiyemo, A.O.; Brim, H.; Ashktorab, H. Global epidemiology of nonalcoholic fatty liver disease and perspectives on US minority populations. *Dig. Dis. Sci.* **2016**, *61*, 1214–1225. [CrossRef] [PubMed]
6. Watanabe, S.; Hashimoto, E.; Ikejima, K.; Uto, H.; Ono, M.; Sumida, Y.; Seike, M.; Takei, Y.; Takehara, T.; Tokushige, K.; et al. Evidence-based clinical practice guidelines for nonalcoholic fatty liver disease/nonalcoholic steatohepatitis. *J. Gastroenterol.* **2015**, *50*, 364–377. [CrossRef] [PubMed]
7. Eguchi, Y.; Hyogo, H.; Ono, M.; Mizuta, T.; Ono, N.; Fujimoto, K.; Chayama, K.; Saibara, T. JSG-NAFLD. Prevalence and associated metabolic factors of nonalcoholic fatty liver disease in the general population from 2009 to 2010 in Japan: A multicenter large retrospective study. *J. Gastroenterol.* **2012**, *47*, 586–595. [CrossRef] [PubMed]
8. Farrell, G.C.; Wong, V.W.; Chitturi, S. NAFLD in Asia—As common and important as in the West. *Nat. Rev. Gastroenterol. Hepatol.* **2013**, *10*, 307–318. [CrossRef] [PubMed]
9. Brunt, E.M. Nonalcoholic steatohepatitis. *Semin. Liver Dis.* **2004**, *24*, 3–20. [PubMed]
10. Freni, M.A.; Artuso, D.; Gerken, G.; Spanti, C.; Marafioti, T.; Alessi, N.; Spadaro, A.; Ajello, A.; Ferraù, O. Focal lymphocytic aggregates in chronic hepatitis C: Occurrence, immunohistochemical characterization, and relation to markers of autoimmunity. *Hepatology* **1995**, *22*, 389–394. [CrossRef] [PubMed]
11. Wong, V.S.; Wight, D.G.; Palmer, C.R.; Alexander, G.J. Fibrosis and other histological features in chronic hepatitis C virus infection: A statistical model. *J. Clin. Pathol.* **1996**, *49*, 465–469. [CrossRef] [PubMed]
12. Abe, M.; Miyake, T.; Kuno, A.; Imai, Y.; Sawai, Y.; Hino, K.; Hara, Y.; Hige, S.; Sakamoto, M.; Yamada, G.; et al. Association between *Wisteria floribunda* agglutinin-positive Mac-2 binding protein and the fibrosis stage of non-alcoholic fatty liver disease. *J. Gastroenterol.* **2015**, *50*, 776–784. [CrossRef] [PubMed]
13. Yamasaki, K.; Tateyama, M.; Abiru, S.; Komori, A.; Nagaoka, S.; Saeki, A.; Hashimoto, S.; Sasaki, R.; Bekki, S.; Kugiyama, Y.; et al. Elevated serum levels of *Wisteria floribunda* agglutinin-positive human Mac-2 binding protein predict the development of hepatocellular carcinoma in hepatitis C patients. *Hepatology* **2014**, *60*, 1563–1570. [CrossRef] [PubMed]
14. Tamaki, N.; Kurosaki, M.; Kuno, A.; Korenaga, M.; Togayachi, A.; Gotoh, M.; Nakakuki, N.; Takada, H.; Matsuda, S.; Hattori, N.; et al. *Wisteria floribunda* agglutinin positive human Mac-2-binding protein as a predictor of hepatocellular carcinoma development in chronic hepatitis C patients. *Hepatol. Res.* **2015**, *45*, E82–E88. [CrossRef] [PubMed]
15. Johnson, D.W.; Stringer, W.A.; Marks, M.P.; Yonas, H.; Good, W.F.; Gur, D. Stable xenon CT cerebral blood flow imaging: Rationale for and role in clinical decision making. *Am. J. Neuroradiol.* **1991**, *12*, 201–213. [PubMed]
16. Gur, D.; Good, W.F.; Wolfson, S.K., Jr.; Yonas, H.; Shabason, L. In vivo mapping of local cerebral blood flow by xenonenhanced computed tomography. *Science* **1982**, *215*, 1267–1268. [CrossRef] [PubMed]
17. Ikeda, H.; Suzuki, M.; Kobayashi, M.; Takahashi, H.; Matsumoto, N.; Maeyama, S.; Iino, S.; Sase, S.; Itoh, F. Xenon computed tomography shows hemodynamic change during the progression of chronic hepatitis C. *Hepatol. Res.* **2007**, *37*, 104–112. [CrossRef] [PubMed]
18. Shigefuku, R.; Takahashi, H.; Kato, M.; Yoshida, Y.; Suetani, K.; Noguchi, Y.; Hatsugai, M.; Nakahara, K.; Ikeda, H.; Kobayashi, M.; et al. Evaluation of hepatic tissue blood flow using xenon computed tomography with fibrosis progression in nonalcoholic fatty liver disease: Comparison with chronic hepatitis C. *Int. J. Mol. Sci.* **2014**, *15*, 1026–1039. [CrossRef] [PubMed]

19. Shigefuku, R.; Takahashi, H.; Kobayashi, M.; Ikeda, H.; Matsunaga, K.; Okuse, C.; Matsumoto, N.; Maeyama, S.; Sase, S.; Suzuki, M.; et al. Pathophysiological analysis of nonalcoholic fatty liver disease by evaluation of fatty liver changes and blood flow using xenon computed tomography: Can early-stage nonalcoholic steatohepatitis be distinguished from simple steatosis? *J. Gastroenterol.* **2012**, *47*, 1238–1247. [CrossRef] [PubMed]

20. Kobayashi, M.; Suzuki, M.; Ikeda, H.; Takahashi, H.; Matsumoto, N.; Maeyama, S.; Sase, S.; Iino, S.; Itoh, F. Assessment of hepatic steatosis and hepatic tissue blood flow by xenon computed tomography in nonalcoholic steatohepatitis. *Hepatol. Res.* **2009**, *39*, 31–39. [CrossRef] [PubMed]

21. Takahashi, H.; Suzuki, M.; Ikeda, H.; Kobayashi, M.; Sase, S.; Yotsuyanagi, H.; Maeyama, S.; Iino, S.; Itoh, F. Evaluation of quantitative portal venous, hepatic arterial, and total hepatic tissue blood flow using xenon CT in alcoholic liver cirrhosis—Comparison with liver cirrhosis related to hepatitis C virus and nonalcoholic steatohepatitis. *Alcohol. Clin. Exp. Res.* **2010**, *34*, S7–S13. [CrossRef] [PubMed]

22. Takahashi, H.; Shigefuku, R.; Yoshida, Y.; Ikeda, H.; Matsunaga, K.; Matsumoto, N.; Okuse, C.; Sase, S.; Itoh, F.; Suzuki, M. Correlation between hepatic blood flow and liver function in alcoholic liver cirrhosis. *World J. Gastroenterol.* **2014**, *20*, 17065–17074. [CrossRef] [PubMed]

23. Brunt, E.M.; Janney, C.G.; di Bisceglie, A.M.; Neuschwander-Tetri, B.A.; Bacon, B.R. Non-alcoholic steatohepatitis: A proposal for grading and staging the histological lesions. *Am. J. Gastroenterol.* **1999**, *94*, 2467–2474. [CrossRef] [PubMed]

24. Desmet, V.J.; Gerber, M.; Hoofnagle, J.H.; Manns, M.; Scheuer, P.J. Classification of chronic hepatitis: Diagnosis, grading and staging. *Hepatology* **1994**, *19*, 1513–1520. [CrossRef] [PubMed]

25. Linden, M.A.; Sheldon, R.D.; Meers, G.M.; Ortinau, L.C.; Morris, E.M.; Booth, F.W.; Kanaley, J.A.; Vieira-Potter, V.J.; Sowers, J.R.; Ibdah, J.A.; et al. Aerobic exercise training in the treatment of NAFLD related fibrosis. *J. Physiol.* **2016**. [CrossRef] [PubMed]

26. Finelli, C.; Tarantino, G. Have guidelines addressing physical activity been established in nonalcoholic fatty liver disease? *World J. Gastroenterol.* **2012**, *18*, 6790–6800. [CrossRef] [PubMed]

27. Tarantino, G.; Citro, V.; Finelli, C. Recreational drugs: A new health hazard for patients with concomitant chronic liver diseases. *J. Gastrointest. Liver Dis.* **2014**, *23*, 79–84.

28. Gadd, V.L.; Patel, P.J.; Jose, S.; Horsfall, L.; Powell, E.E.; Irvine, K.M. Altered peripheral blood monocyte phenotype and function in chronic liver disease: Implications for hepatic recruitment and systemic inflammation. *PLoS ONE* **2016**, *11*, e0157771. [CrossRef] [PubMed]

29. Neuschwander-Tetri, B.A. Hepatic lipotoxicity and the pathogenesis of nonalcoholic steatohepatitis: The central role of nontriglyceride fatty acid metabolites. *Hepatology* **2010**, *52*, 774–788. [CrossRef] [PubMed]

30. Makuuchi, M.; Kosuge, T.; Takayama, T.; Yamazaki, S.; Kakazu, T.; Miyagawa, S.; Kawasaki, S. Surgery for small liver cancers. *Semin. Surg. Oncol.* **1993**, *9*, 298–304. [CrossRef] [PubMed]

31. Lisotti, A.; Azzaroli, F.; Buonfiglioli, F.; Montagnani, M.; Cecinato, P.; Turco, L.; Calvanese, C.; Simoni, P.; Guardigli, M.; Arena, R.; et al. Indocyanine Green retention test as a noninvasive marker of portal hypertension and esophageal varices in compensated liver cirrhosis. *Hepatology* **2014**, *59*, 643–650. [CrossRef] [PubMed]

32. Yamazaki, S.; Takayama, N.; Nakamura, M.; Higaki, T.; Matsuoka, S.; Mizuno, S.; Moriyama, M. Prophylactic impact of endoscopic treatment for esophageal varices in liver resection: A prospective study. *J. Gastroenterol.* **2014**, *49*, 917–922. [CrossRef] [PubMed]

33. Seifalian, A.M.; Mallet, S.V.; Rolles, K.; Davidson, B.R. Hepatic microcirculation during human orthotopic liver transplantation. *Br. J. Surg.* **1997**, *84*, 1391–1395. [CrossRef] [PubMed]

34. Seifalian, A.M.; Chidambaram, V.; Rolles, K.; Davidson, B.R. In vivo demonstration of impaired microcirculation in steatotic human liver grafts. *Liver Transplant. Surg.* **1998**, *4*, 71–77. [CrossRef]

35. Seifalian, A.M.; Piasecki, C.; Agarwal, A.; Davidson, B.R. The effect of graded steatosis on flow in the hepatic parenchymal microcirculation. *Transplantation* **1999**, *68*, 780–784. [CrossRef] [PubMed]

36. Samia, I.; Wenxuan, Y.; Winslet, M.C.; Alexander, M.; Seifalian, A.M. Impairment of hepatic microcirculation in fatty liver. *Microcirculation* **2003**, *10*, 447–456.

37. Hayashi, N.; Kasahara, A.; Kurosawa, K.; Sasaki, Y.; Fusamoto, H.; Sato, N.; Kamada, T. Oxygen supply to the liver in patients with alcoholic liver disease assessed by organ-reflectance spectrophotometry. *Gastroenterology* **1985**, *88*, 881–886. [CrossRef]

38. Farrell, G.C.; Teoh, N.C.; McCuskey, R.S. Hepatic microcirculation in fatty liver disease. *Anat. Rec. (Hoboken)* **2008**, *291*, 684–692. [CrossRef] [PubMed]
39. Pasarín, M.; La Mura, V.; Gracia-Sancho, J.; García-Calderó, H.; Rodríguez-Vilarrupla, A.; García-Pagán, J.C.; Bosch, J.; Abraldes, J.G. Sinusoidal endothelial dysfunction precedes inflammation and fibrosis in a model of NAFLD. *PLoS ONE* **2012**, *7*, e32785. [CrossRef] [PubMed]
40. Yang, Y.-Y.; Tsai, T.-H.; Huang, Y.-T.; Lee, T.-Y.; Chan, C.-C.; Lee, K.-C.; Lin, H.-C. Hepatic endothelin-1 and endocannabinoids-dependent effects of hyperleptinemia in nonalcoholic steatohepatitis-cirrhotic Rats. *Hepatology* **2012**, *55*, 1540–1550. [CrossRef] [PubMed]
41. Francque, S.; Verrijken, A.; Mertens, I.; Hubens, G.; van Marck, E.; Pelckmans, P.; van Gaal, L.; Michielsen, P. Noncirrhotic human nonalcoholic fatty liver disease induces portal hypertension in relation to the histological degree of steatosis. *Eur. J. Gastroenterol. Hepatol.* **2010**, *22*, 1449–1457. [CrossRef] [PubMed]
42. Hashimoto, E.; Yatsuji, S.; Kaneda, H.; Yoshioka, Y.; Taniai, M.; Tokushige, K.; Shiratori, K. The characteristics and natural history of Japanese patients with nonalcoholic fatty liver disease. *Hepatol. Res.* **2005**, *33*, 72–76. [CrossRef] [PubMed]
43. Nakamura, S.; Konishi, H.; Kishino, M.; Yatsuji, S.; Tokushige, K.; Hashimoto, E.; Shiratori, K. Prevalence of esophagogastric varices in patients with nonalcoholic steatohepatitis. *Hepatol. Res.* **2008**, *38*, 572–579. [CrossRef] [PubMed]
44. Mendes, F.D.; Suzuki, A.; Sanderson, S.O.; Lindor, K.D.; Angulo, P. Prevalence and indicators of portal hypertension in patients with nonalcoholic fatty liver disease. *Clin. Gastroenterol. Hepatol.* **2012**, *10*, 1028–1033. [CrossRef] [PubMed]
45. Hirooka, M.; Koizumi, Y.; Miyake, T.; Ochi, H.; Tokumoto, Y.; Tada, F.; Matsuura, B.; Abe, M.; Hiasa, Y. Nonalcoholic fatty liver disease: Portal hypertension due to outflow block in patients without cirrhosis. *Radiology* **2015**, *274*, 597–604. [CrossRef] [PubMed]
46. Yeh, M.M.; Brunt, E.M. Pathological features of fatty liver disease. *Gastroenterology* **2014**, *147*, 754–764. [CrossRef] [PubMed]
47. Brunt, E.M. Nonalcoholic fatty liver disease: Pros and cons of histologic systems of evaluation. *Int. J. Mol. Sci.* **2016**, *17*, 97. [CrossRef] [PubMed]
48. Sase, S.; Monden, M.; Oka, H.; Dono, K.; Fukuta, T.; Shibata, I. Hepatic blood flow measurements with arterial and portal blood flow mapping in the human liver by means of xenon CT. *J. Comput. Assist. Tomogr.* **2002**, *26*, 243–249. [CrossRef] [PubMed]
49. Sase, S.; Takahashi, H.; Ikeda, H.; Kobayashi, M.; Matsumoto, N.; Suzuki, M. Determination of time-course change rate for arterial xenon using the time course of tissue xenon concentration in xenonenhanced computed tomography. *Med. Phys.* **2008**, *35*, 2331–2338. [CrossRef] [PubMed]
50. Kuno, A.; Ikehara, Y.; Tanaka, Y.; Ito, K.; Matsuda, A.; Sekiya, S.; Hige, S.; Sakamoto, M.; Kage, M.; Mizokami, M.; et al. A serum "sweet-doughnut" 272 protein facilitates fibrosis evaluation and therapy assessment in patients 273 with viral hepatitis. *Sci. Rep.* **2013**, *3*, 1065. [CrossRef] [PubMed]

International Journal of
Molecular Sciences

MDPI

Article

Nutritional Strategies for the Individualized Treatment of Non-Alcoholic Fatty Liver Disease (NAFLD) Based on the Nutrient-Induced Insulin Output Ratio (NIOR)

Ewa Stachowska [1,*], Karina Ryterska [1], Dominika Maciejewska [1], Marcin Banaszczak [1], Piotr Milkiewicz [2,3], Małgorzata Milkiewicz [4], Izabela Gutowska [1], Piotr Ossowski [1], Małgorzata Kaczorowska [1], Dominika Jamioł-Milc [1], Anna Sabinicz [1], Małgorzata Napierała [5], Lidia Wądołowska [6] and Joanna Raszeja-Wyszomirska [3]

[1] Department of Biochemistry and Human Nutrition, Pomeranian Medical University, Szczecin 71-460, Poland; ryterska.karina@gmail.com (K.R.); domi.maciejka@wp.pl (D.M.); banaszczak.marcin@gmail.com (M.B.); izagut@poczta.onet.pl (I.G.); zbizcz@pum.edu.pl (P.O.); szpital@szpital-zdroje.szczecin.pl (M.K.); dominikajamiol@interia.pl (D.J.-M.); kldiab@pum.edu.pl (A.S.)

[2] Department of Clinical and Molecular Biochemistry, Pomeranian Medical University, Szczecin 70-111, Poland; p.milkiewicz@wp.pl

[3] Liver and Internal Medicine Unit, Department of General, Transplant and Liver Surgery of the Medical University of Warsaw, Warsaw 02-097, Poland; jorasz@gmail.com

[4] Department of Medical Biology, Pomeranian Medical University, Szczecin 70-111, Poland; milkiewm@pum.edu.pl

[5] Department of Diabetology and Internal Diseases Pomeranian Medical University, Szczecin 72-010, Poland; malnap@sci.pum.edu.pl

[6] Department of Human Nutrition, University of Warmia and Mazury, Olsztyn 10-718, Poland; lidia.wadolowska@wum.edu.pl

* Correspondence: ewa.stachowska@pum.edu.pl; Tel.: +48-91-441-48-06

Academic Editors: Amedeo Lonardo and Giovanni Targher
Received: 25 June 2016; Accepted: 11 July 2016; Published: 22 July 2016

Abstract: Nutrients play a fundamental role as regulators of the activity of enzymes involved in liver metabolism. In the general population, the action of nutrients may be affected by gene polymorphisms. Therefore, individualization of a diet for individuals with fatty liver seems to be a fundamental step in nutritional strategies. In this study, we tested the nutrient-induced insulin output ratio (NIOR), which is used to identify the correlation between the variants of genes and insulin resistance. We enrolled 171 patients, Caucasian men ($n = 104$) and women ($n = 67$), diagnosed with non-alcoholic fatty liver disease (NAFLD). From the pool of genes sensitive to nutrient content, we selected genes characterized by a strong response to the NIOR. The polymorphisms included Adrenergic receptor (*b3AR*), Tumor necrosis factor (*TNFα*), Apolipoprotein C (*Apo C III*). Uncoupling Protein type I (*UCP-1*), Peroxisome proliferator activated receptor γ2 (*PPAR-2*) and Apolipoprotein E (*APOEs*). We performed three dietary interventions: a diet consistent with the results of genotyping (NIOR (+)); typical dietary recommendations for NAFLD (Cust (+)), and a diet opposite to the genotyping results (NIOR (−) and Cust (−)). We administered the diet for six months. The most beneficial changes were observed among fat-sensitive patients who were treated with the NIOR (+) diet. These changes included improvements in body mass and insulin sensitivity and normalization of blood lipids. In people sensitive to fat, the NIOR seems to be a useful tool for determining specific strategies for the treatment of NAFLD.

Keywords: NAFLD; NAFLD diet; insulin sensitivity; NIOR; reduction of body mass; fat reduction; liver fat

---

1. Introduction

Non-alcoholic fatty liver disease (NAFLD) is one of the most frequently diagnosed liver diseases in the industrialized world—approximately 20%–30% of nations' populations are affected by it [1, 2]. With the increase in obesity, NAFLD has become a major risk factor for cirrhosis (and other diseases, e.g., cardiovascular diseases) [3]. Multiple trials have demonstrated that weight loss reduces histological steatosis (intrahepatic fat content) and the amount of serum enzymes [4].

One of the key causes of NAFLD is an improper diet based on caloric oversupply, the excessive intake of fats, and, at the same time, the low intake of grains, fruits, vegetables, proteins and ω-3 fatty acids [2]. This pattern of nutrition leads to the development of hyperinsulinemia, insulin resistance and obesity [2,5–7]. Therefore, on the one hand, nutrition is a major cause of NAFLD, but on the other, it presents an effective form of treatment [5,8,9].

In NAFLD, nutrition can be characterized by an appropriate choice of active nutrients that can play a regulatory role in metabolism. Nutrients regulate the activity of enzymes involved in metabolic processes, acting at the level of the proteome and metabolome and functioning as sensors that influence metabolic pathways [10–12]. Importantly, the same nutrient may have different influences on given people due to genetic polymorphisms found in the population [12]. The interactions between nutrients, genetic factors (polymorphism/mutations) and health are the subject matter of nutrigenomics [12]. This field of science aims to establish personalized nutrition strategies for the prevention and treatment of lifestyle diseases [12,13]. It be assumed that if the action of nutrients is affected by polymorphisms, it is advisable to search for methods of individualizing a patient's nutrition. Therefore, in this study, we focused on testing a tool that could be used for the individualization of nutrition in patients with NAFLD. The specific tool used in this study was the nutrient-induced insulin output ratio (NIOR), which was selected to determine the genotype-phenotype interaction [14]. The NIOR has already been used to identify a correlation between the variants of genes (associated with the metabolism of carbohydrates and fat) and the output of insulin and the development of diet-induced insulin resistance. Using the NIOR, we identified the carriers of the alleles of gene variants characterized by a reduced tolerance to fat or carbohydrates in the diet. The pool of genes associated with NIOR includes glucose-sensitive genes, such as genes for Adrenergic receptors (*b3AR*), Tumor necrosis factor (*TNF-α*) and Apolipoprotein C (*APOC3*) [14]. The variants of these genes are described in the literature as being responsible for an increased risk of developing insulin resistance (gene *b3AR*, rs 4994) [15], the induction and development of insulin resistance and metabolic syndrome (gene *TNF-α*, rs 1800629) [16] and severe forms of hyperlipidemia (gene *APOC3*, rs 5128) [17].

Fat-sensitive genes associated with NIOR include the genes of Uncoupling Protein type I (*UCP-1*, rs 1800592), Peroxisome proliferator-activated receptor γ 2 (*PPAR-γ2*, rs 18012820) and Apolipoprotein E (*ApoE*). Selected variants of these genes are responsible for the regulation of body weight and the concentration of plasma high density lipoprotein (Type 1 uncoupling protein (*UCP1*)) [18], an increased risk of metabolic syndrome by the regulation of energy homeostasis and glucose (Peroxisome proliferator activated receptor γ2 *PPAR-γ2* gene) [19], the furthering of insulin-resistance, the development of hyperlipidemia and hypertriglyceridemia and the progression of coronary heart disease (*APOE* rs 405509, rs 7412 rs 429358) [17].

The aim of this study was to determine whether the NIOR can be useful in planning the individualized nutrition of patients with NAFLD and whether its use contributes to a more effective inhibition of NAFLD progression, defined as a reduced degree of hepatic steatosis and improved biochemical and anthropometric parameters.

2. Results

2.1. The Analysis of the Data Using Model 1

2.1.1. Changes in Anthropometric Parameters after Six Months Depending on the Type of Diet

The most beneficial changes in body composition were observed among patients treated with the NIOR (+) diet (Table 1). The body mass reduction, the reduction in waist circumference, and the reduction in fat mass were significant.

Weight reductions were also recorded in the Cust (+) group, but in comparison to NIOR (+), the reduction in fat content was less significant (-3.40 ± 6.27, $p < 0.002$ vs. -0.66 ± 3.67, $p < 0.02$) (Table 1). In Cust (+) patients, negative changes associated with the loss of lean body mass and arm circumference were also recorded (Table 1).

Slight changes in body mass, waist circumference, and hip circumference were observed in the group contrary to NIOR (−) and Cust (−) (called CONTRA in Table 1).

The analysis of changes between these groups provided interesting results. The most significant changes were observed when NIOR (+) and NIOR (−) and Cust (−) were compared (CONTRA NIOR (−) and Cust (−)). Between these groups, there were significant differences in the reduction of body mass (-6.79 ± 4.79 kg, NIOR (+) vs. -2.56 ± 2.88 kg NIOR (−), $p < 0.026$), BMI (-2.41 ± 1.73 kg/m^2 NIOR (+) vs. -0.83 ± 1.04 kg/m^2 NIOR (−), $p < 0.015$), fat mass (-5.39 ± 6.19, $p < 0.006$ NIOR (+) vs. -0.136 ± 2.97 NIOR (−), $p < 0.007$) and fat content (-2.45 ± 7.01 NIOR (+) vs. -0.88 ± 3.00 NIOR (−), $p < 0.005$) (Table 1).

Between the groups Cust (+) and NIOR (+), we observed a significant difference in the reduction of fat mass (-3.40 ± 6.27 kg Cust (+) vs. -5.39 ± 6.19 kg NIOR (+), $p < 0.04$) (Table 1).

Between the groups Cust (+) and Cust (−), we found a difference in arm circumference change (-1.45 ± 1.60 cm Cust (+) vs. 1.05 ± 3.01 cm Cust (−), $p < 0.04$) (Table 1).

2.1.2. Changes in Biochemical Parameters after Six Months in Model 1

One of the most important objectives to achieve during nutritional therapy in patients with NAFLD is a reduction in insulin resistance [20]. This effect was measured by determining. The homeostatc model assessment HOMA IR and HOMA B (used to estimate the improved β-cell "function") [21]. HOMA IR under normal physiological conditions is 1.0; higher values indicate peripheral insulin resistance or resistance of hepatic origin [22,23]. Patients in all groups were characterized by insulin resistance at the beginning (Table 1). The highest average HOMA IR value was observed for the NIOR (−) and Cust (−) groups. The reduction in HOMA IR in both of these groups reached -2.64 ± 4.57, $p < 0.05$. The initial HOMA IR in NIOR (+) patients was 3.76 ± 1.94. The recorded reduction in HOMA IR after six months was -1.34 ± 1.86, $p < 0.05$ (Table 1).

Additionally, the normalization of blood lipids (total cholesterol, triglyceride (TG), low density lipoprotein (LDL), high density lipoprotein (HDL) is an important element of nutritional therapy. Positive trends toward blood lipid normalization were observed in all types of diets (Table 1).

2.1.3. A Significant Reduction in the Degree of Fatty Liver Disease Was Observed in Patients with a Diet Selected According to NIOR

In the NIOR (+) group, the average reduction in the degree of fatty liver disease was -1.31 ± 1.01, $p < 0.002$. The difference in the reduction of fatty liver disease was significant between the NIOR (+) and NIOR (−) groups, $p < 0.04$—Mann-Whitney U test (Table 1).

Table 1. Anthropological and biochemical characteristics of the study participants' blood parameters at baseline and after six months of the diet in Model 1, with *p*-values of the comparison between subjects within this same intervention before and after six months. [a] $p < 0.0005$ Wilcoxon test, comparison between baseline and the fourth visit in this same group; [b] $p < 0.005$ Wilcoxon test, comparison between baseline and the fourth visit in this same group; [*] Mann-Whitney *U* test, comparison between NIOR (+) and Cust (+); [#] Mann-Whitney *U* test, comparison between NIOR (+) and contrary diets NIOR (−)/Cust (−); [&] Mann-Whitney *U* test, comparison between Cust (+) and contrary diets Cust (−) and NIOR (−). BMI: Body mass index; MUFA: monounsaturated fatty acids; PUFA: polyunsaturated fatty acids; HA: hyaluronic acid.

Parameters	Baseline			24W			p Value
	CUST (+)	NOR (+)	CONTRA CUST (−) and NOR (−)	CUST (+)	NOR (+)	CONTRA CUST (−) and NOR (−)	
Age	52.12 ± 14.74	52.80 ± 12.37	51.87 ± 12.11	52.12 ± 14.74	52.80 ± 12.37	51.87 ± 12.11	
Body mass (kg)	94.70 ± 22.55 [a]	89.01 ± 15.26 [a]	92.20 ± 19.34 [b]	87.59 ± 17.96 [a]	82.21 ± 15.35 [a,#]	89.63 ± 20.79 [b,#]	[a] $p < 0.0005$ [b] $p < 0.005$
BMI (kg/m²)	32.10 ± 4.13	30.70 ± 3.64	32.27 ± 6.59	30.01 ± 2.84	28.29 ± 15.35 [#]	28.29 ± 15.35 [#]	[#] $p < 0.015$
Arm circumference (cm)	33.30 ± 3.64 [a]	31.66 ± 2.87	32.33 ± 3.86	31.85 ± 2.56 [a,&]	30.75 ± 3.46	33.38 ± 4.53 [&]	[a] $p < 0.0005$ & $p < 0.04$
Waist circumference (cm)	105.14 ± 14.69 [a]	100.12 ± 11.75 [b]	106.25 ± 14.45 [b]	97.02 ± 10.63 [a]	94.00 ± 11.97 [b]	102.60 ± 16.02 [b]	[a] $p < 0.0009$ [b] $p < 0.005$
Hip circumference (cm)	105.14 ± 14.69 [a]	100.12 ± 11.75 [b]	106.25 ± 15.73 [b]	104.20 ± 14.89 [a]	94.00 ± 13.33 [b]	102.60 ± 17.04 [b]	[a] $p < 0.0009$ [b] $p < 0.005$
Fat mass (%)	34.71 ± 5.78 [b]	35.41 ± 5.67 [a]	36.02 ± 14.09	31.31 ± 5.78 [b,*]	29.74 ± 8.21 [a,*,#]	35.09 ± 14.94 [#]	[a] $p < 0.0006$ [b] $p < 0.002$ [#] $p < 0.007$ [*] $p < 0.04$
Fat content (%)	37.00 ± 6.63 [b]	35.61 ± 10.96 [b]	38.07 ± 7.79	36.34 ± 5.75 [b,*]	31.03 ± 13.46 [b,*,#]	38.95 ± 7.90 [#]	[b] $p < 0.005$ [#] $p < 0.005$ [*] $p < 0.04$
Lean mass (%)	60.02 ± 16.47 [b]	53.48 ± 10.96	55.94 ± 7.80 [b]	55.92 ± 14.17 [b]	51.03 ± 13.46	53.66 ± 9.28 [b]	[b] $p < 0.002$
AST (U/L)	36.10 ± 25.83 [b]	30.70 ± 13.99 [b]	32.71 ± 10.46 [b]	35.10 ± 29.60 [b]	34.20 ± 26.31 [b,#]	23.85 ± 5.21 [b,#]	[b] $p < 0.035$ [#] $p < 0.041$
ALT (U/L)	54.00 ± 36.86 [b]	46.70 ± 26.56 [a]	47.92 ± 15.85 [a]	44.40 ± 27.86 [b]	39.40 ± 33.04 [a]	32.57 ± 18.40 [a]	[a] $p < 0.0006$ [a] $p < 0.038$
Triglyceride (mg/dL)	129.30 ± 36.30 [b]	123.80 ± 52.82	238.42 ± 482.09	106.40 ± 56.24 [b]	121.80 ± 90.52	204.78 ± 319.17	[b] $p < 0.04$
HDL (mg/dL)	51.00 ± 12.22 [b]	54.40 ± 12.83	51.57 ± 15.73	54.00 ± 16.39 [b]	54.30 ± 12.82	52.14 ± 14.31	[b] $p < 0.025$
Insulin (mcU/L)	15.80 ± 9.05	14.59 ± 8.20 [b]	18.54 ± 19.69 [b]	12.07 ± 8.62	9.58 ± 6.81 [b]	9.63 ± 9.46 [b]	[b] $p < 0.05$
HOMA-IR	4.03 ± 2.31	3.76 ± 1.94 [b]	5.44 ± 6.65 [b]	3.08 ± 2.08	2.41 ± 1.74 [b]	2.80 ± 3.00 [b]	[b] $p < 0.05$
Hyaluronic acid (U/L)	54.56 ± 29.57	45.47 ± 25.82 [b]	50.23 ± 31.76	45.93 ± 22.62	32.56 ± 16.28 [b]	37.42 ± 22.21	[b] $p < 0.04$
Fatty liver Hamaguchi score	2.13 ± 0.74 [b]	2.47 ± 0.94 [b]	2.11 ± 0.98 [b]	1.2 ± 1.0 [b]	1.12 ± 1.08 [b,#]	1.11 ± 0.92 [b,#]	[b] $p < 0.01$ [#] $p < 0.04$

2.2. The Data Analysis in Model 2

Individuals from Different Groups Who Had a Similar Range of Reduction in Body Weight Obtained Different Reductions in Hepatic Steatosis and Other Parameters

Only individuals in the NIOR (+) group showed improvement in the degree of hepatic steatosis (Figure 1, Table S1).

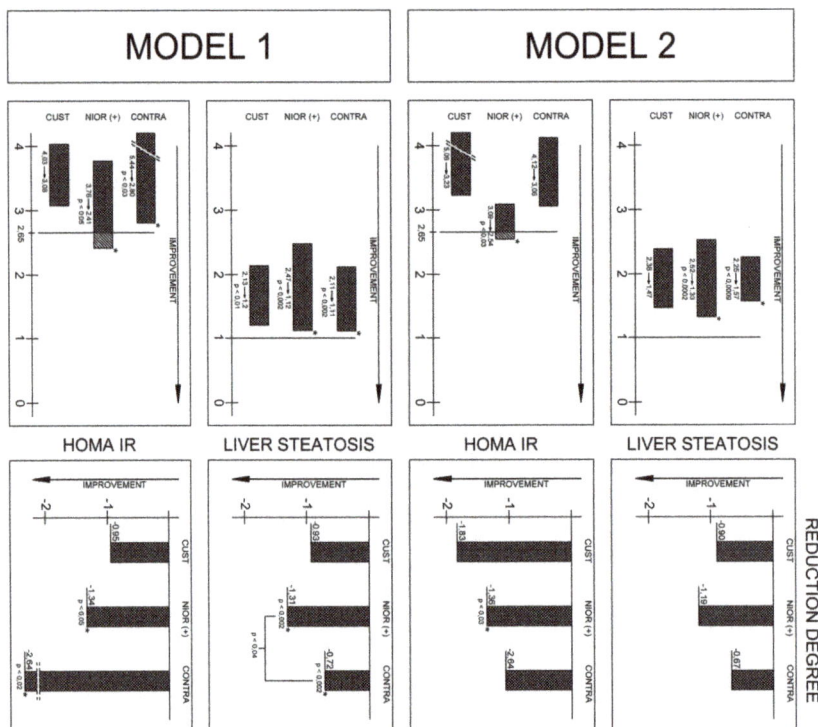

Figure 1. Changes in biochemical blood parameters in Model 1 and 2Note: All data represent the mean (standard deviation).

The analysis of the differences between the groups showed that the reduction in hepatic steatosis in the NIOR (+) group significantly differed from that observed in the NIOR (−) group (Mann-Whitney U test, $p < 0.04$). A similar significant difference between groups was observed for hyaluronic acid, with levels differing significantly between the Cust (+) and NIOR (+) groups (-26.45 ± 17.72 NIOR (+) vs. -1.94 ± 5.4 Cust (−) and NIOR (−), Mann-Whitney U test, $p < 0.005$).

3. Discussion

Obesity and insulin resistance present a considerable challenge in the nutrition plans of patients with NAFLD [24,25]. Current dietary guidelines are based on epidemiological data showing a link between diets enriched in saturated fatty acids and in fructose and the development of insulin resistance [26]. However, the response to diet differs depending on individual variations in genetic and metabolic phenotypes. Therefore, it is important to personalize patients' diets, taking into account their genetic predispositions [13,14].

One potentially interesting tool is the nutrient-induced insulin output ratio (NIOR). The NIOR makes it possible to categorize patients (gene variant carriers) into two groups: phenotypically sensitive to glucose or fat in the diet. The polymorphisms of genes associated with the NIOR have previously been associated with the severity of metabolic syndrome and susceptibility to the effects of nutrients [14–19]. In our work, we examined polymorphisms (linked with NIOR) according to their impact on the output of insulin after a meal [14]. The usefulness of NIOR as a potential tool to individualize diets was examined through the introduction of quantitative changes in nutrients (fat or simple carbohydrates), consistent with the results of genetic tests. To exclude the impact of polymorphisms themselves, some people were randomly assigned to a group in which the key nutrient contents were chosen in quantities contrary to the indications of genetic research.

The second important objective of this study was to create a nutritional plan that would be accepted by the respondents for an extended period of time. We succeeded in obtaining the results of a half-year-long diet, resulting in an acceptable reduction in the content of the tested nutrients in the diet.

We showed that a selection of nutrients consistent with the indications of the NIOR contributed to an effective reduction in hepatic steatosis in both Model 1 and Model 2. This is a very important result, as fat droplets accumulating in hepatocytes are considered the main hepatotoxic factor, inducing hepatic steatosis and fibrosis [27–29]. The reduction of lipid content in the liver, therefore, means a reduction in the intensity of fibrosis [27], which is marked by hyaluronic acid content in the blood [28,29]. Such a reduction in hyaluronic acid was recorded in all groups, but the largest decline in hyaluronic acid content was found in the NIOR (+) group, regardless of the research model (Table 1 and Figure 1).

Additionally, individual selections of nutrients based on the NIOR were intended to contribute to the reduction of fat mass (Table 1). The results seem to confirm the usefulness of NIOR for the efficient reduction in body fat mass and fat content when comparing the NIOR (+) and NIOR (−) groups. It seems that the reduction of fat mass and fat tissue was most effective in the group in which the amount of dietary fat or dietary sugar was adjusted to gene polymorphisms. Of note is that there was no significant effect of NIOR on the reduction of insulin resistance between groups. The HOMA IR ratio was effectively reduced in all groups, regardless of the type of diet (Table 1). Fats are components that play a crucial role in the progression of NAFLD [27,30–34]. The positive changes in the liver were the result of a decrease in the fat content of the diet, especially among fat-sensitive polymorphism carriers (Table 1 and Figure 1). Our study confirms the results of other authors, e.g., Marina et al. [31], who found that fat (in different contents in the diet—20% vs. 55% the total daily energy expenditure (TDEE) caused minor effects in the content of intra-abdominal fat and intrahepatic lipids. In another study (a short-term intervention), a three-week isocaloric low-fat diet (20% TDEE) decreased intrahepatic lipids by 13%, whereas a high fat diet (55% TDEE) increased the amount of lipids in the liver by up to 17% [30]. Unfortunately, both studies were limited to a short period of observation [30,31].

Though our study was longer, it suffered from a significant limitation, which was the exclusion of variants sensitive to simple sugars (after six months, only one person remained—Figure 2). This was a substantial loss because simple sugars, especially fructose (a common nutrient in western diets), is reported to be associated with an increased risk of NAFLD [35–37]. Although the consumption of fructose is high and continues to be on the rise [38], there are still no conclusive results that indicate a connection between the high intake of fructose and NAFLD [35,37]. The available evidence is not sufficiently robust to draw conclusions regarding the effects of fructose, high fructose corn syrup (HFCS) or sucrose consumption on NAFLD [37].

It seems that the lack of clear associations between the consumption of simple sugars and hepatic steatosis can result from yet another important variable, i.e., gender. Research from 2014 shows that the severity of hepatic steatosis may be significantly influenced by feeding patterns associated with gender [27]. Unfortunately, our study cannot be included in the discussion in this area. Slightly more severe hepatic steatosis was shown in our analysis of diets before the initiation of the prescribed diet. The analysis of the FFQ results indicates a lack of a relationship between the consumption of products containing large amounts of sugars and the degree of hepatic steatosis among our respondents, regardless of gender (unpublished results). Understanding the specific interaction between nutrients and dietary needs and maintaining this balance is extremely important in providing treatment for NAFLD [39,40].

4. Materials and Methods

4.1. Patients

A group of 171 eligible participants, Caucasian men (n = 104) and women (n = 67) diagnosed with NAFLD, were prospectively enrolled in the study (Figure 2). Of the 171 total recruited patients, only 166 confirmed patients with NAFLD met the inclusion criteria. We conducted the measurements at the beginning of the study and at check points conducted at the first visit, after the first month, the second month and after six months—the final check point (Figure 2).

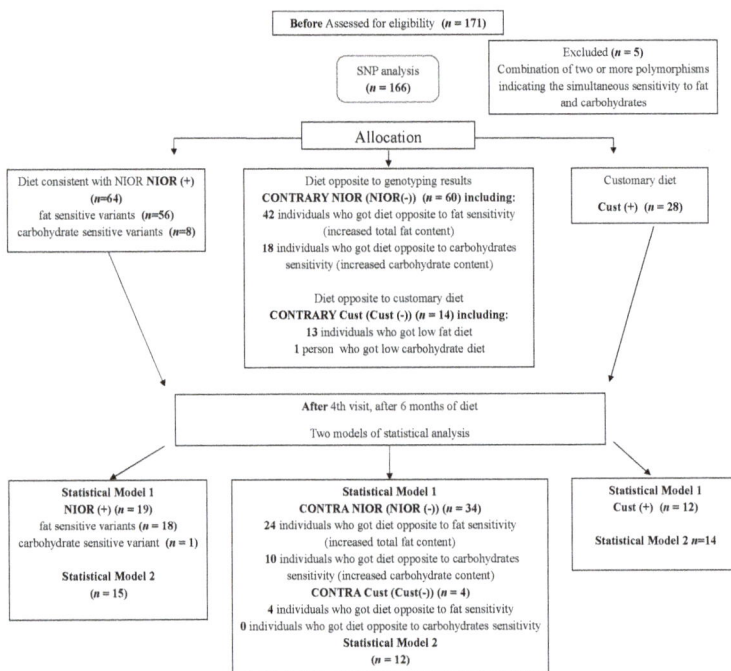

Figure 2. Flowchart for the selection of individuals from the nutrient-induced insulin output ratio (NIOR) cohort. Participants entering subsequent phases of the study as well as dropouts out are indicated in the total. NIOR (+) represents individuals consuming a diet consistent with the results of genotyping; Cust (+), individuals consuming a diet comprising the typical dietary recommendations for non-alcoholic fatty liver disease (NAFLD); NIOR (−) and Cust (−), individuals consuming a diet contrary to the genotyping results.

The exclusion criteria included the following: diabetes mellitus (DMII); infection with either HBV (Hepatitis B Virus) or HCV (Hepatitis C Virus); obesity (body mass index (BMI) >30 kg/m^2); high levels of physical activity (>3000 kcal/week in leisure-time physical activity); changes in physical activity during the dietary intervention; use of statins; any condition that could limit the mobility of the participant; not being able to attend control visits; vegetarianism or a need for other special diets; the excessive consumption of alcohol (≥20 g in women and ≥30 g in men, per day); and other drug addiction.

Physical activity was assessed during the first visit and in subsequent appointments using the International Physical Activity Questionnaire (IPAQ) [41]. In this study we recommended moderate activity and we advised our patients not to change physical activity during the time of intervention. The degree of fatty liver disease was assessed by a trained physician according to the Hamaguchi score [42], using a high-resolution B-mode abdominal ultrasound scanner (Acuson X300, Simens, San Jose, CA, USA).

The study protocol was approved by the ethics committee of the Pomeranian Medical University (Szczecin, Poland, 25 01 2010 KB-0012/09/10) and conformed to the ethical guidelines of the 1975 Declaration of Helsinki. The volunteers provided written informed consent before the study.

4.2. The Anthropometric Data

Anthropometric assessments were performed routinely during each of the four visits. The study included measurements of height (m), body weight (kg), skinfold thickness (mm), arm circumference (cm), waist circumference (cm) and hip circumference (cm). The measurements of body weight and height were obtained by means of medical scales with a stadiometer. Body mass index was calculated according to these measurements (BMI = body weight (kg)/square of height (m)) [24,43]. Using a medical tape measure, waist circumference was measured (midway between the bottom edge of the ribs and the iliac crest) as was hip circumference. Based on these measurements, WHR was calculated (WHR = waist circumference (cm)/hip circumference (cm)) [24]. A caliper was used to measure skinfold thicknesses: biceps, triceps, subscapular and abdominal skinfolds. In addition, in each subject, body composition was measured with a multifrequency bioimpedance meter, BIA-101 (Akern, Bioresearch SRL, PONASSIEVE, Florence, Italy).

4.3. Methods and Experimental Design

A randomized parallel controlled clinical trial with three dietary interventions was performed:

1. A diet consistent with the results of genotyping, called NIOR (+);
2. A diet with typical dietary recommendations for NAFLD, called Cust (+) [8];
3. A diet opposite to genotyping results, called (NIOR (−) and Cust (−) (CONTRA NIOR and Cust) (Figure 3).

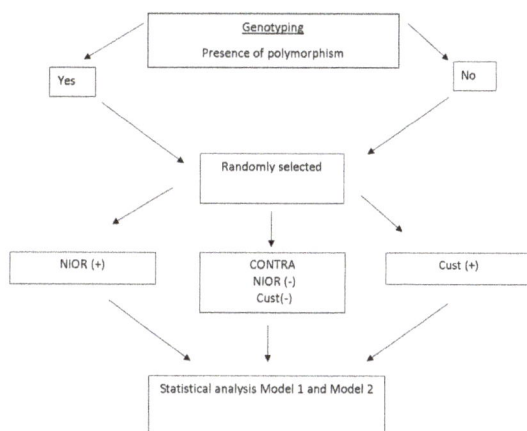

Figure 3. Baseline treatment characteristics. NIOR (+) represents individuals consuming a diet consistent with the results of genotyping; Cust (+), individuals consuming a diet comprising the typical dietary recommendations for NAFLD; NIOR (−) and Cust (−), individuals consuming a diet contrary to the genotyping results.

4.4. Allocation to Groups

The patients were randomly assigned to the NIOR (+) group. They represented:

(a) a single polymorphism indicative of sensitivity to carbohydrates or fats
(b) more than one polymorphism indicative of sensitivity to carbohydrates or to fats (e.g., two polymorphisms indicative of sensitivity to fat)

Only eight patients from the NIOR (+) group had polymorphisms indicative of sensitivity to carbohydrates. Unfortunately, these people dropped out of the study at various stages of the study. Only one carrier of sensitivity to carbohydrates completed the study (19 patients remained in the group).

Persons with a combination of two or more polymorphisms indicating simultaneous sensitivity to fat and carbohydrates were excluded from the study.

4.5. Dietary Intervention

4.5.1. General Recommendation

The diet was calculated individually according to the patient's caloric needs. Individuals with a BMI indicating that they were overweight or obese received a reduced caloric diet of 500 kcal/day. People with a BMI within the normal range were given a normocaloric diet that allowed them to maintain their current body weight.

The total daily energy expenditure (TDEE) was calculated using the direct measurement of resting metabolic rate (RMR). RMR was measured during the first visit and in subsequent follow-up visits with a Fitmate apparatus (Pro, COSMED). The activity factor (AF) was determined in accordance with the generally accepted norm (TDEE = AF × RMR). The caloric content of the diet was adjusted during visits to the changing values of the patient's TDEE.

All patients received weekly menus and guidelines on the timing of meals throughout the day, their composition and the size of the portions. Menus were prepared in the form of a daily plan for the seven days of the week and included guidance on the timing during the day of the five meal times.

The recommended sources of fat included vegetable fats, with a predominance of rapeseed oil and olive oil. It was permissible to use butter and margarine. Animal fats such as lard were excluded.

The recommended sources of carbohydrates included products with a low and medium glycemic index (GI). These included whole wheat bread, whole wheat pasta, cereal and brown rice. Sweets were excluded from the diet.

The recommended protein sources comprised poultry, fish (oily fish three times a week), fermented dairy products (two times a day), eggs (four to five times a week), lean cottage cheese, and cheese with a reduced fat content. Pork fat and offal products were excluded from the diet. The amount of fruit and vegetables recommended in the diets included three portions of vegetables and two portions of fruit. The amount of fluid intake was calculated to be 35 mL/kg of actual body weight.

4.5.2. Recommendations Based on the Nutrient-Induced Insulin Output Ratio (NIOR)

(a) NIOR (+) patients received dietary recommendations with a reduced fat content (20% TDEE when NIOR polymorphisms showed sensitivity to fat) or reduced carbohydrate content (55% of TDEE, including <5% of sugars, when the polymorphisms showed sensitivity to simple carbohydrates).
(b) Cust (+) patients received dietary advice with the following nutrient content: fat content at 30% of TDEE and carbohydrates at 55% of TDEE (including 10% of simple carbohydrates).
(c) NIOR (−) patients, when they had "fat-sensitive" gene variants, received dietary recommendations that increased total fat content up to 30% of TDEE.

When participants had sugar-sensitive variants of genes, they received an increased amount of carbohydrates (10% simple carbohydrates).

Cust (−) patients were randomly assigned to groups with a reduced fat content or lower carbohydrate content.

4.5.3. Dietary Control

Nutrition patterns were analyzed with a Food Frequency Questionnaire (FFQ) and a 72 h food diary (including two working days and one day free of work) during the first visit. At all check points, the patients brought their completed 72 h food diary. The amounts consumed were recorded in household units, by volume or by measuring with a ruler. The dietary records were validated by a nutritionist according to a corresponding food table and nutrient database (Table 2).

4.6. Laboratory Analyses

After overnight fasting, venous blood was collected into tubes containing anticoagulant Ethylenediaminetetraacetic acid (EDTA).

Blood samples were centrifuged at 3500 rpm for 10 min at 4 °C within 2 h of collection. Standard blood biochemical analyses were carried out at the University Hospital Laboratory (Szczecin, Poland). Hyaluronic acid was determined with an ELISA kit (Wuhan EIAab Science, A1710 Guangguguoji, Wuhan, China).

4.7. Genotyping

From the pool of genes sensitive to nutrient content, we selected genes that were characterized by a strong response to the oral glucose tolerance test after 75 g of glucose or after a high-fat meal. These included the b3-adrenergic receptor (b3AR), tumor necrosis factor (TNF-α) and apolipoprotein C III (apo CIII) [14].

From the pool of carbohydrate-sensitive genes, we selected Type 1 uncoupling protein (UCP-1), peroxisome proliferator-activated receptor γ 2 (PPAR-Y2) and apolipoprotein E (ApoE).

DNA from mononuclear peripheral blood was isolated using a DNeasy Blood and Tissue kit (Qiagen, Valencia, CA, USA). Genotypes were determined by the real-time polymerase chain reaction using TaqMan® Genotyping 36 g Assays for polymorphisms, including b3AR rs4994 (Applied Biosystems Assay ID C___2215549_20); TNF-rs1800629 (C___7514879_10); Apo C III-rs5128 (C___8907537_1); Ucp-1-rs1800592 (C___8866368_20); PPAR-2-rs 1801282 (C___1129864_10); APOE-rs 405509 (C____905013_10); APOE-rs7412 (C_904973_10); and APOE-rs429358 (C___3084793_20). Fluorescence data were analyzed with allelic discrimination—7500 Software v 2.0.2 (Foster City, CA, USA).

4.8. Statistical Analysis

Statistica 7.1 software (Statsoft, Poznań, Poland) was used for the statistical analysis, and all results are expressed as the mean ± standard deviation. As the distribution, in most cases, deviated from normal (Shapiro-Wilk's test), non-parametric tests were used: Wilcoxon tests were used for comparisons among groups and Mann-Whitney U tests were used for comparisons between groups. A $p < 0.05$ was considered significant.

Two Models of Statistical Analysis

Model 1 included the analysis of the results of the anthropometric and biochemical measurements with the criterion of the dietary recommendations that were adopted by the patients throughout the study (six months). The caloric value of the patients' menus was estimated during checkups, which took place after one, two and six months, based on their 72 h diaries. The patients who were included in the statistical analysis followed the diet carefully (which was estimated based on menus in relation to the recommended caloric content ±200 kcal/day). Patients who exceeded that value at any stage of the study were excluded from the statistical analysis in Model 1.

Int. J. Mol. Sci. **2016**, *17*, 1192

Table 2. Characteristics of dietary interventions. Nutrient-induced insulin output ratio (NIOR) (+) represents individuals consuming a diet consistent with the results of genotyping; Cust (+), individuals consuming a diet comprising the typical dietary recommendations for non-alcoholic fatty liver disease (NAFLD); NIOR (−) and Cust (−), individuals consuming a diet contrary to the genotyping results. * Group with a lower amount of carbohydrate (CHO) or fat.

Content of Diet	NIOR (+) Variant Sensitive for Fat	NIOR (+) Variant Sensitive for Carbohydrate	Cust (+)	CONTRA NIOR NIOR (−) If Variant Was Sensitive for Fat	CONTRA NIOR NIOR (−) If Variant Was Sensitive for Carbohydrate	CONTRA Cust Cust (−) Randomly Selected to Group with Lower Amount of Fat of CHO *
Energy	Calculated individually	Calculated individually	Calculated individually	Calculated individually	Calculated individually	Calculated individually
Fat percent of total caloric in %	20	30	30	30	20	20 or 30 *
Carbohydrates in %	65	55	55	55	65	65 or 55 *
Simple carbohydrate in %	≥10	<5	≥10	<5	≥10	≥10 or <5 *
Protein (%)	15	15	15	15	15	15
Fiber (g/day)	30–35	30–35	30–35	30–35	30–35	30–35
Fluid (mL/kg)	35	35	35	35	35	35

Model 2 included the analysis of the anthropometric and biochemical results with the criterion of weight loss in the range of 8–10 kg over six months. We excluded patients who were characterized by normal weight at the beginning of the experiment from this analysis.

5. Conclusions

It seems that by introducing an individual nutrition and genotyping plan that takes into account the normal supply of calories, nutrients, proteins, and micro- and macronutrients, we are able to prevent problems that result from the progression of disease. Therefore, individualization, understood as the work of a dietitian with the patient, seems to be a therapeutic necessity, and the nutrient-induced insulin output ratio in people sensitive to fat seems to be n useful tool for determining specific strategies for patients with NAFLD.

Supplementary Materials: Supplementary materials can be found at http://www.mdpi.com/1422-0067/17/7/1192/s1.

Acknowledgments: Supported by a grant from the Narodowe Centrum Nauki (NCN), Nr N404 150539.

Author Contributions: Ewa Stachowska conceived and designed the experiments, wrote the paper; Karina Ryterska performed the experiments; Dominika Maciejewska performed the experiments (biochemistry); Marcin Banaszczak performed the experiments (biochemistry); Piotr Milkiewicz conceived and designed the experiments (medical support); Małgorzata Milkiewicz performed the experiments (biochemistry-PCR); Izabela Gutowska analyzed the data; Piotr Ossowski performed the experiments (biochemistry); Małgorzata Kaczorowska performed the experiments (nutrition); Dominika Jamioł-Milc performed the; experiments (nutrition); Anna Sabinicz performed the experiments (nutrition); Małgorzata Napierała performed the experiments (nutrition); Lidia Wądołowska contributed reagents/materials/analysis tools (nutritional analysis); Raszeja-Wyszomirska Joanna analyzed the data (medical support).

Conflicts of Interest: The authors declare no conflict of interest.

References

1. Vernon, G.; Baranova, A.; Younossi, Z.M. Systematic review: The epidemiology and natural history of non-alcoholic fatty liver disease and non-alcoholic steatohepatitis in adults. *Aliment. Pharmacol. Ther.* **2011**, *34*, 274–285. [CrossRef] [PubMed]

2. Argo, C.K.; Northup, P.G.; Al-Osaimi, A.M.; Caldwell, S.H. Systematic review of risk factors for fibrosis progression in non-alcoholic steatohepatitis. *J. Hepatol.* **2009**, *51*, 371–379. [CrossRef] [PubMed]

3. Targher, G.; Day, C.P.; Bonora, E. Risk of cardiovascular disease in patients with nonalcoholic fatty liver disease. *N. Engl. J. Med.* **2010**, *363*, 1341–1350. [CrossRef] [PubMed]

4. Promrat, K.; Kleiner, D.E.; Niemeier, H.M.; Jackvony, E.; Kearns, M.; Wands, JR.; Fava, J.L.; Wing, R.R. Randomized controlled trial testing the effects of weight loss on nonalcoholic steatohepatitis. *Hepatology* **2010**, *51*, 121–129. [CrossRef] [PubMed]

5. Yoon, H.J.; Cha, B.S. Pathogenesis and therapeutic approaches for non-alcoholic fatty liver disease. *World J. Hepatol.* **2014**, *6*, 800–811. [CrossRef] [PubMed]

6. Hassan, K.; Bhalla, V.; El Regal, M.E.; A-Kader, H.H. Nonalcoholic fatty liver disease: A comprehensive review of a growing epidemic. *World J. Gastroenterol.* **2014**, *20*, 12082–120101. [CrossRef] [PubMed]

7. Weiß, J.; Rau, M.; Geier, A. Non-alcoholic fatty liver disease: Epidemiology, clinical course, investigation, and treatment. *Dtsch. Ärzteblatt Int.* **2014**, *111*, 447–452.

8. Kargulewicz, A.; Stankowiak-Kulpa, H.; Grzymisławski, M. Dietary recommendations for patients with nonalcoholic fatty liver disease. *Prz. Gastroenterol.* **2014**, *9*, 18–23. [CrossRef] [PubMed]

9. Barrera, F.; George, J. The role of diet and nutritional intervention for the management of patients with NAFLD. *Clin. Liver. Dis.* **2014**, *18*, 91–112. [CrossRef] [PubMed]

10. Keijer, J.; Hoevenaars, F.P.; Nieuwenhuizen, A.; van Schothorst, E.M. Nutrigenomics of body weight regulation: A rationale for careful dissection of individual contributors. *Nutrients* **2014**, *6*, 4531–4551. [CrossRef] [PubMed]

11. Arslan, N. Obesity, fatty liver disease and intestinal microbiota. *World J. Gastroenterol.* **2014**, *20*, 16452–16463. [CrossRef] [PubMed]

12. Hesketh, J.; Wybranska, I.; Dommels, Y.; King, M.; Elliott, R.; Pico, C.; Keijer, J. Nutrient-gene interactions in benefit-risk analysis. *Br. J. Nutr.* **2006**, *95*, 1232–1239. [CrossRef] [PubMed]

13. Kang, J.X. The coming of age of nutrigenetics and nutrigenomics. *J. Nutr. Nutr.* **2012**, *5*. [CrossRef] [PubMed]

14. Wybranska, I.; Malczewska-Malec, M.; Partyka, L.; Kiec-Wilk, B.; Kosno, K.; Leszczynska-Golabek, I.; Zdzienicka, A.; Gruca, A.; Kwasniak, M.; Dembinska-Kiec, A. Evaluation of genetic predisposition to insulin resistance by nutrient-induced insulin output ratio (NIOR). *Clin. Chem. Lab. Med.* **2007**, *45*, 1124–1132. [CrossRef] [PubMed]

15. Zafarmand, M.H.; van der Schouw, Y.T.; Grobbee, D.E.; de Leeuw, P.W.; Bots, M.L. T64A polymorphism in β3-adrenergic receptor gene (*ADRB3*) and coronary heart disease: A case-cohort study and meta-analysis. *J. Intern. Med.* **2008**, *263*, 79–89. [CrossRef] [PubMed]

16. Miranda, J.L.; Perez-Martinez, P.P.; Marin, C.F.; Fuentes, F.; Delgado, J.; Pérez-Jiménez, F. Dietary fat, genes, and insulin sensitivity. *J. Mol. Med.* **2007**, *85*, 213–226. [CrossRef] [PubMed]

17. Henneman, P.; van der Sman-de Beer, F.; Moghaddam, P.H.; Huijts, P.; Stalenhoef, AF.; Kastelein, J.J.; van Duijn, C.M.; Havekes, L.M.; Frants, R.R.; van Dijk, K.W.; et al. The expression of type III hyperlipoproteinemia: Involvement of lipolysis genes. *Eur. J. Hum. Genet.* **2009**, *54*, 3043–3048. [CrossRef] [PubMed]

18. Hamada, T.; Kotani, K.; Nagai, N. Low-calorie diet-induced reduction in serum HDL cholesterol is ameliorated in obese women with the −3826 G allele in the uncoupling protein-1 gene. *Tohoku J. Exp. Med.* **2009**, *219*, 337–342. [CrossRef] [PubMed]

19. Meirhaeghem, A.; Cottel, D.; Amouyel, P.; Dallongeville, J. Association between peroxisome proliferator-activated receptor γ haplotypes and the metabolic syndrome in French men and women. *Diabetes* **2005**, *54*, 3043–3048. [CrossRef]

20. Marchesini, G.; Pagotto, U.; Bugianesi, E.; De Iasio, R.; Manini, R.; Vanni, E.; Pasquali, R.; Melchionda, N.; Rizzetto, M. Low ghrelin concentrations in nonalcoholic fatty liver disease are related to insulin resistance. *J. Clin. Endocrinol. Metab.* **2003**, *88*, 5674–5679. [CrossRef] [PubMed]

21. Pfützner, A.; Derwahl, M.; Jacob, S.; Hohberg, C.; Blümner, E.; Lehmann, U.; Fuchs, W.; Forst, T. Limitations of the HOMA-B score for assessment of β-cell functionality in interventional trials-results from the PIOglim study. *Diabetes. Technol. Ther.* **2010**, *12*, 599–604.

22. Haffner, S.M.; Kennedy, E.; Gonzalez, C.; Stern, M.P.; Miettinen, H. A prospective analysis of the HOMA model. The Mexico City Diabetes Study. *Diabetes Care* **1996**, *19*, 1138–1141. [CrossRef] [PubMed]

23. Eslamparast, T.; Eghtesad, S.; Poustchi, H.; Hekmatdoost, A. Recent advances in dietary supplementation, in treating non-alcoholic fatty liver disease. *World J. Hepatol.* **2015**, *7*, 204–212. [CrossRef] [PubMed]

24. Zheng, R.D.; Chen, Z.R.; Chen, J.N.; Lu, Y.H.; Chen, J. Role of body mass index, waist-to-height and waist-to-hip ratio in prediction of nonalcoholic fatty liver disease. *Gastroenterol. Res. Pract.* **2012**, *2012*, 362147. [CrossRef] [PubMed]

25. Dudekula, A.; Rachakonda, V.; Shaik, B.; Behari, J. Weight loss in nonalcoholic Fatty liver disease patients in an ambulatory care setting is largely unsuccessful but correlates with frequency of clinic visits. *PLoS ONE* **2014**, *9*, e111808. [CrossRef]

26. Deer, J.; Koska, J.; Ozias, M.; Reaven, P. Dietary models of insulin resistance. *Metabolism* **2015**, *64*, 163–171. [CrossRef] [PubMed]

27. Jia, Q.; Xia, Y.; Zhang, Q.; Wu, H.; Du, H.; Liu, L.; Wang, C.; Shi, H.; Guo, X.; Liu, X.; et al. Dietary patterns are associated with prevalence of fatty liver disease in adults. *Eur. J. Clin. Nutr.* **2015**, *69*, 914–921. [CrossRef] [PubMed]

28. Adams, L.A. Biomarkers of liver fibrosis. *J. Gastroenterol. Hepatol.* **2011**, *26*, 802–809. [CrossRef] [PubMed]

29. Rossi, E.; Adams, L.A.; Ching, H.L.; Bulsara, M.; MacQuillan, G.C.; Jeffrey, G.P. High biological variation of serum hyaluronic acid and Hepascore, a biochemical marker model for the prediction of liver fibrosis. *Clin. Chem. Lab. Med.* **2013**, *51*, 1107–1114. [CrossRef] [PubMed]

30. Van Herpen, N.A.; Schrauwen-Hinderling, V.; Schaart, G.; Mensink, R.P.; Schrauwen, P. Three weeks on a high-fat diet increases intrahepatic lipid accumulation and decreases metabolic flexibility in healthy overweight men. *JCEM* **2011**, *96*, E691–E695. [CrossRef] [PubMed]

31. Marina, A.; von Frankenberg, A.D.; Suvag, S.; Callahan, H.S.; Kratz, M.; Richards, T.L.; Utzschneider, K.M. Effects of dietary fat and saturated fat content on liver fat and markers of oxidative stress in overweight/obese men and women under weight-stable conditions. *Nutrients* **2014**, *6*, 4678–4690. [CrossRef] [PubMed]

32. Westerbacka, J.; Lammi, K.; Hakkinen, A.M.; Rissanen, A.; Salminen, I.; Aro, A.; Yki-Järvinen, H. Dietary fat content modifies liver fat in overweight nondiabetic subjects. *J. Clin. Endocrinol. Metab.* **2005**, *90*, 2804–2809. [CrossRef] [PubMed]

33. Moore, J.B.; Gunn, P.J.; Fielding, B.A. The role of dietary sugars and de novo lipogenesis in non-alcoholic fatty liver disease. *Nutrients* **2014**, *6*, 5679–5703. [CrossRef] [PubMed]

34. Bémeur, C.; Butterworth, R.F. Nutrition in the management of cirrhosis and its neurological complications. *J. Clin. Exp. Hepatol.* **2014**, *4*, 141–150. [CrossRef] [PubMed]

35. Jin, R.; Welsh, J.A.; Le, N.A.; Holzberg, J.; Sharma, P.; Martin, D.R.; Vos, M.B. Dietary fructose reduction improves markers of cardiovascular disease risk in Hispanic-American adolescents with NAFLD. *Nutrients* **2014**, *6*, 3187–3201. [CrossRef] [PubMed]

36. Chiu, S.; Sievenpiper, J.L.; de Souza, R.J.; Cozma, A.I.; Mirrahimi, A.; Carleton, A.J.; Ha, V.; di Buono, M.; Jenkins, A.L.; Leiter, L.A.; et al. Effect of fructose on markers of non-alcoholic fatty liver disease (NAFLD): A systematic review and meta-analysis of controlled feeding trials. *Eur. J. Clin. Nutr.* **2014**, *68*, 416–423. [CrossRef] [PubMed]

37. Chung, M.; Ma, J.; Patel, K.; Berger, S.; Lau, J.; Lichtenstein, A.H. Fructose, high-fructose corn syrup, sucrose, and nonalcoholic fatty liver disease or indexes of liver health: A systematic review and meta-analysis. *Am. J. Clin. Nutr.* **2014**, *100*, 833–849. [CrossRef] [PubMed]

38. Sluik, D.; Engelen, A.I.; Feskens, E.J. Fructose consumption in the Netherlands: The Dutch National Food Consumption Survey 2007–2010. *Eur. J. Clin. Nutr.* **2015**, *69*, 475–481. [CrossRef] [PubMed]

39. Veena, J.; Muragundla, A.; Sidgiddi, S.; Subramaniam, S. Non-alcoholic fatty liver disease: Need for a balanced nutritional source. *Br. J. Nutr.* **2014**, *112*, 1858–1872. [CrossRef] [PubMed]

40. Rinella, M.E.; Sanyal, A.J. Management of NAFLD: A stage-based approach. *Nat. Rev. Gastroenterol. Hepatol.* **2016**, *13*, 196–205. [CrossRef] [PubMed]

41. Hagströmer, M.; Oja, P.; Sjöström, M. The International Physical Activity Questionnaire (IPAQ): A study of concurrent and construct validity. *Public Health Nutr.* **2006**, *9*, 755–762. [CrossRef] [PubMed]

42. Hamaguchi, M.; Kojima, T.; Itoh, Y.; Harano, Y.; Fujii, K.; Nakajima, T.; Kato, T.; Takeda, N.; Okuda, J.; Ida, K.; et al. The severity of ultrasonographic findings in nonalcoholic fatty liver disease reflects the metabolic syndrome and visceral fat accumulation. *Am. J. Gastroenterol.* **2007**, *102*, 2708–2715. [CrossRef] [PubMed]

43. Wells, J.C. Commentary: The paradox of body mass index in obesity assessment: Not a good index of adiposity, but not a bad index of cardio-metabolic risk. *Int. J. Epidemiol.* **2014**, *43*, 672–674. [CrossRef] [PubMed]

International Journal of
Molecular Sciences

MDPI

Review

Relevant Aspects of Nutritional and Dietary Interventions in Non-Alcoholic Fatty Liver Disease

Maria Catalina Hernandez-Rodas [1], Rodrigo Valenzuela [1,*] and Luis A. Videla [2]

[1] Department of Nutrition, Faculty of Medicine, University of Chile, Santiago 8380453, Chile;
     cata.hernandezr@gmail.com
[2] Molecular and Clinical Pharmacology Program, Institute of Biomedical Sciences, Faculty of Medicine,
     University of Chile, Santiago 8380453, Chile; lvidela@med.uchile.cl
*   Author to whom correspondence should be addressed; rvalenzuelab@med.uchile.cl; Tel.: +56-229-786-014.

Academic Editors: Amedeo Lonardo and Giovanni Targher
Received: 9 September 2015; Accepted: 14 October 2015; Published: 23 October 2015

Abstract: Non-alcoholic fatty liver disease (NAFLD) is the main cause of liver disease worldwide. NAFLD is linked to circumstances such as type 2 diabetes, insulin resistance, obesity, hyperlipidemia, and hypertension. Since the obesity figures and related comorbidities are increasing, NAFLD has turned into a liver problem that has become progressively more common. Currently, there is no effective drug therapy for NAFLD; therefore, interventions in lifestyles remain the first line of treatment. Bearing in mind that adherence rates to this type of treatment are poor, great efforts are currently focused on finding novel therapeutic agents for the prevention in the development of hepatic steatosis and its progression to nonalcoholic steatohepatitis and cirrhosis. This review presents a compilation of the scientific evidence found in the last years showing the results of interventions in lifestyle, diet, and behavioral therapies and research results in human, animal and cell models. Possible therapeutic agents ranging from supplementation with vitamins, amino acids, prebiotics, probiotics, symbiotics, polyunsaturated fatty acids and polyphenols to interventions with medicinal plants are analyzed.

Keywords: NAFLD; lifestyle; diet; exercise; vitamins; amino acids; prebiotics; polyunsaturated fatty acids; polyphenols; medicinal plants

---

1. Introduction

The burden of nonalcoholic fatty liver disease (NAFLD) has a clinical significance in the health system and is a public health problem affecting about a third of the Western population [1]. NAFLD afflicts 30% of the adult population [2] and the majority of obese individuals [3], making obesity the main promoter disease condition. In the pediatric population, NAFLD has also begun to be a relevant problem in public health due to the etiology and pathogenesis are not fully understood, the significant increase in prevalence and the impact of its progression in level of hepatic dysfunction and associated diseases such as diabetes and cardiovascular diseases [4]. Traditionally, the NAFLD has been considered the hepatic manifestation of the metabolic syndrome. However, recently, researchers indicated that this conventional view of NAFLD is outdated and it has been suggested that NAFLD is a precondition to the development of type 2 diabetes mellitus and metabolic syndrome [5]. Lonardo *et al.* [5] in a systematic review found that in 28 longitudinal studies provided sufficient evidence to consider NAFLD as a risk factor for the emergence of future metabolic syndrome and in 19 longitudinal studies reported that NAFLD precedes the metabolic syndrome and is a risk factor for its development [5]. Liver steatosis is mainly a consequence of excess caloric intake and lack of physical activity, which points to the correction of unhealthy lifestyles as first step to follow in the prevention and handling of NAFLD. When such intervention is inefficient or inadequate, then drug therapy becomes the second strategy; however, the efficacy and safety of the proposed drug treatments for treating NAFLD are still unclear [6].

2. Lifestyle Intervention and NAFLD

Today, the therapeutic strategies are aimed at reducing the incidence of risk factors involved in the progression of the hepatic disease and comorbidities associated with NAFLD [7]. Nowadays, all the international guidelines report that lifestyle changes that include diet are the only therapeutic approach recommended (Figure 1). As can be observed in Table 1, a variety of human trials and reviews have evaluated the effects of lifestyle interventions in NAFLD. There are limited data on details of how much and how fast weight loss through diet modification must be attained [8], and, besides, extrahepatic and benefits in the liver granted by weight loss are not well explained [9]. The quality and speed of weight loss have been reported to be important, but not explicitly beneficial [10]. In this regard, a moderate weight loss in the same way that physical activity induces a reduction in insulin resistance, and both behaviors are considered as the current therapeutic strategy for patients with NAFLD who are overweight or obese. However, it has been observed that liver biochemistry (alanine aminotransferase (ALT) serum) and the hepatic steatosis share is modified in the presence of dietary treatment, but inflammation and fibrosis are unchanged [9]. Likewise, physical inactivity and type of physical activity are factors that have different effects on the health of the liver and the achievement and maintenance of a healthy body weight. In this regard, vigorous physical exercise reduces insulin resistance, helps maintain weight loss over time and improves hepatic histology. However, mild or moderate exercise intensity does not provide a significant benefit over protection in the development of NAFLD [11]. Similarly, intervention studies looking to increase adherence to the Mediterranean diet and level of physical activity have reported that adherence to the Mediterranean diet is considered a significant predictor of changes in liver fat content in patients with fatty liver, who are non-alcoholic and overweight and that the effect of the diet is gradual and favorable and it is independent of other changes in lifestyle; so the qualitative profile of the intervention from the diet is responsible for the benefits and instead the concurrent weight loss is negligible [12]. Therefore, weight loss and calorie restriction can be a poor approach for the problem of metabolic liver disease, since other factors like the quality of food, lifestyle and exercise, have a significant impact on non-alcoholic fatty liver and these have been less studied.

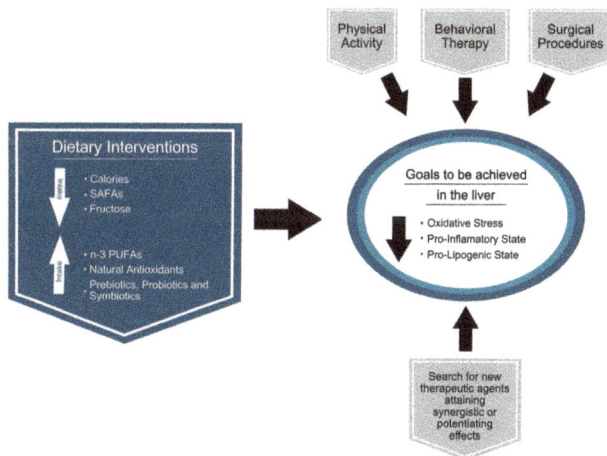

Figure 1. Interventions for the prevention and treatment of non-alcoholic fatty liver disease (NAFLD). *Abbreviations*: n-3 PUFAs, n-3 polyunsaturated fatty acids; SAFAs, saturated fatty acids.

Since there is no consensus about weight loss in the NAFLD treatment, Ghaemi *et al.* [13] implemented a pilot study that assessed the effects of weight loss on characteristics of NAFLD and associated conditions. For this purpose, 44 NAFLD patients received a diet including a reduction in the daily intake from 1000 to 500 kcal, with a distribution with respect to the total caloric value of 30% fat, 15% protein and 55% carbohydrate for six months. At the end of follow-up period, patients were classified as adherent or non-adherent to treatment according to a weight loss ≥5% or <5% of initial body weight, respectively. After the intervention, 56.8% of patients were classified as adherent group and the 43.2% as non-adherent group, and significant reductions were found in the adherent group in relation to diastolic blood pressure (80.2 to 76.9 mmHg) and the serum levels of total cholesterol (TC), low-density lipoprotein LDL cholesterol (LDL-C), triglycerides (TGs), alanine aminotransferase (ALT), aspartate aminotransferase (AST) and gamma-glutamyl transpeptidase (GGT) activities. These results suggest that reduction in weight is a good therapeutic strategy for obese patients with NAFLD, which reach a weight loss of 9.7% of initial body weight after six months of dietary therapy [13]. Similarly, a systematic review of the impact of non-surgical treatments currently available for liver disease and NASH was conducted in order to determine the metabolic risk in publications, which included a total of 78 randomized trials (30 in nonalcoholic steatohepatitis (NASH) and 40 in NAFLD) [14]. It was found that weight loss was safe, improved the cardiometabolic risk profile, and that a weight loss of ≥7% recovered the histological features of the disease; however, this weight loss was only achieved in less than 50% of patients [14].

The interventions focused on changes in lifestyle are considered a key element for the treatment of NAFLD and metabolic syndrome, and although the optimal strategy has not been developed, and that weight loss and exercise are essential, the long-term sustainability of any intervention is a key factor for this to be successful [15]. While interventions aimed at weight loss are recommended, the reduction in weight by dietary restriction is on average unsustainable in the long term, considering that weight loss usually returns to the initial weight over time [16]. Therefore, appropriate strategies to reduce NAFLD that not only include weight loss are necessary, physical activity being an important factor playing a protective healthy role in NAFLD [17] (Figure 1).

Few studies have demonstrated the efficacy of physical activity, in combination with a diet and weight loss. In a prospective study of 141 individuals with NAFLD who were approached in interventions in lifestyle with mild or moderate intensity, those who increased or maintained their physical activity at a level of 150 min/week or more had greater improvement in liver enzymes, regardless of changes in the weight [18]. In another study of 44 patients who completed a regular exercise program, serum ALT was normalized in 55% of patients, whereas 34% that did not meet the exercise program did not present any standardization [19]. Even small gains in fitness and physical activity can have significant health benefits for patients with NAFLD, as found when practiced training exercise by a very short period (4 weeks) attained decreased liver lipids in obese patients without changes in body weight [20].

However, as the success in changing lifestyle is influenced by personal beliefs and values, it becomes complex to encourage patients to make changes in unhealthy behaviors. Accordingly, behavioral and psychological strategies are considered necessary [6]. Behavioral treatments are global therapeutic approaches that give patients practical tools to achieve their goals of intake and exercise [21]. Few studies have evaluated the effects of behavioral approaches in patients with NAFLD; two out of 10 were controlled trials [22]. These studies compared the effects of Vitamin E and Orlistat against behavioral treatments, and both were in favor of the behavioral approach, with an added effect of Orlistat in weight loss. More recently, intensive interventions of lifestyles in patients with different backgrounds of disease (28 with suspected of fatty liver) were shown to be more effective than the prescription of a dietary standard, both in terms of weight loss and in liver enzymes [23].

Few randomized controlled trials (RCTs) have evaluated the effectiveness of treatments for NAFLD in pediatric population. At present, weight loss by controlling caloric intake, the improvement in the quality of diet and exercise are considered the first line of treatment [24]. An analysis of the current management of pediatric NAFLD showed bariatric surgery and drug treatment with Orlistat and insulin sensitizers are not recommended as first or second line treatment for NAFLD. Thus, interventions focused on changes in lifestyle through diet and exercise remain the first line treatment of NAFLD in children population [5]. Trials have shown that treatments with cysteamine bitartrate, probiotics, polyunsaturated fatty acids (PUFAs) and pentoxifylline have beneficial effects. However, few RCTs with powered statistical that have evaluated the impact of these treatments on histological changes. In the case of vitamin E, it was shown to have beneficial effects and was able to improve liver morphology in children with non-alcoholic steatohepatitis. In conclusion, in pediatric patients the interventions in lifestyle are the first choice of treatment and vitamin E should be considered for children with demonstrated NASH or for those at risk of NASH who have failed to the first choice of treatment. While other therapies show promising results, large RCTs with persuasive endpoints are needed [5].

Table 1. Studies on lifestyle interventions in non-alcoholic fatty liver disease (NAFLD).

Intervention	Findings	Reference
Weight loss ≥5% of initial body weight	Significant reduction in systolic blood pressure, total cholesterol, low-density lipoprotein cholesterol, triglycerides, alanine aminotransferase (ALT), aspartate aminotransferase, and γ-glutamyl transferase in the adherent group (weight loss ≥5% of initial body weight)	[13]
Weight loss (≥7%)	Weight loss is safe and improves liver histology and cardiometabolic profile, but it is only achieved in <50% of patients	[16]
Increasing or maintaining the level of physical activity in 150 min/week or more	Greater improvement in levels of liver enzymes, independently of changes in weight	[18]
Complete a regular exercise program	ALT normalization	[19]
Training exercises for 4 weeks	Reduction in liver lipids in obese patients even in the absence of changes in body weight	[20]
Intensive lifestyle interventions	Intensive lifestyle interventions were more effective than the prescription of dietary standard, both in weight loss and in liver enzymes	[23]
Review of the current management of pediatric NAFLD	Lifestyle interventions should be the first line treatment for pediatric NAFLD. Vitamin E could be considered for those with non-alcoholic steatohepatitis (NASH) demonstrated by biopsy or those at risk for NASH where the first line therapy has failed. Other therapies require large RCTs in pediatric population	[5]

3. Dietary Interventions

Various changes in dietary intake have occurred in recent years, which are characterized by an increase in energy intake (24%) due to enhancements in the consumption of flour, cereal products, added sugar and fats, and/or in total fat and fruit intake [25]. The use of corn syrup or high fructose as sweeteners in beverages has increased to comprise 41% of the total sweeteners, with added sucralose accounting for 45%, changes that have undoubtedly helped to increase the prevalence of NAFLD, in association with enhanced obesity and fructose intake from soft drinks [26]. Consequently, a number of diet interventions in different models of NAFLD have been evaluated, as shown in Table 2. In Addition, given the high prevalence of NAFLD in adolescents and its close relationship with cardiovascular disease (CVD), it is imperative to implement strategies focused on prevention through diet and changes in lifestyle, and the validation of effective treatment options [27].

3.1. Caloric Restriction and Macronutrient Distribution

With the central point that insulin resistance is one of the main problems in NAFLD, a diet with low carbohydrate intake could be considered a reasonable treatment option for these patients

(Figure 1). Similarly, studies have reported the benefits of a diet with caloric restriction independent of macronutrients distribution [28], and soy products also have been considered as an important component in the diet for the treatment of NAFLD in the animal model [29], since soy isoflavones increase the antioxidant capacity and reduce hepatic lipid deposits [30]. The latter effect may be related to inhibition of lipogenic transcription factor sterol regulatory element binding protein 1c (SREBP-1c) and activation of peroxisome proliferator-activated receptor alpha (PPAR-α), upregulating fatty acids (FA) oxidation enzymes in the liver [30]. Kani *et al.* [31] evaluated the effects of a diet low in calories and low in carbohydrate containing soy in patients with NAFLD through a RCT of 45 patients with NAFLD who received three different diets: The low calorie diet (restriction of 200–500 calories according to the requirements of each participant and a distribution of 55% of calories from carbohydrates, 15% from proteins and 30% from fat), the low-calorie and low-carbohydrate diet (the same calorie restriction but the distribution was 45% carbohydrates, 35% fat and 25% protein), or a diet low in carbohydrates and in calories, containing soy (the same calorie restriction, the distribution was 45% carbohydrates, 35% fat and 25% protein, but 30 g of soy nut was incorporated instead of 30 g of red meat) for 6 weeks. It was found that changes in both weight and in lipid profile were not significantly different between the 3 groups, but the low-calorie, low-carbohydrate containing soy diet could reduce further the levels of serum ALT, AST, fibrinogen, and of the lipid peroxidation indicator malondialdehyde (MDA), over those achieved by the low-calorie diet [31].

Few studies have evaluated the relationship between protein intake and NAFLD. Protein supplements have offered short-term benefits against hepatic steatosis and lipid profile in sedentary and obese women [32]. In this regard, the research focus has been on the functional properties of soy intake and nitrogen, because soy protein has been shown to be successful in this scenario [33]. In this respect, dietary recommendations in NAFLD patients are 1.000/1.200 kcal/day for overweight women and 1.200/1.600 kcal/day for overweight men. Ideal diet: 50% carbohydrates, 30% lipids (7%–10% saturated fatty acids), and 20% proteins. Diets are developed to provide a calorie deficit of approximately 500 kcal from usual food consumption causing a weight loss of 0.5–1.0 kg/week [34]. Facts interventions with this type of diet (25% of the caloric value from fat (7% saturated fat, 10% monounsaturated fat and 8% polyunsaturated fat), 35% from protein (animal and plant) and 40% from carbohydrates (50% from whole grains, sugar 25 g and 20 g protein/day)) show that the body mass index (BMI), waist circumference, and body fat mass remained relatively stable, whereas high-density lipoprotein HDL cholesterol (HDL-C) increased significantly and TC, LDL-C, VLDL cholesterol (VLDL-C), TGs, AST, GGT, alkaline phosphatase (ALP), fasting blood glucose, and glycosylated hemoglobin (HbA1c) decreased significantly [34]. When stratify patients according to the increase or reduction in BMI, an association between weight loss and liver profit reflected through the ALP and ALT markers was found, and the AST/ALT ratio was observed, with failure to show any changes in patients that increased their weight. Multivariate analysis showed that waist circumference, ferritin, TGs and markers of glucose homeostasis were the parameters most associated with liver enzymes [34].

Studies in an animal model with high-protein diets have also been developed, evaluating whether a high-protein diet prevents the development of steatosis in C57BL/6 male mice with or without pre-existing liver failure, using diets including low-fat or high-fat, low in protein (11% protein) or high in protein (35% protein), high fat/high protein (42% fat and 35% protein), or high fat/low protein (42% fat and 11% protein) for 3 weeks [35]. The results indicate that diets high in protein decreased the hepatic lipid content to ~40% of the corresponding low protein diets, high protein diets being more effective in this regard that reducing energy intake by 80%, which were able to reverse the steatosis induced by pre-existing diet. Compared to diets with low protein, mice fed high protein diets showed increased mitochondrial oxidative capacity and elongation of long chain fatty acids (LCFA), a selective enhancement in plasma branched chain amino acids (BCAA) levels, stellate cells diminution, and a trend towards reduced inflammation [35].

3.2. Fructose Restriction

The fructose intake in American adolescents (mainly as soft drink) representing the 12% of daily calories, this high fructose intake exceeds current recommendations and is considered as one of the components dietary responsible for promoting NAFLD in this demographic group [36]. In studies of short-term feeding in experimental animals and humans, fructose intake increases the accumulation of fats in the liver and of TGs in plasma due in part to increased *de novo* lipogénesis [37]. In this sense, it has been seen that patients with NAFLD have a fructose intake 2-fold greater than the average intake in control patients, according to population studies, exhibited significant increases in the hepatic mRNA expression of fructokinase and FA synthase, suggesting a high pro-lipogenic potential with consequent ATP depletion that can promote necroinflammation [38]. Also, fructose is involved in oxidative damage through the reduction of antioxidant defense and improvement in the production of reactive oxygen species (ROS) [39]. Both lipid overload and oxidative stress promote the fructose as a triggering factor in the onset and progression of NAFLD [40]. Dyslipidemia, insulin resistance and oxidative damage induced by high fructose intake may contribute to increased risk of CVD that is evident in patients with NAFLD [41]; it makes lack direct evidence demonstrating the benefits of the restriction of fructose in the liver steatosis and CVD. An intervention double-blind, controlled, randomized trial in 24 Hispanic-American adolescents with overweight who had a frequent intake of sweet drinks and a content of liver fat greater than 8% as determined by magnetic resonance spectroscopy, showed that when patients were submitted to take only beverages with fructose or glucose only (33 g of sugar that match the standard amount of sugar in a typical drink) for four weeks, no significant changes in liver fat or body weight in either group were found. However, in the glucose drinking group there was a significant progress in adipose tissue insulin sensitivity, high-sensitivity C-reactive protein (hs-CRP), and in LDL oxidation, suggesting that fructose reduction improves markers of CVD despite the lack of recovery in hepatic steatosis [27].

3.3. Mediterranean Diet

The Mediterranean diet has been extensively investigated in terms of benefits with regard to cardiovascular risk reduction and improved insulin sensitivity. However, studies have specifically examined their effects on NAFLD are scarce.

Protective effects have been attributed to the Mediterranean diet because of the high intake of antioxidants; vegetables are the main source of phenolic compounds on this diet. Moreover, polyunsaturated fatty acids of the n-3 series from fish regulate haemostatic factors that induce protection against a variety of chronic diseases, and besides, the olive oil represents a high intake of monounsaturated fatty acids and a good source of phytochemicals, and some protective properties of the Mediterranean diet on human health have been granted to the polyphenols present in wine [42]. A recent meta-analysis showed that n-3 PUFAs found in the Mediterranean diet were beneficial in reducing hepatic steatosis [43]. In order to evaluate whether intervention with Mediterranean diet could improve insulin sensitivity in individuals with NAFLD and reduce steatosis to a greater extent than current dietary recommendations, 12 nondiabetic subjects (six males and six females) with biopsy-proven NAFLD were enrolled for a transverse randomized dietary intervention for 6 weeks. All participants were subjected to the Mediterranean diet and to a control diet (low in fat and high in carbohydrates) in a random order with a period of six weeks of washing between each of the diets. As a result, the weight loss was not different between the two types of diet; there was a significant reduction in relative hepatic steatosis after the Mediterranean diet compared to control diet, with improved insulin sensitivity being observed only with the Mediterranean diet [44]. However, this diet should be further investigated in subjects with NAFLD since the size of the groups evaluated was very small in this investigation.

Table 2. Studies on dietary interventions in non-alcoholic fatty liver disease (NAFLD).

Intervention	Model	Conclusions	Reference
Diets restricted in calories and carbohydrates with soy protein addition	Human	Intervention can have beneficial effects on serum levels of liver enzymes, malonaldehyde and fibrinogen in patients with NAFLD	[31]
Low calorie diet rich in proteins	Human	A protein diet is associated with improved lipid profile, glucose homeostasis, and improved liver enzymes in NAFLD, independently of decreases in body mass index (BMI) or in body fat mass	[34]
High protein diet	Animal	The high-protein diet prevents and reverses the steatosis, regardless of fat and carbohydrate intake, and is more efficient than a 20% reduction in energy intake	[35]
Soft drinks with fructose compared to glucose sodas	Human	Reducing fructose improves several important factors to cardiovascular disease, despite the lack of appreciable improvement in hepatic steatosis in overweight adolescents	[27]
Mediterranean diet	Human	The Mediterranean diet reduces hepatic steatosis and improves insulin sensitivity in insulin-resistant people with NAFLD compared to current dietary recommendations, even in the absence of weight loss	[44]

4. Therapeutic Agents

As mentioned above, fatty liver is mainly generated from the excessive caloric intake and lack of physical activity, pointing to correction of unhealthy styles as the first line approach in the prevention and treatment of NAFLD, which when this intervention is insufficient, drug therapy becomes a strategic line [6] (Figure 1). Because weight loss has been reported to have a low rate of success in the long term [45], research has focused on the development and validation of new dietary therapies aimed at preventing the hepatic steatosis and its progression to NASH [46]. The challenge for the development of therapies for NASH is related to the complexity of the disease, which is directly associated with to visceral obesity, dyslipidemia, hyperglycemia, insulin resistance, and oxidative stress [47,48]. Effective treatments are needed in order to prevent progression of simple steatosis to chronic liver disease [49], considering that fatty liver disease is a reversible condition which if not treated early can lead to a terminal liver disease [50]. Although the pathophysiology of NASH is still not fully understood and the treatments available are not entirely satisfactory, therapies that limit liver injury and the occurrence of inflammation and fibrosis are particularly attractive for this condition [51]. Currently, it is a great challenge for the pharmaceutical industry to develop a combined therapy that is effective in NAFLD patients exhibiting obesity, insulin resistance, dyslipidemia, and oxidative stress. Therefore, serious efforts have been directed to explore novel therapeutic agents that may be directed to multiple targets [52], natural products extracted from medicinal plants being rich sources of biologically active substances having effects on health benefits and disease prevention in humans [53]. Accordingly, current investigations have focused on herbal extracts and natural products with antihyperlipidemic and hepatoprotective effects against NAFLD [54], particularly potential sources of antioxidants [55] (Table 3).

4.1. Amino Acid Supplementation Interventions

4.1.1. Tryptophan

Earlier studies conducted in hens have suggested that supplementation with the amino acid tryptophan (Trp) reduces hepatic lipid accumulation [56]. Recently, the influence of Trp supplementation on NAFLD induced by a fructose-rich diet was studied in C57BL/6J mice, as precursor of serotonin, a regulator of the intestinal motility and permeability [51]. Under these conditions, NAFLD underlying lipid accumulation and increased portal plasma lipopolysaccharide (LPS) concentrations, resulted in derangement of intestinal barrier functions, as evidenced by depressed expression of the tight-junction protein occluding and the serotonin re-uptake transporter (SERT), changes that were attenuated or abolished by Trp. The authors suggested that modulation of the intestinal barrier and the serotonergic system by Trp supplementation may be of importance as a protective mechanism against development of NAFLD in mice [57], although further studies are required to validate this proposal in humans.

4.1.2. Glutamine

In recent years, glutamine was shown to improve hepatic ischemia-reperfusion injury, alcohol-induced liver injury, and gut-derived endotoxemia, promoting resistance to oxidative stress, reducing inflammatory cytokine release, and regulating immune reactions [58]. Assessment of the influence of glutamine on NAFLD induced in rats by a high fat diet (HFD) revealed that hepatic steatosis was accompanied by significant increased liver lipid peroxidation, tumor necrosis factor α (TNF-α) levels, and of p65 NF-κB expression, with concomitant glutathione (GSH) depletion.

Glutamine supplementation reduced the oxidative status of the liver and inhibited NF-κB expression, in association with improvement of hepatic steatosis, suggesting a protective effect of glutamine in NAFLD [58].

4.1.3. L-Carnitine Intervention

L-carnitine plays a critical role in lipid metabolism as it acts as an essential cofactor for β-oxidation of PUFAs by facilitating their transport into the mitochondrial matrix associated with carnitine palmitoyltransferase I (CPT-I) activation, thus converting fat into energy [59]. In recent years, L-carnitine has been proposed as a treatment option for various diseases including liver disease [59]. Using a NASH model mouse subjected to either HFD, HFD plus L-carnitine, or HFD with α-tocopherol, L-carnitine induced an enhancement in the hepatic expression of genes implicated in the transport of long chain PUFAs, mitochondrial β-oxidation, and antioxidant enzymes, with suppression of markers of oxidative stress and inflammatory cytokines in NASH, changes that were similar to those elicited by α-tocopherol. It was concluded that L-carnitine acts as a protective agent to prevent progression of NASH by favoring mitochondrial β-oxidation and redox systems [59].

4.2. n-3 Polyunsaturated Fatty Acids (n-3 PUFAs) Interventions

The n-3 PUFAs are crucial structural components of cellular lipids, substrates for the biosynthesis of physiological mediators, and signaling molecules regulating liver lipid metabolism. The latter feature is achieved by (i) transcriptional activation of the expression of enzymes involved in FA oxidation acting as ligands of PPAR-α; and (ii) suppression of *de novo* lipogenesis by down-regulation of SREBP-1c [60]. Therefore, n-3 PUFA depletion in the liver of NAFLD patients favoring FA and TGs formation over FA oxidation [61] points n-3 PUFAs as specific anti-steatotic drugs for NAFLD (Figure 1) [62]. A systematic review by Parker *et al.* [43] on studies pertaining to the effect of n-3 PUFA supplementation in NAFLD patients, including 9 reports and 355 individuals who were administered either n-3 PUFA treatment or placebo, confirmed a significant reduction in hepatic lipid content. Although there was significant heterogeneity between studies, pooled data suggest that supplementation of n-3 PUFAs reduces liver fat, an effect that persists when data from RCTs are analyzed; however, the optimal dose remains to be established. Interestingly, n-3 PUFAs also improved circulating liver functions markers, TGs and TNF-α level, and hepatic microcirculatory function [43]. It was suggested that future designs of RCTs quantifying the magnitude of the effects of n-3 PUFA supplementation on liver fat are necessary [43], which are also important for liver inflammation and fibrosis outcomes [63].

Studies in pediatric patients with NAFLD have also been developed, the most prominent being the RCT of Nobili *et al.* [64] using docosahexaenoic acid (DHA) treatment (250 and 500 mg/day) *versus* placebo in 60 pediatric patients with NAFLD, with evaluation of the changes in the fat liver content by ultrasonography after 6, 12, 18 and 24 months of intervention, and changes in TGs, ALT, BMI, and the homeostatic model assessment (HOMA) index of insulin resistance. Data reported indicate that DHA decreased liver fat content after 6 months of supplementation, an effect that persists up to 24 months and is equally effective at the two dosages studied, when compared with the placebo group. Furthermore, TGs were lower in DHA-treated children than in controls at any time intervention, ALT was lower in groups with 12 months of DHA treatment onwards, and HOMA was lower in the group given 250 mg DHA/day *versus* placebo group at 6 and 12 months [64], in agreement with the positive outcomes reported in adult NAFLD patients.

4.3. Vitamin Supplementation Interventions

4.3.1. Niacin

Niacin is the precursor of nicotinamide coenzymes acting either as oxidants $(NAD(P)^+)$ in catabolic processes or as reductants (NADPH) in anabolic reactions or in the recovery of the reduced form of antioxidant components, thus decreasing oxidative stress [65]. It has been used for the treatment of dyslipidemia and CVD [66], and proposed to prevent hepatic steatosis and delay NASH induced by HFD [67]. This proposal was tested in Sprague-Dawley rats fed either a standard rodent diet, HFD, or HFD containing 0.5% or 1.0% niacin for 4 weeks. Under these conditions, niacin supplementation in the HFD significantly decreased the content of liver fat, liver weight, liver oxidative products, preventing fatty liver [67]. While niacin had no effect on the mRNA expression of enzymes related to FA synthesis and oxidation including acetyl CoA carboxylase 1 (ACC-1), FAS, and CPT-1, and lipogenic transcription factor SREBP-1c, it significantly down-regulated the mRNA and protein expression and the activity of diacylglycerol acyltransferase (DGAT), a key enzyme in triglyceride synthesis, thus in agreement with its receding effect on steatosis [67].

4.3.2. Vitamin E

Natural vitamin E is fat soluble tocopherol comprising eight isomers including four tocopherols and four tocotrienols, RRR-α-tocopherol being the most abundant and with the highest biological activity, which is mainly related to antioxidation by avoid the propagation of free radical reactions at the cell membrane level [68,69]. The potential role of vitamin E in preventing fat infiltration in the liver was assessed in Wistar rats fed either a standard diet (SD), a diet high in cholesterol and saturated fat (HCSF), or a diet high in cholesterol and saturated fat with added of water soluble vitamin E (10 IU/kg/day; HCSF-E) for ten weeks. The results indicate that vitamin E exerted hypolipidemic and hepatoprotective effects, as evidenced by the lower levels of total cholesterol found in HCSF-E treated rats over the HCSF group, in addition to lower serum glutamic oxaloacetic transaminase (SGOT) and steatosis scores at the end of the study compared with the initial values [70]. However, no significant differences between the different experimental groups were observed in relation to blood glucose and serum lipids [70]. In addition, it has been found that when vitamin E is supplied for a period of 2 years to patients with NAFLD, the histological features of the disease improve but, in turn, an increase in insulin resistance and plasma levels of TGs was observed [14].

4.4. Interventions with Prebiotics, Probiotics, and Synbiotics

Current evidence suggests that the accumulation of triglycerides in the liver responds not only to obesity, but also, the intestinal microbiota plays a key role in the development of insulin resistance, fatty liver, fibrosis and necroinflammatory score, and thereby becomes an endogenous factor that favors the development of NAFLD [71,72]. The link between the liver-intestinal axis and NAFLD is associated with bacterial overgrowth in the small intestine and increased intestinal permeability [73].

The intestine has a complex array of species of microorganisms, wherein the concentration and type of these microorganisms is mainly influenced by the host genotype and availability nutrient [74]. The liver is susceptible to exposure to intestinal bacterial-derived products through a functional and anatomical connection with the intestinal lumen via the portal vein system [75]. The contribution of the microflora in the progression of NAFLD is given mainly by the improvement in hepatic oxidative stress as a result of increased ethanol production and LPS in the intestinal lumen, and the subsequent release of inflammatory cytokines from the inflammatory cells [76]. High concentrations of cytokines may increase intestinal permeability via disruption of intercellular tight junctions, resulting in progressive inflammation and fibrosis within the liver [77], TNF-α plays a critical role in both insulin resistance and uptake by the liver of inflammatory cells in NAFLD [78]. In recent years, it became clear that a high degree of inflammation due to metabolic endotoxemia has an implication in various diseases, including that induced by high fructose intake that changes the intestinal microbiota and intestinal barrier permeability, resulting in increased bacteria derived LPS [79]. As the various species of the gut microbiota are involved in different intestinal biological functions, such as the defense against colonization by opportunistic pathogens, development of a suitable gut architecture can contribute to immune system homeostasis [80]. In this respect, it has been found that manipulating the enteric flora may represent a key therapeutic strategy in the treatment of NASH. Intake of probiotics (living microorganisms), prebiotics (oligosaccharides), and symbiotics (mixture of probiotics and prebiotics) has been reported by their ability to modify the composition of the microbiota and thereby restore the microbial balance. So, exert benefits for health protection [81] (Figure 1).

Animal model studies have shown that probiotics can reduce the progression of NAFLD. Among these, one study evaluated the effect of supplementation with the mixture VSL Pharmaceuticals, Inc., Ft. Lauderdale, FL, USA (VSL#3); a probiotic containing 450 billion bacteria in various strains (three types of bacteria: *Streptococcus*, *Bifidobacterium* and *Lactobacillus*), to ob/ob mice for a period of four weeks and showed that in response to supplementation was observed a reduction in hepatic fatty acid content, in liver inflammation and, in addition to an improvement in the insulin resistance in the liver [82]. It has also been shown that treatment with probiotics lead to a direct reduction in the release of pro-inflammatory cytokines by a down-regulation in the activity of transcription factor NF-κB [83]. In the model of NASH induced by HFD in rats, the treatment with VSL#3 resulted in a reduction in the expression of markers of lipid peroxidation, TNF-α, inducible nitric oxide synthase (iNOS) and cyclooxygenase 2 (COX-2), when compared with the control group [84]. Similarly, treatment with VSL#3 resulted in a minor insulin resistance in liver and adipose tissue, thus counteracting the development of NASH and atherosclerosis in genetically dyslipidemic ApoE(−/−) mice [85]. Moreover, Ritze *et al.* [86] studied whether supplementation with *Lactobacillus* rhamnosus (LGG) could alleviate experimental NAFLD in C57BL/J6 mice, through administration of fructose via drinking water containing 30% fructose with or without LGG at a concentration of 5×10^7 colony-forming units (cfu) per g body weight. Upon completion of the intervention period, it was found that treatment with LLG generated an increase of beneficial bacteria in the small intestine as well as a restoration in the duodenal tight-junction protein concentration and reduced of portal LPS levels. In addition, attenuation in the hepatic mRNA expression of TNF-α, interleukin-8 (IL-8), and IL-1β, liver fat accumulation, and portal ALT levels were observed in animals fed the high fructose diet plus LGG [86]. Similar studies with *Lactobacillus casei* strain Shirota (LcS) given orally to mice fed a methionine-choline-deficient diet (MCD) that reduces lactic acid bacteria such as *Lactobacillus* and *Bifidobacterium* in feces, increased not only the LcS subgroup but also the lactic acid types, with concomitant suppression of MCD-diet-induced NASH development [87].

In agreement with experimental studies [82], the use of the probiotic VSL#3 in NAFLD patients for 2 to 3 months improved routine liver damage tests and oxidative stress-related indicators, without improvement in pro-inflammatory cytokines, suggesting that manipulation of intestinal flora should be taken into consideration as adjunctive therapy in NAFLD [88]. Two randomized placebo-controlled double-blind studies showed a significant decrease in liver AST with the administration of probiotics in children [89] and in adults [90]. Also, symbiotic studies have been developed in humans, which are included in a recent meta-analysis reporting favorable results in four RCTs, two of which involved the use of symbiotic by co-treatment of probiotics with fructo-oligosaccharides (FOS), the latter prebiotics being potentially promoters of the growth of beneficial bifidobacteria in the intestinal tract [91]. It is noteworthy that one of the previous trials in patients with NASH including liver biopsies showed improvement in liver histology after 6 months of symbiotic treatment containing *Bifidobacterium longum* and FOS [92]. With the intention of defining whether treatment with symbiotics imply greater effectiveness on changes in lifestyle for the treatment of NAFLD, Eslamparast *et al.* [78] designed a RCT with 52 NAFLD patients treated with either a symbiotic or placebo for 28 days, concomitantly with diet and physical activity recommendations. It was found that symbiotic supplementation with lifestyle modification is a better strategy than life style adjustment alone in NAFLD treatment, leading to attenuation of markers of liver damage, inflammation, and fibrosis [78].

4.5. Interventions with Polyphenols

Polyphenols are natural compounds produced by plants comprising a heterogeneous group of agents characterized by hydroxylated phenyl moieties. Among them, two types of compounds are distinguished, namely (i) flavonoids containing a common diphenylpropane skeleton (e.g., flavonoids, flavones, flavonols, flavanols, isoflavones, proanthocyanidins, and anthocyanins); and (ii) non flavonoids mainly comprising mono-phenols alcohols (e.g., hydroxytyrosol), or stilbene phenolic acids (e.g., resveratrol) [93]. Several polyphenols have beneficial actions on human health, with potential mechanisms including (i) non-specific antioxidant action due to the existence of a phenol group capable of scavenging free radicals (Figure 1); and (ii) certain mechanisms focused on interactions of particular structural characteristics of polyphenols with proteins or defined membrane domains [94].

4.5.1. Resveratrol, Catechin and Quercetin

The cardioprotective, anti-cancer, and anti-inflammatory properties of resveratrol have been well characterized, a polyphenol that has been reported to present suitable protective effects on the liver against the hepatic lipid accumulation in response to a HFD [95]. The beneficial effects attributed to resveratrol have been awarded mainly to its antioxidant and anti-inflammatory effects that exert protective tissues such as the liver, kidney and brain against a variety of damage caused by oxidative stress and inflammation [96], raising the proposal that resveratrol can be used in the treatment for metabolic disorders including fatty liver disease [97]. In this context, resveratrol was reported to activate sirtuin 1 (SIRT1) with the consequent stimulation of AMP-activated protein kinase (AMPK) [98] through phosphorylation mediated by liver kinase B1 (LKB1) that protects against liver lipid accumulation by down-regulation of FAS expression induced by high glucose [97]. Similarly, resveratrol also blocks the expression of SREBP-1 through the SIRT1/forkhead box O1 (FOXO1) pathway leading to a lipid-lowering effect in HepG2 cells treated with palmitate [99]. A recent randomized, double-blind, placebo-controlled study assessed the scope of resveratrol supplementation in 50 individuals with NAFLD over subjects given placebo for 12 weeks, both groups being subjected to lifestyle improvement. In both groups, the anthropometric measurements, liver enzymes, and degree of steatosis improved. However, resveratrol supplementation was associated with a significant reduction in liver ALT, inflammatory cytokines, NF-κβ activity, serum cytokeratin 18, and grade of hepatic steatosis, compared to placebo-supplemented group. The authors concluded that resveratrol supplementation along with lifestyle modification is a better treatment for NAFLD than lifestyle improvement alone, which is mainly due to attenuation of inflammation and hepatocyte apoptosis [100]. Diminutions in hepatic inflammation and lipogenesis are also observed in HFD fed mice given 30 mg resveratrol/kg/day for 60 days over control values, as evidenced by significant decreases in mRNA expression of either TNF-α, interleukin-6 (IL-6) and NF-κB or the lipogenic factors PPAR-γ, SREBP-1, and ACC-1 [101].

Epidemiological evidence has reported that intake of green tea (Camellia sinensis) may protect against liver injury due to inverse association with lipid profile and serum ALT [102]. While this approach has not yet been confirmed through RCTs in humans, epigallocatechin gallate (EGCG), the main polyphenol catechin in green tea, have been shown to generate a reduction in hepatic lipid accumulation and serum monocyte chemoattractant protein-1 (MCP-1) levels, in a mouse model of diet-induced NASH [103]. Liver protection against HFD-induced NASH in rats was also attained by a green tea extract after 8 weeks supplementation, as shown by an increase in glutathione status related with the inhibition of liver and adipose tissue inflammatory responses mediated by NF-κβ [46].

Quercetin is a flavonoid present in the human diet with a variety of preventive effects in typical human diseases [104], through mechanisms that include a down-regulation in the activation of NF-κB, inducible nitric oxide synthase expression in IL-1β activated rat hepatocytes [105] and also in the improvement in hepatic damage in rats with biliary obstruction [106]. Other significant beneficial effects of quercetin include a reduction in plasma concentrations of oxidized LDL in patients with overweight [107] and a decreased hepatic steatosis induced by Western diet in C57BL/6J mice [108] and attenuation of inflammation and fibrosis in a mouse model of NASH by MCD [51].

4.5.2. Proanthocyanidins and Anthocyanidins

Proanthocyanidins from grape seeds (GSP) are a complex mixture of polyphenolic bioflavonoids having high antioxidant activity, with preventive effects in some forms of cancer and oxidative injury [109]. In a recent study, the effects of GSP and the insulin sensitizer metformin were assessed individually or in combination in a diet-induced NAFLD in Wistar rats subjected to a high fat and high fructose diet (HFFD) [110]. GSP (100 mg/kg/day) and metformin (50 mg/kg/day) were given orally once a day and for the combined treatment, GSP and metformin was administered at 4 h intervals. HFFD resulted in an abnormal plasma lipid profile, with liver inflammation and steatosis, hepatic TGs levels being reduced by 69%, 23%, and 63% after GSP, metformin, and combined treatment, respectively. Accordingly, GSP reduced the mRNA expression of SREBP-1c and increased that of PPAR-α more effectively compared to metformin in HFFD-treated rats; however, no additive effect restoring lipid levels was observed when GSP and metformin were combined [110].

Anthocyanidins (ACNs) are hydrosoluble flavonoids within the polyphenol class, which are responsible for the red, purple, and blue colors of many flowers, cereal grains, fruits, and vegetables [111]. ACNs alleviate hyperglycemia, modulate endothelial function, and reduce inflammation [112], and are able to modulate lipid metabolism and fat deposits in various tissues including the liver [113]. Since the impact of ACNs on NAFLD is not well defined, a literature search grouping experimental *in vitro* and *in vivo* models and human trials was conducted [111]. Although the interpretation of the evidence from *in vitro* studies is hampered by differences in cell models, experimental protocols, and molecular pathways evaluated, most studies are consistent in that ACNs reduced hepatocellular accumulation of lipids by inhibiting lipogenesis and possibly by promoting lipolysis. In addition, interpretation of the data from *in vivo* studies is difficult, due to the large difference in experimental models of NASH used and the utilization of animals exposed to either synthetic ACNs (e.g., Cyanidin-3-*o*-β-glucoside) or to extracts of foods rich in ACNs (e.g., sweet potato, berries, and oranges). Nonetheless, these studies reported an improvement in systemic and hepatic insulin resistance and serum lipids, sometimes related to weight loss and increased PPAR-α activation inducing lipolysis and diminished lipogenesis, thus decreasing hepatic fat content [111]. Finally, a clinical trial enrolling 48 adult borderline hepatitis patients with increased liver enzymes supplemented with 200 mg ANCs of purple sweet potato (PSP) or placebo twice a day for 8 weeks showed that ACNs are associated with reduced levels of liver enzymes, particularly GGT [114]. Although this feature was not associated with liver damage and liver fat was not confirmed by direct imaging, the researchers suggest that the PSP beverage can offer potential activity hepatoprotective against oxidative stress [114]. The final conclusion of the literature search by Valenti *et al.* [111] is that ACNs can prevent the progression of liver damage related to NAFLD by three independent mechanisms, namely, inhibition of lipogenesis by decrease of SREBP-1c, lipolysis promotion by induction of PPAR-α activity, and reduction of oxidative stress, pointing to foods rich in ACNs as a promising strategy for preventing NAFLD and its complications, however future RCTs are needed to test their hepatoprotective efficacy in NAFLD [113].

4.6. Medicinal Plants Interventions

For centuries, products made from natural herbs derived from Traditional Chinese Medicine have been used to treat almost all types of diseases in China [115]. Natural products extracted from medicinal plants are rich sources of biologically active substances and have desirable effects on health benefits and disease prevention in humans [53]; therefore, an increasing number of investigations has been focused on extracts of herbs or natural products with anti-hyperlipidemic and hepatoprotectives effects against NAFLD. Considering the above and also that the use of medicinal herbs is becoming increasingly common for handling of NAFLD, Liu *et al.* [50] conducted a systematic review in order to evaluate both beneficial and detrimental effects of them. The study included 77 randomized trials covering 6753 participants with fatty liver disease, the average sample size was 88 participants per test, and 75 different herbal products were evaluated including single herb products, commercially available proprietary medicinal herbs, and combination formulas prescribed by physicians. It was found that (i) six trials showed a statistically significant effect on hepatic B-ultrasound; (ii) four trials showed a significant increase on liver/spleen computed tomography ratio; and (iii) forty two trials showed reduction in AST levels, forty nine trials in ALT, three trials in ALP, and thirty-two in GGT levels in the herbal group. Overall, these findings indicate that herbal medicines may have positive consequences on fatty liver disease, However, there is insufficient evidence to recommend these medicinal herbs for the management of NAFLD because of the high risk of bias and lack of homogeneous data in studies [50].

4.6.1. Tamarindus Indica Linn

At present time, Tamarindus indica Linn is one of the most important resources of plants for supply of foods and materials [52]. Considering that the seed coat of tamarind contains polyphenols including tannins, anthocyanins, and anthocyanidin oligomers, Sasidharan *et al.* [52] evaluated the ameliorative potential of seed coat of Tamarindus indica (ETS) extracts on HFD-induced NAFLD in rats. At dosages of 45, 90, and 180 mg/kg ETS significantly attenuated the pathological changes associated with NAFLD induced by HFD, namely, hepatomegaly, elevated liver lipids and lipid peroxides, serum ALT levels, free fatty acids, and macro and micro hepatic steatosis. In addition, ETS treatment markedly reduced body weight and adiposity, probably acting in part through anti-obesity, insulin sensitizing, and antioxidant mechanisms [52].

4.6.2. Salvia-Nelumbinis Naturalis (SNN)

Salvia-Nelumbinis naturalis (SNN) formulae (initially called Jiangzhi Granula) was designed, in which Salvia as being the principal element and Nelumbinis, Rhizoma Polygoni Cuspidati, Herba Artemisiae Scopariae the ancillary components [115]. In a study of *in vivo* and *in vitro* model the researchers found that intervention with SNN components in HepG2 cells decreased lipid accumulation and in rats the SNN extract improved the steatohepatitis and conferred a normal lipoproteinemia profile in rats fed high-calorie diet, where the effectiveness of the extract SNN to improve liver function and insulin sensitivity was comparable with medications such as simvastatin and pioglitazone [115].

4.6.3. Ostol Treatment

Ostol is the active compound of Cnidium monnieri extract. Ostol has been described by its anti-inflammatory and cytoprotective effects to promote the oxidation of fat. In an animal model of fatty liver in rats, the ostol treatment induced a decrease in fasting glucose levels and hepatic fat content, besides, resulted in improved insulin resistance [116]. Another study reported that treatment with ostol decreased liver fat content by increasing in the hepatic expression of PPAR-α/γ [117]. Similarly, in a model of NASH, ostol treatment led to an increase in the activation of superoxide dismutase (SOD) and decrease in oxidative stress [118]. Nam *et al.* [119] treated rats Sprague-Dawley with HFD plus ostol (20 mg/kg) 5 times a week and found that compared with the group only HFD, HFD plus ostol group showed a significant decrease in intrahepatic fat (39.4% *versus* 21.0%), the expression of SREBP-1c, FAS and intrahepatic stearoyl CoA desaturase-1 (SCD-1) significantly decreased and the expression of PPAR-α was also significantly higher [119].

4.6.4. Sapindus Mukorossi Gaertn

Studies by Chinese have reported Sapindus mukorossi Gaertn skin is rich in saponins and has properties to regulate fat metabolism and to grant protection to the endothelial cells of blood vessels. However, researchs to provide detailed information about the efficacy of Sapindus mukorossi Gaertn in the prevention and treatment of NAFLD are scarce [120]. Peng *et al.* [120] evaluated in a rat model of NAFLD treatment with an alcohol extract of Sapindus mukorossi Gaertn (AESM) in high dosage (0.5 g/kg), moderate dosage (0.1 g/kg) and low dose (0.05 g/kg). The researchers found that high doses of AESM could relieve AST, ALT, TC, triglycerides, LDL-C, GGT, and also raise HDL-C. Also, the morphology of liver tissue and liver cells began to be normal with this treatment [120].

4.6.5. Sasa Borealis (SBS)

The medicinal benefits of Sasa Borealis Bamboo are mainly given by antidiabetic effects in improving insulin secretion as well as for their hypoglycemic and hypolipidemic, anti-obesogenic and antioxidants effects [121]. For Bamboo, the clinical use for the treatment of hypertension, atherosclerosis, cardiovascular disease and cancer has been reported [122]. However, there have been few studies that have investigated the effects of dietary supplementation with extracts of cane Sasa borealis (SBS) in NAFLD. A recent study examined the effect of supplementation with SBS (150 mg/kg/day) in the presence of a HFD for a cycle of action of 5-week in rats and found that the body weight, liver weight, TGs, TC and lipid accumulation in the liver was significantly lower in the HFD plus SBS group compared with only HFD group. Also in the group supplemented with SBS, the transcription factor PPAR-α is increased significantly and conversely SREBP-1c was suppressed in a meaningful way, in addition, supplementation with SBS lead to a significant reduction in hepatic levels of PPAR-γ mRNA, FAS, ACC1, and enzyme diacylglycerol and acyltransferase-2 (DGAT-2) [121].

Table 3. Studies on therapeutic agents used in non-alcoholic fatty liver disease (NAFLD).

Intervention	Model	Findings	Ref.
Tryptophan supplementation	Animal	Increased occludin concentrations and reduced ratios liver weight/body weight	[57]
Glutamine supplementation	Animal	Reduced oxidative stress in the liver, inhibition of the expression of p65 NF-κB (nuclear factor kappa-light-chain-enhancer of activated B cells), and hepatic steatosis improvement	[58]
L-carnitine supplementation	Animal	Prevention of NAFLD progression through upregulation of mitochondrial β-oxidation and the redox system	[59]
Docosahexaenoic acid (DHA) supplementation	Human	Improvement of hepatic steatosis in children with NAFLD. Doses of 250 and 500 mg/day appear to be equally effective in reducing liver fat content	[64]
Niacin supplementation	Animal	Decreased liver fat content, liver weight, liver oxidative products, and prevention of fatty liver. Inhibition of mRNA and protein expression and diacylglycerol acyltransferase (DGAT) activity. No effects on mRNA expression of sterol regulatory element binding protein 1c (SREBP-1c), acetylCoA carboxylase 1 (ACC-1), fatty acid synthase (FAS), and carnitinepalmitoil transferase 1 (CPT-1)	[67]
Vitamin E supplementation	Animal	Vitamin E combined with exercise exert hypolipidemic and hepatoprotective effects in the presence of an atherogenic diet	[70]
VSL mixture (*Streptococcus, Bifidobacterium, Lactobacillus*)	Animal	Reduction in total fatty acid content in the liver and in hepatic inflammation, with improvement of hepatic insulin sensitivity	[82]
Probiotic treatment	Animal	Down-regulation of the activity of the transcription factor NF-κB	[83]
Lactobacillus rhamnosus treatment	Animal	Attenuation of fat accumulation in the liver and in the concentration of portal alanine aminotransferase (ALT)	[86]
Lactobacillus casein cepa Shirota treatment	Animal	Suppression in NASH development, reduced serum concentrations of lipopolysaccharide (LPS), inhibition of liver inflammation or fibrosis, and diminished inflammation of the colon	[87]
Supplementation with synbiotic, probiotic and prebiotic cultures along with recommendations on healthy lifestyles	Human	The synbiotic supplementation combined with changes in lifestyle is greater than just changes in lifestyle alone for the treatment of NASH	[78]
Resveratrol supplementation	Human	Resveratrol supplementation together with changes in lifestyle is more effective than just changes in lifestyle alone. This is at least partially due to attenuation of inflammatory markers and hepatocellular apoptosis	[100]
Resveratrol supplementation	Animal	Improvement in lipid metabolism and decreased the pro-inflammatory profile of NAFLD in the liver of mice with diet-induced obesity	[101]
Green tea extract	Animal	Higher glutathione levels, lower protein and mRNA contents of inflammatory cytokines, and lower DNA binding activity of NF-κB in liver and adipose tissue of mice supplemented with a green tea extract 2%	[46]
Quercetin treatment	Animal	Total or partial prevention of hepatic steatosis, inflammatory cell accumulation, oxidative stress, and fibrosis caused by the a methionine-choline deficient (MCD)	[51]
Proanthocyanidins from grape seed (GSP) plus metformin	Animal	Improvement of lipid metabolism, but the effects were not additive to normalize lipid levels	[110]
Review of interventions with anthocyanidins (ACNs) in NAFLD patients	Human	Foods rich in ACNs may be promising for prevention of NAFLD and its complications. However, further studies are required	[111]
Seed tamarindus indica	Animal	Intervention has a therapeutic potential against NAFLD, acting in part through insulin sensitization, antioxidant, and anti-obesity mechanisms	[52]
Ostol treatment	Animal	Decreased intrahepatic fat content and in the expression of SREBP-1c, FAS and stearoyl-CoA desaturase-1 (SCD-1), with increased expression of peroxisome proliferator activated receptor α (PPAR-α)	[119]
Sapindus alcohol extract mukorossi Gaertn supplementation	Animal	Regulation of the level of blood fat and improvement in the pathological changes in liver tissue in a rat model of NAFLD	[120]
Sasa borealis (SBS) supplementation	Animal	Improvement in cholesterol metabolism, decreased lipogenesis, and increased oxidation of lipids in rats with high-fat diet (HFD)-induced hepatic steatosis	[121]

4.6.6. Silimarin

Milk thistle has been known for over 2000 years as a herbal medicinal that has been traditionally used for a variety of pathologies. It has been particularly used for handling to diseases related to the liver and gallbladder. Silibum marianum (Latin term for the plant) and its seeds are rich in a variety of natural compounds called flavonolignans. Silimarin is known as a mixture of these compounds, which is extracted after being processed with ethanol, methanol and acetone and contains mainly silibin A, silibin B, taxofolin, isosilibin A, isolsilibin B, silichristin A, silidianin, and other compounds in smaller concentrationes. Apart from its use in liver and gallbladder disorders, milk thistle has recently gained attention due to its hypoglycemic and hypolipidemic properties [123]. Loguercio *et al.* [124] carried out a multicenter, phase III, doubled-blind critical trial to asses RA (comprises the silybin phytosome complex (silybin plus phosphatidylcholine) coformulated with vitamin E) in individuals with NAFLD histologically documented. The participants were distributed (1:1) to receive active treatment (RA; active components: silybin 94 mg, phosphatidylcholine 194 mg, vitamin E acetate 50% (α-tocopherol 30 mg) 89.28 mg) or placebo (P; extrawhite saccharine replacing active components) with a daily dose of 2 times orally and for a period of 12 consecutive months, and the authors found that patients treated with RA showed relief in values of transaminases (AST, ALT) and GGT, insulin resistance and different histological features of the liver [124]. Similarly, a recent study compare the metabolic effects of the Mediterranean diet *versus* the diet associated with silybin, phosphatidylcholine and vitamin E complex (RE complex) in overweight patients with NAFLD and reported that the treatment for six months with the Mediterranean diet and the RE complex, exhibited improvement not only in anthropometric parameters (reduction in BMI and waits circumference) but also in insulin resistance and hepatic fat accumulation [125].

4.7. Miscellaneous Therapeutic Agents' Interventions in NAFLD: Astaxanthin, Cinnamon, and Coffee

Astaxanthin (ASTX) is a xanthophyll carotenoid this primarily in marine animals, among them in salmon and crustaceans [126], which is a potent antioxidant acting as a free radical scavenger including ROS [127] and peroxyl radicals, thus protecting PUFAs in biological membranes from lipid peroxidation [128]. Seeking to define an effective dose of dietary treatment with ASTX to address metabolic dysfunctions, male C57BL/6J mice were fed a HFD (35%) and were treated with 0, 0.003%, 0.01% or 0.03% of ASTX (*w/w*) for 12 weeks [129]. At the highest dosage used, ASTX significantly decreased plasma TGs, AST, and ALT concentrations, and increased expression of endogenous antioxidants genes in liver was observed, with lower sensitivity of isolated splenocytes to LPS stimulation, thereby suggesting that ASTX can have a role in preventing of obesity-associated metabolic disturbances and inflammation [129].

Askari *et al.* [130] designed a RCT to evaluate the effects of cinnamon supplementation in patients with NAFLD, involving 55 patients with NAFLD randomized supplemented either with 2 cinnamon capsules (each capsule containing 750 mg of cinnamon) or placebo capsule daily for 12 weeks, and all patients were instructed to implement a balanced diet and physical activity. Under these conditions, the treatment group exhibited significantly decreased HOMA, fasting blood glucose, TC, LDL-C, TGs, ALT, AST, GGT, hs-CRP, however, the serum levels of HDL-C and in both groups remained unaltered [130].

The coffee is regarded as the most consumed beverage worldwide. A recent large prospective study showed that consumption of pure and decaffeinated coffee is associated with decreased all-cause death [131]. Similarly, it has been reported that the intake of coffee reduces the risk of advanced liver disease and complications associated with this [132], and equally of hepatocellular carcinoma independent of the etiology [133]. However, despite the above benefits, the molecular mechanisms that contribute to the protective effect of coffee are not well clarified. In this regard, a study evaluated the effects of the administration of decaffeinated espresso coffee *versus* placebo in rats fed with HFD and changes in the proteomic profile of the liver. It was found that rats receiving HFD plus placebo developed periacinar steatosis, lobular inflammation, and average fibrosis; while those receiving HFD plus coffee exhibited only average steatosis. Coffee consumption increased the hepatic expression of chaperones of the endoplasmic reticulum and induced the expression of master regulators of redox state. In addition, coffee intake was associated with decreased expression of the α-subunit flavoprotein electron transfer, an element of the mitochondrial respiratory chain related with *de novo* lipogénesis [134].

5. Conclusions and Projections

Currently, an effective pharmacological therapy for the NAFLD treatment is not available. Lifestyle interventions involving diet and exercise remain the first line treatment (Figure 1), however, the weight loss long term has a low success rate as well as dietary restrictions adherence. This situation has prompted the exploration of new therapeutic agents for the prevention of hepatic steatosis and the progression of the disease. Scientific evidence of potential therapeutic agents remains lacking, partly because of the lack of clinical trials with based on evidence of liver histopathology data, but also due to the fact that NAFLD is a multifactorial disease involving deep and complex metabolic changes in the liver, which are in close relationship with other tissues such as adipose tissue and skeletal muscle, making the possibility of successfully respond to monotherapy unlikely. This situation points to the need for new therapeutic approaches considering the assessment of the effectiveness of combined bioactive compounds that have proven hepatoprotective actions, in order to find possible additive or potentiating effects in the prevention and treatment of NAFLD. In addition, it would be of importance to consider the effects of therapeutic agents in conjunction with other non-pharmacological therapies, such as those focused on behavioral therapies and surgical procedures, to evaluate the usefulness of complementary mechanisms of actions on NAFLD outcomes.

Acknowledgments: The authors are grateful to project (11140174) from Initiation FONDECYT (National Fund for Scientific and Technological Development) of Rodrigo Valenzuela, Department of Nutrition, Faculty of Medicine, Chile. And the Enlaza-Mundos Program of the Mayor of Medellin (Colombia)—Agency for Higher Education of Medellin-SAPIENCIA, for the support to co-finance postgraduate study abroad (Maria Catalina Hernandez-Rodas).

Author Contributions: Maria Catalina Hernandez-Rodas, Rodrigo Valenzuela and Luis A. Videla. Analysis of the information and writing the manuscript. All authors reviewed and approved the final version of the manuscript.

Conflicts of Interest: The authors declare no conflict of interest.

References

1. Thoma, C.; Day, C.P.; Trenell, M.I. Lifestyle interventions for the treatment of non-alcoholic fatty liver disease in adults: A systematic review. *J. Hepatol.* **2012**, *56*, 255–266. [CrossRef] [PubMed]
2. Browning, J.D.; Szczepaniak, L.S.; Dobbins, R.; Nuremberg, P.; Horton, J.D.; Cohen, J.C.; Grundy, S.M.; Hobbs, H.H. Prevalence of hepatic steatosis in an urban population in the United States: Impact of ethnicity. *Hepatology* **2004**, *40*, 1387–1395. [CrossRef] [PubMed]
3. Bellentani, S.; Saccoccio, G.; Masutti, F.; Crocè, L.S.; Brandi, G.; Sasso, F.; Cristanini, G.; Tiribelli, C. Prevalence of and risk factors for hepatic steatosis in Northern Italy. *Ann. Intern. Med.* **2000**, *132*, 112–117. [CrossRef] [PubMed]
4. Mitchel, E.B.; Lavine, J.E. Review article: The management of paediatric nonalcoholic fatty liver disease. *Aliment. Pharmacol. Ther.* **2014**, *40*, 1155–1170. [CrossRef] [PubMed]
5. Lonardo, A.; Ballestri, S.; Marchesini, G.; Angulo, P.; Loria, P. Nonalcoholic fatty liver disease: A precursor of the metabolic syndrome. *Dig. Liver Dis.* **2015**, *47*, 181–190. [CrossRef] [PubMed]
6. Centis, E.; Marzocchi, R.; di Domizio, S.; Ciaravella, M.F.; Marchesini, G. The effect of lifestyle changes in non-alcoholic fatty liver disease. *Dig. Dis.* **2010**, *28*, 267–273. [CrossRef] [PubMed]
7. Giorgio, V.; Prono, F.; Graziano, F.; Nobili, V. Pediatric non alcoholic fatty liver disease: Old and new concepts on development, progression, metabolic insight and potential treatment targets. *BMC Pediatr.* **2013**, *13*, 40. [CrossRef] [PubMed]
8. Vuppalanchi, R.; Chalasani, N. Nonalcoholic fatty liver disease and nonalcoholic steatohepatitis: Selected practical issues in their evaluation and management. *Hepatology* **2009**, *49*, 306–317. [CrossRef] [PubMed]

9. Dixon, J.B.; Bhathal, P.S.; Hughes, N.R.; O'Brien, P.E. Nonalcoholic fatty liver disease: Improvement in liver histological analysis with weight loss. *Hepatology* **2004**, *39*, 1647–1654. [CrossRef] [PubMed]
10. Catalano, D.; Trovato, G.M.; Martines, G.F.; Randazzo, M.; Tonzuso, A. Bright liver, body composition and insulin resistance changes with nutritional intervention: A follow-up study. *Liver Int.* **2008**, *28*, 1280–1287. [CrossRef] [PubMed]
11. Trovato, G.M.; Catalano, D.; Martines, G.F.; Pirri, C.; Trovato, F.M. Western dietary pattern and sedentary life: Independent effects of diet and physical exercise intensity on NAFLD. *Am. J. Gastroenterol.* **2008**, *108*, 1932–1933. [CrossRef] [PubMed]
12. Trovato, F.M.; Catalano, D.; Martines, G.F.; Pace, P.; Trovato, G.M. Mediterranean diet and non-alcoholic fatty liver disease: The need of extended and comprehensive interventions. *Clin. Nutr.* **2015**, *34*, 86–88. [CrossRef] [PubMed]
13. Ghaemi, A.; Taleban, F.A.; Hekmatdoost, A.; Rafiei, A.; Hosseini, V.; Amiri, Z.; Homayounfar, R.; Fakheri, H. How Much Weight Loss is Effective on Nonalcoholic Fatty Liver Disease? *Hepat. Mon.* **2013**, *13*, 15227. [CrossRef] [PubMed]
14. Musso, G.; Cassader, M.; Rosina, F.; Gambino, R. Impact of current treatments on liver disease, glucose metabolism and cardiovascular risk in non-alcoholic fatty liver disease (NAFLD): A systematic review and meta-analysis of randomised trials. *Diabetologia* **2012**, *55*, 885–904. [CrossRef] [PubMed]
15. Bradford, V.; Dillon, J.; Miller, M. Lifestyle interventions for the treatment of non-alcoholic fatty liver disease. *Hepat. Med.* **2013**, *6*, 1–10. [PubMed]
16. Franz, M.J.; VanWormer, J.J.; Crain, A.L.; Boucher, J.L.; Histon, T.; Caplan, W.; Bowman, J.D.; Pronk, N.P. Weight-loss outcomes: A systematic review and meta-analysis of weight-loss clinical trials with a minimum 1-year follow-up. *J. Am. Diet. Assoc.* **2007**, *107*, 1755–1767. [CrossRef] [PubMed]
17. Zelber-Sagi, S.; Nitzan-Kaluski, D.; Goldsmith, R.; Webb, M.; Zvibel, I.; Goldiner, I.; Blendis, L.; Halpern, Z.; Oren, R. Role of leisure-time physical activity in nonalcoholic fatty liver disease: A population-based study. *Hepatology* **2008**, *48*, 1791–1798. [CrossRef] [PubMed]
18. St George, A.; Bauman, A.; Johnston, A.; Farrell, G.; Chey, T.; George, J. Independent effects of physical activity in patients with nonalcoholic fatty liver disease. *Hepatology* **2009**, *50*, 68–76. [CrossRef] [PubMed]
19. Sreenivasa Baba, C.; Alexander, G.; Kalyani, B.; Pandey, R.; Rastogi, S.; Pandey, A.; Choudhuri, G. Effect of exercise and dietary modification on serum aminotransferase levels in patients with nonalcoholic steatohepatitis. *J. Gastroenterol. Hepatol.* **2006**, *21*, 191–198. [CrossRef] [PubMed]
20. Johnson, N.A.; Sachinwalla, T.; Walton, D.W.; Smith, K.; Armstrong, A.; Thompson, M.W.; George, J. Aerobic exercise training reduces hepatic and visceral lipids in obese individuals without weight loss. *Hepatology* **2009**, *50*, 1105–1112. [CrossRef] [PubMed]
21. Wadden, T.A.; Butryn, M.L. Behavioral treatment of obesity. *Endocrinol. Metab. Clin. N. Am.* **2003**, *32*, 981–1003. [CrossRef]
22. Bellentani, S.; Dalle Grave, R.; Suppini, A.; Marchesini, G.; Fatty Liver Italian Network. Behavior therapy for nonalcoholic fatty liver disease: The need for a multidisciplinary approach. *Hepatology* **2008**, *47*, 746–754. [CrossRef] [PubMed]
23. Osland, E.J.; Powell, E.E.; Banks, M.; Jonsson, J.R.; Hickman, I.J. Obesity management in liver clinics: Translation of research into clinical practice. *J. Gastroenterol. Hepatol.* **2007**, *22*, 504–509. [CrossRef] [PubMed]
24. Ovchinsky, N.; Lavine, J.E. A critical appraisal of advances in pediatric nonalcoholic Fatty liver disease. *Semin. Liver Dis.* **2012**, *32*, 317–324. [PubMed]
25. Tappy, L.; Lê, K.A.; Tran, C.; Paquot, N. Fructose and metabolic diseases: New findings, new questions. *Nutrition* **2010**, *26*, 1044–1049. [CrossRef] [PubMed]
26. Abid, A.; Taha, O.; Nseir, W.; Farah, R.; Grosovski, M.; Assy, N. Soft drink consumption is associated with fatty liver disease independent of metabolic syndrome. *J. Hepatol.* **2009**, *51*, 918–924. [CrossRef] [PubMed]
27. Jin, R.; Welsh, J.A.; Le, N.A.; Holzberg, J.; Sharma, P.; Martin, D.R.; Vos, M.B. Dietary fructose reduction improves markers of cardiovascular disease risk in Hispanic-American adolescents with NAFLD. *Nutrients* **2014**, *6*, 3187–3201. [CrossRef] [PubMed]
28. Carvalhana, S.; Machado, M.V.; Cortez-Pinto, H. Improving dietary patterns in patients with nonalcoholic fatty liver disease. *Curr. Opin. Clin. Nutr. Metab. Care* **2012**, *15*, 468–473. [CrossRef] [PubMed]

29. Yang, H.Y.; Tzeng, Y.H.; Chai, C.Y.; Hsieh, A.T.; Chen, J.R.; Chang, L.S.; Yang, S.S. Soy protein retards the progression of non-alcoholic steatohepatitis via improvement of insulin resistance and steatosis. *Nutrition* **2011**, *27*, 943–948. [CrossRef] [PubMed]
30. Leng, L.; Jiang, Z.Q.; Ji, G.Y. Effects of soybean isoflavone on liver lipid metabolism in nonalcoholic fatty liver rats. *Zhonghua Yu Fang Yi Xue Za Zhi* **2011**, *45*, 335–339. [PubMed]
31. Kani, A.H.; Alavian, S.M.; Esmaillzadeh, A.; Adibi, P.; Azadbakht, L. Effects of a novel therapeutic diet on liver enzymes and coagulating factors in patients with non-alcoholic fatty liver disease: A parallel randomized trial. *Nutrition* **2014**, *30*, 814–812. [CrossRef] [PubMed]
32. Bortolotti, M.; Maiolo, E.; Corazza, M.; van Dijke, E.; Schneiter, P.; Boss, A.; Carrel, G.; Giusti, V.; Lê, K.A.; Quo Chong, D.G.; *et al.* Effects of a whey protein supplementation on intrahepatocellular lipids in obese female patients. *Clin. Nutr.* **2011**, *30*, 494–498. [CrossRef] [PubMed]
33. Cave, M.; Deaciuc, I.; Mendez, C.; Song, Z.; Joshi-Barve, S.; Barve, S.; McClain, C. Nonalcoholic fatty liver disease: Predisposing factors and the role of nutrition. *J. Nutr. Biochem.* **2007**, *18*, 184–195. [CrossRef] [PubMed]
34. Bezerra Duarte, S.M.; Faintuch, J.; Stefano, J.T.; de Oliveira, M.B.; de Campos Mazo, D.F.; Rabelo, F.; Vanni, D.; Nogueira, M.A.; Carrilho, F.J.; de Oliveira, C.P. Hypocaloric high-protein diet improves clinical and biochemical markers in patients with nonalcoholic fatty liver disease (NAFLD). *Nutr. Hosp.* **2014**, *29*, 94–101. [PubMed]
35. Garcia-Caraballo, S.C.; Comhair, T.M.; Verheyen, F.; Gaemers, I.; Schaap, F.G.; Houten, S.M.; Hakvoort, T.B.; Dejong, C.H.; Lamers, W.H.; Koehler, S.E. Prevention and reversal of hepatic steatosis with a high-protein diet in mice. *Biochim. Biophys. Acta* **2013**, *1832*, 685–695. [CrossRef] [PubMed]
36. Vos, M.B.; Kimmons, J.E.; Gillespie, C.; Welsh, J.; Blanck, H.M. Dietary fructose consumption among US children and adults: The Third National Health and Nutrition Examination Survey. *Medscape J. Med.* **2008**, *10*, 160. [PubMed]
37. Bergheim, I.; Weber, S.; Vos, M.; Krämer, S.; Volynets, V.; Kaserouni, S.; McClain, C.J.; Bischoff, S.C. Antibiotics protect against fructose-induced hepatic lipid accumulation in mice: Role of endotoxin. *J. Hepatol.* **2008**, *48*, 983–992. [CrossRef] [PubMed]
38. Ouyang, X.; Cirillo, P.; Sautin, Y.; McCall, S.; Bruchette, J.L.; Diehl, A.M.; Johnson, R.J.; Abdelmalek, M.F. Fructose consumption as a risk factor for non-alcoholic fatty liver disease. *J. Hepatol.* **2008**, *48*, 993–999. [CrossRef] [PubMed]
39. Girard, A.; Madani, S.; Boukortt, F.; Cherkaoui-Malki, M.; Belleville, J.; Prost, J. Fructose-enriched diet modifies antioxidant status and lipid metabolism in spontaneously hypertensive rats. *Nutrition* **2006**, *22*, 758–766. [CrossRef] [PubMed]
40. Vos, M.B.; Lavine, J.E. Dietary fructose in nonalcoholic fatty liver disease. *Hepatology* **2013**, *57*, 2525–2531. [CrossRef] [PubMed]
41. Targher, G. Non-alcoholic fatty liver disease, the metabolic syndrome and the risk of cardiovascular disease: The plot thickens. *Diabet. Med.* **2007**, *24*, 1–6. [CrossRef] [PubMed]
42. Abenavoli, L.; Milic, N.; Peta, V.; Alfieri, F.; de Lorenzo, A.; Bellentani, S. Alimentary regimen in non-alcoholic fatty liver disease: Mediterranean diet. *World J. Gastroenterol.* **2014**, *20*, 16831–16840. [CrossRef] [PubMed]
43. Parker, H.M.; Johnson, N.A.; Burdon, C.A.; Cohn, J.S.; O'Connor, H.T.; George, J. Omega-3 supplementation and non-alcoholic fatty liver disease: A systematic review and meta-analysis. *J. Hepatol.* **2012**, *56*, 944–951. [CrossRef] [PubMed]
44. Ryan, M.C.; Itsiopoulos, C.; Thodis, T.; Ward, G.; Trost, N.; Hofferberth, S.; O'Dea, K.; Desmond, P.V.; Johnson, N.A.; Wilson, A.M. The Mediterranean diet improves hepatic steatosis and insulin sensitivity in individuals with non-alcoholic fatty liver disease. *J. Hepatol.* **2013**, *59*, 138–143. [CrossRef] [PubMed]
45. Ayyad, C.; Andersen, T. Long-term efficacy of dietary treatment of obesity: A systematic review of studies published between 1931 and 1999. *Obes. Rev.* **2000**, *1*, 113–119. [CrossRef] [PubMed]
46. Park, H.J.; Lee, J.Y.; Chung, M.Y.; Park, Y.K.; Bower, A.M.; Koo, S.I.; Giardina, C.; Bruno, R.S. Green tea extract suppresses NFκB activation and inflammatory responses in diet-induced obese rats with nonalcoholic steatohepatitis. *J. Nutr.* **2012**, *142*, 57–63. [CrossRef] [PubMed]
47. Rector, R.S.; Thyfault, J.P.; Wei, Y.; Ibdah, J.A. Non-alcoholic fatty liver disease and the metabolic syndrome: An update. *World J. Gastroenterol.* **2008**, *14*, 185–192. [CrossRef] [PubMed]

48. Videla, L.A.; Rodrigo, R.; Araya, J.; Poniachik, J. Oxidative stress and depletion of hepatic long-chain polyunsaturated fatty acids may contribute to nonalcoholic fatty liver disease. *Free Radic. Biol. Med.* **2004**, *37*, 1499–1507. [CrossRef] [PubMed]

49. Pagano, G.; Pacini, G.; Musso, G.; Gambino, R.; Mecca, F.; Depetris, N.; Cassader, M.; David, E.; Cavallo-Perin, P.; Rizzetto, M. Nonalcoholic steatohepatitis, insulin resistance, and metabolic syndrome: Further evidence for an etiologic association. *Hepatology* **2002**, *35*, 367–372. [CrossRef] [PubMed]

50. Liu, Z.L.; Xie, L.Z.; Zhu, J.; Li, G.Q.; Grant, S.J.; Liu, J.P. Herbal medicines for fatty liver diseases. *Cochrane Database Syst. Rev.* **2013**, *8*. [CrossRef]

51. Marcolin, E.; San-Miguel, B.; Vallejo, D.; Tieppo, J.; Marroni, N.; González-Gallego, J.; Tuñón, M.J. Quercetin treatment ameliorates inflammation and fibrosis in mice with nonalcoholic steatohepatitis. *J. Nutr.* **2012**, *142*, 1821–1828. [CrossRef] [PubMed]

52. Sasidharan, S.R.; Joseph, J.A.; Anandakumar, S.; Venkatesan, V.; Madhavan, C.N.; Agarwal, A. Ameliorative potential of Tamarindus indica on high fat diet induced nonalcoholic fatty liver disease in rats. *Sci. World J.* **2014**, *2014*, 507197. [CrossRef] [PubMed]

53. Balunas, M.J.; Kinghor, A.D. Drug discovery from medicinal plants. *Life Sci.* **2005**, *78*, 431–441. [CrossRef] [PubMed]

54. Zhang, S.; Zheng, L.; Dong, D.; Xu, L.; Yin, L.; Qi, Y.; Han, X.; Lin, Y.; Liu, K.; Peng, J. Effects of flavonoids from Rosa laevigata Michx fruit against high-fat diet-induced non-alcoholic fatty liver disease in rats. *Food Chem.* **2013**, *141*, 2108–2116. [CrossRef] [PubMed]

55. Prior, R.L.; Cao, G. Antioxidant capacity and polyphenolic components of teas: Implications for altering *in vivo* antioxidant status. *Proc. Soc. Exp. Biol. Med.* **1999**, *220*, 255–261. [CrossRef] [PubMed]

56. Akiba, Y.; Takahashi, K.; Horiguchi, M.; Ohtani, H.; Saitoh, S.; Ohkawara, H. L-tryptophan alleviates fatty liver and modifies hepatic microsomal mixed function oxidase in laying hens. *Comp. Biochem. Physiol. Comp. Physiol.* **1992**, *102*, 769–774. [CrossRef]

57. Ritze, Y.; Bárdos, G.; Hubert, A.; Böhle, M.; Bischoff, S.C. Effect of tryptophan supplementation on diet-induced non-alcoholic fatty liver disease in mice. *Br. J. Nutr.* **2014**, *112*, 1–7. [CrossRef] [PubMed]

58. Lin, Z.; Cai, F.; Lin, N.; Ye, J.; Zheng, Q.; Ding, G. Effects of glutamine on oxidative stress and nuclear factor-κB expression in the livers of rats with nonalcoholic fatty liver disease. *Exp. Ther. Med.* **2014**, *7*, 365–370. [CrossRef] [PubMed]

59. Kerner, J.; Bieber, L. Isolation of a malonyl-CoA-sensitive CPT/β-oxidation enzyme complex from heart mitochondria. *Biochemistry* **1990**, *29*, 4326–4334. [CrossRef] [PubMed]

60. Lombardo, Y.B.; Chicco, A.G. Effects of dietary polyunsaturated n-3 fatty acids on dyslipidemia and insulin resistance in rodents and humans. A review. *J. Nutr. Biochem.* **2006**, *17*, 1–13. [CrossRef] [PubMed]

61. Araya, J.; Rodrigo, R.; Videla, L.A.; Thielemann, L.; Orellana, M.; Pettinelli, P.; Poniachik, J. Increase in long-chain polyunsaturated fatty acid n-6/n-3 ratio in relation to hepatic steatosis in patients with non-alcoholic fatty liver disease. *Clin. Sci.* **2004**, *106*, 635–643. [CrossRef] [PubMed]

62. Xin, Y.N.; Xuan, S.Y.; Zhang, J.H.; Zheng, M.H.; Guan, H.S. Omega-3 polyunsaturated fatty acids: A specific liver drug for non-alcoholic fatty liver disease (NAFLD). *Med. Hypothese.* **2008**, *71*, 820–821. [CrossRef] [PubMed]

63. Shapiro, H.; Tehilla, M.; Attal-Singer, J.; Bruck, R.; Luzzatti, R.; Singer, P. The therapeutic potential of long-chain omega-3 fatty acids in nonalcoholic fatty liver disease. *Clin. Nutr.* **2011**, *30*, 6–19. [CrossRef] [PubMed]

64. Nobili, V.; Alisi, A.; Della Corte, C.; Risé, P.; Galli, C.; Agostoni, C.; Bedogni, G. Docosahexaenoic acid for the treatment of fatty liver: Randomised controlled trial in children. *Nutr. Metab. Cardiovasc. Dis.* **2013**, *23*, 1066–1070. [CrossRef] [PubMed]

65. Ganji, S.H.; Qin, S.; Zhang, L.; Kamanna, V.S.; Kashyap, M.L. Niacin inhibits vascular oxidative stress, redox-sensitive genes, and monocyte adhesion to human aortic endothelial cells. *Atherosclerosis* **2009**, *202*, 68–75. [CrossRef] [PubMed]

66. Meyers, C.D.; Kamanna, V.S.; Kashyap, M.L. Niacin therapy in atherosclerosis. *Curr. Opin. Lipidol.* **2004**, *15*, 659–665. [CrossRef] [PubMed]

67. Ganji, S.H.; Kukes, G.D.; Lambrecht, N.; Kashyap, M.L.; Kamanna, V.S. Therapeutic role of niacin in the prevention and regression of hepatic steatosis in rat model of nonalcoholic fatty liver disease. *Am. J. Physiol. Gastrointest. Liver Physiol.* **2014**, *306*, G320–G327. [CrossRef] [PubMed]

68. Herrera, E.; Barbas, C. Vitamin E: Action, metabolism and perspectives. *J. Physiol. Biochem.* **2001**, *57*, 43–56. [CrossRef] [PubMed]
69. Wefers, H.; Sies, H. The protection by ascorbate and glutathione against microsomal lipid peroxidation is dependent on vitamin E. *Eur. J. Biochem.* **1988**, *174*, 353–357. [CrossRef] [PubMed]
70. Tzanetakou, I.P.; Doulamis, I.P.; Korou, L.M.; Agrogiannis, G.; Vlachos, I.S.; Pantopoulou, A.; Mikhailidis, D.P.; Patsouris, E.; Vlachos, I.; Perrea, D.N. Water Soluble Vitamin E Administration in Wistar Rats with Non-alcoholic Fatty Liver Disease. *Open Cardiovasc. Med. J.* **2012**, *6*, 88–97. [CrossRef] [PubMed]
71. Eslamparast, T.; Eghtesad, S.; Hekmatdoost, A.; Poustchi, H. Probiotics and Nonalcoholic Fatty liver Disease. *Middle East. J. Dig. Dis.* **2013**, *5*, 129–136. [PubMed]
72. Farrell, G.C. Is bacterial ash the flash that ignites NASH? *Gut* **2001**, *48*, 148–149. [CrossRef] [PubMed]
73. Maddur, H.; Neuschwander-Tetri, B.A. More evidence that probiotics may have a role in treating fatty liver disease. *Am. J. Clin. Nutr.* **2014**, *99*, 425–426. [CrossRef] [PubMed]
74. Tandon, P.; Garcia-Tsao, G. Bacterial infections, sepsis, and multiorgan failure in cirrhosis. *Semin. Liver Dis.* **2008**, *28*, 26–42. [CrossRef] [PubMed]
75. Yang, L.; Seki, E. Toll-like receptors in liver fibrosis: Cellular crosstalk and mechanisms. *Front. Physiol.* **2012**, *3*, 138. [CrossRef] [PubMed]
76. Miele, L.; Valenza, V.; La Torre, G.; Montalto, M.; Cammarota, G.; Ricci, R.; Mascianà, R.; Forgione, A.; Gabrieli, M.L.; Perotti, G.; *et al.* Increased intestinal permeability and tight junction alterations in nonalcoholic fatty liver disease. *Hepatology* **2009**, *49*, 1877–1887. [CrossRef] [PubMed]
77. Wigg, A.J.; Roberts-Thomson, I.C.; Dymock, R.B.; McCarthy, P.J.; Grose, R.H.; Cummins, A.G. The role of small intestinal bacterial overgrowth, intestinal permeability, endotoxaemia, and tumour necrosis factor alpha in the pathogenesis of non-alcoholic steatohepatitis. *Gut* **2001**, *48*, 206–211. [CrossRef] [PubMed]
78. Eslamparast, T.; Poustchi, H.; Zamani, F.; Sharafkhah, M.; Malekzadeh, R.; Hekmatdoost, A. Synbiotic supplementation in nonalcoholic fatty liver disease: A randomized, double-blind, placebo-controlled pilot study. *Am. J. Clin. Nutr.* **2014**, *99*, 535–542. [CrossRef] [PubMed]
79. Cani, P.D.; Bibiloni, R.; Knauf, C.; Waget, A.; Neyrinck, A.M.; Delzenne, N.M.; Burcelin, R. Changes in gut microbiota control metabolic endotoxemia-induced inflammation in high-fat diet-induced obesity and diabetes in mice. *Diabetes* **2008**, *57*, 1470–1481. [CrossRef] [PubMed]
80. Round, J.L.; Mazmanian, S.K. The gut microbiota shapes intestinal immune responses during health and disease. *Nat. Rev. Immunol.* **2009**, *9*, 313–323. [CrossRef] [PubMed]
81. Malaguarnera, M.; Greco, F.; Barone, G.; Gargante, M.P.; Malaguarnera, M.; Toscano, M.A. *Bifidobacterium longum* with fructo-oligosaccharide (FOS) treatment in minimal hepatic encephalopathy: A randomized, double-blind, placebo-controlled study. *Dig. Dis. Sci.* **2007**, *52*, 3259–3265. [CrossRef] [PubMed]
82. Li, Z.; Yang, S.; Lin, H.; Huang, J.; Watkins, P.A.; Moser, A.B.; Desimone, C.; Song, X.Y.; Diehl, A.M. Probiotics and antibodies to TNF inhibit inflammatory activity and improve nonalcoholic fatty liver disease. *Hepatology* **2003**, *37*, 343–350. [CrossRef] [PubMed]
83. Ma, X.; Hua, J.; Li, Z. Probiotics improve high fat diet-induced hepatic steatosis and insulin resistance by increasing hepatic NKT cells. *J. Hepatol.* **2008**, *49*, 821–830. [CrossRef] [PubMed]
84. Esposito, E.; Iacono, A.; Bianco, G.; Autore, G.; Cuzzocrea, S.; Vajro, P.; Canani, R.B.; Calignano, A.; Raso, G.M.; Meli, R. Probiotics reduce the inflammatory response induced by a high-fat diet in the liver of young rats. *J. Nutr.* **2009**, *139*, 905–911. [CrossRef] [PubMed]
85. Mencarelli, A.; Distrutti, E.; Renga, B.; D'Amore, C.; Cipriani, S.; Palladino, G.; Donini, A.; Ricci, P.; Fiorucci, S. Probiotics modulate intestinal expression of nuclear receptor and provide counter-regulatory signals to inflammation-driven adipose tissue activation. *PLoS ONE* **2011**, *6*, 22978. [CrossRef] [PubMed]
86. Ritze, Y.; Bárdos, G.; Claus, A.; Ehrmann, V.; Bergheim, I.; Schwiertz, A.; Bischoff, S.C. *Lactobacillus* rhamnosus GG protects against non-alcoholic fatty liver disease in mice. *PLoS ONE* **2014**, *9*, 80169. [CrossRef] [PubMed]
87. Okubo, H.; Sakoda, H.; Kushiyama, A.; Fujishiro, M.; Nakatsu, Y.; Fukushima, T.; Matsunaga, Y.; Kamata, H.; Asahara, T.; Yoshida, Y.; *et al.* Lactobacillus casei strain Shirota protects against nonalcoholic steatohepatitis development in a rodent model. *Am. J. Physiol. Gastrointest. Liver Physiol.* **2013**, *305*, G911–G918. [CrossRef] [PubMed]

88. Loguercio, C.; Federico, A.; Tuccillo, C.; Terracciano, F.; D'Auria, M.V.; de Simone, C.; del Vecchio Blanco, C. Beneficial effects of a probiotic VSL#3 on parameters of liver dysfunction in chronic liver diseases. *J. Clin. Gastroenterol.* **2005**, *39*, 540–543. [PubMed]

89. Vajro, P.; Mandato, C.; Licenziati, M.R.; Franzese, A.; Vitale, D.F.; Lenta, S.; Caropreso, M.; Vallone, G.; Meli, R. Effects of Lactobacillus rhamnosus strain GG in pediatric obesity-related liver disease. *J. Pediatr. Gastroenterol. Nutr.* **2011**, *52*, 740–743. [CrossRef] [PubMed]

90. Aller, R.; de Luis, D.A.; Izaola, O.; Conde, R.; Gonzalez Sagrado, M.; Primo, D.; de La Fuente, B.; Gonzalez, J. Effect of a probiotic on liver aminotransferases in nonalcoholic fatty liver disease patients: A double blind randomized clinical trial. *Eur. Rev. Med. Pharmacol. Sci.* **2011**, *15*, 1090–1095. [PubMed]

91. Ma, Y.Y.; Li, L.; Yu, C.H.; Shen, Z.; Chen, L.H.; Li, Y.M. Effects of probiotics on nonalcoholic fatty liver disease: A meta-analysis. *World J. Gastroenterol.* **2013**, *19*, 6911–6918. [CrossRef] [PubMed]

92. Malaguarnera, M.; Vacante, M.; Antic, T.; Giordano, M.; Chisari, G.; Acquaviva, R.; Mastrojeni, S.; Malaguarnera, G.; Mistretta, A.; Li Volti, G.; *et al. Bifidobacterium longum* with fructo-oligosaccharides in patients with non alcoholic steatohepatitis. *Dig. Dis. Sci.* **2012**, *57*, 545–553. [CrossRef] [PubMed]

93. Cardona, F.; Andrés-Lacueva, C.; Tulipani, S.; Tinahones, F.J.; Queipo-Ortuño, M.I. Benefits of polyphenols on gut microbiota and implications in human health. *J. Nutr. Biochem.* **2013**, *24*, 1415–1422. [CrossRef] [PubMed]

94. Fraga, C.G.; Galleano, M.; Verstraeten, S.V.; Oteiza, P.I. Basic biochemical mechanisms behind the health benefits of polyphenols. *Mol. Aspe. Med.* **2010**, *31*, 435–445. [CrossRef] [PubMed]

95. Baur, J.A.; Sinclair, D.A. Therapeutic potential of resveratrol: The *in vivo* evidence. *Nat. Rev. Drug Discov.* **2006**, *5*, 493–506. [CrossRef] [PubMed]

96. Schmatz, R.; Perreira, L.B.; Stefanello, N.; Mazzanti, C.; Spanevello, R.; Gutierres, J.; Bagatini, M.; Martins, C.C.; Abdalla, F.H.; Daci da Silva Serres, J.; *et al.* Effects of resveratrol on biomarkers of oxidative stress and on the activity of delta aminolevulinic acid dehydratase in liver and kidney of streptozotocin-induced diabetic rats. *Biochimie* **2012**, *94*, 374–383. [CrossRef] [PubMed]

97. Hou, X.; Xu, S.; Maitland-Toolan, K.A.; Sato, K.; Jiang, B.; Ido, Y.; Lan, F.; Walsh, K.; Wierzbicki, M.; Verbeuren, T.J.; *et al.* SIRT1 regulates hepatocyte lipid metabolism through activating AMP-activated protein kinase. *J. Biol. Chem.* **2008**, *283*, 20015–20026. [CrossRef] [PubMed]

98. Borra, M.T.; Smith, B.C.; Denu, J.M. Mechanism of human SIRT1 activation by resveratrol. *J. Biol. Chem.* **2005**, *280*, 17187–17195. [CrossRef] [PubMed]

99. Wang, G.L.; Fu, Y.C.; Xu, W.C.; Feng, Y.Q.; Fang, S.R.; Zhou, X.H. Resveratrol inhibits the expression of SREBP1 in cell model of steatosis via Sirt1-FOXO1 signaling pathway. *Biochem. Biophys. Res. Commun.* **2009**, *380*, 644–649. [CrossRef] [PubMed]

100. Faghihzadeh, F.; Adibi, P.; Rafiei, R.; Hekmatdoost, A. Resveratrol supplementation improves inflammatory biomarkers in patients with nonalcoholic fatty liver disease. *Nutr. Res.* **2014**, *34*, 837–843. [CrossRef] [PubMed]

101. Andrade, J.M.; Paraíso, A.F.; de Oliveira, M.V.; Martins, A.M.; Neto, J.F.; Guimarães, A.L.; de Paula, A.M.; Qureshi, M.; Santos, S.H. Resveratrol attenuates hepatic steatosis in high-fat fed mice by decreasing lipogenesis and inflammation. *Nutrition* **2014**, *30*, 915–919. [CrossRef] [PubMed]

102. Imai, K.; Nakachi, K. Cross sectional study of effects of drinking green tea on cardiovascular and liver diseases. *BMJ* **1995**, *310*, 693–696. [CrossRef] [PubMed]

103. Bose, M.; Lambert, J.D.; Ju, J.; Reuhl, K.R.; Shapses, S.A.; Yang, C.S. The major green tea polyphenol, (-)-epigallocatechin-3-gallate, inhibits obesity, metabolic syndrome, and fatty liver disease in high-fat-fed mice. *J. Nutr.* **2008**, *138*, 1677–1683. [PubMed]

104. Tuñón, M.J.; García-Mediavilla, M.V.; Sánchez-Campos, S.; González-Gallego, J. Potential of flavonoids as anti-inflammatory agents: Modulation of pro-inflammatory gene expression and signal transduction pathways. *Curr. Drug Metab.* **2009**, *10*, 256–271. [CrossRef] [PubMed]

105. Martínez-Flórez, S.; Gutiérrez-Fernández, B.; Sánchez-Campos, S.; González-Gallego, J.; Tuñón, M.J. Quercetin attenuates nuclear factor-kappaB activation and nitric oxide production in interleukin-1β-activated rat hepatocytes. *J. Nutr.* **2005**, *135*, 1359–1365. [PubMed]

106. Peres, W.; Tuñón, M.J.; Collado, P.S.; Herrmann, S.; Marroni, N.; González-Gallego, J. The flavonoid quercetin ameliorates liver damage in rats with biliary obstruction. *J. Hepatol.* **2000**, *33*, 742–750. [CrossRef]

107. Egert, S.; Bosy-Westphal, A.; Seiberl, J.; Kürbitz, C.; Settler, U.; Plachta-Danielzik, S.; Wagner, A.E.; Frank, J.; Schrezenmeir, J.; Rimbach, G.; *et al.* Quercetin reduces systolic blood pressure and plasma oxidised low-density lipoprotein concentrations in overweight subjects with a high-cardiovascular disease risk phenotype: A double-blinded, placebo-controlled cross-over study. *Br. J. Nutr.* **2009**, *102*, 1065–1074. [CrossRef] [PubMed]
108. Kobori, M.; Masumoto, S.; Akimoto, Y.; Oike, H. Chronic dietary intake of quercetin alleviates hepatic fat accumulation associated with consumption of a Western-style diet in C57/BL6J mice. *Mol. Nutr. Food Res.* **2011**, *55*, 530–540. [CrossRef] [PubMed]
109. Engelbrecht, A.M.; Mattheyse, M.; Ellis, B.; Loos, B.; Thomas, M.; Smith, R.; Peters, S.; Smith, C.; Myburgh, K. Proanthocyanidin from grape seeds inactivates the PI3-kinase/PKB pathway and induces apoptosis in a colon cancer cell line. *Cancer Lett.* **2007**, *258*, 144–153. [CrossRef] [PubMed]
110. Yogalakshmi, B.; Sreeja, S.; Geetha, R.; Radika, M.K.; Anuradha, C.V. Grape seed proanthocyanidin rescues rats from steatosis: A comparative and combination study with metformin. *J. Lipids* **2013**, *2013*, 153897. [CrossRef] [PubMed]
111. Valenti, L.; Riso, P.; Mazzocchi, A.; Porrini, M.; Fargion, S.; Agostoni, C. Dietary anthocyanins as nutritional therapy for nonalcoholic fatty liver disease. *Oxidative Med. Cell. Longev.* **2013**, *2013*, 145421. [CrossRef] [PubMed]
112. Prior, R.L.; Wu, X. Anthocyanins: Structural characteristics that result in unique metabolic patterns and biological activities. *Free Radic. Res.* **2006**, *40*, 1014–1028. [CrossRef] [PubMed]
113. Tsuda, T.; Horio, F.; Uchida, K.; Aoki, H.; Osawa, T. Dietary cyanidin 3-*o*-β-D-glucoside-rich purple corn color prevents obesity and ameliorates hyperglycemia in mice. *J. Nutr.* **2003**, *133*, 2125–2130. [PubMed]
114. Suda, I.; Ishikawa, F.; Hatakeyama, M.; Miyawaki, M.; Kudo, T.; Hirano, K.; Ito, A.; Yamakawa, O.; Horiuchi, S. Intake of purple sweet potato beverage affects on serum hepatic biomarker levels of healthy adult men with borderline hepatitis. *Eur. J. Clin. Nutr.* **2008**, *62*, 60–67. [CrossRef] [PubMed]
115. Zhang, L.; Xu, J.; Song, H.; Yao, Z.; Ji, G. Extracts from Salvia-Nelumbinis naturalis alleviate hepatosteatosis via improving hepatic insulin sensitivity. *J. Transl. Med.* **2014**, *12*, 236. [CrossRef] [PubMed]
116. Qi, Z.; Xue, J.; Zhang, Y.; Wang, H.; Xie, M. Osthole ameliorates insulin resistance by increment of adiponectin release in high-fat and high-sucrose-induced fatty liver rats. *Planta Med.* **2011**, *77*, 231–235. [CrossRef] [PubMed]
117. Zhang, Y.; Xie, M.L.; Xue, J.; Gu, Z.L. Osthole regulates enzyme protein expression of CYP7A1 and DGAT2 via activation of PPARalpha/gamma in fat milk-induced fatty liver rats. *J. Asian Nat. Prod. Res.* **2008**, *10*, 807–812. [CrossRef] [PubMed]
118. Zhang, J.; Xue, J.; Wang, H.; Zhang, Y.; Xie, M. Osthole improves alcohol-induced fatty liver in mice by reduction of hepatic oxidative stress. *Phytother. Res.* **2011**, *25*, 638–643. [CrossRef] [PubMed]
119. Nam, H.H.; Jun, D.W.; Jeon, H.J.; Lee, J.S.; Saeed, W.K.; Kim, E.K. Osthol attenuates hepatic steatosis via decreased triglyceride synthesis not by insulin resistance. *World J. Gastroenterol.* **2014**, *20*, 11753–11761. [CrossRef] [PubMed]
120. Peng, Q.; Zhang, Q.; Xiao, W.; Shao, M.; Fan, Q.; Zhang, H.; Zou, Y.; Li, X.; Xu, W.; Mo, Z.; Cai, H. Protective effects of Sapindus mukorossi Gaertn against fatty liver disease induced by high fat diet in rats. *Biochem. Biophys. Res. Commun.* **2014**, *450*, 685–691. [CrossRef] [PubMed]
121. Song, Y.; Lee, S.J.; Jang, S.H.; Ha, J.H.; Song, Y.M.; Ko, Y.G.; Kim, H.D.; Min, W.; Kang, S.N.; Cho, J.H. Sasa borealis stem extract attenuates hepatic steatosis in high-fat diet-induced obese rats. *Nutrients* **2014**, *6*, 2179–2195. [CrossRef] [PubMed]
122. Shibata, M.; Yamatake, Y.; Sakamoto, M.; Kanamori, M.; Takagi, K. Phamacological studies on bamboo grass (1). Acute toxicity and anti-inflammatory and antiulcerogenic activities of water-soluble fraction(Folin) extracted from Sasa albomarginata Makino et Shibata. *Nihon Yakurigaku Zasshi Folia Pharmacol. Jpn.* **1975**, *71*, 481–490. [CrossRef]
123. Kazazis, C.E.; Evangelopoulos, A.A.; Kollas, A.; Vallianou, N.G. The therapeutic potential of milk thistle in diabetes. *Rev. Diabet. Stud.* **2014**, *11*, 167–174. [CrossRef] [PubMed]
124. Loguercio, C.; Andreone, P.; Brisc, C.; Brisc, M.C.; Bugianesi, E.; Chiaramonte, M.; Cursaro, C.; Danila, M.; de Sio, I.; Floreani, A.; *et al.* Silybin combined with phosphatidylcholine and vitamin E in patients with nonalcoholic fatty liver disease: A randomized controlled trial. *Free Radic. Biol. Med.* **2012**, *52*, 1658–1665. [CrossRef] [PubMed]

125. Abenavoli, L.; Greco, M.; Nazionale, I.; Peta, V.; Milic, N.; Accattato, F.; Foti, D.; Gulletta, E.; Luzza, F. Effects of Mediterranean diet supplemented with silybin-vitamin E-phospholipid complex in overweight patients with non-alcoholic fatty liver disease. *Expert Rev. Gastroenterol. Hepatol.* **2015**, *9*, 519–527. [CrossRef] [PubMed]

126. Hussein, G.; Sankawa, U.; Goto, H.; Matsumoto, K.; Watanabe, H. Astaxanthin, a carotenoid with potential in human health and nutrition. *J. Nat. Prod.* **2006**, *69*, 443–449. [CrossRef] [PubMed]

127. Guerin, M.; Huntley, M.E.; Olaizola, M. Haematococcus astaxanthin: Applications for human health and nutrition. *Trends Biotechnol.* **2003**, *21*, 210–216. [CrossRef]

128. Goto, S.; Kogure, K.; Abe, K.; Kimata, Y.; Kitahama, K.; Yamashita, E.; Terada, H. Efficient radical trapping at the surface and inside the phospholipid membrane is responsible for highly potent antiperoxidative activity of the carotenoid astaxanthin. *Biochim. Biophys. Acta* **2001**, *1512*, 251–258. [CrossRef]

129. Yang, Y.; Pham, T.X.; Wegner, C.J.; Kim, B.; Ku, C.S.; Park, Y.K.; Lee, J.Y. Astaxanthin lowers plasma TAG concentrations and increases hepatic antioxidant gene expression in diet-induced obesity mice. *Br. J. Nutr.* **2014**, *112*, 1797–1804. [CrossRef] [PubMed]

130. Askari, F.; Rashidkhani, B.; Hekmatdoost, A. Cinnamon may have therapeutic benefits on lipid profile, liver enzymes, insulin resistance, and high-sensitivity C-reactive protein in nonalcoholic fatty liver disease patients. *Nutr. Res.* **2014**, *34*, 143–148. [CrossRef] [PubMed]

131. Freedman, N.D.; Park, Y.; Abnet, C.C.; Hollenbeck, A.R.; Sinha, R. Association of coffee drinking with total and cause-specific mortality. *N. Engl. J. Med.* **2012**, *366*, 1891–1904. [CrossRef] [PubMed]

132. Corrao, G.; Zambon, A.; Bagnardi, V.; D'Amicis, A.; Klatsky, A. Collaborative SIDECIR Group. Coffee, caffeine, and the risk of liver cirrhosis. *Ann. Epidemiol.* **2001**, *11*, 458–465. [CrossRef]

133. Montella, M.; Polesel, J.; La Vecchia, C.; Dal Maso, L.; Crispo, A.; Crovatto, M.; Casarin, P.; Izzo, F.; Tommasi, L.G.; Talamini, R.; *et al.* Coffee and tea consumption and risk of hepatocellular carcinoma in Italy. *Int. J. Cancer* **2007**, *120*, 1555–1559. [CrossRef] [PubMed]

134. Salomone, F.; Li Volti, G.; Vitaglione, P.; Morisco, F.; Fogliano, V.; Zappalà, A.; Palmigiano, A.; Garozzo, D.; Caporaso, N.; D'Argenio, G.; *et al.* Coffee enhances the expression of chaperones and antioxidant proteins in rats with nonalcoholic fatty liver disease. *Transl. Res.* **2014**, *163*, 593–602. [CrossRef] [PubMed]

International Journal of
Molecular Sciences

MDPI

Article

Weekly Treatment of 2-Hydroxypropyl-β-cyclodextrin Improves Intracellular Cholesterol Levels in LDL Receptor Knockout Mice

Sofie M. A. Walenbergh [1], Tom Houben [1], Tim Hendrikx [1], Mike L. J. Jeurissen [1], Patrick J. van Gorp [1], Nathalie Vaes [1], Steven W. M. Olde Damink [2,3], Fons Verheyen [4], Ger H. Koek [5], Dieter Lütjohann [6], Alena Grebe [7], Eicke Latz [7,8,9] and Ronit Shiri-Sverdlov [1,*]

[1] Department of Molecular Genetics, School of Nutrition and Translational Research in Metabolism (NUTRIM), Maastricht University, Maastricht 6229ER, The Netherlands; s.walenbergh@maastrichtuniversity.nl (S.M.A.W.); tom.houben@maastrichtuniversity.nl (To.H.); t.hendrikx@maastrichtuniversity.nl (Ti.H.); m.jeurissen@maastrichtuniversity.nl (M.L.J.J.); p.vangorp@maastrichtuniversity.nl (P.J.G.); n.vaes@maastrichtuniversity.nl (N.V.)

[2] Department of General Surgery, Maastricht University, Maastricht 6229ER, The Netherlands; steven.oldedamink@maastrichtuniversity.nl

[3] Department of HPB and Liver Transplantation Surgery, Royal Free Hospital, University College London, London NW3 2PF, UK

[4] Department of Molecular Cell Biology and Electron Microscopy, Maastricht University, Maastricht 6229ER, The Netherlands; f.verheyen@maastrichtuniversity.nl

[5] Department of Internal Medicine, Division of Gastroenterology and Hepatology, Maastricht University Medical Center (MUMC), Maastricht 6202AZ, The Netherlands; gh.koek@mumc.nl

[6] Institute of Clinical Chemistry and Clinical Pharmacology, University of Bonn, Bonn D-53105, Germany; dieter.luetjohann@ukb.uni-bonn.de

[7] Institute of Innate Immunity, University Hospital, University of Bonn, Bonn D-53127, Germany; alena.grebe@uni-bonn.de (A.G.); eicke.latz@umassmed.edu (E.L.)

[8] German Center for Neurodegenerative Diseases (DZNE), Bonn D-53127, Germany

[9] Division of Infectious Diseases and Immunology, University of Massachusetts Medical School, Worcester, MA 01605, USA

[*] Author to whom correspondence should be addressed; r.sverdlov@maastrichtuniversity.nl; Tel.: +31-43-388-1746; Fax: +31-43-388-4574.

Academic Editors: Amedeo Lonardo and Giovanni Targher
Received: 4 June 2015; Accepted: 20 August 2015; Published: 2 September 2015

Abstract: Recently, the importance of lysosomes in the context of the metabolic syndrome has received increased attention. Increased lysosomal cholesterol storage and cholesterol crystallization inside macrophages have been linked to several metabolic diseases, such as atherosclerosis and non-alcoholic fatty liver disease (NAFLD). Two-hydroxypropyl-β-cyclodextrin (HP-B-CD) is able to redirect lysosomal cholesterol to the cytoplasm in Niemann-Pick type C1 disease, a lysosomal storage disorder. We hypothesize that HP-B-CD ameliorates liver cholesterol and intracellular cholesterol levels inside Kupffer cells (KCs). Hyperlipidemic low-density lipoprotein receptor knockout ($Ldlr^{-/-}$) mice were given weekly, subcutaneous injections with HP-B-CD or control PBS. In contrast to control injections, hyperlipidemic mice treated with HP-B-CD demonstrated a shift in intracellular cholesterol distribution towards cytoplasmic cholesteryl ester (CE) storage and a decrease in cholesterol crystallization inside KCs. Compared to untreated hyperlipidemic mice, the foamy KC appearance and liver cholesterol remained similar upon HP-B-CD administration, while hepatic campesterol and 7α-hydroxycholesterol levels were back increased. Thus, HP-B-CD could be a useful tool to improve intracellular cholesterol levels in the context of the metabolic syndrome, possibly through modulation of phyto- and oxysterols, and should be tested in the future. Additionally, these data underline the existence of a shared etiology between lysosomal storage diseases and NAFLD.

Int. J. Mol. Sci. **2015**, *16*, 21056–21069

Keywords: NAFLD; metabolic syndrome; cyclodextrin; electron microscopy; lysosomes

---

1. Introduction

Non-alcoholic fatty liver disease (NAFLD) describes several stages of liver disease characterized by no or little alcohol use, and is currently viewed as the precursor of the metabolic syndrome [1]. Initially, the excessive buildup of fat inside the liver, also referred to as steatosis, is a benign and reversible condition. However, later stages of NAFLD are characterized by liver inflammation, the formation of irreversible scar tissue (fibrosis-cirrhosis) and severe end-stage liver disease [2]. Currently, the prevalence of NAFLD is estimated to grow as a direct result of the global obesity epidemic [3]. Better insights into the mechanisms that cause NAFLD are required in order to develop novel therapeutic interventions.

Under healthy circumstances, lipoproteins are endocytosed by macrophages and initially directed to the endolysosomal compartment where further processing will take place. Subsequently, cholesterol is transferred from the lysosomes to the cytoplasm. Interestingly, previous studies from our group revealed that during hyperlipidemic conditions in mice, such as NAFLD, cholesterol is not transported into the cytoplasm, but rather accumulates inside lysosomes of the Kupffer cells (KCs). In addition to a resistance of cholesterol efflux from the lysosome, we observed increased cholesterol crystals in the livers of these mice [4,5]. These cholesterol crystals are so-called cholesterol deposits, formed upon excessive cholesterol uptake. Similar to our data, lysosomal cholesterol storage and cholesterol crystallization inside macrophages was also observed during atherosclerosis [6]. Therefore, the suggestion was raised that both these metabolic diseases share disease mechanisms and could be referred to as acquired lysosomal storage disorders [7,8]. A classical lysosomal storage disorder, such as Niemann-Pick type C (NPC) disease, is caused by a mutation in either the *Npc1* or *Npc2* gene, which encodes for a key protein that is responsible for cholesterol transport from the lysosomes to the cytoplasm. As a result, NPC disease patients demonstrate progressive accumulation of cholesterol inside lysosomes that severely damages almost all organs, leading to neurological disease, liver dysfunction and eventually premature death [9]. Notably, increased lysosomal cholesterol accumulation in $Npc1^{-/-}$ mice could be reversed by the administration of two-hydroxypropyl-β-cyclodextrin (HP-B-CD) and normalized the cholesterol metabolism in nearly every organ of the body [10–14]. Thus far, the effect of HP-B-CD on the cholesterol metabolism during NAFLD has never been studied.

The aim of the current study was to investigate whether HP-B-CD treatment is able to modify the cholesterol metabolism in the liver, as well as inside the KCs, in an established hyperlipidemic low-density lipoprotein receptor knockout ($Ldlr^{-/-}$) mouse model. Unlike wildtype mice, the $Ldlr^{-/-}$ mice demonstrate a human-like lipoprotein profile characterized by mildly elevated cholesterol levels which is mostly carried in the intermediate-density lipoprotein (IDL)/LDL fractions [15]. Additionally, recent research demonstrated that the presence of steatosis and hepatic inflammation is persisted for a long period of time, and even progressed into liver fibrosis [16]. The resemblance with a human-like lipoprotein profile, the sustained hepatic inflammatory response and the development of fibrosis makes hyperlipidemic $Ldlr^{-/-}$ mice an excellent mouse model to study the onset and progression of NAFLD. We hypothesized that HP-B-CD ameliorates liver cholesterol and intracellular cholesterol levels inside KCs. Once a week, we administered HP-B-CD to $Ldlr^{-/-}$ mice fed a high-fat, high-cholesterol (HFC) diet. Mice receiving phosphate-buffered saline (PBS) were used as a control. After HP-B-CD treatment, we found that lysosomal cholesterol levels and cholesterol crystallization were decreased inside KCs compared to control-treated hyperlipidemic mice. In contrast, no changes in the total level of liver cholesterol and KC area were seen. These data indicate for the first time that HP-B-CD could be a useful tool to improve intracellular cholesterol levels in the context of the metabolic syndrome.

2. Results

2.1. No Difference in Liver and Plasma Cholesterol Levels upon HP-B-CD Treatment

The mean spleen and liver weight in the HFC group was increased compared to chow, but remained similar upon weekly HP-B-CD treatment for a 12-week time period (Figure 1A). In line with these data, liver and plasma cholesterol levels were significantly higher upon HFC feeding than after 12 weeks of regular chow. However, no differences in cholesterol concentrations were found between PBS and HP-B-CD-treated mice on an HFC diet (Figure 1B). Thus, these data indicate that HP-B-CD has no effect on organ weight and cholesterol concentrations in plasma and liver.

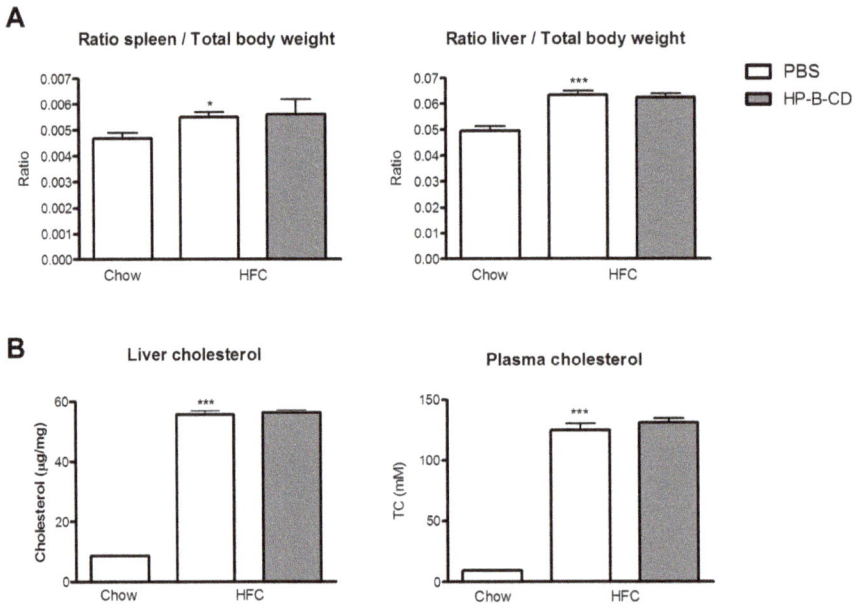

Figure 1. Relative spleen, liver weights and cholesterol levels. (**A**) Relative spleen and liver weights after 12-weeks of regular chow or HFC diet in $Ldlr^{-/-}$ mice with and without HP-B-CD treatment; and (**B**) Cholesterol levels were analyzed in liver as well as plasma of $Ldlr^{-/-}$ mice after 12 weeks of regular chow or HFC diet. TC: total cholesterol. Data are expressed as mean $\pm$ SEM (n = 10 for the chow-fed mice; n = 12 for the mice fed an HFC diet without treatment; n = 12 for the HFC-fed mice receiving HP-B-CD treatment). * Significantly different from chow. * and *** indicate $p < 0.05$, and 0.001, respectively.

2.2. Foamy KC Appearance Is Similar between Control- and HP-B-CD-Injected Mice

To determine whether HP-B-CD affects the foamy appearance of KCs, liver sections were stained against CD68, a marker specifically for macrophages. As expected, HFC feeding increased the area of the KCs, compared to mice fed regular chow. No difference in CD68-positive area was observed between PBS- and HP-B-CD-injected mice on an HFC diet (Figure 2A). These data were confirmed upon quantification of the CD68-positive area of these livers (Figure 2B) and gene expression analysis of *Cd68* (Figure 2C), which both demonstrated no difference in the CD68 expression after HP-B-CD. To summarize, the HFC diet leads to a foamy KC appearance and was not affected upon HP-B-CD treatment.

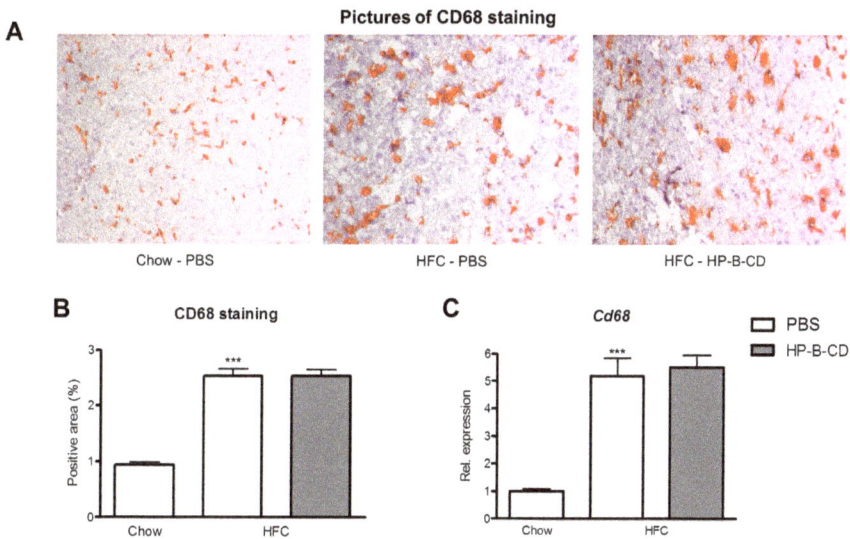

Figure 2. Hepatic CD68 expression. (**A**) Representative histological pictures of the CD68 staining (original magnification, 200×) performed on liver sections of chow, PBS-injected and HP-B-CD-injected HFC-fed mice; (**B**) Quantification of the percentage CD68-positive area; (**C**) Hepatic gene expression analysis of *Cd68*. Gene expression data are shown relative to chow. Data are expressed as mean ± SEM ($n = 10$ for the chow-fed mice; $n = 12$ for the mice fed an HFC diet without treatment; $n = 12$ for the HFC-fed mice receiving HP-B-CD treatment). * Significantly different from chow. *** indicates $p < 0.001$.

2.3. HP-B-CD-Treated Mice Demonstrate Decreased Lysosomal Cholesterol Accumulation and Cholesterol Crystallization

Electron microscopy was performed to investigate the effect of HP-B-CD on redirecting lysosomal cholesterol to the cytoplasm and cholesterol crystallization. Livers were fixed and stained for acid phosphatase (ACPase), a marker for lysosomes. As demonstrated in Figure 3A, KCs of the non-treated HFC group displayed increased lysosomal cholesterol accumulation and cholesterol crystals compared to KCs of HP-B-CD-treated mice upon HFC feeding (Figure 3B). In the latter group, cholesterol droplets were mainly observed inside the cytoplasm. Scoring electron microscopy pictures of approximately 50 KCs from both HFC groups confirmed that lysosomal cholesterol was significantly decreased, while cytoplasmic cholesteryl ester (CE) droplets were increased upon HP-B-CD treatment. Moreover, mice administered HP-B-CD had less cholesterol crystals inside their KCs compared to control PBS-injected mice after a 12-week HFC diet (Figure 3C). These results suggest that HP-B-CD is able to redirect cholesterol from the lysosomes to the cytoplasm.

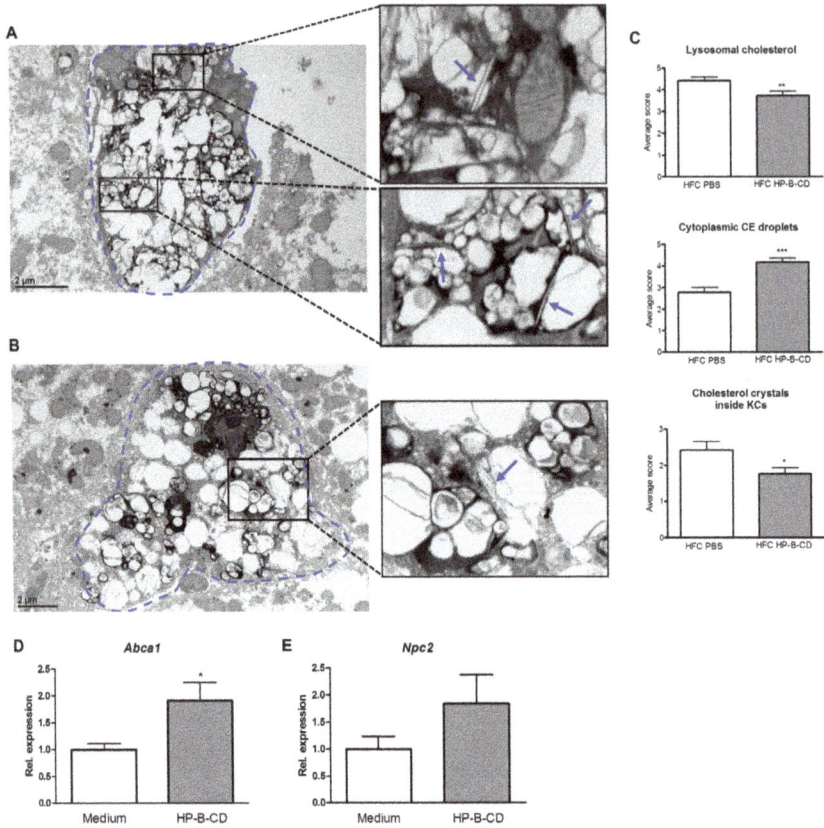

Figure 3. Effect of HP-B-CD on intracellular cholesterol distribution and cholesterol transporters. Representative electron microscopy pictures of Kupffer cells (KCs) of HFC-fed *Ldlr*$^{-/-}$ mice without (**A**) and with HP-B-CD treatment (**B**). Lysosomes are indicated in black by ACPase staining. KCs are depicted by the dashed line. Arrows point to cholesterol crystals; (**C**) Scoring of lysosomal cholesterol, cytoplasmic cholesteryl ester (CE) droplets and cholesterol crystals after 12 weeks of HFC diet. In total, 40 to 50 KCs were scored per HFC group and an average score was calculated. Gene expression levels of the cholesterol transporters *Abca1* (**D**) and *Npc2* (**E**) in oxLDL-loaded BMDM with or without HP-B-CD treatment. The *in vitro* results are the mean ± SEM from two separate experiments performed in triplicate. * Significantly different from control. *, ** and *** indicate $p < 0.05$, 0.01 and 0.001, respectively.

Previous studies found that it is mainly oxidized LDL (oxLDL) that tends to accumulate inside the lysosomes of *Ldlr*$^{-/-}$ mice and in cultured macrophages [5,17]. To show that HP-B-CD is able to modify lysosomal oxLDL, we isolated bone marrow-derived macrophages (BMDM) from wildtype mice and stimulated these with oxLDL. Subsequently, BMDM were treated with HP-B-CD (0.3%) or with control medium. Upon HP-B-CD treatment, gene expression of ATP-binding cassette transporter A1 (*Abca1*), a key regulator of cholesterol efflux, was elevated compared to control treatment (Figure 3D). Additionally, the gene expression of Niemann-Pick type C2 (*Npc2*), an intracellular lysosomal cholesterol transporter responsible for cholesterol transport out of the lysosome, was also elevated after HP-B-CD treatment compared to control (Figure 3E). These data demonstrate the ability of HP-B-CD to lower lysosomal oxLDL levels.

2.4. Campesterol and 7α-Hydroxycholesterol Are Increased after HP-B-CD Treatment

To obtain a better understanding in the cholesterol metabolism after HP-B-CD treatment, we analyzed campesterol, a phytosterol, and 7α-hydroxycholesterol (7aOH), an oxysterol, in the livers of control chow-fed and non-treated and HP-B-CD-treated HFC-fed mice. Hepatic campesterol and 7aOH levels were dramatically reduced upon an HFC diet compared to chow. Interestingly, campesterol and 7aOH were significantly increased after HP-B-CD treatment, although the elevation was minimal (Figure 4A,B).

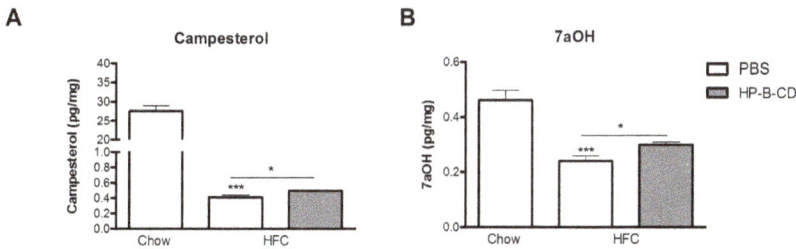

Figure 4. Hepatic levels of campesterol and 7α-hydroxycholesterol (7aOH). Campesterol (**A**) and 7aOH (**B**) were analyzed in liver pieces of *Ldlr*$^{-/-}$ mice after 12 weeks of regular chow or HFC diet. Data are expressed as mean ± SEM (n = 10 for the chow-fed mice; n = 12 for the mice fed an HFC diet without treatment; n = 12 for the HFC-fed mice receiving HP-B-CD treatment). * Significantly different from chow. * and *** indicate $p < 0.05$ and 0.001, respectively.

3. Discussion

Currently, no registered therapeutic interventions against NAFLD are available. Previous studies from our group suggest that lysosomal cholesterol accumulation can be considered as a key mechanism for the pathogenesis of NAFLD in mice. As such, we tested HP-B-CD, a compound known to redirect cholesterol from the lysosomes to the cytoplasm in the context of lysosomal storage diseases, to improve the cholesterol metabolism in an established hyperlipidemic mouse model to study NAFLD [16]. Unlike total hepatic cholesterol levels, we now show that it is the intracellular localization of cholesterol in hyperlipidemic mice that is improved after HP-B-CD treatment. Our novel data demonstrate that HP-B-CD reduces lysosomal cholesterol accumulation and cholesterol crystallization in KCs during hyperlipidemic conditions. Moreover, these data underline the shared etiology between lysosomal storage diseases and NAFLD.

Lysosomal cholesterol accumulation could be efficiently overcome by the administration of HP-B-CD to *Npc1*$^{-/-}$ mice and cells deficient for the *Npc1* gene [10,13]. In the current study, a similar dosage (20% w/v, 4000 mg per kg body weight) and product (H107, Sigma-Aldrich) of HP-B-CD was administered subcuteanously as described in previous *in vivo* studies [11–14,18] and showed to decrease lysosomal cholesterol storage and increase cytoplasmic CE droplets inside KCs. Thus, HP-B-CD was able to reduce lysosomal cholesterol in a lysosomal storage disease and fatty liver disease and suggests a shared disease mechanism. Lysosomal cholesterol accumulation in macrophages is an underlying mechanism in diseases associated with the metabolic syndrome, such as atherosclerosis and NAFLD [4,7,8]. Unlike non-oxidized LDL that accumulates in lysosomes of NPC mice, recent evidence points toward the specific lysosomal trapping of oxLDL in *Ldlr*$^{-/-}$ mice and in cultured macrophages [5,17,19,20]. Besides NAFLD, increasing attention has been directed to the crucial role of oxLDL in the pathogenesis of various metabolic diseases, including atherosclerosis [7] and diabetes [21]. However, thus far, oxLDL has been shown to be highly resistant to removal from the lysosome [22] and to intracellular degradation [23]. As such, the ability of HP-B-CD to liberate lysosomal cholesterol in $Ldlr^{-/-}$ mice is an exciting opportunity for the amelioration of various metabolic diseases underlying lysosomal oxLDL accumulation.

HP-B-CD has cholesterol-binding capacities and normalizes cholesterol homeostasis in *Npc1* deficient cells [24]. Upon absorption, HP-B-CD has been shown to be distributed over several tissues including the liver [25]. In line, numerous studies demonstrated a clear improvement in liver function of $Npc1^{-/-}$ mice after subcutaneous administration of HP-B-CD [11–14,26]. Much to our surprise, no changes in plasma and liver cholesterol levels and the foamy KC appearance were found in HP-B-CD-treated mice compared to their control. A possible explanation for these data is that cholesterol storage inside lysosomes is much less extreme in the $Ldlr^{-/-}$ model compared to the $Npc1^{-/-}$ mice fed an HFC diet. Therefore, the effect of HP-B-CD on total cholesterol levels, and also liver weight, in the $Ldlr^{-/-}$ model is not significant. In line with our observations, Taylor *et al.* demonstrated that HP-B-CD treatment does not lead to increased cholesterol levels in urine and plasma, leaving HP-B-CD to liberate lysosomal cholesterol for further processing within the cytosolic compartment only [27]. However, these results may be related to the fact that HP-B-CD was injected only one single time in the latter study.

In line with the unaffected plasma and liver cholesterol levels between HP-B-CD- and control-treated mice, we could not detect any differences in the foamy KC appearance. This is a striking result, since the amount of cholesterol crystals were lowered in mice treated with HP-B-CD compared to PBS and suggest that foamy KCs do not correlate with cholesterol crystallization. This is contrary to the current view that foamy macrophages are strongly associated with cholesterol crystallization [5,28–30]. Of note, cholesterol crystallization occurs within lipid-loaded lysosomes and not in the cytoplasm, hereby confirming that the actual formation of cholesterol crystals is dependent on lysosomal cholesterol levels [31]. Indeed, in line with a decreased level of lysosomal cholesterol, we observed less cholesterol crystallization. Altogether, these data indicate that there is dissociation between foam cell formation and cholesterol crystallization.

Despite much effort, the exact mechanism by which HP-B-CD normalizes cholesterol homeostasis is still under debate. After injection, HP-B-CD has the ability to be internalized into the lysosomes of cells via bulk phase endocytosis and release sequestered cholesterol from the lysosome into the cytosol [32]. Due to the unique structure of HP-B-CD, it can serve as a cholesterol sink, extract cholesterol and trap cholesterol in the presence of high cholesterol concentrations. However, during low cholesterol levels, HP-B-CD rather acts as a cholesterol shuttle, transporting cholesterol between membranes. Other evidence points towards HP-B-CD as a compound that extracts cholesterol from cell membranes by which the resulting HP-B-CD-cholesterol complex is then cleared via the kidneys.

In the current study, we have found that the HFC diet leads to a dramatic reduction of liver campesterol compared to chow. In the plasma, campesterol can be considered as a surrogate marker for intestinal cholesterol absorption, and likely has the same function when found in the liver [33]. Intestinal cholesterol absorption, and thus campesterol, is likely to be inhibited during consumption of a high fat diet, as a protective mechanism to prevent excess plasma cholesterol levels. Our data are in line with other studies pointing towards an inverse correlation between campesterol and BMI/obesity [34,35]. Likewise, elimination of overweight by lifestyle interventions normalized intestinal cholesterol absorption [33]. Campesterol and 7aOH in the liver were elevated upon HP-B-CD administration. While the molecular mechanisms behind this observation are not clear, it is known that both campesterol and 7aOH are liver X receptor (LXR) agonists which serve as an intracellular sensor of cholesterol content and mobilize cholesterol to the plasma membrane upon activation [36]. Thus, the upregulation of campesterol and 7aOH levels upon HP-B-CD could possibly contribute to the improved intracellular cholesterol trafficking observed upon administration of HP-B-CD. Despite the upregulation of campesterol and 7aOH upon HP-B-CD treatment, we did not observe a decrease in plasma and liver cholesterol. This observation can be explained by the fact that dietary phytosterols, including campesterol, have been shown to increase the affinity and efficiency of the LDLR for adequate cholesterol removal [37]. Since our study was performed in *Ldlr*$^{-/-}$ mice, campesterol was not able to enhance efficiency of the LDLR. Moreover, these results indicate that lysosomal cholesterol levels were reduced independent of the LDLR and support the view of campesterol and 7aOH being an LXR-agonist. Thus, campesterol and 7aOH levels were upregulated upon HP-B-CD and possibly improved intracellular cholesterol trafficking via LXR signaling.

4. Experimental Section

4.1. Mice, Diet and Injections

The mice were housed under standard conditions and given free access to food and water. All experiments were approved by the Committee for Animal Welfare of Maastricht University and performed according to Dutch regulations. Eleven to twelve-week old female *Ldlr*$^{-/-}$ mice on a C57/Bl6 background were either fed regular chow (*n* = 10) or an HFC diet (*n* = 12 per HFC group with and without HP-B-CD treatment) for 12 weeks. The effects of HP-B-CD were investigated by giving weekly subcuteanous injections at the start of the HFC diet with 4000 mg per kg of body weight of 20% *w/v* HP-B-CD (H107, Sigma-Aldrich GmbH, St. Louis, MO, USA) (*n* = 12). PBS was used for control injections. The HFC diet contained 21% milk butter, 0.2% cholesterol, 46% carbohydrates and 17% casein. Collection of blood and tissue specimens, biochemical determination of lipids in plasma, liver histology, electron microscopy, acid phosphatase (ACPase) enzyme cytochemistry, RNA isolation, complementary DNA synthesis and quantitative polymerase chain reaction were determined as described previously [4,5,38–41]. Pieces of liver were used for quantification of liver cholesterol and the hepatic levels of campesterol and 7α-hydroxycholesterol as described previously [42].

4.2. CD68 Staining

For the CD68 staining, six microscopical views (200× magnification) of each liver were obtained. Adobe Photoshop CS2 v.9.0 was used to analyze CD68-positive (red) pixels as well as total unstained tissue pixels of each microscopical picture. Subsequently, these data were used to calculate the percentage of CD68-positive area.

4.3. Scoring of Lysosomal Lipid Droplets, Cytoplasmic CE Droplets and Cholesterol Crystals

Electron microscopy was performed by an expert in the electron microscopical field of the liver. By using electron microscopy pictures, analysis of lysosomal cholesterol was performed by scoring the area of lysosomal lipid droplets, those that are inside ACPase-positive lysosomes indicated by the black membrane, and the area of cytoplasmic CE droplets in 40 to 50 KCs from each HFC group. Each KC was scored between 0 and 6; 0 indicated no lipid droplets inside lysosomes or no cytoplasmic CE droplets, whereas an extremely large area of lysosomal lipid droplets or cytoplasmic CE droplets was scored with a 6. Subsequently, the average lysosomal cholesterol and cytoplasmic CE area per KC was calculated. The scoring and the average calculation for cholesterol crystallization were performed similarly; the score 0 indicated no cholesterol crystals, while 5 indicated the highest area of cholesterol crystals and was performed as described previously [29].

4.4. Bone Marrow-Derived Macrophages

Bone marrow-derived macrophages (BMDM) were isolated from the tibiae and femurs of wildtype C57BL/6 mice. Cells were cultured in RPMI-1640 (GIBCO Invitrogen, Breda, The Netherlands) with 10% heat-inactivated fetal calf serum (Bodinco B.V. Alkmaar, The Netherlands), penicillin (100 U/mL), streptomycin (100 μg/mL) and L-glutamine 2 mM (all GIBCO Invitrogen), supplemented with 20% L929-conditioned medium (LCM) for 8–9 days to generate BMDM. After attachment, macrophages were seeded at 350,000 cells per well in 24-well plates and incubated for 72 h with oxLDL (25 μg/mL; Alfa Aesar: J65591, Wardhill, MA, USA), followed by a treatment with or without 0.3% HP-B-CD (H107, Sigma-Aldrich GmbH, St. Louis, MO, USA). Then cells were washed and stimulated with lipopolysaccharide (100 ng/mL) for 4 h. Finally, cells were lysed and further processed for gene expression analysis.

4.5. Statistical Analysis

Data were analyzed by two-tailed, unpaired, *t*-tests using GraphPad Prism, version 4.0 for Windows (GraphPad Software Inc., La Jolla, CA, USA). Data are represented as mean ± standard error of mean (SEM) and considered significant at $p < 0.05$ (* $p < 0.05$; ** $p < 0.01$ and *** $p < 0.001$, respectively).

5. Conclusions

Unlike total liver cholesterol, administration of HP-B-CD improves intracellular cholesterol localization inside KCs of NAFLD-susceptible $Ldlr^{-/-}$ mice. Therefore, HP-B-CD could be a useful tool to improve intracellular cholesterol levels and cholesterol crystals in the context of the metabolic syndrome and should be tested in the future. Further studies are necessary to determine the novel role of oxysterols and phytosterols in improving intracellular cholesterol trafficking. Additionally, these data underline the existence of a shared etiology between lysosomal storage diseases and NAFLD.

Acknowledgments: This research was supported by the Maag Lever Darm Stichting (MLDS) (WO 08-16 and WO 11-35), the Netherlands Organisation for Scientific Research (NWO) (Vidi grant number: 016.126.327), and by the Cardiovascular Research Netherlands (CVON) IN-CONTROL grant (CVON 2012-03).

Author Contributions: Sofie M. A. Walenbergh, Alena Grebe, Eicke Latz, Ronit Shiri-Sverdlov conceived and designed experiments; Sofie M. A. Walenbergh, Tom Houben, Tim Hendrikx, Mike L. J. Jeurissen, Patrick J. van Gorp, Nathalie Vaes, Fons Verheyen, Dieter Lütjohann, Ronit Shiri-Sverdlov performed the experiments; Sofie M. A. Walenbergh, Tom Houben, Nathalie Vaes, Ronit Shiri-Sverdlov analyzed data; Sofie M. A. Walenbergh, Steven W. M. Olde Damink, Ger H. Koek, Ronit Shiri-Sverdlov wrote the paper.

Conflicts of Interest: The authors declare no conflict of interest.

Abbreviations

NAFLD: Non-alcoholic fatty liver disease; KCs: Kupffer cells; NPC: Niemann-Pick Type C; HP-B-CD: Two-hydroxypropyl-β-cyclodextrin; LDL(R): Low-density lipoprotein (receptor); IDL: Intermediate-density lipoprotein; HFC: High-fat, high-cholesterol; PBS: Phosphate-buffered saline; CE: Cholesteryl ester; ACPase: Acid phosphatase; 7aOH: 7α-Hydroxycholesterol; OxLDL: Oxidized LDL; LXR: Liver X receptor.

References

1. Lonardo, A.; Ballestri, S.; Marchesini, G.; Angulo, P.; Loria, P. Nonalcoholic fatty liver disease: A precursor of the metabolic syndrome. *Dig. Liver Dis.* **2015**, *47*, 181–190. [CrossRef] [PubMed]
2. Angulo, P. Nonalcoholic fatty liver disease. *N. Engl. J. Med.* **2002**, *346*, 1221–1231. [CrossRef] [PubMed]
3. Starley, B.Q.; Calcagno, C.J.; Harrison, S.A. Nonalcoholic fatty liver disease and hepatocellular carcinoma: A weighty connection. *Hepatology* **2010**, *51*, 1820–1832. [CrossRef] [PubMed]
4. Bieghs, V.; Hendrikx, T.; van Gorp, P.J.; Verheyen, F.; Guichot, Y.D.; Walenbergh, S.M.; Jeurissen, M.L.; Gijbels, M.; Rensen, S.S.; Bast, A.; *et al.* The cholesterol derivative 27-hydroxycholesterol reduces steatohepatitis in mice. *Gastroenterology* **2013**, *144*, 167–178.e1. [CrossRef] [PubMed]
5. Bieghs, V.; van Gorp, P.J.; Walenbergh, S.M.; Gijbels, M.J.; Verheyen, F.; Buurman, W.A.; Briles, D.E.; Hofker, M.H.; Binder, C.J.; Shiri-Sverdlov, R. Specific immunization strategies against oxidized low-density lipoprotein: A novel way to reduce nonalcoholic steatohepatitis in mice. *Hepatology* **2012**, *56*, 894–903. [CrossRef] [PubMed]
6. Duewell, P.; Kono, H.; Rayner, K.J.; Sirois, C.M.; Vladimer, G.; Bauernfeind, F.G.; Abela, G.S.; Franchi, L.; Nunez, G.; Schnurr, M.; *et al.* NLRP3 inflammasomes are required for atherogenesis and activated by cholesterol crystals. *Nature* **2010**, *464*, 1357–1361. [CrossRef] [PubMed]
7. Hendrikx, T.; Walenbergh, S.M.; Hofker, M.H.; Shiri-Sverdlov, R. Lysosomal cholesterol accumulation: Driver on the road to inflammation during atherosclerosis and non-alcoholic steatohepatitis. *Obes. Rev.* **2014**, *15*, 424–433. [CrossRef] [PubMed]

8. Jerome, W.G. Advanced atherosclerotic foam cell formation has features of an acquired lysosomal storage disorder. *Rejuv. Res.* **2006**, *9*, 245–255. [CrossRef] [PubMed]
9. Vanier, M.T. Niemann-Pick disease type C. *Orphanet J. Rare Dis.* **2010**, *5*, 16. [CrossRef] [PubMed]
10. Abi-Mosleh, L.; Infante, R.E.; Radhakrishnan, A.; Goldstein, J.L.; Brown, M.S. Cyclodextrin overcomes deficient lysosome-to-endoplasmic reticulum transport of cholesterol in Niemann-Pick type C cells. *Proc. Natl. Acad. Sci. USA* **2009**, *106*, 19316–19321. [CrossRef] [PubMed]
11. Davidson, C.D.; Ali, N.F.; Micsenyi, M.C.; Stephney, G.; Renault, S.; Dobrenis, K.; Ory, D.S.; Vanier, M.T.; Walkley, S.U. Chronic cyclodextrin treatment of murine Niemann-Pick C disease ameliorates neuronal cholesterol and glycosphingolipid storage and disease progression. *PLoS ONE* **2009**, *4*, e6951. [CrossRef] [PubMed]
12. Liu, B.; Ramirez, C.M.; Miller, A.M.; Repa, J.J.; Turley, S.D.; Dietschy, J.M. Cyclodextrin overcomes the transport defect in nearly every organ of NPC1 mice leading to excretion of sequestered cholesterol as bile acid. *J. Lipid Res.* **2010**, *51*, 933–944. [CrossRef] [PubMed]
13. Liu, B.; Turley, S.D.; Burns, D.K.; Miller, A.M.; Repa, J.J.; Dietschy, J.M. Reversal of defective lysosomal transport in NPC disease ameliorates liver dysfunction and neurodegeneration in the $npc1^{-/-}$ mouse. *Proc. Natl. Acad. Sci. USA* **2009**, *106*, 2377–2382. [CrossRef] [PubMed]
14. Ramirez, C.M.; Liu, B.; Taylor, A.M.; Repa, J.J.; Burns, D.K.; Weinberg, A.G.; Turley, S.D.; Dietschy, J.M. Weekly cyclodextrin administration normalizes cholesterol metabolism in nearly every organ of the Niemann-Pick type C1 mouse and markedly prolongs life. *Pediatr. Res.* **2010**, *68*, 309–315. [CrossRef] [PubMed]
15. Ishibashi, S.; Brown, M.S.; Goldstein, J.L.; Gerard, R.D.; Hammer, R.E.; Herz, J. Hypercholesterolemia in low density lipoprotein receptor knockout mice and its reversal by adenovirus-mediated gene delivery. *J. Clin. Investig.* **1993**, *92*, 883–893. [CrossRef] [PubMed]
16. Bieghs, V.; van Gorp, P.J.; Wouters, K.; Hendrikx, T.; Gijbels, M.J.; van Bilsen, M.; Bakker, J.; Binder, C.J.; Lutjohann, D.; Staels, B.; *et al.* LDL receptor knock-out mice are a physiological model particularly vulnerable to study the onset of inflammation in non-alcoholic fatty liver disease. *PLoS ONE* **2012**, *7*, e30668. [CrossRef] [PubMed]
17. Bieghs, V.; Walenbergh, S.M.; Hendrikx, T.; van Gorp, P.J.; Verheyen, F.; Olde Damink, S.W.; Masclee, A.A.; Koek, G.H.; Hofker, M.H.; Binder, C.J.; *et al.* Trapping of oxidized LDL in lysosomes of Kupffer cells is a trigger for hepatic inflammation. *Liver Int.* **2013**, *33*, 1056–1061. [CrossRef] [PubMed]
18. Ramirez, C.M.; Liu, B.; Aqul, A.; Taylor, A.M.; Repa, J.J.; Turley, S.D.; Dietschy, J.M. Quantitative role of LAL, NPC2, and NPC1 in lysosomal cholesterol processing defined by genetic and pharmacological manipulations. *J. Lipid Res.* **2011**, *52*, 688–698. [CrossRef] [PubMed]
19. Jerome, W.G.; Cash, C.; Webber, R.; Horton, R.; Yancey, P.G. Lysosomal lipid accumulation from oxidized low density lipoprotein is correlated with hypertrophy of the Golgi apparatus and trans-Golgi network. *J. Lipid Res.* **1998**, *39*, 1362–1371. [PubMed]
20. Schmitz, G.; Grandl, M. Endolysosomal phospholipidosis and cytosolic lipid droplet storage and release in macrophages. *Biochim. Biophys. Acta* **2009**, *1791*, 524–539. [CrossRef] [PubMed]
21. Sims-Robinson, C.; Bakeman, A.; Rosko, A.; Glasser, R.; Feldman, E.L. The role of oxidized cholesterol in diabetes-induced lysosomal dysfunction in the brain. *Mol. Neurobiol.* **2015**. [CrossRef] [PubMed]
22. Yancey, P.G.; Jerome, W.G. Lysosomal cholesterol derived from mildly oxidized low density lipoprotein is resistant to efflux. *J. Lipid Res.* **2001**, *42*, 317–327. [PubMed]
23. Lougheed, M.; Zhang, H.F.; Steinbrecher, U.P. Oxidized low density lipoprotein is resistant to cathepsins and accumulates within macrophages. *J. Biol. Chem.* **1991**, *266*, 14519–14525. [PubMed]
24. Peake, K.B.; Vance, J.E. Normalization of cholesterol homeostasis by 2-hydroxypropyl-β-cyclodextrin in neurons and glia from Niemann-Pick C1 (NPC1)-deficient mice. *J. Biol. Chem.* **2012**, *287*, 9290–9298. [CrossRef] [PubMed]
25. Stella, V.J.; He, Q. Cyclodextrins. *Toxicol. Pathol.* **2008**, *36*, 30–42. [CrossRef] [PubMed]
26. Lopez, A.M.; Terpack, S.J.; Posey, K.S.; Liu, B.; Ramirez, C.M.; Turley, S.D. Systemic administration of 2-hydroxypropyl-β-cyclodextrin to symptomatic NPC1-deficient mice slows cholesterol sequestration in the major organs and improves liver function. *Clin. Exp. Pharmacol. Physiol.* **2014**, *41*, 780–787. [CrossRef] [PubMed]

27. Taylor, A.M.; Liu, B.; Mari, Y.; Liu, B.; Repa, J.J. Cyclodextrin mediates rapid changes in lipid balance in *Npc1*$^{-/-}$ mice without carrying cholesterol through the bloodstream. *J. Lipid Res.* **2012**, *53*, 2331–2342. [CrossRef] [PubMed]

28. Grebe, A.; Latz, E. Cholesterol crystals and inflammation. *Curr. Rheumatol. Rep.* **2013**, *15*, 313. [CrossRef] [PubMed]

29. Hendrikx, T.; Bieghs, V.; Walenbergh, S.M.; van Gorp, P.J.; Verheyen, F.; Jeurissen, M.L.; Steinbusch, M.M.; Vaes, N.; Binder, C.J.; Koek, G.H.; *et al.* Macrophage specific caspase-1/11 deficiency protects against cholesterol crystallization and hepatic inflammation in hyperlipidemic mice. *PLoS ONE* **2013**, *8*, e78792. [CrossRef] [PubMed]

30. Ioannou, G.N.; Haigh, W.G.; Thorning, D.; Savard, C. Hepatic cholesterol crystals and crown-like structures distinguish nash from simple steatosis. *J. Lipid Res.* **2013**, *54*, 1326–1334. [CrossRef] [PubMed]

31. Tangirala, R.K.; Jerome, W.G.; Jones, N.L.; Small, D.M.; Johnson, W.J.; Glick, J.M.; Mahlberg, F.H.; Rothblat, G.H. Formation of cholesterol monohydrate crystals in macrophage-derived foam cells. *J. Lipid Res.* **1994**, *35*, 93–104. [PubMed]

32. Rosenbaum, A.I.; Zhang, G.; Warren, J.D.; Maxfield, F.R. Endocytosis of β-cyclodextrins is responsible for cholesterol reduction in Niemann-Pick type C mutant cells. *Proc. Natl. Acad. Sci. USA* **2010**, *107*, 5477–5482. [CrossRef] [PubMed]

33. Simonen, P.; Gylling, H.; Howard, A.N.; Miettinen, T.A. Introducing a new component of the metabolic syndrome: Low cholesterol absorption. *Am. J. Clin. Nutr.* **2000**, *72*, 82–88. [PubMed]

34. Pinedo, S.; Vissers, M.N.; von Bergmann, K.; Elharchaoui, K.; Lutjohann, D.; Luben, R.; Wareham, N.J.; Kastelein, J.J.; Khaw, K.T.; Boekholdt, S.M. Plasma levels of plant sterols and the risk of coronary artery disease: The prospective EPIC-Norfolk Population Study. *J. Lipid Res.* **2007**, *48*, 139–144. [CrossRef] [PubMed]

35. Chan, D.C.; Watts, G.F.; Barrett, P.H.; O'Neill, F.H.; Thompson, G.R. Plasma markers of cholesterol homeostasis and apolipoprotein B-100 kinetics in the metabolic syndrome. *Obes. Res.* **2003**, *11*, 591–596. [CrossRef] [PubMed]

36. Rigamonti, E.; Helin, L.; Lestavel, S.; Mutka, A.L.; Lepore, M.; Fontaine, C.; Bouhlel, M.A.; Bultel, S.; Fruchart, J.C.; Ikonen, E.; *et al.* Liver X receptor activation controls intracellular cholesterol trafficking and esterification in human macrophages. *Circ. Res.* **2005**, *97*, 682–689. [CrossRef] [PubMed]

37. Ruiu, G.; Pinach, S.; Veglia, F.; Gambino, R.; Marena, S.; Uberti, B.; Alemanno, N.; Burt, D.; Pagano, G.; Cassader, M. Phytosterol-enriched yogurt increases LDL affinity and reduces CD36 expression in polygenic hypercholesterolemia. *Lipids* **2009**, *44*, 153–160. [CrossRef] [PubMed]

38. Bieghs, V.; Verheyen, F.; van Gorp, P.J.; Hendrikx, T.; Wouters, K.; Lutjohann, D.; Gijbels, M.J.; Febbraio, M.; Binder, C.J.; Hofker, M.H.; *et al.* Internalization of modified lipids by CD36 and SR-A leads to hepatic inflammation and lysosomal cholesterol storage in kupffer cells. *PLoS ONE* **2012**, *7*, e34378. [CrossRef] [PubMed]

39. Bieghs, V.; Wouters, K.; van Gorp, P.J.; Gijbels, M.J.; de Winther, M.P.; Binder, C.J.; Lutjohann, D.; Febbraio, M.; Moore, K.J.; van Bilsen, M.; *et al.* Role of scavenger receptor A and CD36 in diet-induced nonalcoholic steatohepatitis in hyperlipidemic mice. *Gastroenterology* **2010**, *138*, 2477–2486.e3. [CrossRef] [PubMed]

40. Wisse, E.; Braet, F.; Duimel, H.; Vreuls, C.; Koek, G.; Olde Damink, S.W.; van den Broek, M.A.; de Geest, B.; Dejong, C.H.; Tateno, C.; *et al.* Fixation methods for electron microscopy of human and other liver. *World J. Gastroenterol.* **2010**, *16*, 2851–2866. [CrossRef] [PubMed]

41. Wouters, K.; van Gorp, P.J.; Bieghs, V.; Gijbels, M.J.; Duimel, H.; Lutjohann, D.; Kerksiek, A.; van Kruchten, R.; Maeda, N.; Staels, B.; *et al.* Dietary cholesterol, rather than liver steatosis, leads to hepatic inflammation in hyperlipidemic mouse models of nonalcoholic steatohepatitis. *Hepatology* **2008**, *48*, 474–486. [CrossRef] [PubMed]

42. Lutjohann, D.; Stroick, M.; Bertsch, T.; Kuhl, S.; Lindenthal, B.; Thelen, K.; Andersson, U.; Bjorkhem, I.; Bergmann Kv, K.; Fassbender, K. High doses of simvastatin, pravastatin, and cholesterol reduce brain cholesterol synthesis in guinea pigs. *Steroids* **2004**, *69*, 431–438. [CrossRef] [PubMed]

International Journal of
Molecular Sciences

MDPI

Article

The Dipeptidyl Peptidase-4 Inhibitor Teneligliptin Attenuates Hepatic Lipogenesis via AMPK Activation in Non-Alcoholic Fatty Liver Disease Model Mice

Takayasu Ideta [1], **Yohei Shirakami** [1,2,]*, **Tsuneyuki Miyazaki** [1], **Takahiro Kochi** [1], **Hiroyasu Sakai** [1], **Hisataka Moriwaki** [1] and **Masahito Shimizu** [1]

[1] Department of Gastroenterology, Internal Medicine, Gifu University Graduate School of Medicine, 1-1 Yanagido, Gifu 501-1194, Japan; taka.mailbox.789@gmail.com (T.I.); tsunemiyazaking@yahoo.co.jp (T.M.); kottii924@yahoo.co.jp (T.K.); sakaih03@gifu-u.ac.jp (H.S.); hmori@gifu-u.ac.jp (H.M.); shimim-gif@umin.ac.jp (M.S.)
[2] Informative Clinical Medicine, Gifu University Graduate School of Medicine, 1-1 Yanagido, Gifu 501-1194, Japan
*   Correspondence: ys2443@gifu-u.ac.jp; Tel.: +81-58-230-6308; Fax: +81-58-230-6310

Academic Editor: Amedeo Lonardo
Received: 19 October 2015; Accepted: 30 November 2015; Published: 8 December 2015

Abstract: Non-alcoholic fatty liver disease (NAFLD), which is strongly associated with metabolic syndrome, is increasingly a major cause of hepatic disorder. Dipeptidyl peptidase (DPP)-4 inhibitors, anti-diabetic agents, are expected to be effective for the treatment of NAFLD. In the present study, we established a novel NAFLD model mouse using monosodium glutamate (MSG) and a high-fat diet (HFD) and investigated the effects of a DPP-4 inhibitor, teneligliptin, on the progression of NAFLD. Male MSG/HFD-treated mice were divided into two groups, one of which received teneligliptin in drinking water. Administration of MSG and HFD caused mice to develop severe fatty changes in the liver, but teneligliptin treatment improved hepatic steatosis and inflammation, as evaluated by the NAFLD activity score. Serum alanine aminotransferase and intrahepatic triglyceride levels were significantly decreased in teneligliptin-treated mice ($p < 0.05$). Hepatic mRNA levels of the genes involved in *de novo* lipogenesis were significantly downregulated by teneligliptin ($p < 0.05$). Moreover, teneligliptin increased hepatic expression levels of phosphorylated AMP-activated protein kinase (AMPK) protein. These findings suggest that teneligliptin attenuates lipogenesis in the liver by activating AMPK and downregulating the expression of genes involved in lipogenesis. DPP-4 inhibitors may be effective for the treatment of NAFLD and may be able to prevent its progression to non-alcoholic steatohepatitis.

Keywords: AMPK; DPP-4 inhibitor; lipogenesis; non-alcoholic fatty liver disease; NAFLD; SREBP1c; teneligliptin

1. Introduction

Obesity is considered to be a serious health problem, as it frequently causes various medical concerns, including type 2 diabetes mellitus (T2DM), cardiovascular diseases, dyslipidemia and many types of cancer [1]. Non-alcoholic fatty liver disease (NAFLD), which is strongly associated with obesity, has become one of the most common causes of chronic liver disease in developed countries. The clinical importance of NAFLD is illustrated by its high prevalence (6.3%–33%, with a median of 20%) in the general population [2]. NAFLD is defined as a chronic hepatic status with fat accumulation in the liver after the exclusion of secondary causes of hepatic fat accumulation, such as remarkable alcohol consumption, autoimmune or viral hepatitis and certain medications [3]. Some patients with

NAFLD develop a more serious disease condition, non-alcoholic steatohepatitis (NASH), and 10%–15% of patients with NASH develop liver cirrhosis, leading to hepatocellular carcinoma (HCC) [4–6]. The incidence of HCC due to NASH is almost the same as that due to chronic hepatitis C virus [7], which suggests that chronic liver damage or liver carcinogenesis associated with NAFLD/NASH are critical healthcare problems that should be resolved.

NAFLD is strongly associated with several aspects of metabolic syndrome, *i.e.*, obesity, dyslipidemia (primarily increased triglycerides), insulin resistance and concomitant glucose intolerance, including T2DM [6,8,9]. Therefore, improvement of these medical conditions may be beneficial to ameliorate NAFLD. For instance, pitavastatin, a drug used for the treatment of dyslipidemia, improved liver steatosis and decreased serum levels of free fatty acid (FFA) and alanine aminotransferase (ALT) in obese and diabetic *db/db* mice [10]. In the same strain of mice, treatment with green tea catechins, which have characteristics facilitating the prevention of metabolic syndrome, attenuated liver steatosis and suppressed chronic inflammation in the liver [11]. In addition, metformin, an anti-diabetic agent, markedly improve insulin resistance and inhibited obesity-related liver tumorigenesis in *db/db* mice [12]. Recently, it was reported that NAFLD is a strong determinant for the development of metabolic syndrome [13,14], suggesting that interventions purposing to ameliorate NAFLD are appropriate for the prevention and treatment of metabolic syndrome and related diseases.

Intestinal hormone incretins, such as glucagon-like peptide-1 (GLP1), regulate blood glucose levels by promoting insulin secretion in pancreatic β cells, as well as decreasing glucagon secretion in pancreatic α cells. Following their secretion from the intestines, incretins are rapidly decomposed by dipeptidyl peptidase (DPP)-4. DPP-4 inhibitors prevent GLP1 from decomposing, and this leads to appropriate secretion of insulin and glucagon from the pancreas. Therefore, DPP-4 inhibitors are commonly used in practice as medicinal agents for T2DM [15,16]. Recently, incretins have been reported to have various bioactivities, not only in pancreas cells, but also outside the pancreas [17]. Moreover, several studies have revealed the potential roles of incretin-based therapies, including DPP-4 inhibitors and GLP-1 receptor agonists, in the treatment of NAFLD [18,19]. DPP-4 inhibitors may be able to attenuate the pathology of NASH, because patients with NAFLD/NASH have increased DPP-4 activity, which correlates with the histological severity of NASH [20–22].

Monosodium glutamate (MSG)-treated animals exhibit obesity and metabolic dysfunction [23–25]. In the present study, we established a novel mouse model of NAFLD by injecting them with MSG and then feeding them a high-fat diet (HFD); these mice display obesity and severe fatty changes in the liver with an early onset. Using this model, we evaluated the preventive and therapeutic efficacy of teneligliptin, a DPP-4 inhibitor, on NAFLD and investigated the underlying mechanisms.

2. Results and Discussion

2.1. Results

2.1.1. General Observations

At the end of the experiment, there were no significant differences in body weight or relative weight of organs, including the liver and white adipose tissue (periorchis and retroperitoneum), between the two groups (Table 1). No significant difference was seen in the amount of food ingested by the two groups during the experiment. No clinical symptoms of adverse event by teneligliptin were observed throughout the experiment. Histopathological examination also displayed no toxicity due to teneligliptin treatment in important organs, including the liver, kidney and spleen (data not shown).

Table 1. Body, liver and fat weights of the experimental mice.

Measurement Item	Control	Teneligliptin
Body weight (g)	83.4 ± 7.1 [a]	80.7 ± 8.3
Liver weight (g)	5.5 ± 1.4	5.1 ± 0.8
Liver-to-body weight ratio	0.066 ± 0.013	0.063 ± 0.016
White adipose tissue [b] (g)	2.8 ± 0.7	2.8 ± 1.1

[a] Mean ± SD; [b] white adipose tissue of the periorchis and retroperitoneum.

2.1.2. Effects of Teneligliptin on the Histopathology of the Experimental Mouse Liver

The hematoxylin and eosin (H&E)-stained liver sections showed fatty degeneration, inflammation and hepatocellular ballooning in both groups. Macrovesicular fat deposits and glycogen storage were observed in the livers of both groups, but teneligliptin treatment attenuated fat accumulation in the experimental mice (Figure 1A). Liver sections were histologically evaluated using the NAFLD activity score (NAS) system [26]. The total NAS in Group 2 was significantly decreased compared to that in Group 1 (Figure 1B). When comparing each scoring factor in the NAS system, hepatic steatosis and inflammation were significantly attenuated in Group 2 compared to those in Group 1 at this experimental time point (14 weeks of age) (Figure 1C). Liver fibrosis was not detected in either group.

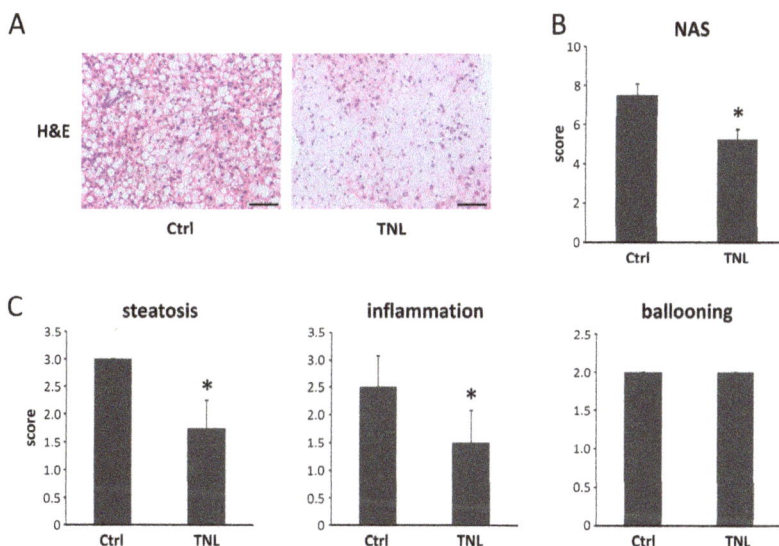

Figure 1. Effects of teneligliptin on hepatic histopathology in experimental mice. (**A**) Hematoxylin and eosin (H&E) staining of liver sections from experimental mice. Representative photomicrographs of the liver sections of MSG/high-fat diet (HFD)-administered mice treated with or without teneligliptin. Bar, 100 μm; (**B,C**) The NAFLD activity score (NAS) was determined based on histopathological analysis (steatosis, inflammation and ballooning). Ctrl, control. TNL, teneligliptin. The values are expressed as the mean ± SD. * *p* < 0.05 *versus* the control group.

2.1.3. Effects of Teneligliptin on the Intrahepatic Triglyceride Levels and the Activation of AMP-Activated Protein Kinase in the Livers of Experimental Mice

Triglyceride levels in the liver were significantly decreased in the teneligliptin-treated group (Figure 2A). This was consistent with histological findings of attenuated hepatic steatosis in the livers of mice in the group treated with teneligliptin, as evaluated by Oil Red *O*-stained liver sections

(Figure 2B). Moreover, tenegliptin administration significantly increased the hepatic expression levels of phosphorylated (*i.e.*, activated) AMPK (p-AMPK) protein (Figure 2C), which may be associated with the improvement of liver steatosis [27].

2.1.4. Effects of Tenegliptin on the Expression Levels of Acetyl-CoA Carboxylase, Fatty Acid Synthetase, Sterol Regulatory Element-Binding Protein 1c and Elongation of Very Long Chain Fatty Acid-Like Family Member 6 mRNA in the Livers of Experimental Mice

We determined the mRNA expression levels of *Acc*, *Fas*, *Srebp1c* and *Elovl6* to elucidate the effects of tenegliptin on lipid metabolism in the livers of experimental mice. As shown in Figure 3, the expression levels of *Acc*, *Fas* and *Srebp1c*, which regulate lipogenesis [28,29], were significantly decreased in the mice treated with tenegliptin when compared to those without tenegliptin. In addition, tenegliptin administration also decreased the hepatic expression levels of *Elovl6*, which is also one of the key molecules controlling fatty acid metabolism and lipotoxicity [28].

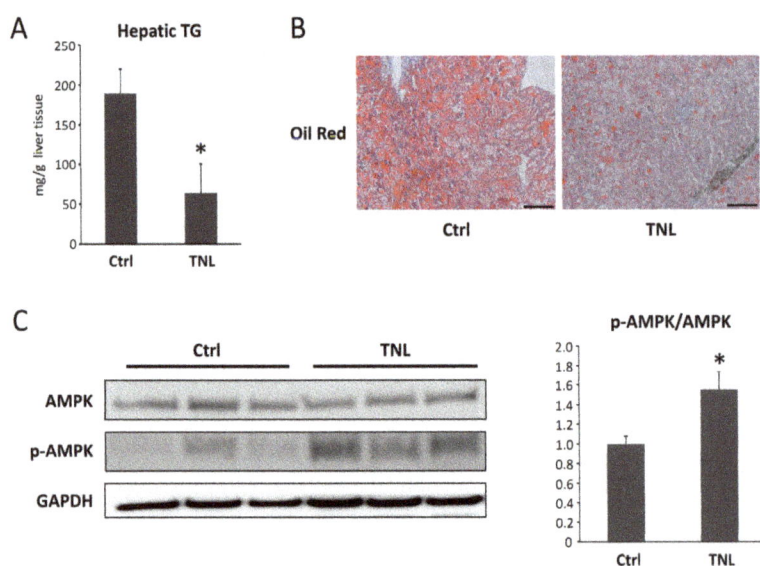

Figure 2. Effects of tenegliptin on hepatic steatosis and the levels of AMPK and p-AMPK in the livers of experimental mice. (A) Hepatic lipids were extracted from liver samples, and intrahepatic triglyceride (TG) levels were measured ($n = 6$); (B) steatosis in frozen liver sections from experimental mice treated with or without tenegliptin was analyzed with Oil Red O staining. Bar, 100 μm; (C) Total proteins were extracted from the livers of experimental mice, and the expression levels of AMPK and p-AMPK proteins were examined by Western blot analysis using the respective antibodies. GAPDH served as a loading control (**left** panel). Band intensities were quantified using densitometry. After the average of band intensity ratios of p-AMPK to GAPDH and AMPK to GAPDH were calculated in each sample, the ratios of these calculated values, which was expressed as p-AMPK/AMPK, were determined (**right** panel). Similar results were obtained in repeat experiments. The values are expressed as the mean ± SD. * $p < 0.05$ *versus* the control group.

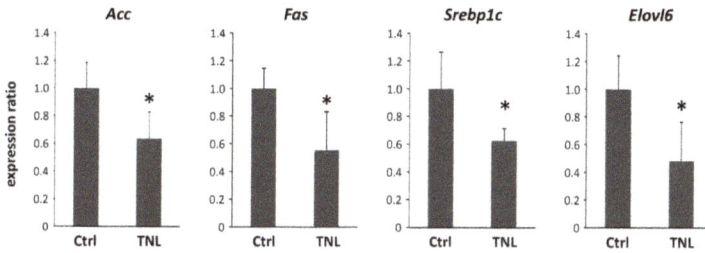

Figure 3. Effects of teneligliptin on the expression levels of genes related to lipogenesis in the livers of experimental mice. Total RNA was isolated from the livers of the experimental mice ($n = 6$), and the expression levels of *Acc*, *Fas*, *Srebp1c* and *Elovl6* mRNAs were examined using quantitative real-time RT-PCR with specific primers. The values are expressed as the mean $\pm$ SD. * $p < 0.05$ *versus* the control group.

2.1.5. Effects of Teneligliptin on Biochemical Parameters

Blood samples were collected from the inferior vena cava at sacrifice after six hours of fasting for chemical analyses. The levels of serum ALT were significantly reduced by teneligliptin administration. On the other hand, other parameters, including FFA, glucose, insulin and triglyceride, were not significantly different between the groups (Table 2).

Table 2. Serum parameters in serum of the experimental mice. FFA, free fatty acid.

Measurement Item	Control	Teneligliptin
FFA (μEQ/mL)	2091.0 $\pm$ 328.9 [a]	1550.4 $\pm$ 267.5
Glucose (mg/dL)	295.2 $\pm$ 108.2	528.0 $\pm$ 102.0
Insulin (ng/mL)	2.3 $\pm$ 0.9	2.14 $\pm$ 1.8
ALT (IU/L)	239.8 $\pm$ 20.4	162.0 $\pm$ 16.5 [b]
Triglyceride (mg/mL)	56.4 $\pm$ 32.2	65.2 $\pm$ 9.3

[a] Mean $\pm$ SD; [b] significantly different from the control group by the Welch t-test.

2.2. Discussion

The incidence of NAFLD/NASH is expected to continue to increase because of the global obesity epidemic. Therefore, efficacious therapeutic medications and preventive strategies for NAFLD/NASH are required. The novel animal model used in our present study is considered to reflect the pathological conditions in human NAFLD/NASH characterized by macrovesicular steatosis and chronic liver inflammation and is thought to be a practical and feasible model for investigating NAFLD and for testing preventive and therapeutic modalities that can suppress the progression of simple hepatic steatosis into NASH. In addition, this mouse model has the advantage of developing NAFLD with earlier onset compared to other animal models reported previously [11,23,30]. Although NAFLD/NASH has been considered as a hepatic manifestation of metabolic syndrome, it was recently found that NAFLD appears to be a precursor and a strong risk factor for the future development of metabolic syndrome [13,14]. A previous report by Misu *et al.* [31] suggested this reciprocal causality by demonstrating that the serum level of selenoprotein P, which is a liver-derived secretory protein and which is higher in subjects with NAFLD [32], causes insulin resistance. From this point of view, it is considered an appropriate action to intervene in ameliorating NAFLD by various medications, including the DPP-4 inhibitors, for the prevention and treatment of metabolic syndrome and related diseases.

DPP-4 inhibitors are commonly used in practice as medical agents for T2DM [15,16]. The present study clearly demonstrated that teneligliptin, a DPP-4 inhibitor, suppresses lipogenesis and steatosis in the liver of NAFLD model mice generated by administering MSG and HFD, whereas body weight and white adipose tissue weight were not reduced by this condition. We consider that the positive effect of teneligliptin on hepatic steatosis is associated, at least in part, with the suppression of the expression of specific genes, including *Srebp1c*, *Acc* and *Fas*, which play a key role in *de novo* lipogenesis [29]. *Srebp1c* is a key lipogenic transcription factor abundantly present in the mammalian liver [33]. It has been reported that hepatic gene expression of *Srebp1c* is increased in subjects with NAFLD as compared to those without [34]. In addition, treatment with linagliptin, the other DPP-4 inhibitor, also decreased liver expression of *Srebp1c* and *Fas* and, thus, improved steatosis in a mouse model of diet-induced obesity [35]. These reports may suggest that targeting lipogenic molecules, such as *Srebp1c* and *Fas*, with a DPP-4 inhibitor is a promising strategy for improving hepatic steatosis.

Among various agents investigated and thought to be candidates targeting NAFLD, the effects on fibrosis, ballooning degeneration, steatosis and lobular inflammation are analyzed in a recent publication comparing vitamin E, thiazolidinediones (TZDs), pentoxifylline and obeticholic acid (OCA) [36]. The effects of these agents are different; pentoxifylline, TZDs and OCA have ameliorating effects on lobular inflammation, but vitamin E has no effect on that compared to placebo. Furthermore, only pentoxifylline shows no effect on ballooning [36]. According to the results in our present study displaying the effects of teneligliptin on histopathology in the liver, teneligliptin could ameliorate hepatic steatosis and inflammation, but not ballooning in the NAS system (Figure 1). This might be because the major effect of teneligliptin as well as pentoxifylline [37] on NAFLD is inhibition of lipogenesis in the liver.

In the present study, the teneligliptin-treated group showed the tendency of a higher serum glucose level. This is assumed to be due possibly to the effect of fasting before sacrifice. In the feeding state, the serum glucose level must be lower than that in the control group, because the effect of this medicine on the serum glucose level has already been proven in experiments in the drug development process, as well as in clinical practice. Furthermore, in the feeding state, serum incretin levels appear to be higher in the teneligliptin-treated group, and it can be suspected that serum glucose metabolism was relatively dependent on the functions of incretins, including the functions that induce insulin secretion from the pancreas and enhance the insulin signaling pathway in the hepatocyte [17], due to the continuous influence of the DPP-4 inhibitor. Then, in the fasting state at sacrifice, intestines did not secrete incretins, leading probably to the relatively higher glucose levels shown in teneligliptin-treated mice. Although the serum levels of incretins and insulin, as well as glucose in the feeding state were not measured in our study, the levels of these might be able to let us interpret those unexpected data.

AMPK is a key regulator of energy balance and nutrient metabolism [38]. In the liver, AMPK has been demonstrated to inhibit cholesterol and triglyceride biosynthesis by reducing the activities of *Srebp1c* and *Fas* [27]. AMPK activation also promotes fatty acid β-oxidation by inactivation of ACC activity [39]. Moreover, GLP-1 suppresses hepatic lipogenesis through the activation of the AMPK pathway [40]. Other studies reported by Svegliati-Baroni *et al.* [41] and Lee *et al.* [42] also demonstrate that enhanced AMPK signaling due to GLP-1 activation can lead to inhibiting hepatic steatosis. Therefore, AMPK is considered to be a therapeutic target for NAFLD/NASH associated with metabolic syndrome [27]. In the present study, teneligliptin treatment significantly increased the levels of phosphorylated AMPK in the livers of NAFLD model mice (Figure 2C). These findings suggest that teneligliptin may attenuate lipogenesis in hepatocytes through the activation of AMPK and, subsequently, downregulation of *Srebp1c* and *Fas* (Figure 3). These findings are also consistent with the results of a previous report showing that AMPK inhibition resulted in elevated cleavage and transcription of hepatic *Srebp1c* in insulin-resistant mice [27]. In our study, it can be considered that teneligliptin elevated the level of GLP-1 due to attenuating the effect of the DDP-4 inhibitor and then enhanced AMPK in hepatocytes through the GLP-1 receptor (GLP-1R). The levels of GLP-1 and other incretins, however, were not determined in this study, as mentioned above. In addition, it is still controversial whether GLP-1R is present or responsible for the GLP-1 signal in the hepatocyte [43]. Moreover, there may be direct effects of DPP-4 inhibitors on hepatic steatosis through AMPK activation or other signaling pathways. Further investigations are required in order to clarify the effect of DPP-4 inhibitors and incretins on lipid metabolism in the hepatocyte.

One of the key mechanisms of incretin-based therapies, including DPP-4 inhibitors, for improving liver steatosis is the reduction of FFA [44] and improvement of glucose metabolism [15,16]. Therefore, we initially expected that teneligliptin would attenuate liver steatosis in the MSG/HFD-treated mice by improving these metabolic abnormalities. However, serum levels of FFA, glucose, insulin and triglycerides were not decreased by treatment with teneligliptin in the present study. We speculated that this was likely due to the study protocols, because MSG plus HFD treatment induced very severe obesity and steatosis within a short period of time. The present experimental condition (10 weeks of treatment with teneligliptin) may have been insufficient to obtain anti-diabetic effects, which is one of the limitations of the present study. Another limitation is that plasma levels of GLP-1 were not measured, and therefore, inhibition of DPP-4 by teneligliptin was not evaluated. We also did not assay the plasma DPP-4 activity or concentration. Therefore, future long-term studies should be conducted to confirm that teneligliptin improves liver steatosis by decreasing serum levels of FFA and improving glucose metabolism, focusing on the serum levels of GLP-1 and the activity of DPP-4 in several animal models.

3. Experimental Section

3.1. Animals and Chemicals

ICR mice were obtained from Charles River Japan (Kanagawa, Japan), and their newborns were employed in the study. MSG was purchased from Wako Pure Chemical (Osaka, Japan). CRF-1, a basal diet and HFD were from Oriental Yeast (Tokyo, Japan). Teneligliptin (Tenelia™) was kindly provided by Mitsubishi Tanabe Pharma Corporation (Tokyo, Japan). We fully complied with the Guidelines Concerning Experimental Animals issued by the Japanese Association for Laboratory Animal Science [45] and exercised due consideration to minimize pain and suffering.

3.2. Experimental Procedure

MSG was administered into the neonatal ICR mice at birth as a single-dose subcutaneous injection (4 mg/g body weight). Among these mice, males were divided into two groups at 4 weeks of age: the MSG/HFD group (n = 6, Group 1) and the MSG/HFD/teneligliptin-treated group (n = 6, Group 2). The mice in Group 2 were administered teneligliptin (30 mg/kg per day) in the drinking water from 4 weeks of age. The treatment dose of teneligliptin was determined according to the data from the animal experiments in the drug development process. Although the dose was relatively higher than that for humans in clinical practice, no notable adverse effect was observed in the treatment with the dose for the experimental animal in the process. Both groups were fed HFD from 4–14 weeks of age. At the termination of the experiment (14 weeks of age), all animals were sacrificed by CO_2 asphyxiation to analyze hepatic histopathology.

3.3. Histopathological Examination

Maximum sagittal sections of three hepatic sublobes were used for histopathological examination. For all experimental mice, 4 μm-thick sections of formalin-fixed and paraffin-embedded livers were stained with H&E for conventional histopathology. The histological features of the liver were evaluated using the NAS system [26].

3.4. Clinical Chemistry

Blood samples were collected from the inferior vena cava at sacrifice after 6 h of fasting for chemical analyses. Unfortunately, one blood sample could not be taken properly in the sampling procedure in each group; therefore, 5 blood samples in each were used to analyze. The serum concentrations of glucose (BioVision Research Products, Mountain View, CA, USA), triglycerides (Wako Pure Chemical), FFAs (Wako Pure Chemical) and insulin (Shibayagi, Gunma, Japan) were measured as previously reported [46]. ALT was measured using a standard clinical automatic analyzer (Type 7180; Hitachi, Tokyo, Japan).

3.5. RNA Extraction and Quantitative Real-Time Reverse Transcription-PCR Analysis

Total RNA was extracted from the mice livers using the RNeasy Mini Kit (QIAGEN, Venlo, The Netherlands). cDNA was synthesized from 0.2 µg of total RNA with the High Capacity cDNA Reverse Transcription Kit (Applied Biosystems, Foster City, CA, USA). A quantitative real-time reverse transcription-PCR (RT-PCR) analysis was applied using a LightCycler Nano (Roche Diagnostics, Indianapolis, IN, USA) and FastStart Essential DNA Green Master (Roche Diagnostics). The sequences of specific primers for amplifying e*Elovl6*, *Fas*, *Acc*, *Srebp1c* and *18S* genes were obtained by Primer-BLAST [47] (Table 3). The expression level of each gene was normalized to that of *18S*.

Table 3. Primer sequences.

Genes	5′-Primer	3′-Primer
Acc	GGCTCAAACTGCAGGTATCC	TTGCCAATCCACTCGAAGA
Elovl6	CAGCAAAGCACCCGAACTA	AGGAGCACAGTGATGTGGTG
Fas	GCTGCTGTTGGAAGTCAGC	AGTGTTCGTTCCTCGGAGTG
Srebp1c	CTGGAGCTGCGTGGTTT	GCCTCATGTAGGAATACCCTCCTCATA
18s	CCATCCAATCGGTAGTAGCG	GTAACCCGTTGAACCCCATT

3.6. Hepatic Lipid Analysis

Approximately 200 mg of frozen liver samples were homogenized, and lipids were extracted using Folch's method [48]. The triglyceride levels in the liver were measured with the Triglyceride E-test Kit (Wako Pure Chemical), as previously reported [49]. To visualize the intrahepatic lipids, Oil Red O staining was performed based on the standard protocol for frozen liver sections.

3.7. Protein Extraction and Western Blot Analysis

Total protein was extracted from the mice livers, and equivalent amounts of proteins (10 µg/lane) were examined by Western blot analysis [11]. Primary antibodies were obtained from Cell Signaling Technology (Beverly, MA, USA), including AMPK (#2603), p-AMPK (#2535) and GAPDH (#2118). The antibody for p-AMPK was used to detect the phosphorylation site at Thr172 in the activation loop. GAPDH served as the loading control. The intensities of the bands were quantified with NIH Image software ver. 1.62 (Bethesda, MD, USA). After the average of band intensity ratios of p-AMPK to GAPDH and AMPK to GAPDH was calculated in each sample, the ratio of these calculated values, which was expressed as p-AMPK/AMPK, were determined.

3.8. Statistical Analysis

The results are presented as the means ± SD and were analyzed using JMP software Version 10 (SAS Institute, Cary, NC, USA). Differences among the two groups were analyzed by Welch's *t*-test. The differences were considered significant at *p*-values of less than 0.05.

4. Conclusions

Teneligliptin, the DPP4 inhibitor, improved the histopathological appearance of the liver and decreased intrahepatic triglyceride levels in an NAFLD model mouse, which was associated with downregulation of hepatic lipogenesis-related genes due to AMPK activation. Interestingly, the hepatic *Dpp-4* mRNA expression level is significantly higher in patients with NAFLD compared to healthy subjects [50]. The results of the present study, together with those of previous reports [19,21,22], have prompted us to conduct a clinical trial to determine the effectiveness of DPP-4 inhibitors for the prevention and treatment of NAFLD.

Acknowledgments: This work was supported in part by Grants-in-Aid from the Ministry of Education, Science, Sports, and Culture of Japan (Nos. 22790638, 25460988 and 26860498).

Author Contributions: Takayasu Ideta, Yohei Shirakami and Masahito Shimizu conceived of and designed the experiments. Tsuneyuki Miyazaki, Takahiro Kochi and Hiroyasu Sakai performed the experiments. Takayasu Ideta, Yohei Shirakami analyzed the data. Takayasu Ideta, Yohei Shirakami, Hisataka Moriwaki and Masahito Shimizu wrote the paper.

Conflicts of Interest: The authors declare no conflict of interest.

References

1. Calle, E.E.; Rodriguez, C.; Walker-Thurmond, K.; Thun, M.J. Overweight, obesity, and mortality from cancer in a prospectively studied cohort of U.S. adults. *N. Engl. J. Med.* **2003**, *348*, 1625–1638. [CrossRef] [PubMed]
2. Chalasani, N.; Younossi, Z.; Lavine, J.E.; Diehl, A.M.; Brunt, E.M.; Cusi, K.; Charlton, M.; Sanyal, A.J. The diagnosis and management of non-alcoholic fatty liver disease: Practice guideline by the american association for the study of liver diseases, american college of gastroenterology, and the american gastroenterological association. *Hepatology* **2012**, *55*, 2005–2023. [CrossRef] [PubMed]
3. Sass, D.A.; Chang, P.; Chopra, K.B. Nonalcoholic fatty liver disease: A clinical review. *Dig. Dis. Sci.* **2005**, *50*, 171–180. [CrossRef] [PubMed]
4. Bacon, B.R.; Farahvash, M.J.; Janney, C.G.; Neuschwander-Tetri, B.A. Nonalcoholic steatohepatitis: An expanded clinical entity. *Gastroenterology* **1994**, *107*, 1103–1109. [PubMed]
5. Kim, C.H.; Younossi, Z.M. Nonalcoholic fatty liver disease: A manifestation of the metabolic syndrome. *Clevel. Clin. J. Med.* **2008**, *75*, 721–728.
6. Vanni, E.; Bugianesi, E.; Kotronen, A.; De Minicis, S.; Yki-Jarvinen, H.; Svegliati-Baroni, G. From the metabolic syndrome to NAFLD or vice versa? *Dig. Liver Dis.* **2010**, *42*, 320–330. [CrossRef] [PubMed]
7. Ascha, M.S.; Hanouneh, I.A.; Lopez, R.; Tamimi, T.A.; Feldstein, A.F.; Zein, N.N. The incidence and risk factors of hepatocellular carcinoma in patients with nonalcoholic steatohepatitis. *Hepatology* **2010**, *51*, 1972–1978. [CrossRef] [PubMed]
8. Marchesini, G.; Brizi, M.; Morselli-Labate, A.M.; Bianchi, G.; Bugianesi, E.; McCullough, A.J.; Forlani, G.; Melchionda, N. Association of nonalcoholic fatty liver disease with insulin resistance. *Am. J. Med.* **1999**, *107*, 450–455. [CrossRef]
9. Sanyal, A.J.; American Gastroenterological, A. Aga technical review on nonalcoholic fatty liver disease. *Gastroenterology* **2002**, *123*, 1705–1725. [CrossRef] [PubMed]
10. Shimizu, M.; Yasuda, Y.; Sakai, H.; Kubota, M.; Terakura, D.; Baba, A.; Ohno, T.; Kochi, T.; Tsurumi, H.; Tanaka, T.; *et al.* Pitavastatin suppresses diethylnitrosamine-induced liver preneoplasms in male C57BL/KsJ-*db/db* obese mice. *BMC Cancer* **2011**, *11*, 281. [CrossRef] [PubMed]
11. Shimizu, M.; Sakai, H.; Shirakami, Y.; Yasuda, Y.; Kubota, M.; Terakura, D.; Baba, A.; Ohno, T.; Hara, Y.; Tanaka, T.; *et al.* Preventive effects of (−)-epigallocatechin gallate on diethylnitrosamine-induced liver tumorigenesis in obese and diabetic C57BL/KsJ-*db/db* mice. *Cancer Prev. Res.* **2011**, *4*, 396–403. [CrossRef] [PubMed]
12. Ohno, T.; Shimizu, M.; Shirakami, Y.; Baba, A.; Kochi, T.; Kubota, M.; Tsurumi, H.; Tanaka, T.; Moriwaki, H. Metformin suppresses diethylnitrosamine-induced liver tumorigenesis in obese and diabetic C57BL/KsJ-+Lepr^{db}/+Lepr^{db} mice. *PLoS ONE* **2015**, *10*, e0124081. [CrossRef] [PubMed]
13. Lonardo, A.; Ballestri, S.; Marchesini, G.; Angulo, P.; Loria, P. Nonalcoholic fatty liver disease: A precursor of the metabolic syndrome. *Dig. Liver Dis.* **2015**, *47*, 181–190. [CrossRef] [PubMed]
14. Zhang, Y.; Zhang, T.; Zhang, C.; Tang, F.; Zhong, N.; Li, H.; Song, X.; Lin, H.; Liu, Y.; Xue, F. Identification of reciprocal causality between non-alcoholic fatty liver disease and metabolic syndrome by a simplified bayesian network in a chinese population. *BMJ Open* **2015**, *5*, e008204. [CrossRef] [PubMed]
15. Aschner, P.; Kipnes, M.S.; Lunceford, J.K.; Sanchez, M.; Mickel, C.; Williams-Herman, D.E.; Sitagliptin Study, G. Effect of the dipeptidyl peptidase-4 inhibitor sitagliptin as monotherapy on glycemic control in patients with type 2 diabetes. *Diabetes Care* **2006**, *29*, 2632–2637. [CrossRef] [PubMed]
16. Pi-Sunyer, F.X.; Schweizer, A.; Mills, D.; Dejager, S. Efficacy and tolerability of vildagliptin monotherapy in drug-naive patients with type 2 diabetes. *Diabetes Res. Clin. Pract.* **2007**, *76*, 132–138. [CrossRef] [PubMed]

17. Gupta, N.A.; Mells, J.; Dunham, R.M.; Grakoui, A.; Handy, J.; Saxena, N.K.; Anania, F.A. Glucagon-like peptide-1 receptor is present on human hepatocytes and has a direct role in decreasing hepatic steatosis *in vitro* by modulating elements of the insulin signaling pathway. *Hepatology* **2010**, *51*, 1584–1592. [CrossRef] [PubMed]

18. Trevaskis, J.L.; Griffin, P.S.; Wittmer, C.; Neuschwander-Tetri, B.A.; Brunt, E.M.; Dolman, C.S.; Erickson, M.R.; Napora, J.; Parkes, D.G.; Roth, J.D. Glucagon-like peptide-1 receptor agonism improves metabolic, biochemical, and histopathological indices of nonalcoholic steatohepatitis in mice. *Am. J. Physiol. Gastrointest. Liver Physiol.* **2012**, *302*, G762–G772. [CrossRef] [PubMed]

19. Klein, T.; Fujii, M.; Sandel, J.; Shibazaki, Y.; Wakamatsu, K.; Mark, M.; Yoneyama, H. Linagliptin alleviates hepatic steatosis and inflammation in a mouse model of non-alcoholic steatohepatitis. *Med. Mol. Morphol.* **2014**, *47*, 137–149. [CrossRef] [PubMed]

20. Balaban, Y.H.; Korkusuz, P.; Simsek, H.; Gokcan, H.; Gedikoglu, G.; Pinar, A.; Hascelik, G.; Asan, E.; Hamaloglu, E.; Tatar, G. Dipeptidyl peptidase IV (DDP IV) in nash patients. *Ann. Hepatol.* **2007**, *6*, 242–250. [PubMed]

21. Schuppan, D.; Gorrell, M.D.; Klein, T.; Mark, M.; Afdhal, N.H. The challenge of developing novel pharmacological therapies for non-alcoholic steatohepatitis. *Liver Int.* **2010**, *30*, 795–808. [CrossRef] [PubMed]

22. Yilmaz, Y.; Atug, O.; Yonal, O.; Duman, D.; Ozdogan, O.; Imeryuz, N.; Kalayci, C. Dipeptidyl peptidase IV inhibitors: Therapeutic potential in nonalcoholic fatty liver disease. *Med. Sci. Res.* **2009**, *15*, HY1-5. [CrossRef]

23. Collison, K.S.; Makhoul, N.J.; Zaidi, M.Z.; Al-Rabiah, R.; Inglis, A.; Andres, B.L.; Ubungen, R.; Shoukri, M.; Al-Mohanna, F.A. Interactive effects of neonatal exposure to monosodium glutamate and aspartame on glucose homeostasis. *Nutr. Metabol.* **2012**, *9*, 58. [CrossRef] [PubMed]

24. Nagata, M.; Suzuki, W.; Iizuka, S.; Tabuchi, M.; Maruyama, H.; Takeda, S.; Aburada, M.; Miyamoto, K. Type 2 diabetes mellitus in obese mouse model induced by monosodium glutamate. *Exp. Anim. Jpn. Assoc. Lab. Anim. Sci.* **2006**, *55*, 109–115. [CrossRef]

25. Roman-Ramos, R.; Almanza-Perez, J.C.; Garcia-Macedo, R.; Blancas-Flores, G.; Fortis-Barrera, A.; Jasso, E.I.; Garcia-Lorenzana, M.; Campos-Sepulveda, A.E.; Cruz, M.; Alarcon-Aguilar, F.J. Monosodium glutamate neonatal intoxication associated with obesity in adult stage is characterized by chronic inflammation and increased mRNA expression of peroxisome proliferator-activated receptors in mice. *Basic Clin. Pharmacol. Toxicol.* **2011**, *108*, 406–413. [CrossRef] [PubMed]

26. Kleiner, D.E.; Brunt, E.M.; Van Natta, M.; Behling, C.; Contos, M.J.; Cummings, O.W.; Ferrell, L.D.; Liu, Y.C.; Torbenson, M.S.; Unalp-Arida, A.; et al. Design and validation of a histological scoring system for nonalcoholic fatty liver disease. *Hepatology* **2005**, *41*, 1313–1321. [CrossRef] [PubMed]

27. Li, Y.; Xu, S.; Mihaylova, M.M.; Zheng, B.; Hou, X.; Jiang, B.; Park, O.; Luo, Z.; Lefai, E.; Shyy, J.Y.; et al. AMPK phosphorylates and inhibits *Srebp* activity to attenuate hepatic steatosis and atherosclerosis in diet-induced insulin-resistant mice. *Cell Metabol.* **2011**, *13*, 376–388. [CrossRef] [PubMed]

28. Serviddio, G.; Bellanti, F.; Vendemiale, G. Free radical biology for medicine: Learning from nonalcoholic fatty liver disease. *Free Radic. Biol. Med.* **2013**, *65*, 952–968. [CrossRef] [PubMed]

29. Blaslov, K.; Bulum, T.; Zibar, K.; Duvnjak, L. Incretin based therapies: A novel treatment approach for non-alcoholic fatty liver disease. *World J. Gastroenterol.* **2014**, *20*, 7356–7365. [CrossRef] [PubMed]

30. Shimizu, M.; Sakai, H.; Shirakami, Y.; Iwasa, J.; Yasuda, Y.; Kubota, M.; Takai, K.; Tsurumi, H.; Tanaka, T.; Moriwaki, H. Acyclic retinoid inhibits diethylnitrosamine-induced liver tumorigenesis in obese and diabetic C57BLKS/J- +lepr^{db}/+lepr^{db} mice. *Cancer Prev. Res.* **2011**, *4*, 128–136. [CrossRef] [PubMed]

31. Misu, H.; Takamura, T.; Takayama, H.; Hayashi, H.; Matsuzawa-Nagata, N.; Kurita, S.; Ishikura, K.; Ando, H.; Takeshita, Y.; Ota, T.; et al. A liver-derived secretory protein, selenoprotein p, causes insulin resistance. *Cell Metabol.* **2010**, *12*, 483–495. [CrossRef] [PubMed]

32. Choi, H.Y.; Hwang, S.Y.; Lee, C.H.; Hong, H.C.; Yang, S.J.; Yoo, H.J.; Seo, J.A.; Kim, S.G.; Kim, N.H.; Baik, S.H.; et al. Increased selenoprotein p levels in subjects with visceral obesity and nonalcoholic fatty liver disease. *Diabetes Metabol. J.* **2013**, *37*, 63–71. [CrossRef] [PubMed]

33. Musso, G.; Gambino, R.; Cassader, M. Recent insights into hepatic lipid metabolism in non-alcoholic fatty liver disease (NAFLD). *Progress Lipid Res.* **2009**, *48*, 1–26. [CrossRef] [PubMed]

34. Higuchi, N.; Kato, M.; Shundo, Y.; Tajiri, H.; Tanaka, M.; Yamashita, N.; Kohjima, M.; Kotoh, K.; Nakamuta, M.; Takayanagi, R.; *et al.* Liver X receptor in cooperation with *Srebp*-1c is a major lipid synthesis regulator in nonalcoholic fatty liver disease. *Hepatol. Res.* **2008**, *38*, 1122–1129. [CrossRef] [PubMed]

35. Kern, M.; Kloting, N.; Niessen, H.G.; Thomas, L.; Stiller, D.; Mark, M.; Klein, T.; Bluher, M. Linagliptin improves insulin sensitivity and hepatic steatosis in diet-induced obesity. *PLoS ONE* **2012**, *7*, e38744. [CrossRef] [PubMed]

36. Singh, S.; Khera, R.; Allen, A.M.; Murad, M.H.; Loomba, R. Comparative effectiveness of pharmacological interventions for nonalcoholic steatohepatitis: A systematic review and network meta-analysis. *Hepatology* **2015**, *62*, 1417–1432. [CrossRef] [PubMed]

37. Shirakami, Y.; Shimizu, M.; Kubota, M.; Ohno, T.; Kochi, T.; Nakamura, N.; Sumi, T.; Tanaka, T.; Moriwaki, H.; Seishima, M. Pentoxifylline prevents nonalcoholic steatohepatitis-related liver pre-neoplasms by inhibiting hepatic inflammation and lipogenesis. *Eur. J. Cancer Prev.* **2015**. [CrossRef] [PubMed]

38. Hardie, D.G.; Ross, F.A.; Hawley, S.A. Ampk: A nutrient and energy sensor that maintains energy homeostasis. *Nat. Rev. Mol. Cell Biol.* **2012**, *13*, 251–262. [CrossRef] [PubMed]

39. Viollet, B.; Mounier, R.; Leclerc, J.; Yazigi, A.; Foretz, M.; Andreelli, F. Targeting AMP-activated protein kinase as a novel therapeutic approach for the treatment of metabolic disorders. *Diabetes Metab.* **2007**, *33*, 395–402. [CrossRef] [PubMed]

40. Ben-Shlomo, S.; Zvibel, I.; Shnell, M.; Shlomai, A.; Chepurko, E.; Halpern, Z.; Barzilai, N.; Oren, R.; Fishman, S. Glucagon-like peptide-1 reduces hepatic lipogenesis via activation of AMP-activated protein kinase. *J. Hepatol.* **2011**, *54*, 1214–1223. [CrossRef] [PubMed]

41. Svegliati-Baroni, G.; Saccomanno, S.; Rychlicki, C.; Agostinelli, L.; de Minicis, S.; Candelaresi, C.; Faraci, G.; Pacetti, D.; Vivarelli, M.; Nicolini, D.; *et al.* Glucagon-like peptide-1 receptor activation stimulates hepatic lipid oxidation and restores hepatic signalling alteration induced by a high-fat diet in nonalcoholic steatohepatitis. *Liver Int.* **2011**, *31*, 1285–1297. [CrossRef] [PubMed]

42. Lee, J.; Hong, S.W.; Chae, S.W.; Kim, D.H.; Choi, J.H.; Bae, J.C.; Park, S.E.; Rhee, E.J.; Park, C.Y.; Oh, K.W.; *et al.* Exendin-4 improves steatohepatitis by increasing Sirt1 expression in high-fat diet-induced obese C57BL/6J mice. *PLoS ONE* **2012**, *7*, e31394. [CrossRef] [PubMed]

43. Samson, S.L.; Bajaj, M. Potential of incretin-based therapies for non-alcoholic fatty liver disease. *J. Diabetes Complicat.* **2013**, *27*, 401–406. [CrossRef] [PubMed]

44. Boschmann, M.; Engeli, S.; Dobberstein, K.; Budziarek, P.; Strauss, A.; Boehnke, J.; Sweep, F.C.; Luft, F.C.; He, Y.; Foley, J.E.; *et al.* Dipeptidyl-peptidase-IV inhibition augments postprandial lipid mobilization and oxidation in type 2 diabetic patients. *J. Clin. Endocrinol. Metab.* **2009**, *94*, 846–852. [CrossRef] [PubMed]

45. The Japanese Association for Laboratory Animal Science (JALAS). Available online: http://www.jalas.jp/english/en_about_jalas.html (accessed on 26 July 2013).

46. Shimizu, M.; Shirakami, Y.; Iwasa, J.; Shiraki, M.; Yasuda, Y.; Hata, K.; Hirose, Y.; Tsurumi, H.; Tanaka, T.; Moriwaki, H. Supplementation with branched-chain amino acids inhibits azoxymethane-induced colonic preneoplastic lesions in male C57BL/KsJ-*db/db* mice. *Clin. Cancer Res.* **2009**, *15*, 3068–3075. [CrossRef] [PubMed]

47. Primer Blast. Available online: http://www.ncbi.nlm.nih.gov/tools/primer-blast/ (accessed on 26 July 2013).

48. Folch, J.; Lees, M.; Sloane Stanley, G.H. A simple method for the isolation and purification of total lipids from animal tissues. *J. Biol. Chem.* **1957**, *226*, 497–509. [PubMed]

49. Iwasa, J.; Shimizu, M.; Shiraki, M.; Shirakami, Y.; Sakai, H.; Terakura, Y.; Takai, K.; Tsurumi, H.; Tanaka, T.; Moriwaki, H. Dietary supplementation with branched-chain amino acids suppresses diethylnitrosamine-induced liver tumorigenesis in obese and diabetic C57BL/KsJ-*db/db* mice. *Cancer Sci.* **2010**, *101*, 460–467. [CrossRef] [PubMed]

50. Miyazaki, M.; Kato, M.; Tanaka, K.; Tanaka, M.; Kohjima, M.; Nakamura, K.; Enjoji, M.; Nakamuta, M.; Kotoh, K.; Takayanagi, R. Increased hepatic expression of dipeptidyl peptidase-4 in non-alcoholic fatty liver disease and its association with insulin resistance and glucose metabolism. *Mol. Med. Rep.* **2012**, *5*, 729–733. [CrossRef] [PubMed]

MDPI

St. Alban-Anlage 66

4052 Basel

Switzerland

Tel. +41 61 683 77 34

Fax +41 61 302 89 18

www.mdpi.com

International Journal of Molecular Sciences Editorial Office

E-mail: ijms@mdpi.com

www.mdpi.com/journal/ijms